STRESS AND DEVELOPMENTAL PROGRAMMING OF HEALTH AND DISEASE

BEYOND PHENOMENOLOGY

PUBLIC HEALTH IN THE 21ST CENTURY

Additional books in this series can be found on Nova's website
under the Series tab.

STRESS AND DEVELOPMENTAL PROGRAMMING OF HEALTH AND DISEASE

BEYOND PHENOMENOLOGY

LUBO ZHANG, PH.D.

AND

LAWRENCE D. LONGO, M.D.

EDITORS

New York

NOTICE TO THE READER

The Publisher has taken reasonable care in the preparation of this book, but makes no expressed or implied warranty of any kind and assumes no responsibility for any errors or omissions. No liability is assumed for incidental or consequential damages in connection with or arising out of information contained in this book. The Publisher shall not be liable for any special, consequential, or exemplary damages resulting, in whole or in part, from the readers' use of, or reliance upon, this material. Any parts of this book based on government reports are so indicated and copyright is claimed for those parts to the extent applicable to compilations of such works.

Independent verification should be sought for any data, advice or recommendations contained in this book. In addition, no responsibility is assumed by the publisher for any injury and/or damage to persons or property arising from any methods, products, instructions, ideas or otherwise contained in this publication.

This publication is designed to provide accurate and authoritative information with regard to the subject matter covered herein. It is sold with the clear understanding that the Publisher is not engaged in rendering legal or any other professional services. If legal or any other expert assistance is required, the services of a competent person should be sought. FROM A DECLARATION OF PARTICIPANTS JOINTLY ADOPTED BY A COMMITTEE OF THE AMERICAN BAR ASSOCIATION AND A COMMITTEE OF PUBLISHERS.

Additional color graphics may be available in the e-book version of this book.

Library of Congress Cataloging-in-Publication Data

ISBN: 978-1-63321-836-9

Published by Nova Science Publishers, Inc. † New York

Contents

Preface

Stress is a constant experience and threat throughout life. In his monumental volume *The physiology and pathology of exposure to Stress*, the McGill University endocrinologist, Hans Selye (1907-1982), observed that stress to the organism, in essentially any of its forms – dietary, environmental, disease, and others – could result in cellular, hormonal, and related damage, with the body mounting a response he termed the "General-Adaptation-Syndrome" (Selye, 1950). Writing years before many of the nuances of biochemical and molecular mechanisms were established, and before the phenomenon of epigenesis was appreciated, Selye envisioned an orchestrated brain to tissue system-wide biological defensive response to the challenge of stress of whatever origin. Subsequent investigation has clarified that while stress of relatively short duration is often followed by successful adaptation, that of longer duration and/or repeated insult many result in cell damage and death (Bale et al., 2010; McEwen, 2004).

In the present volume, we have attempted to bring together some of the latest thinking on the role of antenatal environmental stress to the pregnant mother and the developmental origins of health and diseases in the adult. Since the earliest days that David J. Barker (1937-2013), those before him, and others first articulated this Thesis/Hypothesis, epidemiologists have explored its many facets. As is well known, these include but not limited to cardiovascular diseases (hypertension, ischemic heart disease, cerebrovascular accident), metabolic syndrome/type 2 diabetes, schizophrenia and other neuropsychiatric diseases, and some cancers. It is a dizzying array of a multitude of serious disorders, the fundamental pathophysiology of which little is known. Developing the epidemiologic associations for these conditions to stress *in utero* often has not been easy, and at times, has been labeled as descriptive.

This depiction is unfortunate. For it is by establishing such relationships that one can postulate hypothesis as to the manner of origin and their fundamental mechanisms. Even so, as one journeys through the several hierarchical levels of organ, tissue, cell, subcellular, and molecular, too often we discover that we have only punted discovery of the fundamental mechanisms further down into the morass of complexity within the organism.

In the present collection of essays, each author has attempted to bring the latest, deepest thinking to bear on the subject. This includes providing background for rationale of the study, some details but more general principles of the methodologic aspects of study, findings of consequence, and their interpretation. Each of these Chapters has the goal of understanding, at a deeper level, the meaning of the investigation.

We trust that this offering may provide the reader with a more profound grasp of the issues involved, the complexity of the problem, and the diversity of challenges that lie ahead.

References

Bale, T.L., T.Z. Baram, A.S. Brown, J.M. Goldstein, T.R. Insel, M.M. McCarthy, et al. (2010). Early life programming and neurodevelopmental disorders. *Biol Psychiatry*, 68, 314-9.

McEwen, B.S. (2004). Protection and damage from acute and chronic stress: allostasis and allostatic overload and relevance to the pathophysiology of psychiatric disorders. *Ann N Y Acad Sci*, 1032, 1-7.

Selye, H. (1950). *The physiology and pathology of exposure to STRESS. A treatise based on the concepts of the General-Adaptation-Syndrome and the Diseases of Adaptation.* Montreal: Acta Inc.

Lubo Zhang, Ph.D.
Professor of Physiology and Pharmacology
Director, Center for Perinatal Biology
Department of Basic Sciences
Loma Linda University School of Medicine
Loma Linda, CA
Tel: 909-558-4325
Fax: 909-558-4029
E-mail: lzhang@llu.edu

Lawrence D. Longo, M.D., Dr.H.C. (hon), FACOG, FRCOG
Bernard D. Briggs Distinguished Professor of Physiology
Center for Perinatal Biology
Department of Basic Sciences
Loma Linda University School of Medicine
Loma Linda, CA
Tel: 909-558-4325
Fax: 909-558-4029
E-mail:llongo@llu.edu

Acknowledgments

We are in great debt to Jimin Suh for her tireless efforts in helping to prepare and edit the chapters of this book in their present forms. She is the finest associate for whom one could wish.

In: Stress and Developmental Programming …
Editors: Lubo Zhang and Lawrence D. Longo

ISBN: 978-1-63321-836-9
© 2014 Nova Science Publishers, Inc.

Chapter 1

Developmental Origins of Health and Disease: The Past and the Future

Peter D. Gluckman[*] *and Tatjana Buklijas*
Liggins Institute, the University of Auckland, Grafton, Auckland, New Zealand

Abstract

Developmental Origins of Health and Disease (DOHaD) is a conceptual paradigm used to describe a cluster of phenomena and processes that link the environmental conditions of the early life with the state of health and risk of disease in later life. Based on this paradigm, a field bringing together experimental science with clinical medicine, epidemiology and public health has emerged over the past three decades. This chapter examines the history of the paradigm and the field; discusses criticisms of DOHaD and barriers to its acceptance within the broader research community as well as to its integration into policy; and, finally, considers future directions that the field may take, and its potential impact on reducing the global burden of non-communicable diseases (NCDs).

Keywords: Development, disease, fetal growth restriction, nutrition, programming, stress

Introduction

Developmental Origins of Health and Disease (DOHaD) is a conceptual paradigm used to describe a cluster of phenomena and processes that link the environmental conditions of the early life with the state of health and risk of disease in later life (Gluckman et al., 2010). In its narrowest sense, the term has been used to describe associations between normative conditions of prenatal and infant life with the risks of developing metabolic or cardiovascular disease in later life. Since the beginnings of the field in the 1980s, most research has focused

---

[*] Corresponding author: Professor Peter D. Gluckman, FRS, Liggins Institute, The University of Auckland, E-mail: pd.gluckman@auckland.ac.nz.

on the associations between changes in maternal and infant nutrition, and between maternal behaviour and glucocorticoid-mediated stress on the offspring, and later health risks. There is now a growing recognition that many of the processes underpinning the DOHaD phenomena involve epigenetic mechanisms shaping the normative processes of developmental plasticity. Consideration of other environmental exposures, such as environmental toxins, has been incorporated into the field and research has expanded to include a much broader range of observed phenomena, including allergies and immune disorders, osteoporosis, cancer and mental illness. As developmental toxicology has extended beyond overt teratogenesis, there is now a strong overlap between that field and DOHaD research. More recently the period of interest has expanded to include the preconceptional period and then role of paternal factors. In this chapter, following a brief overview of the origins of the paradigm and the field, we will discuss key research directions in the DOHaD, major critiques and obstacles to broader recognition, as well as possible future research areas and ways in which DOHaD could contribute to the reduction in the global burden of NCDs.

Historical Origins

That the conditions of early life might have an effect on later life health was alluded as early as the Hippocratic writings in the Classical Greece, but the modern history of this problem has arguably begun with the Scottish mathematical epidemiologist William Ogilvy Kermack who in the 1930s argued that life expectancy crucially depended on the "conditions existing during the years 0-15" (Smith and Kuh, 2001). In the same period, experimental teratologists working with animal models collected convincing evidence for the importance of certain environmental factors, especially nutrients, for healthy development (Kalter, 2003). Yet human data remained fairly unpersuasive until the "natural experiments"—that is the exposure of civilian populations to long-lasting famines—of the Second World War. The earliest information came from the siege of Leningrad in the Soviet Union, showing how severe famine in the third trimester of pregnancy resulted in more underweight and stillborn children, while starvation around conception and in the early weeks radically reduced the number of births (Antonov, 1947). Similar but much more detailed and conclusive data were collected during the food shortages in Western Holland under German siege between September 1944 and May 1945, a period that came to be known as "Dutch Winter Famine" (Smith, 1947a, 1947b).

Post-Second World War, working in East Germany in the 1960s and 1970s, the Berlin endocrinologist Günther Dörner undertook a number of experimental and clinical studies (on the cohort of men born before, during and after Second World War) to look for links between fetal conditions and later phenotype and argue for the importance of maternal nutrition for the later susceptibility to metabolic and cardiovascular disease (Dörner et al., 1973). Dörner advocated a new science of *functional teratology* that would study such prenatally and early postnatally acquired predispositions to later disease (Dörner et al., 2008, Plagemann, 2004). He argued that the concentrations of hormones, metabolites and neurotransmitters during critical early developmental periods could 'preprogramme' feedback loops regulating reproduction and metabolism and thus predispose the organism to disease (Dörner, 1975, Koletzko, 2005). At the same time, Norbert Freinkel introduced the term *metabolic teratogenesis* to describe the effect of gestational diabetes on the offspring (Freinkel, 1980). In the same period and working with a rat model of experimentally induced intrauterine growth restriction (IUGR), Frans Van Assche and associates showed that the growth-retarded offspring developed insulinopenia and insulin resistance (De Prins and Van Assche, 1982). However, the clinical relevance of this critical study was not recognized at the time.

In the 1970s, Anders Forsdahl found positive correlation between mortality from cardiovascular disease in people aged 40-69 years in individual Norwegian counties and county infant mortality in the early years of the same cohorts (Forsdahl, 1977). Arguably the first clinical observations that directly supported what became the DOHaD paradigm were those of Gian-Paolo Ravelli, Mervyn Susser and Zena Stein who found higher rates of obesity in the offspring of women in whom the first half of their pregnancies (with the studied offspring) took place during the "Dutch Winter Famine" of 1944-45 (Ravelli et al., 1976). Then in 1980 Millicent Higgins and colleagues, using a birth cohort in Michigan, U. S. A., found significantly higher systolic blood pressure in sons of mothers who had preeclampsia or gestational hypertension during the pregnancy (with that child), suggesting "the possibility of an intrauterine environmental effect" (Higgins et al., 1980). But this work failed to attract much attention.

In the 1980s, Gerhard Gennser and Michael Wadsworth showed independently that low birth weight was associated with a greater risk of hypertension (Gennser et al., 1986, Wadsworth et al., 1985). At about the same time, using historical data from the early twentieth century, David Barker and Clive Osmond reported an association between the geographical distribution of infant mortality and of later coronary heart disease mortality in England and Wales (Barker and Osmond, 1986). From there, Barker and his collaborators went on to show a relationship between birth weight, blood pressure and heart rate at the age of 10 and cardiovascular mortality (Barker et al., 1989). These studies were then expanded to show the relationships between birth size and later risks of diabetes and hypertension. Around this time, Alan Lucas proposed the term *programming* to describe the long-term consequences of different forms of infant nutrition (breast milk, enriched and standard formula) upon later risk of cardiovascular and metabolic disease (Lucas, 1991). He defined it as a process whereby a stimulus or insult, at a critical period of development, has lasting or lifelong significance. Barker adopted this term in the proposed meaning (Barker, 1994); it soon came into wide usage.

While there was a complex and long gestation for the DOHaD paradigm, it was the commitment of Barker to popularise the phenomena for which he invented the umbrella term of *fetal origins of adult disease* that initiated an explosion of interest in the field. Barker's own group produced multiple observations supporting the idea; soon others too began making epidemiological observations linking birth size to later risks of hypertension and insulin resistance. A key event in the evolution of the DOHaD field took place in 1990, when Barker, at the advice of the doyen of fetal physiology, Geoffrey Dawes, met with scholars of the physiology of fetal growth at a conference on "Fetal autonomy and adaptation" (Dawes et al., 1990). In 1994, the first workshop on fetal origins of adult disease was held in Sydney (Barker et al., 1995). It comprised a meeting between Barker's group, Nicholas Hales from Cambridge, UK, Jeffrey Robinson's group in Adelaide, Australia and Peter Gluckman's group in Auckland, New Zealand. The latter two were large experimental physiology groups focused on fetal growth. That meeting of perhaps 25 people was the start of a rapidly expanding series of annual workshops. By the end of the decade, this meeting had grown to over 200 attendees and it was clear that the field had both solid epidemiological and experimental basis.

Prospective studies in children born with IUGR had shown they had marked insulin resistance in childhood (Hofman et al., 1997). A range of experiments in rodents had linked poor maternal nutrition with hypertension and metabolic compromise in the offspring as adults (Erhuma et al., 2007, Langley-Evans et al., 1994, Vickers et al., 2000, Woodall et al., 1996). Under David Barker's leadership, leading investigators of that period created the Council for the Fetal Origins of Adult Disease (FOAD) and the first global congress on FOAD was held in Mumbai in 2001. At the second congress, in Brighton, UK, in 2003, it was decided to transform from a council into an academic society. Gluckman, who was at that time chair of the Council of FOAD, became the founding president. At the same time, the founders of the society took the opportunity to change the brand from FOAD to *developmental origins of health and disease* (DOHaD), to recognize observations suggesting the importance of the first two years of life to programming, such as the work of Lucas and others on the long term consequences of breastfeeding.

At the same time an increasing amount of new research has been presented in many other venues, particularly in those related to fetal physiology. Despite all this activity and progress the field had little impact on public health and clinical medicine. The lack of influence had continued to bedevil the field until recently: most notably, in 2011, the implications of DOHaD were recognized in the UN High Level Declaration on Non-Communicable Disease (United Nations General Assembly, 2012).

Barriers to the Acceptance of the DOHaD Concept

The concept of DOHaD is supported by a vast amount of experimental, clinical and epidemiological data, yet its integration into medical and public health thinking has been slow and it remains peripheral to the dominant paradigm in these fields. This marginality has implications for the future research agenda. Several reasons can be identified.

First, the initial focus arising from the work of Barker (and then others) was on the consequences of low birth weight. This focus influenced the direction of a raft of experimental studies, which induced IUGR in animal models, and clinical studies, comparing the later outcomes of normal-weight and IUGR offspring. The centrality of low birth weight became entrenched, even though there was, within the data sets, clear evidence that the association between birth size and health outcomes was continuous across the birth size range. Given that low birth weight represented a minority of infants (in developed world), its implications for explaining the epidemic of NCDs were not credible. Similarly, while the early arguments relied heavily on data obtained from the offspring of pregnancies during the Dutch Winter Famine (Painter et al., 2005, Ravelli et al., 1976), data from other famines, e.g. the Leningrad siege, were far less clear (Stanner and Yudkin, 2001).

Secondly, initial thinking assumed the existence of a single programming pathway. Thus, the finding of negative associations between birth size and outcomes in some studies led to a critical stance regarding the importance of the claimed relationship (Huxley et al., 2002). Only later the recognition grew that there were multiple ways in which early life events could inform later disease outcomes (Kuzawa et al., 2007) and that birth weight was only a proxy for intrauterine events. Programming could happen in the absence of birth weight effects, as supported by a study showing the impact of the variation in maternal nutrition upon childhood carotid intima-media thickness independent from birth weight (Gale et al., 2006). A more sophisticated understanding of the developmental events was required. There are at least two major classes of inductive process: those associated with suboptimal nutritional conditions or excessive maternal stress and later disease risk—so the processes that most were studying in the initial studies—as well as those associated with gestational diabetes, maternal obesity and infant overfeeding. The latter class was studied by another group of scholars and results were often presented in different venues. The relative importance of these pathways clearly differed in different populations and at different stages of the nutritional transition.

Thirdly, plausible biological mechanisms were not apparent in the 1990s although much effort did and continues to focus on the physiological underpinnings of DOHaD. The recognition that both nutritional and glucocorticoid-mediated mechanisms could have programming-type effects in experimental animals dominated these studies. Many empirical observations on fetal and offspring cardiovascular and metabolic physiology emerged from studies where the level of maternal manipulation was significant. This emphasis reflected in part the strong influence of scholars whose background was in fetal physiology. It was not until the mid-2000s that experimental studies began to suggest the key underlying role of molecular epigenetic processes (Lillycrop et al., 2005). Now epigenetic research is a dominant component of the DOHaD research agenda both experimentally and clinically (Gluckman et al., 2009, Godfrey et al., 2011). This shift to epigenetic studies has placed DOHaD research into the mainstream of current molecular research endeavours.

Fourthly, there was need for a compelling conceptual framework to link the events of early life to consequences that did not appear until middle age. In 1992, Hales and Barker proposed the influential "thrifty phenotype" hypothesis, using the thrifty "label" to position themselves as a credible alternative to James Neel's "thrifty genotype" explanation of the modern epidemic of NCDs (Hales and Barker, 1992, Neel, 1962). Namely, in the 1960s Neel argued that in the human past "thrifty genes" had been selected to survive the periods of famine; in the affluent modern world, such a genetic makeup contributed to disease risk. For all the problems and limitations, "thrifty genotype" has remained popular, with the search for "thrifty genes" still ongoing. The developmental "thrifty phenotype" hypothesis argued that nutritionally inadequate conditions in pregnancy induced offspring phenotype that included low birth weight and insulin resistance. While well adapted to starvation, in a nutritionally abundant postnatal environment such a fetus had a higher risk of metabolic disease. This hypothesis, however, still placed birth weight on the causal pathway. It also assumed that insulin resistance found in diabetes appears in utero, yet evidence has shown that growth-restricted offspring may first go through a period of increased insulin sensitivity, before they become insulin resistant several years after birth (Mericq et al., 2005).

Nevertheless, this model provided a useful stimulus to reflect on possible evolutionary and adaptive significance of mechanisms implied in the DOHaD paradigm, and it was from this basis that subsequent theoretical models emerged. Gluckman and Hanson on one hand and Bateson on the other, initially independently and then jointly, proposed a more robust and integrated formulation. They suggested that it was important to distinguish environmental influences in development that disrupt the developmental programme (i.e. were teratogenic) from those of potentially adaptive significance (in Darwinian terms). The latter processes of developmental plasticity were evolutionarily conserved and allowed the developing organism to respond to normative cues in ways that promote its survival and reproductive potential (Bateson and Gluckman, 2011, Bateson et al., 2004, 2014, Gluckman et al., 2005, Hanson and Gluckman, 2014). Extreme environmental cues may induce immediate responses in the fetus, leading, for example, to growth retardation (Gluckman et al., 2005). By contrast, responses to moderate environmental cues may only become apparent later. The latter came to be termed predictive adaptive responses (PARs). Gluckman and Hanson suggested that it was the mismatch between early life experience, which informed adaptive developmental plasticity, and later environment that could explain the DOHaD phenomena induced by normative exposures *in utero*.

The PARs paradigm has been criticized primarily on arguments relating to maternal-fetal conflict theory (e. g., Wells, 2007), but has received considerable empirical support (Hanson and Gluckman, 2014). Theoretical criticisms have been extensively addressed (Bateson and Gluckman, 2011, Bateson et al., 2014, Gluckman et al., 2008). Gluckman and Hanson have also pointed out that exposures that were novel in evolutionary terms would potentially act through other mechanisms to induce long-term effects. Gestational diabetes (Ma et al., 2013), maternal obesity and infant formula feeding can be considered as such evolutionarily novel exposures. While much focus has been on the role of the adipogenic effects of fetal or neonatal hyperinsulinemia in these latter circumstances, epigenetic mechanisms may also be involved (reviewed in Low et al., 2014).

Perhaps the biggest issue impeding acceptance of DOHaD as an epidemiologically important phenomenon was the inability to estimate its significance for the rising incidence of non-communicable diseases. The escalating epidemic of gestational diabetes in Asia, where up to 25% of pregnant women suffer from this condition, highlights the growing importance of non-adaptive pathways to later disease risk (Tutino et al., 2014). However, the role of pathways operative in normative situations has been unclear. As suggested above, the early focus on small-for-gestational-age (SGA) had limited the significance of DOHaD in the minds of many. Recent development of specific epigenetic tools has helped show that some epigenetic marks at birth both reflect prenatal experience and predict postnatal phenotypic outcomes. While this work is still in early stages, it does suggest a much bigger role for early life determinants in the aetiology of NCDs than the role that has generally been accepted. For example, more than 20% of the variance in childhood body composition can be explained by variance in a single epigenetic mark at birth, which in turn is influenced by maternal nutrition in the first trimester (Godfrey et al., 2011). This finding should be contrasted with current estimates of the role of fixed genomic variation in the origin of obesity, where known polymorphisms have a combined effect around 3% (Li et al., 2010).

The Future of DOHAD Research

There are some exciting new components to the research agenda. Molecular epigenetic approaches seem likely to help both detail the mechanism of programming and identify the role of a broader range of inducing cues. It is hoped they will also allow better estimates of risk and help construct approaches to prevention or intervention. Data suggesting the role of pre-conceptional and early pregnancy conditions are rapidly accumulating; strong evidence may well lead to fundamental changes in public health strategies. Recent data suggest the role of paternal factors operating through sperm mediated epigenetic changes: this is now a rapidly expanding area of research (e. g., Carone et al., 2010, Wei et al., 2014). Finally, the potential for epigenetic inheritance has moved from a theoretical "neo-Lamarckian" concept (Jablonka and Lamb, 2005) to being empirically proven in many comparative studies (Jablonka and Raz, 2009). There are now some suggestive human data (Pembrey et al., 2006, Savage et al., 2014). Small but important literature has furthermore pointed out that taste and food preference and satiety are established in early life: in some of the animal models of programming major effects on appetite control, food preference and free exercise have been noted (Bellinger et al., 2004, Vickers et al., 2003). The DOHaD community is yet to give sufficient attention to the role of central processes in the pathway to metabolic compromise.

DOHaD and the Global NCD Agenda

In the last decade there has been an escalating concern globally over the burden of NCDs. The projections for the burden of these diseases on the global health budget are frightening (Sassi and Hurst, 2008), so in both developed and developing countries demands for strategies to reduce the burden of obesity and its associated morbidities have been growing. While the WHO agenda continues to focus on attempts to modify adult lifestyle, the science of DOHaD suggests that a broader agenda is needed. The basic argument is that early life exposures alter the sensitivity of the individual to an obesogenic environment (Gluckman et al., 2011). While attempts at lifestyle modification will continue to be important, primary prevention may be best achieved by focusing on the conditions of early life. This approach was suggested in the UK Foresight analysis (Government Office for Science (UK), 2007). In 2011, the UN General Assembly organized a high level meeting on NCDs. The clause 26 of the resulting political declaration referred directly to the DOHaD phenomenon while other clauses brought up the need for a life course approach (United Nations General Assembly, 2012).

What the DOHaD community needs to provide is convincing evidence regarding appropriate and effective ways in which to use the knowledge of DOHaD in a public health context. Ways to reverse the induction of programming have been shown experimentally (Pinney et al., 2011, Vickers et al., 2005). While such findings do not easily translate into clinically feasible solutions, assuming that biomarkers of risk to justify intervention could be found, preventative approaches targeted at parental health before and during pregnancy, and perhaps also to the offspring health during infancy, seem a more likely approach. Formal interventional trials addressing maternal and potentially paternal lifestyle will be required. In addition to providing evidence, the DOHaD community needs to put more effort into integrating its research findings with the broader maternal, neonatal, infant and reproductive community. This remains a major challenge.

Conclusion

While research into the impact of the conditions of early development for later-life disease risk has a history extending over many decades, the DOHaD field only consolidated in the 1990s, after the efforts first of David Barker and then many others. The extensive empirical research supported by conceptual development and many of the issues raised above which inhibited the uptake of DOHaD into mainstream, pathophysiological thought have been addressed. But, as discussed above, there are also many important outstanding questions that need to be addressed before it is clear how and to what extent this knowledge can advance the human condition.

References

Antonov, A. N. (1947). Children born during the siege of Leningrad in 1942. *J Pediatr, 30,* 250-9.

Barker, D. J., Gluckman, P. D. & Robinson, J. S. (1995). Conference report: fetal origins of adult disease. Report of the First International Study Group, Sydney, 29-30 October 1994. *Placenta, 16,* 317-20.

Barker, D. J. P. (1994). *Mothers, babies, and disease in later life*. London: BMJ Publishing Group.

Barker, D. J. P. & Osmond, C. (1986). Infant mortality, childhood nutrition, and ischaemic heart disease in England and Wales. *Lancet, 1,* 1077-81.

Barker, D. J. P., Osmond, C., Golding, J., Kuh, D. & Wadsworth, M. E. J. (1989). Growth in utero, blood pressure in childhood and adult life, and mortality from cardiovascular disease. *Br Med J, 298,* 564-7.

Bateson, P., Barker, D. J. P., Clutton-Brock, T., Deb, D., D'Udine, B., Foley, R. A., et al. (2004). Developmental plasticity and human health. *Nature, 430,* 419-21.

Bateson, P. & Gluckman, P. D. (2011). *Plasticity, robustness, development and evolution*. Cambridge: Cambridge University Press.

Bateson, P., Gluckman, P. D. & Hanson, M. A. (2014). The biology of developmental plasticity and the hypothesis of the Predictive Adaptive Response. *J Physiol,592,* 2357-68.

Bellinger, L., Lilley, C. & Langley-Evans, S. C. (2004). Prenatal exposure to a maternal low-protein diet programmes a preference for high-fat foods in the young rat. *Br J Nutr, 92,* 513-20.

Carone, B. R., Fauquier, L., Habib, N., Shea, J. M., Hart, C. E., Li, R., et al. (2010). Paternally induced transgenerational environmental reprogramming of metabolic gene expression in mammals. *Cell, 143,* 1084-96.

Dawes, G. S., Borruto, F., Zacutti, A. & Zacutti, A. J. (Eds). (1990). *Fetal autonomy and adaptation*. Chichester: John Wiley & Sons.

De Prins, F. A. & Van Assche, F. A. (1982). Intrauterine growth retardation and development of endocrine pancreas in the experimental rat. *Biol Neonate, 41,* 16-21.

Dörner, G., Haller, H. & Leonhardt, W. (1973). Zur möglichen Bedeutung der prä- und/oder frühpostnatalen Ernährung für die Pathogenese der Arteriosklerose. *Acta Biol Med Ger, 31,* K31-5.

Dörner, G. (1975). Perinatal hormone levels and brain organization. In: W.E.Stumpf & L.D.Grant (Eds.), *Anatomical Neuroendocrinology* (pp. 245-252). Basel: Karger.

Dörner, G., Rodekamp, E. & Plagemann, A. (2008). Maternal deprivation and overnutrition in early postnatal life and their primary prevention: Historical reminiscence of an "ecologic experiment" in Germany. *human_ontogenetics*, *2*, 51-9.

Erhuma, A., Salter, A. M., Sculley, D. V., Langley-Evans, S. C. & Bennett, A. J. (2007). Prenatal exposure to a low-protein diet programs disordered regulation of lipid metabolism in the aging rat. *Am J Physiol Endocrinol Metab*, *292*, E1702-14.

Forsdahl, A. (1977). Are poor living conditions in childhood and adolescence an important risk for arteriosclerotic heart disease? *Br J Prev Soc Med*, *31*, 91-5.

Freinkel, N. (1980). Banting lecture 1980. Of pregnancy and progeny. *Diabetes*, *29*, 1023-35.

Gale, C. R., Jian, B., Robinson, S. M., Godfrey, K. M., Law, C. M. & Martyn, C. N. (2006). Maternal diet during pregnancy and carotid intima-media thickness in children. *Arterioscler Thromb Vasc Biol*, *26*, 1877-82.

Gennser, G., Rymark, P. & Isberg, P. E. (1986). Low birth weight and risk of high blood pressure in adulthood. *Br Med J (Clin Res Ed)*, *296*, 1498-500.

Gluckman, P. D., Hanson, M. A. & Buklijas, T. (2010). A conceptual framework for the developmental origins of health and disease. *J Dev Orig Health Dis*, *1*, 6-18.

Gluckman, P. D., Hanson, M. A., Buklijas, T., Low, F. M. & Beedle, A. S. (2009). Epigenetic mechanisms that underpin metabolic and cardiovascular diseases. *Nat Rev Endocrinol*, *5*, 401-8.

Gluckman, P. D., Hanson, M. A. & Spencer, H. G. (2008). Predictive adaptive responses and human evolution. *Trends Ecol Evol*, *20*, 527-33.

Gluckman, P. D., Hanson, M. A., Spencer, H. G. & Bateson, P. (2005). Environmental influences during development and their later consequences for health and disease: implications for the interpretation of empirical studies. *Proc Biol Sci*, *272*, 671-7.

Gluckman, P. D., Hanson, M. A., Zimmet, P. & Forrester, T. (2011). Losing the war against obesity: the need for a developmental perspective. *Sci Transl Med*, *3*, 93cm19.

Godfrey, K. M., Sheppard, A., Gluckman, P. D., Lillycrop, K. A., Burdge, G. C., McLean, C., et al. (2011). Epigenetic gene promoter methylation at birth is associated with child's later adiposity. *Diabetes*, *60*, 1528-34.

Government Office for Science (UK) (2007). Foresight: tacking obesities: future choices-- project report. Available online at http://www.bis.gov.uk/foresight/our-work/projects/ published-projects/tackling-obesities. London.

Hales, C. N. & Barker, D. J. P. (1992). Type 2 (non-insulin-dependent) diabetes mellitus: the thrifty phenotype hypothesis. *Diabetologia*, *35*, 595-601.

Hanson, M. A. & Gluckman, P. D. (2014). Early developmental conditioning: implications for health and disease. *Physiol Rev*, in press.

Higgins, M., Keller, J., Moore, F., Ostrander, L., Metzner, H. & Stock, L. (1980). Studies of blood pressure in Tecumseh, Michigan: Familial characteristics and complications of pregnancy in mothers. *Am J Epidemiol*, *111*, 142-55.

Hofman, P. L., Cutfield, W. S., Robinson, E. M., Bergman, R. N., Menon, R. K., Sperling, M. A., et al. (1997). Insulin resistance in short children with intrauterine growth retardation. *J Clin Endocrinol Metab*, *82*, 402-6.

Huxley, R., Neil, A. & Collins, R. (2002). Unravelling the fetal origins hypothesis: is there really an inverse association between birthweight and subsequent blood pressure? *Lancet*, *360*, 659-65.

Jablonka, E. & Lamb, M. (2005). *Evolution in four dimensions: genetic, epigenetic, behavioral and symbolic variation in the history of life*. Cambridge: MIT Press.

Jablonka, E. & Raz, G. (2009). Transgerational epigenetic inheritance: prevalence, mechanisms, and implications for the study of heredity and evolution. *Q Rev Biol, 84*, 131-76.

Kalter, H. (2003). Teratology in the 20th century: Environmental causes of congenital malformations in humans and how they were established. *Neurotoxicol Teratol, 25*, 131-282.

Koletzko, B. (2005). Letter to the editor: Developmental origins of adult disease: Barker's or Dörner's hypothesis? *Am J Hum Biol* 17:381-382.

Kuzawa, C. W., Gluckman, P. D. & Hanson, M. A. (2007). Developmental perspectives on the origin of obesity. In: G. Fantuzzi & T. Mazzone (Eds.), *Adipose tissue and adipokines in health and disease* (pp. 207-19). Totowa, NJ: Humana Press.

Langley-Evans, S. C., Phillips, G. J. & Jackson, A. A. (1994). In utero exposure to maternal low protein diets induces hypertension in weanling rats, independently of maternal blood pressure changes. *Clin Nutr, 13*, 319-24.

Li, S., Zhao, J. H., Luan, J., Luben, R. N., Rodwell, S. A., Khaw, K. T., et al. (2010). Cumulative effects and predictive value of common obesity-susceptibility variants identified by genome-wide association studies. *Am J Clin Nutr, 91*, 184-90.

Lillycrop, K. A., Phillips, E. S., Jackson, A. A., Hanson, M. A. & Burdge, G. C. (2005). Dietary protein restriction of pregnant rats induces and folic acid supplementation prevents epigenetic modificaiton of hepatic gene expression in the offspring. *J Nutr, 135*, 1382-6.

Low, F. M., Gluckman, P. D. & Hanson, M. A. (2014). Epigenetic and developmental basis of risk of obesity and metabolic disease. In: A. Ulloa-Aguirre & P. M. Conn (Eds.), *Cellular endocrinology in health and disease* (pp. 111-32). Burlington: Elsevier Science.

Lucas, A. (1991). Programming by early nutrition in man. In: G. R. Bock & J. Whelan, (Eds.), *The childhood environment and adult disease. CIBA Foundation Symposium 156* (pp. 38-55). Chichester, UK: Wiley.

Ma, R. C., Chan, J. C., Tam, W. H., Hanson, M. A. & Gluckman, P. D. (2013). Gestational diabetes, maternal obesity, and the NCD burden. *Clin Obstet Gynecol, 56*, 633-41.

Mericq, V., Ong, K. K., Bazaes, R. A., Pena, V., Avila, A., Salazar, T., et al. (2005). Longitudinal changes in insulin sensitivity and secretion from birth to age three years in small- and appropriate-for-gestational-age children. *Diabetologia, 48*, 2609-14.

Neel, J. V. (1962). Diabetes mellitus: a "thrifty" genotype rendered detrimental by "progress"? *Am J Hum Genet, 14*, 353-62.

Painter, R. C., Roseboom, T. J. & Bleker, O. P. (2005). Prenatal exposure to the Dutch famine and disease in later life: an overview. *Reprod Toxicol, 20*, 345-52.

Pembrey, M. E., Bygren, L. O., Kaati, G., Edvinsson, S., Northstone, K. & Sjöström, M. (2006). Sex-specific, male-line transgenerational responses in humans. *Eur J Hum Genet, 14*, 159-66.

Pinney, S. E., Jaeckle Santons, L. J., Han, Y., Stoffers, D. A. & Simmons, R. A. (2011). Exendin-4 increases histone acetylase activity and reverses epigenetic modifications that silence Pdx1 in the intrauterine growth retarded rat. *Diabetologia, 54*, 2606-14.

Plagemann, A. (2004). "Fetal programming" and "functional teratogenesis": on epigenetic mechanisms and prevention of perinatally acquired lasting health risks. *J Perinat Med, 32*, 297-305.

Ravelli, G. P., Stein, Z. A. & Susser, M. W. (1976). Obesity in young men after famine exposure in utero and early infancy. *N Engl J Med, 295*, 345-53.

Sassi, F. & Hurst, J. (2008). The prevention of lifestyle-related chronic diseases: an economic framework. OECD Health Working Paper no. 32. Available online at http://www.oecd.org/els/health-systems/40324263.pdf.

Savage, T., Derraik, J. G., Miles, H. L., Mouat, F., Hofman, P. L. & Cutfield, W. S. (2014). Increasing paternal age at childbirth is associated with taller stature and less favourable lipid profiles in their children. *Clin Endocrinol (Oxf), 80*, 253-60.

Smith, C. A. (1947a). The effect of wartime starvation in Holland upon pregnancy and its product. *Am J Obstet Gynecol, 53*, 599-608.

Smith, C. A. (1947b). Effects of maternal undernutrition upon the newborn infant in Holland (1944-45). *J Pediatr, 30*, 229-43.

Smith, G. D. & Kuh, D. (2001). William Ogilvy Kermack and the childhood origins of adult health and disease. *Int J Epidemiol, 30*, 696-703.

Stanner, S. A. & Yudkin, J. S. (2001). Fetal programming and the Leningrad siege study. *Twin Res*, 4, 287-92.

Tutino, G. E., Tam, W. H., Yang, X., Chan, J. C., Lao, T. T. & Ma, R. C. (2014). Diabetes and pregnancy: perspectives from Asia. *Diabet Med, 31*, 302-18.

United Nations General Assembly (2012). Resolution adopted by the General Assembly. Political Declaration of the High-level Meeting of the General Assembly on the Prevention and Control of Non-communicable Diseases. 24 Jan 2012. http://www.who.int/nmh/events/un_ncd_summit2011/political_declaration_en.pdf.

Vickers, M. H., Breier, B. H., Cutfield, W. S., Hofman, P. L. & Gluckman, P. D. (2000). Fetal origins of hyperphagia, obesity and hypertension and postnatal amplification by hypercaloric nutrition. *Am J Physiol, 279*, E83-7.

Vickers, M.H., Breier, B.H., McCarthy, D. & Gluckman, P.D. (2003). Sedentary behaviour during postnatal life is determined by the prenatal environment and exacerbated by postnatal hypercaloric nutrition. *Am J Physiol, 285*, R271-3.

Vickers, M. H., Gluckman, P. D., Coveny, A. H., Hofman, P. L., Cutfield, W. S., Gertler, A., et al. (2005). Neonatal leptin treatment reverses developmental programming. *Endocrinology, 146*, 4211-6.

Wadsworth, M. E., Cripps, H. A., Midwinter, R. E. & Colley, J. R. (1985). Blood pressure in a national birth cohort at the age of 36 related to social and familial factors, smoking, and body mass. *Br Med J (Clin Res Ed), 291*, 1534-8.

Wei, Y., Yang, C. R., Wei, Y. P., Zhao, Z. A., Hou, Y., Schatten, H., et al. (2014). Paternally induced transgenerational inheritance of susceptibility to diabetes in mammals. *Proc Natl Acad Sci U S A, 111*, 1873-8.

Wells, J. C. (2007). Flaws in the theory of predictive adaptive responses. *Trends Endocrinol Metab, 18*, 331-7.

Woodall, S. M., Johnston, B. M., Breier, B. H. & Gluckman, P. D. (1996). Chronic maternal undernutrition in the rat leads to delayed postnatal growth and elevated blood pressure of offspring. *Pediatr Res, 40*, 438-43.

In: Stress and Developmental Programming …
Editors: Lubo Zhang and Lawrence D. Longo

ISBN: 978-1-63321-836-9
© 2014 Nova Science Publishers, Inc.

Chapter 2

Programming and the Barker Hypothesis

Kent Thornburg[1], Andrew J. Patterson[2] and Lubo Zhang[2]*

[1]Oregon Health Sciences University, Department of Medicine, Knight Cardiovascular Institute and Moore Institute for Nutrition and Wellness, Portland, OR, US
[2]Center for Perinatal Biology, Loma Linda University, School of Medicine, Loma Linda, CA, US

Abstract

Over the past half century, cardiovascular disease has been thought to arise more from abnormal genes and poor lifestyle choices than from underlying environmental-induced vulnerability. However, studies in the field of programming suggest a different view. Barker and colleagues demonstrated that the underpinnings of cardiovascular disease such as hypertension, type 2 diabetes and obesity are the direct result of inadequate growth during the formative stages of development or from exposure to stressors including hypoxemia and/or cortisol. It is now known that there are definite stages of embryonic and fetal development when the heart and blood vessels are especially vulnerable to these stressors. The pre-septation heart of the embryo is sensitive to a long list of stressors with hypoxia, hyperglycemia and altered sheer and stretch forces. Exposure to these stressors leads to structural and epigenetic changes that underlie heart defects and/or vulnerabilities for abnormal growth thereafter. The near term stage, when cardiomyocytes are undergoing terminal differentiation represents another critical period during which exposures to hormonal, nutritional or hypoxic episodes change the number of cardiomyocytes and coronary microvessels for life and lead for vulnerability to heart failure and coronary disease. In the later stages of heart development hypoxia leads to a suppression of cardiomyocyte hyperplasia and hearts are born endowed with fewer working cells that are larger than normal and hearts are more vulnerable to ischemic damage for life. Glucocorticoids are   steroid hormones that are required for normal development of the cardiovascular system but when present in excess before term

---

* Corresponding author: Kent L. Thornburg, PhD, Department of Medicine, Knight Cardiovascular Institute, Moore Institute for Nutrition and Wellness, Oregon Health and Science University, Portland, OR, E-mail: thornbur@ohsu.edu.

can lead to programming effects in the hearts of offspring. Abused drugs like cocaine and ethanol also have specific effects on the developing myocardium. In addition, the mechanisms that protect against ischemic damage such as PKC epsilon are suppressed in males through the methylation of specific sites on the promoter. Thus, epigenetic mechanisms, including DNA methylation and histone protein modifications are key to understanding the link between the intrauterine environment and later cardiovascular vulnerability. DNA methylation plays a critical role in gene repression. Methylated cytosines recruit methyl-binding proteins that restrict binding of transcription factors to promoter regions. Histone protein modifications regulate access of transcription machinery for selected genes. Histone proteins are modified by acetylation of lysine residues via histone acetyltransferases, deacetylation of lysine residues via histone deacetylases and methylation of lysine 4 on histone H3 is generally associated with transcriptional active promoters while multiple methylation of histone restricts transcription. Thus, vulnerability for cardiovascular disease has its primary roots in prenatal life. A growing number of underlying mechanisms have been identified. However, the field is in urgent need of investigation.

Keywords: Cardiovascular disease, cardiomyocytes, DNA methylation, epigenetic, glucocorticoids, histone protein, programming

Introduction

For half of the last century, chronic diseases like heart disease, type 2 diabetes and obesity have been thought to be either the direct result of a poor genetic endowment handed down from parents or the result of an unhealthy lifestyle. While there is no debating the evidence that these two purported causes are associated with these chronic conditions, it has been difficult to explain their roles in any mechanistic detail. For example, of the known risk factors for contracting coronary heart disease, some 10%-50% of people who contract the disease carry none of the well-advertised cardiovascular risk factors (Braunwald, 1997, Futterman and Lemberg, 1998, Khot et al., 2003) -- though the prevalence of people who have no risk factors is diminishing (CDC, 1999). People who do acquire heart disease in the absence of risk factors have been assumed to carry invisible detrimental risks derived from their poor genetic endowment. In addition there are unknown numbers of people who have one or more risk factors but who never acquire the disease. The people in the high risk group who never acquire the disease have been thought to carry protective genes. Thus, heart disease risk has been thought to reside mostly within the gene code itself.

However, the genetic roots of heart disease have been difficult to define in large populations even though a number of specific gene coding variants that lead to abnormal amino acid sequences and specific cardiovascular conditions are well characterized. A host of genome wide association studies (GWAS) have discovered a large number of single nucleotide polymorphisms (SNP) associated with specific cardiac conditions including coronary heart disease (Davies et al., 2012) and heart failure (Larson et al., 2007) as well as others. However, the usefulness of understanding these genetic variants as risk factors has not become evident thus far. In 2007 Cambien and Tiret stated, "The new strategy of genome-wide association studies coupled with the availability of very large cohorts is beginning to reveal novel genetic factors that contribute to disease risk. Whether these variants will be clinically more useful than those that were derived from the study of candidate genes still needs to be demonstrated" (Cambien and Tiret, 2007). SNPs that have been associated with disease often reside in non-coding regions of the genome and do not associate well with known risk factors.

GWAS proponents continue to predict that the complexity of minor gene variants will ultimately explain most of the current cardiovascular disease burden and, indeed, there are examples of gene variant discoveries that relate risk factors that are known to be important (Lieb et al., 2013). However, known disease risk alleles do not compromise human longevity making it less clear how genetic risks relate to long life in a large population (Beekman et al., 2010). Thus, it is too soon to know the degree to which genetic variation will explain cardiac disease susceptibility in different populations. All in all, SNP frequencies are not yet able to explain the large number of people who acquire heart disease and their geographic distribution.

If one compares the prevalence of mortality from these chronic diseases county by county within each of the lower 48 states, it becomes immediately clear that counties bearing the highest rates of cardiac deaths are found in the Deep South as are those with the highest rates of deaths from stroke, diabetes and obesity (CDC, 2004). If one attempted to assign a mostly genetic cause to the cardiovascular deaths, it would require not only that the most vulnerable genotypes for cardiovascular disease be found in the specific counties where excessively large numbers of people had cardiovascular disease, but also that all the genotypes that lead to the other major chronic diseases, including stroke, type 2 diabetes and obesity, be assigned to the same population. Thus one would be required to argue that people in the South carry a greater burden of deleterious genes for the most lethal of the chronic diseases than do people in other regions of the country. Given the difficulty of this argument, an alternative explanation is that the geographic distribution of chronic diseases has an overriding environmental cause.

A purely genetic explanation of the secular trends of mortality from heart disease in the USA and the Soviet Union is also not tenable. Early in the 20th Century, mortality rates from heart disease in the USA were low but rose rapidly so that by 1921 ischemic heart disease was the leading cause of death, its leadership position being held ever since (CDC, 1999, Jones et al., 2012). (See Figure 1) In the early 1950s the USA suffered an average of over 350 deaths/100,000, a figure which has declined to half that rate since the 1970s (See Figure 2) (CDC, 1999, Jones et al., 2012). During that same period of time, cardiac related diseases increased in the former Soviet Union countries even among populations with diverse ethnic backgrounds (Cooper, 1983) and heart disease deaths remain high today across those regions. Large, rapid changes in disease burden in a population, such as with rapid increases in rates of cardiac death in the early 20th century or with rapid increases in obesity over the past 20 years, cannot be explained by random mutation rates in the genome. Rather, an environmental explanation is required.

Without an overwhelming genetic explanation, it is tempting to blame victims who suffer chronic diseases in the South as perpetrators of their own demise because of their deleterious diets and other lifestyle choices. However, such an argument would not explain why people who live in other parts of the world who eat similar diets acquire these diseases less often or why even higher rates of disease are found in the former Soviet Union countries. While the search for genetic variants and lifestyle links to cardiovascular risk remain worthy pursuits, other more powerful disease drivers must be at play.

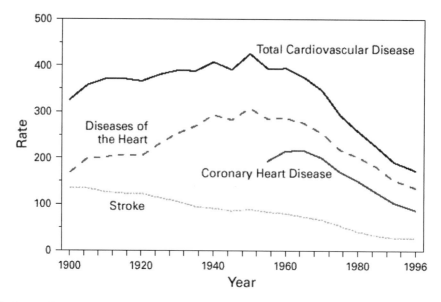

Figure 1. Age-Adjusted death rates* for total cardiovascular disease, diseases of the heart, coronary heart disease, and stroke, by year- United States, 1900-1996. *Per 100,000 population, standardized to the 1940 U.S. population. Centers for Disease Control. Achievements in public health U.S. 1900-1999, decline in deaths from heart disease and stroke – United States, 1900-1999.

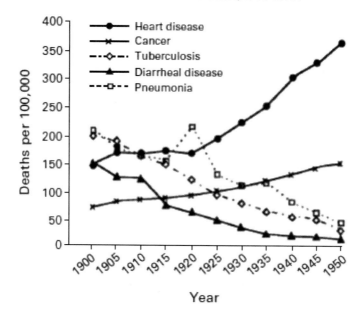

Figure 2. Crude Death Rates for Leading Causes of Death in the United States from 1900 to 1950. Data are from the Centers for Disease Control and Prevention.

The work of David Barker and colleagues points to additional sources of risk that go beyond genetic endowment and adult behavior (Barker, 1989). In the mid-1980s, Barker noticed that the industrial areas of England in the North had the highest rates of neonatal deaths and also had the highest mortality rates from ischemic heart disease in adulthood (Barker and Osmond, 1986, Barker et al., 1989b). Barker did not assign genetic variants or environmental pollutants as the culprits as he might have. Rather, he concluded that those who survived the high risk of being an infant continued, nevertheless, to be vulnerable for acquiring adult-onset heart disease and that this vulnerability arose from poor conditions in the womb (Barker et al., 1989b). Barker's team then went on to strengthen the point. They showed that in Hertfordshire, UK, people who had the lowest birthweights carried the highest risk for death from ischemic heart disease and those with the highest birthweights had the lowest risk over the 5lb to 9lb range (Barker et al., 1989a). From these data, Barker hypothesized that a person's risk for chronic disease was directly related to their acquisition of nutrients before birth and in infancy.

Thus, the resulting *Barker Hypothesis*, suggesting that prenatal growth determines a person's predisposition for heart disease, became well known and laid the foundation for a groundswell of studies around the world that has produced thousands of papers unfolding the relationship between intrauterine conditions and later disease. A new field of medicine, the Developmental Origins of Health and Disease (DOHaD), arose from the clear cut findings by fetal biologists (Gluckman et al., 2008). Over the past 25 years, a great deal has been learned about the developmental underpinnings of adult onset cardiovascular disease. The theory suggests that the plasticity of the genome during development accommodates shortages or excesses of nutrients, inadequate oxygen and excess glucocorticoid steroid hormones by modifying fetal growth and other less visible biological processes. Under these adverse conditions, fetal organs become compromised, i.e. manufactured "on the cheap," and are then more vulnerable for disease in later life. The compromise is structural, physiological and epigenetic (Gluckman et al., 2008, McMillen and Robinson, 2005). The emerging body of knowledge in the field demonstrates that specific organ systems in the developing fetus and infant can be detrimentally affected for life by insufficient nutrient flow across the placenta and that such shortages result in fetal compromises detrimentally affecting the systems that protect against oxidative stress, determine stem cell quality and stimulate inflammatory processes.

Now, in addition to cardiovascular disease, high and low birthweights are known to be related to a wide range of conditions including type 2 diabetes, stroke, hypertension, obesity, osteoporosis, asthma and many cancers (Barker and Thornburg, 2013a, Gluckman et al., 2008). While the risk for ischemic heart disease ranges some 3 to 5 fold across the normal birthweight range, the risk among English men for type 2 diabetes and metabolic syndrome appears to be much higher, approaching 8 to 15 fold (Hales and Barker, 2001). Thus, a 5 lb baby boy born in the '30s had an 8 fold greater risk for insulin resistance and/or type 2 diabetes than does a baby born at 9 lb. The metabolic syndrome, including type 2 diabetes, is foundational for cardiovascular disease (Braunwald, 1997).

The powerful inverse associations between prenatal growth and type 2 diabetes and metabolic syndrome have spawned the generation of new ideas about the evolutionary roots of type 2 diabetes, cardiovascular disease, obesity and cancer (Barker and Thornburg, 2013b). For example it has shed new light on the *thrifty genotype hypothesis*, proposed by Neel in 1962 (Neel, 1962) suggesting that over the millennia, human genes have come to favor putting on fat during times of plenty to ensure adequate energy stores during times of famine. Hales and Barker (2013) suggested that the hypothesis should now be interpreted in light of the developmental origins of disease. Their additional point was that developmental plasticity leads to changes in the individual phenotype in times of adversity in the womb, which provides the underpinnings for disease under conditions of plenty in postnatal life. They proposed the *thrifty phenotype hypothesis*.

The mismatch concept (Godfrey et al., 2007) is based on the idea that genetic processes driving development are influenced by intrauterine levels of nutrition that regulate metabolic and structural systems under the expectation or "prediction" that similar levels of nutrition are likely to exist after birth. If perchance, nutrient levels in the postnatal world are greater than "predicted" by prenatal environmental signals, the biological mismatch between the fetal prediction and the vastly different post-natal condition leads to a high risk for acquiring chronic diseases because of prenatal genetic patterns already in operation. While the thrifty phenotype and the mismatch ideas will undoubtedly be refined as the field develops, they have nevertheless been important for focusing the debate on the ancient genetic underpinnings of developmental plasticity that link environmental stressors to long term disease-promoting outcomes.

The finding that chronic disease risk is strongly related to the embryonic and fetal nutritional environment has solidified the original ideas proposed by Barker and his team through a large body of literature derived from animal and human studies. Thus, there are now well established links between the compromises required by the body as it was constructed in the womb and during infancy and later vulnerability for disease. *The phenomenon whereby suboptimal conditions in the womb lead to increased risks for chronic disease, called "programming"* (Lucas, 1991)*, now accounts for a substantial portion of the chronic disease burden across the globe* (Gluckman et al., 2008). This concept has changed the basic paradigm for understanding the origins of chronic disease. Where it was once thought to be driven by nefarious genes and self-destructive behavior, it is now more widely recognized that people who suffer chronic diseases are especially vulnerable to the ravages of life not only because of their genetic endowment but more because of their early life environment. And yes, life style undoubtedly influences the risk for disease over the life course-- but only to the degree that a person's vulnerability has been determined by experiences in early life.

The implications of this concept are profound. First, it means that the human race can now seriously discuss, for the first time, the eradication of chronic disease and second, it suggests that the increasingly expensive cost of medical treatment for chronic diseases could be reduced on a grand scale if well-constructed babies were born to well-nourished and unstressed mothers. This should be the stated goal of every society across the globe.

There are several features of programming that have come to light as the field has developed.

1. Developmental Sensitivity

Because individual embryonic organs arise, grow and mature at different rates over the duration of pregnancy, each is uniquely sensitive to the effects of stressors at any particular time of gestation, especially when it is growing most rapidly. Such periods have been recognized for the embryo for more than 60 years (Romanoff, 1949). Thus each organ has a critical window of development during which it is most vulnerable to the effects of inadequate nutrition, low oxygen or high levels of glucocorticoid hormones. In large mammals, most organs have become miniature versions of their fully grown counterparts by the time of parturition. However, a few systems, like the brain (Rice and Barone, 2000) and immune systems (Galic et al., 2009) are not mature at birth and continue to be easily modified by external environmental conditions throughout infancy and into early childhood.

2. Preimplantation Nutritional Stress

If sperm are present in the oviduct at the time of ovulation, the newly formed ovum will undergo its early stages of embryogenesis as it travels down the oviduct powered by ciliary forces. After some 6-8 days, it will be at the blastocyst stage and will have reached the body of the uterus where it will implant (Niakan et al., 2012). Over the past two decades it has become increasingly clear that the intratubal nutrient environment has a powerful influence on the development of the early embryo (Fleming et al., 2004). Both *in vivo* animal studies and *in vitro* human studies demonstrate the sensitivity of the early embryo to nutrient deprivation or excesses in the ductal fluid or culture medium (Duranthon et al., 2008, Watkins et al., 2008, Young et al., 2001). Changes in the nutritional environment lead to increased rates of cardiovascular and pulmonary abnormalities in the offspring (Fleming et al., 2004). In addition, rodent studies suggest that maternal nutrient deprivation that is restricted to the peri-ovulatory period affects the ovarian environment and maturing eggs, and leads to programming of offspring (Bernal et al., 2010, Watkins et al., 2008).

3. Transgenerational Effects

There is ample evidence that stressors that affect the flow of nutrients, restrict oxygen exchange across the placenta or lead to elevated levels of glucocorticoids in the fetal plasma influence the structural and epigenetic profile of offspring (Gluckman et al., 2008, Meaney, 2001, Patterson and Zhang, 2010). What is surprising, however, is the increasing evidence that not only is the F1 generation affected by intrauterine conditions but the F2 and even the F3 generation can also be affected (Aiken and Ozanne, 2014). Transgenerational environmental influences have been observed in human epidemiological studies as well as in numerous animal studies. The environmentally induced transgenerational epigenetic reprogramming of primordial germ cells and the subsequent germ line is only now being investigated (Migicovsky and Kovalchuk, 2011, Skinner et al., 2013). However, this area of programming is understudied.

4. Placental Influences

While it was learned some 20 years ago that placental weight as a proportion of fetal weight predicted a "U" shaped cardiovascular risk, (Martyn et al., 1996) (See Figure 3) recent studies of the role of the placenta in programming show that it is more complex and yet more important. Both animal and epidemiological studies have enlightened the field (Barker et al., 2013c, Godfrey, 2002, Jansson and Powell, 2013, Myatt, 2006, Thornburg et al., 2010). Recent work shows that the shape and size of the placenta, the length of the umbilical cord and the number of cotyledons are all factors that have associations with longevity and risk for chronic disease (Alwasel et al., 2013, Barker and Thornburg, 2013a, 2013b, Barker et al.,

2010b, 2013a, 2013b, Eriksson et al., 2013). Data from the Helsinki Birth Cohort have been especially helpful in determining the role of the placenta in predicting a number of chronic conditions. Studies from The Netherlands, Saudi Arabia, United Kingdom, and United States of America have also been helpful. The placenta plays an important theme in the development of heart disease and all evidence suggests that it is the organ most central to the programming process.

5. Maternal Influences

Maternal phenotype is known to influence the outcome of a pregnancy. Obesity and type 2 diabetes are examples. Recent data from the Helsinki Birth Cohort suggest that the combination of maternal body size and composition together with placental phenotype are more powerful predictors of many chronic diseases than is birthweight alone (Barker and Thornburg, 2013a, 2013b). For example, a woman's height, body mass index and hip width have all been shown to be associated with independent risk for a number of chronic diseases (Barker et al., 2008).

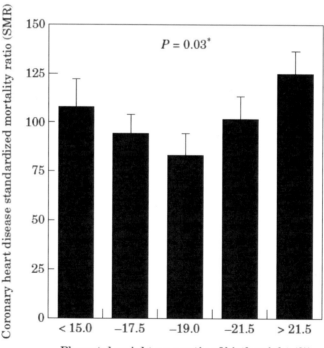

Figure 3. Death rates from coronary heart disease in 2571 men born in Sheffield, UK, during 1907-1930 (derived from Martyn, Barker and Osmond, 1996). *$P=$ for quadratic trend by log-linear regression. Values are SMR and standard error. (With permission from Godfrey et al. 2002).

Vulnerable Periods of Embryonic Development

Across the entire vertebrate development time scale, spanning fertilization to birth, the cardiovascular system is susceptible to stage-specific influences of stressors that interfere with normal developmental processes and result in long term abnormalities ranging from lethal structural defects to subtle propensities for late life chronic pathological conditions (Fahed et al., 2013, Gluckman et al., 2008, Srivastava and Olson, 2000, Thornburg et al., 2010). However, there are two stages of development, cardiogenesis in the embryo and cardiac maturation in the late term fetus during which the heart is particularly vulnerable to external stressors. During these two phases, developmental processes can be easily modified by environmental influences that put the heart on a path toward disease vulnerability. These two phases of development will be discussed below.

Embryonic Heart Development

The overriding question that haunts cardiac scientists is, why do the processes underlying the development of heart and vasculature get interrupted so often as to explain the nearly 1% of babies born alive suffer structural abnormalities of the heart and great vessels (Hoffman and Kaplan, 2002)? Thousands of papers have been written on the intricacies of heart construction during embryonic life. We now know that cardiac morphogenesis is highly complex and guided by a tightly regulated orchestration of gene expression patterns which when abnormally expressed lead to the long list of structural abnormalities that are well recognized clinically (Olson, 2006, Rossant, 1996, Srivastava, 2006a, 2006b, Srivastava and Olson, 2000). Abnormal gene expression patterns can arise from abnormal gene sequences or from alterations in the regulation of expression of normal gene sequences.

Therefore, there are two important processes that lead to structural abnormalities, 1) gene defects containing coding variants that lead to dysfunctional gene products (Srivastava and Olson, 2000), and 2) environmental effects where stressors alter the normal processes of development through gene-environment interactions (Zhu et al., 2009). Some of these interactions fit within the definition of epigenetics and some do not (van Weerd et al., 2011). Environmental factors include an extensive list of influences: abnormal incubation temperatures (De la Cruz et al., 1966), toxins (Wikenheiser et al., 2013), teratogens (Dawson et al., 1993), inappropriate oxygen levels (McCutcheon et al., 1982), inadequate nutrient supply (Zile, 2010), hyperglycemia (Corrigan et al., 2013, Scott-Drechsel et al., 2013), abnormal hormonal environment (Nesan and Vijayan, 2012) and altered hemodynamic forces (Granados-Riveron and Brook, 2012a, 2012b, Liu et al., 2012, Rugonyi et al., 2008).

There is a strong evolutionary theme that underlies heart developmental patterns across the animal kingdom (Kirby and Schachat, 2007, Olson, 2006, Perez-Pomares et al., 2009). While the stages of development have unique peculiarities among vertebrate phyla that are highly instructive, the general schemes are similar. The commonalities of structure and gene expression patterns among vertebrates are striking. The hearts of chicken (Kirby and Schachat, 2007, Martinsen, 2005) and mouse embryos (Olson, 2006, Savolainen et al., 2009, Xu and Baldini, 2007) have been most studied because of their obvious advantages in accessibility and genetic manipulation, respectively. In recent decades, the zebra fish model has been highly instructive as well because it offers both accessibility as well as genetic advantages (Auman et al., 2007).

The development of the vertebrate heart can be divided into stages based on molecular events and morphological milestones. Stages include the formation of the 1) heart fields, 2) heart tube, 3) looping heart and 4) septation during which the atrial, ventricular, outflow tract septa and valves are formed (See Figure 4). The newly formed 4-chambered heart including outflow structures is not yet a complete functional organ without added features including the epicardium, coronary circulation and conduction system. Each cell that contributes to the cardiac organ has an interesting developmental history and each is characterized by the expression of unique genes that drove its differentiation and maturation processes. In addition to the formation of the heart chambers, there are specific maturation processes in the cardiomyocytes that span the whole of gestation (Moorman and Christoffels, 2003, Xin et al., 2013).

As the developmental process moves seamlessly from one stage to the next, groups of transcription factors and other developmental genes are characteristically expressed often in overlapping temporal and spatial sequence. In general, precardiac mesoderm arises before and during the gastrulation stage of embryo development and forms the primitive heart field in the area designated as the cardiac crescent. Avian hearts are largely derived from two lateral primary heart fields (Kirby, 2007). As the progenitor cells accompany the folding tissue and migrate toward the midline, they begin the process of differentiation into endocardial and myocardial lineages. A primitive heart tube is formed by the folding and eventual fusion of the lateral heart fields as pharyngeal structures are being constructed. These lateral cells give rise to the heart tube which begins to beat soon after it has been formed.

In 2001, a trio of studies demonstrated the importance of a second heart field that populates cells in the extending outflow tract and the right ventricle in avian and murine hearts during the looping process (Kelly et al., 2001, Mjaatvedt et al., 2001, Waldo et al., 2001). There is now clear evidence that the growth of the mammalian outflow tract arises from contributions of pharyngeal mesoderm progenitors (Kelly et al., 2001) and furthermore, explant and DiI labeling experiments have confirmed that pharyngeal mesoderm gives rise to second field-derived cells that contribute to right ventricular and outflow tract structures (Zaffran et al., 2004). Thus, one new revelation of the 21st century is that the original heart tube does not contain all the regions of the definitive heart as was once thought (Waldo et al., 2001) and depicted in Figure 4.

A number of important gene expression patterns are clearly associated with cells that participate in the construction of the cardiac tube as shown in Figure 5 (Olson, 2006). Our current understanding of the contributions of specific patterns of gene expression that guide the differentiation and function of each cell type at every stage of development has been possible because of a host of new tools in molecular biology (Xu and Baldini, 2007).

Heart Tube

The early cardiac tube is composed of an inner endocardial layer which lines the lumen and an external compact myocardial layer that is separated by a gelatinous layer of extracellular matrix called cardiac jelly. The details can be found in a number of outstanding reviews (Harvey and Rosenthal, 1999, Kirby and Schachat, 2007, Rosenthal and Harvey, 2010). The heart begins to beat at this stage, on about day 21 to 23 postconception in the human; a detailed description of human heart development is available (Sizarov et al., 2011).

Looping

The heart tube lengthens and bends rightward in a process known as looping where the two ends of the heart tube approximate. As mentioned above, it is during this process that cells from the second heart field are incorporated into the outflow portion and unlike during the heart tube stage, the looped heart now contains cell precursors for each future segment including outflow tract, right ventricle, left ventricle, atrial chamber and sinus venosus.

Septation

The formation of the cardiac chambers is complex and requires tissue accretion, local site specific apoptosis and cellular migration in a temporally orchestrated fashion. The basic anatomic sequences have been known for the chicken embryo for nearly 100 years. Walls (septa) are formed within the primitive ventricles, atria and outflow tract to generate distinct chambers and vessels, including the right and left ventricles, right and left atria, aorta and pulmonary arteries (Kirby, 2007). However since the early descriptive studies it has become known that three different populations of extracardiac cells migrate into the heart to contribute to anatomic structures. Neural crest derived cells are important in the outflow septum, vestibular spine cells in the primary atrial septum and proepicardial cells populate the epicardium (Kirby, 2007).

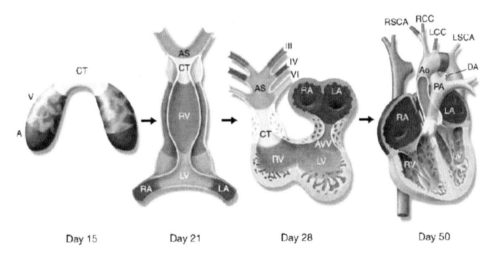

Figure 4. Human cardiac development, ventral view. Color coding represents morphologically related regions. Left panel is a crescent shaped region of cardiogenic precursors specified to form segments of the linear heart tube, which is patterned along the anterior–posterior axis to form the various regions and chambers of the looped and mature heart. Since this figure was first published cells from the second heart field are now known to contribute to the elongation of the outflow region and the right ventricle. The aortic arch arteries (III, IV and VI) and aortic sac (AS) are populated with neural crest that contributes to specific regions of the aortic arch. Mesenchymal cells form the cardiac valves from the conotruncal (CT) and atrioventricular valve (AVV) segments. A, atrium; Ao, aorta; DA, ductus arteriosus; LA, left atrium; LCC, left common carotid; LSCA, left subclavian artery; LV, left ventricle; PA, pulmonary artery; RA, right atrium; RCC, right common carotid; RSCA, right subclavian artery; RV, right ventricle; V, ventricle. (With permission, Srivastava and Olson, 2000).

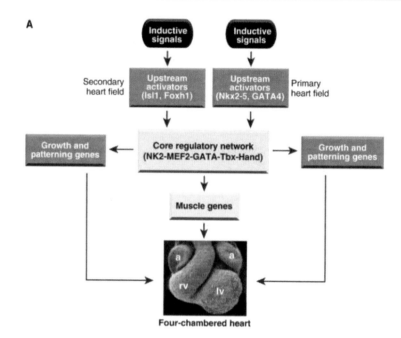

Figure 5. Inductive signals activate a set of upstream regulatory genes, encoding transcription factors, in the primary and secondary heart fields. The products of these genes activate the genes in the core cardiac network (NK2-MEF2-GATA-Tbx-Hand). Some components of the network, such as Nkx2-5, are also activated in the primary heart field in response to inductive signals. The core network genes cross- and autoregulate their expression and serve as the central regulatory network for the activation of muscle-specific genes and genes that control the growth and patterning of derivatives of the primary and secondary heart fields. The primary heart field gives rise to the left ventricle (lv) and portions of the atria (a), whereas the secondary heart field gives rise to the right ventricle (rv), portions of the atria, and the outflow tract. A scanning electron micrograph of a mouse heart at embryonic day 14.5 is shown at the bottom. Derivatives of primary and secondary heart fields are shown in blue and pink, respectively. The atria, which are derived from the primary and secondary heart fields, are shown in purple. (With permission, Olson, 2006).

The atria are separated from the ventricles by physical septal structures and valves derived from specialized embryonic tissue called cushions. The atrioventricular cushions form the atrioventricular septum which separates the atrioventricular canal and when complete allows separate pulmonary and systemic circulations. Atrioventricular and arterial valves are formed from remodeled endocardial cushions at the atrioventricular and the ventriculoarterial junctions.

Separate right and left atria are formed from the atrial chamber by the primary septum which originates from vestibular spine cells from outside the heart and migrates downward from the dorso-cranial wall and eventually fuses with cushion tissue. To maintain a parallel circulation until hatching or birth, a hole is formed in the septum as it is formed which allows right to left blood flow via this so-called foramen ovale. A secondary membranous layer of myocardial tissue grows downward alongside the primary septum on the right side and allows right to left chamber flow but not the reverse when left atrial pressures exceed those on the right, as occurs after birth. In some mammals, a variant but equally effective valve prevents left to right flow. In sheep, the foramen ovale has a wind sock appearance as it protrudes into the left atrium (Anderson et al., 1985). It preferentially directs oxygenated blood from the inferior vena cava to the left atrium.

The outflow tract must deliver blood to the pulmonary circulation and independently to the systemic circulation. This is accomplished through the division of the tract by the aorticopulmonary septum which is formed under the influence of neural crest cells which migrate from the developing neural tube outside the heart and become important in the formation of the septum and valves (Hutson and Kirby, 2003). The septum arises at the aortic arches and spirals toward the ventricular region where it ultimately fuses with cushion tissue in the forming right and left ventricular outlets.

The epicardium is derived from proepicardial cells that originate near the forming liver (Kirby, 2007) and the coronary arterial vessels arise by angiogenesis from epicardial precursors (Olivey et al., 2004). The conduction system derives from rapidly conducting cardiomyocytes within the myocardium.

Much of the driving force for research in the developing heart in recent decades has been directed toward understanding cell lineages and differentiation. This work has led to a better understanding of the genetic features of cardiogenesis but has not brought about many new clinical treatments. Fahed et al., (2013) recently made the point regarding the lessons that we have learned so far: "First, human congenital heart disease (CHD) mutations impact a heterogeneous set of molecules that orchestrate cardiac development. Second, CHD mutations often alter gene/protein dosage. Third, identical pathogenic CHD mutations cause a variety of distinct malformations, implying that higher order interactions account for particular CHD phenotypes." It is highly likely that the next frontier that promises revolutionary therapeutic potential will be found in understanding gene-environment interactions and epigenetics.

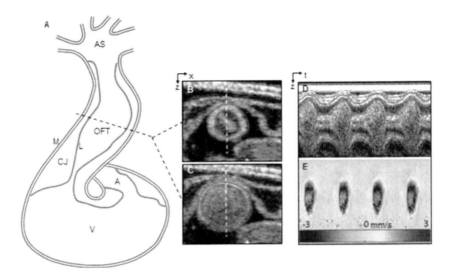

Figure 6. Mechanical features of the HH18 chick embryo heart. (A) Sketch of the developing, tubular heart. (B) and (C) show optical coherence tomography cross-sections of the OFT sampled from the black dashed line in (A) at maximum contraction and expansion in the cardiac cycle, respectively. (D) and (E) show the M-mode (structure over time) and M-phase (Doppler velocity over time) sampled from the white dashed line in (B) and (C). A, atrium; AS, aortic sac; OFT, outflow tract; V, ventricle; M, myocardium with outer and inner walls shown with blue lines; CJ, cardiac jelly; L, lumen shown with red lines. (Liu A, Midgett M, Rugonyi S. Unpublished).

There are a growing number of studies that point to mechanical underpinnings of abnormal gene expression in the embryo. Based on theoretical considerations, it is possible that errors in the vascularization of primitive placental structures alter mechanical gene expression patterns that govern the composition of the heart chambers, the outflow tract and cushion tissues. Thus, the application of engineering principles to the hemodynamic forces that affect cardiac wall and shear forces has brought new insight to the interaction of developmental gene expression patterns and their sensitivity to moment by moment mechanical forces (Egorova et al., 2011, Groenendijk et al., 2007). Much of the energy for the understanding of the mechanics of the embryo heart was driven by Clark and Keller (Hu et al., 1991, Keller et al., 1990, 1991) and has been refined in recent years by engineers (Liu et al., 2011a, 2012, Rugonyi et al., 2008, Taber et al., 1992, 1994). (See Figure 6) This line of investigation may bring new insight into both structural defects in the heart and to abnormalities of the myocardium and the coronary circulation that lead to ischemic heart disease in later life.

Vulnerable Periods of Fetal Development

As mentioned above, heart disease related deaths have decreased by half in the USA since about 1970. Similar decreases have been observed in Europe. (See Figure 7) These impressive decreases represent important milestones in the history of medicine. It is likely that improvements in medical care as well as improved management of risk factors have played important roles in the decline. In the past 20 years, however, the overall health of the American population has been worsening according to a number of indicators, with prevalence of type 2 diabetes mellitus (CDC, 2011), obesity (Flegal et al., 2012, Nader et al., 2014), and uncontrolled hypertension (Olives et al., 2013) leading the way. These indicators have been increasing so much so that one wonders whether it will be financially possible to care for the sequelae of these diseases should the trend continue. Some 65-70% of people with type 2 diabetes eventually acquire coronary heart disease (Braunwald, 1997, Grundy et al., 1999); the current rapid rise in diabetes (CDC, 2011, Mainous et al., 2007) and obesity (Bibbins-Domingo et al., 2007) predict that ischemic heart disease rates will also rise rapidly during the next few decades (Go et al., 2014). The relationship between diabetes and heart disease is so tightly linked that some medical scientists have emphasized the point by stating that "diabetes is a cardiovascular disease" (Grundy et al., 1999). Thus, as exciting as the heart statistics appear, one cannot interpret the declining heart disease mortality rate as clear evidence that the prevalence of heart disease is declining.

New epidemiological evidence from the Helsinki Birth Cohort provides further evidence that adult-onset ischemic heart disease has its roots in early life (Barker et al., 2010a, 2012, Eriksson et al., 2011). The three primary causes of cardiac death, coronary disease, heart failure and sudden cardiac death are related to specific maternal or placental phenotypes. Three phenotype combinations predicted coronary heart disease--an oblong placental shape in short mothers; a small placental surface in tall mothers and a high placenta to birth weight ratio in tall, thin mothers (Eriksson et al., 2011). Heart failure was associated with a small placental surface (Barker et al., 2010a) and sudden death was related to a thin poorly invaded placenta (Barker et al., 2012). Although our current understanding of the biology of placental and fetal growth and how it underlies cardiovascular disease risk in later life is quite primitive, each of the developmental conditions that lead to heart disease can be theoretically linked to specific stressors that alter developmental patterns in the fetus.

The physiologic stressors that lead to cardiovascular disease in adult life are becoming known, as are the critical periods of development during which they act. The last third of gestation is a critical period for the hearts of large mammals because of two primary events: 1) cardiomyocyte numbers are set during that time and 2) the heart goes through its maturation stages (Barbera et al., 2000, Jonker et al., 2010, Thornburg et al., 2011). Both of these processes are associated with long term alterations in the anatomy and physiology of the heart that carry lifelong consequences. Biological processes that underlie programmed cardiovascular disease include altered coronary tree structure and physiology (Yang et al., 2008), oxidative stress (Simmons, 2006, von Bergen et al., 2009), hypertension (Woods et al., 2001), augmented sympathetic tone (Jansson and Lambert, 1999), metabolic disorders (Cleasby et al., 2003, Cottrell and Ozanne, 2007), altered cellular processes (Vo and Hardy, 2012) and decreased cardiomyocyte number (Barbera et al., 2000, Li et al., 2003). As discussed below, the Zhang laboratory showed that hypoxia in the womb leads to a decreased cardiomyocyte endowment in adult rats and an increased vulnerability to ischemia-reperfusion damage (Li et al., 2003).

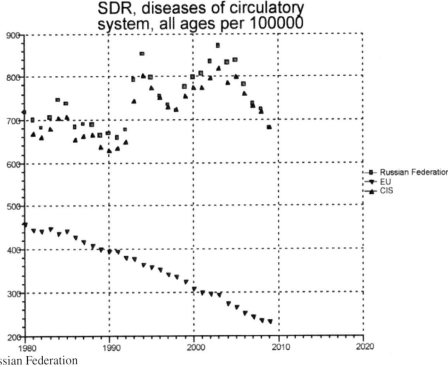

■ Russian Federation
▲CIS=Commonwealth of Independent States (former USSR)
▼EU=European Union.

Figure 7. Standardized death rates (SDR): diseases of the circulatory system, all ages per 100,000, European Region, 1980-2009. Source: Health for All Data Base, WHO European Region, July 2011. Available from URL: http://www.euro.who.int/HFADB (Accessed 21 September 2011).

During the last 40 years, the rates of hospitalization for heart failure have increased even as heart deaths decreased (Owan et al., 2006, Roger et al., 2012). The increase in heart failure rates is often attributed to increased survival of people with coronary heart disease. In addition, however, there are increasing numbers of people who suffer from heart failure with preserved ejection fraction of unknown etiology (Owan et al., 2006). One apparently common feature of heart failure is the loss of cardiomyocytes. One may therefore speculate that low cardiomyocyte numbers underlie heart failure in adults (Thornburg et al., 2011); this speculation has support from human studies of apoptosis in failing hearts (Sabbah and Sharov, 1998) and from recent animal models (Wencker et al., 2003).

The establishment of the cardiomyocyte endowment is controversial. In small rodents cell numbers can be increased with growth factor treatment soon after birth (Reiss et al., 1996). However, the fact that hearts in small rodents seem unable to compensate for myocyte deficits that arise from stress in the womb (Corstius et al., 2005, Li et al., 2003) suggests that "decisions" regarding myocardial cellular composition are made during the perinatal period. The inability to compensate for inadequate cardiomyocyte number may also hold for hearts of large mammals including humans even though it is increasingly clear that there is mitotic activity among cardiomyocytes during the postnatal period into childhood (Bergmann et al., 2009, 2012, Mollova et al., 2013). What is often not obvious, however, is that mitotic activity does not necessarily indicate net accretion of myocardial tissue. In sheep it appears that the number of cardiomyocytes plateaus before birth and that the cardiomyocyte endowment is not increased ever after. This suggests that sheep, like rats, determine their cardiomyocyte endowment around the time of birth. The biological lessons for the human have yet to be learned. Since every heart attains a final number of cardiomyocytes by the age of 20 years, it is not known whether underendowed human hearts at birth can be compensated through catch up growth or whether the set point for the final number was set before birth as it is in sheep.

In the ovine fetal heart, like the heart of the developing rat, working myocytes become binucleated as they mature. See Figure 8. We and others have shown that binucleation is equivalent to terminal differentiation and that once binucleated, cardiomyocytes cannot be coerced to divide (Jonker et al., 2010). Binucleation is thus one indicator that a cardiomyocyte has entered a new maturation phase. It is the process of maturation that makes the fetal heart vulnerable for detrimental influences that affect cell number and cell function. It is also clear that there is a very small but measurable population of quadrinucleated cardiomyocytes that persists into adulthood (Jonker et al., 2007b). Cardiomyocytes in preterm neonatal sheep, mononucleated cardiomyocytes, undergo DNA duplication and become polyploid without karyokinesis—that is-- terminal differentiation without binucleation (Bensley et al., 2010). Normal human mononucleated cardiomyocytes are also often polyploid. The presence of a polyploid myocyte is not a certain indicator that the cell has terminally differentiated, however, because cells that are in G2 phase of the cycle normally, if temporarily, reside in this condition.

There are a number of conditions that cause the fetal heart to be underendowed. These include placental insufficiency, increased mechanical load, abnormal levels of growth related hormones and low levels of oxygen in the womb (Barbera et al., 2000, Chattergoon et al., 2007, Davis et al., 2003, Giraud et al., 2006, Jonker et al., 2007a, Louey et al., 2007, O'Tierney et al., 2010a, 2010b, Pinson et al., 1991, Sundgren et al., 2003a, 2003b). While insulin-like growth factor-2, IGF-2, is important in early development, its influence in the ovine heart dwindles in the later stages of gestation (Reini et al., 2008). Even though IGF-2 does not seem to be a strong regulator of proliferation in the womb in the large mammal it may support the hypertrophic growth of the myocardium near term (Morrison et al., 2007). Both tri-iodo-L-thyronine (T3) (Chattergoon et al., 2012a, 2012b) and atrial natriuretic peptide (ANP) (O'Tierney et al., 2010b) are powerful inhibitors of serum-stimulated cardiomyocyte proliferation while other factors like angiotensin II (Sundgren et al., 2003b) and cortisol (Giraud et al., 2006, Jensen et al., 2002) stimulate proliferation. The number of capillaries in the mature heart is related to the number of cardiomyocytes. It is therefore likely that cardiomyocyte number influences the ultimate architecture of the cardiac microcirculation.

Fetal sheep that were growth restricted because of placental insufficiency had small hearts for gestational age that were, however, proportional in size to body weight (Bubb et al., 2007, Louey et al., 2007). Hearts from undergrown fetuses were different than normal hearts in that they had a very low population of myocytes that were proliferating and further they had a low number of cardiomyocytes that were maturing as indicated by the low number of nucleated cells. One can speculate that such hearts will be vulnerable for later life cardiac disease including heart failure should they be further stressed.

The hormonal environment is a powerful regulator of cell cycle activity among cardiomyocytes in the near term sheep. The hormone that drives cardiomyocyte proliferation in the fetus is IGF-1 (Sundgren et al., 2003a). However, T$_3$ completely inhibits the actions of IGF-1 among cardiomyocytes (Chattergoon et al., 2007, 2012a). There is increasing evidence that thyroid hormone in the form of T$_3$ is the primary driver of myocardial maturation in that it suppresses proliferation, enhances binucleation and stimulates maturation of the cardiomyocyte including hypertrophic growth (Chattergoon et al., 2012a, 2012b). Excesses or deficits in thyroid hormone levels in the fetus lead to reduced numbers of cardiomyocytes at birth (Chattergoon and Thornburg, unpublished).

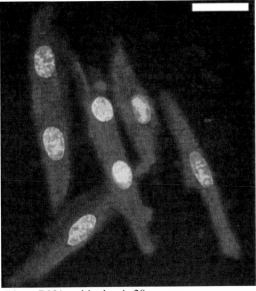

Red= myosin heavy chain; Blue= DNA; white bar is 20μm.

Figure 8. Cardiomyocytes isolated from the 135d fetal sheep. Cells are mono-nucleated cells over most of gestation but become bi-nucleated in late gestation as they mature.

The new frontier in cardiovascular development will be to determine how these growth signals are integrated and prioritized by the cardiomyocyte as well as by fibroblasts and other cells that contribute to the architecture of the extracellular matrix. It will not be possible to understand or even reverse cardiac vulnerability for disease without understanding the mechanisms by which the myriad of signaling molecules are processed by the cardiomyocyte.

Mechanical factors are important modulators of fetal heart development (Barbera et al., 2000, Jonker et al., 2007a, 2010, O'Tierney et al., 2010a). One common pathological condition under which the heart is faced with increased afterload is placental insufficiency. In this condition, the heart must eject its stroke volume against a placenta that is inadequately vascularized. Thus arterial impedance is increased in such fetuses. This condition can be so extreme that blood flow in the umbilical artery is absent or even reversed during diastole (Battaglia et al., 1993). The near term fetal myocardium accommodates an increase in systolic pressure in two ways: 1) It briefly augments cardiomyocyte proliferation followed by a powerful cessation of proliferation and 2) it stimulates the maturation of the myocardium so that cardiomyocytes become terminally differentiated and enlarged (Barbera et al., 2000). The outcome is a thicker ventricular wall at the expense of chamber volume and a reduction in systolic wall stress. Such hearts will be born with fewer cardiomyocytes than normal because they augment cardiomyocyte numbers at a reduced rate over the remaining course of gestation (Barbera et al., 2000).

It is interesting to note that when fetal arterial pressure is reduced the heart is undergrown (O'Tierney et al., 2010a). Under the conditions of hypotension, the fetal heart does not receive adequate mechanical signals to sustain cardiomyocyte proliferation and the heart is small for fetal body weight and contains fewer proliferating cardiomyocytes.

Shear stress modulates the development of the coronary tree in the near term fetus (Wothe et al., 2002). Fetuses that are made anemic in the last third of gestation have a drastically augmented coronary tree (Davis et al., 2003). Total myocardial conductance, that is flow per unit driving pressure when the vascular bed is fully dilated, is doubled during fetal anemic stress in a matter of days and the condition persists into adulthood. There are several physiological changes in the anemic fetus that could trigger myocardial responses. Blood oxygen content is decreased, blood viscosity is decreased, cardiac output is increased and coronary flow is increased (Davis et al., 2003, 2005, Yang et al., 2008). Nevertheless, it appears that the vascular remodeling stimulus is due in large part to increased shear forces within the coronary arteries. If fetal coronary flow is artificially increased by infusing adenosine in a near chronic fashion, the same remodeling occurs even when fetal hematocrit is normal. Although an augmented coronary tree benefits the adult heart and renders it resistant to acute hypoxic episodes (Broberg et al., 2003), there is a detrimental side to the condition. Adult hearts that were anemic in the womb are more sensitive to ischemic events than are normal hearts (Yang et al., 2008).

Thus, adverse conditions in the womb, especially in the form of abnormal hemodynamic forces, lead to permanent modifications of the myocardium. Heart muscle may have reduced numbers of cardiomyocytes or an augmented coronary tree that is vulnerable to ischemia reperfusion injury in the adult. These factors predict abnormal heart function. In addition, the vascular elements of the body have increased levels of oxidative stress and inadequate vascular function for life.

Maternal Undernutrition and Overnutrition

A host of animal models have been developed for the purpose of understanding the mechanisms that underlie programming across species (Bertram and Hanson, 2001, Hill et al., 2010, Langley-Evans et al., 2005, Nathanielsz, 2006, Poston, 2010, Seki et al., 2012, Williams et al., 2014). It was the use of animal models that provided much needed biological evidence for programming soon after several epidemiological reports first showed an inverse relationship between birthweight and adult onset disease. Simon Langley-Evans and co-workers were among the first to show the programming effect using the rat model (Langley-Evans et al., 1994). The field of developmental origins of disease may have never taken root if not for the biological data which showed plausibility for the transgenerational effect of a poor maternal diet. Among the myriad of animal models used in hundreds of investigations are studies in the chicken (Giussani et al., 2007), rat (Jansson and Lambert, 1999; Woods et al., 2004), mouse (van Straten et al., 2010), guinea pig (Evans et al., 2012b, Kind et al., 2005), pig (Denisenko et al., 2011, Liu et al., 2011b), sheep (Begum et al., 2013, Cleal et al., 2010, Kandadi et al., 2013, Zhang et al., 2010) and non-human primate (McDonald et al., 2013, Nicol et al., 2013). These models have brought enormous benefit to our understanding of the basic biological mechanisms that underlie the propensity for cardiovascular disease that derives from a variety of stress laden environments. The term "stress," while somewhat arbitrary and often controversial, nevertheless suggests that there are stimuli to which developing organisms respond that lead to long term detrimental consequences.

One of the first and most obvious outcomes in offspring of maternal protein restriction in rats was hypertension. The data from rats fit with similar findings in people who had low birthweight. The details of the findings of multiple rat studies are nicely summarized by McMillan and Robinson (2005) in their excellent and thorough review of programming. Many different investigators reduced the protein content of rat chow by 50% over specific periods of gestation while maintaining caloric content by increasing carbohydrate levels (Kwong et al., 2000, Langley-Evans et al., 1996a, 1996b, Langley and Jackson, 1994, Manning et al., 2002, Nwagwu et al., 2000, Ozaki et al., 2001, Woods et al., 2001). Regardless of the stage of exposure to low protein, most studies showed increases in systolic blood pressure in postnatal life and in some animals, decreases in kidney weight and nephron number (Edwards and McMillen, 2002, Gardner et al., 2004, Gilbert et al., 2007, Hawkins et al., 2000). Sheep studies show many similarities to rat studies. Fetal and postnatal sheep show elevated blood pressures following protein restriction in the periconceptional period through mid-gestation.

Non-human primate studies have provided many new insights into the roles that diets play in offspring health. Most mothers of the species Macaca fuscata becomes obese when exposed to a high-fat diet, while some will be resistant to the calorie effect and not gain much weight. Fetal offspring from both lean and obese mothers consuming a high fat diet had a 3-fold increase in liver triglycerides and had indicators of oxidative stress consistent with the development of nonalcoholic fatty liver disease (McCurdy et al., 2009). In addition, juveniles that were exposed to a high fat diet in the womb displayed an increased plasma insulin level and glucose-stimulated insulin secretion in comparison with control animals. In the abdominal aorta, acetylcholine-induced vasorelaxation was decreased in the experimental group compared to controls, indicating endothelial dysfunction. High fat juvenile animals also had a thicker intimal wall and an abnormal vascular-morphology, concurrent with elevated expression levels of several markers related to vascular inflammation and fibrinolytic function (Fan et al., 2013). The most profound effects on the fetus were related to uterine blood flow. There was a 38-56% reduction in uterine volume blood flow from HFD animals, whether lean or obese. Consumption of a high fat diet by mothers increased her placental inflammatory cytokines and the expression of Toll-like receptor 4. Obese mothers with hyperinsulinemia had a reduced blood flow on the fetal side of the placenta and increased frequency of placental infarctions and stillbirth (Frias et al., 2011). In fetal baboons born to high fat/high fructose-diet fed mothers, 80 cardiac miRNAs were differentially expressed; 55 miRNAs were upregulated and 25 downregulated. Of the eighty differentially expressed, fourteen were known to be associated with human cardiovascular disease (Maloyan et al., 2013).

One of the most interesting features of programming is its constancy among mammals. While there are a number of different responses to prenatal stresses that are clearly species specific, the similarities across species are, perhaps, even more striking. For example, a reduction in the number of nephrons in the kidney is a common, though not universal, response to mid-gestation maternal undernutrition in several animal models (Bagby, 2007). Nephron deficits are known to be associated with changes in glomerular structure and hypertension in humans (Hoy et al., 2008).

It is clear than the genomic endowment of vertebrates and even invertebrates have evolved to provide for specific modifications of phenotype in response to varied environmental conditions present during development. It is easy to find species-specific examples of plastic changes that occur in response to limited nutritional resources, like the absence of horns on the sneaker form of dung beetles (Smallegange and Johansson, 2014) or increased dispersal abilities of western bluebirds (Duckworth, 2009). Evolutionists have considered how genomic plasticity gives rise to innovation within a species (Moczek et al., 2011) and how epigenetic regulation of gene expression might bridge the need for short-term reaction to environmental changes while also providing subsequent long-term stabilization of adaptive phenotypes (Duckworth, 2013). The evolutionary aspects of programming responses among mammals have also been addressed (Bateson, 2007, Gluckman and Hanson, 2004). One might ask, how did similar gene expression responses to fetal adversity among a range of mammals first arise? That remains an unanswered question. However, more insight into such questions is likely as the field of developmental plasticity rapidly gains momentum among theoretical evolutionists.

Another example of a common response to an early life programming event is the so-called catch up growth or compensatory growth phenomenon that occurs in response to nutrient deprivation during fetal development or early childhood. There is increasing evidence that an organism's capacity to achieve accelerated growth in a lush postnatal nutritional environment is a common feature of a permissive genome found widely across the animal kingdom. The historical views on the subject of human catch up growth, nicely reviewed by Boersma and Wit (1997), predate the concept of fetal programming by some 80 years. There are many technicalities in defining catch up growth and many controversies underlying its biological underpinnings (Boersma and Wit, 1997). These issues are now in the spotlight because the field of programming has brought a new urgency to understanding its causes. It is no longer controversial to state that rapid growth in offspring that resided in a low growth centile at birth and in a much higher centile in childhood carries risk for adult onset cardiovascular disease (Eriksson et al., 1999) and a shortened lifespan (Barker et al., 2011). The metabolic syndrome is linked to poor prenatal growth and may be in part related to endowment of skeletal muscle cells and their physiology. People and animals that had low birthweight are born with fewer skeletal muscle cells (Brown, 2014), a condition that remains for life (Baker et al., 2010), even if there is postnatal catch-up growth (Louey et al., 2005). Most of the catch up in body weight observed in people and animals that were poorly endowed with muscle at birth is accounted for by an accelerated accumulation of body fat mass over muscle mass. Thus the resulting increased velocity of growth is disordered and leads to metabolic disturbances including hypertension, dyslipidemia and coronary heart disease (Bagby, 2004, Barker et al., 2005).

Maternal Nutrition, Birthweight and Later Disease

Heart disease, type 2 diabetes and hypertension are predicted by slow intrauterine growth across the normal birthweight range (Barker, 1995, Curhan et al., 1996, Whincup et al., 2008). While there are a host of particulars that may be associated with body size at birth, maternal and placental phenotypes are, in broad strokes, the most important determinants of the robustness of fetal development and, in combination, are the best predictors of future cardiovascular disease. Maternal fat and muscle masses dictate the varying degrees of tissue turnover during pregnancy and thus nutrient supply to support a pregnancy. It has been difficult to determine the roles of maternal obesity, insulin resistance and type 2 diabetes as determinants of metabolic disorder in offspring in spite of animal studies that are more secure (Fernandez-Twinn and Ozanne, 2010, Mostyn and Symonds, 2009, Poston, 2010). There are human studies that convincingly make the link and others that do find strong associations. Catalano found that among 89 women, maternal BMI (>30kg/m2) predicted childhood fat mass more than did maternal glucose status (Catalano et al., 2009). Gestational diabetes was associated with childhood skin fold thickness at 3 years after adjustment for maternal and paternal BMI (Catalano et al., 2009, Wright et al., 2009). There are increasing numbers of studies showing harm to the fetus as a result of elevated levels of glucose that go beyond congenital structural defects. Several studies suggest that a neonate with poor insulin/glucose control may face a persisting problem with metabolic physiology later in life (Plagemann et al., 1997, Silverman et al., 1995).

Studies of people who were conceived or grown in the womb during periods of famine have elucidated the role of maternal diet in determining the health of offspring. Famine in regions of the former Soviet Union (Anderson & Silver, 1989, Antonov, 1947) and China (Chen and Zhou, 2007) is known to have affected population health well into the decades that followed. Mothers who reduce their food intake for weeks to months during pregnancy because of famine often give birth to babies of average birthweight (Roseboom et al., 2006), but low weight for length (Stein et al., 1975) and who, nevertheless, carry a high risks for cardiovascular disease and metabolic syndrome into adulthood.

During the Dutch Hunger Winter of 1944, food delivery to Amsterdam and surrounds were blocked by German forces for some months. Daily energy availability decreased to as little as 400 calories per day. Now, some 70 years later, retrospective studies are able to reconstruct the developmental periods in which people were exposed to famine and outcomes compared to pre and post-famine births. Tessa Roseboom and colleagues (Roseboom et al., 2006) have reported on a number of associations between famine and disease outcomes in people who were in the womb during the Dutch Hunger Winter. Figure 9 summarizes the detrimental health effects on people who were conceived and developed before, during and after the famine by trimester. Interestingly birthweight was not reduced among people exposed to famine in any trimester. Nevertheless, glucose intolerance was associated with famine exposure in all three trimesters. However, exposure to famine during the first two trimesters of pregnancy but not the third led to an altered glucose regulation by an insulin secretion defect (de Rooij et al., 2006). People exposed to famine in mid-gestation had increased prevalence of chronic obstructive airways disease (Lopuhaa et al., 2000). There was no general association between diastolic or systolic blood pressure in offspring exposed to famine. However, those who were born at the low end of the birthweight scale had hypertension as adults as seen in any population. (Roseboom et al., 1999). Adults whose mothers ate low amounts of protein relative to carbohydrate while in the womb during the last trimester had higher blood pressure (Roseboom et al., 2001). Coronary heart disease was found more often in people who were exposed to the famine during early gestation (Roseboom et al., 2000); early onset of coronary heart disease was observed in people who were conceived during the famine (Painter et al., 2006). In summary, nearly all of the detrimental health outcomes that were found in people exposed to famine in early gestation place those individuals at high risk for cardiovascular disease.

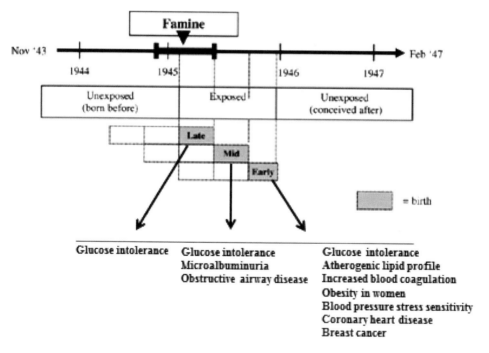

Figure 9. shows diagrammatically the trimesters in which people were exposed to the Dutch Famine and associated outcomes. Most of the diseases that were related to early life exposure to famine were related to the cardiovascular system. Obstructive airways disease and breast cancer were the exceptions. (Modified from Roseboom et al., 2006).

Glucocorticoids and Heart Development

In this section, current literature regarding the intrauterine effects of glucocorticoids on heart development and risk for ischemic heart disease will be discussed. Glucocorticoids are indispensable for survival in mammalian life. Removal of adrenal organs without exogenous steroid replacement would result in death. Glucocorticoids are important in regulating blood glucose through the stimulation of gluconeogenesis and glycogen storage. They maintain vascular responsiveness to catecholamines by increasing the synthesis and promoting the expression of α_1 adrenergic receptors (α_1AR). In addition, glucocorticoids mediate anti-inflammatory effects through the synthesis of lipocortin (an inhibitor of phospholipase A_2), inhibition of interleukin-2 (IL-2) and inhibiting the release of histamine and serotonin from mast cells and platelets. Glucocorticoids are synthesized and stored in the zona fasiculata of the adrenal cortex. The synthesis and release of glucocorticoids are governed by a feedback mechanism involving hypothalamic-pituitary axis (HPA). HPA axis regulation and stress response is covered in chapter 5.

In pregnancy, the levels of circulating glucocorticoids are higher in the maternal versus the fetal compartment. The fetus is protected from excessive levels of maternal glucocorticoids by placenta enzymatic regulation of 11β-hydroxysteriod dehydrogenase type 2 (11βHSD2). 11βHSD2 is abundantly expressed in the placenta and functions by metabolizing maternal glucocorticoids, rending them inert. This allows the fetal adrenals to normally develop (Chatelain et al., 1980). Due to the low affinity of dexamethasome and betamethasome to 11βHSD2, these two glucocorticoids traverse the placenta and readily concentrate in fetal circulation (Seckl, 2004). These features make them ideal to administer to pregnant women at risk for premature delivery. In rats, 11βHSD2 declines in 3rd trimester which may allow increasing concentrations of glucocorticoids to act on fetal lung tissue, whereas humans have high glucocorticoids in maternal circulation which necessitate the need for elevated 11βHSD2 levels in the placenta.

The role glucocorticoids play in fetal life presents two distinct paradigms. On the one hand, glucocorticoids regulate and promote organ maturation and growth. They are frequently given to promote fetal lung maturation and the production of surfactant, which reduces the risk of respiratory distress syndrome in premature newborns. On the other hand, depending on the timing, dose and duration of exposure, glucocorticoids program the fetus for cardiovascular disorders. Excessive intrauterine levels of glucocorticoids may occur as a result of increased circulating maternal glucocorticoids, reduced placental 11βHSD2 activity or increased fetal adrenal production of glucocorticoids (Seckl , 2004). Elevated production of glucocorticoids occurs in chronic disease states or with exogenous administration of glucocorticoids. Maternal stress from undernutrition is a classic condition that decreases the expression of placental 11βHSD2 (Bertram et al., 2001), allowing increased circulating glucocorticoids in the fetal compartment.

Elevated levels of glucocorticoids have adverse effects on fetal physiology. Excessive glucocorticoids reduce fetal growth and birthweight (Seckl, 2004). They also program the fetus for cardiovascular disease. The chronic infusion of cortisol in fetal sheep day 103-120 or 130-137 of gestation increased both systolic and diastolic blood pressure and increased the reactivity of those animals to angiotensin II injection (Tangalakis et al., 1992). Sheep tend to be more sensitive to the programming of high blood pressure by glucocorticoids earlier in gestation while rats are more susceptible to programming later in gestation (Dodic et al., 1998, Langley-Evans et al., 1999). In 6-week-old wistar rats whose mothers were exposed to low protein diet, adrenalectomy significantly reduced their blood pressure (Gardner et al., 1997). However, when these same animals were given exogenous glucocorticoids, their blood pressure returned to baseline (Gardner et al., 1997). This suggests postnatal hypertension depends on *in utero* programming of vascular reactivity to glucocorticoids. Prenatal glucocorticoids cause endothelial dysfunction and increase expression of angiotensin converting enzyme in lung tissue (Molnar et al., 2003, Wintour et al., 2003, Zimmermann et al., 2003). These factors may play a role in inducing increased blood pressure in animals exposed to excessive glucocorticoids. In addition, glucocorticoids can impair nephrogenesis (Wintour et al., 2003). Aberrant nephrogenesis can promote hypertension in adult offspring. It has been reported that unilateral nephrectomy *in utero* leads to hypertension and congenital absence of a kidney is associated with increased blood pressure in humans (Mei-Zahav et al., 2001, Moritz et al., 2002, Woods, 1999). Thus the absence or impairment of nephrogenesis programs fetuses for cardiovascular dysfunction.

Likewise, exogenous administration of glucocorticoids causes hypertrophy of the fetal heart. Infants born to mothers with preexisting maternal Cushing disease and infants with severe adrenal hyperplasia requiring high doses of steroids have increased heart size (Bertram and Hanson, 2002). Whether these effects are due to alterations in the fetal cardiovascular system or are a direct effect of glucocorticoid on the fetal heart is not clear. Beginning on day 27 in gestation, two day exposure to intrauterine glucocorticoid caused cardiac dysfunction in adult offspring with evidence of ventricular hypertrophy, cardiac fibrosis, reduced cardiac output and contractile reserve in adult sheep offspring (Dodic et al., 2001, Wintour et al., 2003). Perhaps cardiovascular dysfunction in the form of hypertension may increase afterload, which causes compensatory myocardial remodeling and subsequent long-term cardiac dysfunction. Interestingly, studies in rats have found neonatal dexamethasone treatment caused cardiac dysfunction in prepubertal (4 weeks) rats characterized by reduced systolic function (Bal et al., 2005). Although this study looked only at male rats, these findings suggest an extended period of myocardial susceptibility to programming with glucocorticoid treatment.

In addition to programming for hypertension, excessive exposure to glucocorticoids may cause dysfunction in β-islet cells (Nyirenda et al., 1998). In *ex vivo* mouse pancreas, glucocorticoids increased the expression of the transcription factor C/EBPb (CCAAT/enhancer-binding protein b) and decreased expression of the transcription factor Pdx-1 (pancreatic duodenal homeobox-1) (Shen et al., 2003). C/EBPb suppresses insulin gene transcription while Pdx-1 binds and increases insulin promoter activity (Lu et al., 1997, Ohlsson et al., 1993). Prenatal glucocorticoid exposure selectively programs hepatic acini by increasing phosphenolpyruvate carboxylase (the rate limiting step in gluconeogenesis) mRNA in hepatocytes (Nyirenda and Seckl, 1998). Overexpression of phosphenolpyruvate carboxylase in heptoma cell lines impairs insulin suppression of gluconeogenesis. These factors support the notion that prenatal glucocorticoids program the postnatal endocrine system leading to increased risk of diabetes mellitus later in life. Diabetes is an important risk equivalent for coronary vessel disease, which can lead to ischemic heart disease.

Although the predominant effects of glucocorticoids on myocardium appear to be indirectly related to cardiovascular changes including increased afterload, vascular and endocrine dysfunction, there are direct effects on fetal heart metabolism and gene expression that occur from prenatal glucocorticoid exposure. Glucose is shuttled into the heart through the actions of GLUT1 and GLUT4. Studies have found increased expression of glucose transporter 1 (GLUT1) in growth restricted male rats exposed to late gestation intrauterine glucocorticoids (Langdown et al., 2001). Upregulation of AKT/PKB and Protein kinas C isoforms was noted which suggest programming of abnormal glucose metabolism and possibly compensatory hypertrophic growth in response to programmed hypertension (Manning and Cantley, 2007, Paul et al., 1997, Takeishi et al., 1999). High doses of cortisol in fetal sheep reduced GLUT1 mRNA, increased angiotensinogen expression and cardiac hypertrophy (Lumbers et al., 2005). The disparate effects of glucocorticoids on glut1 expression perhaps is explained by species differences and the timing of insult with rats being more sensitive in late gestation and sheep having increased vulnerability in early gestation (Dodic et al., 1998, Langley-Evans et al., 1999).

Glucocorticoids elicit their effects on gene expression through glucocorticoid and mineralcorticoid receptor (GR & MR) nuclear transcriptional activity. Normally, glucocorticoids diffuse across plasma membrane and bind to the GR, causing their activation and release from chaperone proteins. GR then translocates to the nucleus where it binds glucocorticoid response elements (GRE) located on prospective gene promoters and modulates gene expression. Mice devoid of GR demonstrated signs of impaired fetal heart maturation (Rog-Zielinska et al., 2013). Studies in neonatal rats have shown GR to be important in remodeling of electrical pathways and chronotropic response to glucocorticoids and myocyte hypertrophy (Rossier et al., 2010). Genomic arrays have shown dexamethasome-induced hypertrophy is mediated through GR transcriptional regulation (Ren et al., 2012). Consistent with these findings, administration of dexamethasome to neonatal rat pups reduced cardiomyocyte proliferation and caused hypertrophy suggesting postnatal sensitivity to glucocorticoids (de Vries et al., 2002, 2006). Normal neonatal cardiomyocytes maintain their proliferative capacity but may prematurely lose this function do to glucocorticoid exposure.

Glucocorticoids also act on mineralcorticoid receptors (MR), which are expressed in the fetal heart and whose activation is similar to GR. Glucocorticoid activation of MR receptor is governed by 11βHSD2 abundance, which is low in fetal hearts (Seckl, 2004). Blockade of MR is linked to the improved mortality and morbidity in heart failure patients (Messaoudi et al., 2012). Studies have shown that activation of MR receptor with cortisol after myocardial infarction increased cardiac damage (Mihailidou et al., 2009). Chronic MR stimulation has deleterious effects on the heart. Using intrapericardial infusion of GR and MR antagonists, Feng and colleauges found MR mediates cardiac proliferation whereas GR caused apoptosis of purkinje fibers (Feng et al., 2013). In embryonic ventricular H9c2 cells or freshly isolated cultured neonatal cardiomyocytes, synthetic glucocorticoids caused hypertrophy in normal serum solution and inhibited apoptosis in serum free solution through a GR dependent upreguation of anti-apoptic genes Bcl-xl and down-regulation of pro-apoptic genes, gas2 (Ren et al., 2012). Consistent with these findings, dexamethosone upregulates BcL-xL in cultured cardiomyocytes (Xu et al., 2011). GR also regulates angiotensin II receptor type 1 & 2 (AT$_1$R & AT$_2$R) promoter through binding to GRE sites (Guo et al., 1995, Xue et al., 2011). Late gestational chronic hypoxia decreased nuclear GR binding to AT$_2$R promoter, which increased AT$_2$R expression leading to increased vulnerability to ischemia reperfusion (I/R) injury in adult rat offspring (Xue et al., 2011). The regulation of AT$_2$R expression by GR provides an additional potential mechanism through which intrauterine glucocorticoid may program the myocardium. These programming effects of GR may be dependent on the timing of insult. Blockade of GR with mifepristone in adult mice inhibited the dexamethasone protective effect against ischemia/reperfusion injury (Xu et al., 2011). This suggests elevated glucocorticoids program fetal hearts, but they may be protective to the heart against I/R injury through a GR-mediated mechanism.

The essential role of glucocorticoids in normal fetal maturation is in contrast to pathophysiological elevation of stress hormones that have significant programming effects on the heart. Glucocorticoids program the cardiovascular system leading to hypertension and increased risk of metabolic disorders. In addition, depending on the timing and duration of the insult, glucocorticoids may alter myocardial structure and function. Its direct effects are mediated through GR, however glucocorticoids in sufficient amounts may act on MR receptors in fetal cardiomyocytes leading to alterations in cardiomyocyte growth, morphology and perhaps survival.

Substance Abuse

An ongoing challenge to perinatal health and disease is the risk afforded to the developing fetus from commonly abused substances such as nicotine from tobacco smoke, illicit drug and ethanol use. Epidemiological and clinical evidence suggest these compounds may have profound effects on heart development by increasing the risk for cardiovascular anomalies as well as altering the function, structure and the potential for fetal programming of ischemic heart disease. In this section, we will summarize current literature regarding the intrauterine effects of nicotine, cocaine and ethanol on heart development and risk for ischemic heart disease later in life.

Nicotine

Cigarette smoking has profound effects on fetal physiology and survivability. Studies have shown smoking increased the risk of sudden infant death syndrome (SIDS), intrauterine growth restriction and cardiovascular disease (Slotkin, 1998). Prospective cohort evidence linked maternal cigarette smoking to elevation in systolic blood pressure and reduced birth weight in offspring (Blake et al., 2000). In a cross-sectional study among pregnant Dutch women, a dose response relationship was found between the number of cigarettes smoked per day and the birth weight of offspring (Adriaanse et al., 1996). Tobacco smoking causes vasoconstriction of placental blood vessels and has damaging effects on fetal vasculature (Asmussen, 1979, Economides and Braithwaite, 1994, Longo, 1977). These studies illustrate the harmful effects of tobacco smoking to the developing fetus.

Nicotine is an important component of tobacco smoke and is considered a major factor in sustaining smoking addiction. In human and animal studies, nicotine increased maternal heart rate and blood pressure which is likely due to increased catecholamine release. It crosses the placenta and breast milk in humans and concentrates in fetal blood (Lambers and Clark, 1996). Interestingly, nicotine levels tend to be 15% higher in the concentration in the fetal compartment than in the maternal compartment (Lambers and Clark, 1996). In rats, prenatal nicotine exposure does not affect basal function of the heart, but influences EKG waveforms with rapid bradycardia in response to neonatal hypoxia and attenuates responsiveness to beta adrenergic stimulation that persist into adulthood (Navarro et al., 1990, Slotkin et al., 1997). In addition, prenatal nicotine modulates nicotinic receptors, influencing excitatory conduction of cardiac vagal neurons (Huang et al., 2004). It appears that these effects may provide a possible explanation for the cardiopulmonary failure in response to hypoxia that occurs in SIDS.

Fetuses exposed to prenatal nicotine, have reduced body weights as compared to their age matched controls. This is consistent with the reduced maternal food intake observed during early gestation. However, the same offspring showed no differences in body weight, nor any significant effect on the thickness of left and right ventricular walls and ventricular septum in control and treatment groups in adults (Lawrence et al., 2008). Both male and female offspring exposed to nicotine *in utero* had poor recovery of LV function following ischemic reperfusion insult as compared to age matched control. Nicotine exposed groups had significantly less recovery of LVDP and elevated LVEDP as compared to controls (Lawrence et al., 2008). Infarct size of these animals was larger as well, suggesting increased tissue loss. Likewise, second hand smoke exposure *in utero* increased infarct size of pups that were subjected to I/R injury by left coronary artery occlusion (Zhu et al., 1997). These findings demonstrate that nicotine influences the hearts ability to respond to stress in the postnatal environment.

To account for the observed functional and structural changes attributed to prenatal exposure, investigators examined physiological and molecular events for clarity. Utilizing pulmonary artery effluent as an index of coronary flow, researchers found that female but not male hearts exposed to nicotine *in utero* had decreased flow at baseline and at postischemic recovery as compared to age and gender matched controls (Lawrence et al., 2008). These changes may not be relevant to cardiac function at baseline; however they may increase the risk of inadequate perfusion of myocardial tissue during periods of stress. Moreover, basal levels of nitric oxide as measured by chemiluminescence were decreased in male but not female offspring, which is consistent with the finding that endothelial nitric oxide activity is decreased in the aorta of male rats exposed to prenatal nicotine (Lawrence et al., 2008, Xiao et al., 2007). These factors may reduce the ability of the heart to respond adequately to increased demand.

Understanding which genes and what regulatory factors are important to increased vulnerability of hearts is essential. In rats, the genes important in the regulation of apoptosis and cell death were differentially regulated in animals exposed to prenatal nicotine (Lawrence et al., 2008). Researchers found no significant change in the expression of Caspase-3, 8 & 9 among control and treatment groups, but gender specific differences were observed in terms of abundance (Lawrence et al., 2008). In contrast, they found a significant reduction in PKCε in both male and female offspring and reduced PKCδ in female but not male offspring (Lawrence et al., 2008). These findings suggest that an increase in myocardial tissue lost after an ischemic reperfusion insult observed in animals treated with prenatal nicotine may result from decreased expression of a cardioprotective gene, PKCε.

PKCε & PKCδ belong to the novel subset of Protein Kinase C's whose activation is independent of calcium but modulated through diacylglycerol (DAG). Both are highly expressed in heart tissues and are activated during ischemic preconditioning (IPC)

(Bogoyevitch et al., 1993, Gray et al., 1997). Knockout studies indicated PKCε is not necessary for normal heart development, but plays a key role in cardioprotection from I/R injury (Saurin et al., 2002). Studies using PKCε translocation inhibitory peptide (PKCε-TIP) and PKCε activating peptide provide a cause and effect relationship for PKCε expression in myocardial protection from ischemic reperfusion injury (Meyer et al., 2009b, Xue and Zhang, 2009). The mechanism by which PKCε protect cardiomyocytes from cell death is not completely understood. However, PKCε attenuates the function of Bcl-2-associated death promoter protein (BAD) proteins and stabilizes mitochondria through phosphorylation of mitochondria K_{ATP} resulting in hyperpolarization of mitochondrial membranes (Bertolotto et al., 2000, Hausenloy et al., 2003, Jaburek et al., 2006). In contrast to PKCε, PKCδ has an opposing function in ischemia precondition. PKCδ promotes an apoptotic phenotype (Duquesnes et al., 2011). Transient episodes of ischemia activate PKCδ through a ROS-dependent mechanism (Duquesnes et al., 2011). Studies with transgenic mice have shown activation of PKCδ to increase injury from ischemia reperfusion and inhibition of PKCδ activation to be protective (Chen et al., 2001). Some researchers have postulated that the relative ratios of PKCε to PKCδ may influence overall cell viability during ischemic insults (Churchill and Mochly-Rosen, 2007). Given their similarities in structure and opposing roles in cell death, this is an interesting prospect. Interestingly, both PKCε and PKCδ play concurrent roles in cardiomyocyte hypertrophy (Chen et al., 2001, Duquesnes et al., 2011).

Since expression of PKCε was reduced in adult offspring exposed to prenatal nicotine, researchers looked into epigenetic modification of the PKCε gene as a possible mechanism. Epigenetics is an exploding field looking into heritable changes to genes without changes to nucleotide base sequence. Major epigenetic modifications include methylation of cytosine in CpG dinucleotide, and post-translation modification of histone proteins (e.g. acetylation). DNA methylation plays a critical role in gene repression and has been implicated in gene imprinting and embryogenesis (Hirst and Marra, 2009). Methylated cytosines recruit methyl-binding proteins that restrict binding of transcription factors to promoter regions. Methylation of CpG is normally conserved during somatic replication. Modifications of histone proteins can either increase or reduce the association of DNA with histones thereby regulating access of transcription machinery for selected genes. These modifications are dynamic and are influenced by a range of factors including the expression of cofactors, phase of cell cycle (i.e. G_1, S, mitosis), and environmental stimuli (Nafee et al., 2008). Major histone modifications include acetylation of lysine residues via histone acetyltransferases that are associated with transcription activity; deacetylation of lysine residues via histone deacetylases that are commonly associated with transcription repression; methylation of lysine 4 on histone H3 is generally associated with transcriptional active promoters while multiple methylation of histone restricts transcription (Hirst and Marra, 2009). Further modifications include phosphorylation, ubiquitousation, hydroxylation, and sumolation. Histone modification not only influences transcription, but DNA replication, repair, and condensation. In addition, DNA methylation and histone modification, microRNA (miRNA), is another form of epigenetic regulation that is gaining increasing attention. miRNA regulates posttranscriptional gene expression through RNA-induced Silencing Complex (RISC) which acts by targeting complementary nucleotide sequences of message RNA for degradation (Creemers et al., 2012). miRNA is expressed throughout the body and thought to play an important role in cardiovascular disease (Creemers et al., 2012).

In rats, studies identified eight putative transcription factor binding sites with CpG dinucleotides within their sequences on the PKCε promoter (See Figure 10) (Zhang et al., 2009). Late gestational hypoxia significantly increased promoter methylation for EGR-1 (-1008) and MTF-1 (-603) binding sites (Lawrence et al., 2011). It was reported that EGR but not MTF-1 binds the PKCε promoter (Lawrence et al., 2011, Zhang et al., 2009). Reporter gene assay in rat embryonic ventricular myocyte cell line H9c2 showed a 37% decline in promoter activity with deletion from -1163 to -826 and 26% decrease in promoter activity with site directed mutation, indicating EGR-1 binding strongly influences PKCε promoter activity (Lawrence et al., 2011). Nicotine does not alter EGR-1 nuclear abundance or the binding affinity of EGR-1 to unmethylated sites, but methylation abolished EGR-1 binding to PKCε promoter (Lawrence et al., 2011). This suggests the PKCε transcriptional activity is modulated by nicotine induced methylation of CpG dinucleotides on the EGR-1 binding site. These experiments provide a causative mechanism through which nicotine programs cardioprotective genes *in utero*.

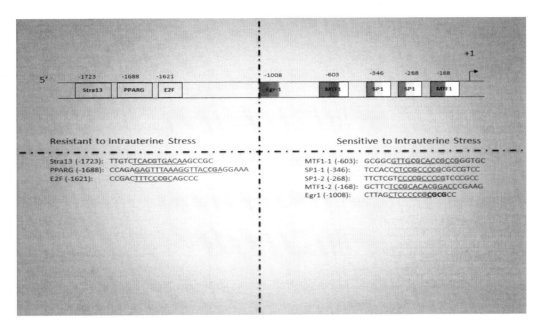

Figure 10. The epigenetic regulation of PKCε promoter by methylation of CpG dinucleotides for transcription factor binding sites. The various colors indicate sites sensitive to the following stressors: hypoxia (blue), nicotine (red), norepinephrine (yellow) and cocaine (white).

The mechanism through which maternal nicotine treatment induces methylation of PKCε promoter is through enhanced sympathetic stimulation resulting in elevated norepinephrine content in fetal hearts (Lawrence et al., 2011). In freshly isolated hearts, norepinephrine but not nicotine directly induced repression of PKCε gene. Direct treatment of norepinephrine in freshly isolated fetal hearts and H9c2 cell line increased methylation of the PKCε promoter at two Sp1 (-346, -268) and EGR-1 (-1008) binding sites (Xiong et al., 2012). This differs from maternal administration of nicotine, which increased EGR-1 and MTF-1 methylation. This evidence suggests that the underlying mechanism of maternal nicotine repression of PKCε gene is multifactorial with alternative pathways of repression.

Which receptor is responsible for the norepinephrine induced repression of PKCε gene is an intriguing question. In the embryonic ventricular H9c2 cell model, α_1 blockade with prazosin but not β_1 blockade attenuated norepinephrine induced repression of PKCε gene. This suggests that norepinephrine mediates repression of PKCε gene through stimulation of α_1-adrenoceptors. Interestingly, studies have found α_{1B}-adrenoceptors stimulation mimics ischemic preconditioning in the acute setting through PKCε activation and mitoK (ATP) channel opening in adult rat hearts (Gao et al., 2007). However, other studies have found α_{1A}-adrenoceptors, but not α_{1B}-adrenoceptors mediate cardioprotective phenotype during I/R injury (Rorabaugh et al., 2005). Determining whether subtype specific activation of α_1-adrenoceptors causes varied phenotypes in the fetal heart model is an intriguing prospect. Additionally, the identification of the receptor responsible for nicotine-induced repression of PKCε gene may have therapeutic implications. Whether α_1 agonist *in utero* can reproduce myocardial vulnerability is an interesting question that may have implications in terms of therapy.

How α_1-adrenoceptors mediates repression of PKCε gene is another intriguing question. Cardiomyocytes are major producers of reactive oxygen species (ROS) due to their high metabolic demand. In adult hearts, α_1-adrenoceptor stimulation increases oxidative stress through NADPH oxidase activation, a superoxide producing enzyme (Liang et al., 2000, Murdoch et al., 2006). Norepinephrine represses PKCε gene activity through an NADPH oxidase dependent mechanism (See Figure 11) (Xiong et al., 2012). NADPH oxidases (Nox) are divided into seven subtypes whose expression and localization varies depending on tissue. In cardiomyocytes, the subtypes Nox1, Nox2, and Nox4 are expressed in association with cardiovascular disease states (Kuroda et al., 2010, Looi et al., 2008, Matsuno et al., 2005). The expression of Nox2 was reported in H9c2 cells exposed to ischemia reperfusion insult. Using a pharmacological approach and a knockdown model with SiRNA, researchers demonstrated that Nox1 but not Nox4 was vital in mediating norepinephrine-induced ROS production (Xiong et al., 2012). These findings implicate NOX1 activity in norepinephrine-induced epigenetic repression of PKCε (See Figure 11).

Together, these findings shed light on how nicotine exposure *in utero* weakens the heart's ability to respond to stress and increases the risk of ischemic heart disease. The fact that nicotine mediates its effects through catecholamines, namely norepinephrine, is fascinating. Several *in utero* insults such as cocaine, maternal stress, and hypoxia can increase catecholamine release and thereby potentially regulate cardioprotective genes, such as PKCε (See Figures 11, 12 & 13). Determining whether increased doses of antioxidants during prenatal nicotine exposure protects against fetal programming of cardioprotective genes is an intriguing prospect and warrants further investigation.

Cocaine

Cocaine is the second most commonly abused illicit drug and is a frequent contributor in drug-related death. The use of cocaine is associated with acute and chronic cardiovascular complications. In humans, it produces adverse cardiovascular effects in adults, such as left ventricular hypertrophy, myocardial ischemia, coronary artery spasm, acute myocardial infarction (MI), atherosclerosis, myocarditis, cardiomyopathy, arrhythmia, hypertension, endocarditis, aortic dissection and rupture, vasculitis and stroke (Brickner et al., 1991, Egred and Davis, 2005, Lange and Hillis, 2001). Cocaine acts as a potent sympathomimetic agent. It blocks the reuptake of norepinephrine and dopamine resulting in increased neurotransmitters at the postsynaptic receptors (Lange and Hillis, 2001). Cocaine increases the release of catecholamines from central and peripheral stores (Gradman, 1988). It also acts as a local anesthetic by inhibiting membrane permeability to sodium ions resulting in decreased electrical conduction (Gradman, 1988).

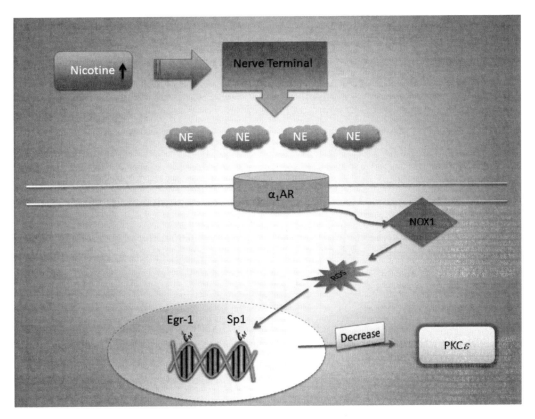

Figure 11. Circulating nicotine mediates repression of PKC epsilon gene through enhanced norepinephrine (NE) release from nerve terminals. Norepinephrine acts on $\alpha_1 AR$, which subsequently activates NOX1 and increases oxidative stress. This signals repression of the PKCε promoter through methylation of Egr-1 binding sites. This alteration increases myocardial vulnerability to I/R injury later in life.

With a molecular weight of 303.4, cocaine is able to cross the placenta and accumulate within the fetal compartment (Schenker et al., 1993). Therefore, in pregnant women who abuse cocaine, the fetus is adversely affected. Several disorders have been attributed to cocaine use in pregnancy. These include prematurity, Sudden Infant Death Syndrome (SIDS), low birthweight, placenta previa, hypertension, and tachycardia (Handler et al., 1991, Silvestri et al., 1991). Interestingly, intravascular or intraperitoneal administration of cocaine in rats did not alter maternal body or birthweight (Bae et al., 2005). However, subcutaneous administration of cocaine did slightly reduce birthweight (Bae and Zhang, 2005). This suggests the route of injection effects maternal satiety. Intravascular injection of cocaine into pregnant sheep alters hemodynamics by causing a transient decrease in uterine blood flow producing hypoxemia within the fetal compartment (Woods et al., 1987).

These findings suggest cocaine has a systemic effect on maternal and fetal physiology, which may result in an adverse intrauterine environment.

Children born to mothers with a history of cocaine abuse have an increased incidence of cardiovascular malformations, including functional and structural deficits, arrhythmias and intracardiac abnormalities that persist in adulthood (Mehta et al., 1993, Meyer and Zhang, 2009, Shaw et al., 1991). In bovine coronary artery endothelial cells, cocaine reduced the basal release of nitric oxide, decreased eNOS protein abundance and reduced intracellular calcium mobilization thereby reducing the active state of calcium dependent eNOS (He et al., 2005). The endothelium plays a critical role in regulating coronary vascular tone by eNOS mediated release of nitric oxide. Inhibition of nitric oxide generation causes an increase in coronary vascular resistance and reduction in perfusion of the myocardium (Chu et al., 1991). Consistent with these findings, 3-month-old male offspring exposed to prenatal cocaine from day 15-21 had decreased pressure dependent myogenic tone in coronary arteries through altered calcium sensitivity (Xiao et al., 2009). Furthermore, high doses of prenatal cocaine abolished the IGF-1 mediated undoing of the positive inotropic effect of angiotensin II in atrial muscle of aged (19-24.5 mo) rat offspring (Haddad et al., 2005).

Prenatal cocaine exposure increased programmed cell death in fetal rat hearts (Bae and Zhang, 2005, Li et al., 2005). Molecular analysis revealed cocaine induced cardiomyocyte cell death through rapid induction of p38α/MAPK which resulted in the downregulation of Bcl-2 (prosurvival protein), increased cytochrome C release and increased caspase-9 but not caspase 8 activation, suggesting a mitochondrial dependent pathway of apoptosis (Li et al., 2005). Consistent with these findings, studies in neonatal rat cardiomyocytes have shown p38α/MAPK blockade with PDSB203580 reduced ischemia reperfusion injury in cardiomyocytes (Barancik et al., 2000, Mackay and Mochly-Rosen, 1999). Linking p38/MAPK to increased perinatal cardiomyocyte apoptosis is intriguing given that studies have shown p38/MAPK inhibits growth of adult cardiomyocytes and that inhibition of the p38/MAPK pathway with dispensation of growth hormones may reinstall cardiomyocyte proliferative capacity (Engel, 2005, Engel et al., 2005). Interestingly, apoptosis plays an important role in the cardiogenesis and maturation of rodent hearts during the first 2 postnatal weeks (Fernandez et al., 2001, Kajstura et al., 1995). Additionally, evidence such as increased DNA fragmentation and sustained Bcl-2/BAX was observed in neonatal rats exposed to prenatal cocaine (Bae and Zhang, 2005), suggesting sustained apoptotic features well into postnatal life. Even with the increased apoptosis, there was no significant difference in the hearts of neonates or adults treated with or without prenatal cocaine (Bae and Zhang, 2005, Bae et al., 2005, Meyer et al., 2009b). Because of its remarkable plasticity, the developing myocardium is able to compensate for myocyte loss by increasing the size of the residue cell population (Bae et al., 2003). Consistent with these studies, cocaine increased the total protein and β-MHC expression in adolescent and adult rat ventricles through a protein kinase C α dependent mechanism (Henning and Cuevas, 2006, Henning and Li, 2003, Henning et al., 2000). This response may sustain basal ventricular function but reduce the heart's capacity to adequately meet demands in situations of stress.

To assess whether hearts exposed to prenatal cocaine respond differently to stress than controls, researchers have used animal models to simulate ischemia reperfusion injury. Although they found no significant difference in baseline function when the hearts were exposed to ischemia reperfusion insult, they found that adult male rats exposed to prenatal cocaine had poorer recovery compared to control animals (Bae and Zhang, 2005). The myocardial infarct size was significantly larger LVDP recovery was compromised and LVEDP was elevated in treatment animals, suggesting cocaine induced increased vulnerability of the myocardium causing reduced myocardial performance (Bae and Zhang, 2005). Conversely, there was no difference between female control and treatment groups, suggesting gender specific cardiac vulnerability to cocaine. When animals exposed to prenatal cocaine were subjected to ischemia preconditioning (IPC), a process whereby several minor or short bouts of ischemia afford increased protection to the myocardium, the protective affects observed in control groups were abolished in treatment groups suggesting long-term susceptibility in these animals (Meyer et al., 2009b).

The molecular events underpinning the increased vulnerability of myocardial tissue in response to prenatal cocaine exposure are not completely understood. Yet, recent work has shown a reduction in overall abundance of the cardioprotective genes PKCε and phospho-PKCε in the ventricles of rat male offspring exposed to prenatal cocaine (Meyer et al., 2009b, Zhang et al., 2007b). The decrease in PKCε expression is a direct effect of cocaine on fetal heart cells (Meyer et al., 2009a). However, maternal administration of cocaine did not alter PKCδ mRNA or protein, suggesting differential regulation of PKCε in response to intrauterine stress (Meyer and Zhang, 2009). As in the nicotine model of fetal programming, prenatal cocaine modulates the PKCε promoter through alterations in the methylation status for transcription factor binding sites (See Figure 10). Prenatal cocaine increases CpG dinucleotides methylation for Sp1 transcription factor binding sites -346 and -268 and MTF-1 -603 and -168 (Meyer et al., 2009a, Zhang et al., 2009). Sp1 was shown to interact with both sites and that binding affinity was completely abolished with methylation at the core of both bindings sites (Zhang et al., 2009). Interestingly, mutation of CpG dinucleotides within two out of three Sp1 binding sites did not change binding of Sp1 but did decrease gene expression (Bogdarina et al., 2009). However, most studies support the idea that CpG methylation inhibits Sp1 promoter binding (Liedtke et al., 2005, Zhu et al., 2003). Additionally, the regions encompassing both sites play an important role in PKCε promoter activity (See Figure 10) (Meyer et al., 2009a, Zhang et al., 2009). Nuclear abundance of Sp1 protein was decreased in cocaine treated fetal hearts, but returned to control values in adult offspring (Meyer et al., 2009a). The use of DNA methylation inhibitors completely abolished the direct effect of cocaine on PKCε expression, clearly linking epigenetic repression in the regulation of PKCε gene *in utero*.

These findings implicate cocaine as a potent programming agent capable of altering the expression patterns of cardioprotective genes resulting in increased risk of ischemic heart disease later in life (See Figure 12). The exact mechanism by which cocaine increased methylation of PKCε promoter is not known. Cocaine causes increased oxidative stress in cardiomyocytes and is known to activate redox sensitive p38/MAPK pathways (Devi and Chan, 1999, Zhang et al., 1999a).

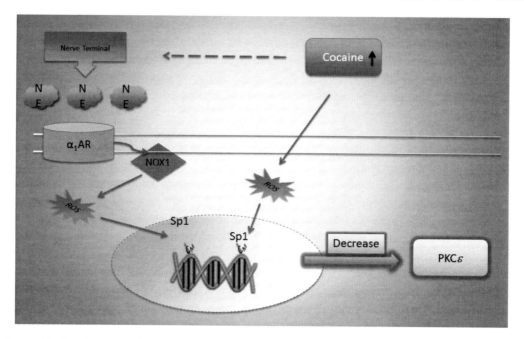

Figure 12. Cocaine indirectly through enhanced sympathetic release of neurotransmitters or through direct toxicity causes increased oxidative stress in fetal cardiomyocytes. This signal's repression of PKC epsilon promoter through methylation of Sp1 binding sites. This alteration increases myocardial vulnerability to I/R injury later in life.

In addition, it is well documented that cocaine causes enhanced sympathetic release of neurotransmitter. Studies examining the effect of prenatal nicotine and increased risk of I/R injury have found nicotine increased the norepinephrine content in hearts and that norepinephrine is sufficient to induce repression of PKCε gene expression. It is possible that in addition to cocaine's direct effect on fetal cardiomyocytes, indirect regulation of PKCε gene occurs via catecholamines (See Figure 12). Future studies in the area of cocaine-induced oxidative stress and norepinephrine may help to explain the mechanism by which prenatal cocaine regulates PKCε gene in male offspring.

Ethanol

It is estimated that there are at least 10 million chronic alcoholics in the United States. The consumption of ethanol is responsible for 100,000 deaths annually. Although it is not known how many pregnant women consume ethanol regularly, it is estimated that ethanol is the most commonly used teratogen. When consumed in sufficient amounts in pregnancy, the fetus is at risk of a constellation of findings that involve structural anomalies with cognitive and behavior abnormalities. These features include growth retardation, facial and neural abnormalities such as microcephaly, short palpebral fissures, and maxillary hypoplasia, and cardiovascular anomalies such as atrial septal defect, pulmonary artery hypoplasia, interruption of the aortic arch, atrio-ventricular defects, patent ductus arteriosus and teratology of Fallot (Mena et al., 1986).

Ethanol is metabolized by alcohol dehydrogenase (ADH) and the mitochondrial form of aldehyde dehydrogenase (ADH2) to acetaldehyde in normal liver. Ethanol crosses the placenta and is not eliminated in the fetal compartment because the fetus does not express significant quantities of ADH in the liver as it does in later postnatal life (Nava-Ocampo et al., 2004). Ethanol impairs fetal heart contractility. Acutely, low and high doses of ethanol in pregnant ewes impair fetal heart function, with the high dose causing suppression of heart function for 4 hours after exposure (Lafond et al., 1985). Consistent with these findings, prenatal alcohol suppressed peak tension development in the rat left ventricular papillary muscle but not isolated ventricular myocytes which may be a reflection of loss of myocytes (Ren et al., 2002). Studies have found a dose-dependent effect of ethanol on the myocardium by increasing apoptosis of cardiomyocytes through increased Bar and caspase-3 activation (Chen et al., 2000, Ren et al., 2002). Furthermore, prenatal ethanol caused increased intracellular calcium levels, which may reflect defects in calcium handling. In avian models, acute exposure to ethanol reduced the cellular contents of actin and myosin in cardiomyocytes (Ni et al., 1992). However, Goh et al. demonstrated in pregnant ewes that chronic infusion of a moderate dose of ethanol during late gestation caused accelerated cardiomyocyte maturation and increased extracellular matrix deposition with increased heart size (Goh et al., 2011). Whether the increase in ventricular size was sustained in postnatal life is not known. These findings indicate that ethanol produces an adverse intrauterine environment that suppresses fetal heart function and may reduce fetal cardiomyocyte number, thus increasing vulnerability of the heart to injury.

It is well established that intrauterine exposure to ethanol is adverse to fetal heart development, however, clinical studies suggest that low to moderate doses of ethanol may be beneficial against I/R injury affording the term "ethanol preconditioning," a state where ethanol exposure confers similar resistance to ischemic insults as myocardial preconditioning (Miyamae et al., 2010). In one study, acute ethanol exposure confers cardioprotection from I/R injury through the upregulation of PKCε that is mediated by A$_1$ adenosine receptor. However, Torres et al., showed that 3 weeks of ethanol exposure caused suppression of PKCε translocation to membrane, which was sustained for 12 days after ethanol withdrawal (Torres et al., 2010). In addition to PKCε, ethanol increased NO release through the modulation of eNOS expression (Jones et al., 2004). Also, chronic treatment of moderate doses of ethanol increased vasodilatation and increased circulating NO in plasma with elevation in eNOS protein (Venkov et al., 1999). Perhaps the effect of alcohol on the heart is dependent on the timing, duration and dose of ethanol exposure. The effect of low and moderate doses of ethanol on cardiac gene expression is not known and deserves future inquiry.

It appears the heart may be more susceptible to prenatal ethanol exposure than postnatal. This vulnerability perhaps is related to alterations in structure and cardiomyocyte number. Interestingly, ethanol increases oxidative stress *in utero* (Henderson et al., 1999). Although it is not clear whether ethanol programs genes necessary for cardioprotection, its ability to alter myocyte growth and morphology may significantly increase the risk of ischemic heart disease later in life.

Table 1. Common causes of intrauterine hypoxia

Environmental Factors	Maternal factors	Placenta Factors
High Altitude	Prexisting disease (i.e. Heart & Lung Disease)	Placenta Insufficiency
Carbon monoxide Exposure	Tobacco Use	Placental Abruption
Toxin exposure (i.e. Cyanide)	Gestational Diabetes	Cord Compression
	Pre-Ecclampsia/Ecclampisa	
	Chronic Hypertension	
	Hematological Disease (i.e. anemia)	
	Anemia	
	Illicit Drug Abuse	
	Medication	
	Infections	
	Chronic Inflammation	

Prenatal Hypoxia and Anemia

Hypoxia is a common gestation insult to the fetus. There is profound clinical relevance in understanding the relationship between *in utero* oxygen insufficiency and the risk of ischemic heart disease. Hypoxia can occur through multiple etiologies during gestation. The most common causes of prenatal hypoxia are listed in Table 1. In this section, we will explore current literature as to the effect of intrauterine hypoxia and the risk of ischemic heart disease.

Hypoxia is the state where the demand for oxygen within tissue exceeds the supply available. This is commonly brought about through insufficient gas exchange and low partial pressure of oxygen in blood. Hypoxia has both systemic and organ specific effects on the fetus. In humans, fetal hypoxia causes intrauterine growth restriction (IUGR), low birth weight and is associated with prematurity, and infant mortality (Jensen and Moore, 1997, Patterson and Zhang, 2010). In fetal hearts, it suppresses function, modifies cardiac gene expression and increases heart to body weight ratio (Bae et al., 2003, Kamitomo et al., 1992, Martin et al., 1998, Ohtsuka and Gilbert, 1995, Val'Kovich et al., 1986, Zhang, 2005). Common maternal and placental derived insults, such as tobacco smoking, cord compression and aberrant placental function, may reduce gas exchange between the mother and fetus causing hypoxemia and tissue hypoxia *in utero* (Patterson and Zhang, 2010). Systemically, the fetus compensates by adjusting fetal blood flow away from peripheral tissues to vital organs such as the brain and heart. The heart itself adapts by activating hypoxia-dependent genes such as Hypoxia Inducible Factor-1 and 2 (HIF-1 & 2), which facilitates the shift from aerobic to greater utilization of anaerobic respiratory pathways, increasing capillary density (Thompson, 2003) and the recruitment of factors necessary for expansion of the coronary tree such as vascular endothelium growth factor (VEGF). Interestingly, the fetal heart is more resistant to hypoxia induced cellular demise than the adult heart due to its superior ability to increase glycolytic flux and enhanced anaerobic respiration (Ascuitto and Ross-Ascuitto, 1996).

Hypoxia and Normal Heart Development

The complexity of the intrauterine environment is thus illustrated by the irony of the fact that the fetus is known to develop in a relative state of hypoxia and that hypoxia plays a vital role in fetal heart development. Although oxidative metabolism is fundamental to building energy reserves necessary for sustained fetal growth, fluctuations in oxygen availability are necessary for normal growth and maturation of the myocardium. It has been well documented in mammalian and avian models the critical role hypoxia plays in outflow tract (OFT) remodeling and coronary vessel patterning and growth (Fishman and Chien, 1997, Wikenheiser et al., 2006). The remodeling of the OFT is required for proper transition from single to dual circulation in mammalian and avian models. Revision of the OFT myocardium and correct alignment of the aorta with the left ventricle involves programmed cell death of OFT cardiomyocytes through a hypoxia dependent mechanism (Fishman and Chien, 1997, Patterson and Zhang, 2010). Additionally, the migration of endothelial progenitor cells to the myocardium and their subsequent organization into the coronary vessels tree coincides with and involves genes regulated by hypoxic stress (Garcia-Martinez and Schoenwolf, 1993, Liu et al., 2009). Importantly, hypoxia mediated induction of VEGF through both mechanical or metabolic stimulus is important in conducting the events necessary for patterning and growth of coronary vessels (Tomanek et al., 2003). The growth and cardiogenic effects of hypoxia are abolished in conditions of hyperoxia (Tomanek et al., 2003). The role of hypoxia in the earlier cardiac development illustrates how fluctuations in oxygen availability can change gene expression patterns leading to morphological and physiological maturation.

Hypoxia Inducible Factor

Hypoxia regulates a number of genes of which the Hypoxia Inducible Factor (HIF) family of transcription factors is the most important. HIF is a heterodimeric transcription factor that plays a pivotal role in cellular sensing and response to low oxygen tension. HIF belongs to the basic helix-loop-helix (bHLH)/Per-ARNT-Sim (PAS) domain family of transcription factors and is composed of an oxygen-sensitive α subunit and constitutively expressed β subunit (Jiang et al., 1996a, Semenza, 1998, Ward, 2008). It regulates numerous processes such as energy metabolism, erythropoiesis, cell survival and death, vascularization, angiogenesis, and differentiation (Adelman et al., 2000, Covello et al., 2006, Cowden Dahl et al., 2005, Galanis et al., 2008, Semenza et al., 1999). Oxygen availability regulates HIF-1 expression *via* prolyl hydroxylase activity. Normoxic conditions promote PHDs -mediated hydroxylation of two proline residues (402 and 564) of the HIF-1α subunit. Hydroxylation promotes recruitment and binding of the von Hippel-Lindau protein, an E3 ubiquitin protein ligase, which primes HIF-1α for subsequent proteasome degradation. The transcriptional activity of HIF-1 is regulated by the hydroxylation of arginine 803 by Factor inhibiting HIF-1 (FIH). FIH prevents the association of HIF-1 and its cofactor CREB-binding protein

(CBP)/p300, precluding the transactivation of HIF-1 dependent genes (Mahon et al., 2001). When cellular oxygen levels fall, the activity of PHDs and FIH are attenuated, stabilizing the HIF-1α subunit. Stable HIF-1α subunit rapidly translocates into the nucleus where it dimerizes with HIF-1β and transactivates genes that possess hypoxic response elements (HRE) (short sequences of DNA that include 5'-CGTGC/T-3'). HIF-1 stability is inversely proportional to oxygen concentration within the cell with severe hypoxia or anoxia producing the most robust response (Jiang et al., 1996b). Across several species, investigators have reported HIF-1 nuclear accumulation in fetal hearts (Bae et al., 2003, Martin et al., 1998, Wikenheiser et al., 2006). HIF-1α knockout models have demonstrated the essential role HIF-1 has in normal myocardium maturation and coronary vessel development (Kotch et al., 1999). Whether aberrant expression of HIF *in utero* predisposes the myocardium to ischemic disease is not well understood. Studies have shown prenatal hypoxia regulates cardioprotective genes (Li et al., 2003, Xue and Zhang, 2009). Pharmacological blockade of HIF-1α nuclear accumulation with YC-1 and 2-me2 does not affect the hypoxia-induced repression of the PKCε expression, a known cardioprotective gene (Patterson et al., 2012). Although the role of HIF-2 is directly identified, studies have shown both YC-1 and 2-me2 inhibits HIF-2 nuclear accumulation which may suggest the HIF family of genes are not involved in hypoxia-induced PKCε gene repression (Hwang et al., 2008, Mabjeesh et al., 2003). Whether the HIF family of genes regulates other cardioprotective genes such as eNOS and Hsp70 *in utero* is not known and warrants further study.

Structural Deficits

The essential role of hypoxia in myocardium maturation and growth is in contrast to the detrimental effects attributed to sustained pathophysiological oxygen insufficiency *in utero*. Chronic prenatal hypoxia influences myocardium structure and architecture. These findings are typically characterized by abnormal myocardial growth that is based on changes in myocyte morphology and proliferation as well as the extracellular matrix remodeling (See Figure 13). Fluctuations in growth characteristics may depend on the severity, timing or species in which the hypoxic insult is transmitted. Grossly, studies have found simulated high altitude in pregnant rats increased the rate of ventricular septal defects in rat offspring (Clemmer and Telford, 1966). This finding is supported by studies in midgestional mouse fetuses (E11.5-E13.5) exposed to 8% maternal hypoxia that found myocardial hypoplasia and ventricular dilation suggesting reduced cardiomyocyte proliferation (Ream et al., 2008). In fetal and neonatal rats exposed to late gestational maternal hypoxia (10.5% O_2), the thickness of the anterior wall, posterior wall, septal wall, and free wall of left ventricle was decreased and epicardial detachment observed as compared to age matched controls (Tong et al., 2011). This implies that reduction in oxygen availability reduces the proliferative capacity leading to decreased tissue bulk. In avian models, prenatal hypoxia caused ventricular dilation, decreased wall mass and increased apoptosis (Tintu et al., 2009). These findings indicate that aberrant hypoxic stress reduces myocardial wall thickness and increases the risk of congenital cardiac anomalies, predisposing the myocardium to disease later in life.

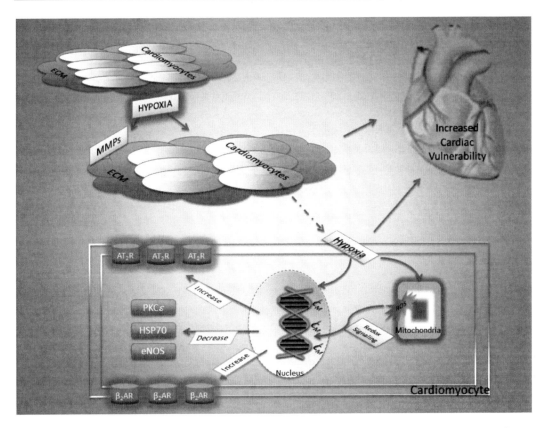

Figure 13. Chronic intrauterine hypoxia accelerates cardiomyocyte maturation leading to decreased proliferation and increased cell size. It also promotes extracellular matrix (ECM) remodeling alterations in matrix metalloproteinases (MMPs) and increased collagen content. Hypoxia directly down regulates cardioprotective genes (i.e., PKCε, HSP70 & eNOS) and upregulates maladaptive genes (i.e. AT$_2$R, β_2AR).

Conversely, ventricular hypertrophy has been documented in ovine fetuses exposed to isovolemic hemorrhage producing chronic anemia for 21 days (Martin et al., 1998) and anemic fetuses whose placentas were subjected to chronic embolization resulting in 50% reduced oxygen content (Murotsuki et al., 1997). Perhaps increased catecholamines from stress may have induced a hypertensive state, which increased afterload and ventricular mass. In rats, chronic intermittent hypoxia for both 4 and 8 weeks caused eccentric ventricular hypertrophy with 4 week insults increasing tumor necrosis factor-alpha (TNF-α), insulin-like growth factor II (IGF-II), phosphorylated p38/MAPK and signal transducers and activators of transcription I and III (STAT-1&3) (Chen et al., 2007). In the group exposed to 8-week hypoxic insult, researchers found the additional activation of interleukin-6 (IL-6), mitogen-activated protein kinase 5 and extracellular signal-regulated kinase 5 (ERK5), which suggest the involvement of pro-inflammatory activity in hypoxia-induced eccentric myocardial hypertrophy (Chen et al., 2007). Davidge et al. reported that rat offspring ages 4, 7, and 12 months that were exposed to prenatal hypoxia (12% O$_2$) during late gestation significantly reduced birthweight and increased relative right and left ventricle weights (Rueda-Clausen et al., 2009, Xu et al., 2006b). These studies suggest pathophysiological hypoxia can conversely produce myocardial hypertrophy. These changes may reflect individual alterations in fetal cardiomyocytes morphology or modification to the extracellular mesh housing fetal cardiomyocytes.

To gain insight into the role of fetal hypoxia in determining the risk of ischemic heart disease, it is vital to understand normal fetal cardiomyocyte behavior. Cardiomyocytes are derived from cardiac progenitor cells that form two cardiac fields located anterior to the mesoderm germ layer early in cardiogenesis (Garcia-Martinez and Schoenwolf, 1993, Schoenwolf and Garcia-Martinez, 1995). Normal development of the heart involves a process in which cardiomyocytes become terminally differentiated. During late fetal development in humans, many cardiomyocytes transition from a mononucleate to binucleate phenotype. These binucleate cells are terminally differentiated and lack the ability to proliferate. Thus the majority of proliferation and hyperplasia of the heart occurs during fetal development (Jonker et al., 2007b). Once cardiomyocytes reach terminal differentiation, the population of these cells in the heart is determined. Therefore the amount of cardiomyocytes residing in the adult heart is greatly dependent on the development of the fetal heart.

An adverse intrauterine environment has been well established to lead to an increased predisposition to cardiovascular disease later in life (Barker, 1995, 1997, 2004). As previously mentioned, hypoxic exposure *in utero* is a major stress that can create an unfavorable environment for fetal growth. Maternal hypoxia during gestation has adverse effects on the fetal and neonatal heart structure and architecture. These effects are characterized by fewer and larger cardiomyocytes with an increase in number of binucleate cells in the heart of its offspring (Bae et al., 2003). Several studies have also shown this increase in cell size of neonatal rat cardiomyocytes via hypoxia-induced hypertrophy both *in vitro* (Chu et al., 2012, Ito et al., 1996) and *in vivo* (Radom-Aizik et al., 2013). Of importance in rats, cardiomyocytes continue to proliferate after birth and do not become terminally differentiated until 1–2 weeks after birth (Clubb and Bishop, 1984). Furthermore, *in vitro* hypoxia followed by reoxygenation led to premature senescence and reduced proliferation of neonatal rat cardiomyocytes (Zhang et al., 2007a). Altogether these studies suggest that hypoxia stimulates the transition of cardiomyocytes to a terminally differentiated form, or binucleate phenotype (See Figure 13).

Fetal studies give further evidence that hypoxia decreases proliferation of cardiomyocytes, marked by reduced expression of Ki-67, a proliferation marker (Tong et al., 2011, 2013). The downregulation of cyclin D2, a cell cycle activator, and upregulation of p27, a cell cycle inhibitor, were associated with reduced proliferation in hypoxia.

Similarly, chronic anemia in fetal sheep has also been shown to increase cardiomyocyte size and terminal differentiation while cell cycle activity was unchanged (Jonker et al., 2010). Hypoxic conditions also upregulated the tissue inhibitor of metalloproteinases, TIMP-3 and -4, suggesting these inhibitors as potential candidates for enhanced cardiac remodeling and reduced proliferation (Tong et al., 2013). These findings are intriguing given that, in transgenic mice and cultured neonatal mouse cardiomyocytes, eNOS knockdown inhibited myocyte proliferation through a TIMP-3 dependent mechanism (Hammoud et al., 2007). Ironically, the effects of TIMP-3 are mediated through inhibition of EGFR expression/phosphorylation, and decreases in JNK and SP-1 transcription factor signaling (Hammoud et al., 2009). Chronic maternal hypoxia has been documented to reduce eNOS levels and thus serve as an additional pathway of increased vulnerability of hearts exposed to chronic intrauterine hypoxia (Li et al., 2003). Additionally, SP1 transcription factor binding sites are sensitive to epigenetic modification in hypoxic models and may also be regulated by

TIMP-3 activity (Patterson et al., 2010). Overall these studies imply a complex role for hypoxia in reducing proliferation of cardiomyocytes.

On the contrary, there are a number of studies in support of hypoxia-induced proliferation of cardiomyocytes. In adult zebrafish, hypoxia-induced ventricular amputation has been shown to mediate heart regeneration (Jopling et al., 2012), which occurs through the proliferation and dedifferentiation of cardiomyocytes (Jopling et al., 2010). Furthermore, transgenic mice overexpressing hypoxia-inducible factor 1alpha (HIF1α) had reduced infarct size and enhanced cardiac function at 4 weeks after injury with myocardial infarction (Kido et al., 2005). Additionally, neonatal cardiomyocytes treated with C3 or f58, a hypoxia and Akt induced stem cell factor (HASF), exhibited increased DNA synthesis and number of cells in mitosis and cytokinesis. Altogether this demonstrates that HASF can induce proliferation of cardiomyocytes, specifically via the PI3K-AKT-CDK7 pathway (Beigi et al., 2013).

Growth restriction *in utero* can lead to reduced oxygen supply to the fetus. Intrauterine growth restriction (IUGR) is associated with hypoxia (Bae et al., 2003, Moore, 2003, Xiao et al., 2000, Zhang, 2005) and has been shown to reduce the percentage of binucleated cardiomyocytes (Bubb et al., 2007). Morrison et al. showed that placental restriction leads to chronic fetal hypoxia, which results in increased percentage of mononucleated cardiomyocytes in the fetal sheep. The restricted fetuses have smaller individual cardiomyocytes but when compared relative to heart weight, the cells were larger (Morrison et al., 2007). The results of this study suggest that placental restriction-induced hypoxia reduces the total number of cardiomyocytes in the heart. Other studies demonstrate that after 20 days of uteroplacental insufficiency, the percentage of binucleated cardiomyocytes as well as cell cycle activity decreased. In addition, fewer mononucleated cardiomyocytes expressed Ki-67, indicating reduced proliferative capacity of these hearts (Louey et al., 2007).

There is evidence to support both a positive and negative effect of hypoxia on cardiomyocyte proliferation. This could be due to the differences in the age and species of animal used, as well as methods of hypoxia induction and proliferation quantification. A possible explanation for hypoxia's effect on binucleation is that cardiomyocytes respond by initiating proliferation but are unable to complete cell division and thus become binucleated. Altogether, studies give evidence that hypoxia is a major fetal stressor capable of modulating cardiomyocyte endowment in the heart—ultimately influencing cardiac health throughout life.

In addition to proliferative alterations, hypoxia may alter myocardial extracellular matrix. The extracellular matrix of cardiomyocytes is a complex 3-dimensional network of matrix proteins, signaling molecules, proteases and cell types that collectively regulate myocardial organization (Spinale, 2007). The dominant form of collagen in heart tissue is type I and III. The regulation of fibrillar proteins is influenced by the rate of synthesis and degradation. Excessive synthesis may cause fibrosis while reduced degradation may cause ventricular stiffening and lead to diastolic dysfunction. Matrix metalloproteinase (MMPs) belong to a group of enzymes important in the remodeling. They regulate gelatin, collagen, fibrillin and other extracellular components (Tong and Zhang, 2012). MMPs cleave collagen at a Gly-Leu or Gly-Ile site, which produces an unstable conformation allowing degradation by nonspecific proteases (Tong and Zhang, 2012). MMPs are regulated by endogenous mechanisms in heart tissue. One important family of regulators is Tissue inhibitors of Matrix metalloproteinases (TIMP). TIMP regulate MMP activity through competitively binding to MMP active sites, thus eliminating their ability to act on substrate. TIMP-1 & 2 regulate the activity of MMP 9

& 2 respectively (Vaillant et al., 1999). TIMP-3 regulates ECM proteins while TIMP-4 has activity against proMMP-2.

Intrauterine hypoxia alters the expression profile of MMPs and collagen composition in fetal hearts. Chronic late gestational hypoxia from day 15 to 21 increased the expression of collagen 1 and differentially regulated MMP expression in perinatal rat hearts (Tong et al., 2011). In 4 & 7 month old offspring exposed to maternal hypoxia, type collagen I and III were increased as was the β/α MHC isoform ratio, which suggested increased myocardial remodeling (Xu et al., 2006b). In rat, α MHC is the predominant isoform in healthy hearts, while β MHC increases in expression in pathological states (Buttrick et al., 1991, Takahashi et al., 1992). Consistent with these findings, maternal hypoxia decreased the expression of MMP-1 and increased the expression of MMP-13 and membrane type (MT) 1 MMP in fetal heart while increasing MMP-1 & 9 in neonatal rats (Tong et al., 2011). While Tong et al. (Tong et al., 2011) found prenatal hypoxia did not affect the expression of MMP-2 & 9 in fetal and neonatal hearts, Xu et al., found MMP-2 activity was decreased in adults suggesting an age related decline in function. Likewise, prenatal hypoxia increased MMP9 expression and collagen deposition (Evans et al., 2012a). These findings suggest prenatal hypoxia influences cardiac remodeling, which may alter cardiac function and increase the risk of ischemic heart disease later in life.

Functional Programming

The changes in cardiomyocyte morphology, number, and ECM may alter myocardial performance. In support of this idea, chronic hypoxia *in utero* decreased cardiac performance as demonstrated by decreased LV ejection fractions, decreased dP/dT maximum accompanied by signs of diastolic dysfunction in avian models (Tintu et al., 2009). Likewise, fetuses exposed to hypoxemia have reduced cardiac output and contractility in ovine models. These findings are likely the result of abnormal calcium handling and reduction in Mg^{2+}-activated myofibrillar ATPase activity (Gilbert, 1998, Gilbert et al., 2003, Kamitomo et al., 1994). In anemic sheep subjected to isovolumic hemorrhage, intrauterine hypoxemia remodeled the coronary vessel tree, resulting in increased coronary blood flow and conductance and enhanced coronary reserves (Davis et al., 2003, 2005). These changes persisted into adulthood suggesting programming of coronary vasculature.

Remarkably, many hearts subjected to intrauterine hypoxia maintain normal basal function. However, when these hearts are exposed to stress later in life, there is an increased susceptibility to myocardial dysfunction. For example, 7-month-old sheep subjected to chronic anemia *in utero* had poorer cardiac performance in response to hypoxic insult as compared to aged matched controls (Broberg et al., 2003). In 3, 4 & 6 month old male Sprague-Dawley rats, prenatal hypoxia caused a significant increase in myocardial infarct size, and showed signs of persistent decrease in postischemic recovery from simulated I/R injury (Li et al., 2003, Patterson et al., 2010, Xu et al., 2006b, Xue and Zhang, 2009). The hearts of these animals have elevated markers of apoptosis as seen by caspase-3 activity, FAS ligand expression, and DNA fragmentation, while showing signs of decreased cardioprotection and myocardial remodeling as evidenced by MMP-2 activity and decreased eNOS and PKCε expression. In male 2 month old rats, prenatal hypoxia abolished the protective effects attributed to whole body heat stress (Li et al., 2004). In this study, researchers found prenatal hypoxia did not affect basal levels of heat shock protein 70 (HSP70), but abolished the whole body heat stress induced rise in HSP70 abundance and decreased the PKCε content (Li et al., 2004). On the contrary, a study utilizing 3-month-old Wistar rats subjected to intermittent hypobaric hypoxia *in utero* and 10 days after birth did not find changes in heart recovery between experimental and control groups after open chest I/R insult (Netuka et al., 2006). They did report sex specific susceptibility to arrhythmias with protection afforded to females but not males (Netuka et al., 2006). The most plausible explanation for the different outcomes is likely related to prenatal hypoxia induced differential effects on myocardial vulnerability to I/R injury, which is likely dependent on the gender, species, duration and method of I/R insult.

Cardioprotective Genes

How genes important to myocardial protection are regulated *in utero* is a fascinating question. Several genes appear to be sensitive to chronic intrauterine hypoxic stress. So far, the genes that show sensitivity include PKCε, eNOS, HSP70, β_2-adrenoceptors, and Angiotensin II Receptors (ATRs) (See Figure 13). Whether regulation of cardioprotective genes involves a similar or different mechanism of repression is intriguing.

PKCε

New discoveries have increased our understanding pertaining to the mechanism of hypoxia-induced repression of cardioprotective genes. PKCε is arguably one of the most important cardioprotective genes and consequently has been studied most extensively in the field of fetal programming of ischemic heart disease. Thus, it is an excellent example to demonstrate the intrauterine modulation of gene expression. Intrauterine stress can induce DNA methylation of CpG dinucleotides of transcription factor binding sites causing long-term down-regulation of PKCε gene activity. In rats, nicotine and cocaine mediated repressive effects on PKCε gene through increased DNA methylation of CpG dinucleotides of Sp1 (-346, -268) and EGR-1 (-1008) binding sites (See Figure 10) (Lawrence et al., 2008, 2011, Meyer et al., 2009a, Zhang et al., 2009). Similarly, prenatal hypoxia increased the methylation Sp1 (-346, -268) and EGR-1 (-1008) of PKCε promoter in fetal hearts (Chen et al., 2013, Patterson et al., 2010). As mentioned in previous sections, the regions encompassing Sp1 and Egr-1 binding sites play an important role in PKCε promoter activity (Meyer et al., 2009a, Zhang et al., 2009). Interestingly, the embryonic rat ventricular h9c2 cell line PKCε promoter was differentially regulated compared to whole hearts with both having increased methylation of Sp1 (-346, -268) binding sites, but only whole hearts having increased methylation of EGR-1 (-1008). Although H9c2 cells retain many properties consistent with freshly isolated cardiomyocytes, they lack the contractile properties and are capable of continuous growth (Hescheler et al., 1991). These data may reflect the unique relationship of the direct effects of hypoxia on isolated cells versus whole organs and systemic responses. In whole animals, additional factors such as catecholamines and stress hormones may in conjunction with hypoxia produce a different pattern of PKCε gene activity. Interestingly, the nuclear levels and binding affinities of both Sp1 and Egr-1 were unaffected by hypoxia with the exception being in H9c2 cells which had an increase in Sp1 abundance (Patterson et al., 2010). Consistent with these findings, the use of 5-aza-2-deoxycytidine reversed the hypoxia-induced methylation of Sp1 (-346, -268) and EGR-1 (-1008) and restored PKCε expression (Chen et al., 2013, Patterson et al., 2010). This pattern of increased promoter methylation persevered into adulthood (Patterson et al., 2010, Xue and Zhang, 2009).

On the other hand, hypoxia is known to increase oxidative stress in cardiomyocytes and play a role in the development of heart disease (Dai et al., 2011, Duranteau et al., 1998, Patterson et al., 2012). The mitochondria is believed to be the major source of hypoxia derived ROS with complex III of the electron transport chain being the most likely source (Galanis et al., 2008). In fetal hearts, N-acetylcysteine and tempol (ROS scavengers) but not apocynin (inhibitor of NADPH oxidase) blocked the hypoxia-induced repression of PKCε expression and restored normal basal levels of methylation and Sp1 binding (See Figure 13) (Patterson et al., 2012). Consistent with these findings, studies have found norepinephrine through NOX-1 dependent and cocaine through NAPDH oxidase independent mechanisms reduced PKCε gene activity in fetal rat hearts, which suggests a similar mechanism of repression (See Figure 11 & 12). In cancer cell lines, studies have found hypoxia & oxidative stress upregulate SNAIL transcription factor which leads to the suppression of E-cadherin (a gene involved in cell adhesion) expression through hypermethylation of E-cadherin promoter that involves the activation of ROS sensitive pathways (Cannito et al., 2008, Lim et al., 2008). Functionally, antioxidant exposure with N-acetylcysteine during intrauterine hypoxic insult blocked myocardial vulnerability to I/R injury in adult offspring by preserving normal postischemic LVDP and LVEDP in male rats subjected to prenatal hypoxia (Patterson et al., 2012). These findings point to redox sensitive pathways as mediators of epigenetic repression of cardioprotective genes and subsequent increased cardiac vulnerability to I/R injury. They also suggest that the repressive intrauterine effects of hypoxia on cardioprotective genes may be ameliorated by increase antioxidant defense *in utero*.

eNOS

In addition to PKCε, maternal hypoxia (10.5% O_2) caused a reduction in the expression of endothelial nitric oxide synthase (eNOS) in adult rat offspring (Li et al., 2003). In pregnant guinea pigs exposed to either 14 days or 28 days of hypoxia (12%, O_2), intrauterine hypoxia decreased eNOS protein and mRNA in fetal heart but was found to subsequently increase in the adult heart and carotid arteries (Thompson and Dong, 2005). Additional studies have found chronic hypoxia increased iNOS expression in fetal guinea pigs (Thompson et al., 2009), which may be a compensatory response to the reduced eNOS expression. Nitric oxide (NO) regulates and promotes vascular integrity. While its cardioprotective role is controversial, with studies suggesting NO accumulation is important in ischemia reperfusion injury (Csonka et al., 1999) and others showing NO to be protective (Bolli, 2001), the use of gain of function/loss of function experiments in transgenic mice seems to suggest a strong correlation of NO in promoting a cardioprotective phenotype (Jones and Bolli, 2006).

Interestingly, SP1 transcription factor is important for critical basal expression of eNOS in endothelial cells (Zhang et al., 1999b). Furthermore, mutation of Sp1 consensus sequence at -104 of the eNOS promoter significantly reduced basal eNOS activity (Kumar and Sitasawad, 2009). The GC rich region at -104 contains two CpG dinucleotide sequence at the core binding motif (Kumar and Sitasawad, 2009). Kumar and Sitasawad (2009) were able to demonstrate H_2O_2 significantly reduced eNOS promoter activity by decreasing SP1 activity. Furthermore, methylation of eNOS promoter plays an important role in regulating cell specific expression of eNOS (Chen et al., 2004). These findings seem to strongly correlate with PKCε pattern of repression. Whether chronic intrauterine hypoxia directly regulates eNOS promoter through increased methylation of CpG dinucleotide for Sp1 binding sites in fetal hearts is intriguing and warrants further investigation.

Hsp70

In addition to PKCε and eNOS, Hsp70 presents another interesting cardioprotective gene that was reported to be sensitive to maternal hypoxic insult. Chronic maternal hypoxia significantly reduced Hsp70 protein and mRNA levels in fetal hearts (Bae et al., 2003). The down regulation on Hsp70 gene persisted into adulthood (Li et al., 2003). Hsp70 plays an important role in protection against ischemia reperfusion injury and injury from heat shock (Jayakumar et al., 2001, Okubo et al., 2001, Snoeckx et al., 2001). The amount of Hsp70 directly correlates with the degree of cardioprotection conferred (Hutter et al., 1994). Chronic maternal hypoxia reduced the expression of Hsp70 and reduced recovery from heat shock in adult rat hearts (Li et al., 2004). Morgan (Morgan, 1989) demonstrated Sp1 binding to Hsp70 promoter promotes transcriptional activity. Interestingly, Morgan (Morgan, 1989) identified two Sp1 binding sites at the proximal promoter (-172 to -163 and -50 to -41) that possess CpG dinucleotides in their consensus sequence. Whether methylation regulates SP1 binding to Hsp70 promoter and whether alterations change promoter activity are intriguing questions. Characterizing the SP1 transcriptional regulation of Hsp70 promoter deserves further attention.

ATR

Angiotensin II Receptors (ATRs) are G-protein coupled, 7 transmembrane receptors that are found as two primary subtypes, AT_1R and AT_2R that share 30% homology. Both are stimulated by the renin-angiotensin-system (RAS) with the primary mediator being angiotensin II. However, they differ in terms of 2nd messenger pathways with stimulation of AT_1R resulting in Gq/Gi coupling, with activation of calcium voltage channels through a phospholipase C dependent pathway that results in the phosphorylation of Ras/ERK and activation of JAK2/STATS 2nd messenger pathways (Dasgupta and Zhang, 2011). AT_2R activates Gi coupling which initiates tyrosine phosphatase activation. This results in 2nd messenger activation of downstream targets such as NO, cGMP, and phospholipase A_2 (Dasgupta and Zhang, 2011). Whereas short-term stimulation of AT_1R mediates cardioprotective effects against I/R injury, chronic stimulation of AT_1R increases oxidative stress, endothelial damage and promotes adverse myocardial remodeling and fibrosis through the upregulation of TGF-β. AT_2R stimulation seems to offset the acute and chronic effects of AT_1R stimulation. Acute stimulation of AT_2R increased myocardial dysfunction and damage from I/R injury, but chronic stimulation of AT_2R antagonizes AT_1R signaling through inhibiting cell growth and proliferation as well as increasing vasodilatation through enhanced release of nitric oxide. Interestingly, AT_2R expression is inhibited by glucocorticoid receptor binding glucocorticoid response elements (GRE) on the AT_2R promoter (Xue et al., 2011). Deletion of regions containing GRE's sites significantly increased AT_2R promoter activity suggesting an inhibitor role for GR receptor. In fetal tissue, glucocorticoids are found in relatively low levels in blood but increase substantially in the post gestation environment. Prenatal hypoxia reduced the expression of GR in fetal, neonatal and adult offspring leading to increased AT_2R density and subsequent enhanced cardiac vulnerability to I/R injury (Xue et al., 2011). Interestingly, 5 minute pretreatment with AT_2R inhibitor (PD123, 319) blocked prenatal hypoxia-mediated enhanced injury during I/R injury (Xue et al., 2011). These findings indicate hypoxia modifies GR expression leading to increased myocardial injury from enhanced AT_2R expression.

β₂AR

Previous studies have shown prenatal hypoxia increased expression of β₂-adrenoceptors and increased the ratio of $G_s\alpha/G_i\alpha$ in fetal rat hearts (Li et al., 2003). β₂AR is coupled to both $G_s\alpha$ and $G_i\alpha$ in rat and human hearts (Xiao, 2000). The functional significance of these finding are not clear given that intrauterine hypoxia increases catecholamine release. Overexpression of $G_s\alpha$ resulted in increased activation of β₂AR with increased apoptotic features in cardiomyocytes (Geng et al., 1999). Studies indicate $G_i\alpha$ is important in promoting a survival phenotype in cardiomyocytes (Zhu et al., 2001). In addition, β₂AR knockout mice reduced injury from middle cerebral artery occlusion as in wild-type mice pretreated with β₂AR antagonist. Studies looking at epigenetic modifications to the proximal promoter of β₂AR gene are few; however, work done by McAlees et al. (McAlees et al., 2011) found that methylation of proximal promoter of β₂AR influences CD4+ T cells. Perhaps this region may be sensitive to intrauterine stress in fetal cardiomyocytes, resulting in aberrant β₂AR gene expression and consequent enhanced vulnerability to ischemia reperfusion injury.

Sex-Dimorphorism

Previous studies have reported significant sex differences in the effect of maternal hypoxia on cardiac vulnerability in adulthood. Maternal hypoxia increased the susceptibility to ischemia reperfusion injury in male rat offspring (Xue and Zhang, 2009). Although the extent of gender specific difference in gene expression patterns is not known in fetal hearts, PKCε is a suitable example of the gender disparities. Investigation has revealed reduced expression of PKCε protein in male rats compared to female rats. Maternal hypoxia caused significant decrease in PKCε mRNA and increased methylation of both SP1 bindings sites (-346 and -268) for fetuses and adult offspring. The degree to which methylation was increased in female hearts was considerably lower than in male hearts. Fetal hearts exposed to maternal cocaine responded in a similar sex dependent manner (Zhang et al., 2009). Maternal cocaine exposure caused increased CpG methylation for SP1 binding sites -346 and -268 in male and -268 only in female offspring (Zhang et al., 2009). Likewise, maternal nicotine exposure caused increased susceptibility to ischemia reperfusion injury in both male and female offspring, with poorer recovery in female offspring (Lawrence et al., 2008). PKCε protein was significantly reduced in both male and female hearts exposed to prenatal nicotine, which suggests that nicotine induces a different pattern of regulation in fetal hearts (Lawrence et al., 2008). Furthermore, Netuka et al. (Netuka et al., 2006) found maternal hypoxia significantly improved cardiac tolerance to ischemic arrhythmias in female offspring, but had the opposite effect in male offspring. These findings indicate sex dependent mechanisms for *in utero* programming of the myocardium.

There is a general tendency for female offspring to be more resistant to cardiovascular diseases induced by prenatal stressors (Xue and Zhang, 2009, Zhang et al., 2009). Freshly isolated cardiomyocytes from female hearts express more K(ATP) channels that may support resistance to ischemia reperfusion injury (Ranki et al., 2001). According to previous studies, sex specific differences in gene expression become evident by midgestation in rodents (Dewing et al., 2003). The contribution of (XX) and (XY) dependent genes in reduced or enhanced cardioprotection of male or female offspring respectively is not well understood. The increased cardioprotection observed in female offspring may be explained by the presence of estrogens sex hormone. Removal of the ovaries and estrogen replacement in rats has implicated estrogens in cardioprotection against ischemia reperfusion injury in female rat hearts (Zhai et al., 2000b). The exact mechanism is not clear, but studies in female rat hearts have found estrogen replacement reduced the expression of tumor necrosis factor-alpha (Xu et al., 2006a). Further studies have found estrogen receptor alpha agonist [PPT] or selective beta agonist [DPN] improved myocardial recovery from acute ischemia reperfusion insult (Vornehm et al., 2009). These findings are interesting given that male and female fetuses are likely exposed to similar concentrations of steroid hormones. Studies have reported significantly higher expression of ERα and ERβ in female fetal hearts compared to male, which may explain the enhanced protection afforded in female hearts (Chen et al., 2013, Patterson et al., 2010). ERα knockout in male mice have significantly increased damage from ischemic reperfusion injury (Zhai et al., 2000a). Of interest, chromatin immunoprecipitation has shown ERα and ERβ interact with SP1 (-346 and -268) and EGR-1 (-1008) binding sites at PKCε promoter. The functional significance of this interaction is yet to be understood, however, several studies examining multiple genes have demonstrated ERα and ERβ bind GC rich regions and form ER-SP1 complexes that are significant in gene transactivation (Nilsson et al., 2001, Safe and Kim, 2008, Sisci et al., 2010). It is not known whether the promoters of cardioprotective genes such as eNOS or Hsp70 have enhanced binding of SP1 with ER. The relative gender differences in PKCε promoter methylation and ERα and ERβ expression *in utero* are fascinating and deserve future study.

Conclusion

The intrauterine environment plays a vital role in determining the functional and structural resiliency of the heart. This often unnoticed risk factor for ischemic heart disease is modulated primarily through both maternal and environmental factors. Inadequate caloric intake along with excessive exposure to stress hormones such as glucocorticoids lead to aberrant myocardial development and systemic changes that lead to cardiovascular dysfunction. Substance abuse may negatively influence fetal heart development and alter the expression of cardioprotective genes. Being the most common gestation insult, hypoxia programs the heart for disease by decreasing cardioprotective genes and increasing genes that increase injury during I/R insults. Intrauterine adaptations to an adverse environment may acutely be protective and maintain vital cardiac function, but in the long-term can program the heart for ischemic heart disease later life.

References

Adelman, D. M., Gertsenstein, M., Nagy, A., Simon, M. C. & Maltepe, E. (2000). Placental cell fates are regulated in vivo by HIF-mediated hypoxia responses. *Genes Dev, 14,* 3191-203.

Adriaanse, H. P., Knottnerus, J. A., Delgado, L. R., Cox, H. H. & Essed, G. G. (1996). Smoking in Dutch pregnant women and birth weight. *Patient Educ Couns, 28,* 25-30.

Aiken, C. E. & Ozanne, S. E. (2014). Transgenerational developmental programming. *Hum Reprod Update, 20,* 63-75.

Alwasel, S. H., Harrath, A. H., Aljarallah, J. S., Abotalib, Z., Osmond, C., Al Omar, S. Y., et al. (2013). The velocity of fetal growth is associated with the breadth of the placental surface, but not with the length. *Am J Hum Biol, 25,* 534-7.

Anderson, B. A. & Silver, B. D. (1989). Patterns of cohort mortality in the Soviet population. *Population and Development Review, 15,* 471-501.

Anderson, D. F., Faber, J. J., Morton, M. J., Parks, C. M., Pinson, C. W. & Thornburg, K. L. (1985). Flow through the foramen ovale of the fetal and new-born lamb. *J Physiol, 365,* 29-40.

Antonov, A. N. (1947). Children born during the siege of Leningrad in 1942. *J Pediatr, 30,* 250-9.

Ascuitto, R. J. & Ross-Ascuitto, N. T. (1996). Substrate metabolism in the developing heart. *Semin Perinatol, 20,* 542-63.

Asmussen, I. (1979). Fetal cardiovascular system as influenced by maternal smoking. *Clin Cardiol, 2,* 246-56.

Auman, H. J., Coleman, H., Riley, H. E., Olale, F., Tsai, H. J. & Yelon, D. (2007). Functional modulation of cardiac form through regionally confined cell shape changes. *PLoS Biol, 5,* e53.

Bae, S., Gilbert, R. D., Ducsay, C. A. & Zhang, L. (2005). Prenatal cocaine exposure increases heart susceptibility to ischaemia-reperfusion injury in adult male but not female rats. *J Physiol, 565,* 149-58.

Bae, S., Xiao, Y., Li, G., Casiano, C. A. & Zhang, L. (2003). Effect of maternal chronic hypoxic exposure during gestation on apoptosis in fetal rat heart. *Am J Physiol Heart Circ Physiol, 285,* H983-90.

Bae, S. & Zhang, L. (2005). Prenatal cocaine exposure increases apoptosis of neonatal rat heart and heart susceptibility to ischemia-reperfusion injury in 1-month-old rat. *Br J Pharmacol, 144,* 900-7.

Bagby, S. P. (2004). Obesity-initiated metabolic syndrome and the kidney: a recipe for chronic kidney disease? *J Am Soc Nephrol, 15*, 2775-91.

Bagby, S. P. (2007). Maternal nutrition, low nephron number, and hypertension in later life: pathways of nutritional programming. *J Nutr, 137*, 1066-72.

Baker, J., Workman, M., Bedrick, E., Frey, M. A., Hurtado, M. & Pearson, O. (2010). Brains versus brawn: an empirical test of Barker's brain sparing model. *Am J Hum Biol, 22*, 206-15.

Bal, M. P., De Vries, W. B., Van der Leij, F. R., Van Oosterhout, M. F., Berger, R. M., Baan, J., et al. (2005). Neonatal glucocorticosteroid treatment causes systolic dysfunction and compensatory dilation in early life: studies in 4-week-old prepubertal rats. *Pediatr Res, 58*, 46-52.

Barancik, M., Htun, P., Strohm, C., Kilian, S. & Schaper, W. (2000). Inhibition of the cardiac p38-MAPK pathway by SB203580 delays ischemic cell death. *J Cardiovasc Pharmacol, 35*, 474-83.

Barbera, A., Giraud, G. D., Reller, M. D., Maylie, J., Morton, M. J. & Thornburg, K. L. (2000). Right ventricular systolic pressure load alters myocyte maturation in fetal sheep. *Am J Physiol Regul Integr Comp Physiol, 279*, R1157-64.

Barker, D. J. (1989). Rise and fall of Western diseases. *Nature, 338*, 371-2.

Barker, D. J. (1995). Fetal origins of coronary heart disease. *BMJ, 311*, 171-4.

Barker, D. J. (1997). Fetal nutrition and cardiovascular disease in later life. *Br Med Bull, 53*, 96-108.

Barker, D. J. (2004). The developmental origins of chronic adult disease. *Acta Paediatr Suppl, 93*, 26-33.

Barker, D. J., Gelow, J., Thornburg, K., Osmond, C., Kajantie, E. & Eriksson, J. G. (2010a). The early origins of chronic heart failure: impaired placental growth and initiation of insulin resistance in childhood. *Eur J Heart Fail, 12*, 819-25.

Barker, D. J., Larsen, G., Osmond, C., Thornburg, K. L., Kajantie, E. & Eriksson, J. G. (2012). The placental origins of sudden cardiac death. *Int J Epidemiol, 41*, 1394-9.

Barker, D. J. & Osmond, C. (1986). Infant mortality, childhood nutrition, and ischaemic heart disease in England and Wales. *Lancet, 1*, 1077-81.

Barker, D. J., Osmond, C., Forsen, T. J., Kajantie, E. & Eriksson, J. G. (2005). Trajectories of growth among children who have coronary events as adults. *N Engl J Med, 353*, 1802-9.

Barker, D. J., Osmond, C., Golding, J., Kuh, D. & Wadsworth, M. E. (1989a). Growth in utero, blood pressure in childhood and adult life, and mortality from cardiovascular disease. *BMJ, 298*, 564-7.

Barker, D., Osmond, C., Grant, S., Thornburg, K. L., Cooper, C., Ring, S., et al. (2013a). Maternal cotyledons at birth predict blood pressure in childhood. *Placenta, 34*, 672-5.

Barker, D. J., Osmond, C., Thornburg, K. L., Kajantie, E. & Eriksson, J. G. (2011). The lifespan of men and the shape of their placental surface at birth. *Placenta, 32*, 783-7.

Barker, D. J., Osmond, C., Thornburg, K. L., Kajantie, E. & Eriksson, J. G. (2013b). The intrauterine origins of Hodgkin's lymphoma. *Cancer Epidemiol, 37*, 321-3.

Barker, D. J., Osmond, C., Thornburg, K. L., Kajantie, E. & Eriksson, J. G. (2013c). The shape of the placental surface at birth and colorectal cancer in later life. *Am J Hum Biol, 25*, 566-8.

Barker, D. J., Osmond, C., Thornburg, K. L., Kajantie, E., Forsen, T. J. & Eriksson, J. G. (2008). A possible link between the pubertal growth of girls and breast cancer in their daughters. *Am J Hum Biol*, *20*, 127-31.

Barker, D. J. & Thornburg, K. L. (2013a). The obstetric origins of health for a lifetime. *Clin Obstet Gynecol*, *56*, 511-9.

Barker, D. J. & Thornburg, K. L. (2013b). Placental programming of chronic diseases, cancer and lifespan: A review. *Placenta*, *34*, 841-5.

Barker, D. J., Thornburg, K. L., Osmond, C., Kajantie, E. & Eriksson, J. G. (2010b). The surface area of the placenta and hypertension in the offspring in later life. *Int J Dev Biol*, *54*, 525-30.

Barker, D. J., Winter, P. D., Osmond, C., Margetts, B. & Simmonds, S. J. (1989b). Weight in infancy and death from ischaemic heart disease. *Lancet*, *2*, 577-80.

Bateson, P. (2007). Developmental plasticity and evolutionary biology. *J Nutr*, *137*, 1060-2.

Battaglia, C., Artini, P. G., Galli, P. A., D'Ambrogio, G., Droghini, F. & Genazzani, A. R. (1993). Absent or reversed end-diastolic flow in umbilical artery and severe intrauterine growth retardation. An ominous association. *Acta Obstet Gynecol Scand*, *72*, 167-71.

Beekman, M., Nederstigt, C., Suchiman, H. E., Kremer, D., Van der Breggen, R., Lakenberg, N., et al. (2010). Genome-wide association study (GWAS)-identified disease risk alleles do not compromise human longevity. *Proc Natl Acad Sci U S A*, *107*, 18046-9.

Begum, G., Davies, A., Stevens, A., Oliver, M., Jaquiery, A., Challis, J., et al. (2013). Maternal undernutrition programs tissue-specific epigenetic changes in the glucocorticoid receptor in adult offspring. *Endocrinology*, *154*, 4560-9.

Beigi, F., Schmeckpeper, J., Pow-Anpongkul, P., Payne, J. A., Zhang, L., Zhang, Z., et al. (2013). C3orf58, a Novel Paracrine Protein, Stimulates Cardiomyocyte Cell-Cycle Progression Through the PI3K-AKT-CDK7 Pathway. *Circ Res*, *113*, 372-80.

Bensley, J. G., Stacy, V. K., De Matteo, R., Harding, R. & Black, M. J. (2010). Cardiac remodelling as a result of pre-term birth: implications for future cardiovascular disease. *Eur Heart J*, *31*, 2058-66.

Bergmann, O., Bhardwaj, R. D., Bernard, S., Zdunek, S., Barnabe-Heider, F., Walsh, S., et al. (2009). Evidence for cardiomyocyte renewal in humans. *Science*, *324*, 98-102.

Bergmann, O., Zdunek, S., Frisen, J., Bernard, S., Druid, H. & Jovinge, S. (2012). Cardiomyocyte renewal in humans. *Circ Res*, *110*, e17-8.

Bernal, A. B., Vickers, M. H., Hampton, M. B., Poynton, R. A. & Sloboda, D. M. (2010). Maternal undernutrition significantly impacts ovarian follicle number and increases ovarian oxidative stress in adult rat offspring. *PLoS One*, *5*, e15558.

Bertolotto, C., Maulon, L., Filippa, N., Baier, G. & Auberger, P. (2000). Protein kinase C theta and epsilon promote T-cell survival by a rsk-dependent phosphorylation and inactivation of BAD. *J Biol Chem*, *275*, 37246-50.

Bertram, C., Trowern, A. R., Copin, N., Jackson, A. A. & Whorwood, C. B. (2001). The maternal diet during pregnancy programs altered expression of the glucocorticoid receptor and type 2 11beta-hydroxysteroid dehydrogenase: potential molecular mechanisms underlying the programming of hypertension in utero. *Endocrinology*, *142*, 2841-53.

Bertram, C. E. & Hanson, M. A. (2001). Animal models and programming of the metabolic syndrome. *Br Med Bull*, *60*, 103-21.

Bertram, C. E. & Hanson, M. A. (2002). Prenatal programming of postnatal endocrine responses by glucocorticoids. *Reproduction, 124,* 459-67.

Bibbins-Domingo, K., Coxson, P., Pletcher, M. J., Lightwood, J. & Goldman, L. (2007). Adolescent overweight and future adult coronary heart disease. *N Engl J Med, 357,* 2371-9.

Blake, K. V., Gurrin, L. C., Evans, S. F., Beilin, L. J., Landau, L. I., Stanley, F. J., et al. (2000). Maternal cigarette smoking during pregnancy, low birth weight and subsequent blood pressure in early childhood. *Early Hum Dev, 57,* 137-47.

Boersma, B. & Wit, J. M. (1997). Catch-up growth. *Endocr Rev, 18,* 646-61.

Bogdarina, I. G., King, P. J. & Clark, A. J. (2009). Characterization of the angiotensin (AT1b) receptor promoter and its regulation by glucocorticoids. *J Mol Endocrinol, 43,* 73-80.

Bogoyevitch, M. A., Parker, P. J. & Sugden, P. H. (1993). Characterization of protein kinase C isotype expression in adult rat heart. Protein kinase C-epsilon is a major isotype present, and it is activated by phorbol esters, epinephrine, and endothelin. *Circ Res, 72,* 757-67.

Bolli, R. (2001). Cardioprotective function of inducible nitric oxide synthase and role of nitric oxide in myocardial ischemia and preconditioning: an overview of a decade of research. *J Mol Cell Cardiol, 33,* 1897-918.

Braunwald, E. (1997). Shattuck lecture--cardiovascular medicine at the turn of the millennium: triumphs, concerns, and opportunities. *N Engl J Med, 337,* 1360-9.

Brickner, M. E., Willard, J. E., Eichhorn, E. J., Black, J. & Grayburn, P. A. (1991). Left ventricular hypertrophy associated with chronic cocaine abuse. *Circulation, 84,* 1130-5.

Broberg, C. S., Giraud, G. D., Schultz, J. M., Thornburg, K. L., Hohimer, A. R. & Davis, L. E. (2003). Fetal anemia leads to augmented contractile response to hypoxic stress in adulthood. *Am J Physiol Regul Integr Comp Physiol, 285,* R649-55.

Brown, L. (2014). Endocrine regulation of fetal skeletal muscle growth: impact on future metabolic health. *J Endocrinol.*

Bubb, K. J., Cock, M. L., Black, M. J., Dodic, M., Boon, W. M., Parkington, H. C., et al. (2007). Intrauterine growth restriction delays cardiomyocyte maturation and alters coronary artery function in the fetal sheep. *J Physiol, 578,* 871-81.

Buttrick, P., Malhotra, A., Factor, S., Greenen, D., Leinwand, L. & Scheuer, J. (1991). Effect of aging and hypertension on myosin biochemistry and gene expression in the rat heart. *Circ Res, 68,* 645-52.

Cambien, F. & Tiret, L. (2007). Genetics of cardiovascular diseases: from single mutations to the whole genome. *Circulation, 116,* 1714-24.

Cannito, S., Novo, E., Compagnone, A., Valfre Di Bonzo, L., Busletta, C., Zamara, E., et al. (2008). Redox mechanisms switch on hypoxia-dependent epithelial-mesenchymal transition in cancer cells. *Carcinogenesis, 29,* 2267-78.

Catalano, P. M., Farrell, K., Thomas, A., Huston-Presley, L., Mencin, P., De Mouzon, S. H., et al. (2009). Perinatal risk factors for childhood obesity and metabolic dysregulation. *Am J Clin Nutr, 90,* 1303-13.

Centers for Disease Control and Prevention (CDC). (1999). Decline in deaths from heart disease and stroke--United States, 1900-1999. (MMWR) *Morb Mortal Wkly Rep, 48,* 649-56.

Centers for Disease Control and Prevention (CDC). (2004). Declining Prevalence of no known major risk factors for heart disease and stroke among adults -- United States, 1991—2001. (MMWR) *Morb Mortal Wkly Rep, 53*, 4-7.

Centers for Disease Control and Prevention (CDC). (2011). *CDC. Diabetes: Successes and Opportunities for Population-Based Prevention and Control At A Glance* [Online]. Available: http://www. cdc. gov/chronicdisease/resources/publications/AAG/ddt. htm.

Chatelain, A., Dupouy, J. P. & Allaume, P. (1980). Fetal-maternal adrenocorticotropin and corticosterone relationships in the rat: effects of maternal adrenalectomy. *Endocrinology, 106*, 1297-303.

Chattergoon, N. N., Giraud, G. D., Louey, S., Stork, P., Fowden, A. L. & Thornburg, K. L. (2012a). Thyroid hormone drives fetal cardiomyocyte maturation. *FASEB J, 26*, 397-408.

Chattergoon, N. N., Giraud, G. D. & Thornburg, K. L. (2007). Thyroid hormone inhibits proliferation of fetal cardiac myocytes in vitro. *J Endocrinol, 192*, R1-8.

Chattergoon, N. N., Louey, S., Stork, P., Giraud, G. D. & Thornburg, K. L. (2012b). Mid-gestation ovine cardiomyocytes are vulnerable to mitotic suppression by thyroid hormone. *Reprod Sci, 19*, 642-9.

Chen, D. B., Bird, I. M., Zheng, J. & Magness, R. R. (2004). Membrane estrogen receptor-dependent extracellular signal-regulated kinase pathway mediates acute activation of endothelial nitric oxide synthase by estrogen in uterine artery endothelial cells. *Endocrinology, 145*, 113-25.

Chen, D. B., Wang, L. & Wang, P. H. (2000). Insulin-like growth factor I retards apoptotic signaling induced by ethanol in cardiomyocytes. *Life Sci, 67*, 1683-93.

Chen, L., Hahn, H., Wu, G., Chen, C. H., Liron, T., Schechtman, D., et al. (2001). Opposing cardioprotective actions and parallel hypertrophic effects of delta PKC and epsilon PKC. *Proc Natl Acad Sci U S A, 98*, 11114-9.

Chen, L. M., Kuo, W. W., Yang, J. J., Wang, S. G., Yeh, Y. L., Tsai, F. J., et al. (2007). Eccentric cardiac hypertrophy was induced by long-term intermittent hypoxia in rats. *Exp Physiol, 92*, 409-16.

Chen, M., Xiong, F. & Zhang, L. (2013). Promoter methylation of Egr-1 site contributes to fetal hypoxia-mediated PKC{varepsilon} gene repression in the developing heart. *Am J Physiol Regul Integr Comp Physiol, 304*, R683-9.

Chen, Y. & Zhou, L. A. (2007). The long-term health and economic consequences of the 1959-1961 famine in China. *J Health Econ, 26*, 659-81.

Chu, A., Chambers, D. E., Lin, C. C., Kuehl, W. D., Palmer, R. M., Moncada, S., et al. (1991). Effects of inhibition of nitric oxide formation on basal vasomotion and endothelium-dependent responses of the coronary arteries in awake dogs. *J Clin Invest, 87*, 1964-8.

Chu, W., Wan, L., Zhao, D., Qu, X., Cai, F., Huo, R., et al. (2012). Mild hypoxia-induced cardiomyocyte hypertrophy via up-regulation of HIF-1alpha-mediated TRPC signalling. *J Cell Mol Med, 16*, 2022-34.

Churchill, E. N. & Mochly-Rosen, D. (2007). The roles of PKCdelta and epsilon isoenzymes in the regulation of myocardial ischaemia/reperfusion injury. *Biochem Soc Trans, 35*, 1040-2.

Cleal, J. K., Thomas, M., Hanson, M. A., Paterson-Brown, S., Gardiner, H. M. & Green, L. R. (2010). Noninvasive fetal electrocardiography following intermittent umbilical cord occlusion in the preterm ovine fetus. *BJOG, 117*, 438-44.

Cleasby, M. E., Kelly, P. A., Walker, B. R. & Seckl, J. R. (2003). Programming of rat muscle and fat metabolism by in utero overexposure to glucocorticoids. *Endocrinology, 144,* 999-1007.

Clemmer, T. P. & Telford, I. R. (1966). Abnormal development of the rat heart during prenatal hypoxic stress. *Proc Soc Exp Biol Med, 121,* 800-3.

Clubb, F. J., Jr. & Bishop, S. P. (1984). Formation of binucleated myocardial cells in the neonatal rat. An index for growth hypertrophy. *Lab Invest, 50,* 571-7.

Cooper, R. S. (1983). Epidemiologic features of recent trends in coronary heart disease in the Soviet Union. *J Am Coll Cardiol, 2,* 557-64.

Corrigan, N., Treacy, A., Brazil, D. P. & McAuliffe, F. M. (2013). Cardiomyopathy and diastolic dysfunction in the embryo and neonate of a type 1 diabetic mouse model. *Reprod Sci, 20,* 781-90.

Corstius, H. B., Zimanyi, M. A., Maka, N., Herath, T., Thomas, W., van der Laarse, A., et al. (2005). Effect of intrauterine growth restriction on the number of cardiomyocytes in rat hearts. *Pediatr Res, 57,* 796-800.

Cottrell, E. C. & Ozanne, S. E. (2007). Developmental programming of energy balance and the metabolic syndrome. *Proc Nutr Soc, 66,* 198-206.

Covello, K. L., Kehler, J., Yu, H., Gordan, J. D., Arsham, A. M., Hu, C. J., et al. (2006). HIF-2alpha regulates Oct-4: effects of hypoxia on stem cell function, embryonic development, and tumor growth. *Genes Dev, 20,* 557-70.

Cowden Dahl, K. D., Fryer, B. H., Mack, F. A., Compernolle, V., Maltepe, E., Adelman, D. M., et al. (2005). Hypoxia-inducible factors 1alpha and 2alpha regulate trophoblast differentiation. *Mol Cell Biol, 25,* 10479-91.

Creemers, E. E., Tijsen, A. J. & Pinto, Y. M. (2012). Circulating microRNAs: novel biomarkers and extracellular communicators in cardiovascular disease? *Circ Res, 110,* 483-95.

Csonka, C., Szilvassy, Z., Fulop, F., Pali, T., Blasig, I. E., Tosaki, A., et al. (1999). Classic preconditioning decreases the harmful accumulation of nitric oxide during ischemia and reperfusion in rat hearts. *Circulation, 100,* 2260-6.

Curhan, G. C., Willett, W. C., Rimm, E. B., Spiegelman, D., Ascherio, A. L. & Stampfer, M. J. (1996). Birth weight and adult hypertension, diabetes mellitus, and obesity in US men. *Circulation, 94,* 3246-50.

Dai, D. F., Chen, T., Szeto, H., Nieves-Cintron, M., Kutyavin, V., Santana, L. F., et al. (2011). Mitochondrial targeted antioxidant Peptide ameliorates hypertensive cardiomyopathy. *J Am Coll Cardiol, 58,* 73-82.

Dasgupta, C. & Zhang, L. (2011). Angiotensin II receptors and drug discovery in cardiovascular disease. *Drug Discov Today, 16,* 22-34.

Davies, R. W., Wells, G. A., Stewart, A. F., Erdmann, J., Shah, S. H., Ferguson, J. F., et al. (2012). A genome-wide association study for coronary artery disease identifies a novel susceptibility locus in the major histocompatibility complex. *Circ Cardiovasc Genet, 5,* 217-25.

Davis, L., Roullet, J. B., Thornburg, K. L., Shokry, M., Hohimer, A. R. & Giraud, G. D. (2003). Augmentation of coronary conductance in adult sheep made anaemic during fetal life. *J Physiol, 547,* 53-9.

Davis, L., Thornburg, K. L. & Giraud, G. D. (2005). The effects of anaemia as a programming agent in the fetal heart. *J Physiol, 565,* 35-41.

Dawson, B. V., Johnson, P. D., Goldberg, S. J. & Ulreich, J. B. (1993). Cardiac teratogenesis of halogenated hydrocarbon-contaminated drinking water. *J Am Coll Cardiol, 21,* 1466-72.

De la Cruz, M. V., Campillo-Sainz, C. & Munoz-Armas, S. (1966). Congenital heart defects in chick embryos subjected to temperature variations. *Circ Res, 18,* 257-62.

De Rooij, S. R., Painter, R. C., Phillips, D. I., Osmond, C., Michels, R. P., Godsland, I. F., et al. (2006). Impaired insulin secretion after prenatal exposure to the Dutch famine. *Diabetes Care, 29,* 1897-901.

De Vries, W. B., Bal, M. P., Homoet-van der Kraak, P., Kamphuis, P. J., Van der Leij, F. R., Baan, J., et al. (2006). Suppression of physiological cardiomyocyte proliferation in the rat pup after neonatal glucocorticosteroid treatment. *Basic Res Cardiol, 101,* 36-42.

De Vries, W. B., Van der Leij, F. R., Bakker, J. M., Kamphuis, P. J., Van Oosterhout, M. F., Schipper, M. E., et al. (2002). Alterations in adult rat heart after neonatal dexamethasone therapy. *Pediatr Res, 52,* 900-6.

Denisenko, O., Lin, B., Louey, S., Thornburg, K., Bomsztyk, K. & Bagby, S. (2011). Maternal malnutrition and placental insufficiency induce global downregulation of gene expression in fetal kidneys. *J Dev Origins Health and Dis, 2,* 124-33.

Devi, B. G. & Chan, A. W. (1999). Effect of cocaine on cardiac biochemical functions. *J Cardiovasc Pharmacol, 33,* 1-6.

Dewing, P., Shi, T., Horvath, S. & Vilain, E. (2003). Sexually dimorphic gene expression in mouse brain precedes gonadal differentiation. *Brain Res Mol Brain Res, 118,* 82-90.

Dodic, M., May, C. N., Wintour, E. M. & Coghlan, J. P. (1998). An early prenatal exposure to excess glucocorticoid leads to hypertensive offspring in sheep. *Clin Sci (Lond), 94,* 149-55.

Dodic, M., Samuel, C., Moritz, K., Wintour, E. M., Morgan, J., Grigg, L., et al. (2001). Impaired cardiac functional reserve and left ventricular hypertrophy in adult sheep after prenatal dexamethasone exposure. *Circ Res, 89,* 623-9.

Duckworth, R. A. (2009). Maternal effects and range expansion: a key factor in a dynamic process? *Philos Trans R Soc Lond B Biol Sci, 364,* 1075-86.

Duckworth, R. A. (2013). Epigenetic inheritance systems act as a bridge between ecological and evolutionary timescales. *Behavioral Ecology, 24,* 327-8.

Duquesnes, N., Lezoualc'h, F. & Crozatier, B. (2011). PKC-delta and PKC-epsilon: foes of the same family or strangers? *J Mol Cell Cardiol, 51,* 665-73.

Duranteau, J., Chandel, N. S., Kulisz, A., Shao, Z. & Schumacker, P. T. (1998). Intracellular signaling by reactive oxygen species during hypoxia in cardiomyocytes. *J Biol Chem, 273,* 11619-24.

Duranthon, V., Watson, A. J. & Lonergan, P. (2008). Preimplantation embryo programming: transcription, epigenetics, and culture environment. *Reproduction, 135,* 141-50.

Economides, D. & Braithwaite, J. (1994). Smoking, pregnancy and the fetus. *J R Soc Health, 114,* 198-201.

Edwards, L. J. & McMillen, I. C. (2002). Periconceptional nutrition programs development of the cardiovascular system in the fetal sheep. *Am J Physiol Regul Integr Comp Physiol, 283,* R669-79.

Egorova, A. D., Van der Heiden, K., Van de Pas, S., Vennemann, P., Poelma, C., DeRuiter, M. C., et al. (2011). Tgfbeta/Alk5 signaling is required for shear stress induced klf2 expression in embryonic endothelial cells. *Dev Dyn, 240,* 1670-80.

Egred, M. & Davis, G. K. (2005). Cocaine and the heart. *Postgrad Med J*, *81*, 568-71.

Engel, F. B. (2005). Cardiomyocyte proliferation: a platform for mammalian cardiac repair. *Cell Cycle*, *4*, 1360-3.

Engel, F. B., Schebesta, M., Duong, M. T., Lu, G., Ren, S., Madwed, J. B., et al. (2005). p38 MAP kinase inhibition enables proliferation of adult mammalian cardiomyocytes. *Genes Dev*, *19*, 1175-87.

Eriksson, J. G., Forsen, T., Tuomilehto, J., Winter, P. D., Osmond, C. & Barker, D. J. (1999). Catch-up growth in childhood and death from coronary heart disease: longitudinal study. *BMJ*, *318*, 427-31.

Eriksson, J. G., Kajantie, E., Phillips, D. I., Osmond, C., Thornburg, K. L. & Barker, D. J. (2013). The developmental origins of chronic rheumatic heart disease. *Am J Hum Biol*, *25*, 655-8.

Eriksson, J. G., Kajantie, E., Thornburg, K. L., Osmond, C. & Barker, D. J. (2011). Mother's body size and placental size predict coronary heart disease in men. *Eur Heart J*, *32*, 2297-303.

Evans, L. C., Liu, H., Pinkas, G. A. & Thompson, L. P. (2012a). Chronic hypoxia increases peroxynitrite, MMP9 expression, and collagen accumulation in fetal guinea pig hearts. *Pediatr Res*, *71*, 25-31.

Evans, L. C., Liu, H. & Thomspon, L. P. (2012b). Differential effect of intrauterine hypoxia on caspase 3 and DNA fragmentation in fetal guinea pig hearts and brains. *Reprod Sci*, *19*, 298-305.

Fahed, A. C., Gelb, B. D., Seidman, J. G. & Seidman, C. E. (2013). Genetics of congenital heart disease: the glass half empty. *Circ Res*, *112*, 707-20.

Fan, L., Lindsley, S. R., Comstock, S. M., Takahashi, D. L., Evans, A. E., He, G. W., et al. (2013). Maternal high-fat diet impacts endothelial function in nonhuman primate offspring. *Int J Obes (Lond)*, *37*, 254-62.

Feng, X., Reini, S. A., Richards, E., Wood, C. E. & Keller-Wood, M. (2013). Cortisol stimulates proliferation and apoptosis in the late gestation fetal heart: differential effects of mineralocorticoid and glucocorticoid receptors. *Am J Physiol Regul Integr Comp Physiol*, *305*, R343-50.

Fernandez-Twinn, D. S. & Ozanne, S. E. (2010). Early life nutrition and metabolic programming. *Ann N Y Acad Sci*, *1212*, 78-96.

Fernandez, E., Siddiquee, Z. & Shohet, R. V. (2001). Apoptosis and proliferation in the neonatal murine heart. *Dev Dyn*, *221*, 302-10.

Fishman, M. C. & Chien, K. R. (1997). Fashioning the vertebrate heart: earliest embryonic decisions. *Development*, *124*, 2099-117.

Flegal, K. M., Carroll, M. D., Kit, B. K. & Ogden, C. L. (2012). Prevalence of obesity and trends in the distribution of body mass index among US adults, 1999-2010. *JAMA*, *307*, 491-7.

Fleming, T. P., Wilkins, A., Mears, A., Miller, D. J., Thomas, F., Ghassemifar, M. R., et al. (2004). Society for Reproductive Biology Founders' Lecture 2003. The making of an embryo: short-term goals and long-term implications. *Reprod Fertil Dev*, *16*, 325-37.

Frias, A. E., Morgan, T. K., Evans, A. E., Rasanen, J., Oh, K. Y., Thornburg, K. L., et al. (2011). Maternal high-fat diet disturbs uteroplacental hemodynamics and increases the frequency of stillbirth in a nonhuman primate model of excess nutrition. *Endocrinology*, *152*, 2456-64.

Futterman, L. G. & Lemberg, L. (1998). Fifty percent of patients with coronary artery disease do not have any of the conventional risk factors. *Am J Crit Care, 7*, 240-4.

Galanis, A., Pappa, A., Giannakakis, A., Lanitis, E., Dangaj, D. & Sandaltzopoulos, R. (2008). Reactive oxygen species and HIF-1 signalling in cancer. *Cancer Lett, 266*, 12-20.

Galic, M. A., Spencer, S. J., Mouihate, A. & Pittman, Q. J. (2009). Postnatal programming of the innate immune response. *Integr Comp Biol, 49*, 237-45.

Gao, H., Chen, L. & Yang, H. T. (2007). Activation of alpha1B-adrenoceptors alleviates ischemia/reperfusion injury by limitation of mitochondrial Ca2+ overload in cardiomyocytes. *Cardiovasc Res, 75*, 584-95.

Garcia-Martinez, V. & Schoenwolf, G. C. (1993). Primitive-streak origin of the cardiovascular system in avian embryos. *Dev Biol, 159*, 706-19.

Gardner, D. S., Jackson, A. A. & Langley-Evans, S. C. (1997). Maintenance of maternal diet-induced hypertension in the rat is dependent on glucocorticoids. *Hypertension, 30*, 1525-30.

Gardner, D. S., Pearce, S., Dandrea, J., Walker, R., Ramsay, M. M., Stephenson, T., et al. (2004). Peri-implantation undernutrition programs blunted angiotensin II evoked baroreflex responses in young adult sheep. *Hypertension, 43*, 1290-6.

Geng, Y. J., Ishikawa, Y., Vatner, D. E., Wagner, T. E., Bishop, S. P., Vatner, S. F., et al. (1999). Apoptosis of cardiac myocytes in Gsalpha transgenic mice. *Circ Res, 84*, 34-42.

Gilbert, J. S., Ford, S. P., Lang, A. L., Pahl, L. R., Drumhiller, M. C., Babcock, S. A., et al. (2007). Nutrient restriction impairs nephrogenesis in a gender-specific manner in the ovine fetus. *Pediatr Res, 61*, 42-7.

Gilbert, R. D. (1998). Fetal myocardial responses to long-term hypoxemia. *Comp Biochem Physiol A Mol Integr Physiol, 119*, 669-74.

Gilbert, R. D., Pearce, W. J., Longo, L. D. (2003). Fetal cardiac and cerebrovascular acclimatization responses to high altitude, long-term hypoxia. *High Alt Med Biol, 4*, 203-13.

Giraud, G. D., Louey, S., Jonker, S., Schultz, J. & Thornburg, K. L. (2006). Cortisol stimulates cell cycle activity in the cardiomyocyte of the sheep fetus. *Endocrinology, 147*, 3643-9.

Giussani, D. A., Salinas, C. E., Villena, M. & Blanco, C. E. (2007). The role of oxygen in prenatal growth: studies in the chick embryo. *J Physiol, 585*, 911-7.

Gluckman, P. D. & Hanson, M. A. (2004). Developmental origins of disease paradigm: a mechanistic and evolutionary perspective. *Pediatr Res, 56*, 311-7.

Gluckman, P. D., Hanson, M. A., Cooper, C. & Thornburg, K. L. (2008). Effect of in utero and early-life conditions on adult health and disease. *N Engl J Med, 359*, 61-73.

Go et al., Heart Disease and Stroke Statistics—2014 Update. Circulation. 2014; 129: e28-e292

Godfrey, K. M. (2002). The role of the placenta in fetal programming-a review. *Placenta, 23* Suppl A, S20-7.

Godfrey, K. M., Lillycrop, K. A., Burdge, G. C., Gluckman, P. D. & Hanson, M. A. (2007). Epigenetic mechanisms and the mismatch concept of the developmental origins of health and disease. *Pediatr Res, 61*, 5R-10R.

Goh, J. M., Bensley, J. G., Kenna, K., Sozo, F., Bocking, A. D., Brien, J., et al. (2011). Alcohol exposure during late gestation adversely affects myocardial development with implications for postnatal cardiac function. *Am J Physiol Heart Circ Physiol*, *300*, H645-51.

Gradman, A. H. (1988). Cardiac effects of cocaine: a review. *Yale J Biol Med*, *61*, 137-47.

Granados-Riveron, J. T. & Brook, J. D. (2012a). Formation, contraction, and mechanotransduction of myofribrils in cardiac development: clues from genetics. *Biochem Res Int*, *2012*, 504906.

Granados-Riveron, J. T. & Brook, J. D. (2012b). The impact of mechanical forces in heart morphogenesis. *Circ Cardiovasc Genet*, *5*, 132-42.

Gray, M. O., Karliner, J. S. & Mochly-Rosen, D. (1997). A selective epsilon-protein kinase C antagonist inhibits protection of cardiac myocytes from hypoxia-induced cell death. *J Biol Chem*, *272*, 30945-51.

Groenendijk, B. C., Van der Heiden, K., Hierck, B. P. & Poelmann, R. E. (2007). The role of shear stress on ET-1, KLF2, and NOS-3 expression in the developing cardiovascular system of chicken embryos in a venous ligation model. *Physiology (Bethesda)*, *22*, 380-9.

Grundy, S. M., Benjamin, I. J., Burke, G. L., Chait, A., Eckel, R. H., Howard, B. V., et al. (1999). Diabetes and cardiovascular disease: a statement for healthcare professionals from the American Heart Association. *Circulation*, *100*, 1134-46.

Guo, D. F., Uno, S., Ishihata, A., Nakamura, N. & Inagami, T. (1995). Identification of a cis-acting glucocorticoid responsive element in the rat angiotensin II type 1A promoter. *Circ Res*, *77*, 249-57.

Haddad, G. E., Scheer, A., Clarke, E., Jr., Arguinzoni, J. K. & Sobrian, S. K. (2005). Prenatal cocaine alone and combined with nicotine alters ANG II and IGF-1 induced left atrial contractions in aging male offspring. *Can J Physiol Pharmacol*, *83*, 957-65.

Hales, C. N. & Barker, D. J. (2001). The thrifty phenotype hypothesis. *Br Med Bull*, *60*, 5-20.

Hales, C. N. & Barker, D. J. (2013). Type 2 (non-insulin-dependent) diabetes mellitus: the thrifty phenotype hypothesis. *Int J Epidemiol*, *42*, 1215-22.

Hammoud, L., Burger, D. E., Lu, X. & Feng, Q. (2009). Tissue inhibitor of metalloproteinase-3 inhibits neonatal mouse cardiomyocyte proliferation via EGFR/JNK/SP-1 signaling. *Am J Physiol Cell Physiol*, *296*, C735-45.

Hammoud, L., Xiang, F., Lu, X., Brunner, F., Leco, K. & Feng, Q. (2007). Endothelial nitric oxide synthase promotes neonatal cardiomyocyte proliferation by inhibiting tissue inhibitor of metalloproteinase-3 expression. *Cardiovasc Res*, *75*, 359-68.

Handler, A., Kistin, N., Davis, F. & Ferre, C. (1991). Cocaine use during pregnancy: perinatal outcomes. *Am J Epidemiol*, *133*, 818-25.

Harvey, R. P. & Rosenthal, N. (Eds). (1999). *Heart development*. London: Academic Press.

Hausenloy, D. J., Duchen, M. R. & Yellon, D. M. (2003). Inhibiting mitochondrial permeability transition pore opening at reperfusion protects against ischaemia-reperfusion injury. *Cardiovasc Res*, *60*, 617-25.

Hawkins, P., Steyn, C., McGarrigle, H. H., Calder, N. A., Saito, T., Stratford, L. L., et al. (2000). Cardiovascular and hypothalamic-pituitary-adrenal axis development in late gestation fetal sheep and young lambs following modest maternal nutrient restriction in early gestation. *Reprod Fertil Dev*, *12*, 443-56.

He, J., Yang, S. & Zhang, L. (2005). Effects of cocaine on nitric oxide production in bovine coronary artery endothelial cells. *J Pharmacol Exp Ther*, *314*, 980-6.

Henderson, G. I., Chen, J. J. & Schenker, S. (1999). Ethanol, oxidative stress, reactive aldehydes, and the fetus. *Front Biosci*, *4*, D541-50.

Henning, R. J. & Cuevas, J. (2006). Cocaine activates calcium/calmodulin kinase II and causes cardiomyocyte hypertrophy. *J Cardiovasc Pharmacol*, *48*, 802-13.

Henning, R. J. & Li, Y. (2003). Cocaine produces cardiac hypertrophy by protein kinase C dependent mechanisms. *J Cardiovasc Pharmacol Ther*, *8*, 149-60.

Henning, R. J., Silva, J., Reddy, V., Kamat, S., Morgan, M. B., Li, Y. X., et al. (2000). Cocaine increases beta-myosin heavy-chain protein expression in cardiac myocytes. *J Cardiovasc Pharmacol Ther*, *5*, 313-22.

Hescheler, J., Meyer, R., Plant, S., Krautwurst, D., Rosenthal, W. & Schultz, G. (1991). Morphological, biochemical, and electrophysiological characterization of a clonal cell (H9c2) line from rat heart. *Circ Res*, *69*, 1476-86.

Hill, R. A., Connor, E. E., Poulos, S. P., Welsh, T. H. & Gabler, N. K. (2010). Growth and development symposium: fetal programming in animal agriculture. *J Anim Sci*, *88*, E38-9.

Hirst, M. & Marra, M. A. (2009). Epigenetics and human disease. *Int J Biochem Cell Biol*, *41*, 136-46.

Hoffman, J. I. & Kaplan, S. (2002). The incidence of congenital heart disease. *J Am Coll Cardiol*, *39*, 1890-900.

Hoy, W. E., Bertram, J. F., Denton, R. D., Zimanyi, M., Samuel, T. & Hughson, M. D. (2008). Nephron number, glomerular volume, renal disease and hypertension. *Curr Opin Nephrol Hypertens*, *17*, 258-65.

Hu, N., Connuck, D. M., Keller, B. B. & Clark, E. B. (1991). Diastolic filling characteristics in the stage 12 to 27 chick embryo ventricle. *Pediatr Res*, *29*, 334-7.

Huang, Z. G., Wang, X., Evans, C., Gold, A., Bouairi, E. & Mendelowitz, D. (2004). Prenatal nicotine exposure alters the types of nicotinic receptors that facilitate excitatory inputs to cardiac vagal neurons. *J Neurophysiol*, *92*, 2548-54.

Hutson, M. R. & Kirby, M. L. (2003). Neural crest and cardiovascular development: a 20-year perspective. *Birth Defects Res C Embryo Today*, *69*, 2-13.

Hutter, M. M., Sievers, R. E., Barbosa, V. & Wolfe, C. L. (1994). Heat-shock protein induction in rat hearts. A direct correlation between the amount of heat-shock protein induced and the degree of myocardial protection. *Circulation*, *89*, 355-60.

Hwang, J. M., Weng, Y. J., Lin, J. A., Bau, D. T., Ko, F. Y., Tsai, F. J., et al. (2008). Hypoxia-induced compensatory effect as related to Shh and HIF-1alpha in ischemia embryo rat heart. *Mol Cell Biochem*, *311*, 179-87.

Ito, H., Adachi, S., Tamamori, M., Fujisaki, H., Tanaka, M., Lin, M., et al. (1996). Mild hypoxia induces hypertrophy of cultured neonatal rat cardiomyocytes: a possible endogenous endothelin-1-mediated mechanism. *J Mol Cell Cardiol*, *28*, 1271-7.

Jaburek, M., Costa, A. D., Burton, J. R., Costa, C. L. & Garlid, K. D. (2006). Mitochondrial PKC epsilon and mitochondrial ATP-sensitive K+ channel copurify and coreconstitute to form a functioning signaling module in proteoliposomes. *Circ Res*, *99*, 878-83.

Jansson, T. & Lambert, G. W. (1999). Effect of intrauterine growth restriction on blood pressure, glucose tolerance and sympathetic nervous system activity in the rat at 3-4 months of age. *J Hypertens*, *17*, 1239-48.

Jansson, T. & Powell, T. L. (2013). Role of placental nutrient sensing in developmental programming. *Clin Obstet Gynecol*, *56*, 591-601.

Jayakumar, J., Suzuki, K., Sammut, I. A., Smolenski, R. T., Khan, M., Latif, N., et al. (2001). Heat shock protein 70 gene transfection protects mitochondrial and ventricular function against ischemia-reperfusion injury. *Circulation, 104,* I303-7.

Jensen, E. C., Gallaher, B. W., Breier, B. H. & Harding, J. E. (2002). The effect of a chronic maternal cortisol infusion on the late-gestation fetal sheep. *J Endocrinol, 174,* 27-36.

Jensen, G. M. & Moore, L. G. (1997). The effect of high altitude and other risk factors on birthweight: independent or interactive effects? *Am J Public Health, 87,* 1003-7.

Jiang, B. H., Rue, E., Wang, G. L., Roe, R. & Semenza, G. L. (1996a). Dimerization, DNA binding, and transactivation properties of hypoxia-inducible factor 1. *J Biol Chem, 271,* 17771-8.

Jiang, B. H., Semenza, G. L., Bauer, C. & Marti, H. H. (1996b). Hypoxia-inducible factor 1 levels vary exponentially over a physiologically relevant range of O2 tension. *Am J Physiol, 271,* C1172-80.

Jones, D. S., Podolsky, S. H. & Greene, J. A. (2012). The burden of disease and the changing task of medicine. *N Engl J Med, 366,* 2333-8.

Jones, S. P. & Bolli, R. (2006). The ubiquitous role of nitric oxide in cardioprotection. *J Mol Cell Cardiol, 40,* 16-23.

Jones, S. P., Greer, J. J., Kakkar, A. K., Ware, P. D., Turnage, R. H., Hicks, M., et al. (2004). Endothelial nitric oxide synthase overexpression attenuates myocardial reperfusion injury. *Am J Physiol Heart Circ Physiol, 286,* H276-82.

Jonker, S. S., Faber, J. J., Anderson, D. F., Thornburg, K. L., Louey, S. & Giraud, G. D. (2007a). Sequential growth of fetal sheep cardiac myocytes in response to simultaneous arterial and venous hypertension. *Am J Physiol Regul Integr Comp Physiol, 292,* R913-9.

Jonker, S. S., Giraud, M. K., Giraud, G. D., Chattergoon, N. N., Louey, S., Davis, L. E., et al. (2010). Cardiomyocyte enlargement, proliferation and maturation during chronic fetal anaemia in sheep. *Exp Physiol, 95,* 131-9.

Jonker, S. S., Zhang, L., Louey, S., Giraud, G. D., Thornburg, K. L. & Faber, J. J. (2007b). Myocyte enlargement, differentiation, and proliferation kinetics in the fetal sheep heart. *J Appl Physiol, 102,* 1130-42.

Jopling, C., Sleep, E., Raya, M., Marti, M., Raya, A. & Izpisua Belmonte, J. C. (2010). Zebrafish heart regeneration occurs by cardiomyocyte dedifferentiation and proliferation. *Nature, 464,* 606-9.

Jopling, C., Sune, G., Faucherre, A., Fabregat, C. & Izpisua Belmonte, J. C. (2012). Hypoxia induces myocardial regeneration in zebrafish. *Circulation, 126,* 3017-27.

Kajstura, J., Mansukhani, M., Cheng, W., Reiss, K., Krajewski, S., Reed, J. C., et al. (1995). Programmed cell death and expression of the protooncogene bcl-2 in myocytes during postnatal maturation of the heart. *Exp Cell Res, 219,* 110-21.

Kamitomo, M., Longo, L. D. & Gilbert, R. D. (1992). Right and left ventricular function in fetal sheep exposed to long-term high-altitude hypoxemia. *Am J Physiol, 262,* H399-405.

Kamitomo, M., Longo, L. D. & Gilbert, R. D. (1994). Cardiac function in fetal sheep during two weeks of hypoxemia. *Am J Physiol, 266,* R1778-85.

Kandadi, M. R., Hua, Y., Zhu, M., Turdi, S., Nathanielsz, P. W., Ford, S. P., et al. (2013). Influence of gestational overfeeding on myocardial proinflammatory mediators in fetal sheep heart. *J Nutr Biochem, 24,* 1982-90.

Keller, B. B., Hu, N. & Clark, E. B. (1990). Correlation of ventricular area, perimeter, and conotruncal diameter with ventricular mass and function in the chick embryo from stages 12 to 24. *Circ Res, 66*, 109-14.

Keller, B. B., Hu, N., Serrino, P. J. & Clark, E. B. (1991). Ventricular pressure-area loop characteristics in the stage 16 to 24 chick embryo. *Circ Res, 68*, 226-31.

Kelly, R. G., Brown, N. A. & Buckingham, M. E. (2001). The arterial pole of the mouse heart forms from Fgf10-expressing cells in pharyngeal mesoderm. *Dev Cell, 1*, 435-40.

Khot, U. N., Khot, M. B., Bajzer, C. T., Sapp, S. K., Ohman, E. M., Brener, S. J., et al. (2003). Prevalence of conventional risk factors in patients with coronary heart disease. *JAMA, 290*, 898-904.

Kido, M., Du, L., Sullivan, C. C., Li, X., Deutsch, R., Jamieson, S. W., et al. (2005). Hypoxia-inducible factor 1-alpha reduces infarction and attenuates progression of cardiac dysfunction after myocardial infarction in the mouse. *J Am Coll Cardiol, 46*, 2116-24.

Kind, K. L., Roberts, C. T., Sohlstrom, A. I., Katsman, A., Clifton, P. M., Robinson, J. S., et al. (2005). Chronic maternal feed restriction impairs growth but increases adiposity of the fetal guinea pig. *Am J Physiol Regul Integr Comp Physiol, 288*, R119-26.

Kirby, M. L. (2007). *Cardiac Development*. Oxford, UK: Oxford University Press.

Kirby, M. L. & Schachat, F. (2007). Evolutionary developmental biology of the heart. In: *Cardiac Development*. Oxford, UK: Oxford University Press.

Kotch, L. E., Iyer, N. V., Laughner, E. & Semenza, G. L. (1999). Defective vascularization of HIF-1alpha-null embryos is not associated with VEGF deficiency but with mesenchymal cell death. *Dev Biol, 209*, 254-67.

Kumar, S. & Sitasawad, S. L. (2009). N-acetylcysteine prevents glucose/glucose oxidase-induced oxidative stress, mitochondrial damage and apoptosis in H9c2 cells. *Life Sci, 84*, 328-36.

Kuroda, J., Ago, T., Matsushima, S., Zhai, P., Schneider, M. D. & Sadoshima, J. (2010). NADPH oxidase 4 (Nox4) is a major source of oxidative stress in the failing heart. *Proc Natl Acad Sci U S A, 107*, 15565-70.

Kwong, W. Y., Wild, A. E., Roberts, P., Willis, A. C. & Fleming, T. P. (2000). Maternal undernutrition during the preimplantation period of rat development causes blastocyst abnormalities and programming of postnatal hypertension. *Development, 127*, 4195-202.

Lafond, J. S., Fouron, J. C., Bard, H. & Ducharme, G. (1985). Effects of maternal alcohol intoxication on fetal circulation and myocardial function: an experimental study in the ovine fetus. *J Pediatr, 107*, 947-50.

Lambers, D. S. & Clark, K. E. (1996). The maternal and fetal physiologic effects of nicotine. *Semin Perinatol, 20*, 115-26.

Langdown, M. L., Holness, M. J. & Sugden, M. C. (2001). Early growth retardation induced by excessive exposure to glucocorticoids in utero selectively increases cardiac GLUT1 protein expression and Akt/protein kinase B activity in adulthood. *J Endocrinol, 169*, 11-22.

Lange, R. A. & Hillis, L. D. (2001). Cardiovascular complications of cocaine use. *N Engl J Med, 345*, 351-8.

Langley, S. C. & Jackson, A. A. (1994). Increased systolic blood pressure in adult rats induced by fetal exposure to maternal low protein diets. *Clin Sci (Lond), 86*, 217-22; discussion 121.

Langley-Evans, S. C., Bellinger, L. & McMullen, S. (2005). Animal models of programming: early life influences on appetite and feeding behaviour. *Matern Child Nutr, 1*, 142-8.

Langley-Evans, S. C., Gardner, D. S. & Jackson, A. A. (1996a). Maternal protein restriction influences the programming of the rat hypothalamic-pituitary-adrenal axis. *J Nutr, 126*, 1578-85.

Langley-Evans, S. C., Phillips, G. J. & Jackson, A. A. (1994). In utero exposure to maternal low protein diets induces hypertension in weanling rats, independently of maternal blood pressure changes. *Clin Nutr, 13*, 319-24.

Langley-Evans, S. C., Welham, S. J. & Jackson, A. A. (1999). Fetal exposure to a maternal low protein diet impairs nephrogenesis and promotes hypertension in the rat. *Life Sci, 64*, 965-74.

Langley-Evans, S. C., Welham, S. J., Sherman, R. C. & Jackson, A. A. (1996b). Weanling rats exposed to maternal low-protein diets during discrete periods of gestation exhibit differing severity of hypertension. *Clin Sci (Lond), 91*, 607-15.

Larson, M. G., Atwood, L. D., Benjamin, E. J., Cupples, L. A., D'Agostino, R. B., Sr., Fox, C. S., et al. (2007). Framingham Heart Study 100K project: genome-wide associations for cardiovascular disease outcomes. *BMC Med Genet, 8*, Suppl 1, S5.

Lawrence, J., Chen, M., Xiong, F., Xiao, D., Zhang, H., Buchholz, J. N., et al. (2011). Foetal nicotine exposure causes PKCepsilon gene repression by promoter methylation in rat hearts. *Cardiovasc Res, 89*, 89-97.

Lawrence, J., Xiao, D., Xue, Q., Rejali, M., Yang, S. & Zhang, L. (2008). Prenatal nicotine exposure increases heart susceptibility to ischemia/reperfusion injury in adult offspring. *J Pharmacol Exp Ther, 324*, 331-41.

Li, G., Bae, S. & Zhang, L. (2004). Effect of prenatal hypoxia on heat stress-mediated cardioprotection in adult rat heart. *Am J Physiol Heart Circ Physiol, 286*, H1712-9.

Li, G., Xiao, Y., Estrella, J. L., Ducsay, C. A., Gilbert, R. D. & Zhang, L. (2003). Effect of fetal hypoxia on heart susceptibility to ischemia and reperfusion injury in the adult rat. *J Soc Gynecol Investig, 10*, 265-74.

Li, G., Xiao, Y. & Zhang, L. (2005). Cocaine induces apoptosis in fetal rat myocardial cells through the p38 mitogen-activated protein kinase and mitochondrial/cytochrome c pathways. *J Pharmacol Exp Ther, 312*, 112-9.

Liang, C., Rounds, N. K., Dong, E., Stevens, S. Y., Shite, J. & Qin, F. (2000). Alterations by norepinephrine of cardiac sympathetic nerve terminal function and myocardial beta-adrenergic receptor sensitivity in the ferret: normalization by antioxidant vitamins. *Circulation, 102*, 96-103.

Lieb, W., Jansen, H., Loley, C., Pencina, M. J., Nelson, C. P., Newton-Cheh, C., et al. (2013). Genetic predisposition to higher blood pressure increases coronary artery disease risk. *Hypertension, 61*, 995-1001.

Liedtke, C., Zschemisch, N. H., Cohrs, A., Roskams, T., Borlak, J., Manns, M. P., et al. (2005). Silencing of caspase-8 in murine hepatocellular carcinomas is mediated via methylation of an essential promoter element. *Gastroenterology, 129*, 1602-15.

Lim, S. O., Gu, J. M., Kim, M. S., Kim, H. S., Park, Y. N., Park, C. K., et al. (2008). Epigenetic changes induced by reactive oxygen species in hepatocellular carcinoma: methylation of the E-cadherin promoter. *Gastroenterology, 135*, 2128-40, 2140. e1-8.

Liu, A., Nickerson, A., Troyer, A., Yin, X., Cary, R., Thornburg, K., et al. (2011a). Quantifying blood flow and wall shear stresses in the outflow tract of chick embryonic hearts. *Comput Struct, 89*, 855-67.

Liu, A., Yin, X., Shi, L., Li, P., Thornburg, K. L., Wang, R., et al. (2012). Biomechanics of the chick embryonic heart outflow tract at HH18 using 4D optical coherence tomography imaging and computational modeling. *PLoS One, 7*, e40869.

Liu, H., Yang, Q., Radhakrishnan, K., Whitfield, D. E., Everhart, C. L., Parsons-Wingerter, P., et al. (2009). Role of VEGF and tissue hypoxia in patterning of neural and vascular cells recruited to the embryonic heart. *Dev Dyn, 238*, 2760-9.

Liu, X., Wang, J., Li, R., Yang, X., Sun, Q., Albrecht, E., et al. (2011b). Maternal dietary protein affects transcriptional regulation of myostatin gene distinctively at weaning and finishing stages in skeletal muscle of Meishan pigs. *Epigenetics, 6*, 899-907.

Longo, L. D. (1977). The biological effects of carbon monoxide on the pregnant woman, fetus, and newborn infant. *Am J Obstet Gynecol, 129*, 69-103.

Looi, Y. H., Grieve, D. J., Siva, A., Walker, S. J., Anilkumar, N., Cave, A. C., et al. (2008). Involvement of Nox2 NADPH oxidase in adverse cardiac remodeling after myocardial infarction. *Hypertension, 51*, 319-25.

Lopuhaa, C. E., Roseboom, T. J., Osmond, C., Barker, D. J., Ravelli, A. C., Bleker, O. P., et al. (2000). Atopy, lung function, and obstructive airways disease after prenatal exposure to famine. *Thorax, 55*, 555-61.

Louey, S., Cock, M. L. & Harding, R. (2005). Long term consequences of low birthweight on postnatal growth, adiposity and brain weight at maturity in sheep. *J Reprod Dev, 51*, 59-68.

Louey, S., Jonker, S. S., Giraud, G. D. & Thornburg, K. L. (2007). Placental insufficiency decreases cell cycle activity and terminal maturation in fetal sheep cardiomyocytes. *J Physiol, 580*, 639-48.

Lu, M., Seufert, J. & Habener, J. F. (1997). Pancreatic beta-cell-specific repression of insulin gene transcription by CCAAT/enhancer-binding protein beta. Inhibitory interactions with basic helix-loop-helix transcription factor E47. *J Biol Chem, 272*, 28349-59.

Lucas, A. (1991). Programming by early nutrition in man. *Ciba Found Symp, 156*, 38-50.

Lumbers, E. R., Boyce, A. C., Joulianos, G., Kumarasamy, V., Barner, E., Segar, J. L., et al. (2005). Effects of cortisol on cardiac myocytes and on expression of cardiac genes in fetal sheep. *Am J Physiol Regul Integr Comp Physiol, 288*, R567-74.

Mabjeesh, N. J., Escuin, D., Lavallee, T. M., Pribluda, V. S., Swartz, G. M., Johnson, M. S., et al. (2003). 2ME2 inhibits tumor growth and angiogenesis by disrupting microtubules and dysregulating HIF. *Cancer Cell, 3*, 363-75.

Mackay, K. & Mochly-Rosen, D. (1999). An inhibitor of p38 mitogen-activated protein kinase protects neonatal cardiac myocytes from ischemia. *J Biol Chem, 274*, 6272-9.

Mahon, P. C., Hirota, K. & Semenza, G. L. (2001). FIH-1: a novel protein that interacts with HIF-1alpha and VHL to mediate repression of HIF-1 transcriptional activity. *Genes Dev, 15*, 2675-86.

Mainous, A. G., 3rd, Baker, R., Koopman, R. J., Saxena, S., Diaz, V. A., Everett, C. J., et al. (2007). Impact of the population at risk of diabetes on projections of diabetes burden in the United States: an epidemic on the way. *Diabetologia, 50*, 934-40.

Maloyan, A., Muralimanoharan, S., Huffman, S., Cox, L. A., Nathanielsz, P. W., Myatt, L., et al. (2013). Identification and comparative analyses of myocardial miRNAs involved in the fetal response to maternal obesity. *Physiol Genomics, 45*, 889-900.

Manning, B. D. & Cantley, L. C. (2007). AKT/PKB signaling: navigating downstream. *Cell, 129*, 1261-74.

Manning, J., Beutler, K., Knepper, M. A. & Vehaskari, V. M. (2002). Upregulation of renal BSC1 and TSC in prenatally programmed hypertension. *Am J Physiol Renal Physiol, 283*, F202-6.

Martin, C., Yu, A. Y., Jiang, B. H., Davis, L., Kimberly, D., Hohimer, A. R., et al. (1998). Cardiac hypertrophy in chronically anemic fetal sheep: Increased vascularization is associated with increased myocardial expression of vascular endothelial growth factor and hypoxia-inducible factor 1. *Am J Obstet Gynecol, 178*, 527-34.

Martinsen, B. J. (2005). Reference guide to the stages of chick heart embryology. *Dev Dyn, 233*, 1217-37.

Martyn, C. N., Barker, D. J. & Osmond, C. (1996). Mothers' pelvic size, fetal growth, and death from stroke and coronary heart disease in men in the UK. *Lancet, 348*, 1264-8.

Matsuno, K., Yamada, H., Iwata, K., Jin, D., Katsuyama, M., Matsuki, M., et al. (2005). Nox1 is involved in angiotensin II-mediated hypertension: a study in Nox1-deficient mice. *Circulation, 112*, 2677-85.

McAlees, J. W., Smith, L. T., Erbe, R. S., Jarjoura, D., Ponzio, N. M. & Sanders, V. M. (2011). Epigenetic regulation of beta2-adrenergic receptor expression in T(H)1 and T(H)2 cells. *Brain Behav Immun, 25*, 408-15.

McCurdy, C. E., Bishop, J. M., Williams, S. M., Grayson, B. E., Smith, M. S., Friedman, J. E., et al. (2009). Maternal high-fat diet triggers lipotoxicity in the fetal livers of nonhuman primates. *J Clin Invest, 119*, 323-35.

McCutcheon, I. E., Metcalfe, J., Metzenberg, A. B. & Ettinger, T. (1982). Organ growth in hyperoxic and hypoxic chick embryos. *Respir Physiol, 50*, 153-63.

McDonald, T. J., Wu, G., Nijland, M. J., Jenkins, S. L., Nathanielsz, P. W. & Jansson, T. (2013). Effect of 30% nutrient restriction in the first half of gestation on maternal and fetal baboon serum amino acid concentrations. *Br J Nutr, 109*, 1382-8.

McMillen, I. C. & Robinson, J. S. (2005). Developmental origins of the metabolic syndrome: prediction, plasticity, and programming. *Physiol Rev, 85*, 571-633.

Meaney, M. J. (2001). Maternal care, gene expression, and the transmission of individual differences in stress reactivity across generations. *Annu Rev Neurosci, 24*, 1161-92.

Mehta, S. K., Finkelhor, R. S., Anderson, R. L., Harcar-Sevcik, R. A., Wasser, T. E. & Bahler, R. C. (1993). Transient myocardial ischemia in infants prenatally exposed to cocaine. *J Pediatr, 122*, 945-9.

Mei-Zahav, M., Korzets, Z., Cohen, I., Kessler, O., Rathaus, V., Wolach, B., et al. (2001). Ambulatory blood pressure monitoring in children with a solitary kidney - a comparison between unilateral renal agenesis and uninephrectomy. *Blood Press Monit, 6*, 263-7.

Mena, M., Pacheco, V., Lama, A., Otero, C., Tapia, J. & Schurman, R. (1986). [Congenital heart defects in fetal alcohol syndrome]. *Rev Chil Pediatr, 57*, 398-400.

Messaoudi, S., Azibani, F., Delcayre, C. & Jaisser, F. (2012). Aldosterone, mineralocorticoid receptor, and heart failure. *Mol Cell Endocrinol, 350*, 266-72.

Meyer, K., Zhang, H. & Zhang, L. (2009a). Direct effect of cocaine on epigenetic regulation of PKCepsilon gene repression in the fetal rat heart. *J Mol Cell Cardiol, 47*, 504-11.

Meyer, K. D., Zhang, H. & Zhang, L. (2009b). Prenatal cocaine exposure abolished ischemic preconditioning-induced protection in adult male rat hearts: role of PKCepsilon. *Am J Physiol Heart Circ Physiol*, *296*, H1566-76.

Meyer, K. D. & Zhang, L. (2009). Short- and long-term adverse effects of cocaine abuse during pregnancy on the heart development. *Ther Adv Cardiovasc Dis*, *3*, 7-16.

Migicovsky, Z. & Kovalchuk, I. (2011). Epigenetic memory in mammals. *Front Genet*, *2*, 28.

Mihailidou, A. S., Loan Le, T. Y., Mardini, M. & Funder, J. W. (2009). Glucocorticoids activate cardiac mineralocorticoid receptors during experimental myocardial infarction. *Hypertension*, *54*, 1306-12.

Miyamae, M., Kaneda, K., Domae, N. & Figueredo, V. M. (2010). Cardioprotection by regular ethanol consumption: potential mechanisms and clinical application. *Curr Drug Abuse Rev*, *3*, 39-48.

Mjaatvedt, C. H., Nakaoka, T., Moreno-Rodriguez, R., Norris, R. A., Kern, M. J., Eisenberg, C. A., et al. (2001). The outflow tract of the heart is recruited from a novel heart-forming field. *Dev Biol*, *238*, 97-109.

Moczek, A. P., Sultan, S., Foster, S., Ledon-Rettig, C., Dworkin, I., Nijhout, H. F., et al. (2011). The role of developmental plasticity in evolutionary innovation. *Proc Biol Sci*, *278*, 2705-13.

Mollova, M., Bersell, K., Walsh, S., Savla, J., Das, L. T., Park, S. Y., et al. (2013). Cardiomyocyte proliferation contributes to heart growth in young humans. *Proc Natl Acad Sci U S A*, *110*, 1446-51.

Molnar, J., Howe, D. C., Nijland, M. J. & Nathanielsz, P. W. (2003). Prenatal dexamethasone leads to both endothelial dysfunction and vasodilatory compensation in sheep. *J Physiol*, *547*, 61-6.

Moore, L. G. (2003). Fetal growth restriction and maternal oxygen transport during high altitude pregnancy. *High Alt Med Biol*, *4*, 141-56.

Moorman, A. F. & Christoffels, V. M. (2003). Cardiac chamber formation: development, genes, and evolution. *Physiol Rev*, *83*, 1223-67.

Morgan, W. D. (1989). Transcription factor Sp1 binds to and activates a human hsp70 gene promoter. *Mol Cell Biol*, *9*, 4099-104.

Moritz, K. M., Wintour, E. M. & Dodic, M. (2002). Fetal uninephrectomy leads to postnatal hypertension and compromised renal function. *Hypertension*, *39*, 1071-6.

Morrison, J. L., Botting, K. J., Dyer, J. L., Williams, S. J., Thornburg, K. L. & McMillen, I. C. (2007). Restriction of placental function alters heart development in the sheep fetus. *Am J Physiol Regul Integr Comp Physiol*, *293*, R306-13.

Mostyn, A. & Symonds, M. E. (2009). Early programming of adipose tissue function: a large-animal perspective. *Proc Nutr Soc*, *68*, 393-400.

Murdoch, C. E., Zhang, M., Cave, A. C. & Shah, A. M. (2006). NADPH oxidase-dependent redox signalling in cardiac hypertrophy, remodelling and failure. *Cardiovasc Res*, *71*, 208-15.

Murotsuki, J., Challis, J. R., Han, V. K., Fraher, L. J. & Gagnon, R. (1997). Chronic fetal placental embolization and hypoxemia cause hypertension and myocardial hypertrophy in fetal sheep. *Am J Physiol*, *272*, R201-7.

Myatt, L. (2006). Placental adaptive responses and fetal programming. *J Physiol*, *572*, 25-30.

Nader, N., Singhal, V., Javed, A., Weaver, A. & Kumar, S. (2014). Temporal trends in the diagnosis and management of childhood obesity/overweight in primary care. *J Prim Care Community Health, 5*, 44-9.

Nafee, T. M., Farrell, W. E., Carroll, W. D., Fryer, A. A. & Ismail, K. M. (2008). Epigenetic control of fetal gene expression. *BJOG, 115*, 158-68.

Nathanielsz, P. W. (2006). Animal models that elucidate basic principles of the developmental origins of adult diseases. *ILAR J, 47*, 73-82.

Nava-Ocampo, A. A., Velazquez-Armenta, Y., Brien, J. F. & Koren, G. (2004). Elimination kinetics of ethanol in pregnant women. *Reprod Toxicol, 18*, 613-7.

Navarro, H. A., Mills, E., Seidler, F. J., Baker, F. E., Lappi, S. E., Tayyeb, M. I., et al. (1990). Prenatal nicotine exposure impairs beta-adrenergic function: persistent chronotropic subsensitivity despite recovery from deficits in receptor binding. *Brain Res Bull, 25*, 233-7.

Neel, J. V. (1962). Diabetes mellitus: a "thrifty" genotype rendered detrimental by "progress"? *Am J Hum Genet, 14*, 353-62.

Nesan, D. & Vijayan, M. M. (2012). Embryo exposure to elevated cortisol level leads to cardiac performance dysfunction in zebrafish. *Mol Cell Endocrinol, 363*, 85-91.

Netuka, I., Szarszoi, O., Maly, J., Besik, J., Neckar, J., Kolar, F., et al. (2006). Effect of perinatal hypoxia on cardiac tolerance to acute ischaemia in adult male and female rats. *Clin Exp Pharmacol Physiol, 33*, 714-9.

Ni, Y., Feng-Chen, K. C. & Hsu, L. (1992). A tissue culture model for studying ethanol toxicity on embryonic heart cells. *Cell Biol Toxicol, 8*, 1-11.

Niakan, K. K., Han, J., Pedersen, R. A., Simon, C. & Pera, R. A. (2012). Human pre-implantation embryo development. *Development, 139*, 829-41.

Nicol, L. E., Grant, W. F., Comstock, S. M., Nguyen, M. L., Smith, M. S., Grove, K. L., et al. (2013). Pancreatic inflammation and increased islet macrophages in insulin-resistant juvenile primates. *J Endocrinol, 217*, 207-13.

Nilsson, T., Zetterberg, H., Wang, Y. C. & Rymo, L. (2001). Promoter-proximal regulatory elements involved in oriP-EBNA1-independent and -dependent activation of the Epstein-Barr virus C promoter in B-lymphoid cell lines. *J Virol, 75*, 5796-811.

Nwagwu, M. O., Cook, A. & Langley-Evans, S. C. (2000). Evidence of progressive deterioration of renal function in rats exposed to a maternal low-protein diet in utero. *Br J Nutr, 83*, 79-85.

Nyirenda, M. J., Lindsay, R. S., Kenyon, C. J., Burchell, A. & Seckl, J. R. (1998). Glucocorticoid exposure in late gestation permanently programs rat hepatic phosphoenolpyruvate carboxykinase and glucocorticoid receptor expression and causes glucose intolerance in adult offspring. *J Clin Invest, 101*, 2174-81.

Nyirenda, M. J. & Seckl, J. R. (1998). Intrauterine events and the programming of adulthood disease: the role of fetal glucocorticoid exposure (Review). *Int J Mol Med, 2*, 607-14.

O'Tierney, P. F., Anderson, D. F., Faber, J. J., Louey, S., Thornburg, K. L. & Giraud, G. D. (2010a). Reduced systolic pressure load decreases cell-cycle activity in the fetal sheep heart. *Am J Physiol Regul Integr Comp Physiol, 299*, R573-8.

O'Tierney, P. F., Chattergoon, N. N., Louey, S., Giraud, G. D. & Thornburg, K. L. (2010b). Atrial natriuretic peptide inhibits angiotensin II-stimulated proliferation in fetal cardiomyocytes. *J Physiol, 588*, 2879-89.

Ohlsson, H., Karlsson, K. & Edlund, T. (1993). IPF1, a homeodomain-containing transactivator of the insulin gene. *EMBO J*, *12*, 4251-9.

Ohtsuka, T. & Gilbert, R. D. (1995). Cardiac enzyme activities in fetal and adult pregnant and nonpregnant sheep exposed to high-altitude hypoxemia. *J Appl Physiol (1985)*, *79*, 1286-9.

Okubo, S., Wildner, O., Shah, M. R., Chelliah, J. C., Hess, M. L. & Kukreja, R. C. (2001). Gene transfer of heat-shock protein 70 reduces infarct size in vivo after ischemia/reperfusion in the rabbit heart. *Circulation*, *103*, 877-81.

Olives, C., Myerson, R., Mokdad, A. H., Murray, C. J. & Lims S. S. (2013). Prevalence, awareness, treatment, and control of hypertension in United States counties, 2001-2009. *PLoS One*, *8*, e60308.

Olivey, H. E., Compton, L. A. & Barnett, J. V. (2004). Coronary vessel development: the epicardium delivers. *Trends Cardiovasc Med*, *14*, 247-51.

Olson, E. N. (2006). Gene regulatory networks in the evolution and development of the heart. *Science*, *313*, 1922-7.

Owan, T. E., Hodge, D. O., Herges, R. M., Jacobsen, S. J., Roger, V. L. & Redfield, M. M. (2006). Trends in prevalence and outcome of heart failure with preserved ejection fraction. *N Engl J Med*, *355*, 251-9.

Ozaki, T., Nishina, H., Hanson, M. A. & Poston, L. (2001). Dietary restriction in pregnant rats causes gender-related hypertension and vascular dysfunction in offspring. *J Physiol*, *530*, 141-52.

Painter, R. C., De Rooij, S. R., Bossuyt, P. M., Simmers, T. A., Osmond, C., Barker, D. J., et al. (2006). Early onset of coronary artery disease after prenatal exposure to the Dutch famine. *Am J Clin Nutr*, *84*, 322-7; quiz 466-7.

Patterson, A. J., Chen, M., Xue, Q., Xiao, D. & Zhang, L. (2010). Chronic prenatal hypoxia induces epigenetic programming of PKC{epsilon} gene repression in rat hearts. *Circ Res*, *107*, 365-73.

Patterson, A. J., Xiao, D., Xiong, F., Dixon, B. & Zhang, L. (2012). Hypoxia-derived oxidative stress mediates epigenetic repression of PKCepsilon gene in foetal rat hearts. *Cardiovasc Res*, *93*, 302-10.

Patterson, A. J. & Zhang, L. (2010). Hypoxia and fetal heart development. *Curr Mol Med*, *10*, 653-66.

Paul, K., Ball, N. A., Dorn, G. W., 2nd & Walsh, R. A. (1997). Left ventricular stretch stimulates angiotensin II--mediated phosphatidylinositol hydrolysis and protein kinase C epsilon isoform translocation in adult guinea pig hearts. *Circ Res*, *81*, 643-50.

Perez-Pomares, J. M., Gonzalez-Rosa, J. M. & Munoz-Chapuli, R. (2009). Building the vertebrate heart - an evolutionary approach to cardiac development. *Int J Dev Biol*, *53*, 1427-43.

Pinson, C. W., Morton, M. J. & Thornburg, K. L. (1991). Mild pressure loading alters right ventricular function in fetal sheep. *Circ Res*, *68*, 947-57.

Plagemann, A., Harder, T., Kohlhoff, R., Rohde, W. & Dorner, G. (1997). Glucose tolerance and insulin secretion in children of mothers with pregestational IDDM or gestational diabetes. *Diabetologia*, *40*, 1094-100.

Poston, L. (2010). Developmental programming and diabetes - The human experience and insight from animal models. *Best Pract Res Clin Endocrinol Metab*, *24*, 541-52.

Radom-Aizik, S., Zaldivar, F. P., Nance, D. M., Haddad, F., Cooper, D. M. & Adams, G. R. (2013). Growth inhibition and compensation in response to neonatal hypoxia in rats. *Pediatr Res*, *74*, 111-20.

Ranki, H. J., Budas, G. R., Crawford, R. M. & Jovanovic, A. (2001). Gender-specific difference in cardiac ATP-sensitive K(+) channels. *J Am Coll Cardiol*, *38*, 906-15.

Ream, M., Ray, A. M., Chandra, R. & Chikaraishi, D. M. (2008). Early fetal hypoxia leads to growth restriction and myocardial thinning. *Am J Physiol Regul Integr Comp Physiol*, *292*, 583-95.

Reini, S. A., Dutta, G., Wood, C. E. & Keller-Wood, M. (2008). Cardiac corticosteroid receptors mediate the enlargement of the ovine fetal heart induced by chronic increases in maternal cortisol. *J Endocrinol*, *198*, 419-27.

Reiss, K., Cheng, W., Ferber, A., Kajstura, J., Li, P., Li, B., et al. (1996). Overexpression of insulin-like growth factor-1 in the heart is coupled with myocyte proliferation in transgenic mice. *Proc Natl Acad Sci U S A*, *93*, 8630-5.

Ren, J., Wold, L. E., Natavio, M., Ren, B. H., Hannigan, J. H. & Brown, R. A. (2002). Influence of prenatal alcohol exposure on myocardial contractile function in adult rat hearts: role of intracellular calcium and apoptosis. *Alcohol Alcohol*, *37*, 30-7.

Ren, R., Oakley, R. H., Cruz-Topete, D. & Cidlowski, J. A. (2012). Dual role for glucocorticoids in cardiomyocyte hypertrophy and apoptosis. *Endocrinology*, *153*, 5346-60.

Rice, D. & Barone, S., Jr. (2000). Critical periods of vulnerability for the developing nervous system: evidence from humans and animal models. *Environ Health Perspect*, *108*, Suppl 3, 511-33.

Rog-Zielinska, E. A., Thomson, A., Kenyon, C. J., Brownstein, D. G., Moran, C. M., Szumska, D., et al. (2013). Glucocorticoid receptor is required for foetal heart maturation. *Hum Mol Genet*, *22*, 3269-82.

Roger, V. L., Go, A. S., Lloyd-Jones, D. M., Benjamin, E. J., Berry, J. D., Borden, W. B., et al. (2012). Heart disease and stroke statistics--2012 update: a report from the American Heart Association. *Circulation*, *125*, e2-e220.

Romanoff, A. L. (1949). Critical periods and causes of death in avian embryonic development. *Auk*, *66*, 264-70.

Rorabaugh, B. R., Ross, S. A., Gaivin, R. J., Papay, R. S., McCune, D. F., Simpson, P. C., et al. (2005). alpha1A- but not alpha1B-adrenergic receptors precondition the ischemic heart by a staurosporine-sensitive, chelerythrine-insensitive mechanism. *Cardiovasc Res*, *65*, 436-45.

Roseboom, T., De Rooij, S. & Painter, R. (2006). The Dutch famine and its long-term consequences for adult health. *Early Hum Dev*, *82*, 485-91.

Roseboom, T. J., Van der Meulen, J. H., Osmond, C., Barker, D. J., Ravelli, A. C., Schroeder-Tanka, J. M., et al. (2000). Coronary heart disease after prenatal exposure to the Dutch famine, 1944-45. *Heart*, *84*, 595-8.

Roseboom, T. J., Van der Meulen, J. H., Ravelli, A. C., Van Montfrans, G. A., Osmond, C., Barker, D. J., et al. (1999). Blood pressure in adults after prenatal exposure to famine. *J Hypertens*, *17*, 325-30.

Roseboom, T. J., Van der Meulen, J. H., Van Montfrans, G. A., Ravelli, A. C., Osmond, C., Barker, D. J., et al. (2001). Maternal nutrition during gestation and blood pressure in later life. *J Hypertens*, *19*, 29-34.

Rosenthal, N. & Harvey, R. P. (2010) *Heart development and regeneration*. Vol. 1 & 2., London, UK: Academic Press.

Rossant, J. (1996). Mouse mutants and cardiac development: new molecular insights into cardiogenesis. *Circ Res, 78*, 349-53.

Rossier, M. F., Python, M. & Maturana, A. D. (2010). Contribution of mineralocorticoid and glucocorticoid receptors to the chronotropic and hypertrophic actions of aldosterone in neonatal rat ventricular myocytes. *Endocrinology, 151*, 2777-87.

Rueda-Clausen, C. F., Morton, J. S. & Davidge, S. T. (2009). Effects of hypoxia-induced intrauterine growth restriction on cardiopulmonary structure and function during adulthood. *Cardiovasc Res, 81*, 713-22.

Rugonyi, S., Shaut, C., Liu, A., Thornburg, K. & Wang, R. K. (2008). Changes in wall motion and blood flow in the outflow tract of chick embryonic hearts observed with optical coherence tomography after outflow tract banding and vitelline-vein ligation. *Phys Med Biol, 53*, 5077-91.

Sabbah, H. N. & Sharov, V. G. (1998). Apoptosis in heart failure. *Prog Cardiovasc Dis, 40*, 549-62.

Safe, S. & Kim, K. (2008). Non-classical genomic estrogen receptor (ER)/specificity protein and ER/activating protein-1 signaling pathways. *J Mol Endocrinol, 41*, 263-75.

Saurin, A. T., Pennington, D. J., Raat, N. J., Latchman, D. S., Owen, M. J. & Marber, M. S. (2002). Targeted disruption of the protein kinase C epsilon gene abolishes the infarct size reduction that follows ischaemic preconditioning of isolated buffer-perfused mouse hearts. *Cardiovasc Res, 55*, 672-80.

Savolainen, S. M., Foley, J. F. & Elmore, S. A. (2009). Histology atlas of the developing mouse heart with emphasis on E11. 5 to E18. 5. *Toxicol Pathol, 37*, 395-414.

Schenker, S., Yang, Y., Johnson, R. F., Downing, J. W., Schenken, R. S., Henderson, G. I., et al. (1993). The transfer of cocaine and its metabolites across the term human placenta. *Clin Pharmacol Ther, 53*, 329-39.

Schoenwolf, G. C. & Garcia-Martinez, V. (1995). Primitive-streak origin and state of commitment of cells of the cardiovascular system in avian and mammalian embryos. *Cell Mol Biol Res, 41*, 233-40.

Scott-Drechsel, D. E., Rugonyi, S., Marks, D. L., Thornburg, K. L. & Hinds, M. T. (2013). Hyperglycemia slows embryonic growth and suppresses cell cycle via cyclin D1 and p21. *Diabetes, 62*, 234-42.

Seckl, J. R. (2004). Prenatal glucocorticoids and long-term programming. *Eur J Endocrinol, 151* Suppl 3, U49-62.

Seki, Y., Williams, L., Vuguin, P. M. & Charron, M. J. (2012). Minireview: Epigenetic programming of diabetes and obesity: animal models. *Endocrinology, 153*, 1031-8.

Semenza, G. L. (1998). Hypoxia-inducible factor 1: master regulator of O2 homeostasis. *Curr Opin Genet Dev, 8*, 588-94.

Semenza, G. L., Agani, F., Iyer, N., Kotch, L., Laughner, E., Leung, S., et al. (1999). Regulation of cardiovascular development and physiology by hypoxia-inducible factor 1. *Ann N Y Acad Sci, 874*, 262-8.

Shaw, G. M., Malcoe, L. H., Lammer, E. J. & Swan, S. H. (1991). Maternal use of cocaine during pregnancy and congenital cardiac anomalies. *J Pediatr, 118*, 167-8.

Shen, C. N., Seckl, J. R., Slack, J. M. & Tosh, D. (2003). Glucocorticoids suppress beta-cell development and induce hepatic metaplasia in embryonic pancreas. *Biochem J, 375*, 41-50.

Silverman, B. L., Metzger, B. E., Cho, N. H. & Loeb, C. A. (1995). Impaired glucose tolerance in adolescent offspring of diabetic mothers. Relationship to fetal hyperinsulinism. *Diabetes Care, 18*, 611-7.

Silvestri, J. M., Long, J. M., Weese-Mayer, D. E. & Barkov, G. A. (1991). Effect of prenatal cocaine on respiration, heart rate, and sudden infant death syndrome. *Pediatr Pulmonol, 11*, 328-34.

Simmons, R. A. (2006). Developmental origins of diabetes: the role of oxidative stress. *Free Radic Biol Med, 40*, 917-22.

Sisci, D., Middea, E., Morelli, C., Lanzino, M., Aquila, S., Rizza, P., et al. (2010). 17beta-estradiol enhances alpha(5) integrin subunit gene expression through ERalpha-Sp1 interaction and reduces cell motility and invasion of ERalpha-positive breast cancer cells. *Breast Cancer Res Treat, 124*, 63-77.

Sizarov, A., Ya, J., de Boer, B. A., Lamers, W. H., Christoffels, V. M. & Moorman, A. F. (2011). Formation of the building plan of the human heart: morphogenesis, growth, and differentiation. *Circulation, 123*, 1125-35.

Skinner, M. K., Haque, C. G., Nilsson, E., Bhandari, R. & McCarrey, J. R. (2013). Environmentally induced transgenerational epigenetic reprogramming of primordial germ cells and the subsequent germ line. *PLoS One, 8*, e66318.

Slotkin, T. A. (1998). Fetal nicotine or cocaine exposure: which one is worse? *J Pharmacol Exp Ther, 285*, 931-45.

Slotkin, T. A., Saleh, J. L., McCook, E. C. & Seidler, F. J. (1997). Impaired cardiac function during postnatal hypoxia in rats exposed to nicotine prenatally: implications for perinatal morbidity and mortality, and for sudden infant death syndrome. *Teratology, 55*, 177-84.

Smallegange, I. M. & Johansson, J. (2014). Life-history differences favor evolution of male dimorphism in competitive games. *Am Nat, 183*, 188-98.

Snoeckx, L. H., Cornelussen, R. N., Van Nieuwenhoven, F. A., Reneman, R. S. & Van der Vusse, G. J. (2001). Heat shock proteins and cardiovascular pathophysiology. *Physiol Rev, 81*, 1461-97.

Spinale, F. G. (2007). Myocardial matrix remodeling and the matrix metalloproteinases: influence on cardiac form and function. *Physiol Rev, 87*, 1285-342.

Srivastava, D. (2006a). Genetic regulation of cardiogenesis and congenital heart disease. *Annu Rev Pathol, 1*, 199-213.

Srivastava, D. (2006b). Making or breaking the heart: from lineage determination to morphogenesis. *Cell, 126*, 1037-48.

Srivastava, D. & Olson, E. N. (2000). A genetic blueprint for cardiac development. *Nature, 407*, 221-6.

Stein, Z., Susser, M., Saenger, G. & Marolla, F. (1975). *Famine and human development: The Dutch Hunger Winter of 1944-1945*. New York: Oxford University Press.

Sundgren, N. C., Giraud, G. D., Schultz, J. M., Lasarev, M. R., Stork, P. J. & Thornburg, K. L. (2003a). Extracellular signal-regulated kinase and phosphoinositol-3 kinase mediate IGF-1 induced proliferation of fetal sheep cardiomyocytes. *Am J Physiol Regul Integr Comp Physiol, 285*, R1481-9.

Sundgren, N. C., Giraud, G. D., Stork, P. J., Maylie, J. G. & Thornburg, K. L. (2003b). Angiotensin II stimulates hyperplasia but not hypertrophy in immature ovine cardiomyocytes. *J Physiol*, *548*, 881-91.

Taber, L. A., Keller, B. B. & Clark, E. B. (1992). Cardiac mechanics in the stage-16 chick embryo. *J Biomech Eng*, *114*, 427-34.

Taber, L. A., Sun, H., Clark, E. B. & Keller, B. B. (1994). Epicardial strains in embryonic chick ventricle at stages 16 through 24. *Circ Res*, *75*, 896-903.

Takahashi, T., Schunkert, H., Isoyama, S., Wei, J. Y., Nadal-Ginard, B., Grossman, W., et al. (1992). Age-related differences in the expression of proto-oncogene and contractile protein genes in response to pressure overload in the rat myocardium. *J Clin Invest*, *89*, 939-46.

Takeishi, Y., Bhagwat, A., Ball, N. A., Kirkpatrick, D. L., Periasamy, M. & Walsh, R. A. (1999). Effect of angiotensin-converting enzyme inhibition on protein kinase C and SR proteins in heart failure. *Am J Physiol*, *276*, H53-62.

Tangalakis, K., Lumbers, E. R., Moritz, K. M., Towstoless, M. K. & Wintour, E. M. (1992). Effect of cortisol on blood pressure and vascular reactivity in the ovine fetus. *Exp Physiol*, *77*, 709-17.

Thompson, L., Dong, Y. & Evans, L. (2009). Chronic hypoxia increases inducible NOS-derived nitric oxide in fetal guinea pig hearts. *Pediatr Res*, *65*, 188-92.

Thompson, L. P. (2003). Effects of chronic hypoxia on fetal coronary responses. *High Alt Med Biol*, *4*, 215-24.

Thompson, L. P. & Dong, Y. (2005). Chronic hypoxia decreases endothelial nitric oxide synthase protein expression in fetal guinea pig hearts. *J Soc Gynecol Investig*, *12*, 388-95.

Thornburg, K., Jonker, S., O'Tierney, P., Chattergoon, N., Louey, S., Faber, J., et al. (2011). Regulation of the cardiomyocyte population in the developing heart. *Prog Biophys Mol Biol*, *106*, 289-99.

Thornburg, K. L., O'Tierney, P. F. & Louey, S. (2010). Review: The placenta is a programming agent for cardiovascular disease. *Placenta*, *31* Suppl, S54-9.

Tintu A, Rouwet, E., Verlohren, S., Brinkmann, J., Ahmad, S., Crispi, F., et al. (2009). Hypoxia induces dilated cardiomyopathy in the chick embryo: mechanism, intervention, and long-term consequences. *PLoS One*, *4*, e5155.

Tomanek, R. J., Lund, D. D. & Yue, X. (2003). Hypoxic induction of myocardial vascularization during development. *Adv Exp Med Biol*, *543*, 139-49.

Tong, W., Xiong, F., Li, Y. & Zhang, L. (2013). Hypoxia inhibits cardiomyocyte proliferation in fetal rat hearts via upregulating TIMP-4. *Am J Physiol Regul Integr Comp Physiol*, *304*, R613-20.

Tong, W., Xue, Q., Li, Y. & Zhang, L. (2011). Maternal hypoxia alters matrix metalloproteinase expression patterns and causes cardiac remodeling in fetal and neonatal rats. *Am J Physiol Heart Circ Physiol*, *301*, H2113-21.

Tong, W. & Zhang, L. (2012). Fetal hypoxia and programming of matrix metalloproteinases. *Drug Discov Today*, *17*, 124-34.

Torres, L. M., Konopnika, B., Berti-Mattera, L. N., Liedtke, C. & Romani, A. (2010). Defective translocation of PKCepsilon in EtOH-induced inhibition of $Mg2+$ accumulation in rat hepatocytes. *Alcohol Clin Exp Res*, *34*, 1659-69.

Vaillant, C., Didier-Bazes, M., Hutter, A., Belin, M. F. & Thomasset, N. (1999). Spatiotemporal expression patterns of metalloproteinases and their inhibitors in the postnatal developing rat cerebellum. *J Neurosci, 19,* 4994-5004.

Val'Kovich, E. I., Molchanova, V. V., Davydova, M. K. & Davydova, O. K. (1986). [Changes in the myocardium of fetuses and newborn infants as a result of hypoxia]. *Arkh Anat Gistol Embriol, 90,* 35-9.

Van Straten, E. M., Bloks, V. W., Huijkman, N. C., Baller, J. F., Van Meer, H., Lütjohann, D., et al. (2010). The liver X-receptor gene promoter is hypermethylated in a mouse model of prenatal protein restriction. *Am J Physiol Regul Integr Comp Physiol, 298,* R275-82.

Van Weerd, J. H., Koshiba-Takeuchi, K., Kwon, C. & Takeuchi, J. K. (2011). Epigenetic factors and cardiac development. *Cardiovasc Res, 91,* 203-11.

Venkov, C. D., Myers, P. R., Tanner, M. A., Su, M. & Vaughan, D. E. (1999). Ethanol increases endothelial nitric oxide production through modulation of nitric oxide synthase expression. *Thromb Haemost, 81,* 638-42.

Vo, T. & Hardy, D. B. (2012). Molecular mechanisms underlying the fetal programming of adult disease. *J Cell Commun Signal, 6,* 139-53.

Von Bergen, N. H., Koppenhafer, S. L., Spitz, D. R., Volk, K. A., Patel, S. S., Roghair, R. D., et al. (2009). Fetal programming alters reactive oxygen species production in sheep cardiac mitochondria. *Clin Sci (Lond), 116,* 659-68.

Vornehm, N. D., Wang, M., Abarbanell, A., Herrmann, J., Weil, B., Tan, J., et al. (2009). Acute postischemic treatment with estrogen receptor-alpha agonist or estrogen receptor-beta agonist improves myocardial recovery. *Surgery, 146,* 145-54.

Waldo, K. L., Kumiski, D. H., Wallis, K. T., Stadt, H. A., Hutson, M. R., Platt, D. H., et al. (2001). Conotruncal myocardium arises from a secondary heart field. *Development, 128,* 3179-88.

Ward, J. (2008). Oxygen sensors in context. *Biochim Biophys Acta, 1777,* 1-14.

Watkins, A. J., Wilkins, A., Cunningham, C., Perry, V. H., Seet, M. J., Osmond, C., et al. (2008). Low protein diet fed exclusively during mouse oocyte maturation leads to behavioural and cardiovascular abnormalities in offspring. *J Physiol, 586,* 2231-44.

Wencker, D., Chandra, M., Nguyen, K., Miao, W., Garantziotis, S., Factor, S. M., et al. (2003). A mechanistic role for cardiac myocyte apoptosis in heart failure. *J Clin Invest, 111,* 1497-504.

Whincup, P. H., Kaye, S. J., Owen, C. G., Huxley, R., Cook, D. G., Anazawa, S., et al. (2008). Birth weight and risk of type 2 diabetes: a systematic review. *JAMA, 300,* 2886-97.

Wikenheiser, J., Doughman, Y. Q., Fisher, S. A. & Watanabe, M. (2006). Differential levels of tissue hypoxia in the developing chicken heart. *Dev Dyn, 235,* 115-23.

Wikenheiser, J., Karunamuni, G., Sloter, E., Walker, M. K., Roy, D., Wilson, D. L., et al. (2013). Altering HIF-1alpha through 2,3,7,8-tetrachlorodibenzo-p-dioxin (TCDD) exposure affects coronary vessel development. *Cardiovasc Toxicol, 13,* 161-7.

Williams, L., Seki, Y., Vuguin, P. M. & Charron, M. J. (2014). Animal models of in utero exposure to a high fat diet: A review. *Biochim Biophys Acta, 1842,* 507-19.

Wintour, E. M., Johnson, K., Koukoulas, I., Moritz, K., Tersteeg, M. & Dodic, M. (2003). Programming the cardiovascular system, kidney and the brain--a review. *Placenta, 24* Suppl A, S65-71.

Woods, J. R., Jr., Plessinger, M. A. & Clark, K. E. (1987). Effect of cocaine on uterine blood flow and fetal oxygenation. *JAMA*, *257*, 957-61.

Woods, L. L. (1999). Neonatal uninephrectomy causes hypertension in adult rats. *Am J Physiol*, *276*, R974-8.

Woods, L. L., Ingelfinger, J. R., Nyengaard, J. R. & Rasch, R. (2001). Maternal protein restriction suppresses the newborn renin-angiotensin system and programs adult hypertension in rats. *Pediatr Res*, *49*, 460-7.

Woods, L. L., Weeks, D. A. & Rasch, R. (2004). Programming of adult blood pressure by maternal protein restriction: role of nephrogenesis. *Kidney Int*, *65*, 1339-48.

Wothe, D., Hohimer, A., Morton, M., Thornburg, K., Giraud, G. & Davis, L. (2002). Increased coronary blood flow signals growth of coronary resistance vessels in near-term ovine fetuses. *Am J Physiol Regul Integr Comp Physiol*, *282*, R295-302.

Wright, C. S., Rifas-Shiman, S. L., Rich-Edwards, J. W., Taveras, E. M., Gillman, M. W. & Oken, E. (2009). Intrauterine exposure to gestational diabetes, child adiposity, and blood pressure. *Am J Hypertens*, *22*, 215-20.

Xiao, D., Ducsay, C. A. & Zhang, L. (2000). Chronic hypoxia and developmental regulation of cytochrome c expression in rats. *J Soc Gynecol Investig*, *7*, 279-83.

Xiao, D., Huang, X., Lawrence, J., Yang, S. & Zhang, L. (2007). Fetal and neonatal nicotine exposure differentially regulates vascular contractility in adult male and female offspring. *J Pharmacol Exp Ther*, *320*, 654-61.

Xiao, D., Yang, S. & Zhang, L. (2009). Prenatal cocaine exposure causes sex-dependent impairment in the myogenic reactivity of coronary arteries in adult offspring. *Hypertension*, *54*, 1123-8.

Xiao, R. P. (2000). Cell logic for dual coupling of a single class of receptors to G(s) and G(i) proteins. *Circ Res*, *87*, 635-7.

Xin, M., Olson, E. N. & Bassel-Duby, R. (2013). Mending broken hearts: cardiac development as a basis for adult heart regeneration and repair. *Nat Rev Mol Cell Biol*, *14*, 529-41.

Xiong, F., Xiao, D. & Zhang, L. (2012). Norepinephrine causes epigenetic repression of PKCepsilon gene in rodent hearts by activating Nox1-dependent reactive oxygen species production. *FASEB J*, *26*, 2753-63.

Xu, B., Strom, J. & Chen, Q. M. (2011). Dexamethasone induces transcriptional activation of Bcl-xL gene and inhibits cardiac injury by myocardial ischemia. *Eur J Pharmacol*, *668*, 194-200.

Xu, H. & Baldini, A. (2007). Genetic pathways to mammalian heart development: Recent progress from manipulation of the mouse genome. *Semin Cell Dev Biol*, *18*, 77-83.

Xu, Y., Arenas, I. A., Armstrong, S. J., Plahta, W. C., Xu, H. & Davidge, S. T. (2006a). Estrogen improves cardiac recovery after ischemia/reperfusion by decreasing tumor necrosis factor-alpha. *Cardiovasc Res*, *69*, 836-44.

Xu, Y., Williams, S. J., O'Brien, D. & Davidge, S. T. (2006b). Hypoxia or nutrient restriction during pregnancy in rats leads to progressive cardiac remodeling and impairs postischemic recovery in adult male offspring. *FASEB J*, *20*, 1251-3.

Xue, Q., Dasgupta, C., Chen, M. & Zhang, L. (2011). Foetal hypoxia increases cardiac AT(2)R expression and subsequent vulnerability to adult ischaemic injury. *Cardiovasc Res*, *89*, 300-8.

Xue, Q. & Zhang, L. (2009). Prenatal hypoxia causes a sex-dependent increase in heart susceptibility to ischemia and reperfusion injury in adult male offspring: role of protein kinase C epsilon. *J Pharmacol Exp Ther*, *330*, 624-32.

Yang, Q., Hohimer, A. R., Giraud, G. D., Van Winkle, D. M., Underwood, M. J., He, G. W., et al. (2008). Effect of fetal anaemia on myocardial ischaemia-reperfusion injury and coronary vasoreactivity in adult sheep. *Acta Physiol (Oxf)*, *194*, 325-34.

Young, L. E., Fernandes, K., McEvoy, T. G., Butterwith, S. C., Gutierrez, C. G., Carolan, C., et al. (2001). Epigenetic change in IGF2R is associated with fetal overgrowth after sheep embryo culture. *Nat Genet*, *27*, 153-4.

Zaffran, S., Kelly, R. G., Meilhac, S. M., Buckingham, M. E. & Brown, N. A. (2004). Right ventricular myocardium derives from the anterior heart field. *Circ Res*, *95*, 261-8.

Zhai, P., Eurell, T. E., Cooke, P. S., Lubahn, D. B. & Gross, D. R. (2000a). Myocardial ischemia-reperfusion injury in estrogen receptor-alpha knockout and wild-type mice. *Am J Physiol Heart Circ Physiol*, *278*, H1640-7.

Zhai, P., Eurell, T. E., Cotthaus, R., Jeffery, E. H., Bahr, J. M. & Gross, D. R. (2000b). Effect of estrogen on global myocardial ischemia-reperfusion injury in female rats. *Am J Physiol Heart Circ Physiol*, *279*, H2766-75.

Zhang, F. X., Chen, M. L., Shan, Q. J., Zou, J. G., Chen, C., Yang, B., et al. (2007a). Hypoxia reoxygenation induces premature senescence in neonatal SD rat cardiomyocytes. *Acta Pharmacol Sin*, *28*, 44-51.

Zhang, H., Darwanto, A., Linkhart, T. A., Sowers, L. C. & Zhang, L. (2007b). Maternal cocaine administration causes an epigenetic modification of protein kinase Cepsilon gene expression in fetal rat heart. *Mol Pharmacol*, *71*, 1319-28.

Zhang, H., Meyer, K. D. & Zhang, L. (2009). Fetal exposure to cocaine causes programming of Prkce gene repression in the left ventricle of adult rat offspring. *Biol Reprod*, *80*, 440-8.

Zhang, L. (2005). Prenatal hypoxia and cardiac programming. *J Soc Gynecol Investig*, *12*, 2-13.

Zhang, L., Xiao, Y. & He, J. (1999a). Cocaine and apoptosis in myocardial cells. *Anat Rec*, *257*, 208-16.

Zhang, M., Luo, B., Chen, S. J., Abrams, G. A. & Fallon, M. B. (1999b). Endothelin-1 stimulation of endothelial nitric oxide synthase in the pathogenesis of hepatopulmonary syndrome. *Am J Physiol*, *277*, G944-52.

Zhang, S., Rattanatray, L., MacLaughlin, S. M., Cropley, J. E., Suter, C. M., Molloy, L., et al. (2010). Periconceptional undernutrition in normal and overweight ewes leads to increased adrenal growth and epigenetic changes in adrenal IGF2/H19 gene in offspring. *FASEB J*, *24*, 2772-82.

Zhu, B. Q., Sun, Y. P., Sudhir, K., Sievers, R. E., Browne, A. E., Gao, L., et al. (1997). Effects of second-hand smoke and gender on infarct size of young rats exposed in utero and in the neonatal to adolescent period. *J Am Coll Cardiol*, *30*, 1878-85.

Zhu, H., Kartiko, S. & Finnell, R. H. (2009). Importance of gene-environment interactions in the etiology of selected birth defects. *Clin Genet*, *75*, 409-23.

Zhu, W. G., Srinivasan, K., Dai, Z., Duan, W., Druhan, L. J., Ding, H., et al. (2003). Methylation of adjacent CpG sites affects Sp1/Sp3 binding and activity in the p21(Cip1) promoter. *Mol Cell Biol*, *23*, 4056-65.

Zhu, W. Z., Zheng, M., Koch, W. J., Lefkowitz, R. J., Kobilka, B. K. & Xiao, R. P. (2001). Dual modulation of cell survival and cell death by beta(2)-adrenergic signaling in adult mouse cardiac myocytes. *Proc Natl Acad Sci U S A*, *98*, 1607-12.

Zile, M. H. (2010). Vitamin A-not for your eyes only: requirement for heart formation begins early in embryogenesis. *Nutrients*, *2*, 532-50.

Zimmermann, H., Gardner, D. S., Jellyman, J. K., Fowden, A. L., Giussani, D. A. & Forhead, A. J. (2003). Effect of dexamethasone on pulmonary and renal angiotensin-converting enzyme concentration in fetal sheep during late gestation. *Am J Obstet Gynecol*, *189*, 1467-71.

In: Stress and Developmental Programming …
Editors: Lubo Zhang and Lawrence D. Longo

ISBN: 978-1-63321-836-9
© 2014 Nova Science Publishers, Inc.

Chapter 3

Stress and Programming of Metabolic Disease

Song Zhang[1], Shervi Lie[1], Lisa M. Nicholas[1], Leewen Rattanatray[1],
*Janna L. Morrison[1] and I. Caroline McMillen[1,2]**
[1]University of South Australia, Adelaide, SA Australia
[2]University of Newcastle, NSW, Australia

Abstract

It has been proposed that the developmental programming of the hypothalamo-pituitary-adrenocortical (HPA) axis is a conserved evolutionary response to a suboptimal early environment which originates in the embryo, fetus or neonate and which persists into postnatal life in anticipation of 'a life of adversity' (Worthman and Kuzara, 2005). Such a programmed response may result in an increased stress responsiveness and hypercortisolism in postnatal life and may in turn exacerbate the metabolic and cardiovascular sequelae of a poor early environment which include central obesity, insulin resistance, glucose intolerance and hypertension (Barker and Osmond, 1986, Barker et al., 1989, McMillen and Robinson, 2005, Phillips, 2007).

Results from a worldwide series of experimental, clinical and epidemiological studies have demonstrated that exposure of the embryo, fetus or neonate to adverse environmental stressors such as poor nutrition, poor placental growth or function, excess glucocorticoids or poor maternal care increases the risk of hyperactivation of the HPA axis and poor metabolic and cardiovascular health in later life (Butler et al., 2002, de Vries et al., 2007, Levitt et al., 1996, Phillips et al., 2000, Weaver et al., 2004). There is evidence that the developmental programming of the HPA axis occurs in parallel with and contributes to the developmental programming of changes within insulin signalling and other key pathways in tissues of metabolic importance including muscle, liver and fat.

In this chapter, we focus firstly on the impact of maternal undernutrition during the period around conception on the programming of the HPA axis and associated health outcomes including poor metabolic health in later life. We then discuss the separate

---

* Corresponding author: I. Caroline McMillen, University of Newcastle, Caroline.McMillen@newcastle.edu.au.

impacts of chronic placental and fetal growth restriction and excess glucocorticoid exposure on the programming of the HPA axis and metabolic function in adult life. Finally, we review the impact of an adverse intrauterine environment on the epigenetic mechanisms which may initiate and/or sustain the long term changes within the HPA axis after birth.

1. The Impact of Poor Maternal Nutrition During the Periconceptional Period on the HPA Axis in Fetal and Postnatal Life

The effects of the Dutch Winter Famine, a 5 month period of malnutrition experienced in Amsterdam between mid-October 1944 and May 1945 on pregnancy outcomes and adult health have been the focus of a series of detailed publications (Roseboom et al., 2001, 2003, Schulz, 2010, Stein and Susser, 1975, Stein et al., 1972). Poor maternal nutrition experienced by a cohort of women exposed to the famine during the first trimester had no effect on either the mean placental or birth weight, however, there were a number of infants in the cohort which were born with very low birth weights and this was attributed to premature delivery (Stein and Susser, 1975). Interestingly it has also been shown that suboptimal growth during the first-trimester is associated with premature delivery (Smith et al., 1998).

It is well established that in the sheep, the prepartum activation of the fetal HPA axis is essential for the normal timing of parturition (term = 150 ± 3 days of gestation) and the maturation of key organ systems before birth which is critical for a successful transition from intrauterine to extrauterine life (Liggins, 1994, MacLaughlin and McMillen, 2007, Whittle et al., 2001). A series of experimental studies in the sheep have highlighted that exposure to poor maternal nutrition in the period around conception results in an earlier activation of the fetal HPA axis before birth and an increased likelihood of preterm delivery.

In sheep, exposure to moderate nutrient restriction from at least 45 days before until one week after conception resulted in an earlier prepartum activation of the HPA axis in twin, but not in singleton fetal sheep, during late gestation (Edwards and McMillen, 2002). When the maternal undernutrition was more severe and the period of exposure was extended from 60 days before conception to day 30 of gestation, prepartum activation of the HPA axis then occurred earlier in the singleton sheep fetus (Bloomfield et al., 2004, Kumarasamy et al., 2005) and this was associated with an increased risk of preterm delivery in ewes carrying singletons (Bloomfield et al., 2003). Thus periconceptional undernutrition appears to result in an earlier activation of the fetal HPA axis with a greater effect in the twin compared to the singleton fetus.

The difference in the impact of maternal undernutrition during the periconceptional period on the HPA axis in twins and singletons suggests that the 'set point' of the function of the HPA axis is already programmed at a different level in twins compared to singletons. Supporting this conclusion is evidence that the timing of the prepartum activation of the fetal HPA axis is normally delayed in twin compared to singleton fetal sheep (Edwards and McMillen, 2002, Gardner et al., 2004, Rumball et al., 2008, Schwartz and Rose, 1998). Plasma adrenocorticotropic hormone (ACTH) concentrations are lower, the prepartum cortisol surge occurs later, and adrenocortical responsiveness to ACTH is blunted in twins compared with singleton fetal sheep in late gestation (Edwards and McMillen, 2002, Gardner et al., 2004, Rumball et al., 2008). It has been proposed that there may be a programmed delay in the prepartum activation of the fetal HPA axis in the twin that acts to protect the twin fetus from preterm delivery, given that twins are exposed to the additional stress of decreased placental substrate supply in late gestation (Bloomfield et al., 2004, MacLaughlin and McMillen, 2007, Muhlhausler et al., 2011). Interestingly, it has been previously reported that the relative adrenal weight was smaller in twin compared to singleton fetal sheep at 55 days of gestation (MacLaughlin et al., 2007), but was greater in twins compared to singleton fetuses during late gestation (Zhang et al., 2013c). This would suggest that the hormonal environment of the early twin pregnancy may have a direct or indirect impact on the fetal HPA axis to result in a programmed delay in the prepartum activation of the axis, which may counter the impact of the adrenocortical hypertrophy present in the normal twin fetus in late gestation. It may be that the mechanisms that initiate the prepartum activation of the HPA axis are those that are also altered by exposure to maternal undernutrition in the periconceptional period and by the early hormonal environment of a twin pregnancy.

A range of studies have also shown that maternal undernutrition during the first 30 or 70 days of pregnancy resulted in higher basal cortisol concentrations and greater ACTH and cortisol responses to a corticotrophin releasing hormone (CRH)/ vasopressin (AVP) challenge in postnatal lambs (Chadio et al., 2007, Gardner et al., 2006, Hawkins et al., 2000).

Interestingly exposure to undernutrition during the periconceptional period from one month before until one week after conception in either normal weight or overweight ewes resulted in an increase in plasma cortisol, but not ACTH, concentrations in response to stress in female lambs at 3-4 months of age (Zhang et al., 2010). This suggests that the impact of maternal undernutrition on the programming of the HPA axis is independent of maternal body weight at conception and is rather dependent on maternal weight loss in the periconceptional period.

The transgenerational effects of maternal undernutrition during the periconceptional period have also been investigated on the HPA function in the guinea pig (term=70 days) (Bertram et al., 2008). Non-sibling F1 females previously exposed to maternal undernutrition were used to generate the F2 generation. Maternal undernutrition from 1-35 days of gestation increased basal cortisol concentrations in the absence of an increase in basal ACTH concentrations in both F1 and F2 generations each at 3 months of age. In F1 and F2 animals, there was a reduced suppression of plasma ACTH and greater suppression of plasma cortisol concentrations following dexamethasone treatment compared to control animals. However, the latter may have been a consequence of higher basal cortisol concentrations present in the dietary restricted group. Interestingly, there were reduced plasma ACTH and cortisol responses to a CRH challenge in the dietary restricted F1 offspring, which were not present in the F2 offspring. In F2 animals, the CRH challenge resulted in a greater ACTH response, in the absence of increased cortisol secretion. These data suggest that altered pituitary sensitivity and adrenal responses to dexamethasone and CRH challenges and the effects of maternal undernutrition may be transmitted to the second generation in the absence of an additional nutritional challenge.

1.1. The Impact of Periconceptional Undernutrition on the Hippocampal-Hypothalmo-Pituitary-Adrenal (HHPA) Axis

There are conflicting reports of the effects of exposure to periconceptional undernutrition on the expression of key regulatory genes in the hypothalamus and anterior pituitary. Maternal undernutrition during the periconceptional period from 60 days before to 30 days after conception did not alter CRH or AVP mRNA expression in the hypothalamic paraventricular nucleus (PVN), glucocorticoid receptor (GR) mRNA expression in either the hypothalamus or anterior pituitary or the mRNA expression of the ACTH precursor, pro-opiomelanocortin (POMC) in the anterior pituitary of the fetal sheep during late gestation (Bloomfield et al., 2004).

Exposure to maternal undernutrition between conception and 70 days of gestation resulted in a decrease in CRH mRNA expression in the hypothalamic PVN and in GR mRNA in the anterior pituitary in the sheep fetus (Hawkins et al., 2001). Similarly, maternal undernutrition during the periconceptional period from at least 45 days before until one week after conception or for just the first week after conception resulted in a decrease in pituitary GR mRNA expression in both singleton and twin fetuses compared to control fetuses (Zhang et al., 2013c). Thus exposure of the single or twin embryos to maternal undernutrition for one week only after conception is sufficient to cause a suppression of pituitary GR expression in late gestation. These changes may contribute to the increased stress responsiveness of the HPA axis in the offspring after exposure to poor nutrition during the periconceptional period.

It is the case, however, that exposure to maternal undernutrition from before to one week after conception was not associated with an increase in pituitary POMC and prohormone convertase 1 (PC1) mRNA expression in either singleton or twin fetuses exposed to periconceptional undenutrition from before until one week after conception (Zhang et al., 2013c). The findings were supported by previous studies where maternal undernutrition imposed up to either 30 or 70 days of gestation did not alter POMC and PC1 mRNA expression in the anterior pituitary of the late gestation fetal sheep (Bloomfield et al., 2004, Hawkins et al., 2001). One possibility is that the decrease in pituitary GR mRNA expression in the periconceptional undernourished group may result in an increase in POMC expression in defined corticotroph subpopulations and thus measurement of POMC expression in whole tissue samples may mask changes occurring within these subpopulations. Farrand and colleagues previously identified three major subpopulations of corticotrophs that expressed POMC and/or ACTH (Farrand et al., 2006). It has also been demonstrated that in the pituitary of the fetal and adult sheep there are subpopulations of corticotrophic cell types that are differentially sensitive to the negative feedback actions of cortisol (Butler et al., 1999, Neill et al., 1987, Schwartz et al., 1994).

Subsequent studies in which maternal undernutrition was imposed from 60 days before to 30 days after conception found that GR mRNA and protein expression was increased in the fetal hypothalamus in late gestation and that these changes persisted into the adult offspring at 5 years of age (Begum et al., 2012, 2013, Stevens et al., 2010). While GR mRNA expression was unaltered in the hippocampus and anterior pituitary in the late gestation sheep fetus, periconceptional undernutrition resulted in a decrease in hippocampal GR mRNA and protein expression and sex-specific changes in pituitary GR mRNA and protein expression in adult offspring at 5 years of age (Begum et al., 2013, Stevens et al., 2010). The discrepancy in the impact of periconceptional undernutrition on pituitary GR mRNA expression in fetal sheep exposed to different periods of undernutrition in early gestation may depend on whether the timing of the undernutrition extends through the period before and after conception, and beyond the preimplantation period and on the severity of the maternal nutritional insult.

Interestingly, in the above studies, hypothalamic POMC mRNA expression was decreased in mature male adult offspring after exposure to periconceptional undernutrition (Begum et al., 2013). POMC is a key anorexigenic neuropeptide in the hypothalamus that regulates food intake and hence energy balance. The decreased expression of hypothalamic POMC was consistent with an increase in fat mass which was also found in adult male offspring after exposure to undernutrition in early pregnancy. The authors therefore proposed that the increase in hypothalamic GR expression in the group exposed to undernutrition may contribute to the decrease in POMC expression and to changes in energy balance in the offspring, up to five years after exposure to maternal undernutrition in early pregnancy.

1.2. The Impact of Periconceptional Undernutrition on Adrenal Growth and Development

Adrenal growth and corticosteroidogenesis are regulated by multiple signalling pathways. ACTH binds to the ACTH receptor (ACTH-R; MC2R) to stimulate production of cyclic AMP (cAMP), which in turn activates protein kinase A (PKA) and phosphorylates the cAMP response element binding protein (CREB), a transcription factor which then activates the transcription of regulators such as steroidogenic acute regulatory (StAR) protein – which mediates the delivery of cholesterol from the outer to the inner mitochondrial membrane for cortisol synthesis (Figure 1) (Lefrancois-Martinez et al., 2011, Li et al., 2008). The six-carbon side chain is removed from cholesterol by the action of the cholesterol side-chain cleavage enzyme, cytochrome P450 (CYP11A1) to result in the formation of pregnenolone. The actions of 17α-hydroxylase (CYP17), 3β hydroxysteroid dehydrogenase (3βHSD), 21-hydroxylase and 11β- hydroxylase then drive cortisol synthesis. Other molecular signalling pathways have also been implicated in the regulation of adrenal growth including the insulin-like growth factor receptor I (IGF1R) pathway with activation of protein kinase B (PKB/Akt), mammalian target of rapamycin (mTOR), mitogen-activated protein kinase/ extracellular signal-regulated kinase (MAPK/ERK), Ca^{2+}/calmodulin-dependent kinase (CAMK), janus kinase/signal transducer and activator of transcription/ suppressors of cytokine signalling (JAK/STAT/SOCS) (Figure 1) (Chen et al., 2005, Condon et al., 2002, Ferreira et al., 2004, 2007, Foster, 2004, Hoeflich and Bielohuby, 2009, Lefrancois-Martinez et al., 2011, Zhang et al., 2013a, 2013b). Adrenocortical hypertrophy is associated with an increase in the adrenal output of cortisol and there have therefore been studies which have determined whether exposure to periconceptional undernutrition resulted in an increase in the expression of genes regulating adrenal growth and/or steroidogenesis.

MacLaughlin and colleagues investigated the impact of exposure to periconceptional undernutrition on fetal adrenal growth and steroidogenesis in early pregnancy at 55 days of gestation (MacLaughlin et al., 2007). There was no effect of periconceptional undernutrition on fetal adrenal weight at 55 days or at 132 days of gestation (Bloomfield et al., 2004), however, fetal adrenal weight was significantly greater at 136-138 days of gestation (Zhang et al., 2013c). This suggests that the effects of periconceptional undernutrition on fetal adrenal growth may emerge in later gestation when adrenal growth and steroidogenesis are normally upregulated during the prepartum period. Exposure to maternal undernutrition for the first 30 days of gestation, however, did not alter the total adrenal weight in postnatal lambs at 1 year of age (Gardner et al., 2006).

It has been shown that maternal undernutrition during the periconceptional period from before until one week after conception resulted in altered relationships between adrenal growth, adrenal IGF expression and steroidogenic enzyme expression during the first 55 days of gestation (MacLaughlin et al., 2007). The relative weight of the fetal adrenal and adrenal IGF1, IGF1R, IGF2 and IGF2R, as well as CYP17 mRNA expression was lower in twin compared with singleton fetuses. In singleton fetuses exposed to maternal undernutrition during the periconceptional period, there was a loss of the relationship which was present in the control fetuses, between adrenal IGF2/IGF2R mRNA expression and either adrenal weight or CYP17 mRNA expression. Similarly in twin fetuses, periconceptional undernutrition resulted in the loss of the relationship (which was present in the controls) between fetal adrenal weight and IGF1 expression and between adrenal CYP17 and IGF2 expression. These findings suggest that the delayed prepartum activation of the HPA axis and blunted adrenal responsiveness in late gestation in twin pregnancies may be programmed early in gestation.

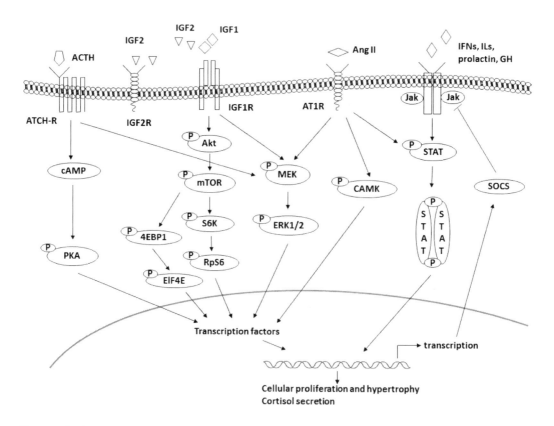

Figure 1. Major molecular signalling pathways which play a role in the stimulation of adrenal growth.

In postnatal life, a moderate restriction of energy intake imposed during a relatively short periconceptional period in normal weight and overweight ewes resulted in an increase in adrenal weight in male and female lambs and a greater cortisol response to stress in female lambs at 3-4 months of age (Zhang et al., 2010). It has also been demonstrated that the increased adrenal mass in male and female lambs after exposure to periconceptional undernutrition in normal weight ewes is a result of increased growth of the adrenal cortex and specifically the zona fasciculata-reticularis (Zhang et al., 2013b). The increase in adrenocortical growth in these lambs appears to be a result of hypertrophy of adrenocortical cells and interestingly the effect of maternal dietary restriction on adrenal growth was relatively greater in the offspring of the normal weight ewe compared to the obese ewe. These findings suggest that the increased cortisol response to stress in lambs exposed to maternal undernutrition during the periconceptional period may be a direct result of early programming of an increase in adrenocortical growth, rather than an increased activation of the HPA axis.

The increase in adrenal weight in lambs exposed to periconceptional undernutrition was associated with a decrease in the adrenal mRNA expression of IGF2, but not with changes in the mRNA expression of IGF2R, ACTH-R, GR, 3βHSD or CYP17 in the adrenals of the lambs (Zhang et al., 2010). This was also supported by previous findings that the increase in plasma ACTH concentrations in twin fetuses exposed to periconceptional undernutrition was not accompanied by either an increase in the expression of adrenal ACTH-R or in adrenal steroidogenic enzyme expression including StAR, CYP11A1, CYP17 and 3βHSD (Edwards et al., 2002). In contrast, a study by Connor et al. reported that maternal periconceptional undernutrition from 60 days before until 30 days after mating resulted in a specific increase in adrenal CYP17 protein abundance in the absence of an increase in adrenal mRNA expression of ACTH-R and steroidogenic enzymes including StAR, 3βHSD and CYP17 in the late gestation singleton sheep fetus (Connor et al., 2009).

Angiotensin II (Ang II) has been shown to stimulate adrenal growth in the zona glomerulosa and the zona fasciculata-reticularis regions of the adrenal cortex (Clyne et al., 1993, Finn et al., 1988, Hattangady et al., 2012, Hoeflich and Bielohuby, 2009, Lebrethon et al., 1994, Nussdorfer et al., 1981, Romero et al., 2006, Viard et al., 1990). In genetically hypertensive Lyon rats, a 4-week infusion of Ang II resulted in an enlargement in both the zona glomerulosa and the zona fasciculata-reticularis regions of the adrenal gland and in an increase in plasma aldosterone and corticosterone concentrations (Aguilar et al., 2004). The increase in volume in the zona fasciculata-reticularis regions accounted for 63% of the adrenal hypertrophy. Maternal dietary restriction in normal weight or obese ewes during the periconceptional period resulted in an activation of the downstream components of the intra-adrenal renin angiotensin system (RAS) through an increase in the abundance of angiotensin converting enzyme (ACE) and angiotensin receptor type I (AT1R) in the adrenal cortex of their offspring at 4 months of age (Zhang et al., 2013a). The intensity of ACE and AT1R, but not ACE2 or AT2R, immunostaining was higher in all zones of the adrenal cortex of lambs in the dietary restricted groups. There was no effect, however, of maternal dietary restriction in either normal weight or obese ewes on ACE and AT1R mRNA expression in the adrenals of the offspring. Similarly, a previous study in the sheep has shown that maternal nutrient restriction during early to mid gestation (28–77 days of gestation) resulted in an increase in AT1R mRNA expression, however, changes in AT1R protein abundance were not examined in this study (Whorwood et al., 2001). It has also been found that there was a decrease in ACE2 mRNA, but not in the abundance of ACE2 in the adrenals of female lambs exposed to maternal undernutrition during the periconceptional period in normal weight ewes, which could potentially contribute to increased angiotensin II activation in adrenals in these lambs (Zhang et al., 2013a). These changes within the intra-adrenal RAS may contribute to the increased adrenal growth and greater adrenal stress response following exposure to signals of adversity in the periconceptional period.

There was no effect of exposure to periconceptional undernutrition on the protein abundance of ERK, CAMKII and their phosphorylated forms in the postnatal lamb adrenal (Zhang et al., 2013a), suggesting other AT1R downstream signalling pathways including c-Jun N-terminal kinases (JNKs) or JAK/STAT may play a role in the increased adrenal growth after exposure to maternal undernutrition during the periconceptional period (Marrero et al., 1995, Zhang et al., 2005). Indeed, exposure to maternal undernutrition in the periconceptional period in the normal weight ewe resulted in the activation of components of the STAT signalling pathway, including an increase in the adrenocortical abundance of STAT1, phospho-STAT1 and phospho-STAT3 in the postnatal lamb adrenals (Figure 2) (Zhang et al., 2013b). Cytokines, as the major ligands, bind to their receptor and activate the JAK/STAT pathway to stimulate cell proliferation, differentiation, migration, apoptosis and cell survival. These cellular responses are critical to numerous developmental and homeostatic processes (Lim and Cao, 2006, Rawlings et al., 2004). Cytokines have been implicated in the regulation of the activation of the HPA axis and an increase in glucocorticoid secretion in the offspring exposed to early-life malnutrition through the JAK/STAT signalling (Palmer, 2011). One possibility therefore is that maternal undernutrition during the periconceptional period results in a programmed upregulation of intrafetal or intraadrenal cytokine production, along with the increase in intraadrenal RAS, to result in the increase in the STAT1 and STAT3 isoforms in the adrenal and increased adrenal growth in lambs exposed to maternal undernutrition.

IGF2 is expressed in the steroidogenic cells of the sheep adrenal from as early as 60 days of gestation (Han et al., 1992) and IGF1 and IGF2 act *in vitro* as specific mitogens for human fetal adrenal cells (Han et al., 1988, Pham-Huu-Trung et al., 1991). There are, however, conflicting data on the role that IGFs may play *in vivo* on adrenal growth and steroidogenesis in early life. It has been previously shown that in growth restricted fetal sheep, a decrease in adrenal IGF2 mRNA expression was also associated with an increase in fetal adrenal weight (Ross et al., 2000). IGF1 and IGF2 can each bind to the IGF1R and stimulate its downstream signalling pathways. Consistent with a decrease in adrenal IGF2 mRNA expression, maternal undernutrition in either normal weight or obese ewes during the periconceptional period resulted in a decrease in the upstream but not downstream part of the IGF1R signalling pathway, including the abundance of adrenal IGF1R, Akt and phospho-Akt in both male and female lambs and mTOR in female lambs (Figure 2) (Zhang et al., 2013b). This suggests that adrenal IGF2 via IGF1R and its downstream signalling molecules might not play an important role in stimulating adrenal growth in the periconceptional undernourished group compared with controls in lambs at 4 months of age. Instead, the decrease in the protein abundance of molecules in the upstream part of the IGF1R signalling pathway in the adrenal cortex of the dietary restricted group may represent a partial compensatory response to the adrenocortical hypertrophy and/or activated STAT pathway present in these offspring. It has been shown that there is crosstalk between the IGF1R and JAK/STAT signalling pathways (Himpe and Kooijman, 2009). Shalita-Chesner et al. have previously reported that IFN-γ activates STAT1, which in turn suppresses IGF1R promoter activity in a human osteosarcoma cell line (Shalita-Chesner et al., 2004).

As highlighted earlier the findings on the impact of periconceptional undernutrition in normal weight or obese ewes, on adrenal growth and steroidogenesis in the offspring, emphasize that it may be the maternal metabolic response to dietary restriction imposed during a critical periconceptional window e.g., the nutritional or hormonal response to maternal weight loss in the ewe around the time of conception, independent of the maternal body weight at conception that is important in programming the longer term outcome of adrenal growth and development in the offspring.

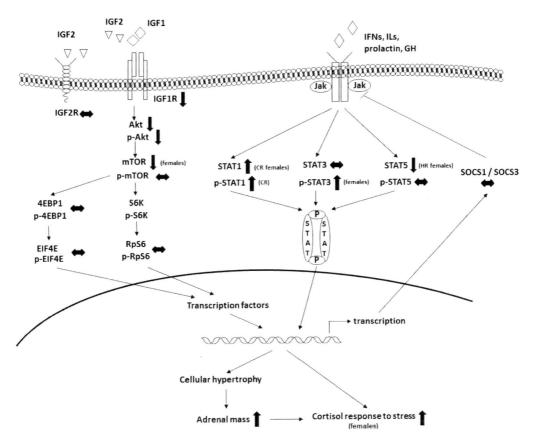

Figure 2. A summary of the protein changes in IGF1R downstream signalling molecules and STAT/SOCS isoforms in the adrenal of lambs in response to maternal dietary restriction in normal weight (CR) and obese ewes (HR) during the periconceptional period compared with the control group (CC). (↑), increased protein abundance; (↓), decreased protein abundance; (↔), no change in protein abundance. (females) indicates that a change in protein abundance only occurred in female lambs in both the CR and HR groups. (CR) indicates that a change in protein abundance only occurred in the CR group. (CR females) indicates that a change in protein abundance only occurred in CR female lambs. (HR females) indicates that a change in protein abundance only occurred in HR female lambs.

1.3. The Effect of Gender and Periconceptional Undernutrition on the HPA Axis

It has been established that there are sex-specific differences in the regulation of the HPA axis (Owen and Matthews, 2003, Silva et al., 2002, van Lier et al., 2003) and that estrogen enhances while androgen inhibits the activation of the HPA axis (Lund et al., 2004, Viau and Meaney, 1996). Plasma ACTH and corticosterone concentrations and CRH expression in the PVN of hypothalamus in response to restraint stress were increased in estradiol benzoate-treated rats but decreased in dihydrotestosterone propionate-treated rats compared to controls (Lund et al., 2004). It has been reported that basal cortisol production was lower, whilst the ACTH stimulated cortisol response was higher in adrenocortical cells from female compared to male sheep. The authors of this study also concluded that the enhanced adrenal responsiveness and steroidogenic response in females was due to differences in the latter stages of steroidogenesis, rather than an effect on ACTH-R (Canny et al., 1999). There was an increase in plasma cortisol response to a CRH challenge in female lambs compared with male lambs at 5.5 and 10 months of age (Chadio et al., 2007). Maternal undernutrition during the periconceptional period from before until 30 days after conception resulted in a decrease in pituitary GR mRNA and protein expression in adult female sheep but an increase in male sheep at 5 years of age (Begum et al., 2013, Stevens et al., 2010). Maternal undernutrition during a relatively short periconceptional period until one week after conception resulted in an increase in adrenal weight in male and female lambs and a greater cortisol response to stress in female lambs only at 3-4 months of age (Zhang et al., 2010). Interestingly adrenal ACTH-R, CYP17 and IGF2R mRNA expression were each lower in female lambs compared to male lambs independent of the periconceptional nutritional environment.

The dissociation in the adrenal growth and cortisol response to stress may be attributed to the effects of sex steroids on adrenal STAT signalling pathways. There is evidence that estrogen plays a role in the JAK/STAT signalling pathways (Björnström and Sjöberg, 2002, Dai et al., 2009, Dziennis et al., 2007). It has been demonstrated that estrogen rapidly induces phosphorylation/ activation of STAT3 and STAT5 *in vitro* and in estrogen-treated rat brains (Björnström and Sjöberg, 2002, Dziennis et al., 2007). The alterations of the abundance of the adrenal STAT1, phospho-STAT3 and STAT5 in female but not male lambs may contribute to a greater cortisol response to stress in the dietary restricted female lambs (Zhang et al., 2013b). The findings highlight that exposure of the oocyte/embryo to a short period of moderate undernutrition around the time of conception has a specific impact on the mechanisms which regulate adrenal signalling pathways, however the precise mechanisms by which transcription factors and signalling cascades cooperate with sex steroids to activate transcription of target genes are not fully understood. Taken together, these data suggest that the periconceptional period is a critical window during which changes in maternal nutrient levels may act to alter the signalling cascades and target genes to change the set point of the function of the HPA axis and stress responsiveness in later life. It is not clear to what extent the changes within the central or peripheral components of the HPA axis recruit or impact on the metabolic outcomes which occur in later life after exposure to poor nutrition *in utero*.

2. The Key Regulators of Metabolic Health in Adult Life

The metabolic syndrome is a pathophysiological condition defined as a cluster of at least three of the following changes in metabolic outcomes; an increased central adiposity, fasting hyperglycemia, dyslipidemia and elevated blood pressure (Wilson and Grundy, 2003). The key organ systems implicated in the development of the metabolic syndrome are adipose tissue, skeletal muscle and liver (Figure 3). A range of clinical and experimental studies have shown that visceral adiposity is the critical risk factor in the development of insulin resistance, which is a major contributor to the development of metabolic syndrome (Despres and Lemieux, 2006, Shaw and Chisholm, 2003). Secretion of free fatty acids (FFAs) from visceral adipose tissue resulting in increased deposition of fat in liver and muscle is implicated in the emergence of the impairment of insulin signalling and insulin resistance in these tissues (Assimacopoulos-Jeannet, 2004, Boden et al., 1994, Cahová et al., 2007, Valverde et al., 2005). Skeletal muscle is the main organ responsible for 75% of postprandial glucose uptake from the circulation through the actions of insulin signalling in stimulating the translocation of the glucose transporter type 4 (GLUT4) to the plasma membrane and thus increasing glucose uptake (Klip and Pâquet, 1990, Maureen et al., 2005, Wallberg-Henriksson and Zierath, 2001). Furthermore, liver is the key organ in maintaining normal blood glucose concentrations through its ability to produce glucose from lactate and pyruvate through gluconeogenesis.

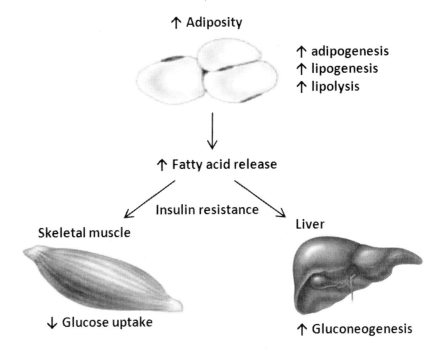

Figure 3. An increase in visceral adiposity results in an increase in free fatty acid secretion and deposition in the skeletal muscle and liver, which impairs insulin action to result in peripheral insulin resistance.

2.1. Leptin, Adiponectin and Obesity

Adipose tissue plays a major role in maintaining whole body energy balance through the action of leptin, adiponectin and lipoprotein lipase (LPL). Leptin is an adipokine that regulates food intake, energy expenditure and fatty acid β-oxidation mainly in skeletal muscle (Mora and Pessin, 2002). The expression of leptin is proportional to adipose tissue mass (Trayhurn, 1996), and thus leptin is often used as a marker of adiposity. Obesity, however, is usually characterised as a state of leptin resistance (Mohiti et al., 2009). In contrast to leptin, the expression of the adipokine, adiponectin is inversely proportional to adipose tissue mass and adiponectin acts to improve insulin sensitivity in skeletal muscle and liver (Mora and Pessin, 2002). Therefore, in obesity, the decreased plasma concentrations of adiponectin may play a role in the development of peripheral insulin resistance. Additionally, plasma adiponectin concentrations have been suggested as the best biomarker for metabolic syndrome in obese children and adolescents (Gilardini et al., 2006). LPL plays a role in regulating fatty acid uptake into the adipocyte by catalysing the hydrolysis of triglycerides from very low density lipoproteins (VLDL) and chylomicrons from the circulation, thus regulating fatty acid uptake and may determine the level of fat deposition in the adipose tissue (Frühbeck and Salvador, 2004).

The targeted deletion of the peroxisome proliferator activated receptor gamma (PPARγ) gene in mice results in an increase in plasma free fatty acids and triglycerides, as well as increased hepatic gluconeogenesis, insulin resistance and a greater susceptibility to high fat induced hepatic steatosis (He et al., 2003). In contrast, PPARγ activation results in increase in triglyceride accumulation in white adipose tissue, but decreased triglyceride accumulation in liver and skeletal muscle which ameliorates insulin resistance (Terauchi, 2007). PPARγ agonists are widely used as therapeutic agents in the treatment for type 2 diabetes (Saraf et al., 2012). PPARγ plays a key role in development in the regulation of adipogenesis and lipogenesis through the stimulation of the target genes, leptin, adiponectin and LPL (Ferre, 2004, Muhlhausler et al., 2009b).

2.2. The Role of the Liver in Maintaining Glucose Homeostasis

The liver plays an important role in maintaining glucose homeostasis, through its ability to store glucose as glycogen and synthesise glucose via gluconeogenesis (Postic et al., 2004), which is regulated by the rate-limiting enzyme phosphoenolpyruvate carboxykinase (PEPCK) including the mitochondrial and cytosolic isoforms (PEPCK-M and PEPCK-C) (Chakravarty et al., 2005). PEPCK-M is constitutively expressed and plays a role in maintaining basal gluconeogenesis (Modaressi et al., 1998). The expression of PEPCK-C, however, is inhibited by the action of insulin via Akt2 (Chakravarty and Hanson, 2007, Sasaki et al., 1984, Savage et al., 2007) and stimulated by transcription factors such as hepatocytes nuclear factor 4 alpha (HNF4α) and cAMP response element-binding (CREB) and CCAAT-enhancer-binding protein alpha and beta (C/EBPα and C/EBPβ) (Chakravarty et al., 2005, Fowden et al., 1993). When the liver is relatively resistant to the actions of insulin, the expression of PEPCK-C is not suppressed by insulin, thus resulting in an inadequate suppression of hepatic glucose output and hyperglycemia (Sun et al., 2002). The action of insulin is through the insulin receptor (IR) resulting in the stimulation of phosphatidylinositol 3-kinase (PI3K) and Akt. In the liver, activation of Akt leads to phosphorylation of transcription factor forkhead box O-1 (FOXO1) and inhibition of PEPCK-C expression (Chakravarty and Hanson, 2007, Pessin and Saltiel, 2000, Sasaki et al., 1984, Savage et al., 2007).

PEPCK-C expression in the liver is also regulated by glucocorticoids which act to counteract the inhibitory actions of insulin, thus promoting gluconeogenesis (Sasaki et al., 1984). Glucocorticoid action in tissues is mediated by GR (Tronche et al., 1998) and the intracellular glucocorticoid activator, 11β-hydroxysteroid dehydrogenase-1 (11βHSD1), which converts the non-active form of glucocorticoid, cortisone, to an active form of glucocorticoid, cortisol (Krozowski, 1999). Increased hepatic glucose production plays a major role in type-2 diabetes (Cline et al., 1994, Consoli et al., 1989, Gallagher et al., 2010) and that this increase in hepatic glucose production may be mediated through the activation of the GR and subsequent increase in PEPCK expression (Friedman et al., 1997). In adult life, intrahepatic triglyceride accumulation is associated with insulin resistance and may result in an increase in hepatic gluconeogenesis (Kotronen et al., 2008, Seppala-Lindroos et al., 2002). It has also been shown that mitochondrial dysfunction contributes to insulin resistance and hepatic steatosis leading to the development of non-alcoholic fatty liver disease (Rector et al., 2010).

2.3. Skeletal Muscle, Insulin Signalling and Glucose Homeostasis

The rate of glucose uptake by the skeletal muscle is regulated by the action of insulin and the activation of subsequent downstream signalling molecules (Sesti, 2006). In skeletal muscle, activation of PI3K leads to phosphorylation of Akt and/or 3-Phosphoinositide-dependent protein kinase 1 (PDPK1), which then leads to phosphorylation of the atypical protein kinase C zeta (PKCζ). Phosphorylation of Akt may result in the phosphorylation of the Akt substrate 160kDa (AS160). Phosphorylated PKCζ and AS160 each play a major role in the translocation of the GLUT4 to the plasma membrane to facilitate glucose uptake into the skeletal muscle (Sesti, 2006, Taniguchi et al., 2006). In type-2 diabetes patients, there is an impairment of glucose uptake by the muscle due to a decrease in insulin stimulated GLUT4 translocation (Kelley et al., 1996, Zierath et al., 1996). In skeletal muscle of non-obese type-2 diabetic model, there was a decrease in the phosphorylation of IR (Maegawa et al., 1991) and insulin receptor substrate (IRS1), as well as reduction in PI3K activity, which may underlie the decrease in glucose uptake present in type-2 diabetes (Björnholm et al., 1997). Triglyceride accumulation in skeletal muscle is associated with the development of insulin resistance and type-2 diabetes (Boden et al., 2001, Hegarty et al., 2002, 2003), which may also be a consequence of a decrease in mitochondrial density and/or function (Kelley et al., 2002, Morino et al., 2005, Petersen et al., 2004).

3. The Metabolic Consequences of Maternal Undernutrition during the Periconceptional Period

Exposure to the Dutch Winter famine during early gestation was associated with an increased prevalence of coronary heart disease (Roseboom et al., 2000), an increase in adiposity (Ravelli et al., 1976, 1999, Roseboom et al., 2001) and higher glucose and insulin concentrations following an oral glucose tolerance test (de Rooij et al., 2006) in later life. These findings have been supported by a study of Gambian children which showed that individuals exposed to nutrient restriction and maternal weight loss during the first trimester were heavier as children and had higher blood pressure, which was positively related to mothers' weight at six months of gestation, when maternal nutrition levels had improved (Margetts et al., 1991). Thus nutrient restriction experienced during early pregnancy, when the nutrient demands of the early conceptus are minimal, can have specific long-term metabolic consequences in adult life.

In the rat, maternal protein restriction for 8 weeks prior to conception resulted in a decrease in brain, heart and liver weight, but an increase in relative liver adiposity and blood glucose concentrations at 94 days after birth (Joshi et al., 2003). Exposure to a maternal low protein diet in the mouse during the preimplantation period also resulted in an increase in postnatal growth of the offspring and the emergence of hypertension and abnormal anxiety related behaviour in the offspring in adult life (Watkins et al., 2008).

It has been shown in the sheep that exposure to maternal undernutrition during different periods around the time of conception and during early gestation results in changes in lamb growth, adiposity, glucose tolerance and insulin sensitivity. Exposure to maternal undernutrition from 1-31 days of gestation resulted in an increase in lamb weight at weaning and in weight gain between birth and weaning at 12 weeks in the male twin offspring (Cleal et al., 2007). Maternal undernutrition from 60 days before until 30 days after mating resulted in an increase in fetal liver weight at 131 days of gestation (Oliver et al., 2005). In contrast, exposure to periconceptional undernutrition from one month before until one week after conception had no effects on fetal weight, liver weight or perirenal fat mass in late gestation (Budge et al., 2004, Edwards et al., 2005, Lie et al., 2013), and also did not alter birth or lamb weight, liver weight or adipose tissue mass at 4 months of age (Rattanatray et al., 2010), suggesting that the period before and the first week after conception may be an important window for programming of lamb body and organ growth.

Ford and colleagues showed that maternal undernutrition in sheep between 28 and 78 days of gestation resulted in lambs which were heavier with more back fat thickness and an increase in basal glucose and leptin concentrations with impaired glucose tolerance at 140 days of age (Ford et al., 2007). Lambs exposed to maternal nutrient restriction for 35 days in early pregnancy also had a higher insulin response to a glucose challenge at 10 weeks of age and persistence of impaired glucose tolerance in later life (Smith et al., 2010) and an increased body weight and impaired glucose tolerance at 10 months of age (Todd et al., 2009) with decreased physical activity (Donovan et al., 2013) and increased fat mass at 5 years of age (Jaquiery et al., 2012). As described above for the HPA axis, there is a different impact of maternal undernutrition during the periconceptional period on metabolic function in singleton and twin offspring. Todd *et al.* reported that the decrease in the first phase insulin secretion was more pronounced in singleton offspring that had been exposed to periconceptional undernutrition than in the twin offspring (Todd et al., 2009). The mechanisms underlying the programming of metabolic outcomes in offspring after exposure to poor maternal nutrition during the period around conception have been investigated to determine the relative contributions of the programming of the central regulation of energy balance versus changes in insulin signalling and other key regulatory pathways within tissues of metabolic importance including the liver, muscle and fat.

3.1. Periconceptional Undernutrition and Effects on the Central Regulation of Energy Balance

It is well established that hypothalamic POMC plays an essential role in energy homeostasis (Cone et al., 1996). Null mutations of POMC in the mouse and POMC mutations in the human are associated with obesity (Challis et al., 2002, Farooqi et al., 2006, Yaswen et al., 1999). In the rat, exposure to maternal undernutrition in the perinatal period perturbed the development of the hypothalamic POMC anorexigenic circuit in neonatal male pups (Delahaye et al., 2008) and in adult male offspring, where it was associated with an increase in food intake and body weight, and in changes in energy metabolism (Breton et al., 2009). Similarly in the sheep maternal undernutrition during the periconceptional period resulted in a lower expression of POMC mRNA in the hypothalamus and a concomitant increase in fat mass in the male adult sheep at 5 years of age (Begum et al., 2013). Begum *et al.* also reported that periconceptional undernutrition resulted in consistent epigenetic modifications and changes in expression of GR in the hypothalamus in the offspring (Begum et al., 2012, 2013, Stevens et al., 2010). As discussed earlier it has therefore been proposed that the programming of metabolic changes in energy intake and fat mass might be a consequence of epigenetic modifications of the GR gene in the hypothalamus.

3.2. Periconceptional Undernutrition and Effects on Adipose Tissue, Liver and Fat

Adipose tissue

In the sheep, exposure to maternal undernutrition from either before until one week after conception or at the first week after conception (preimplantation) resulted in significant changes in the expression and abundance of key factors regulating thermogenesis, insulin signalling and fatty acid β-oxidation in the fetal perirenal adipose tissue (PAT) and these effects were different in singletons and twins in late gestation (Lie et al., 2013). There was a decrease in uncoupling protein 1 (UCP1) expression in fetal PAT in both singletons and twins after exposure maternal undernutrition during the periconceptional or preimplantation period. This suggests that the first week after conception was a sensitive period during which exposure to maternal undernutrition may program a decreased thermogenic capacity in brown fat in late gestation. Similarly, it has recently been shown that exposure to a low protein diet for the first 3.5 days after conception in mouse also resulted in a decrease in UCP1 expression in intrascapular brown fat in the male offspring at 1 year of age (Watkins et al., 2011).

Maternal undernutrition for the first week after conception alone (preimplantation undernutrition) also resulted in higher circulating insulin concentrations, a decrease in the abundance of Akt1, phosphorylated mTOR and PPARγ but an increase in phospho-PKCζ and pyruvate dehydrogenase kinase 4 (PDK4) abundance in PAT in singleton and twin fetuses in late gestation (Lie et al., 2013). In singletons there was a decrease in the abundance of p110β catalytic subunit of PI3K in PAT in the periconceptional or perimplantation undernourished groups and an increase in total AMP-activated protein kinase subunit α (AMPKα) in PAT in the preimplantation undernourished group. In twins, however, there was an increase in the abundance of mTOR in the periconceptional undernourished group and an increase in PDK2 and a decrease in total AMPKα in the preimplantation undernourished group. These findings were important as the thermogenic capacity of brown fat and the insulin sensitivity of visceral fat are important determinants of the risk of developing obesity and an insulin resistance phenotype in later life. In contrast, periconceptional undernutrition from before until one week after conception or during the first week after conception had no effects on the key regulatory genes involved in lipid accumulation and metabolism including PPARγ, LPL, leptin and adiponectin mRNA expression in fetal perirenal fat (Lie et al., 2013) and each omental, perirenal, and subcutaneous fat depots of lambs (Rattanatray et al., 2010).

Interestingly, maternal undernutrition during the first week after conception resulted in a reduction in PPARγ protein abundance in PAT in both singletons and twins.

Table 1. Direction of changes in the abundance of the insulin signalling and gluconeogenic factors in fetal sheep exposed to either periconceptional (PCUN; at least 45 days before and one week after conception) or preimplantation (PIUN; one week after conception) relative to controls in the liver of singleton and twin fetal sheep in late gestation

Protein	Singleton Fetal Sheep		Twin Fetal Sheep	
	PCUN	PIUN	PCUN	PIUN
	Abundance relative to controls	Abundance relative to controls	Abundance relative to controls	Abundance relative to controls
IRS1	↓	↓	↑	↑
PI3K (p85)	↔	↔	↑	↑
PI3K (p110β)	↓	↓	↑	↑
PTEN	↓	↓	↑	↑
Akt2	↓ (P=0.06)	↓ (P=0.06)	↑	↑
FOXO1	↔	↔	↔	↓
CREB	↓	↓	↔	↔
PEPCK-C	↓	↓	↑	↑

Liver

It has been shown that maternal undernutrition between 28 and 80 days of gestation resulted in an increase in hepatic IGF1 expression and a tendency for increased IGF2 expression in the sheep fetus at 140 days of gestation (Brameld et al., 2000). In contrast, maternal undernutrition during the first 95 days of gestation in sheep resulted in a decrease in the relative weight of the liver and a decrease in mRNA expression of growth hormone, prolactin and IGF2R in the liver of the offspring at 3 years of age (Hyatt et al., 2007).

Exposure to maternal undernutrition during the periconceptional (-60 ~ 6 days after conception) or preimplantation (0-6 days after conception) period resulted in a decrease in hepatic PEPCK-C mRNA and protein abundance and the protein abundance of IRS-1, p110β, phosphatase and tensin homolog (PTEN), CREB and phospho-CREB in singleton fetuses in late gestation (Table 1) (Lie et al., 2014a). In contrast, hepatic protein abundance of IRS-1, p85 and p110β subunits of PI3K, PTEN, Akt2, phospho-Akt and phospho-FOXO1 was increased in twin compared with singleton fetuses. There was a decrease in PEPCK-C mRNA in singletons, but paradoxically an increase in PEPCK-C protein abundance in twins. The findings suggest the differential impact of maternal undernutrition in the presence of one or two embryos on mRNAs and proteins involved in the insulin signalling and gluconeogenesis.

Moderate maternal undernutrition from one month before until one week after conception resulted in decreased abundance of insulin signalling molecules namely IRS1, PDPK1, phosphorylated-PDPK1 and PKCζ and in decreased PEPCK-C and glucose-6-phosphatase (G6Pase) expression in the liver of the postnatal lamb at 4 months of age, which may lead to a decreased hepatic response to insulin when exposed to a glucose challenge or a high nutrient environment with a concomitant vulnerability to insulin resistance in later life (Nicholas et al., 2013). Liver 11βHSD1 expression was also increased in female rat fetuses at 20 days of gestation whose mothers were exposed to a low protein diet during the preimplantation period (Kwong et al., 2007). This raises the question to what extent there is a parallel programming of an increase in intrahepatic cortisol signalling together with a decrease in intrahepatic insulin signalling in response to signals of suboptimal nutrition around the time of conception.

Muscle

In sheep, periconceptional undernutrition from 18 days before until 6 days after conception resulted in a 20% decrease in total muscle fibres and a decrease in secondary: primary fibre ratio when measured at 75 days of gestation (Quigley et al., 2005). Exposure to maternal undernutrition in the first 31 days of gestation also resulted in a decrease in total and fast myofibres at 127 days of gestation, suggesting a decrease in glucose uptake capacity which may contribute to hyperglycemia (Costello et al., 2008). There was a decrease in IGF2 expression in skeletal muscle of fetuses in late gestation after exposure to maternal undernutrition between 28 and 80 days of gestation (Brameld et al., 2000). Furthermore, maternal undernutrition during 28-78 days of gestation resulted in an increase in intramuscular triglyceride content in lambs at 8 months of age potentially due to a decrease in fatty acid β-oxidation (Zhu et al., 2006). Exposure to maternal undernutrition during the periconceptional (-60 ~ 6 days after conception) or preimplantation (0-6 days after conception) period resulted in a decrease in the abundance of PI3K (p110β), PKCζ and phospho-PKCζ in skeletal muscle of singleton fetuses in late gestation (Lie et al., 2014b). This suggests that there may be a potential vulnerability to insulin resistance in skeletal muscle in later life after exposure to maternal undernutrition during oocyte maturation and early embryo development. In singleton fetuses exposed to maternal undernutrition during the first week of pregnancy alone, however, there was an increase in the abundance of IRS1, PDPK1 and GLUT4 in skeletal muscle. In twin fetuses exposed to periconceptional undernutrition, there was an increase in the abundance of IRS1, Akt2, PDPK1 and PKCζ and in twins exposed to preimplantation undernutrition, there was an increase in the abundance of IRS1, PKCζ and GLUT4, which suggest that in these groups there is a programming of an insulin sensitive, rather than an insulin resistant phenotype. This is also supported by a previous study that twin lambs had a greater muscle depth at 1.5 years of age and were more insulin sensitive at 2.5 years of age compared to singletons (Poore et al., 2007). Therefore, the early environment of the twin pregnancy may result in the programming of an insulin signalling response to maternal undernutrition which may be appropriate in the context of the substrate limited environment of the twin fetus in later gestation. The authors proposed that the differential impact of periconceptional undernutrition and preimplantation undernutrition in singletons and twins may depend on the sensitivity of the embryo to the mismatch between the nutritional environment of the oocyte and the embryo and the hormonal environment of the singleton and twin pregnancy.

4. The Impact of Restriction of Placental and Fetal Growth on the HPA Axis and Programing of Metabolic Diseases

Chronic placental insufficiency induced in sheep by removing the majority of the placental attachment sites - the uterine caruncles from the uterus of the non-pregnant ewe results in fewer placentomes and thus placental restriction (PR) (Alexander, 1964). The PR fetus is exposed to chronic placental restriction of fetal substrate supply resulting in chronic hypoxemia and fetal growth restriction throughout late gestation (McMillen et al., 2000, Robinson et al., 1979, 1985). Restriction of placental growth results in the birth of low birth weight lambs which then undergo a period of catch-up growth after birth (De Blasio et al., 2007b, Muhlhausler et al., 2009b). Catch-up growth after birth has been implicated as a predictor of later development of central obesity, insulin resistance, type 2 diabetes and cardiovascular diseases (Bavdekar et al., 1999, Curhan et al., 1996, Eriksson et al., 2001, Levy-Marchal and Jaquet, 2004, Veening et al., 2002). There have been a series of studies which have investigated the endocrine and metabolic responses to chronic placental restriction which ensure survival of the growth restricted fetus. The hormonal and metabolic changes which occur, however, in the PR fetus also result in programmed changes which persist in the HPA axis and in the adipose tissue, liver and muscle of the postnatal animal- which as is the case for offspring from undernourished mothers appear to be changes consistent with an expectation of a life of adversity.

4.1. Placental Restriction and the HPA

In the PR fetus, circulating cortisol concentrations were increased in the absence of an increase in fetal plasma concentrations of either immunoreactive (ir)ACTH or ACTH(1-39) in late gestation (Phillips et al., 1996). Indeed the mRNA expression of the ACTH precursor - POMC was decreased in the anterior pituitary of the chronically hypoxemic growth restricted fetus (Phillips et al., 1996). One possibility is that fetal growth restriction programs the developmental changes of the pool of corticotroph cells within the pituitary to maintain ACTH secretion in the face of elevated cortisol concentrations during late gestation. It has been demonstrated that there is a population of non-CRH target cells that secrete high amounts of ACTH in the pituitaries of fetuses exposed to the uterine caruniclectomized environment in early gestation and that this occurred independently of whether those fetuses were hypoxemic in late gestation (Butler et al., 2002). Exposure to chronic hypoxemia during late gestation, however, resulted in a specific reduction in the proportion of ACTH stored in CRH target cells and this effect occurred independently of whether fetuses had been exposed to the caruniclectomy environment in early gestation (Butler et al., 2002). These data suggest that environmental perturbations in early and late gestation can differentially program the development of specific corticotrophic cell types and corticotroph development may be reprogrammed to ensure that fetal ACTH secretion is maintained throughout late gestation in the growth-restricted fetuses.

4.2. Placental Restriction and Programing of Metabolic Diseases

Adipose Tissue

Placental restriction of fetal growth resulted in a decrease in perirenal fat mass with no difference in relative perirenal fat mass compared to control fetuses in late gestation (Duffield et al., 2008). In the placentally restricted sheep model, PR fetuses were chronically hypoxemic, hypoglycaemic and growth restricted (Duffield et al., 2008, Kind et al., 1995, Simonetta et al., 1997). Plasma concentrations of insulin, IGF1, IGF2, thyroid hormones and prolactin were reduced in growth-restricted PR fetuses (Cetin et al., 2001, Duffield et al., 2008, Kind et al., 1995, Owens et al., 1994, Phillips et al., 2001, Robinson et al., 1980). In intrauterine growth restricted PR fetuses, the expression of IGF1 and leptin mRNA expression was lower in PAT in late gestation, although there was no difference in the expression of other adipokine or adipogenic genes in the fetal PAT or in plasma leptin concentrations between the control and PR fetuses (Duffield et al., 2008).

Placental restriction also increased plasma leptin concentrations and expression of leptin mRNA expression in PAT at the end of the first month of life in the young lamb, however, this increased abundance of peripheral leptin did not inhibit feeding activity (suckling event frequency) (De Blasio et al., 2010). An increase in the fasting plasma glucose, leptin and insulin concentrations in conjunction with increased feeding activity in the PR lambs suggested that there may be programmed changes in appetite and energy balance, leading to early onset obesity and impaired insulin secretion (De Blasio et al., 2010). At 6 weeks of age there was an increase in the relative mass of visceral and perirenal fat present in lambs in the PR group (De Blasio et al., 2007b). The key questions for the future studies are how PR regulates plasma leptin before and after birth and how altered molecular signalling in the appetite regulatory networks within the hypothalamus ultimately results in leptin resistance, increased adiposity and later metabolic dysfunction.

Liver

It has been demonstrated that the expression of the hepatic insulin independent glucose transporter, GLUT1 mRNA was increased in PR hypoxic fetuses, in which liver growth was maintained compared with PR hypoxic fetuses in which liver growth was reduced (Gentili et al., 2009). These differences in fetal liver growth did not appear to be explained by the degree of fetal hypoxemia or plasma glucose concentrations. Hepatic expression of 11βHSD1, peroxisome proliferator-activated receptor gamma coactivator 1-alpha (PGC-1α), and PEPCK mRNA was increased in all PR hypoxic fetuses but IGF1 mRNA expression was decreased only in the PR-hypoxic group in which liver growth was reduced. These data suggest that intrahepatic responses to fetal substrate restriction exist that can protect the liver from decreased growth and, potentially, from a decreased responsiveness to the actions of insulin in postnatal life. Similarly, a previous study has also found that there was an increase in 11βHSD1 mRNA expression in the liver of PR fetuses in late gestation compared with controls (McMillen et al., 2000). This suggests that there is increased hepatic exposure to cortisol in the PR fetus, which may be important in the reprogramming of hepatic physiology that occurs after growth restriction *in utero*. In early postnatal life, PR did not alter hepatic expression of insulin signaling and related genes but did result in an increase in hepatic GLUT2 expression in male lambs at 6 weeks of age (De Blasio et al., 2012).

Muscle

It has been demonstrated that the abundance of IR and IGF1R were each increased in the quadriceps muscle of the PR fetus at 140 days of gestation but that this increase was associated with a decrease, rather than an increase in the abundance of the insulin signalling molecule, PKCζ, and of the insulin responsive glucose transporter, GLUT4. At 21 days of postnatal age, the increase in IR abundance which was present in the PR group persisted after birth and was then associated with an up-regulation of Akt1, Akt2 and GLUT4 protein (Muhlhausler et al., 2009a). These data provide the evidence for the *in utero* origins of the increased insulin sensitivity in skeletal muscle which drives accelerated growth after birth and precedes the later emergence of insulin resistance.

In addition, mRNA expression of PPARα and PGC-1α was lower in skeletal muscle of the PR fetus, suggesting that PR may also be implicated on fatty acid metabolism (Muhlhausler et al., 2009a). Interestingly, at 21 days of postnatal age, expression of PGC-1α mRNA was higher in skeletal muscle of growth restricted male, but not female, lambs. In contrast, De Blasio et al. have reported that PR reduced skeletal muscle mRNA expression of IR, IRS1, Akt2, GLUT4 and insulin signalling target molecules glycogen synthase kinase-3α (GSK3α) and glycogen synthase-1 (GYS1) in both male and female lambs and decreased AMPKγ3 mRNA expression in females lambs at 43 days of postnatal age (De Blasio et al., 2012). The differences in muscle insulin signalling molecules after PR in the postnatal lambs may suggest that there is a transition from increased abundance of insulin signalling molecules in skeletal muscle associated with catch-up growth at 3 weeks of age to a reduction in the abundance of these molecules associated with the emergence of insulin resistance, leptin resistance and increased adiposity at 6 weeks of age.

5. The Impact of Maternal Glucocorticoid Exposure on the HPA Axis and Programing of Metabolic Diseases

Exposure to chronic substrate restriction, maternal undernutriton or stress during pregnancy can result in an activation of the maternal and/or fetal HPA axis and there is substantial evidence that fetal cortisol exposure may in turn program changes within the developing HPA axis and within tissues of metabolic importance to result in a postnatal phenotype which is consistent with those present in models of placental restriction or periconceptional undernutrition.

5.1. Glucocorticoid Administration and the HPA Axis

Exposure of the fetus to excess glucocorticoid concentrations can result in long-term programming of the HPA axis (O'Regan et al., 2001). In rats, dexamethasone exposure in the last week of gestation reduced hippocampal GR and mineralocorticoid receptor (MR) expression, increased CRH expression in the PVN of the hypothalamus and increased basal and restraint-stressed plasma ACTH and corticosterone concentrations in the adult offspring (Levitt et al., 1996, O'Regan et al., 2001, Shoener et al., 2006). In guinea pigs, 2 days of antenatal glucocorticoid exposure resulted in a decrease in GR expression in the PVN of the hypothalamus, an increase in GR expression and a decrease in MR expression in the hippocampus, and an increase in plasma cortisol concentrations in adult females (Dean et al., 2001). In contrast, there was an increased hippocampal MR expression and reduced basal and stimulated plasma cortisol concentrations in adult male guinea pigs (Dean et al., 2001).

In sheep, maternal dexamethasone administration for 2 days at 27 days of gestation did not alter GR and MR expression in the hippocampus or hypothalamus and plasma ACTH or cortisol responses to haemorrhage (Dodic et al., 2002). Similarly, while administration of cortisol during the same gestational age window resulted in a transient increase in hippocampal GR and MR expression during late gestation, this was not maintained into the postnatal period (Dodic et al., 2002). Prolonged low-dose dexamethasone treatment between 25 and 45 days of gestation specifically suppressed hippocampal expression of GR and MR during late gestation, but again, these changes were not sustained into postnatal life (Moritz et al., 2002). Maternal dexamethasone treatment at 40-41 days of gestation resulted in an increase in fetal plasma cortisol concentrations, an increase in adrenal CYP17 and 3βHSD mRNA expression in females and a reduction in ACTH-R mRNA expression in male fetuses at 140 days of gestation (Braun et al., 2009). This suggests that adrenal steroidogenic activity may contribute in part to the altered fetal HPA axis after dexamethasone exposure in early gestation. Similarly, it has been shown that the adrenals were more responsive to ACTH in the female offspring at 7 months of age after exposure to early prenatal dexamethasone administration (Li et al., 2012). The alterations in basal and CRH/AVP stimulated ACTH and cortisol concentrations and key regulatory genes in the hippocampus, hypothalamus, pituitary and adrenal glands in this cohort strongly suggest that prenatal exposure to dexamethasone treatments has persisting effects on the HPA axis and these are sex-specific responses.

When betamethasone was administered to ewes or their fetuses at between 104 and 125 days of gestation, however, it resulted in changes in the responsiveness of the HPA axis to a CRH and AVP challenge at between 6 and 12 months of age (Sloboda et al., 2002a). It has been reported that increased cord concentrations of plasma ACTH and corticosteroid binding capacity of the fetuses at 146 days of gestation were not associated with changes in steady state concentrations of POMC and CRH mRNA in the pituitary or hypothalamus after maternal betamethasone treatments at 104, 111 and 118 days of gestation (Sloboda et al., 2000). The lack of changes in these fetuses may be attributed to increased output of ACTH (1–39) relative to large molecular-weight POMC peptides by corticotrophs. A study by Fletcher *et al.* reported that the increased basal cortisol concentration and ACTH responses to acute hypoxemia after dexamethasone infusion to the fetuses for 2 days in late gestation were associated with reductions in pituitary and adrenal GR mRNA contents of the fetuses (Fletcher et al., 2004).

Administration of dexamethasone orally from mid-term to a singleton-bearing nonhuman primate the vervet monkey resulted in an exaggerated cortisol response to mild stress in the juvenile offspring at 12-14 months of age (de Vries et al., 2007). Long *et al.* have investigated the multigenerational effects of fetal dexamethasone exposure on the HPA axis of F1 and F2 female sheep offspring (Long et al., 2012). Pregnant ewes received 4 dexamethasone injections with 12 hours apart at 0.7 gestation and F1 female offspring were bred to produce F2 female offspring. Maternal dexamethasone exposure increased baseline but reduced stimulated HPA activity in F1 and F2 female offspring. Taking together, these findings indicate that prenatal glucocorticoids alter the basal set point of the HPA axis and also the

HPA axis responses to stress and challenges in later life. These data also highlight the importance of timing in relation to glucocorticoid exposure in determining whether such exposure has long-term consequences for the basal and stimulated function of the HPA axis.

5.2. Glucocorticoid Administration and Programing of Metabolic Outcomes

Treatment of pregnant rats with dexamethasone in late pregnancy results in a lower mean birth weight, persistent elevations of arterial blood pressure, and fasting hyperglycemia and hyperglycemia in the adult offspring (Levitt et al., 1996, Nyirenda et al., 1998). Dexamethasone administration in pregnant rats during late gestation also resulted in an increased hepatic mRNA expression of GR and PEPCK and an associated increase in hepatic PEPCK activity in the adult offspring, which may lead to increased hepatic glucose production and impaired glucose tolerance (Nyirenda et al., 1998). It should be noted, however, that in these studies, dexamethasone treatment of the pregnant rat did not alter hepatic 11βHSD1 mRNA expression in the newborn or adult offspring.

In sheep, cortisol, but not dexamethasone, treatment of mothers for 2 days from 26-28 days of gestation resulted in fasting hyperglycemia in adult male offspring at 4 years of age (De Blasio et al., 2007a). Maternal cortisol and dexamethasone exposure in early gestation each induced hyperinsulinemia in adult male offspring. In contrast, dexamethasone treatment in early pregnancy impaired cardiovascular function, but not glucose homeostasis in adult female offspring at 5 years of age (Gatford et al., 2000). These data suggest that maternal glucocorticoid exposure in early pregnancy altered glucose homeostasis and induced hyperinsulinemia in adult male offspring, but not in adult female offspring.

Repeated maternal dexamethasone injections on three occasions at weekly intervals commencing at 104 days of gestation prolonged gestation, reduced fetal weight and weights at birth and 3 months (Ikegami et al., 1997, Newnham et al., 1999). Repeated or single betamethasone injections in either maternal or fetal sheep at between 104 and 125 days of gestation resulted in alterations in fetal cord glucose homeostasis (Sloboda et al., 2002b),and insulin insensitivity as indicated by increased insulin responses to glucose challenge in lambs at 6 months of age (Moss et al., 2001). In the adult sheep offspring, basal plasma insulin concentrations and insulin-to-glucose ratio were elevated after exposure to maternal or fetal betamethasone injections between 104 and 124 days of gestation (Sloboda et al., 2005). Maternal or fetal betamethasone treatments also resulted in significant increases in hepatic G6Pase activity in the adult offspring (Sloboda et al., 2005). Fetal hepatic 11βHSD1 mRNA and protein expression and corticosteroid-binding globulin (CBG) mRNA expression were significantly elevated after repeated maternal betamethasone administration at 104, 111 and 118 days of gestation (Sloboda et al., 2002b). The increase in hepatic 11βHSD1 provided the potential to lead to the increase in intra-liver cortisol concentrations and probably explain the changes in glucocorticoid-dependent hepatic enzymes involved with the regulation of glucose homeostasis and HPA responsiveness.

Administration of cortisol to fetal sheep for 5 days before 130 days of gestation prematurely stimulated the hepatic glycogen deposition and enhanced hepatic glucogenic capacity via the increases in the activity of key gluconeogenic enzymes including G6Pase, fructose diphosphatase, PEPCK and aspartate transaminase in the fetal liver (Fowden et al., 1993). Similarly, it has been recently shown that fetal cortisol infusion for 5 days beginning at

125-126 days of gestation significantly increased protein abundance of Akt2 and phosphorylated Akt, but decreased phosphorylated forms of mTOR and ribosomal protein S6 kinase (S6K) in skeletal muscle of fetal sheep (Jellyman et al., 2012). In contrast, maternal dexamethasone exposure with two injections at 24 intervals from 125 days of gestation increased the glycogen content and G6Pase activity in the liver of the fetuses, although hepatic PEPCK activity of the fetuses was not affected by maternal dexamethasone treatment during late gestation (Franko et al., 2007). These changes were also accompanied by rises in the plasma glucose and insulin concentrations (Franko et al., 2007). Maternal dexamethasone injections resulted in an increase in GLUT4 protein abundance in skeletal muscle of the fetuses (Jellyman et al., 2012). Interestingly, in the adult female sheep offspring whose mothers received a clinically relevant dose of corticosteroids at term, there was increased body weight and a greater fat mass assessed by dual-energy X-ray absorptiometry (Berry et al., 2013). Administration of dexamethasone orally from mid-term to a pregnant monkey resulted in impaired glucose tolerance and hyperinsulinemia in the offspring at 8 months of age and reduced pancreatic β cell number and increase subcutaneous fat mass at 12 months of age (de Vries et al., 2007).

Drake et al. have explored intergenerational effects in the dexamethasone-programmed rats (Drake et al., 2005). The authors reported that the F2 offspring of F1 female or male rats that had been exposed prenatally to dexamethasone during late gestation mated with controls had reduced birth weight, glucose intolerance, and elevated hepatic PEPCK activity, however, these effects resolved in a third generation. These data suggested the potential importance of epigenetic factors in the intergenerational inheritance of the "programming phenotype". The intergenerational effects of maternal dexamethasone exposure have also been studied in sheep (Long et al., 2012). Both F1 and F2 female offspring whose mothers received multiple dexamethasone injections at 0.7 gestation had decreased birth weight, reduced postnatal growth, increased fasting glucose and insulin concentrations, and increased plasma glucose and decreased insulin responses to an intravenous bolus glucose tolerance test.

These findings suggest that the effects of glucocorticoids on glucose intolerance, insulin resistance and postnatal obesity which are mediated through the insulin signalling pathways in the liver and skeletal muscle are species specific and may depend on the duration, dose, route and timing of exposure and are influenced differentially by endogenous and synthetic glucocorticoids.

6. The Epigenetic Programming of the HPA Axis

Epigenetic modifications are heritable changes in gene expression that are not caused by changes in the DNA sequence itself. The mechanisms underlying the programming of the HPA axis and associated metabolic phenotypes occurred in later life are not fully understood. One possibility is that maternal hormonal and metabolic responses to adverse maternal stresses have an impact on the epigenetic regulation of gene expression within the developing embryo.

6.1. The Epigenetic Programming of the Central HPA Axis

Adversity in early life can result in long term changes in the HPA axis as a consequence of epigenetic modifications of key regulatory genes in the rodent, sheep and human (Grace et al., 2011, Murgatroyd et al., 2009, Oberlander et al., 2008, Stevens et al., 2010, Weaver et al., 2004, Zhang et al., 2010). The key important finding was the expression and methylation status of the 5'CpG site within the NGF1-A response element of the hippocampal exon 1_7 GR promoter (Weaver et al., 2004). A series of studies have demonstrated that early environmental events can alter central GR expression through changes in chromatin structure and DNA methylation and have long term effects on the HPA axis and stress response in the offspring (McGowan et al., 2009, Oberlander et al., 2008, Stevens et al., 2010, Weaver et al., 2004).

It has been demonstrated in the rat that there are a range of GR mRNAs which encode a common protein, but which differ in their 5'-leader sequences as a consequence of alternate splicing of around 11 different exon 1 sequences, each with its own upstream promoter region. In the rat there are significant levels of at least six first exon variants, with tissue specific differences in promoter activity between the liver, hippocampus, and thymus (McCormick et al., 2000). Analysis of the 5' region of the human GR gene has revealed 9 untranslated alternative first exons and 13 splice variants and its tissue specific promoter usage has been extensively examined in a range of human tissues (Presul et al., 2007, Turner and Muller, 2005, Turner et al., 2010).

Rat pups exposed to low maternal care resulted in hypermethylation of the 5'CpG dinucleotide within an NGF1-A consensus sequence located within the hippocampal GR promoter, which was associated with lower hippocampal GR and hypothalamic CRH mRNA expression and increased HPA stress response in the postnatal life (Weaver et al., 2004). In mouse pups periodic infant-mother separation during the first 10 days of life led to a hypomethylation of a key regulatory region of the arginine vasopressin (AVP) gene which was accompanied by an upregulation of AVP mRNA expression in hypothalamic paraventribular nucleus and increased HPA axis for at least 1 year (Murgatroyd et al., 2009). Oberlander et al. have found that increased third trimester depressed maternal mood was associated with increased infant HPA stress responsiveness through a potential epigenetic link that involves a hypermethylation of the human GR gene (Oberlander et al., 2008). More recently, it has been reported that CpG methylation within GR promoter, 11β-hydroxysteroid dehydrogenase type 2 (11βHSD2) promoter and the DMR of the IGF2/H19 gene measured on blood buffy coat DNA samples was positively associated with increased adiposity and blood pressure in adulthood (Drake et al., 2012). Methylation levels of GR promoter was increased in offspring of mothers with the most unbalanced diets in pregnancy. In another study, a decrease in methylation of the GR promoter from peripheral blood samples was associated with a decrease in physical stress reactivity as indicated by low cortisol and low heart rate reactivity (de Rooij et al., 2012). Interestingly, these associations could largely be explained by differences in lifestyle and education.

Maternal undernutrition during the periconceptional period from at least 45 days before until one week after conception or for one week after conception only resulted in a decrease in pituitary GR mRNA expression in both singletons and twins compared with control fetuses in late gestation, although this suppression of GR expression was not associated with hypermethylation of the exon1_7 region located 3kb upstream of the translational start site

(TSS) in exon 2 in the sheep *GR* gene (Zhang et al., 2013c). It is therefore possible that periconceptional undernutrition may down regulate GR expression within the pituitary through an action on a pituitary-specific *GR* promoter that is distinct from the hippocampal exon 1_7 promoter, which is yet to be characterised. Thus the possibility remains that maternal undernutrition during the first week after conception results in epigenetic changes at the *GR* in the developing pituitary to ensure an enhanced response to fetal and postnatal stress in anticipation of a life of continuing adversity.

Recent studies in the sheep reported that maternal undernutrition during the periconceptional period from before until 30 days after conception resulted in decreased *GR* promoter methylation, decreased H3K27 trimethylation and increased H3K9 acetylation in the hypothalamus of the late gestation fetus and mature adult offspring (Begum et al., 2012, 2013, Stevens et al., 2010). These findings were entirely compatible with the increased GR mRNA and protein expression observed in the hypothalamus of these animals. Importantly, these studies have shown that all of the epigenetic changes and the resultant increases in GR expression in the hypothalamus which were first observed at the fetal stage, were maintained in adults up to 5 years of age, a time representing late middle age in these sheep. In addition, there was decreased *POMC* promoter methylation and increased H3K9 acetylation in the hypothalamus, but no change in hypothalamic POMC mRNA expression and plasma POMC concentrations in the late gestation sheep fetus (Begum et al., 2012, Stevens et al., 2010).

It has been previously shown that there were no changes in epigenetic status or mRNA levels of GR in the hippocampus or pituitary at the fetal stage (Begum et al., 2012, Stevens et al., 2010). There was, however, an increase in hippocampal *GR* promoter methylation and a decrease in H3K9 acetylation in the adult female offspring as well as an increase in H3K27 trimethylation in both female and male offspring following periconceptional undernutrition in ewes (Begum et al., 2013). These epigenetics changes were also consistent with a decrease in hippocampal GR mRNA and protein in the periconceptional undernourished adult offspring compared to controls. In the pituitary, there were sex-specific changes in the epigenetic status and mRNA expression of GR in these adult offspring. Such differences of hippocampal and pituitary GR between the fetal stage and mature adult animals imply that there may be an adaptive plasticity after birth in epigenetic modifications of the central HPA axis in the tissue and sex specific manner as a consequence of maternal undernutrition during the periconceptional period. The epigenetic programmed alterations in GR, therefore, could have profound implications for the HPA axis and for adaptations to stress in later life.

6.2. The Epigenetic Programming of Adrenal Growth and Development

As discussed earlier, it has been demonstrated that weight loss in both normal and overweight mothers during the periconceptional period resulted in epigenetic modification of *IGF2* in the adrenal, adrenal overgrowth and an increased vulnerability to stress in the offspring. The increase in adrenal weight in the lambs exposed to maternal undernutrition during the periconceptional period in normal weight or obese ewes was paradoxically associated with a decrease in adrenal IGF2 mRNA expression and a decreased level of methylation in the proximal CTCF binding site in the differentially methylated region (DMR) region of the *IGF2/H19* gene (Figure 4) (Zhang et al., 2010). Thus, epigenetic programming of adrenal growth and development through a change in the epigenetic state of *IGF2* may play a role in the subsequent responsiveness of the HPA axis to stress in later life. These findings may be relevant to the human, which is suggested by a recent report that individuals whose mothers were exposed to famine during the Dutch Hunger Winter in 1944-1945, had less *IGF2* methylation in blood cells in adult life compared with their unexposed same-sex siblings (Heijmans et al., 2008). Importantly, epigenetic differences were found among individuals who were exposed to famine in early gestation and had a normal birth weight. In contrast, exposure to famine in late gestation was associated with low birth weight, but not with epigenetic changes (Heijmans et al., 2008). Although it has previously been shown that exposure of the sheep embryo to the nutritional environment of *in vitro* culture resulted in decreased *IGF2R* methylation and IGF2R mRNA expression and overgrowth of a number of fetal tissues (Young et al., 2001), there was no difference of adrenal IGF2R methylation levels and mRNA expression between the control and periconceptional undernourished groups (Zhang et al., 2010).

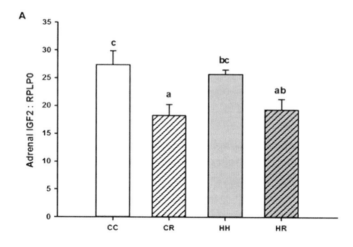

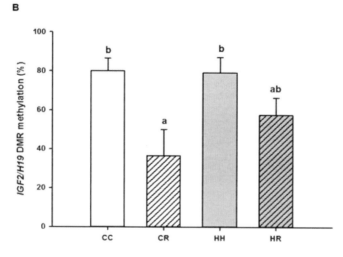

Figure 4. Adrenal IGF2 mRNA expression (A) and *IGF2/H19* DMR methylation (B) in the CC, CR, HH, HR lambs (CC: open bar; CR: striped bar; HH: grey bar; HR: grey striped bar). Different superscripts a, b and c denote treatment groups which are significantly different from each other ($P < 0.05$).

In rats, exposure to a maternal low protein diet in pregnancy resulted in decreased methylation of the adrenal *At1r* and increased *At1r* mRNA expression and protein abundance and adrenal angiotensin responsiveness in offspring (Bogdarina et al., 2007). More recently, Bogdarina *et al.* reported that when rat dams fed a low protein diet were treated with the 11β-hydroxylase inhibitor, metyrapone, which acts to decrease the adrenal output of maternal corticosterone, during the first two weeks of pregnancy, the changes in adrenal *At1r* methylation and mRNA expression in the offspring were reversed (Bogdarina et al., 2010). In contrast, maternal dietary restriction during the periconceptional period in normal weight or obese ewes resulted in an increase in the protein abundance of ACE and AT1R in the absence of changes in the methylation status or mRNA expression of ACE and AT1R in the adrenal of the offspring. These results suggest that the impact of maternal dietary restriction during the periconceptional period on adrenal ACE and AT1R abundance is not a consequence of epigenetic changes in the methylation status or the regulation of ACE and AT1R transcription and may rather be a consequence of a change in the regulation of the post translational clearance of these proteins in the postnatal adrenal.

One alternative explanation is that dietary restriction in the periconceptional period may result in the altered expression of microRNAs, small ~22 nucleotide long non-coding RNAs, which play important roles as key post transcriptional regulators of gene expression (Bartel, 2009, Bushati and Cohen, 2007). Interestingly it has been reported that miR-155 expression is reduced in hypertensive patients with a specific polymorphic genotype at 3' untranslated region of AT1R gene and this is associated with higher AT1R protein abundance, despite similar AT1R mRNA expression (Ceolotto et al., 2011).

Therefore, there is evidence that there is epigenetic programming within every part of the HPA axis and that this occurs during critical windows of development such that the set point of the axis changes resulting in altered basal and/or stress induced glucocorticoid responses in later life.

The extent to which the programming of the HPA axis determines or contributes to the obese, insulin resistant and glucose intolerant phenotype which is also present after exposure to a suboptimal intrauterine environment remains to be determined. In recent studies it was reported that there were specific patterns of the types and direction of changes in the expression of 22 microRNAs in skeletal muscle after exposure to maternal undernutrition during the periconceptional and preimplantation periods and that this suite of microRNAs was implicated in the control of a range of cell signalling systems including insulin signalling (Figure 5) (Lie et al., 2014b). Similarly maternal undernutrition during the periconceptional and preimplantation periods altered the hepatic expression of 23 specific microRNAs (Lie et al., 2014a). These findings provide evidence that maternal undernutrition around the time of conception induces changes in the expression of microRNAs, which may then target specific insulin signalling molecules and determine the insulin sensitivity of these key metabolic tissues in later life.

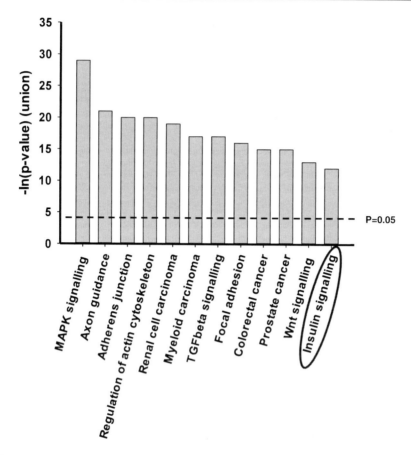

Figure 5. Kyoto Encyclopedia of Genes and Genomes (KEGG) pathways associated with the candidate miRs which are altered in the skeletal muslce of fetal sheep in late gestation which have been exposed to maternal undernutrition during the periconceptional and preimplantation periods. The 22 candidate miRs found to have altered expression were associated with MAPK signalling, axon guidance, adherens junction, regulation of actin cytoskeleton, renal cell carcinoma, chronic myeloid leukemia, TGFβ signalling, focal adhesion, colorectal cancer, prostate cancer, Wnt signalling pathway and insulin signalling defined by targetscan multiple miRs analysis.

Conclusion

Thus underlying the well described 'phenomenology' of the developmental origins of adult metabolic health is a suite of epigenetic mechanisms which are recruited within specific tissues and result in changes within the HPA axis and within key organ systems to result in a deliberate and coordinated set of responses developed to ensure fetal and neonatal survival in the face of a predicted adverse environment. Interestingly it has also been proposed that the differential impact of maternal undernutrition in the presence of either one or two embryos on the HPA axis and on the mRNAs and proteins within the insulin signalling and gluconeogenic pathways may also be explained by differences in the epigenetic mechanisms recruited including specific candidate microRNAs. Finally, the mechanisms which are recruited in response to exposure of the embryo to undernutrition may be similar to those recruited in a multifetal pregnancy. This poses the question of whether studies in polytocous species on the programming of metabolic function are working on an 'epigenetic background' which is different to that present in the singleton embryo and fetus.

References

Aguilar, F., Lo, M., Claustrat, B., Saez, J. M., Sassard, J. & Li, J. Y. (2004). Hypersensitivity of the adrenal cortex to trophic and secretory effects of angiotensin II in lyon genetically-hypertensive rats. *Hypertension, 43*, 87-93.

Alexander, G. (1964). Studies on the placenta of the sheep (ovis aries L.). effect of surgical reduction in the number of caruncles *J Reprod Fertil, 7*, 307-22.

Assimacopoulos-Jeannet, F. (2004). Fat storage in pancreas and in insulin-sensitive tissues in pathogenesis of type 2 diabetes. *Int J Obes Relat Metab Disord, 28*, S53-7.

Barler, D. J., Osmond, C., Golding, J., Kuh, D. & Wadsworth, M. E. (1989). Growth in utero, blood pressure in childhood and adult life, and mortality from cardiovascular disease. *BMJ, 298*, 564-7.

Barker, D. J. & Osmond, C. (1986). Infant mortality, childhood nutrition, and ischaemic heart diseae in England and Wales. *Lancet, 327*, 1077-81.

Bartel, D. P. (2009). MicroRNAs: Target Recognition and Regulatory Functions. *Cell, 136*, 215-33.

Bavdekar, A., Yajnik, C. S., Fall, C. H., Bapat, S., Pandit, A. N., Deshpande, V., et al. (1999). Insulin resistance syndrome in 8-year-old Indian children: small at birth, big at 8 years, or both? *Diabetes, 48*, 2422-9.

Begum, G., Davies, A., Stevens, A., Oliver, M., Jaquiery, A., Challis, J., et al. (2013). Maternal undernutrition programs tissue-specific epigenetic changes in the glucocorticoid receptor in adult offspring. *Endocrinology, 154*, 4560-9.

Begum, G., Stevens, A., Smith, E. B., Connor, K., Challis, J. R., Bloomfield, F., et al. (2012). Epigenetic changes in fetal hypothalamic energy regulating pathways are associated with maternal undernutrition and twinning. *FASEB J, 26*, 1694-703.

Berry, M. J., Jaquiery, A. L., Oliver, M. H., Harding, J. E. & Bloomfield, F. H. (2013). Antenatal corticosteroid exposure at term increases adult adiposity: an experimental study in sheep. *Acta Obstet Gynecol Scand, 92*, 862-5.

Bertram, C., Khan, O., Ohri, S., Phillips, D. I., Matthews, S. G. & Hanson, M. A. (2008). Transgenerational effects of prenatal nutrient restriction on cardiovascular and hypothalamic-pituitary-adrenal function. *J Physiol, 586*, 2217-29.

Björnholm, M., Kawano, Y., Lehtihet, M. & Zierath, J. R. (1997). Insulin receptor substrate-1 phosphorylation and phosphatidylinositol 3-kinase activity in skeletal muscle from NIDDM subjects after in vivo insulin stimulation. *Diabetes, 46*, 524-7.

Björnström, L. & Sjöberg, M. (2002). Signal transducers and activators of transcription as downstream targets of nongenomic estrogen receptor actions. *Mol Endocrinol, 16*, 2202-14.

Bloomfield, F. H., Oliver, M. H., Hawkins, P., Campbell, M., Phillips, D. J., Gluckman, P. D., et al. (2003). A periconceptional nutritional origin for non-infectious preterm birth. *Science, 300*, 561-2.

Bloomfield, F. H., Oliver, M. H., Hawkins, P., Holloway, A. C., Campbell, M., Gluckman, P. D., et al. (2004). Periconceptional undernutrition in sheep accelerates maturation of the fetal HPA axis in late gestation. *Endocrinology, 145*, 4278-85.

Boden, G., Chen, X., Ruiz, J., White, J. V. & Rossetti, L. (1994). Mechanisms of fatty acid-induced inhibition of glucose uptake. *J Clin Invest, 93*, 2438-46

Boden, G., Lebed, B., Schatz, M., Homko, C. & Lemieux, S. (2001). Effects of acute changes of plasma free fatty acids on intramyocellular fat content and insulin resistance in healthy subjects. *Diabetes, 50*, 1612-7.

Bogdarina, I., Haase, A., Langley-Evans, S. & Clark, A. J. (2010). Glucocorticoid effects on the programming of AT1b angiotensin receptor gene methylation and expression in the rat. *PLoS One, 5*, e9237.

Bogdarina, I., Welham, S., King, P. J., Burns, S. P. & Clark, A. J. (2007). Epigenetic modification of the renin-angiotensin system in the fetal programming of hypertension. *Circ Res, 100*, 520-6.

Brameld, J. M., Mostyn, A., Dandrea, J., Stephenson, T. J., Dawson, J. M., Buttery, P. J., et al. (2000). Maternal nutrition alters the expression of insulin-like growth factors in fetal sheep liver and skeletal muscle. *J Endocrinol, 167*, 429-37.

Braun, T., Li, S., Sloboda, D. M., Li, W., Audette, M. C., Moss, T. J., et al. (2009). Effects of maternal dexamethasone treatment in early pregnancy on pituitary-adrenal axis in fetal sheep. *Endocrinology, 150*, 5466-77.

Breton, C., Lukaszewski, M. A., Risold, P. Y., Enache, M., Guillemot, J., Riviere, G., et al. (2009). Maternal prenatal undernutrition alters the response of POMC neurons to energy status variation in adult male rat offspring. *Am J Physiol Endocrinol Metab, 296*, E462-72.

Budge, H., Edwards, L. J., McMillen, I. C., Bryce, A., Warnes, K., Pearce, S., et al. (2004). Nutritional manipulation of fetal adipose tissue deposition and uncoupling protein 1 messenger RNA abundance in the sheep: differential effects of timing and duration. *Biol Reprod, 71*, 359-65.

Bushati, N. & Cohen, S. M. (2007). microRNA functions. *Annu Rev Cell Dev Biol, 23*, 175-205.

Butler, T. G., Schwartz, J. & McMillen, I. C. (1999). Functional heterogeneity of corticotrophs in the anterior pituitary of the sheep fetus. *J Physiol, 516*, 907-13.

Butler, T. G., Schwartz, J. & McMillen, I. C. (2002). Differential effects of the early and late intruterine environment on cortioctrophic cell development. *J Clin Invest, 110*, 783-91.

Cahová, M., Vavrínková, H. & Kazdová, L. (2007). Glucose-fatty acid interaction in skeletal muscle and adipose tissue in insulin resistance. *Physiol Res, 56*, 1-15.

Canny, B. J., O'Farrell, K. A., Clarke, I. J. & Tilbrook, A. J. (1999). The influence of sex and gonadectomy on the hypothalamo-pituitary-adrenal axis of the sheep. *J Endocrinol, 162*, 215-25.

Ceolotto, G., Papparella, I., Bortoluzzi, A., Strapazzon, G., Ragazzo, F., Bratti, P., et al. (2011). Interplay Between miR-155, AT1R A1166C Polymorphism, and AT1R Expression in Young Untreated Hypertensives. *Am J Hypertens, 24*, 241-6.

Cetin, I., Radaelli, T., Taricco, E., Giovannini, N., Alvino, G. & Pardi, G. (2001). The endocrine and metabolic profile of the growth-retarded fetus. *J Pediatr Endocrinol Metab, 14* Suppl 6, 1497-505.

Chadio, S. E., Kotsampasi, B., Papadomichelakis, G., Deligeorgis, S., Kalogiannis, D., Menegatos, I., et al. (2007). Impact of maternal undernutrition on the hypothalamic-pituitary-adrenal axis responsiveness in sheep at different ages postnatal. *J Endocrinol*, *192*, 495-503.

Chakravarty, K., Cassuto, H., Reshef, L. & Hanson, R. W. (2005). Factors that control the tissue-specific transcription of the gene for phosphoenolpyruvate carboxykinase-C. *Crit Rev Biochem Mol Biol*, *40*, 129-54.

Chakravarty, K. & Hanson, R. W. (2007). Insulin regulation of phosphoenolpyruvate carboxykinase-C gene transcription: The role of sterol regulatory element-binding protein 1c. *Nutr Rev*, *65*, S47-S56.

Challis, B. G., Pritchard, L. E., Creemers, J. W., Delplanque, J., Keogh, J. M., Luan, J., et al. (2002). A missense mutation disrupting a dibasic prohormone processing site in pro-opiomelanocortin (POMC) increases susceptibility to early-onset obesity through a novel molecular mechanism. *Hum Mol Genet*, *11*, 1997-2004.

Chen, Y. C., Chang, M. F., Chen, Y. & Wang, S. M. (2005). Signaling pathways of magnolol-induced adrenal steroidogensis. *FEBS Lett*, *579*, 4337-43.

Cleal, J. K., Poore, K. R., Newman, J. P., Noakes, D. E., Hanson, M. A. & Green, L. R. (2007). The effect of maternal undernutrition in early gestation on gestation length and fetal and postnatal growth in sheep. *Pediatr Res*, *62*, 422-7.

Cline, G. W., Rothman, D. L., Magnusson, I., Katz, L. D. & Shulman, G. I. (1994). 13C-nuclear magnetic resonance spectroscopy studies of hepatic glucose metabolism in normal subjects and subjects with insulin-dependent diabetes mellitus. *J Clin Invest*, *94*, 2369-76.

Clyne, C. D., Nicol, M. R., MacDonald, S., Williams, B. C. & Walker, S. W. (1993). Angiotensin II stimulates growth and steroidogenesis in zona fasciculata/reticularis cells from bovine adrenal cortex via the AT1 receptor subtype. *Endocrinology*, *132*, 2206-12.

Condon, J. C., Pezzi, V., Drummond, B. M., Yin, S. & Rainey, W. E. (2002). Calmodulin-dependent kinase I regulates adrenal cell expression of aldosterone synthase. *Endocrinology*, *143*, 3651-7.

Cone, R. D., Lu, D., Koppula, S., Vage, D. I., Klungland, H., Boston, B., et al. (1996). The melanocortin receptors: agonists, antagonists, and the hormonal control of pigmentation. *Recent Prog Horm Res*, *51*, 287-317; discussion 318.

Connor, K. L., Bloomfield, F. H., Oliver, M. H., Harding, J. E. & Challis, J. R. (2009). Effect of periconceptional undernutrition in sheep on late gestation expression of mRNA and protein from genes involved in fetal adrenal steroidogenesis and placental prostaglandin production. *Reprod Sci*, *16*, 573-83.

Consoli, A., Nurjhan, N., Capani, F. & Gerich, J. (1989). Predominant role of gluconeogenesis in increased hepatic glucose production in NIDDM. *Diabetes*, *38*, 550-7.

Costello, P. M., Rowlerson, A., Astaman, N. A., Anthony, F. E., Sayer, A. A., Cooper, C., et al. (2008). Peri-implantation and late gestation maternal undernutrition differentially affect fetal sheep skeletal muscle development. *J Physiol*, *586*, 2371-9.

Curhan, G. C., Willett, W. C., Rimm, E. B., Spiegelman, D., Ascherio, A. L. & Stampfer, M. J. (1996). Birth weight and adult hypertension, diabetes mellitus, and obesity in US men. *Circulation*, *94*, 3246-50.

Dai, R., Phillips, R. A., Karpuzoglu, E., Khan, D. & Ahmed, S. A. (2009). Estrogen regulates transcription factors STAT-1 and NF-κB to promote inducible nitric oxide synthase and inflammatory responses. *J Immunol*, *183*, 6998-7005.

De Blasio, M. J., Blache, D., Gatford, K. L., Robinson, J. S. & Owens, J. A. (2010). Placental restriction increases adipose leptin gene expression and plasma leptin and alters their relationship to feeding activity in the young lamb. *Pediatr Res*, *67*, 603-8.

De Blasio, M. J., Dodic, M., Jefferies, A. J., Moritz, K. M., Wintour, E. M. & Owens, J. A. (2007a). Maternal exposure to dexamethasone or cortisol in early pregnancy differentially alters insulin secretion and glucose homeostasis in adult male sheep offspring. *Am J Physiol Endocrinol Metab*, *293*, E75-82.

De Blasio, M. J., Gatford, K. L., Harland, M. L., Robinson, J. S. & Owens, J. A. (2012). Placental restriction reduces insulin sensitivity and expression of insulin signaling and glucose transporter genes in skeletal muscle, but not liver, in young sheep. *Endocrinology*, *153*, 2142-51.

De Blasio, M. J., Gatford, K. L., Robinson, J. S. & Owens, J. A. (2007b). Placental restriction of fetal growth reduces size at birth and alters postnatal growth, feeding activity, and adiposity in the young lamb. *Am J Physiol Regul Integr Comp Physiol*, *292*, R875-86.

De Rooij, S., Painter, R., Roseboom, T., Phillips, D., Osmond, C., Barker, D., et al. (2006). Glucose tolerance at age 58 and the decline of glucose tolerance in comparison with age 50 in people prenatally exposed to the Dutch famine. *Diabetologia*, *49*, 637-43.

De Rooij, S. R., Costello, P. M., Veenendaal, M. V., Lillycrop, K. A., Gluckman, P. D., Hanson, M. A., et al. (2012). Associations between DNA methylation of a glucocorticoid receptor promoter and acute stress responses in a large healthy adult population are largely explained by lifestyle and educational differences. *Psychoneuroendocrinology*, *37*, 782-8.

De Vries, A., Holmes, M. C., Heijnis, A., Seier, J. V., Heerden, J., Louw, J., et al. (2007). Prenatal dexamethasone exposure induces changes in nonhuman primate offspring cardiometabolic and hypothalamic-pituitary-adrenal axis function. *J Clin Invest*, *117*, 1058-67.

Dean, F., Yu, C., Lingas, R. I. & Matthews, S. G. (2001). Prenatal glucocorticoid modifies hypothalamo-pituitary-adrenal regulation in prepubertal guinea pigs. *Neuro-endocrinology*, *73*, 194-202.

Delahaye, F., Breton, C., Risold, P. Y., Enache, M., Dutriez-Casteloot, I., Laborie, C., et al. (2008). Maternal perinatal undernutrition drastically reduces postnatal leptin surge and affects the development of arcuate nucleus proopiomelanocortin neurons in neonatal male rat pups. *Endocrinology*, *149*, 470-5.

Despres, J. P. & Lemieux, I. (2006). Abdominal obesity and metabolic syndrome. *Nature*, *444*, 881-7.

Dodic, M., Peers, A., Moritz, K., Hantzis, V. & Wintour, E. M. (2002). No evidence for HPA reset in adult sheep with high blood pressure due to short prenatal exposure to dexamethasone. *Am J Physiol Regul Integr Comp Physiol*, *282*, R343-50.

Donovan, E. L., Hernandez, C. E., Matthews, L. R., Oliver, M. H., Jaquiery, A. L., Bloomfield, F. H., et al. (2013). Periconceptional undernutrition in sheep leads to decreased locomotor activity in a natural environment. *J DOHaD*, *4*, 296-9.

Drake, A. J., McPherson, R. C., Godfrey, K. M., Cooper, C., Lillycrop, K. A., Hanson, M. A., et al. (2012). An unbalanced maternal diet in pregnancy associates with offspring epigenetic changes in genes controlling glucocorticoid action and foetal growth. *Clin Endocrinol (Oxf)*, *77*, 808-15.

Drake, A. J., Walker, B. R. & Seckl, J. R. (2005). Intergenerational consequences of fetal programming by in utero exposure to glucocorticoids in rats. *Am J Physiol Regul Integr Comp Physiol*, *288*, R34-8.

Duffield, J. A., Vuocolo, T., Tellam, R., Yuen, B. S., Muhlhausler, B. S. & McMillen, I. C. (2008). Placental restriction of fetal growth decreases IGF1 and leptin mRNA expression in the perirenal adipose tissue of late gestation fetal sheep. *Am J Physiol Regul Integr Comp Physiol*, *294*, R1413-9.

Dziennis, S., Jia, T., Rønnekleiv, O. K., Hurn, P. D. & Alkayed, N. J. (2007). Role of signal transducer and activator of transcription-3 in estradiol-mediated neuroprotection. *J Neurosci*, *27*, 7268-74.

Edwards, L. J., Bryce, A. E., Coulter, C. L. & McMillen, I. C. (2002). Maternal undernutrition throughout pregnancy increases adrenocorticotrophin receptor and steroidogenic acute regulatroy protein gene expression in the adrenal gland of twin fetal sheep during late gestation. *Mol Cell Endocrinol*, *196*, 1-10.

Edwards, L. J., McFarlane, J. R., Kauter, K. G. & McMillen, I. C. (2005). Impact of periconceptional nutrition on maternal and fetal leptin and fetal adiposity in singleton and twin pregnancies. *Am J Physiol Regul Integr Comp Physiol*, *288*, R39-45.

Edwards, L. J. & McMillen, I. C. (2002). Impact of maternal undernutrition during the periconceptional period, fetal number, and fetal sex on the development of the hypothalamo-pituitary adrenal axis in sheep during late gestation. *Biol Reprod*, *66*, 1562-9.

Eriksson, J., Forsen, T., Tuomilehto, J., Osmond, C. & Barker, D. (2001). Size at birth, childhood growth and obesity in adult life. *Int J Obes Relat Metab Disord*, *25*, 735-40.

Farooqi, I. S., Drop, S., Clements, A., Keogh, J. M., Biernacka, J., Lowenbein, S., et al. (2006). Heterozygosity for a POMC-null mutation and increased obesity risk in humans. *Diabetes*, *55*, 2549-53.

Farrand, K., McMillen, I. C., Tanaka, S. & Schwartz, J. (2006). Subpopulations of corticotrophs in the sheep pituitary during late gestation: effects of development and placental restriction. *Endocrinology*, *147*, 4762-71.

Ferre, P. (2004). The biology of peroxisome proliferator-activated receptors: relationship with lipid metabolism and insulin sensitivity. *Diabetes*, *53*, S43-50.

Ferreira, J. G., Cruz, C., Vinson, G. P. & Pignatelli, D. (2004). ACTH modulates ERK phosphorylation in the adrenal gland in a time-dependent manner. *Endocr Res*, *30*, 661-6.

Ferreira, J. G., Cruz, C. D., Neves, D. & Pignatelli, D. (2007). Increased extracellular signal regulated kinases phosphorylation in the adrenal gland in response to chronic ACTH treatment. *J Endocrinol*, *192*, 647-58.

Finn, F. M., Stehle, C., Ricci, P. & Hofmann, K. (1988). Angiotensin stimulation of adrenal fasciculata cells. *Arch Biochem Biophys*, *264*, 160-7.

Fletcher, A. J., Ma, X. H., Wu, W. X., Nathanielsz, P. W., McGarrigle, H. H., Fowden, A. L., et al. (2004). Antenatal glucocorticoids reset the level of baseline and hypoxemia-induced pituitary-adrenal activity in the sheep fetus during late gestation. *Am J Physiol Endocrinol Metab*, *286*, E311-9.

Ford, S. P., Hess, B. W., Schwope, M. M., Nijland, M. J., Gilbert, J. S., Vonnahme, K. A., et al. (2007). Maternal undernutrition during early to mid-gestation in the ewe results in altered growth, adiposity, and glucose tolerance in male offspring. *J Anim Sci, 85,* 1285-94.

Foster, R. H. (2004). Reciprocal influences between the signalling pathways regulating proliferation and steroidogenesis in adrenal glomerulosa cells. *J Mol Endocrinol, 32,* 893-902.

Fowden, A. L., Mijovic, J. & Silver, M. (1993). The effects of cortisol on hepatic and renal gluconeogenic enzyme activities in the sheep fetus during late gestation. *J Endocrinol, 137,* 213-22.

Franko, K. L., Giussani, D. A., Forhead, A. J. & Fowden, A. L. (2007). Effects of dexamethasone on the glucogenic capacity of fetal, pregnant, and non-pregnant adult sheep. *J Endocrinol, 192,* 67-73.

Friedman, J. E., Sun, Y., Ishizuka, T., Farrell, C. J., McCormack, S. E., Herron, L. M., et al. (1997). Phosphoenolpyruvate carboxykinase (GTP) gene transcription and hyperglycemia are regulated by glucocorticoids in genetically obesedb/db transgenic mice. *J Biol Chem, 272,* 31475-81.

Frühbeck, G. & Salvador, J. (2004). Role of adipocytokines in metabolism and disease. *Nutr Res, 24,* 803-26.

Gallagher, E. J., Leroith, D. & Karnieli, E. (2010). Insulin resistance in obesity as the underlying cause for the metabolic syndrome. *Mt Sinai J Med, 77,* 511-23.

Gardner, D. S., Jamall, E., Fletcher, A. J., Fowden, A. L. & Giussani, D. A. (2004). Adrenocortical responsiveness is blunted in twin relative to singleton ovine fetuses. *J Physiol, 557,* 1021-32.

Gardner, D. S., Van Bon, B. W., Dandrea, J., Goddard, P. J., May, S. F., Wilson, V., et al. (2006). Effect of periconceptional undernutrition and gender on hypothalamic-pituitary-adrenal axis function in young adult sheep. *J Endocrinol, 190,* 203-12.

Gatford, K. L., Wintour, E. M., De Blasio, M. J., Owens, J. A. & Dodic, M. (2000). Differential timing for programming of glucose homoeostasis, sensitivity to insulin and blood pressure by in utero exposure to dexamethasone in sheep. *Clin Sci (Lond), 98,* 553-60.

Gentili, S., Morrison, J. L. & McMillen, I. C. (2009). Intrauterine growth restriction and differential patterns of hepatic growth and expression of IGF1, PCK2, and HSDL1 mRNA in the sheep fetus in late gestation. *Biol Reprod, 80,* 1121-7.

Gilardini, L., McTernan, P. G., Girola, A., da Silva, N. F., Alberti, L., Kumar, S., et al. (2006). Adiponectin is a candidate marker of metabolic syndrome in obese children and adolescents. *Atherosclerosis, 189,* 401-7.

Grace, C. E., Kim, S. J. & Rogers, J. M. (2011). Maternal influences on epigenetic programming of the developing hypothalamic-pituitary-adrenal axis. *Birth Defects Res A Clin Mol Teratol, 91,* 797-805.

Han, V. K., Lu, F., Bassett, N., Yang, K. P., Delhanty, P. J. & Challis, J. R. (1992). Insulin-like growth factor-II (IGF-II) messenger ribonucleic acid is expressed in steroidogenic cells of the developing ovine adrenal gland: evidence of an autocrine/paracrine role for IGF-II. *Endocrinology, 131,* 3100-9.

Han, V. K., Lund, P. K., Lee, D. C. & D'Ercole, J. (1988). Expression of somatomedin/insulin-like growth factor messenger ribonucleic acids in the human fetus: identification, characterization, and tissue distribution. *J Clin Endocrinol Metab, 66,* 422-9.

Hattangady, N. G., Olala, L. O., Bollag, W. B. & Rainey, W. E. (2012). Acute and chronic regulation of aldosterone production. *Mol Cell Endocrinol*, *350*, 151-62.

Hawkins, P., Hanson, M. A. & Matthews, S. G. (2001). Maternal undernutrition in early gestation alters molecular regulation of the hypothalamic-pituitary-adrenal axis in the ovine fetus. *J Neuroendocrinol*, *13*, 855-61.

Hawkins, P., Steyn, C., McGarrigle, H. H., Calder, N. A., Saito, T., Stratford, L. L., et al. (2000). Cardiovascular and hypothalamic-pituitary-adrenal axis development in late gestation fetal sheep and young lambs following modest maternal nutrient restriction in early gestation. *Reprod Fertil Dev*, *12*, 443-56.

He, W., Barak, Y., Hevener, A., Olson, P., Liao, D., Le, J., et al. (2003). Adipose-specific peroxisome proliferator-activated receptor knockout causes insulin resistance in fat and liver but not in muscle. *Proc Natl Acad Sci U S A*, *100*, 15712-7.

Hegarty, B. D., Cooney, G. J., Kraegen, E. W. & Furler, S. M. (2002). Increased efficiency of fatty acid uptake contributes to lipid accumulation in skeletal muscle of high fat-fed insulin-resistant rats. *Diabetes*, *51*, 1477-84.

Hegarty, B. D., Furler, S. M., Ye, J., Cooney, G. J. & Kraegen, E. W. (2003). The role of intramuscular lipid in insulin resistance. *Acta Physiol Scand*, *178*, 373-83.

Heijmans, B. T., Tobi, E. W., Stein, A. D., Putter, H., Blauw, G. J., Susser, E. S., et al. (2008). Persistent epigenetic differences associated with prenatal exposure to famine in humans. *Proc Natl Acad Sci U S A*, *105*, 17046-9.

Himpe, E. & Kooijman, R. (2009). Insulin-like growth factor-I receptor signal transduction and the Janus Kinase/Signal Transducer and Activator of Transcription (JAK-STAT) pathway. *BioFactors*, *35*, 76-81.

Hoeflich, A. & Bielohuby, M. (2009). Mechanisms of adrenal gland growth: signal integration by extracellular signal regulated kinases1/2. *J Mol Endocrinol*, *42*, 191-203.

Hyatt, M. A., Gopalakrishnan, G. S., Bispham, J., Gentili, S., McMillen, I. C., Rhind, S. M., et al. (2007). Maternal nutrient restriction in early pregnancy programs hepatic mRNA expression of growth-related genes and liver size in adult male sheep. *J Endocrinol*, *192*, 87-97.

Ikegami, M., Jobe, A., Newnham, J., Polk, D., Willet, K. & Sly, P. (1997). Repetitive prenatal glucocorticoids improve lung function and decrease growth in preterm lambs. *Am J Respir Crit Care Med*, *156*, 178-84.

Jaquiery, A. L., Oliver, M. H., Honeyfield-Ross, M., Harding, J. E. & Bloomfield, F. H. (2012). Periconceptional undernutrition in sheep affects adult phenotype only in males. *J Nutr Metab*, *2012*, 123610.

Jellyman, J. K., Martin-Gronert, M. S., Cripps, R. L., Giussani, D. A., Ozanne, S. E., Shen, Q. W., et al. (2012). Effects of cortisol and dexamethasone on insulin signalling pathways in skeletal muscle of the ovine fetus during late gestation. *PLoS One*, *7*, e52363.

Joshi, S., Garole, V., Daware, M., Girigosavi, S. & Rao, S. (2003). Maternal protein restrction before pregnancy affects vital organs of offspring in Wistar rats. *Metabolism*, *52*, 13-8.

Kelley, D. E., He, J., Menshikova, E. V. & Ritov, V. B. (2002). Dysfunction of mitochondria in human skeletal muscle in type 2 diabetes. *Diabetes*, *51*, 2944-50.

Kelley, D. E., Mintun, M. A., Watkins, S. C., Simoneau, J. A., Jadali, F., Fredrickson, A., et al. (1996). The effect of non-insulin-dependent diabetes mellitus and obesity on glucose transport and phosphorylation in skeletal muscle. *J Clin Invest*, *97*, 2705-13.

Kind, K. L., Owens, J. A., Robinson, J. S., Quinn, K. J., Grant, P. A., Walton, P. E., et al. (1995). Effect of restriction of placental growth on expression of IGFs in fetal sheep: relationship to fetal growth, circulating IGFs and binding proteins. *J Endocrinol, 146*, 23-34.

Klip, A. & Pâquet, M. R. (1990). Glucose transport and glucose transporters in muscle and their metabolic regulation. *Diabetes Care, 13*, 228-43.

Kotronen, A., Seppälä-Lindroos, A., Bergholm, R. & Yki-Järvinen, H. (2008). Tissue specificity of insulin resistance in humans: fat in the liver rather than muscle is associated with features of the metabolic syndrome. *Diabetologia, 51*, 130-8.

Krozowski, Z. (1999). The 11b-hydroxysteroid dehydrogenases: functions and physiological effects. *Mol Cell Endocrinol, 151*, 121-7.

Kumarasamy, V., Mitchell, M. D., Bloomfield, F. H., Oliver, M. H., Campbell, M. E., Challis, J. R., et al. (2005). Effects of periconceptional undernutrition on the initiation of parturition in sheep. *Am J Physiol Regul Integr Comp Physiol, 288*, R67-72.

Kwong, W. Y., Miller, D. J., Wilkins, A. P., Dear, M. S., Wright, J. N., Osmond, C., et al. (2007). Maternal low protein diet restricted to the preimplantation period induces a gender-specific change on hepatic gene expression in rat fetuses. *Mol Reprod Dev, 74*, 52-60.

Lebrethon, M. C., Jaillard, C., Defayes, G., Begeot, M. & Saez, J. M. (1994). Human cultured adrenal fasciculata-reticularis cells are targets for angiotensin-II: effects on cytochrome P450 cholesterol side-chain cleavage, cytochrome P450 17 alpha-hydroxylase, and 3 beta-hydroxysteroid-dehydrogenase messenger ribonucleic acid and proteins and on steroidogenic responsiveness to corticotropin and angiotensin-II. *J Clin Endocrinol Metab, 78*, 1212-9.

Lefrancois-Martinez, A. M., Blondet-Trichard, A., Binart, N., Val, P., Chambon, C., Sahut-Barnola, I., et al. (2011). Transcriptional control of adrenal steroidogenesis: novel connection between Janus kinase (JAK) 2 protein and protein kinase A (PKA) through stabilization of cAMP response element-binding protein (CREB) transcription factor. *J Biol Chem, 286*, 32976-85.

Levitt, N. S., Lindsay, R. S., Holmes, M. C. & Seckl, J. R. (1996). Dexamethasone in the last week of pregnancy attenuates hippocampal glucocorticoid receptor gene expression and elevates blood pressure in the adult offspring in the rat. *Neuroendocrinology, 64*, 412-8.

Levy-Marchal, C. & Jaquet, D. (2004). Long-term metabolic consequences of being born small for gestational age. *Pediatr Diabetes, 5*, 147-53.

Li, L. A., Xia, D., Wei, S., Hartung, J. & Zhao, R. Q. (2008). Characterization of adrenal ACTH signaling pathway and steroidogenic enzymes in Erhualian and Pietrain pigs with different plasma cortisol levels. *Steroids, 73*, 806-14.

Li, S., Nitsos, I., Polglase, G. R., Braun, T., Moss, T. J., Newnham, J. P., et al. (2012). The effects of dexamethasone treatment in early gestation on hypothalamic-pituitary-adrenal responses and gene expression at 7 months of postnatal age in sheep. *Reprod Sci, 19*, 260-70.

Lie, S., Morrison, J. L., Williams-Wyss, O., Ozanne, S. E., Zhang, S., Walker, S. K., et al. (2013). Impact of embryo number and periconceptional undernutrition on factors regulating adipogenesis, lipogenesis, and metabolism in adipose tissuein the sheep fetus. *Am J Physiol Endocrinol Metab, 305*, E931-41.

Lie, S., Morrison, J. L., Williams-Wyss, O., Suter, C. M., Humphreys, D. T., Ozanne, S. E., et al. (2014a). Impact of embryo number and maternal undernutrition around the time of conception on insulin signaling and gluconeogenic factors and microRNAs in the liver of fetal sheep. *Am J Physiol Endocrinol Metab, 306*, E1013-24.

Lie, S., Morrison, J. L., Williams-Wyss, O., Suter, C. M., Humphreys, D. T., Ozanne, S. E., et al. (2014b). Periconceptional undernutrition programs changes in insulin signalling molecules and microRNAs in skeletal muscle in singleton and twin fetal sheep. *Biol Reprod, 90*, 5.

Liggins, G. C. (1994). The role of cortisol in preparing the fetus for birth. *Reprod Fertil Dev, 6*, 141-50.

Lim, C. P. & Cao, X. (2006). Structure, function, and regulation of STAT proteins. *Mol BioSyst, 2*, 536-50.

Long, N. M., Shasa, D. R., Ford, S. P. & Nathanielsz, P. W. (2012). Growth and insulin dynamics in two generations of female offspring of mothers receiving a single course of synthetic glucocorticoids. *Am J Obstet Gynecol, 207*, 203. e1-8.

Lund, T. D., Munson, D. J., Haldy, M. E. & Handa, R. J. (2004). Androgen inhibits, while oestrogen enhances, restraint-induced activation of neuropeptide neurones in the paraventricular nucleus of the hypothalamus. *J Neuroendocrinol, 16*, 272-8.

MacLaughlin, S. M. & McMillen, I. C. (2007). Impact of periconceptional undernutrition on the development of the hypothalamo-pituitary-adrenal axis: does the timing of parturition start at conception? *Curr Drug Targets, 8*, 880-7.

MacLaughlin, S. M., Walker, S. K., Kleemann, D. O., Sibbons, J. P., Tosh, D. N., Gentili, S., et al. (2007). Impact of periconceptional undernutrition on adrenal growth and adrenal insulin-like growth factor and steroidogenic enzyme expression in the sheep fetus during early pregnancy. *Endocrinology, 148*, 1911-20.

Maegawa, H., Shigeta, Y., Egawa, K. & Kobayashi, M. (1991). Impaired autophosphorylation of insulin receptors from abdominal skeletal muscles in nonobese subjects with NIDDM. *Diabetes, 40*, 815-9.

Margetts, B. M., Rowland, M. G., Foord, F. A., Cruddas, A. M., Cole, T. J. & Barker, D. (1991). The relation of maternal weight to the blood pressures of Gambian children. *Int J Epidemiol, 20*, 938-43.

Marrero, M. B., Schieffer, B., Paxton, W. G., Heerdt, L., Berk, B. C., Delafontaine, P., et al. (1995). Direct stimulation of Jak/STAT pathway by the angiotensin II AT1 receptor. *Nature, 375*, 247-50.

Maureen, J. C., Naira, G., Laidlaw, J. S., Mollie, R. & Ellen, B. K. (2005). Use of GLUT-4 null mice to study skeletal muscle glucose uptake. *Clin Exp Pharmacol Physiol, 32*, 308-13.

McCormick, J. A., Lyons, V., Jacobson, M. D., Noble, J., Diorio, J., Nyirenda, M., et al. (2000). 5'-heterogeneity of glucocorticoid receptor messenger RNA is tissue specific: differential regulation of variant transcripts by early-life events. *Mol Endocrinol, 14*, 506-17.

McGowan, P. O., Sasaki, A., D'Alessio, A. C., Dymov, S., Labonté, B., Szyf, M., et al. (2009). Epigenetic regulation of the glucocorticoid receptor in human brain associates with childhood abuse. *Nat Neurosci, 12*, 342-8.

McMillen, I. C. & Robinson, J. S. (2005). Developmental origins of the metabolic syndrome: prediction, plasticity, and programming. *Physiol Rev, 85*, 571-633.

McMillen, I. C., Warnes, K. E., Adams, M. B., Robinson, J. S., Owens, J. A. & Coulter, C. L. (2000). Impact of restriction of placental and fetal growth on expression of 11beta-hydroxysteroid dehydrogenase type 1 and type 2 messenger ribonucleic acid in the liver, kidney, and adrenal of the sheep fetus. *Endocrinology*, *141*, 539-43.

Modaressi, S., Brechtel, K., Christ, B. & Jungermann, K. (1998). Human mitochondrial phosphoenolpyruvate carboxykinase 2 gene. Structure, chromosomal localization and tissue-specific expression. *Biochem J*, *333*, 359-66.

Mohiti, J., Talebi, F. & Afkhami-Ardekani, M. (2009). Circulation free leptin in diabetic patients and its correlation to insulin level. *Pak J Biol Sci*, *12*, 397-400.

Mora, S. & Pessin, J. E. (2002). An adipocentric view of signaling and intracellular trafficking. *Diabetes Metab Res Rev*, *18*, 345-56.

Morino, K., Petersen, K. F., Dufour, S., Befroy, D., Frattini, J., Shatzkes, N., et al. (2005). Reduced mitochondrial density and increased IRS-1 serine phosphorylation in muscle of insulin-resistant offspring of type 2 diabetic parents. *J Clin Invest*, *115*, 3587-93.

Moritz, K., Butkus, A., Hantzis, V., Peers, A., Wintour, E. M. & Dodic, M. (2002). Prolonged low-dose dexamethasone, in early gestation, has no long-term deleterious effect on normal ovine fetuses. *Endocrinology*, *143*, 1159-65.

Moss, T. J., Sloboda, D. M., Gurrin, L. C., Harding, R., Challis, J. R. & Newnham, J. P. (2001). Programming effects in sheep of prenatal growth restriction and glucocorticoid exposure. *Am J Physiol Regul Integr Comp Physiol*, *281*, R960-70.

Muhlhausler, B. S., Duffield, J. A., Ozanne, S. E., Pilgrim, C., Turner, N., Morrison, J. L., et al. (2009a). The transition from fetal growth restriction to accelerated postnatal growth: a potential role for insulin signalling in skeletal muscle. *J Physiol*, *587*, 4199-211.

Muhlhausler, B. S., Hancock, S. N., Bloomfield, F. H. & Harding, R. (2011). Are twins growth restricted? *Pediatr Res*, *70*, 117-22.

Muhlhausler, B. S., Morrison, J. L. & McMillen, I. C. (2009b). Rosiglitazone increases the expression of peroxisome proliferator-activated receptor-{gamma} target genes in adipose tissue, liver, and skeletal muscle in the sheep fetus in late gestation. *Endocrinology*, *150*, 4287-94.

Murgatroyd, C., Patchev, A. V., Wu, Y., Micale, V., Bockmuhl, Y., Fischer, D., et al. (2009). Dynamic DNA methylation programs persistent adverse effects of early-life stress. *Nat Neurosci*, *12*, 1559-66.

Neill, J. D., Smith, P. F., Luque, E. H., Munoz de Toro, M., Nagy, G. & Mulchahey, J. J. (1987). Detection and measurement of hormone secretion from individual pituitary cells. *Recent Prog Horm Res*, *43*, 175-229.

Newnham, J. P., Evans, S. F., Godfrey, M., Huang, W., Ikegami, M. & Jobe, A. (1999). Maternal, but not fetal, administration of corticosteroids restricts fetal growth. *J Matern Fetal Med*, *8*, 81-7.

Nicholas, L. M., Rattanatray, L., MacLaughlin, S. M., Ozanne, S. E., Kleemann, D. O., Walker, S. K., et al. (2013). Differential effects of maternal obesity and weight loss in the periconceptional period on the epigenetic regulation of hepatic insulin-signaling pathways in the offspring. *FASEB J*, *27*, 3786-96.

Nussdorfer, G. G., Robba, C., Mazzochi, G. & Rebuffat, P. (1981). Effects of angiotensin II on the zona fasciculata of the rat adrenal cortex: an ultrastructural stereologic study. *J Anat*, *132*, 235-42.

Nyirenda, M. J., Lindsay, R. S., Kenyon, C. J., Burchell, A. & Seckl, J. R. (1998). Glucocorticoid exposure in late gestation permanently programs rat hepatic phosphoenolpyruvate carboxykinase and glucocorticoid receptor expression and causes glucose intolerance in adult offspring. *J Clin Invest, 101*, 2174-81.

O'Regan, D., Welberg, L. L., Holmes, M. C. & Seckl, J. R. (2001). Glucocorticoid programming of pituitary-adrenal function: mechanisms and physiological consequences. *Semin Neonatol, 6*, 319-29.

Oberlander, T. F., Weinberg, J., Papsdorf, M., Grunau, R., Misri, S. & Devlin, A. M. (2008). Prenatal exposure to maternal depression, neonatal methylation of human glucocorticoid receptor gene (NR3C1) and infant cortisol stress responses. *Epigenetics, 3*, 97-106.

Oliver, M. H., Hawkins, P. & Harding, J. E. (2005). Periconceptional undernutrition alters growth trajectory and metabolic and endocrine responses to fasting in late gestation fetal sheep. *Pediatr Res, 57*, 591-8.

Owen, D. & Matthews, S. G. (2003). Glucocorticoids and Sex-Dependent Development of Brain Glucocorticoid and Mineralocorticoid Receptors. *Endocrinology, 144*, 2775-84.

Owens, J. A., Kind, K. L., Carbone, F., Robinson, J. S. & Owens, P. C. (1994). Circulating insulin-like growth factors-I and -II and substrates in fetal sheep following restriction of placental growth. *J Endocrinol, 140*, 5-13.

Palmer, A. C. (2011). Nutritionally mediated programming of the developing immune system. *Adv Nutr, 2*, 377-95.

Pessin, J. E. & Saltiel, A. R. (2000). Signaling pathways in insulin action: molecular targets of insulin resistance. *J Clin Invest, 106*, 165-9.

Petersen, K. F., Dufour, S., Befroy, D., Garcia, R. & Shulman, G. I. (2004). Impaired mitochondrial activity in the insulin-resistant offspring of patients with type 2 diabetes. *N Engl J Med, 350*, 664-71.

Pham-Huu-Trung, M. T., Villette, J. M., Bogyo, A., Duclos, J. M., Fiet, J. & Binoux, M. (1991). Effects of insulin-like growth factor I (IGF-I) on enzymatic activity in human adrenocortical cells. Interactions with ACTH. *J Steroid Biochem Mol Biol, 39*, 903-9.

Phillips, D. I. (2007). Programming of the stress response: a fundamental mechanism underlying the long-term effects of the fetal environment? *J Intern Med, 261*, 453-60.

Phillips, D. I., Walker, B. R., Reynolds, R. M., Flanagan, D. E., Wood, P. J., Osmond, C., et al. (2000). Low birth weight predicts elevated plasma cortisol concentrations in adults from 3 populations. *Hypertension, 35*, 1301-6.

Phillips, I. D., Anthony, R. V., Simonetta, G., Owens, J. A., Robinson, J. S. & McMillen, I. C. (2001). Restriction of fetal growth has a differential impact on fetal prolactin and prolactin receptor mRNA expression. *J Neuroendocrinol, 13*, 175-81.

Phillips, I. D., Simonetta, G., Owens, J. A., Robinson, J. S., Clarke, I. J. & McMillen, I. C. (1996). Placental restriciton alters the functional development of the pituitary-adrenal axis in the sheep fetus during late gestation. *Pediatr Res, 40*, 861-6.

Poore, K. R., Cleal, J. K., Newman, J. P., Boullin, J. P., Noakes, D. E., Hanson, M. A., et al. (2007). Nutritional challenges during development induce sex-specific changes in glucose homeostasis in the adult sheep. *Am J Physiol Endocrinol Metab, 292*, E32-9.

Postic, C., Dentin, R. & Girard, J. (2004). Role of the liver in the control of carbohydrate and lipid homeostasis. *Diabetes Metab, 30*, 398-408.

Presul, E., Schmidt, S., Kofler, R. & Helmberg, A. (2007). Identification, tissue expression, and glucocorticoid responsiveness of alternative first exons of the human glucocorticoid receptor. *J Mol Endocrinol*, *38*, 79-90.

Quigley, S. P., Kleemann, D. O., Kakar, M. A., Owens, J. A., Nattrass, G. S., Maddocks, S., et al. (2005). Myogenesis in sheep is altered by maternal feed intake during the periconception period. *Anim Reprod Sci*, *87*, 241-51.

Rattanatray, L., MacLaughlin, S. M., Kleemann, D. O., Walker, S. K., Muhlhausler, B. S. & McMillen, I. C. (2010). Impact of maternal periconceptional overnutrition on fat mass and expression of adipogenic and lipogenic genes in visceral and subcutaneous fat depots in the postnatal lamb. *Endocrinology*, *151*, 5195-205.

Ravelli, A., van der Meulen, J., Osmond, C., Barker, D. & Bleker, O. (1999). Obesity at the age of 50 y in men and women exposed to famine prenatally. *Am J Clin Nutr*, *70*, 811-6.

Ravelli, G. P., Stein, Z. A. & Susser, M. W. (1976). Obesity in young men after famine exposure in utero and early infancy. *N Engl J Med*, *295*, 349-53.

Rawlings, J. S., Rosler, K. M. & Harrison, D. A. (2004). The JAK/STAT signaling pathway. *J Cell Sci*, *117*, 1281-3.

Rector, R. S., Thyfault, J. P., Uptergrove, G. M., Morris, E. M., Naples, S. P., Borengasser, S. J., et al. (2010). Mitochondrial dysfunction precedes insulin resistance and hepatic steatosis and contributes to the natural history of non-alcoholic fatty liver disease in an obese rodent model. *J Hepatol*, *52*, 727-36.

Robinson, J. S., Falconer, J. & Owens, J. A. (1985). Intrauterine growth retardation: clinical and experimental. *Acta Paediatr Scand Suppl*, *319*, 135-42.

Robinson, J. S., Hart, I. C., Kingston, E. J., Jones, C. T. & Thorburn, G. D. (1980). Studies on the growth of the fetal sheep. The effects of reduction of placental size on hormone concentration in fetal plasma. *J Dev Physiol*, *2*, 239-48.

Robinson, J. S., Kingston, E. J., Jones, C. T. & Thorburn, G. D. (1979). Studies on experimental growth retardation in sheep. The effect of removal of a endometrial caruncles on fetal size and metabolism. *J Dev Physiol*, *1*, 379-98.

Romero, D. G., Welsh, B. L., Gomez-Sanchez, E. P., Yanes, L. L., Rilli, S. & Gomez-Sanchez, C. E. (2006). Angiotensin II-mediated protein kinase D activation stimulates aldosterone and cortisol secretion in H295R human adrenocortical cells. *Endocrinology*, *147*, 6046-55.

Roseboom, T. J., van der Meulen, J. H., Ravelli, A. C., Osmond, C., Barker, D. J. & Bleker, O. P. (2001). Effects of prenatal exposure to the Dutch famine on adult disease in later life: an overview. *Mol Cell Endocrinol*, *185*, 93-8.

Roseboom, T. J., van der Meulen, J. H., Ravelli, A. C., Osmond, C., Barker, D. J. & Bleker, O. P. (2003). Perceived health of adults after prenatal exposure to the Dutch famine. *Paediatr Perinat Epidemiol*, *17*, 391-7.

Roseboom, T. J., van der Meulen, J. H., Osmond, C., Barker, D. J., Ravelli, A. C., Schroeder-Tanka, J. M., et al. (2000). Coronary heart disease after prenatal exposure to the Dutch famine, 1944-45. *Heart*, *84*, 595-8.

Ross, J. T., Phillips, I. D., Simonetta, G., Owens, J. A., Robinson, J. S. & McMillen, I. C. (2000). Differential effects of placental restriction on IGF-II, ACTH receptor and steroidogenic enzyme mRNA levels in the foetal sheep adrenal. *J Neuroendocrinol*, *12*, 79-85.

Rumball, C. W., Oliver, M. H., Thorstensen, E. B., Jaquiery, A. L., Husted, S. M., Harding, J. E., et al. (2008). Effects of twinning and periconceptional undernutrition on late-gestation hypothalamic-pituitary-adrenal axis function in ovine pregnancy. *Endocrinology, 149*, 1163-72.

Saraf, N., Sharma, P. K., Mondal, S. C., Garg, V. K. & Singh, A. K. (2012). Role of PPARg2 transcription factor in thiazolidinedione-induced insulin sensitization. *J Pharm Pharmacol, 64*, 161-71.

Sasaki, K., Cripe, T. P., Koch, S. R., Andreone, T. L., Petersen, D. D., Beale, E. G., et al. (1984). Multihormonal regulation of phosphoenolpyruvate carboxykinase gene transcription. The dominant role of insulin. *J Biol Chem, 259*, 15242-51.

Savage, D. B., Petersen, K. F. & Shulman, G. I. (2007). Disordered lipid metabolism and the pathogenesis of insulin resistance. *Physiol Rev, 87*, 507-20.

Schulz, L. C. (2010). The Dutch Hunger Winter and the developmental origins of health and disease. *Proc Natl Acad Sci U S A, 107*, 16757-8.

Schwartz, J., Ash, P., Ford, V., Raff, H., Crosby, S. & White, A. (1994). Secretion of adrenocorticotrophin (ACTH) and ACTH precursors in ovine anterior pituitary cells: actions of corticotrophin-releasing hormone, arginine vasopressin and glucocorticoids. *J Endocrinol, 140*, 189-95.

Schwartz, J. & Rose, J. C. (1998). Development of the pituitary adrenal axis in fetal sheep twins. *Am J Physiol, 274*, R1-8.

Seppala-Lindroos, A., Vehkavaara, S., Hakkinen, A. M., Goto, T., Westerbacka, J., Sovijarvi, A., et al. (2002). Fat accumulation in the liver is associated with defects in insulin suppression of glucose production and serum free fatty acids independent of obesity in normal men. *J Clin Endocrinol Metab, 87*, 3023-8.

Sesti, G. (2006). Pathophysiology of insulin resistance. *Best Pract Res Clin Endocrinol Metab, 20*, 665-79.

Shalita-Chesner, M., Glaser, T. & Werner, H. (2004). Signal transducer and activator of transcription-1 (STAT1), but not STAT5b, regulates IGF-I receptor gene expression in an osteosarcoma cell line. *J Pediatr Endocrinol Metab, 17*, 211-8.

Shaw, J. E. & Chisholm, D. J. (2003). Epidemiology and prevention of type 2 diabetes and the metabolic syndrome. *Med J Aust, 179*, 379-83.

Shoener, J. A., Baig, R. & Page, K. C. (2006). Prenatal exposure to dexamethasone alters hippocampal drive on hypothalamic-pituitary-adrenal axis activity in adult male rats. *Am J Physiol Regul Integr Comp Physiol, 290*, R1366-73.

Silva, C., Ines, L. S., Nour, D., Straub, R. H. & Da Silva, J. A. (2002). Differential Male and Female Adrenal Cortical Steroid Hormone and Cortisol Responses to Interleukin-6 in Humans. *Ann N Y Acad Sci, 966*, 68-72.

Simonetta, G., Rourke, A. K., Owens, J. A., Robinson, J. S. & McMillen, I. C. (1997). Impact of placental restriction on the development of the sympathoadrenal system. *Pediatr Res, 42*, 805-11.

Sloboda, D. M., Moss, T. J., Gurrin, L. C., Newnham, J. P. & Challis, J. R. (2002a). The effect of prenatal betamethasone administration on postnatal ovine hypothalamic-pituitary-adrenal function. *J Endocrinol, 172*, 71-81.

Sloboda, D. M., Moss, T. J., Li, S., Doherty, D. A., Nitsos, I., Challis, J. R., et al. (2005). Hepatic glucose regulation and metabolism in adult sheep: effects of prenatal betamethasone. *Am J Physiol Endocrinol Metab, 289*, E721-8.

Sloboda, D. M., Newnham, J. P. & Challis, J. R. (2000). Effects of repeated maternal betamethasone administration on growth and hypothalamic-pituitary-adrenal function of the ovine fetus at term. *J Endocrinol, 165,* 79-91.

Sloboda, D. M., Newnham, J. P. & Challis, J. R. (2002b). Repeated maternal glucocorticoid administration and the developing liver in fetal sheep. *J Endocrinol, 175,* 535-43.

Smith, G. C., Smith, M. F., McNay, M. B. & Fleming, J. E. (1998). First-trimester growth and the risk of low birth weight. *N Engl J Med, 339,* 1817-22.

Smith, N. A., McAuliffe, F. M., Quinn, K., Lonergan, P. & Evans, A. C. (2010). The negative effects of a short period of maternal undernutrition at conception on the glucose-insulin system of offspring in sheep. *Anim Reprod Sci, 121,* 94-100.

Stein, Z. & Susser, M. (1975). The Dutch famine, 1944-1945, and the reproductive process. I. Effects on six indices at birth. *Pediatr Res, 9,* 70-6.

Stein, Z., Susser, M. W., Saenger, G. & Moarolla, F. (1972). Nutrition and mental performance. *Science, 178,* 708-13.

Stevens, A., Begum, G., Cook, A., Connor, K., Rumball, C., Oliver, M., et al. (2010). Epigenetic changes in the hypothalamic proopiomelanocortin and glucocorticoid receptor genes in the ovine fetus after periconceptional undernutrition. *Endocrinology, 151,* 3652-64.

Sun, Y., Liu, S., Ferguson, S., Wang, L., Klepcyk, P., Yun, J. S., et al. (2002). Phosphoenolpyruvate carboxykinase over expression selectively attenuates insulin signaling and hepatic insulin sensitivity in transgenic mice. *J Biol Chem, 277,* 23301-7.

Taniguchi, C. M., Emanuelli, B. & Kahn, C. R. (2006). Critical nodes in signalling pathways: Insights into insulin action. *Nat Rev Mol Cell Biol, 7,* 85-96.

Terauchi, Y. (2007). PPARgamma and metabolic syndrome. *Rinsho Byori, 55,* 447-51.

Todd, S. E., Oliver, M. H., Jaquiery, A. L., Bloomfield, F. H. & Harding, J. E. (2009). Periconceptional undernutrition of ewes impairs glucose tolerance in their adult offspring. *Pediatr Res, 65,* 409-13.

Trayhurn, P. (1996). New insights into the development of obesity: obese genes and the leptin system. *Proc Nutr Soc, 55,* 783-91.

Tronche, F., Kellendonk, C., Reichardt, H. M. & Schutz, G. (1998). Genetic dissection of glucocorticoid receptor function in mice. *Curr Opin Genet Dev, 8,* 532-8.

Turner, J. D., Alt, S. R., Cao, L., Vernocchi, S., Trifonova, S., Battello, N., et al. (2010). Transcriptional control of the glucocorticoid receptor: CpG islands, epigenetics and more. *Biochem Pharmacol, 80,* 1860-8.

Turner, J. D. & Muller, C. P. (2005). Structure of the glucocorticoid receptor (NR3C1) gene 5' untranslated region: identification, and tissue distribution of multiple new human exon 1. *J Mol Endocrinol, 35,* 283-92.

Valverde, A. M., Benito, M. & Lorenzo, M. (2005). The brown adipose cell: a model for understanding the molecular mechanisms of insulin resistance. *Acta Physiol Scand, 183,* 59-73.

Van Lier, E., Pérez-Clariget, R. & Forsberg, M. (2003). Sex differences in cortisol secretion after administration of an ACTH analogue in sheep during the breeding and non-breeding season. *Anim Reprod Sci, 79,* 81-92.

Veening, M. A., Van Weissenbruch, M. M. & Delemarre-van de Waal, H. A. (2002). Glucose tolerance, insulin sensitivity, and insulin secretion in children born small for gestational age. *J Clin Endocrinol Metab, 87,* 4657-61.

Viard, I., Rainey, W. E., Capponi, A. M., Begeot, M. & Saez, J. M. (1990). Ovine adrenal fasciculata cells contain angiotensin-II receptors coupled to intracellular effectors but are resistant to the steroidogenic effects of this hormone. *Endocrinology*, *127*, 2071-8.

Viau, V. & Meaney, M. J. (1996). The inhibitory effect of testosterone on hypothalamic-pituitary-adrenal responses to stress is mediated by the medial preoptic area. *J Neurosci*, *16*, 1866-76.

Wallberg-Henriksson, H. & Zierath, J. R. (2001). GLUT4: a key player regulating glucose homeostasis? Insights from transgenic and knockout mice (review). *Mol Membr Biol*, *18*, 205-11.

Watkins, A. J., Lucas, E. S., Wilkins, A., Cagampang, F. R. & Fleming, T. P. (2011). Maternal periconceptional and gestational low protein diet affects mouse offspring growth, cardiovascular and adipose phenotype at 1 year of age. *PLoS ONE*, *6*, e28745.

Watkins, A. J., Ursell, E., Panton, R., Papenbrock, T., Hollis, L., Cunningham, C., et al. (2008). Adaptive responses by mouse early embryos to maternal diet protect fetal growth but predispose to adult onset disease. *Biol Reprod*, *78*, 299-306.

Weaver, I. C., Cervoni, N., Champagne, F. A., D'Alession, A. C., Sharma, S., Seckl, J. R., et al. (2004). Epigenetic programming by maternal behaviour. *Nat Neurosci*, *7*, 791-2.

Whittle, W. L., Patel, F. A., Alfaidy, N., Holloway, A. C., Fraser, M., Gyomorey, S., et al. (2001). Glucocorticoid regulation of human and ovine parturition: the relationship between fetal hypothalamic-pituitary-adrenal axis activation and intrauterine prostaglandin production. *Biol Reprod*, *64*, 1019-32.

Whorwood, C. B., Firth, K. M., Budge, H. & Symonds, M. E. (2001). Maternal undernutrition during early to midgestation programs tissue-specific alterations in the expression of the glucocorticoid receptor, 11β-hydroxysteroid dehydrogenase isoforms, and type 1 angiotensin II receptor in neonatal sheep. *Endocrinology*, *142*, 2854-64.

Wilson, P. W. & Grundy, S. M. (2003). The metabolic syndrome. *Circulation*, *108*, 1537-40.

Worthman, C. M. & Kuzara, J. (2005). Life history and the early origins of health differentials. *Am J Hum Biol*, *17*, 95-112.

Yaswen, L., Diehl, N., Brennan, M. B. & Hochgeschwender, U. (1999). Obesity in the mouse model of pro-opiomelanocortin deficiency responds to peripheral melanocortin. *Nat Med*, *5*, 1066-70.

Young, L. E., Fernandes, K., McEvoy, T. G., Butterwith, S. C., Gutierrez, C. G., Carolan, C., et al. (2001). Epigenetic change in *IGF2R* is associated with fetal overgrowth after sheep embryo culture. *Nat Genet*, *27*, 153-4.

Zhang, A., Ding, G., Huang, S., Wu, Y., Pan, X., Guan, X., et al. (2005). c-Jun NH2-terminal kinase mediation of angiotensin II-induced proliferation of human mesangial cells. *Am J Physiol Renal Physiol*, *288*, F1118-24.

Zhang, S., Morrison, J. L., Gill, A., Rattanatray, L., MacLaughlin, S. M., Kleemann, D., et al. (2013a). Dietary restriction in the periconceptional period in normal-weight or obese ewes results in increased abundance of angiotensin-converting enzyme (ACE) and angiotensin type 1 receptor (AT1R) in the absence of changes in ACE or AT1R methylation in the adrenal of the offspring. *Reproduction*, *146*, 443-54.

Zhang, S., Morrison, J. L., Gill, A., Rattanatray, L., MacLaughlin, S. M., Kleemann, D., et al. (2013b). Maternal dietary restriction during the periconceptional period in normal weight or obese ewes results in adrenocortical hypertrophy, an upregulation of the JAK/STAT and downregulation of the IGF1R signalling pathways in the adrenal of the postnatal lamb. *Endocrinology, 154*, 4650-62.

Zhang, S., Rattanatray, L., MacLaughlin, S. M., Cropley, J. E., Suter, C. M., Molloy, L., et al. (2010). Periconceptional undernutrition in normal and overweight ewes leads to increased adrenal growth and epigenetic changes in adrenal IGF2/H19 gene in offspring. *FASEB J, 24*, 2772-82.

Zhang, S., Williams-Wyss, O., MacLaughlin, S. M., Walker, S. K., Kleemann, D. O., Suter, C. M., et al. (2013c). Maternal undernutrition during the first week after conception results in decreased expression of glucocorticoid receptor mRNA in the absence of GR exon 17 hypermethylation in the fetal pituitary in late gestation. *J DOHaD, 4*, 391-401.

Zhu, M. J., Ford, S. P., Means, W. J., Hess, B. W., Nathanielsz, P. W. & Du, M. (2006). Maternal nutrient restriction affects properties of skeletal muscle in offspring. *J Physiol, 575*, 241-50.

Zierath, J. R., He, L., Gumà, A., Odegoard Wahlström, E., Klip, A. & Wallberg-Henriksson, H. (1996). Insulin action on glucose transport and plasma membrane GLUT4 content in skeletal muscle from patients with NIDDM. *Diabetologia, 39*, 1180-9.

ISBN: 978-1-63321-836-9
© 2014 Nova Science Publishers, Inc.

Chapter 4

The Stress of Chronic Hypoxia in Fetal Growth Restriction: Some Physiological Considerations

Lawrence D. Longo[*] and Ravi Goyal

Center for Perinatal Biology, Department of Basic Sciences, Division of Physiology,
Loma Linda University School of Medicine, Loma Linda, CA, US

Abstract

Fetal growth restriction (FGR), defined as 10th percentile or less of estimated fetal weight, is a complication of 7 to 10% of pregnancies in the USA and throughout the world. Strikingly, the relation of FGR to chronic hypoxia is complex and poorly understood. Development of the normal embryo has been shown to occur in a state of relative hypoxia. Nonetheless, beyond a certain degree of physiological adjustment, hypoxia is associated with a number of factors inimical to cell growth and function. In response to prolonged or long-term hypoxemia (LTH), a number of compensatory changes transpire in many organ systems and tissues to maintain homeostasis. These result in what has been called intrauterine growth restriction, small for gestational age infants, and more recently fetal growth restriction. The FGR phenomenon, which with the use of contemporary ultrasonography can become evident during the mid- to late-second trimester, is accompanied by a host of specific responses in essentially every tissue and organ system that has been studied. For instance, in the cardiovascular system secondary to a decrease in myocardial cell contractile function, the heart shows a decrease in cardiac output. In turn, the cerebrovasculature demonstrates a number of significant changes including decreased vascular resistance to maintain cerebral blood flow (CBF) at near normal sea levels values. To effect changes in tone, the cerebral arteries undergo a number of other changes in receptor density and functions. For instance, the function of alpha1 adrenergic receptor subtypes, potassium channel function, and a host of other endocrinologic, metabolic, and neurobiologic changes occur. A key element of these responses includes fundamental changes in structure and function of the placenta of the

---

[*] Corresponding author: Lawrence D. Longo, M.D. Center for Perinatal Biology, Loma Linda University, School of Medicine, Loma Linda, CA 92350, Telephone: 909-558-4325, Fax: 909-558-4029, E-mail: llongo@llu.edu.

FGR infant. The results emphasize the role of hypoxemia in modulating a number of signal transduction mechanisms, including those for protein synthesis, in the various organs and tissues to affect a mosaic of cellular and molecular responses. These specifically highlight the implications of these changes for development and the genesis of disease in the adult. Of critical relevance, our challenge is to move beyond phenomenology to gain an understanding of the fundamental cellular and molecular changes and the mechanisms by which hypoxia and/or other stress result in FGR. In addition, we need to understand how we can prevent the lifelong consequences with a panoply of diseases in adult life.

Keywords: Long-term hypoxia, cardiac, cerebrovascular, development

Abbreviations

ACOG	American Congress of Obstetricians and Gynecologists
BW	birthweight
CpG	cytosine phosphodiester guanine
DNA	deoxyribonucleic acid
DOHaD	developmental origins of adult health and disease
DPC	day post conception
FGR	fetal growth restriction
gm	gram
HIF	hypoxia inducible factor
HSD	hydroxysteroid dehydrogenase
IGF	insulin-like growth factor
IUGR	intrauterine growth restriction
LTH	long-term hypoxia
mmHg	millimeters of mercury
mRNA	messenger ribonucleic acid
NO	nitric oxide
NOS	nitric oxide synthase
O_2	oxygen
PKC	protein kinase C
RNA	ribonucleic acid
ROS	reactive oxygen species
SGA	small for gestational age
Torr	Torricelli (unit of pressure)

An Introduction to Fetal Growth Restriction

Fetal growth restriction (FGR) is a condition of less than optimal growth of the fetus within the maternal uterus, e.g., failure of the fetus to achieve its genetically determined growth potential. Defined by being in the lower 10th percentile of estimated body weight, fetal growth restriction is a health issue of vital importance. In the USA, as well as the entire globe, it occurs in 7 to 10 percent of pregnancies, and accounts for a significant increase in the rates of stillbirth (Gardosi et al., 2013), as well as infant morbidity and mortality (Kramer et al., 1990, Lin et al., 1991, Manning, 1995, Marsal, 2002, Resnik, 2002). In fact, FGR is believed to be associated with, and perhaps account for, ~60 percent of the 4 million neonatal deaths that occur annually worldwide (Lawn et al., 2005, Bellamy and UNICEF, 2003). The perinatal morbidity and mortality in these cases often are associated with hypoxic-ischemic encephalopathy, intraventricular hemorrhage, pulmonary hypertension, necrotizing enterocolitis, and related complications (Amon et al., 1987, Baschat et al., 2000, Batalle et al., 2012, Bernstein et al., 2000, Gilbert and Danielsen, 2003, Kramer et al., 1990, Resnik, 2002, Schauseil-Zipf et al., 1989). Based on a number of studies, a related problem is that of the wide variations seen in growth profiles (Bloomfield et al., 2006). Another factor of importance is the failure to detect FGR antenatally. For instance, in the United Kingdom the detection rate varies from 12 to 50% (West Midlands Perinatal KPI Report, 2011), and such figures are similar in other studies (Gardosi et al., 2013, Gardosi and Francis, 1999) including Australia (Roex et al., 2012). Finally, an economic consideration for these infants is that their required prolonged stay in hospital results in enormous health care costs (Bernstein et al., 2000; Gilbert and Danielson, 2003).

Of major importance, the pathophysiology of fetal growth restriction is incompletely understood. As noted, a large body of epidemiologic studies have identified many clinical associations with the FGR infant (Table 1). Of the preventable, environmental causative factors, smoking by the mother during pregnancy probably is the most common (Wollmann, 1998), and some have ascribed the increased prevalence of FGR to the delay in childbearing in contemporary society (Balasch and Gratacos, 2011). The independent role of specific factors has yet to be established, however. In addition, despite some strong statistical correlations, these do not establish causality.

Typically, growth restricted fetuses/newborns demonstrate normal growth of the brain and heart with their bodies thin for their length. Thus, they are described as having a low ponderal index (100 x weight in grams·crown-heel length^{-3}), a measure of leanness (both weight in gm^{-2} and^{-3} are used), although this is not always the case (Sweeting, 2007). It was in the early 1960s that Lula O. Lubchenco (1915-2001) and colleagues at the University of Colorado published their classic study on the relation of birthweight (both in absolute terms and in centiles) to gestational age during the last trimester of pregnancy (Lubchenco et al., 1963). Subsequently, this group demonstrated that for those infants below the 10th percentile, the risk of neonatal death increased at every gestational age (Lubchenco et al., 1972). Recognition of the concept of fetal growth restriction (Battaglia et al., 1966, Battaglia and Lubchenco, 1967), led to dramatic advances in prenatal care, as well as vast improvements in the management of the newborn infant. The Denver population-based growth curves became used widely, setting a normal range of fetal weight between 2 standard deviations of the mean, or between the 10th and 90th centiles for a given gestational age. Initially, the term small for gestational age (SGA) was used to describe newborn infants whose birthweight (BW) was below the 10th centile. Later, this term was used interchangeably with intrauterine growth restriction (IUGR) of the developing fetus (Wollmann, 1998). Still later, IUGR was distinguished from the SGA infant, however this distinction led to considerable confusion (Saenger et al., 2007). More recently with the development of refined serial ultrasonographic techniques to establish with accuracy fetal body size and its growth velocity *in utero*, the term fetal growth restriction has become *Au courant* [up-to-date].

Table 1. The "Mosaic" of Maternal, Placental, and Fetal Factors in the Genesis of Fetal Growth Restriction*

Maternal	Uteroplacental	Fetal
• Persistent hypoxia (e.g., high altitude, pulmonary disease, severe anemia; moderate to heavy smoking; hemoglobinopathies) • Cardiovascular disorders Hypertension (>140/90) Cyanotic heart disease Diabetes mellitus Renal disease Collagen vascular disease • Hypercoagulable disease Thrombophilia Antiphospholipid antibody syndrome • Undernutrition (caloric and/or protein deprivation) • Toxins and Teratogens (e.g., tobacco, alcohol, illicit drugs, medications, irradiation) • Age <15, >45 • History of IUGR	• Uterine malformation or masses • Placental insufficiency Idiopathic Preeclampsia • Abnormal placentation Abnormal trophoblast invasion Placental infarcts Placenta previa Circumvallate placenta Chorioangioma Velamentous insertion of umbilical cord Umbilical-placental vascular anomalies (Twin-to-twin transfusion syndrome)	• Genetic Chromosomal abnormalities Trisomy 18, 13, 21 Congenital malformations Turner's and other syndromes • Epigenetic Hypoxia Undernutrition • Multiple gestation • Intrauterine viral infections Rubella, Cytomegalovirus, Parvovirus, Herpes virus, Human Immunodeficiency Virus • Other infections Syphilis, Malaria, Toxoplasmosis

Overall, FGR encompasses an extremely heterogeneous group that can be categorized into maternal, placental, and fetal factors. A subgroup of infants includes overlapping etiologies. In addition, there are also a significant number of infants with unexplained etiologies. *Table modified from several that are in the literature.

As noted, for several decades neonatologists distinguished fetuses with IUGR from those that were SGA. While IUGR referred to a pattern of fetal growth below the expected norm, the classification of SGA was based on birth weight alone. Related terms are low birthweight (LBW), defined as a newborn infant of less than 2,500 gm regardless of gestational age, very low birth weight (<1,500 gm), and extremely low BW (<1,000 gm). In terms of morphology, and as a consequence of ultrasonic measurement of both head and abdominal circumference, fetal growth restriction has been categorized as asymmetric (or asynchronous) in which the head grows at a near normal rate (head sparing) or symmetric (synchronous or global) with growth restriction of the head as well as the body (Campbell and Thoms, 1977). The former, accounting for 2/3 to 3/4 of cases, is commonly caused by extrinsic factors affecting the fetus during the third trimester of gestation. Chiefly these factors include: hypoxia, inadequate maternal nutrition or other maternal or placental dysfunctions (Table 1). The latter more symmetric growth pattern commences much earlier in pregnancy from a variety of causes including chromosomal abnormalities, infection, and drugs. These result in a higher incidence of preterm delivery and higher rate of neonatal morbidity (Table 1) (ACOG, 2001, Brodsky and Christou, 2004, Lin et al., 1991, Lin and Santolaya-Forgas, 1998, Manning, 1995,

Nardozza et al., 2012, Resnik, 2002, Seeds, 1984). Nonetheless, caution is required as the pattern, or trajectory, of fetal growth can vary widely with organ specific differences and yet result in a given birthweight. A major factor for these differences is that of growth velocity profiles. Because previously to the advances in ultrasonic technology the FGR infant could be diagnosed only as such with certainty following birth, a significant number who are constitutionally healthy have been and will be subjected to high-risk management resulting in iatrogenic prematurity.

Although differences in growth profiles have been thought to occur chiefly during the third trimester, by means of contemporary ultrasonography those for head circumference, femur diaphysis length, and abdominal circumference are evident by 18, 20, and 22 weeks gestation, respectively (Milani et al., 2005), and these growth velocity differences may become evident at weeks 16 to 17 of gestation (Milani et al., 2005). Of great importance to the advancement of perinatology and neonatology, the dramatic consequence of refinements in ultrasonography has led to more rational care of the developing organism with the saving of lives. These advances allow assessment of blood flow/velocity in the uterine artery (Albaiges et al., 2003, Axt-Fliedner, 2004, Hershkovitz et al., 2005, Thaler et al., 1990), the umbilical vessels (Chen et al., 1986, Gill et al., 1981, Sutton et al., 1990), and other vessels including cerebral arteries (Fong et al., 1999, Hershkovitz et al., 2000, Mari et al., 2007). (A caveat of these studies is that the sonograph measures the velocity of blood flow, while flow *per se* is the product of velocity and vascular diameter). Critical aspects of many of these studies have been surveyed by Battaglia (Battaglia, 2011), and will not be re-reviewed here.

Two decades ago it came to be appreciated that custom- rather than population-based fetal growth standards are more likely to discriminate between the fetus/newborn that is constitutionally small but normal from a biologic-physiologic standpoint, from that with true FGR (Gardosi et al., 1992, Gardosi and Francis, 1999, Resnik, 2007). These custom-based standards, with consideration of variables such as maternal ethnicity, parity, height and weight in early pregnancy, as well as fetal sex, utilize optimal birthweight as the proper endpoint of a growth curve, and are based upon the fetus' ability to achieve its full growth potential independent of maternal/placental pathology. As may be obvious, each of these variables plays an important role in the determination of fetal potential. Of considerable relevance here is the distinction of the FGR infant from that which is born prematurely, and preventative methods that may be of value in this regard (Iams, 2014). In a large study from New Zealand, the use of customized-based birthweight centiles identified more preterm infants as FGR. This contrasted with population-based studies that reported more near-term infants as FGR (Groom et al., 2007). In the customized studies, perinatal death among preterm infants occurred only in those classified as FGR. This supports the conclusion that prematurity and true fetal growth restriction are co-morbidities. In contrast, no perinatal deaths and low rates of preterm birth occurred for FGR infants classified by population percentiles (Groom et al., 2007). Other investigators have noted that customized birthweight standards also more accurately predict stillbirth, neonatal deaths, and neurologic sequelae (Clausson et al., 2001, McCowan et al., 2005). As observed by Robert Resnik, "one size does not fit all, and it would seem … time for … obstetricians to adopt the use of customized fetal growth standards" (Resnik, 2007, p. 221).

The two major factors/processes which determine fetal growth and development are genetic and epigenetic. In contrast to the unalterable nucleotide sequences of the DNA, nutritional, metabolic, and other environmental influences operate through epigenetic mechanisms to affect gene expression. Figure 1 shows the interrelationships of fetal demand and maternal supply with some associated variables which can affect the course of fetal development.

An additional consideration concerns the fetus not developing in isolation. Rather, in concert with the placenta and maternal organism, the fetus is an essential element of the maternal-placental-fetal complex or unit (Diczfalusy, 1964). Thus, whether considered from the perspective of its general physiology, endocrinology, metabolism, circulation, immunology, or other elements, the fetus is part of this integrated organic unit, a dynamic module in the matrix of reproductive development. It should be evident that in the maternal-placental-fetal complex a host of biochemical factors at the cellular and molecular level can interact with physiologic variables at the organ and tissue level including that of inadequate trophoblast invasion (see below) to result in growth restriction. Rather than existing as a distinct pathological entity, FGR, in fact, is a symptom complex resulting from many causes. One may posit, therefore, that as in the case of hypertension, metabolic syndrome, and other disorders, the FGR phenotype is a mosaic resulting from many underlying conditions.

During the past several decades, in addition to factors causing fetal growth restriction and its more immediate effects, attention has been directed to the genesis of long-term sequelae of the offspring when they become adolescents and adults, that is the concept of the developmental origins of adult disease (DOHaD). Among conditions so identified in children and adolescents are short stature and premature adrenarche. In adults the host of conditions so identified include: cardiovascular disease (hypertension, coronary artery disease, cardiomyopathy, and cerebral vascular accident), metabolic syndrome and type 2 diabetes, some malignancies, and several neuropsychiatric disorders (Table 2). In addition to the implications of these diseases for the lives of individuals, their social and public health considerations are far from trivial (see below).

Intra-uterine Stress and Epigenetic Mechanisms

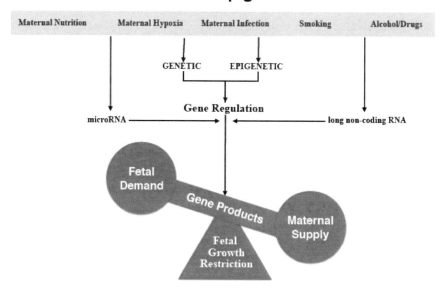

Figure 1. Some intra-uterine stressors and the proposed mechanisms of gene regulation that determine fetal growth.

Table 2. Adolescent and/or Adult Long-term Sequelae of Fetal Growth Restriction in Offspring

- Effects on Growth and Puberty
  Born with low birthweight
  Poor postnatal growth
  Short stature in adolescents and adults
  Premature adrenarche
  Premature pubarche in females
  Body composition: decrease in fat mass at birth, accelerated gain in fat mass during adolescence and later
- Metabolic Conditions
  Glucose tolerance impaired
  Mild-to-moderate insulin resistance
  Resetting of IGF/insulin systems, circulating concentrations of IGF-1 below average for age and sex
  Metabolic syndrome
    Dyslipidemia
    Type 2 Diabetes mellitus
    Obesity
- Other Endocrinopathies
  Mild hyperthyrotropinemia in absence of overt hypothyroidism
  Decreased adiponectin and follistatin in children
  Increased fetal/neonatal glucocorticoid exposure
  Polycystic ovary syndrome
  Early menopause
- Cardiovascular Disease
  Hypertension
  Coronary artery disease
  Cyanotic heart disease
  Atherosclerosis
  Cardiomyopathy with heart failure
  Cerebrovascular accident (stroke)
  Coagulation disorders
- Chronic Pulmonary Disease
  Obstructive lung disease
  Asthma
- Renal Insufficiency
- Immunodeficiency
- Neuropsychiatric Sequelae
  Neurodevelopmental delay
  Multiple syndromes
  Schizophrenia
- Skeletal system
  Osteoporosis

* Table modified from several that are in the literature.

The lack of understanding of this complex syndrome of growth restriction is not unlike a similar situation in the seventeenth century. Until the latter part of that century, specific infectious diseases such as typhus, typhoid, malaria, *et cetera*, were not recognized as such. Rather, these and other febrile illnesses were classified as a single disorder – fever. These were distinguished as continual, intermittent, hectic, recurrent, or remittent, there being little or no understanding of the underlying condition (King, 1958). It took Thomas Sydenham (1624-1689), the English Hippocrates, to differentiate between typhoid fever and typhus, and to define other febrile conditions such as measles and scarlet fever (Payne, 1900). Today, over three centuries later, we need a contemporary Sydenham to cut through the Gordian knot[*] of the various mechanisms and their interactions which produce the fetal growth restriction phenotype.

While falling far short of that goal, the present Chapter attempts to synthesize into a coherent whole some of the hypoxic-induced mechanisms which interact in several key organ systems to result in abnormal fetal growth and development. In addition, as a case study we review background on the idea of FGR, and a few of the key studies at high altitude that have helped to establish the close association of high altitude hypoxia with fetal growth restriction. An additional objective is to consider the manner(s) by which failure of these mechanisms might result in growth restriction of the fetus/newborn infant in those instances when the etiology is not known. For the most part these experimental studies have been performed in species suitable for investigation of physiologic (sheep) and cellular and/or molecular (rodents) mechanisms. Thus, one may view this as an exercise in exploring what is known and what is unknown of the mosaic of interdigitating and complementary factors and mechanisms that eventuate in the developing fetus experiencing growth restriction (Longo, 1984).

The Recognition of Fetal Growth Restriction

Not until the mid-twentieth century did the concept arise that some small neonates gave evidence of growth failure, rather than being born prematurely. To that time, all infants who weighed <2,500 gm were classified as "premature", this being the definition of the "Expert Group on Pre-Maturity" of the World Health Organization (World Health Organization, 1950). Thus, the idea of fetal growth restriction with failure to reach full growth potential was pioneering. In 1947 from Los Angeles "... with much trepidation", a report was presented of 69 SGA newborns near-term who were undernourished (of 6,641 total) (McBurney, 1947). These infant birthweights ranged from ~1.5 to 2.5 kg, and the placentas tended to be smaller than normal. By California State Board of Health statistical requirements, the infants were classified as "premature" despite their having been born at or near full-term (McBurney, 1947). In another series shortly thereafter, 20 such small-for-dates infants were diagnosed *in utero* by both serial measurements of pubic symphysis to uterine fundal height, as well as birthweight. Excluding stillborns and one mongoloid infant, the weight of the 12 surviving infants was 1702 ± 135 gm (Rumbolz and McGoogan, 1953). Since that time, it has become recognized that a number of such low birth weight infants are a consequence of decreased rate of intrauterine growth, rather than their being delivered prior to term. The vital relevance of this concept was affirmed by subsequent studies that demonstrated correlations of stillbirth and fetal asphyxia to restricted growth (North, 1966). As noted, to account for smaller than normal size and weight, the terms "small for gestational age" (SGA), "intrauterine growth

---

[*] An intricate knot tied by King Gordius of Phrygia and cut by Alexander the Great (356 BCE-323 BCE) with his sword after hearing an oracle promise that whoever could undo it would be the next ruler of Asia

restriction" (IUGR; initially "retardation"; Gruenwald et al., 1967, Warkany et al., 1961), and "fetal growth restriction" (FGR) were introduced to describe these infants.

In a 1950 study by the United States Public Health Service of a reported total of 837,736 live births, neonatal and infant mortality were considerably higher in the mountain states than that of other areas of the country (Shapiro et al., 1954). For the USA as a whole, these were mean BW=3,320 gm; neonatal mortality = 20; for infants who weighed 4,000 gm or more, 9.8%, for infants who weighed 2,500 gm or less = 7.4%). For Colorado and other mountain states the values were, mean BW = 3,240 gm, neonatal mortality = 24%, for infants who weighed 4,000 gm or more = 6.3%; for infants who weighed less than 2,500 gm = 9.1%. For Denver, CO, the comparable values were, mean BW = 3,035 gm; for infants that weighed 4,000 gm or more = 3.3%, for infants who weighed less than 2,500 gm = 11.7% (neonatal mortality not given). In comparison, the values for Lake County (Leadville), CO were, mean BW = 2,655 gm, neonatal mortality = 49%; for infants who weighed 4,000 gm or more 0%; for infants weighed 2,500 gm or less 48.3% (McClung, 1969, p. 52). Thus, in comparison to the USA as a whole, the mean birthweights for live born infants at Leadville were 20% less, the neonatal mortality was over twice greater, and the percent of infants who weighed 2,500 gm or less was many-fold greater. It is a sobering reflection.

In light of its relatively large population that lives at high elevations, and with its careful maintenance of health records, the earliest controlled studies that established the inverse relation of birthweight to altitude originated in Colorado. Stimulated by the observation that its Lake County had a several-fold higher incidence of "prematurity" than the state average, in the mid-1950s the Colorado State Department of Public Health initiated a study to explore the reasons for this apparent anomaly. Further analysis of this unexplained dilemma was conducted by a combined effort of the departments of pediatrics and obstetrics and gynecology at the University of Colorado School of Medicine and the State Department of Public Health, and other groups, and was headed by John A. Lichty. This report compared a number of obstetrical and newborn indices at Leadville in Lake County (3,100 m) with those at Denver (1,609 m). Mean birthweights at these two locales were 2,655 gm and 3,035 gm, respectively. For live births of 2,500 gm or less the comparative numerical values were as follows: "Prematurity" 31% versus 10%, neonatal death rate (deaths under one month of age per 1,000 live births), 42% versus 23%. The Lake County birthweights were 380 gm less than Denver controls, with a significant shift to the left of BW distribution curves, as compared to controls (Lichty et al., 1957). The authors also quoted a personal communication from Dr. Elena Boder of Mexico stating that, in a comparison of live birthweights, those in Mexico City (2,134 m) were 8.7% less than those in Mazatlan (sea level). Of critical importance, the authors concluded that these findings "… support the statement of practicing physicians in Lake County that the babies are often small but not otherwise abnormal. Possibly the generally accepted BW of 2,500 gm is not appropriate for distinguishing between full term and premature infants in this community" (Lichty et al., 1957, p. 669). This then was the first study that demonstrated clearly the fact that low BW was a consequence of high altitude, not a *defacto* index of prematurity. In related reports, the authors confirmed these findings and showed that newborn crown-heel length and head length and width were appropriate for gestational age (Howard et al., 1957b). They also reported the paradox that in Lake County newborns neither the oxyhemoglobin saturation nor hematocrit values differed from control (Howard et al., 1957a). Of vital importance, further studies from 1969 to 1973 in Colorado confirmed these conclusions, and also demonstrated that high altitude hypoxia, rather than decreased gestational age with pre-term delivery, accounted for the altitude-associated lessened BW and increase in neonatal mortality. Birthweight was inversely associated with altitude at each gestational age beyond 35 weeks (McCullough and Reeves, 1977, McCullough et al., 1977).

In an historical perspective, the late Joseph Dancis (1916-2010), of New York University and the Bellevue Hospital, recalled regarding normal patterns of newborn growth that it was when he was a senior resident that his chief of Pediatrics, Luther Emmett Holt Jr. (1895-1974), pointed out the lack of standard BW curves for premature infants. This made it difficult to judge the progress of a given infant following birth (Dancis, 1983). In a series of 100 infants that weighed from 1,000 to 2,500 gm at the time of birth, Dancis enlisted a fellow resident to tabulate the weight gains for their first 50 days of life. On analyzing what appeared a "tangled mass of curves", Dr. Holt "… sketched in over them, at 250-gram intervals, simple straight lines seeking to reproduce the summation of the slopes." Following some corrections, with the early weight losses, "… the rough outline of the premie weight grid emerged" (Dancis, 1983, p. 3; Dancis et al., 1948). Here, Dancis confessed the unusual nature of their published report. There were no section on methods (including the population surveyed, criteria for inclusion or exclusion), no careful analysis of results, no regression lines or statistics, and no "… extensive and penetrating discussion" (Dancis, 1983, p. 2). Of note, the shape of the grid demonstrated that less mature preemies reached their weight nadir later than those that are more mature, and their rate of weight gain was slower so that they required more time to regain their original birthweight. These observations on the significant decrease in weight during the first days to week of life confirmed an earlier study of the weight changes of almost 3,000 newborns, which separated males and females and white and blacks (Dunham et al., 1939).

In a follow up study for the years 1950 to 1957 of almost one million live births in the USA, again the mountain states and Lake County, CO stood out for both their high rates of "prematurity" and neonatal deaths (Grahn and Kratchman, 1963). Notable in this review was the association of these variables with high altitude, with minimal association with exposure to terrestrial irradiation. The authors concluded, "The weight of the evidence – historical, experimental, and clinical – strongly suggests that the reduced partial pressure of oxygen is responsible for the reduced fetal growth and subsequently increased neonatal death rate" (Grahn and Kratchman, 1963, p. 350).

A decade and a half following the early Colorado studies, and, in part, motivated by those conclusions, Lula O. Lubchenco and colleagues at the University of Colorado first described the relation of birthweight to gestational age during the third trimester (Lubchenco et al., 1963). Although this study was conducted at moderately high altitude (Denver, CO, 1,609 m, 5,280 ft), it set a new standard for evaluation of the newborn, and the "Lulagram" developmental growth chart became used world-wide. For infants whose growth patterns lie outside normal developmental profiles, the terms small-, appropriate-, and large- for gestational age were introduced on the basis of weight, length, head circumference, and weight-length ratio (ponderal index) (Battaglia and Lubchenco, 1967, Lubchenco, 1970, Lubchenco et al., 1966, 1972). Although the term "low-birth weight" was introduced in the early sixties to replace the word "premature" for infants under 2,500 gm at birth, its acceptance was markedly facilitated by Lubchenco's popularization of matching birthweight with gestation. Too long had the designation for term and premature been based on BW above and below 2,500 gm without awareness of two distinct populations for each weight group.

A study by the University of California Berkeley biostatistician Jacob Yerushalmy (1904-1973) and coworkers showed that there were as many term as preterm infants born weighing under 2,500 gm in the United States, and surprisingly more preterm infants weighing above than below that figure (Yerushalmy et al., 1965).

In her monograph *The high-risk infant*, Lubchenco summarized standards of intrauterine growth from the twenty fourth to the forty second week of gestation. She emphasized the importance of the use of gestational age, along with birthweight, as a dimension to understanding not only peri-natal risk factors, but also in the consideration of long-term outcome (Lubchenco, 1976). Her work became a classic. The studies of Lubchenco and others helped to replace the pediatric concept of "failure to thrive" with that of the extent to which the yet to be born infant grows in an optimal manner. Subsequently, several investigators have reported birthweight-gestational age data for infants born at sea level among different ethnic groups (Altman and Coles, 1980, Ballard et al., 1979, Brenner et al., 1976, Dunn and Wharton, 1985, Gardosi et al., 1992, Usher, 1970, Usher and McLean, 1969, Usher et al., 1966). The introduction of diagnostic ultrasound, with measurements of both head and abdominal circumference and femur length has revolutionized the determination of fetal body size *in utero*. Although continuous throughout pregnancy, fetal growth follows a biphasic curve, with the period ~32 weeks being most rapid for acceleration in mass (weight) gain, and ~18 weeks for the peak rate of increase in body length (Tanner, 1978, Villar and Belizan, 1982). Although many instances of IUGR have been attributed to "placental insufficiency" (Gruenwald, 1963, 1970), the term has caused confusion in the literature, and been defined in various ways.

A more recent analysis was conducted of all live births and infant deaths in the state of Colorado for the years 1978 to 1981 (Yip, 1987). After adjusting for socioeconomic factors, a modest association was noted between altitude and the percentage of preterm births of infants weighing <2,500 gm. This association was much stronger, however, for term births with BW <2,500 gm (Yip, 1987). Among comparable subpopulations of infants with gestational ages of at least 37 weeks, the lower BW at high altitude held for each BW distribution at differing altitudes (Yip, 1987). In terms of BW, one might ask about the extent to which it really matters, and what is its relation to morbidity rates. We are unaware of comparative morbidity rates, a fruitful area to explore. In terms of neonatal mortality, the studies from Lake County have been highly valuable in this regard. Other details of high altitude associated FGR are presented in an accompanying Chapter (Longo and Goyal, 2014).

Fetal Growth Restriction in Laboratory Animals

From an experimental standpoint, in laboratory species fetal hypoxia with resultant FGR can be induced by several means. These include: maternal hypoxia (Giussani et al., 1994, Kitanaka et al., 1989), maternal hyperthermia (Thureen et al., 1992) restricting maternal uterine blood flow (Baserga et al., 2009, 2010, Challis et al., 1989, Phillips et al., 1996, Wilkening and Meschia, 1983), reducing fetal umbilical blood flow (Giussani et al., 1997, Unno et al., 1997), placental embolization (Boyle et al., 1984, Bubb et al., 2007, Clapp et al., 1980, Gagnon et al., 1997), and maternal uterine carunclectomy prior to mating (which restricts the number of placentomes; Alexander, 1964, Dyer et al., 2009, Phillips et al., 1996,

Robinson et al., 1979). Details of many aspects of these approaches with their strengths and weaknesses, as well as similarities and differences in fetal physiologic responses, have been reviewed by others (Morrison, 2008). As a caveat, despite many similarities in the responses to these stresses to the fetus, these several methodologies are associated with differing degrees of acidemia, hypoglycemia, and/or nutrient deprivation.

As a "model" for almost every aspect of reproduction, rodents have been used to explore antenatal maternal hypoxia and its sequelae for the mother, fetus, and offspring as an adult. These include the most vulnerable period of gestation, the degree of hypoxia, and its duration. Based on an analysis of 19 studies in rats and 5 in mice that met criteria of having appropriate controls and stringent statistical analysis (Jang et al., 2014), it is clear that, in addition to the factors given above, the species/breed studied is important and these variables interact. For instance, in the rat 7 days or more and in the mouse 3 days or more of hypoxia at 14% or less O_2 concentration during the third (in some cases second) trimester of pregnancy are required to produce FGR. Also in the rodent, overall analysis suggests that a newborn pup weight reduction of 22% is required to meet the human FGR definitions of below the 10th percentile (Jang et al., 2014). In the rabbit, uteroplacental ischemia produced by ligation of 50% of blood vessels on day 25 (of a 30 day gestation), produced a number of fetal cerebral neurostructural abnormalities associated with functional impairments (Illa et al., 2013).

As noted, prolonged fetal hypoxia, as a consequence of any of the factors noted above can result in considerable changes in cardiovascular function (Kamitomo et al., 1993) with FGR (Giussani et al., 2001, Moore et al., 2011). Many of these have been demonstrated in our "model" of high altitude acclimatized long-term hypoxia in fetal sheep. These include significant reduction (-24%) combined right and left ventricular cardiac output compared to the normoxic fetuses (Kamitomo et al., 1992, 1993).

Cardiovascular Function with Fetal Growth Restriction

In human FGR infants several studies have demonstrated significant alterations in cardiovascular function. For instance, such newborns have increased thickening and stiffness of the aorta with reduced distensibility (Cosmi et al., 2009; Koklu et al., 2006; Skilton et al., 2005), key components of cardiovascular disease in adults (Arnett et al., 1994). Associated pathologies in FGR infants are ventricular hypertrophy with increased heart weight (Veille et al., 1993), decreased myocyte size and ventricular volume (Mayhew et al., 1999), and ventricular ejection force (Rizzo et al., 1995). In a report using ultrasonic measurements to compare myocardial function in late second and throughout the third trimester FGR fetuses, a number of parameters in these fetuses differed from appropriate for gestational age controls. For instance, both isovolumetric contraction and relaxation times were prolonged, ejection time was reduced, and the calculated myocardial performance index was increased (Hassan et al., 2013). These indices of altered myocardial function appeared prior to the observed arterial and venous umbilical and other arterial Doppler abnormalities that characterize hypoxia (Hassan et al., 2013). In view of the evidence in animal models that LTH results in these alterations, it would seem reasonable that hypoxia is the culprit for mediating these changes in the FGR newborn infant.

In response to acute hypoxia, the fetus experiences redistribution of cardiac output from the peripheral circulation to maintain circulation of the brain, heart, and adrenal glands (Cohn et al., 1974, Lorijn and Longo, 1980, Peeters et al., 1979). Such redistribution has been shown to be mediated by a carotid body chemoreflex (Giussani et al., 1993) in concert with the release of catecholamines (Jones and Robinson, 1975), arginine vasopressin (Perez et al., 1989), neuropeptide Y (Fletcher et al., 2000), nitric oxide (NO) (Morrison et al., 2003), and other vasoactive factors. Reactive oxygen species also play a role in this response (Thakor et al., 2010).

Fetal asymmetric growth restriction and cardiovascular dysfunction also have been demonstrated in the rat (Herrera et al., 2012, Williams et al., 2005a, 2005b). Also in the guinea pig, Thompson and his group have demonstrated several cardiovascular sequelae including increased cardiac production of endothelial nitric oxide synthase (NOS) (Dong and Thompson, 2006, Thompson et al., 2000) with increased NO in such dysfunction (Thompson et al., 2009).

To explore aspects of growth and the developing cardiovascular system independently from those influences of maternal physiologic responses, the chicken embryo also has been used to advantage. Several groups have demonstrated the effect of hypoxia in causing asymmetric embryonic/fetal growth as well as the growth of specific organs (Giussani et al., 2007, Lindgren and Altimiras, 2011, Miller et al., 2002, Ruijtenbeek et al., 2003a, 2003b, Sharma et al., 2006). The reported changes include aortic hypertrophy and left ventricular dysfunction (Rouwet et al., 2002), with enlargement of both ventricles (Villamor et al., 2004), and cardiomyopathy (Salinas et al., 2010). Such cardiovascular changes are associated with altered endothelial reactivity (Ruijtenbeek et al., 2003a, 2003b), and sympathetic hyperinnervation of peripheral arteries (Rouwet et al., 2002, Ruijtenbeek et al., 2000). The LTH-induced asymmetric growth restriction and cardiac remodeling were not seen when supplemental O_2 was administered to those chick embryos at high altitude (Giussani et al., 2007, Salinas et al., 2010). As in the fetal lamb, in the chick embryo LTH decreased ventricular $+dT \cdot dt_{max}^{-1}$, peak pressure and ventricular ejection fraction (Sharma et al., 2006).

Hypoxia-Mediated FGR and Neuropsychological Correlates

The correlation of cerebral neuroanatomical and neuropsychological changes with fetal growth restriction has been described by numerous investigators. Chronic hypoxia *per se* or hypoxia-ischemia as a consequence of prolonged reduction in uteroplacental blood flow can have invidious short-term and long-term consequences for the developing brain (Rees et al., 2008). For instance, an association of FGR with poor neurobehavioral and cognitive performance has been reported in neonates (Figueras et al., 2009). Some neurobehavioral impairment appears to be even more pronounced in preterm, as compared to near term, FGR infants (Rees et al., 2008), although these differences were not observed over a long time period of life (Bassan et al., 2011). Nonetheless, long-term follow-up studies have demonstrated significant neurodevelopmental delays persisting into adolescence (Aarnoudse-Moens et al., 2009, Feldman and Eidelman, 2006). Other investigators have reported cognitive impairment and learning deficiencies observed in school being related to a characteristic pattern of altered short-term memory, attention span, and anxiety (Feldman and Eidelman, 2006, Geva et al., 2006a, 2006b, Leitner et al., 2007), with in some cases an increased risk of overt attention deficit disorders (Geva et al., 2006a, 2006b, Heinonen et al., 2010). These behavioral changes have been suggested to serve as indices of specific neurological changes such as the anterior hippocampal-prefrontal cortical network, the parahippocampal complex, the striatum thalamus, and other structures (Cubillo et al., 2012, Eichenbaum et al., 2007, Geva et al., 2006a, 2006b).

Magnetic resonance imaging has demonstrated a number of structural changes in the brain of the FGR fetus and newborn infant (Sanz-Cortés et al., 2013). These include the cerebral cortex (Dubois et al., 2008) and hippocampus (Lodygensky et al., 2008). Rather than gross tissue destruction, FGR is believed to be associated with more subtle disruption of normal neurodevelopment (Rees et al., 2011). To detect such changes in structure and organization requires modifications of imaging. To date, we know of no long-term studies that have evaluated the correlation of functional impairments with the underlying neurological anomalies, however.

Hypoxia-Mediated FGR and the Placenta

Although the focus of this Chapter is on FGR, because of the intimate relations of the placenta to growth of the fetus and the genesis of its restriction (Baschat, 2004, Bell et al., 1999, Cetin and Alvino, 2009, Cetin and Antonazzo, 2009, Mellor, 1983, Myatt, 2006, Sibley et al., 2005, Wallace et al., 2005), it may be of value to consider several aspects of these under conditions of LTH (Charnock-Jones et al., 2004, Tissot van Patot, 2012). Designed for efficient exchange of O_2 and nutrients between the maternal and fetal circulations, the placenta elaborates hormones that determine fetal and, in some respects, maternal metabolism. Among other considerations, the efficiency of placental exchange also is a function of morphology, which varies considerably among species (Amoroso, 1952, Leiser and Kaufmann, 1994, Mossman, 1987).

In addition to its role in serving as the fetal lung in supplying oxygen to the developing organism, the placenta consumes a considerable fraction of the O_2 exchanged to support its own energy demands. During the third trimester, with its period of fetal exponential growth, and with limited enlargement of the placenta, limitation in O_2 availability such as that which occurs at high altitude or in the presence of maternal cyanotic heart, pulmonary disease, and/or hemoglobinopathy, fetal O_2 demands may be limited with resultant growth restriction (Longo, 1987). In patients with preeclampsia or associated oxidative stress, this may be aggravated to be more than a straightened issue of supply and demand (Corso and Thomson, 2001, Murray, 2012, Postigo et al., 2009, Singla et al., 1997, Soleymanlou et al., 2005; Zamudio et al., 2007).

Of relevance, in a relatively recent retrospective report, in the near-term placenta of FGR human newborns, several measures of growth of villi and fetal capillaries have been shown to be abnormal, including a significant 24% decrease in placental weight (from 470±52 to 357±41 gm) (Calvert et al., 2013). Others report reduced villous and capillary growth, without changes in measures of lumen caliber or shape (Mayhew et al., 2004). Perhaps of relevance in FGR placentas, fibrocyte-like cells demonstrate a reduced ability to promote angiogenesis (Riddell et al., 2013). As depicted in Figure 2, inadequate trophoblast invasion may play a key role in the genesis of FGR. As an aside, although it has been suggested that asymmetric growth of the FGR fetus is a consequence of altered trophoblast apoptotic activity, the evidence does not support this thesis (Roje et al., 2014).

In a further attempt to understand the mechanistic basis of some of the LTH-associated FGR changes noted above, in our mouse "model" of FGR, we tested the hypothesis that the placental response to hypoxic stress is associated with important gene expression changes. We quantified such expression in response to 48 hours of hypoxia near term (Gheorghe et al., 2007). Pregnant mice at 15.5 DPC were exposed to 48 hours of hypoxia (10.5% O_2), after which the Affymetrix Mouse 430A_2.0 array was used to measure gene expression changes (Gheorghe et al., 2007). 171 probe sets, corresponding to 163 genes, were regulated by hypoxia (P<0.01). Ninety of these genes were upregulated, and 73 were downregulated. We annotated the regulated genes and examined overrepresented functional categories. Among these we observed several overrepresented functional categories. Upregulated genes included those involved in metabolism, oxygen transport, proteolysis, cell death, metabolism of reactive oxygen species, and DNA methylation. Genes involved in transcription, cell cycle regulation, and cell structure were downregulated. The observation that hypoxia upregulates ROS metabolism, in conjunction with DNA methylation enzymes, suggest that in addition to the placenta, hypoxia may contribute to long-term epigenetic changes in stressed fetal tissues and organs (Gheorghe et al., 2007).

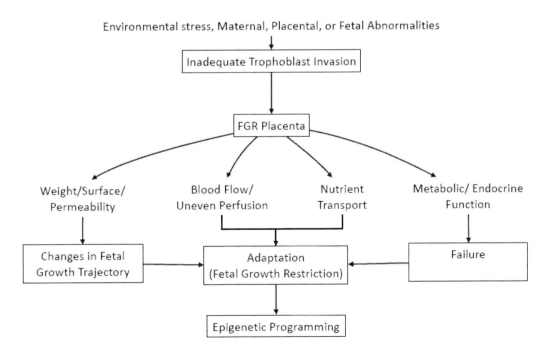

Figure 2. Some of the possible mechanisms involved in environmental stress with maternal, placental, and/or fetal abnormalities that result in inadequate trophoblast invasion and epigenetic programming of diseases.

In the human FGR placenta, microarray gene expression confirmed by real-time polymerase chain reaction studies demonstrated several-fold increased expression of a number of genes, including those for soluble endothelial growth factor receptor, human chorionic gonadotropin, HIF-2α, follistatin-like 3, and leptin. These changes suggest active placental angiogenesis (McCarthy et al., 2007). In the placenta of FGR infants, studies demonstrate significant differences in gene expression patterns of insulin-like growth factor 1 and 2 (IGF 1, 2), and IGF binding protein 3 (Börzsönyi et al., 2011). In addition, underexpression of the *11β-HSD2* gene with impaired feto-maternal glucocorticoid metabolism was seen (Börzsönyi et al., 2012). Of relevance, in cultured human trophoblastic cells, hypoxia reduced the expression and activity of system A amino acid transporters (Nelson et al., 2003), and increased the expression of glucose transporters (Esterman et al., 1997). Also of importance, expression of the ATP binding cassette (ABC) superfamily member G2 (ABCG2), a major membrane transporter for xenobiotics, was reduced significantly in the placenta of infants showing growth restriction (Evseenko et al., 2007). Further, in the human FGR placenta the mitochondrial DNA content was increased significantly (35%), and this change was correlated inversely with umbilical venous PO_2 (Lattuada et al., 2008). These changes all suggest placental adaptation to O_2 and/or nutritional restriction. In pregnancies complicated by FGR, an examination of microRNAs, short non-coding RNAs that regulate gene expression at the post-transcriptional level, disclosed slightly higher levels of several species in maternal plasma with lower levels in the placental tissue (Mouillet et al., 2010). This has great implications for dysregulation of protein synthesis in the placenta and fetus. FGR infants born at high altitude on the *alto plano* of Bolivia, demonstrated inhibition of the peroxisome proliferator-activated antigen gamma, a potential link between long-term hypoxia and growth restriction (Julian et al., 2014).

Not to be overlooked, many (~60) so-called imprinted genes that exhibit parent-of-origin monoallelic differences in expression, play important roles in development of the placenta as well as in embryonic and fetal growth (Angiolini et al., 2006, Fowden et al., 2006b, Reik et al., 2003). Disruption of imprinted gene expression can result in abnormal placental development and FGR (Morgan et al., 2005, Piedrahita, 2011). In humans, over 50 imprinted genes have been identified. These are distributed in distinct clusters that are regulated by a common imprinting control region (Reik and Walter, 2001). In regards to placental and fetal development, two clusters of imprinted genes lie within chromosome 11p15.5, each regulated by a separate imprinting control region, -1 and -2. Decreased expression of the paternally expressed *IGF-2* gene has been reported in the placenta of the FGA infant (Guo et al., 2008).

Among imprinted genes, those for the cullins, a family of hydrophobic proteins that provide a scaffold for ubiquitin ligases, and which combine with RING proteins to form Cullin-RING ubiquitin ligases have been appreciated to be of importance. A family of 7 distinct genes, cullins not only are involved in targeting proteins for ubiquitin-mediated destruction as in embryonic limb patterning, but also serving as a docking site for ubiquitin conjugating enzymes involved in cell cycle control. The placentas of humans (Gascoin-Lachambre et al., 2010) and rats (Buffat et al., 2007) as well as patients with FGR, preeclampsia, and several other conditions show significant elevation of cullin7, 1, 4A, and 4B and these may serve as biomarkers for several varieties of trophoblastic disease. Emphasis should be given to the identification of targets of cullin-mediated protein degeneration in association with FGR. Along this line, homogenized umbilical cord samples from a population of Asian Chinese women showed significant inverse relation of expression of the imprinted gene pleckstrin homology domain, family A, member 2 (PHLDA2) and BW, with downregulation of paternally expressed gene 10 (PEG10). The latter was associated with concomitant methylation patterns of the PEG10 promoter as a biomarker for FGR (Lim et al., 2012).

In a knockout mouse model in which the paternal allele placental-specific transcript of the imprinted *Igf-2* gene was deleted, a placental phenotype similar to that seen in FGR, with a decrement in fetal growth was observed (Constância et al., 2002, Sibley et al., 2004). These studies have led Colin P. Sibley and colleagues to speculate that alterations in the patterns or phenotype of the human placenta can be associated with specific patterns of fetal development under conditions of growth restriction (Sibley et al., 2005).

To return to the human FGR placenta, the ratio of mRNA from the maternally expressed gene *Phlda2* to that of the paternally expressed gene *Mest* has been shown to be increased. No changes in DNA methylation were observed, however. Four other imprinted genes were differentially expressed, as were a number of non-imprinted genes (McMinn et al., 2006). In another study of gene expression in the FGR placenta, signaling pathway analysis disclosed upregulation of 47 genes including those of the inflammation-mediated cytokine and chemokine pathways, as well as those for angiogenesis, with downregulation of genes that encode for ribosomal proteins (the latter suggesting reduced translation) (Sitras et al., 2009). Of interest, in this report none of the known imprinted placental genes were expressed differentially, and those FGR gene expression changes were similar to that seen with preeclampsia (Sitras et al., 2009).

Further studies in this regard in the FGR placenta reported upregulation of leptin, corticotropin releasing hormone IGF-binding protein-1 (Struwe et al., 2010), with differences noted for site of placental sampling (Tzschoppe et al., 2010). Further investigation disclosed increased placental leptin mRNA and protein, as well as in venous umbilical cord blood elevated leptin binding capacity with reduced leptin levels (Tzschoppe et al., 2011). The authors suggest that in the infant this may play an important role in induced dysregulation of appetite regulatory mechanisms leading to further growth restriction (Tzschoppe et al., 2011). Reduced methylation (associated with increased gene expression) of *Icr-1* is associated with FGR in normotensive patients (Bourque et al., 2010). In an analysis of 74 "putatively" imprinted genes in placental tissue of FGR and normal control pregnancies of 52 (70%) imprinted genes expressed, five were upregulated and four downregulated; but loss of imprinting gain of function did not play a major role in these changes (Diplas et al., 2009). A caution to consider is that although perturbation in genomic imprinting have been associated with FGR, no correlation of differentially methylation regions with a specific biologic function has been demonstrated. Rather the correlation was with gene length (Lambertini et al., 2011). A caveat of all of these described differential expression of placental genome studies, the cell of origin (syncytiotrophoblast versus cytotrophoblast, versus other cell types) was not defined.

A related consideration for the growth restricted fetus is that of decreased amniotic fluid volume (oligohydramnios) which may aggravate a non-hospitable environment. The association of low values of amniotic fluid index (an estimate of the amount of amniotic fluid, and part of the biophysical profile; Griffin et al., 2009) with a growth-restricted fetus has been reported by several groups (Banks and Miller, 1999, Chamberlain et al., 1984, Chauhan et al., 1999). We are not aware of more recent studies demonstrating such an association with LTH.

Hypoxia-Mediated FGR and the Developmental Origins of Adult Health and Disease

A major cause of death in the USA and the world, heart disease imposes an enormous burden on patient health as well as the economy in terms of medical costs and lost productivity (Heidenreich et al., 2011, World Health Organization, 2012). Although risk factors such as cigarette smoking, high body mass index, and lack of exercise, play an important role in this pandemic, a number of affected individuals do not have these risk factors (Table 1). Thus, it is becoming recognized that in early life, environmental stresses such as maternal hypoxia, dietary imbalance, and other factors can affect specific gene expression patterns to "program" cardiac or other disease in later life (Barker, 1994, Barker et al., 1989, Fowden et al., 2005, 2006a, 2006b, Hales and Ozanne, 2003, Leon et al., 1998). A number of these have been tabulated (Dessì et al., 2012). As is increasingly becoming appreciated, the factors responsible for FGR may have profound influences beyond childhood in one's life course, including the developmental origins of adult health and disease with intrauterine programming during critical periods of vulnerability, the failure to meet certain developmental milestones, and the permanent nature of specific sequelae (Barker, 1994) (Table 2). Despite the demonstration of strong associations in this regard, little is understood in terms of underlying mechanisms.

The past several decades have witnessed considerable advance in our understanding the role of prolonged antenatal hypoxia, not only in the genesis of FGR and associated disease in the fetus/newborn (Kramer et al., 1990), but in establishing the long-term consequences of this stress in adolescent and adult offspring. These conditions in the adult include the major causes of morbidity and death, cardiovascular and cerebrovascular disease (Barker, 1994, Leon et al., 1998, World Health Organization, 2012), as well as metabolic syndrome (Gluckman et al., 2008), some malignancies and a number of neuropsychiatric disorders (Table 2). In an attempt to understand the association between stress experienced as a fetus and/or infant and disease as a young adult or later in life, the "thrifty phenotype" hypothesis was proposed (Hales and Barker, 1992). That is, epigenetic changes in gene transcription alter cellular metabolic functions to affect receptor and/or enzyme activation and downstream events such as insulin resistance, vascular contractility, and other functions that extend into later life. (The cellular/subcellular mechanisms by which this is affected remain unknown, however). Along this line, the "predictive adaptive response" suggests metabolic responses such as insulin resistance that emerges in anticipation of poor quality adult environment (Wells, 2011). Also to be considered is the competing and "maternal capital" hypotheses which considers thrift to involve reductions in lean body mass and organ phenotype arising from constrains on maternal phenotype (Wells, 2011). These have been suggested to consider resultant cellular-tissue-organ ultimate survival phenotype under given environmental conditions. These may be viewed as the extreme of a continuum of responses (Wells, 2009a, 2009b, 2010, 2011). A major issue in this regard is to move beyond the phenomenology of occurrence and possible relations to that of causative mechanisms. Some of these environmental stresses are diagramed in Figure 3. In turn, some of the epigenetic-induced molecular mechanisms are illustrated in Figure 4. Although a consideration of the nuances of antenatal hypoxia and the fetal programming hypothesis is beyond the scope of this Chapter, several observations by biologic and physiologic associations may be in order.

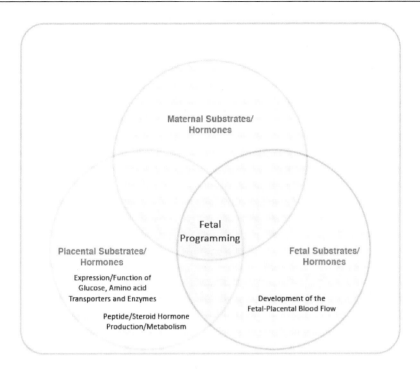

Figure 3. Illustration of the convergence of various environmental stressors and their interaction in the mother, placenta, and/or fetus that interact to affect fetal programming.

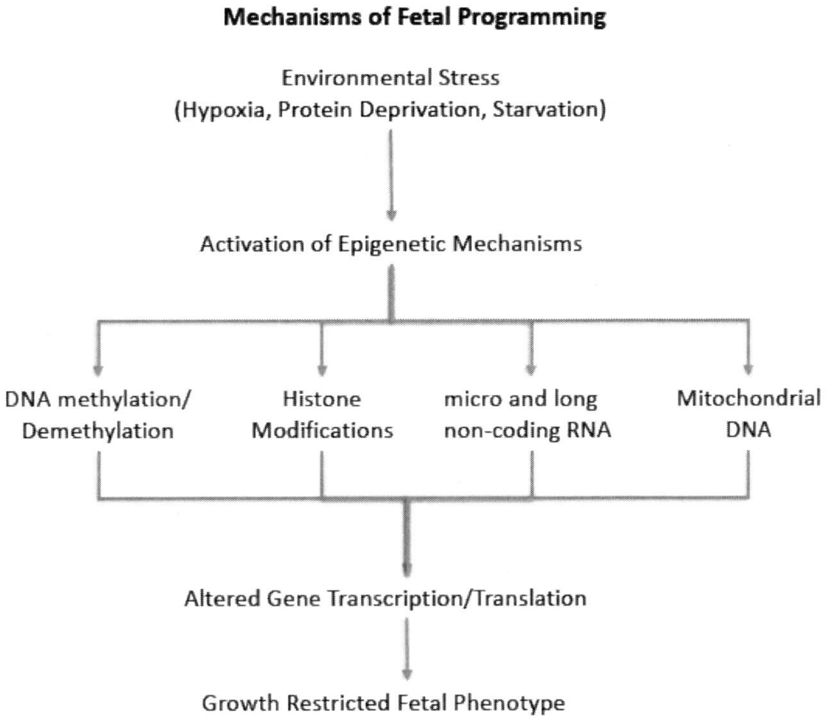

Mechanisms of Fetal Programming

Environmental Stress
(Hypoxia, Protein Deprivation, Starvation)

Activation of Epigenetic Mechanisms

| DNA methylation/ Demethylation | Histone Modifications | micro and long non-coding RNA | Mitochondrial DNA |

Altered Gene Transcription/Translation

Growth Restricted Fetal Phenotype

Figure 4. Overview of different epigenetic mechanisms responsible for fetal growth restriction and programming.

As noted, in the mouse 48hr of hypoxia at 15 to 17 days post conception results in marked deviations in the pattern of gene expression in the placenta (Gheorghe et al., 2007, 2010), accompanied by significant alterations in the placental renin-angiotensin system (Goyal et al., 2011b) as well as the fetal lung (Goyal et al., 2011a). The extent to which the RAS is altered in the human placenta remains to be demonstrated.

In the rat, antenatal chronic hypoxia also has been shown to affect fetal myocardial expression of cardioprotective enzymes such as protein kinase C epsilon (PKCε) with programming of an increase in cardiac susceptibility to ischemia and reperfusion injury in male offspring (Li et al., 2003, Patterson et al., 2010, Xue and Zhang, 2009). Presumably the result of ROS, studies also have demonstrated increased methylation of the promoter of the *PKCε* gene, an epigenetic change which could be prevented by administration of an inhibitor of DNA methylation (Patterson et al., 2012). The adult offspring of dams subjected to antenatal hypoxia also displayed cardiac structural and functional changes including: increased expression of collagen type I and III, and the ratio of beta to alpha myosin heavy chains (Xu et al., 2006), as well as increased left ventricular end diastolic pressure (Rueda-Clausen et al., 2009), and decreased myocardial metabolism (Rueda-Clausen et al., 2011). Further studies have demonstrated decreased beta 1 receptor and increased muscarinic receptor responses in adult offspring of rats so subjected to LTH (Giussani et al., 2012). Also of clinical relevance, cardiovascular disease in adults has been associated with elevated sympathetic and decreased parasympathetic reactivity. Thus, overall studies from several species support the idea of antenatal hypoxia as well as nutritional deficiency resulting in cardiomyopathy in the adult offspring. Provocatively, many of these antenatal hypoxic-mediated (Hemmings et al., 2005, Kuzawa, 2004) changes show gender specificity for many complications, with males being more susceptible than females.

Other studies have reported adult sequelae of antenatal hypoxia. For instance, following hypoxic incubation as chicks the femoral arteries of adult chickens showed increased sensitivity to both pharmacologic and electrical stimulation of periarterial sympathetic nerves, as well as decreased NO-dependent vasodilatation (Ruijtenbeek et al., 2003a). Other investigators also have demonstrated NO-mediated endothelial dysfunction following antenatal hypoxia in the adult rat (Hemmings et al., 2005, Morton et al., 2010, 2011, Williams et al., 2005a, 2005b), and sheep (Giussani et al., 2012). Along this line, FGR offspring show evidence of endothelial dysfunction as manifest by high resolution ultrasound in both 9 to 11 year olds (Leeson et al., 1997), as well as in early adult life (Leeson et al., 2001).

A number of studies have reported that in developed nations, FGR is associated with consequential neurodevelopmental/neurocognitive outcomes later in life (Frisk et al., 2002, Leitner et al., 2007, Paz et al., 1995, Strauss, 2000, Sung et al., 1993, Zubrick et al., 2000). In an attempt to discover the mechanistic basis for this association, Robert H. Lane and colleagues at the University of Utah have explored several aspects of developmental neurogenesis in laboratory animals. In addition to significant changes in composition of the neuronal *N*-methyl-D-aspartate receptor subunits, which are critical for synaptogenesis, the alterations showed gender specificity (Schober et al., 2009). Also FGR newborn infants, as well as those 30 and 60 days of age, showed a significant decrease in the N1/P2 component of the auditory evoked potential to be associated with increased free, and decreased bound, fractions (but no change in total) of plasma L-tryptophan levels (Manjarrez et al., 2005). This suggests impairment of brain serotonergic transmission, and probably that of other cerebral cortical sensory mechanisms as well (Manjarrez et al., 2005).

In a rat bilateral uterine artery ligation FGR "model", the renal expression of 11β-hydroxysteroid dehydrogenase type 2 (11β-HSD2) mRNA and protein were significantly decreased (Baserga et al., 2007). This occurred in association with increased corticosteroid levels at the time of birth as well as at day 21 of life (Baserga et al., 2005). This enzyme plays a key role in the regulation of renal steroid sensitivity, catabolizing glucocorticoids to an inactive form in the kidney and other aldosterone target tissues, its deficiency being an important mechanism that can lead to hypertension. This FGR "model" also has been demonstrated to be associated with decreased binding of the transcription enhancers specificity protein 1 and NF-κB p65, with increased transcriptional repressors early growth response factor NF-κB p 50 to the 11β-HSD2 promoter in males. Some of these changes were more predominant in females. In addition, DNA CpG methylation occurred in a sex specific manner (Baserga et al., 2010).

In light of the host of evidence from both epidemiologic studies in humans and experimental studies in laboratory animals, the role of antenatal hypoxia in the genesis of FGR has raised a number of questions in regards to the underlying mechanisms of signaling for the development of these major long-term sequelae. Additional questions pertain to means of possible preventative intervention. With the evidence of NO oxidative stress and many epigenetic factors playing a role in the pathophysiology of this syndrome, such interventions have been explored by several groups. Additionally, several investigators have exposed the possibility of postnatal treatment to rescue the FGR newborn from long-term sequelae. Many of these recent studies, with their promise and problems have been reviewed (Giussani and Davidge, 2013).

Conclusion with Perspective

The syndrome of fetal growth restriction, a complex interplay of confounding variables, presents a variety of phenotypes. Beyond the phenomenology of having a birthweight at or below the 10th percentile, and beyond genetic- and environmental-epigenetic-mediated factors, a seemingly infinite mosaic of cellular, subcellular, and molecular alterations and mechanisms are involved. That said, we remain in a circular argument. Despite increasing evidence to support hypoxia in the pathogenesis of FGR, at present we have little or no knowledge of the initiating event and the multiplex of signaling networks involved.

Oxygen being an essential requirement for aerobic metabolism and life, from the earliest stages of development, cellular hypoxia poses significant challenges for survival. Fortunately, cardiovascular, endocrinologic, metabolic, and other acclimatization responses mitigate that risk and work to preserve oxygen homeostasis at the organismal level. Hypobaric hypoxic-induced physiologic responses in the mother include increased ventilation and O_2 transport capacity, and compensatory changes in uteroplacental blood flow. Placental function also is optimized with greater capillary blood volume and shorter transcapillary diffusion distance. For the fetus, a number of metabolites, growth factors, and other molecules may influence its tissues to constrain protein synthesis and growth in an attempt to survive limited O_2 availability. In this regard, because of its potent influence on central nervous system function, the pathophysiology of cerebral hypoxia, the regulation of cerebral blood flow, and the mechanisms involved in development of and responses to cerebral edema and ischemia are of profound importance. Whereas cellular hypoxia is perhaps the most important primary stimulus to homeostatic responses, multiple secondary responses in levels of circulating catecholamines, cortisol or other stress-related hormones, the multiple growth factors and cytokines involved in protein synthesis, and other cellular responses are clearly critical to the hypoxic acclimatization process.

As noted, despite a number of studies to explore the fundamental hypoxic-mediated mechanisms that account for FGR, there remain enormous gaps in our understanding. Whereas, to some degree, the changes in the fetal environment are "buffered" by maternal homeostatic mechanisms, it also is clear that under conditions of prolonged hypoxia or other invidious environmental factors, the fetus constitutes a stress for the mother. From this perspective, it would enhance the survival mechanisms for both the mother and conceptus if the latter were to mature more rapidly. Whereas this hypothesis has some attraction, it remains highly speculative and in need of definitive experimental verification.

In particular, identification of the signals whereby cells sense limited O_2 or other nutrient availability remains a critical unknown. How, and by what cells and tissues, the "prime mover" responses to hypoxia are mounted is a fascinating question that has been pursued for decades. Recent advances are promising in that they point the direction for the focus of more cellular and molecular investigation of gene regulation to elucidate their role in this process, and the mechanisms by which they are activated to effect protein synthesis in the developing organism. The rapidly growing diversity and power of new, powerful technology offers unprecedented opportunity and great promise for furthering our understanding. Our challenge today is to promote a new generation of studies of the mosaic of hypoxic- and other mediator-induced gene regulation and/or metabolomics that will yield the key clues to the origins of FGR. These are discoveries for which this field has for so long been in search.

Acknowledgment

Supported by USPHS NIH grants HD-03807 and HD-031226 to LDL. We thank Jimin Suh for her highly professional assistance in preparing this manuscript.

References

Aarnoudse-Moens, C. S., Weisglas-Kuperus, N., van Goudoever, J. B. & Oosterlaan, J. (2009). Meta-analysis of neurobehavioral outcomes in very preterm and/or very low birth weight children. *Pediatrics, 124*, 717-28.

Albaiges, G., Missfelder-Lobos, H., Parra, M., Lees, C., Cooper, D. & Nicolaides, K. H. (2003). Comparison of color Doppler uterine artery indices in a population at high risk for adverse outcome at 24 weeks' gestation. *Ultrasound Obstet Gynecol, 21*, 170-3.

Alexander, G. (1964). Studies on the placenta of the sheep (Ovis aries L.). Effect of surgical reduction in the number of caruncles. *J Reprod Fertil, 7*, 307-22.

Altman, D. G. & Coles, E. C. (1980). Nomograms for precise determination of birth weight for dates. *Br J Obstet Gynaecol, 87*, 81-6.

American College of Obstetricians and Gynecologists (ACOG). (2001). Intrauterine growth restriction. Clinical management guidelines for obstetrician-gynecologists. Committee on Practice Bulletins – Gynecology, American College of Obstetricians and Gynecologists. *Int J Gynaecol Obstet, 71*, 85-96.

Amon, E., Sibai, B. M., Anderson, G. D. & Mabie, W. C. (1987). Obstetric variables predicting survival of the immature newborn (less than or equal to 1000 gm): a five-year experience at a single perinatal center. *Am J Obstet Gynecol, 156*, 1380-9.

Amoroso, E. C. (1952). Placentation. In: *Marshall's Physiology of Reproduction*. Parkes, A.S. (Ed) 3rd edn. London: Longmans, Green, p. 127-311.

Angiolini, E., Fowden, A., Coan, P. Sandovici, I., Smith, P., Dean, W., et al. (2006). Regulation of placental efficiency for nutrient transport by imprinted genes. *Placenta, 27* Suppl A, S98-102.

Arnett, D. K., Evans, G. W. & Riley, W. A. (1994). Arterial stiffness: a new cardiovascular risk factor? *Am J Epidemiol, 140*, 669-82.

Axt-Fliedner, R. (2004). Second trimester uterine artery Doppler ultrasound as a screening test for adverse pregnancy outcome. *Clin Exp Obstet Gynecol, 31*, 9-11.

Balasch, J. & Gratacos, E. (2011). Delayed childbearing: effects on fertility and the outcome of pregnancy. *Fetal Diagn Ther, 29*, 263-73.

Ballard, J. L., Novak, K. K., & Driver, M. (1979). A simplified score for assessment of fetal maturation of newly born infants. *J Pediatr, 95*, 769-74.

Banks, E. H. & Miller, D. A. (1999). Perinatal risks associated with borderline amniotic fluid index. *Am J Obstet Gynecol, 180*, 1461-3.

Barker, D. J. (1994). *Mothers, babies and disease in later life*. London: BMJ Publishing Group.

Barker, D. J., Winter, P. D., Osmond, C., Margetts, B. & Simmonds, S. J. (1989). Weight in infancy and death from ischaemic heart disease. *Lancet, 2*, 577-80.

Baschat, A. A. (2004). Fetal responses to placental insufficiency: an update. *BJOG, 111*, 1031-41.

Baschat, A. A., Gembruch, U., Reiss, I., Gortner, L., Weiner, C. P. & Harman, C. R. (2000). Relationship between arterial and venous Doppler and perinatal outcome in fetal growth restriction. *Ultrasound Obstet Gynecol, 16*, 407-13.

Baserga, M., Bares, A. L., Hale, M. A., Callaway, C. W., McKnight, R. A., Lane, P. H. et al. (2009). Uteroplacental insufficiency affects kidney VEGF expression in a model of IUGR with compensatory glomerular hypertrophy and hypertension. *Early Hum Dev, 85*, 361-7.

Baserga, M., Hale, M. A., McKnight, R. A., Yu, X., Callaway, C. W. & Lane, R. H. (2005). Uteroplacental insufficiency alters hepatic expression, phosphorylation, and activity of the glucocorticoid receptor in fetal IUGR rats. *Am J Physiol Regul Integr Comp Physiol, 289*, R1348-53.

Baserga, M., Hale, M. A., Wang, Z. M., Yu, X., Callaway, C. W., McKnight, R. A., et al. (2007). Uteroplacental insufficiency alters nephrogenesis and downregulates cyclooxygenase-2 expression in a model of IUGR with adult-onset hypertension. *Am J Physiol Regul Integr Comp Physiol, 292*, R1943-55.

Baserga, M., Kaur, R., Hale, M. A., Bares, A., Yu, X., Callaway, C. W., et al. (2010). Fetal growth restriction alters transcription factor binding and epigenetic mechanisms of renal

11beta-hydroxysteroid dehydrogenase type 2 in a sex-specific manner. *Am J Physiol Regul Integr Comp Physiol, 299*, R334-42.

Bassan, H., Stolar, O., Geva, R., Eshel, R., Fattal-Valevski, A., Leitner, Y., et al. (2011). Intrauterine growth-restricted neonates born at term or preterm: how different? *Pediatr Neurol, 44*, 122-130.

Batalle, D., Eixarch, E., Figueras, F., Muñoz-Moreno, E., Bargallo, N., Illa, M., et al. (2012). Altered small-world topology of structural brain networks in infants with intrauterine growth restriction and its association with later neurodevelopmental outcome. *Neuroimage, 60*, 1352-66.

Battaglia, F. C. (2011). Circulatory and metabolic changes accompanying fetal growth restriction. In: *Fetal and neonatal physiology.* Polin, R.A., Fox, W.W. & Abman, S.H. (Eds). 4th edn, Vol 1. Philadelphia: Elsevier/Saunders, p. 302-10.

Battaglia, F. C., Frazier, T. M. & Hellegers, A. E. (1966). Birth weight, gestational age, and pregnancy out-come, with special reference to high birth weight-low gestational age infant. *Pediatrics, 37*, 417-22.

Battaglia, F. C. & Lubchenco, L. O. (1967). A practical classification of newborn infants by weight and gestational age. *J Pediatr, 71*, 159-63.

Bell, A. W., Hay, W. W., Jr. & Ehrhardt, R. A. (1999). Placental transport of nutrients and its implications for fetal growth. *J Reprod Fertil Suppl, 54*, 401-10.

Bellamy, C. & UNICEF. (2003). *The state of the world's children 2004.* New York: United Nations Publications.

Bernstein, M., Horbar, J. D., Badger, G. J., Ohlsson, A. & Golan, A. (2000). Morbidity and mortality among very-low-birth-weight neonates with intrauterine growth restriction. The Vermont Oxford Network. *Am J Obstet Gynecol, 182*, 198-206.

Bloomfield, F. H., Oliver, M. H. & Harding, J. E. (2006). The late effects of fetal growth patterns. *Arch Dis Child Fetal Neonatal Ed, 91*, F299-304.

Börzsönyi, B., Demendi, C., Nagy, Z., Tóth, K., Csanád, M., Pajor, A. et al. (2011). Gene expression patterns of insulin-like growth factor 1, insulin-like growth factor 2 and insulin-like growth factor binding protein 3 in human placenta from pregnancies with intrauterine growth restriction. *J Perinat Med, 39*, 701-7.

Börzsönyi, B., Demendi, C., Pajor, A., Rigó, J., Jr., Marosi, K., Ágota, A., et al. (2012). Gene expression patterns of the 11β-hydroxysteroid dehydrogenase 2 enzyme in human placenta from intrauterine growth restriction: the role of impaired fetal-maternal glucocorticoid metabolism. *Eur J Obstet Gynecol Reprod Biol, 161*, 12-17.

Bourque, D. K., Avila, L., Penaherrera, M., von Dadelszen, P. & Robinson, W. P. (2010). Decreased placental methylation at the H19/IGF2 imprinting control region is associated with normotensive intrauterine growth restriction but not preeclampsia. *Placenta, 31*, 197-202.

Boyle, J. W., Lotgering, F. K. & Longo, L. D. (1984). Acute embolization of the uteroplacental circulation: uterine blood flow and placental CO diffusing capacity. *J Dev Physiol, 6*, 377-86.

Brenner, W. E., Edelman, D. A. & Hendricks, C. H. (1976). A standard of fetal growth for the United States of America. *Am J Obstet Gynecol, 126*, 555-64.

Brodsky, D. & Christou, H. (2004). Current concepts in intrauterine growth restriction. *J Intensive Care Med, 19*, 307-19.

Bubb, K. J., Cock, M. L., Black, M. J., Dodic, M., Boon, W. M., Parkington, H. C., et al. (2007). Intrauterine growth restriction delays cardiomyocyte maturation and alters coronary artery function in the fetal sheep. *J Physiol*, *578*, 871-81.

Buffat, C., Mondon, F., Rigourd, V., Boubred, F., Bessieres, B., Fayol, L., et al. (2007). A hierarchical analysis of transcriptome alterations in intrauterine growth restriction (IUGR) reveals common pathophysiological pathways in mammals. *J Pathol*, *213*, 337-46.

Calvert, S. J., Jones, C. J., Sibley, C. P., Aplin, J. D. & Heazell, A. E. (2013). Analysis of syncytial nuclear aggregates in preeclampsia shows increased sectioning artefacts and decreased inter-villous bridges compared to healthy placentas. *Placenta*, *34*, 1251-4.

Campbell, S. & Thoms, A. (1977). Ultrasound measurement of the fetal head to abdomen circumference ratio in the assessment of growth retardation. *Br J Obstet Gynaecol*, *84*, 165-74.

Cetin, I. & Alvino, G. (2009). Intrauterine growth restriction: implications for placental metabolism and transport. A review. *Placenta*, *30* Suppl A, S77-82.

Cetin, I. & Antonazzo, P. (2009). The role of the placenta in intrauterine growth restriction (IUGR). *Z Geburtshilfe Neonatol*, *213*, 84-8.

Challis, J. R., Fraher, L., Oosterhuis, J., White, S. E. & Bocking, A. D. (1989). Fetal and maternal endocrine responses to prolonged reductions in uterine blood flow in pregnant sheep. *Am J Obstet Gynecol*, *160*, 926-32.

Chamberlain, P. F., Manning, F. A., Morrison, I., Harman, C. R. & Lange, I. R. (1984). Ultrasound evaluation of amniotic fluid volume. I. The relationship of marginal and decreased amniotic fluid volumes to perinatal outcome. *Am J Obstet Gynecol*, *150*, 245-9.

Charnock-Jones, D. S., Kaufmann, P. & Mayhew, T. M. (2004). Aspects of human fetoplacental vasculogenesis and angiogenesis. I. Molecular regulation. *Placenta*, *25*, 103-13.

Chauhan, S. P., Scardo, J. A., Hendrix, N. W., Magann, E. F. & Morrison, J. C. (1999). Accuracy of sonographically estimated fetal weight with and without oligohydramnios. A case-control study. *J Reprod Med*, *44*, 969-73.

Chen, H. Y., Lu, C. C., Cheng, Y. T., Hsieh, F. J. & Liu, J. Y. (1986). Antenatal measurement of fetal umbilical venous flow by pulsed Doppler and B-mode ultrasonography. *J Ultrasound Med*, *5*, 319-21.

Clapp, J. F., 3rd, Szeto, H. H., Larrow, R., Hewitt, J. & Mann, L. I. (1980). Umbilical blood flow response to embolization of the uterine circulation. *Am J Obstet Gynecol*, *138*, 60-7.

Clausson, B., Gardosi, J., Francis, A. & Cnattingius, S. (2001). Perinatal outcome in SGA births defined by customized versus population-based birthweight standards. *BJOG*, *108*, 830-4.

Cohn, H. E., Sacks, E. J., Heymann, M. A. & Rudolph, A. M. (1974). Cardiovascular responses to hypoxemia and academia in fetal lambs. *Am J Obstet Gynecol*, *120*, 817-24.

Constância, M., Hemberger, M., Hughes, J., Dean, W., Ferguson-Smith, A., Fundele, R., et al. (2002). Placental-specific IGF-II is a major modulator of placental and fetal growth. *Nature*, *417*, 945-8.

Corso, M. & Thomson, M. (2001). Protein phosphorylation in mitochondria from human placenta. *Placenta*, *22*, 432-9.

Cosmi, E., Visentin, S., Fanelli, T., Mautone, A. J. & Zanardo, V. (2009). Aortic intima media thickness in fetuses and children with intrauterine growth restriction. *Obstet Gynecol, 114*, 1109-14.

Cubillo, A., Halari, R., Smith, A., Taylor, E. & Rubia, K. (2012). A review of fronto-striatal and fronto-cortical brain abnormalities in children and adults with Attention Deficit Hyperactivity Disorder (ADHD) and new evidence for dysfunction in adults with ADHD during motivation and attention. *Cortex, 48*, 194-215.

Dancis, J. (1983). Historic Perspective [on the weight of premature infants]. *Landmarks in Perinatology/Neonatology, 18*, 1-3.

Dancis, J., O'Connell, J. R. & Holt, L. E., Jr. (1948). A grid for recording the weight of premature infants. *J Pediatr, 33*, 570-2.

Dessì, A., Ottonello, G. & Fanos, V. (2012). Physiopathology of intrauterine growth retardation: from classic data to metabolomics. *J Matern Fetal Neonatal Med*, 25 (Suppl 5), 13-8.

Diczfalusy, E. (1964). Endocrine functions of the human fetoplacental unit. *Fed Proc, 23*, 791-8.

Diplas, A. I., Lambertini, L., Lee, M. J., Sperling, R., Lee, Y. L., Wetmur, J., et al. (2009). Differential expression of imprinted genes in normal and IUGR human placentas. *Epigenetics, 4*, 235-40.

Dong, Y. & Thompson, L. P. (2006). Differential expression of endothelial nitric oxide synthase in coronary and cardiac tissue in hypoxic fetal guinea pig hearts. *J Soc Gynecol Investig, 13*, 483-90.

Dubois, J., Benders, M., Borradori-Tolsa, C., Cachia, A., Lazeyras, F., Ha-Vinh Leuchter, R., et al. (2008). Primary cortical folding in the human newborn: an early marker of later functional development. *Brain, 131*, 2028-41.

Dunham, E. C., Jenss, R. M. & Christie, A. U. (1939). A consideration of race and sex in relation to the growth and development of infants. *J Pediatr, 14*, 156-60.

Dunn, P. M. & Wharton, B. A. (1985). *Perinatal growth: the quest for an international standard for reference*. Stockholm, Sweden: Almqvist & Wiksell Periodical Company.

Dyer, J. L., McMillen, I. C., Warnes, K. E. & Morrison, J. L. (2009). No evidence for an enhanced role of endothelial nitric oxide in the maintenance of arterial blood pressure in the IUGR sheep fetus. *Placenta, 30*, 705-10.

Eichenbaum, H., Yonelinas, A. P. & Ranganath, C. (2007). The medial temporal lobe and recognition memory. *Annu Rev Neurosci, 30*, 123-52.

Esterman, A., Greco, M. A., Mitani, Y., Finlay, T. H., Ismail-Beigi, F. & Dancis, J. (1997). The effect of hypoxia on human trophoblast in culture: morphology, glucose transport and metabolism. *Placenta, 18*, 129-36.

Evseenko, D. A., Murthi, P., Paxton, J. W., Reid, G., Emerald, B. S., Mohankumar, K. M., et al. (2007). The ABC transporter BCRP/ABCG2 is a placental survivor factor, and its expression is reduced in idiopathic human fetal growth restriction. *FASEB J, 21*, 3592-605.

Feldman, R. & Eidelman, A. I. (2006). Neonatal state organization, neuromaturation, mother-infant interaction, and cognitive development in small-for-gestational-age premature infants. *Pediatrics, 118*, e869-78.

Figueras, F., Oros, D., Cruz-Martinez, R., Padilla, N., Hernandez-Andrade, E., Botet, F., et al. (2009). Neurobehavior in term, small-for-gestational age infants with normal placental function. *Pediatrics*, *124*, e934-41.

Fletcher, A. J., Edwards, C. M., Gardner, D. S., Fowden, A. L. & Giussani, D. A. (2000). Neuropeptide Y in the sheep fetus: effects of acute hypoxemia and dexamethasone during late gestation. *Endocrinology*, *141*, 3976-82.

Fong, K. W., Ohlsson, A., Hannah, M. E., Grisaru, S., Kingdom, J., Cohen, H., et al. (1999). Prediction of perinatal outcome in fetuses suspected to have intrauterine growth restriction: Doppler US study of fetal cerebral, renal, and umbilical arteries. *Radiology*, *213*, 681-9.

Fowden, A. L., Giussani, D. A. & Forhead, A. J. (2005). Endocrine and metabolic programming during intrauterine development. *Early Hum Dev*, *81*, 723-34.

Fowden, A. L., Giussani, D. A. & Forhead, A. J. (2006a). Intrauterine programming of physiological systems: causes and consequences. *Physiology*, *21*, 29-37.

Fowden, A. L., Sibley, C., Reik, W. & Constancia, M. (2006b). Imprinted genes, placental development and fetal growth. *Horm Res*, *65* Suppl 3, 50-8.

Frisk, V., Amsel, R. & Whyte, H. E. (2002). The importance of head growth patterns in predicting the cognitive abilities and literacy skills of small-for-gestational-age children. *Dev Neuropsychol*, *22*, 565-93.

Gagnon, R., Murotsuki, J., Challis, J. R., Fraher, L. & Richardson, B. S. (1997). Fetal sheep endocrine responses to sustained hypoxemic stress after chronic fetal placental embolization. *Am J Physiol*, *272*, E817-23.

Gardosi, J., Chang, A., Kalyan, B., Sahota, D. & Symonds, E. M. (1992). Customised antenatal growth charts. *Lancet*, *339*, 283-7.

Gardosi, J. & Francis, A. (1999). Controlled trial of fundal height measurement plotted on customized antenatal growth charts. *Br J Obstet Gynaecol*, *106*, 309-17.

Gardosi, J., Madurasinghe, V., Williams, M., Malik, A. & Francis, A. (2013). Maternal and fetal risk factors for stillbirth: population based study. *BMJ*, *346*, f108.

Gascoin-Lachambre, G., Buffat, C., Rebourcet, R., Chelbi, S. T., Rigourd, V., Mondon, F., et al. (2010). Cullins in human intra-uterine growth restriction: expressional and epigenetic alterations. *Placenta*, *31*, 151-7.

Geva, R., Eshel, R., Leitner, Y., Fattal-Valevski, A. & Harel, S. (2006a). Memory functions of children born with asymmetric intrauterine growth restriction. *Brain Res*, *1117*, 186-94.

Geva, R., Eshel, R., Leitner, Y., Valevski, A. F. & Harel, S. (2006b). Neuropsychological outcome of children with intrauterine growth restriction: a 9-year prospective study. *Pediatrics*, *118*, 91-100.

Gheorghe C. P., Goyal, R., Mittal, A. & Longo, L. D. (2010). Gene expression in the placenta: maternal stress and epigenetic responses. *Int J Develop Biol*, *54*, 507-23.

Gheorghe, C. P., Mohan, S., Oberg, K. & Longo, L. D. (2007). Gene expression patterns in the hypoxic murine placenta: a role in epigenesis? *Reprod Sci*, *14*, 223-33.

Gilbert, W. M. & Danielsen, B. (2003). Pregnancy outcomes associated with intrauterine growth restriction. *Am J Obstet Gynecol*, *188*, 1596-9.

Gill, R. W., Trudinger, B. J., Garrett, W. J., Kossoff, G. & Warren, P. S. (1981). Fetal umbilical venous flow measured in utero by pulsed Doppler and B-mode ultrasound. I. Normal pregnancies. *Am J Obstet Gynecol*, *139*, 720-5.

Giussani, D. A., Camm, E. J., Niu, Y., Richter, H. G., Blanco, C. E., Gottschalk, R., et al. (2012). Developmental programming of cardiovascular dysfunction by prenatal hypoxia and oxidative stress. *PLoS One, 7*, e31017.

Giussani, D. A. & Davidge, S. T. (2013). Developmental programming of cardiovascular disease by prenatal hypoxia. *J Dev Orig Health Dis, 4*, 328-37.

Giussani, D. A., Phillips, P. S., Anstee, S. & Barker, D. J. (2001). Effects of altitude versus economic status on birth weight and body shape at birth. *Pediatr Res, 49*, 490-4.

Giussani, D. A., Salinas, C. E., Villena, M. & Blanco, C. E. (2007). The role of oxygen in prenatal growth: studies in the chick embryo. *J Physiol, 585*, 911-7.

Giussani, D. A., Spencer, J. A. & Hanson, M. A. (1994). Fetal cardiovascular reflex responses to hypoxaemia. *Fetal Matern Med Rev, 6*, 17-37.

Giussani, D. A., Spencer, J. A., Moore, P. J., Bennet, L. & Hanson, M. A. (1993). Afferent and efferent components of the cardiovascular reflex responses to acute hypoxia in term fetal sheep. *J Physiol, 461*, 431-49.

Giussani, D. A., Unno, N., Jenkins, S. L., Wentworth, R. A., Derks, J. B., Collins, J. H., et al. (1997). Dynamics of cardiovascular responses to repeated partial umbilical cord compression in late-gestation sheep fetus. *Am J Physiol, 273*, H2351-60.

Gluckman, P. D., Hanson, M. A., Cooper, C. & Thornburg, K. L. (2008). Effect of in utero and early-life conditions on adult health and disease. *N Engl J Med, 359*, 61-73.

Goyal, R., Leitzke, A., Goyal, D., Gheorghe, C. P. & Longo, L. D. (2011a). Antenatal maternal hypoxic stress: epigenetic adaptations in fetal lung renin-angiotensin system. *Reprod Sci, 18*, 180-9.

Goyal, R., Lister, R. R., Goyal, D., Gheorghe, C. P. & Longo, L. D. (2011b). Antenatal maternal hypoxic stress: Adaptations of the placental renin-angiotensin system in the mouse. *Placenta, 32*, 134-9.

Grahn, D. & Kratchman, J. (1963). Variation in neonatal death rate and birth weight in the United States and possible relations to environmental radiation, geology and altitude. *Am J Hum Genet, 15*, 329-52.

Griffin, M., Attilakos, G., Greenwood, R. & Denbow, M. (2009). Amniotic fluid index in low-risk, post-dates pregnancies. *Fetal Diagn Ther, 26*, 212-5.

Groom, K. M., Poppe, K. K., North, R. A. & McCowan, L. M. (2007). Small-for-gestational-age infants classified by customized or population birthweight centiles: impact of gestational age at delivery. *Am J Obstet Gynecol, 197*, 239.e1-5.

Gruenwald, P. (1963). Chronic fetal distress and placental insufficiency. *Biol Neonat, 5*, 215-65.

Gruenwald, P. (1970). Intrauterine growth. In: *Physiology of the perinatal period, functional and biochemical development in mammals.* Stave, U. (Ed). New York: Appleton-Century-Crofts, 3-27.

Gruenwald, P., Funakawa, H., Mitani, S., Nishimura, T. & Takeuchi, S. (1967). Influence of environmental factors on foetal growth in man. *Lancet, 1*, 1026-8.

Guo, L., Choufani, S., Ferreira, J., Smith, A., Chitayat, D., Shuman, C. et al. (2008). Altered gene expression and methylation of the human chromosome 11 imprinted region in small for gestational age (SGA) placentae. *Dev Biol, 320*, 79-91.

Hales, C. N. & Barker, D. J. (1992). Type 2 (non-insulin-dependent) diabetes mellitus: the thrifty phenotype hypothesis. *Diabetologia, 35*, 595-601.

Hales, C.N. & Ozanne, S.E. (2003). For debate: Fetal and early postnatal growth restriction lead to diabetes, the metabolic syndrome and renal failure. *Diabetologia, 46,* 1013-9.

Hassan, W. A., Brockelsby, J., Alberry, M., Fanelli, T., Wladimiroff, J. & Lees, C. C. (2013). Cardiac function in early onset small for gestational age and growth restricted fetuses. *Eur J Obstet Gynecol Reprod Biol, 171,* 262-5.

Heidenreich, P. A., Trogdon, J. G., Khavjou, O. A., Butler, J., Dracup, K., Ezekowitz, M. D., et al. (2011). Forecasting the future of cardiovascular disease in the United States: a policy statement from the American Heart Association. *Circulation, 123,* 933-44.

Heinonen, K., Raikkonen, K., Pesonen, A. K., Andersson, S., Kajantie, E., Eriksson, J. G., et al. (2010). Behavioural symptoms of attention deficit/hyperactivity disorder in preterm and term children born small and appropriate for gestational age: a longitudinal study. *BMC Pediatr, 10,* 91.

Hemmings, D. G., Williams, S. J. & Davidge, S. T. (2005). Increased myogenic tone in 7-month-old adult male but not female offspring from rat dams exposed to hypoxia during pregnancy. *Am J Physiol Heart Circ Physiol, 289,* H674-82.

Herrera, E. A., Camm, E. J., Cross, C. M., Mullender, J. L., Wooding, F. B. & Giussani, D. A. (2012). Morphological and functional alterations in the aorta of the chronically hypoxic fetal rat. *J Vasc Res, 49,* 50-8.

Hershkovitz, R., de Swiet, M. & Kingdom, J. (2005). Mid-trimester placentation assessment in high-risk pregnancies using maternal serum screening and uterine artery Doppler. *Hypertens Pregnancy, 24,* 273-80.

Hershkovitz, R., Kingdom, J. C., Geary, M. & Rodeck, C. H. (2000). Fetal cerebral blood flow redistribution in late gestation: identification of compromise in small fetuses with normal umbilical artery Doppler. *Ultrasound Obstet Gynecol, 15,* 209-12.

Howard, R. C., Bruns, P. D. & Lichty, J. A. (1957a). Studies on babies born at high altitudes. III. Arterial oxygen saturation and hematocrit values at birth. *AMA J Dis Child, 93,* 674-8.

Howard, R. C., Lichty, J. A. & Bruns, P. D. (1957b). Studies on babies born at high altitude. II. Measurement of birth weight, body length and head size. *AMA J Dis Child, 93,* 670-4.

Iams, J. D. (2014). Clinical practice. Prevention of preterm parturition. *N Engl J Med, 370,* 254-61.

Illa, M., Eixarch, E., Batalle, D., Arbat-Plana, A., Muñoz-Moreno, E., Figueras, F., et al. (2013). Long-term functional outcomes and correlation with regional brain connectivity by MRI diffusion tractography metrics in a near-term rabbit model of intrauterine growth restriction. *PLoS One, 8,* e76453.

Jang, E. A., Longo, L. D. & Goyal, R. (2014). Antenatal maternal hypoxia and fetal growth restriction in rodents. *Reprod Sci* (In Review).

Jones, C. T. & Robinson, R. O. (1975). Plasma catecholamines in foetal and adult sheep. *J Physiol, 248,* 15-33.

Julian, C. G., Yang, I. V., Browne, V. A., Vargas, E., Rodriguez, C., Pedersen, B. S., et al. (2014). Inhibition of peroxisome proliferator-activated receptor γ: a potential link between chronic maternal hypoxia and impaired fetal growth. *FASEB J, 28,* 1268-79.

Kamitomo, M., Alonso, J. G., Okai, T., Longo, L. D. & Gilbert, R. D. (1993). Effects of long-term, high-altitude hypoxemia on ovine fetal cardiac output and blood flow distribution. *Am J Obstet Gynecol, 169,* 701-7.

Kamitomo, M., Longo, L. D. & Gilbert, R. D. (1992). Right and left ventricular function in fetal sheep exposed to long-term high-altitude hypoxemia. *Am J Physiol, 262*, H399-405.

King, L. S. (1958). *The medical world of the eighteenth century*. Huntington, NY: R.E. Krieger.

Kitanaka, T., Gilbert, R. D. & Longo, L. D. (1989). Maternal responses to long-term hypoxemia in sheep. *Am J Physiol, 256*, R1340-7.

Koklu, E., Kurtoglu, S., Akcakus, M., Koklu, S., Buyukkayhan, D., Gumus, H., et al. (2006). Increased aortic intima-media thickness is related to lipid profile in newborns with intrauterine growth restriction. *Horm Res, 65*, 269-75.

Kramer, M. S., Olivier, M., McLean, F. H., Willis, D. M. & Usher, R. H. (1990). Impact of intrauterine growth retardation and body proportionality on fetal and neonatal outcome. *Pediatrics, 86*, 707-13.

Kuzawa, C. W. (2004). Modeling fetal adaptation to nutrient restriction: testing the fetal origins hypothesis with a supply-demand model. *J Nutr, 134*, 194-200.

Lambertini, L., Lee, T. L., Chan, W. Y., Lee, M. J., Diplas, A., Wetmur, J., et al. (2011). Differential methylation of imprinted genes in growth-restricted placentas. *Reprod Sci, 18*, 1111-7.

Lattuada, D., Colleoni, F., Martinelli, A., Garretto, A., Magni, R., Radaelli, T., et al. (2008). Higher mitochondrial DNA content in human IUGR placenta. *Placenta, 29*, 1029-33.

Lawn, J. E., Cousens, S., Zupan, J. & Lancet Neonatal Survival Steering Team. (2005). 4 million neonatal deaths: When? Where? Why? *Lancet, 365*, 891-900.

Leeson, C. P., Kattenhorn, M., Morley, R., Lucas, A. & Deanfield, J. E. (2001). Impact on low birth weight and cardiovascular risk factors on endothelial function in early adult life. *Circulation, 103*, 1264-8.

Leeson, C. P., Whincup, P. H., Cook. D. G., Donald, A. E., Papacosta, O., Lucas, A., et al. (1997). Flow-mediated dilation in 9- to 11-year-old children: the influence of intrauterine and childhood factors. *Circulation, 96*, 2233-8.

Leiser, R. & Kaufmann, P. (1994). Placental structure: in a comparative aspect. *Exp Clin Endocrinol, 102*, 122-34.

Leitner, Y., Fattal-Valevski, A., Geva, R., Eshel, R., Toledano-Alhadef, H., Rotstein, M., et al. (2007). Neurodevelopmental outcome of children with intrauterine growth retardation: a longitudinal, 10-year prospective study. *J Child Neurol, 22*, 580-7.

Leon, D. A., Lithell, H. O., Vagero, D., Koupilova, I., Mohsen, R., Berglund, L., et al. (1998). Reduced fetal growth rate and increased risk of death from ischaemic heart disease: cohort study of 15000 Swedish men and women born in 1915-29. *BMJ, 317*, 241-5.

Li, G., Xiao, Y., Estrella, J. L., Ducsay, C. A., Gilbert, R. D. & Zhang, L. (2003). Effect of fetal hypoxia on heart susceptibility to ischemia and reperfusion injury in the adult rat. *J Soc Gynecol Investig, 10*, 265-74.

Lichty, J. A., Ting, R. Y., Bruns, P. D. & Dyar, E. (1957). Studies of babies born at high altitudes. I. Relation of altitude to birth weight. *AMA J Dis Child, 93*, 666-9.

Lim, A. L., Ng, S., Leow, S. C., Choo, R., Ito, M., Chan, Y. H., et al. (2012). Epigenetic state and expression of imprinted genes in umbilical cord correlates with growth parameters in human pregnancy. *J Med Genet, 49*, 689-97.

Lin, C. C. & Santolaya-Forgas, J. (1998). Current concepts of fetal growth restriction: part I. Causes, classification, and pathophysiology. *Obstet Gynecol, 92*, 1044-55.

Lin, C. C., Su, S. J. & River, L. P. (1991). Comparison of associated high-risk factors and perinatal outcome between symmetric and asymmetric fetal intrauterine growth retardation. *Am J Obstet Gynecol, 164*, 1535-41.

Lindgren, I. & Altimiras, J. (2011). Sensitivity of organ growth to chronically low oxygen levels during incubation in Red Junglefowl and domesticated chicken breeds. *Poult Sci, 90*, 126-35.

Lodygensky, G. A., Seghier, M. L., Warfield, S. K., Tolsa, C. B., Sizonenko, S., Lazeyras, F., et al. (2008). Intrauterine growth restriction affects the preterm infant's hippocampus. *Pediatr Res, 63*, 438-43.

Longo, L. D. (1984). Intrauterine growth retardation: a "mosaic" hypothesis of pathophysiology. *Semin Perinatol, 8*, 62-72.

Longo, L. D. (1987). Respiratory gas exchange in the placenta. In: *Handbook of Physiology. The Respiratory System. Gas Exchange.* (Sect. 3, vol. IV). Bethesda, MD: American Physiological Society, p. 351-401.

Longo, L. D. & Goyal, R. (2014). Fetal stress and growth restriction at high altitude. In: *Stress and developmental programming of health and disease: beyond phenomenology.* Zhang, L. & Longo, L.D. (Eds). New York, Nova Science Publishers, Inc.

Lorijn, R. H. & Longo, L. D. (1980). Norepinephrine elevation in the fetal lamb: oxygen consumption and cardiac output. *Am J Physiol, 239*, R115-22.

Lubchenco, L. O. (1970). Assessment of gestational age and development of birth. *Pediatr Clin North Am, 17*, 125-45.

Lubchenco, L. O. (1976). *The high-risk infant.* Schaffer, A.J. & Markowitz, M. (Eds). Philadelphia: Saunders.

Lubchenco, L. O., Hansman, C. & Boyd, E. (1966). Intrauterine growth in length and head circumference as estimated from live births at gestational ages from 26 to 42 weeks. *Pediatrics, 37*, 403-8.

Lubchenco, L. O., Hansman, C., Dressler, M. & Boyd, E. (1963). Intrauterine growth as estimated from liveborn birth-weight data at 24 to 42 weeks of gestation. *Pediatrics, 32*, 793-800.

Lubchenco, L. O., Searls, D. T. & Brazie, J. V. (1972). Neonatal mortality rate: relationship to birth weight and gestational age. *J Pediatr, 81*, 814-22.

Manjarrez, G., Cisneros, I., Herrera, R., Vazquez, F., Robles, A. & Hernandez, J. (2005). Prenatal impairment of brain serotonergic transmission in infants. *J Pediatr, 147*, 592-6.

Manning, F. A. (1995). Intrauterine growth retardation. In: *Fetal medicine: principal and practice.* Norwalk: Appleton and Lange.

Mari, G., Hanif, F., Kruger, M., Cosmi, E., Santolaya-Forgas, J. & Treadwell, M.C. (2007). Middle cerebral artery peak systolic velocity: a new Doppler parameter in the assessment of growth-restricted fetuses. *Ultrasound Obstet Gynecol, 29*, 310-6.

Marsál, K. (2002). Intrauterine growth restriction. *Curr Opin Obstet Gynecol, 14*, 127-35.

Mayhew, T. M., Gregson, C. & Fagan, D. G. (1999). Ventricular myocardium in control and growth-retarded human fetuses: growth in different tissue compartments and variation with fetal weight, gestational age, and ventricle size. *Hum Pathol, 30*, 655-60.

Mayhew, T. M., Wijesekara, J., Baker, P. N. & Ong, S. S. (2004). Morphometric evidence that villous development and fetoplacental angiogenesis are compromised by intrauterine growth restriction but not by pre-eclampsia. *Placenta, 25*, 829-33.

McBurney, R. D. (1947). The undernourished full term infant; a case report. *West J Surg Obstet Gynecol*, *55*, 363-70.

McCarthy, C., Cotter, F. E., McElwaine, S., Twomey, A., Mooney, E. E., Ryan, F., et al. (2007). Altered gene expression patterns in intrauterine growth restriction: potential role of hypoxia. *Am J Obstet Gynecol*, *196*, 70.e1-6.

McClung, J. (1969). *Effects of high altitude on human birth. Observations on mothers, placentas, and the newborn in two Peruvian populations.* Cambridge, MA: Harvard University Press.

McCowan, L. M., Harding, J. E. & Stewart, A. W. (2005). Customized birthweight centiles predict SGA pregnancies with perinatal morbidity. *BJOG*, *112*, 1026-33.

McCullough, R. E. & Reeves, J. T. (1977). Fetal growth retardation and increased infant mortality at high altitude. *Arch Environ Health*, *32*, 36-9.

McCullough, R. E., Reeves, J. T. & Liljegren, R. L. (1977). Fetal growth retardation and increased infant mortality at high altitude. *Obstet Gynecol Surv*, *32*, 596-8.

McMinn, J., Wei, M., Schupf, N., Cusmai, J., Johnson, E. B., Smith, A. C., et al. (2006). Unbalanced placental expression of imprinted genes in human intrauterine growth restriction. *Placenta*, *27*, 540-9.

Mellor, D. J. (1983). Nutritional and placental determinants of foetal growth rate in sheep and consequences for the newborn lamb. *Br Vet J*, *139*, 307-24.

Milani, S., Bossi, A., Bertino, E., di Battista, E., Coscia, A., Aicardi, G., et al. (2005). Differences in size at birth are determined by differences in growth velocity during early prenatal life. *Pediatr Res*, *57*, 205-10.

Miller, S. L., Green, L. R., Peebles, D. M., Hanson, M. A. & Blanco, C. E. (2002). Effects of chronic hypoxia and protein malnutrition on growth in the developing chick. *Am J Obstet Gynecol*, *186*, 261-7.

Moore, L. G., Charles, S. M. & Julian, C. G. (2011). Humans at high altitude: hypoxia and fetal growth. *Respir Physiol Neurobiol*, *178*, 181-90.

Morgan, H. D., Santos, F., Green, K., Dean, W. & Reik, W. (2005). Epigenetic reprogramming in mammals. *Hum Mol Genet*, 14 Spec No 1, R47-58.

Morrison, J. L. (2008). Sheep models of intrauterine growth restriction: fetal adaptations and consequences. *Clin Exp Pharmacol Physiol*, *35*, 730-43.

Morrison, S., Gardner, D. S., Fletcher, A. J., Bloomfield, M. R. & Giussani, D. A. (2003). Enhanced nitric oxide activity offsets peripheral vasoconstriction during acute hypoxaemia via chemoreflex and adrenomedullary actions in the sheep fetus. *J Physiol*, *547*, 283-91.

Morton, J. S., Rueda-Clausen, C. F. & Davidge, S. T. (2010). Mechanisms of endothelium-dependent vasodilation in male and female, young and aged offspring born growth restricted. *Am J Physiol Regul Integr Comp Physiol*, *298*, R930-8.

Morton, J. S., Rueda-Clausen, C. F. & Davidge, S. T. (2011). Flow-mediated vasodilation is impaired in adult rat offspring exposed to prenatal hypoxia. *J Appl Physiol*, *110*, 1073-82.

Mossman, H. W. (1987). *Vertebrate fetal membranes.* New Brunswick, N.J.: Rutgers University Press.

Mouillet, J. F., Chu, T., Hubel, C. A., Nelson, D. M., Parks, W. T. & Sadovsky, Y. (2010). The levels of hypoxia-regulated microRNAs in plasma of pregnant women with fetal growth restriction. *Placenta*, *31*, 781-4.

Murray, A. J. (2012). Oxygen delivery and fetal-placental growth: beyond a question of supply and demand? *Placenta*, 33 Suppl 2, e16-22.

Myatt, L. (2006). Placental adaptive responses and fetal programming. *J Physiol*, *572*, 25-30.

Nardozza, L. M., Araujo Júnior, E., Barbosa, M. M., Caetano, A. C., Lee, D. J. & Moron, A. F. (2012). Fetal growth restriction: current knowledge to the general Obs/Gyn. *Arch Gynecol Obstet*, *286*, 1-13.

Nelson, D. M., Smith, S. D., Furesz, T. C., Sadovsky, Y., Ganapathy, V., Parvin, C. A., et al. (2003). Hypoxia reduces expression and function of system A amino acid transporters in cultured term human trophoblasts. *Am J Physiol Cell Physiol*, *284*, C310-5.

North, A. F., Jr. (1966). Small-for-dates neonates. I. Maternal, gestational, and neonatal characteristics. *Pediatrics*, *38*, 1013-9.

Patterson, A. J., Chen, M., Xue, Q., Xiao, D. & Zhang, L. (2010). Chronic prenatal hypoxia induces epigenetic programming of PKC{epsilon} gene repression in rat hearts. *Circ Res*, *107*, 365-73.

Patterson, A. J., Xiao, D., Xiong, F., Dixon, B. & Zhang, L. (2012). Hypoxia-derived oxidative stress mediates epigenetic repression of PKCε gene in foetal rat. *Cardiovasc Res*, *93*, 302-10.

Payne, J. F. (1900). *Thomas Sydenham*. London: T. Fisher Unwin.

Paz, I., Gale, R., Laor, A., Danon, Y. L., Stevenson, D. K. & Seidman, D. S. (1995). The cognitive outcome of full-term small for gestational age infants at late adolescence. *Obstet Gynecol*, *85*, 452-6.

Peeters, L. L., Sheldon, R. E., Jones, M. D. Jr., Makowski, E. L. & Meschia, G. (1979). Blood flow to fetal organs as a function of arterial oxygen content. *Am J Obstet Gynecol*, *135*, 637-46.

Perez, R., Espinoza, M., Riguelme, R., Parer, J. T. & Llanos, A. J. (1989). Arginine vasopressin mediates cardiovascular responses to hypoxemia in fetal sheep. *Am J Physiol*, *256*, R1011-8.

Phillips, I. D., Simonetta, G., Owens, J. A., Robinson, J. S., Clarke, I. J. & McMillen, I. C. (1996). Placental restriction alters the functional development of the pituitary-adrenal axis in the sheep fetus during late gestation. *Pediatr Res*, *40*, 861-6.

Piedrahita, J. A. (2011). The role of imprinted genes in fetal growth abnormalities. *Birth Defects Res A Clin Mol Teratol*, *91*, 682-92.

Postigo, L., Heredia, G., Illsley, N. P., Torricos, T., Dolan, C., Echalar, L., et al. (2009). Where the O2 goes to: preservation of human fetal oxygen delivery and consumption at high altitude. *J Physiol*, *587*, 693-708.

Rees, S., Harding, R. & Walker, D. (2008). An adverse intrauterine environment: implications for injury and altered development of the brain. *Int J Dev Neurosci*, *26*, 3-11.

Rees, S., Harding, R. & Walker, D. (2011). The biological basis of injury and neuroprotection in the fetal and neonatal brain. *Int J Dev Neurosci*, *29*, 551-63.

Reik, W., Constância, M., Fowden, A., Anderson, N., Dean, W., Ferguson-Smith, A., et al. (2003). Regulation of supply and demand for maternal nutrients in mammals by imprinted genes. *J Physiol*, *547*, 35-44.

Reik, W. & Walter, J. (2001). Genomic imprinting: parental influence on the genome. *Nat Rev Genet*, *2*, 21-32.

Resnik, R. (2002). Intrauterine growth restriction. *Obstet Gynecol*, *99*, 490-6.

Resnik, R. (2007). One size does not fit all. *Am J Obstet Gynecol 197*, 221-2.

Riddell, M. R., Winkler-Lowen, B., Jiang, Y., Guilbert, L. J. & Davidge, S. T. (2013). Fibrocyte-like cells from intrauterine growth restriction placentas have a reduced ability to stimulate angiogenesis. *Am J Pathol, 183*, 1025-33.

Rizzo, G., Capponi, A., Rinaldo, D., Arduini, D. & Romanini, C. (1995). Ventricular ejection force in growth-retarded fetuses. *Ultrasound Obstet Gynecol, 5*, 247-55.

Robinson, J. S., Kingston, E. J., Jones, C. T. & Thorburn, G. D. (1979). Studies on experimental growth retardation in sheep. The effect of removal of a endometrial caruncles on fetal size and metabolism. *J Dev Physiol, 1*, 379-98.

Roex, A., Nikpoor, P., van Eerd, E., Hodyl, N. & Dekker, G. (2012). Serial plotting on customised fundal height charts results in doubling of the antenatal detection of small for gestational age fetuses in nulliparous women. *Aust N Z J Obstet Gynaecol, 52*, 78-82.

Roje, D., Zekic Tomas, S., Capkun, V., Marusic, J., Resic, J. & Kuzmic Prusac, I. (2014). Asymmetrical fetal growth is not associated with altered trophoblast apoptotic activity in idiopathic intrauterine growth retardation. *J Obstet Gynaecol Res, 40*, 410-7.

Rouwet, E. V., Tintu, A. N., Schellings, M. W., van Bilsen, M., Lutgens, E., Hofstra, L., et al. (2002). Hypoxia induces aortic hypertrophic growth, left ventricular dysfunction, and sympathetic hyperinnervation of peripheral arteries in the chick embryo. *Circulation, 105*, 2791-6.

Rueda-Clausen, C. F., Morton, J. S. & Davidge, S. T. (2009). Effects of hypoxia-induced intrauterine growth restriction on cardiopulmonary structure and function during adulthood. *Cardiovasc Res, 81*, 713-22.

Rueda-Clausen, C. F., Morton, J. S., Lopaschuk, G. D. & Davidge, S. T. (2011). Long-term effects of intrauterine growth restriction on cardiac metabolism and susceptibility to ischaemia/reperfusion. *Cardiovasc Res, 90*, 285-94.

Ruijtenbeek, K., Kessels, C. G., Janssen, B. J., Bitsch, N. J., Fazzi, G. E., Janssen, G. M. et al. (2003a). Chronic moderate hypoxia during in ovo development alters arterial reactivity in chickens. *Pflugers Arch, 447*, 158-67.

Ruijtenbeek, K., Kessels, L. C., De Mey, J. G. & Blanco, C. E. (2003b). Chronic moderate hypoxia and protein malnutrition both induce growth retardation, but have distinct effects on arterial endothelium-dependent reactivity in the chicken embryo. *Pediatr Res, 53*, 573-9.

Ruijtenbeek, K., le Noble, F. A., Janssen, G. M., Kessels, C. G., Fazzi, G. E., Blanco, C. E., et al. (2000). Chronic hypoxia stimulates periarterial sympathetic nerve development in chicken embryo. *Circulation, 102*, 2892-7.

Rumbolz, W. L. & McGoogan, L. S. (1953). Placental insufficiency and the small undernourished full-term infant. *Obstet Gynecol, 1*, 294-301.

Saenger, P., Czernichow, P., Hughes, I. & Reiter, E. O. (2007). Small for gestational age: short stature and beyond. *Endocr Rev, 28*, 219-51.

Salinas, C. E., Blanco, C. E., Villena, M., Camm, E. J., Tuckett, J. D., Weerakkody, R. A., et al. (2010). Cardiac and vascular disease prior to hatching in chick embryos incubated at high altitude. *J Dev Orig Health Dis, 1*, 60-6.

Sanz-Cortés, M., Figueras, F., Bonet-Carne, E., Padilla, N., Tenorio, V., Bargalló, N., et al. (2013). Fetal brain MRI texture analysis identifies different microstructural patterns in adequate and small for gestational age fetuses at term. *Fetal Diagn Ther, 33*,122-9.

Schauseil-Zipf, U., Hamm, W., Stenzel, B., Bolte, A. & Gladtke, E. (1989). Severe intra-uterine growth retardation: obstetrical management and follow up studies in children born between 1970 and 1985. *Eur J Obstet Gynecol Reprod Biol, 30,* 1-9.

Schober, M. E., McKnight, R. A., Yu, X., Callaway, C. W., Ke, X. & Lane, R. H. (2009). Intrauterine growth restriction due to uteroplacental insufficiency decreased white matter and altered NMDAR subunit composition in juvenile rat hippocampi. *Am J Physiol Regul Integr Comp Physiol, 296,* R681-92.

Seeds, J. W. (1984). Impaired fetal growth: definition and clinical diagnosis. *Obstet Gynecol, 64,* 303-10.

Shapiro, S., Unger, J. & U.S. Public Health Service & National Center for Health Statistics (U.S.). (1954). *Weight at birth and its effect on survival of the newborn in the United States, early 1950.* Vital Statistics-Special Reports, Selected Studies, Vol. *39,* No. 1. Rockville, MD: U.S. Dept. of Health, Education, and Welfare, Public Health Service.

Sharma, S. K., Lucitti, J. L., Nordman, C., Tinney, J. P., Tobita, K. & Keller, B. B. (2006). Impact of hypoxia on early chick embryo growth and cardiovascular function. *Pediatr Res, 59,* 116-20.

Sibley, C. P., Coan, P. M., Ferguson-Smith, A. C., Dean, W., Hughes, J., Smith, P., et al. (2004). Placental-specific insulin-like growth factor 2 (Igf2) regulates the diffusional exchange characteristics of the mouse placenta. *Proc Natl Acad Sci USA, 101,* 8204-8.

Sibley, C. P., Turner, M. A., Cetin, I., Ayuk, P., Boyd, C. A., D'Souza, S. W., et al. (2005). Placental phenotypes of intrauterine growth. *Pediatr Res, 58,* 827-32.

Singla, P. N., Tyagi, M., Kumar, A., Dash, D. & Shankar, R. (1997). Fetal growth in maternal anaemia. *J Trop Pediatr, 43,* 89-92.

Sitras, V., Paulssen, R., Leirvik, J., Vårtun, A. & Acharya, G. (2009). Placental gene expression profile in intrauterine growth restriction due to placental insufficiency. *Reprod Sci, 16,* 701-11.

Skilton, M. R., Evans, N., Griffiths, K. A., Harmer, J. A. & Celermajer, D. S. (2005). Aortic wall thickness in newborns with intrauterine growth restriction. *Lancet, 365,* 1484-6.

Soleymanlou, N., Jurisica, I., Nevo, O., Ietta, F., Zhang, X., Zamudio, S., et al. (2005). Molecular evidence of placental hypoxia in preeclampsia. *J Clin Endocrinol Metab, 90,* 4299-308.

Strauss, R. S. (2000). Adult functional outcome of those born small for gestational age: twenty-six-year follow-up of the 1970 British Birth Cohort. *JAMA, 283,* 625-32.

Struwe, E., Berzl, G., Schild, R., Blessing, H., Drexel, L., Hauck, B., et al. (2010). Microarray analysis of placental tissue in intrauterine growth restriction. *Clin Endocrinol, 72,* 241-7.

Sung, I. K., Vohr, B. & Oh, W. (1993). Growth and neurodevelopmental outcome of very low birth weight infants with intrauterine growth retardation: comparison with control subjects matched by birth weight and gestational age. *J Pediatr, 123,* 618-24.

Sutton, M. S., Theard, M. A., Bhatia, S. J., Plappert, T., Saltzman, D. H. & Doubilet, P. (1990). Changes in placental blood flow in the normal human fetus with gestational age. *Pediatr Res, 28,* 383-7.

Sweeting, H. N. (2007). Measurement and definitions of obesity in childhood and adolescence: a field guide for the uninitiated. *Nutr J, 6,* 32.

Tanner, J. M. (1978). *Foetus into man: physical growth from conception to maturity.* Cambridge: Harvard University Press.

Thakor, A. S., Richter, H. G., Kane, A. D., Dunster, C., Kelly, F. J., Poston, L., et al. (2010). Redox modulation of the fetal cardiovascular defence to hypoxaemia. *J Physiol, 588*, 4235-47.

Thaler, I., Manor, D., Itskovitz, J., Rottem, S., Levit, N., Timor-Tritsch, I., et al. (1990). Changes in uterine blood flow during human pregnancy. *Am J Obstet Gynecol, 162*, 121-5.

Thompson, L. P., Aguan, K., Pinkas, G. & Weiner, C. P. (2000). Chronic hypoxia increases the NO contribution of acetylcholine vasodilation of the fetal guinea pig heart. *Am J Physiol Regul Integr Comp Physiol, 279*, R1813-20.

Thompson, L. P., Dong, Y. & Evans, L. (2009). Chronic hypoxia increases inducible NOS-derived nitric oxide in fetal guinea pig hearts. *Pediatr Res, 65*, 188-92.

Thureen, P. J., Trembler, K. A., Meschia, G., Makowski, E. L. & Wilkening, R. B. (1992). Placental glucose transport in heat-induced fetal growth retardation. *Am J Physiol, 263*, R578-85.

Tissot van Patot, M. C., Ebensperger, G., Gassmann, M. & Llanos, A. J. (2012). The hypoxic placenta. *High Alt Med Biol, 13*, 176-84.

Tzschoppe, A. A., Struwe, E., Dörr, H. G., Goecke, T. W., Beckmann, M. W., Schild, R. L., et al. (2010). Differences in gene expression dependent on sampling site in placental tissue of fetuses with intrauterine growth restriction. *Placenta, 31*, 178-85.

Tzschoppe, A., Struwe, E., Rascher, W., Dorr, H. G., Schild, R. L., Goecke, T. W., et al. (2011). Intrauterine growth restriction (IUGR) is associated with increased leptin synthesis and binding capability in neonates. *Clin Endocrinol, 74*, 459-66.

Unno, N., Giussani, D. A., Hing, W. K., Ding, X. Y., Collins, J. H. & Nathanielsz, P. W. (1997). Changes in adrenocorticotropin and cortisol responsiveness after repeated partial umbilical cord occlusions in the late gestation ovine fetus. *Endocrinology, 138*, 259-63.

Usher, R. H. (1970). Clinical and therapeutic aspects of fetal malnutrition. *Pediatr Clin North Am, 17*, 169-83.

Usher, R. & McLean, F. (1969). Intrauterine growth of live-born Caucasian infants at sea level: Standards obtained from measurements in 7 dimensions of infants born between 25 and 44 weeks of gestation. *J Pediatr, 74*, 901-10.

Usher, R., McLean, F. & Scott, K. E. (1966). Judgment of fetal age. II. Clinical significance of gestational age and an objective method for its assessment. *Pediatr Clin North Am, 13*, 835-48.

Veille, J. C., Hanson, R., Sivakoff, M., Hoen, H. & Ben-Ami, M. (1993). Fetal cardiac size in normal, intrauterine growth retarded, and diabetic pregnancies. *Am J Perinatol, 10*, 275-9.

Villamor, E., Kessels, C. G., Ruijtenbeek, K., van Suylen, R. J., Belik, J., de Mey, J. G., et al. (2004). Chronic in ovo hypoxia decreases pulmonary arterial contractile reactivity and induces biventricular cardiac enlargement in the chicken embryo. *Am J Physiol Regul Integr Comp Physiol, 287*, R642-51.

Villar, J. & Belizan, J. M. (1982). The timing factor in the pathophysiology of the intrauterine growth retardation syndrome. *Obstet Gynecol Surv, 37*, 499-506.

Wallace, J. M., Regnault, T. R., Limesand, S. W., Hay, W. W., Jr. & Anthony, R. V. (2005). Investigating the causes of low birth weight in contrasting ovine paradigms. *J Physiol, 565*, 19-26.

Warkany, J., Monroe, B. B. & Sutherland, B. S. (1961). Intrauterine growth retardation. *Am J Dis Child, 102,* 249-79.

Wells, J. C. (2009a). Historical cohort studies and the early origins of disease hypothesis: making sense of the evidence. *Proc Nutr Soc, 68,* 179-88.

Wells, J. C. (2009b). Thrift: a guide to thrifty genes, thrifty phenotypes and thrifty norms. *Int J Obes,* 33, 1331-8.

Wells, J. C. (2010). Maternal capital and the metabolic ghetto: An evolutionary perspective on the transgenerational basis of health inequalities. *Am J Hum Biol, 22,* 1-17.

Wells, J. C. (2011). The thrifty phenotype: An adaptation in growth or metabolism? *Am J Hum Biol, 23,* 65-75.

West Midlands Perinatal Institute. (2011). West Midlands PEER-Perinatal KPI Report Q2 2010/11. Available at: www.pi.nhs.uk/pnm/maternitydata/Q2_2010-11_Perinatal_ KPI_ report.pdf

Wilkening, R. B. & Meschia, G. (1983). Fetal oxygen uptake, oxygenation, and acid-base balance as a function of uterine blood flow. *Am J Physiol, 244,* H749-55.

Williams, S. J., Campbell, M. E., McMillen, I. C. & Davidge, S. T. (2005a). Differential effects of maternal hypoxia or nutrient restriction on carotid and femoral vascular function in neonatal rats. *Am J Physiol Regul Integr Comp Physiol, 288,* R360-7.

Williams, S. J., Hemmings, D. G., Mitchell, J. M., McMillen, I. C. & Davidge, S. T. (2005b). Effects of maternal hypoxia or nutrient restriction during pregnancy on endothelial function in adult male rat offspring. *J Physiol, 565,* 125-35.

Wollmann, H. A. (1998). Intrauterine growth restriction: definition and etiology. *Horm Res,* 49 Suppl 2, 1-6.

World Health Organization (WHO). (1950). *Expert Group on Prematurity: final report [on a meeting held in] Geneva, 17-21 April 1950.* Geneva: World Health Organization.

World Health Organization (WHO). (2012). *World Health Statistics.* Geneva, Switzerland: World Health Organization.

Xu, Y., Williams, S. J., O'Brien, D. & Davidge, S. T. (2006). Hypoxia or nutrient restriction during pregnancy in rats leads to progressive cardiac remodeling and impairs postischemic recovery in adult male offspring. *FASEB J, 20,* 1251-3.

Xue, Q. & Zhang, L. (2009). Prenatal hypoxia causes a sex-dependent increase in heart susceptibility to ischemia and reperfusion injury in adult male offspring: role of protein kinase C epsilon. *J Pharmacol Exp Ther, 330,* 624-32.

Yerushalmy, J., van den Berg, B. J., Erhardt, C. L. & Jacobziner, H. (1965). Birth weight and gestation as indices of "immaturity": neonatal mortality and congenital anomalies of the "immature". *Am J Dis Child, 109,* 43-57.

Yip, R. (1987). Altitude and birth weight. *J Pediatr, 111,* 869-76.

Zamudio, S., Wu, Y., Ietta, F., Rolfo, A., Cross, A., Wheeler, T., et al. (2007). Human placental hypoxia-inducible factor-1alpha expression correlates with clinical outcomes in chronic hypoxia in vivo. *Am J Pathol, 170,* 2171-9.

Zubrick, S. R., Kurinczuk, J. J., McDermott, B. M., McKelvey, R. S., Silburn, S. R. & Davies, L. C. (2000). Fetal growth and subsequent mental health problems in children aged 4 to 13 years. *Dev Med Child Neurol, 42,* 14-20.

In: Stress and Developmental Programming … ISBN: 978-1-63321-836-9
Editors: Lubo Zhang and Lawrence D. Longo © 2014 Nova Science Publishers, Inc.

Chapter 5

Fetal Stress and Growth Restriction at High Altitude

Lawrence D. Longo[*] and Ravi Goyal

Center for Perinatal Biology, Department of Basic Sciences, Division of Physiology,
Loma Linda University School of Medicine, Loma Linda, CA, US

Abstract

In the USA and throughout the world, fetal growth restriction (FGR), defined as 10th percentile or less of estimated fetal weight, is a complication of 7 to 10% of pregnancies. Its relation to chronic hypoxia is complex and poorly understood. Development of the normal embryo has been shown to occur in a state of relative hypoxia. Nonetheless, beyond a certain degree of physiological adjustment, hypoxia is associated with a number of factors inimical to cell growth and function. In response to prolonged or long-term hypoxemia (LTH), a number of compensatory changes transpire in many organ systems and tissues to maintain homeostasis. These result in what has been called intrauterine growth restriction, small for gestational age, and/or growth restricted fetuses/newborn infants. Because of the relatively large fraction of pregnancies that occur in women who live at high altitude, this now is recognized as a not uncommon cause of FGR. Appreciation of the physiologic responses to high altitude acclimatization is of great interest and illustrates the evolution of ideas concerning such a physiologic stress. To explore the mechanisms of high altitude LTH in producing the FGR phenotype, many studies have been performed in the fetal sheep, and in these, a host of specific responses have been recorded in essentially every tissue and organ system that have been studied. In terms of a case study for a specific tissue, cerebral arteries of the LTH fetus demonstrate a number of significant changes that may be adaptive or maladaptive in preserving cerebral blood flow and oxygenation. In various organs a multitude of other endocrinologic, metabolic, and neurobiologic changes occur, as well as fundamental changes in structure of the placenta. In concert with these high altitude, hypoxic-induced

[*] Corresponding author: Lawrence D. Longo, M.D., Center for Perinatal Biology, Loma Linda University, School of Medicine, Loma Linda, CA 92350, Telephone: 909-558-4325, Fax: 909-558-4029, E-mail: llongo @llu.edu.

changes, fetal hemoglobin concentration and blood volume increase to maintain tissue O_2 delivery. In contrast to the sheep, the llama fetus which has been acclimatized to high elevation for many generations demonstrates marked differences in many cardiovascular variables. In response to hypoxia, these include a marked increase in systemic vascular tone, lack of augmentation of cerebral blood flow but dramatic increases in blood flow to the myocardium and adrenal glands, and many other differences in response. The results emphasize the role of high altitude hypoxemia in modulating a number of signal transduction mechanisms in the various organs and tissues to affect protein synthesis and a mosaic of responses. These specifically highlight the array of responses in the fetus and their implications for development under conditions of high altitude induced fetal growth restriction. Of critical relevance and importance the cellular and molecular changes present lifelong consequences with a panoply of diseases in adult life. Discovery of the genes that promote acclimatization and/or prevent high altitude-associated disease may have profound implications for human well-being.

Keywords: Long-term hypoxia, acclimatization, cardiac, cerebrovascular, development

Abbreviations

ACE	angiotensin converting enzyme
ACOG	American Congress of Obstetricians and Gynecologists
ACTH	adrenocorticotropic hormone
Akt	protein kinase B (PKB) serine/threonine-specific protein kinase
AMPD	antenatal maternal protein deprivation
AT1- and 2-	angiotensin II-type 1 and 2
ATP	adenosine triphosphate
AVP	arginine vasopressin
BA	basilar artery
BK	big conductance calcium activated potassium channel
BPM	beats per minute
BW	birthweight
CA	carotid artery
Ca^{2+}	ionized calcium
cAMP	cyclic adenosine monophosphate
CBF	cerebral blood flow
cDNA	complementary DNA
cGMP	cyclic guanosine monophosphate
CREB	cAMP response element binding protein
CRH	corticotropin releasing hormone
CpG	cytosine phosphodiester guanine
CSS	chronic social stress
dl	deciliter
DOHaD	developmental origins of adult health and disease
DNA	deoxyribonucleic acid
DPC	day post conception

2,3-DPG	2-3-diphosphoglycerate
ECoG	electrocorticogram
eNOS	endothelial nitric oxide synthetase
ER	endoplasmic reticulum
ERK	extracellular regulated kinase
F	generation of offspring
FGR	fetal growth restriction
Flk-1	VEGF receptor 1
Flt-1	VEGF receptor 2
gm	gram
HAT	histone acetyl transferase
HDAC	histone deacetylase
HDM	histone demethylase
HIF	hypoxic inducible factor
HMT	histone methyl transferase
HPA	hypothalamic pituitary axis
HSD	hydroxydehydrogenase
5-HT	5 hydroxytryptamine, serotonin
IGF	insulin-like growth factor
IP$_3$	inositol 1,4,5-trisphosphate
IR	immunoreactive
IUGR	intrauterine growth restriction
K$^+$	ionized potassium
kDa	kilodalton
kg	kilogram
L-channel	L Type Ca^{2+} channel
L-Name	N^{ω}-nitro-L-arginine methyl ester
LTH	long-term hypoxia
MAPK	mitogen-activated protein kinase
MCA	middle cerebral artery
MEK	mitogen-activated extracellular kinase
miRNA	micro RNA
mmHg	millimeters of mercury
MRI	magnetic resonance imaging
mRNA	messenger ribonucleic acid
NE	norepinephrine
NO	nitric oxide
NOS	nitric oxide synthase
NPY	neuropeptide Y
O$_2$	oxygen
PCO$_2$	partial pressure of carbon dioxide
PDBU	phorbol 12, 13-dibutyrate
PHE	phenylephrine
PKC	protein kinase C
PKG	protein kinase G

PO_2	partial pressure of oxygen
RAS	renin angiotensin system
ROS	reactive oxygen species
SGA	small for gestational age
SR	sarcoplasmic reticulum
TGF	transforming growth factor
T_{max}	maximum tension
Torr	Torricelli (unit of pressure)
VEGF	vascular endothelial growth factor

High Altitude Long-Term Hypoxia and the Human Condition

In terms of the optimal conditions for fetal development, numerous workers have noted that such growth and development occurs in an environment of maternal homeostasis and well being, and with her ability to respond appropriately to a particular stress. One such stress is that of long-term hypoxia (LTH). Because fetal growth critically depends upon adequate maternal oxygenation, conditions such as residence at high altitude (>2,500 m), or that of mothers who are moderate to heavy smokers or with cyanotic heart disease, lung disease, severe anemia, and other conditions that cause prolonged hypoxia may be associated with FGR (Hutter et al., 2010, Longo, 1984, Neerhof and Thaete, 2008).

In a sense O_2 is a two edged sword, Janus-like gas (Burton 2009). Although essential for oxidative metabolism, in either excess or deficiency O_2 can be metabolized into reactive O_2 species (ROS) such as: superoxide anions, hydrogen peroxide, lipid peroxides, hydroxyl radicals, and other malevolent ions (Burton, 2009, Burton and Jauniaux, 2011, Maiti et al., 2006, Maulik et al., 1998, Pringle et al., 2010). The generation of ROS beyond the cellular antioxidant capacity has a number of invidious effects including disruption of plasma membranes, oxidation of cellular proteins, DNA fragmentation, and other consequences (Giordano, 2005, Longo and Packianathan, 1997). Mammals respond to reduced O_2 levels (hypoxia) in many different ways at the systemic, local, cellular, and molecular levels. These responses are designed, in general terms, to decrease cellular O_2 dependence and to increase tissue O_2 availability. The impact of hypoxia on embryonic/fetal biology is a function of factors such as the stage of gestation and development, severity of the hypoxic event, its duration, and its association with other confounders including acidemia, hypercapnia, and/or ischemia. In addition, fetal growth and development critically depend upon adequate placental substrate transport and metabolism (see below).

Thus, quite obviously for the developing fetus *in utero*, its ability to respond to hypoxia in a manner to optimize tissue cellular oxygenation is of vital importance. Under normoxic physiologic conditions, fetal arterial O_2 tensions are low by adult standards (fetal arterial PO_2 ~25±3 Torr versus ~95±5 Torr in adult; thus the fetal arterial O_2 tension is about one-quarter that of the adult). Many of the cardiovascular, hemodynamic, endocrinologic, metabolic, and other responses to acute or short-term hypoxia (often a decrease in arterial O_2 tension of 50% for minutes to several hours) are defined reasonably well (Giussani et al., 1994a, 1994b), such as higher O_2 affinity of fetal hemoglobin and its relative greater hemoglobin concentration that help to maintain circulation O_2 content at levels near that of the adult. That the normal fetus at near sea level is not hypoxic is suggested by its lack of elevated circulating lactate concentrations, and that increasing fetal arterial O_2 levels does not increase its rate of O_2 consumption (Battaglia and Meschia, 1978), as are some of the mechanisms that mediate these relatively rapid responses.

In contrast, in response to chronic or long-term hypoxia, such as that at high altitude, those alterations and their cellular and subcellular mechanisms are less fully known. Several problems confound consideration of adaptations to environmental stress such as acclimatization to high altitude. One is the challenge of delineating in a rigorous manner the pattern of cellular, structural, functional, and behavioral responses. In addition, one must attempt to assess the adaptive value of a given response in terms of its relative benefit to the individual or the population, that is, the extent to which it is adaptive as opposed to being maladaptive. As with many environmental stresses, the description and defining of responses to high altitude has advanced to a much greater extent than has sophistication in the evaluation of specific adaptive values. Because of it being a not uncommon experience for humans, including women who are pregnant, such understanding of the lessons of high altitude are of vital importance. In the present review we consider some of the cardiovascular, cerebrovascular, metabolic, and related adjustments or acclimatization responses of the developing fetus to hypoxia of prolonged duration that play a major role in the genesis of FGR. In addition, we attempt to gain an understanding of their adaptive value.

In terms of fetal growth restriction, a classic example is that of pregnant women who live at high altitude and experience LTH. World-wide, over 100 million people are believed to be permanent residents at altitudes >2,500 m (8,208 ft). Thus, this hypobaric hypoxia presents a challenge for two groups, permanent residents who have lived at high altitude for generations, show evidence of genetic adaptations to optimize cellular oxygenation. In addition, short term sojourners, individuals who spend a month or more as visitors or mountain climbers must undergo the process of acclimatization of tissues and cellular responses to accomplish the same goal. As established in many studies, acclimatization demonstrates its highest degree of efficiency in those born and raised at high altitude. For the pregnant woman at high altitude, whether permanent resident or sojourner, the long-term hypoxia is a not an uncommon cause of FGR.

For example, in the mountain states of the USA, on the *alto plano* [high plane] of the South American Andes Mountains, and in the Himalayas, many individuals live at elevations of 3,000 m, some as high as 4,600m (West, 2002). It was in the latter part of the 19th century with the publication of Paul Bert's (1833-1886) *La pression barométrique. Recherches de physiologie expérimentale* (Bert, 1878), that established the role of reduced partial pressure of oxygen, rather than the hypobaric pressure *per se* that results in erythropoiesis as well as the principal signs and symptoms of high altitude sickness. As an aside, in this work, in which he was the first to investigate the conditions of ascent to high altitude in a hypobaric chamber, Bert credits his colleague Denis Jourdanet (1815-1892) for collaboration in studies of high altitude effects in remote areas of Latin America and mid-southeast Asia (Jourdanet, 1875). Continuing to the early 20th century a number of investigators explored various aspects of the physiologic effects of high altitude acclimatization in the adult (Barcroft, 1927, Barcroft et al., 1923, Douglas et al., 1913, Haldane, 1922, Hurtado, 1964, Monge, 1948, Monge and Monge, 1966, Mosso, 1897, 1899, Weihe, 1964, West, 2002). (Quite obviously, this is not the place to review *in extenso* the physiology of high altitude, long-term hypoxia).

Essentially none of these studies concerned the physiology of pregnancy at altitude, however. Nonetheless, the Peruvian physiologist Carlos Monge (1884-1970) recounted the early years following the Spanish subjugation of the Incas. During the initial period of occupation of the highlands, fertility of the Spanish woman was low and the infants born died shortly thereafter, it being over 50 years before a newborn survived (Monge, 1948). It was following World War 2 that investigators in South America and other countries commenced studies on the effects of altitude on the pregnant woman and her infant (Hurtado, 1955, 1960, 1964, Monge, 1948, 1960, Sobrevilla et al., 1967). These were criticized, however, on grounds that the observed differences were a consequence of differences other than altitude. Confounding variables that might produce the observed changes in birthweight included: small sample size, racial or nutritional differences, socioeconomic status, the presence of disease, exposure to cosmic rays and/or cold temperatures, maternal parity and age, amount of prenatal care, degree to which mothers smoked cigarettes, multiple gestation, degree of pathology of the placenta, and sex of infant.

The fundamental problem of acclimatization to high altitude is that in contrast to an ambient O_2 partial pressure of about 154 Torr (20.9% of 760 Torr) at sea level, with the hypobaric pressure at high altitude the ambient O_2 tension is only a fraction of that value. For instance, at 5,000 m (16,404 ft; somewhat less than the one-half atmosphere of 5,486 m (18,000 ft)), ambient partial pressure is only about 85 Torr. As noted below, one would anticipate that at this elevation, the arterial O_2 tension of the fetus would be much lower than normal, however, surprisingly, and as illustrated in Figure 1 and as discussed in greater detail below and elsewhere, such is not the case (Longo, 1987).

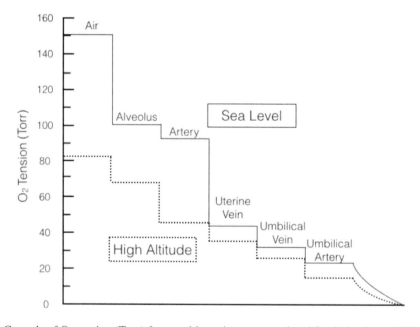

Figure 1. Cascade of O_2 tension (Torr) from ambient air to maternal and fetal blood at ~5,000 m elevation (dotted line) as compared with that at sea level (solid line). (Modified from Longo, 1987).

The Colorado and Mountain States Studies

In a 1950 study by the United States Public Health Service of a reported total of 837,736 live births, neonatal mortality was considerably higher in the mountain states than that of other areas of the country (Shapiro et al., 1954). For the USA as a whole, these were mean BW=3,320 gm; neonatal mortality = 20; for infants who weighed 4,000 gm or more, 9.8%, for infants who weighed 2,500 gm or less = 7.4%) (Table 1 and 2). For all mountain states (~1,790 m) the values were, mean BW = 3,240 gm, neonatal mortality = 24%, for infants who weighed 4,000 gm or more = 6.3%; for infants who weighed less than 2,500 gm = 9.1%. For Denver, CO, the comparable values were, mean BW = 3,035 gm; for infants that weighed 4,000 gm or more = 3.3%, for infants who weighed less than 2,500 gm = 11.7% (neonatal mortality not given). In comparison, the values for Lake County (Leadville), CO were, mean BW = 2,655 gm, neonatal mortality = 49%; for infants who weighed 4,000 gm or more 0%; for infants weighed 2,500 gm or less 48.3% (McClung 1969, p. 52, Shapiro et al., 1954). Thus, in comparison to the USA as a whole, the mean birthweights for live born infants at Leadville were 20% less, the neonatal mortality was over twice greater, and the percent of infants who weighed 2,500 gm or less was many fold greater (Table 1 and 2). It is a sobering reflection.

In light of its relatively large population that lives at high elevations, and with its careful maintenance of health records, the earliest controlled studies that established the inverse relation of birthweight to altitude originated in Colorado. Stimulated by the observation that its Lake County had a several-fold higher incidence of "prematurity" than the state average, in the mid-1950s the Colorado State Department of Public Health initiated a study to explore the reasons for this anomaly. Further analysis of this unexplained dilemma was conducted by a combined effort of the departments of pediatrics and obstetrics and gynecology at the University of Colorado School of Medicine and the State Department of Public Health, and other groups, and was headed by John A. Lichty. This report compared a number of obstetrical and newborn indices at Leadville in Lake County (3,100 m) with those at Denver (1,609 m). For live births of 2,500 gm or less the comparative numerical values were as follows: "Prematurity" 31% versus 10%, neonatal death rate (deaths under one month of age per 1,000 live births), 42% versus 23%. The Lake County birthweights were 380 gm less than Denver controls, with a significant shift to the left of BW distribution curves, as compared to controls (Lichty et al., 1957) (Table 2). The authors also quoted a personal communication from Dr. Elena Boder of Mexico stating that, in a comparison of live birthweights, those in Mexico City (2,134 m) were 8.7% less than those in Mazatlan (sea level). Of critical importance, the authors concluded that these findings "… support the statement of practicing physicians in Lake County that the babies are often small but not otherwise abnormal. Possibly the generally accepted BW of 2,500 gm is not appropriate for distinguishing between full term and premature infants in this community" (Lichty et al., 1957, p. 669). This then was the first study that demonstrated clearly the fact that low BW was a consequence of high altitude, not a *defacto* index of prematurity. In related reports, the authors confirmed these findings and showed that newborn crown-heel length and head length and width were appropriate for gestational age (Howard et al., 1957b). They also reported the paradox that in Lake County newborns neither the oxyhemoglobin saturation nor hematocrit values differed from lowland controls (Howard et al., 1957a). Of vital importance, further studies from 1969 to 1973 in Colorado confirmed these conclusions, and also demonstrated that high altitude hypoxia, rather than decreased gestational age with pre-term delivery, accounted for the altitude-associated lessened BW and increase in neonatal mortality. Birthweight was inversely associated with altitude at each gestational age beyond 35 weeks (McCullough and Reeves, 1977, McCullough et al., 1977) (Table 2).

Table 1. Birth weight and neonatal mortality in the USA Mountain States*

Study	Source	N	Mean birth weight	% less than 2,500 gms	% 4,000 gms or more	Neonatal Mortality†
United States births, 1950	United States, 1965	837,786	3,320	7.4	9.8	20
Mountain States Births, 1950 (~1,790 m)		33,625	3,240	9.1	6.3	24
Denver, 1953 (~1,609 m)	Lichty et al., 1957	10,566	3,035	11.7	3.3	NA
Lake County, Colorado, 1949-1951 (~3,100 m)	Hospital Records	577	2,655	48.3	0.0	49

* From Shapiro et al., 1954; and McClung, 1969, p. 52
† Deaths under 28 days per 1,000 live births, NA=not available

Table 2. Infant Birthweights and Neonatal Mortality Rates at High Altitude

Location	Elevation (m)	Birthweight (gm)	Neonatal Death Rate	Reference
USA	~500	3,320	20.0	Shapiro et al., 1954
Mountain States	~1,790	3,240	24.0	Shapiro et al., 1954
Colorado				
Lake County	~3,100	2,655	49.0	Shapiro et al., 1954
Denver	1,609	3,035	23.4	Lichty et al., 1957
Lake County	3,100	2,655	41.6	Lichty et al., 1957
Denver		3,166	11.9	McCullough & Reeves, 1977
Lake County		2,962	18.5	McCullough et al., 1977
				Grahn & Kratchman, 1963
Low Altitude	<1,500	3,496		Yip, 1987
High Altitude	2,500 †	3,170		Yip, 1987
Denver	~1,600	3,455±112		Julian et al., 2008
Leadville	~3,100	3,035±71		Julian et al., 2008
Leadville	3,100	3,186±70		Moore, 1990
Low Altitude	<1,525	3,271	6.0	Unger et al., 1988
High Altitude	>2,744	3,058	6.5	Unger et al., 1988
Denver		3,415±106		Zamudio et al., 1995
Leadville		3,136±79		Zamudio et al., 1995

Location	Elevation (m)	Birthweight (gm)	Neonatal Death Rate	Reference
South America **Peru**				
Lowland	338		28.4	Mazess, 1965
Highland	3,030		51.8	Mazess, 1965
Lima	203	3,312		McClung, 1969
Cusco	3,416	3,093		McClung,1969
Tacna	568	3,443		Haas et al., 1977
Arequipa	2,363	3,263		Haas et al., 1977
Puno	3,870	3,175		Haas et al., 1977
Tacna	600	3,410		Beall, 1981
Puno	3,860	3,140		Beall, 1981
Lima	~200	~3,240		Mortola et al., 2000
Cerro de Pasco	4,330	2,930		Mortola et al., 2000
Northern Peru	3,360	~3,000		Mortola et al., 2000
Cerra de Paso, Peru	4,300	2,920±90		Moore, 1990
Bolivia				
Santa Cruz	400	Indian 3,345±314 Non Indian 3,559±478	10.6‡	Hass et al., 1980
La Paz	3,600	Indian 3,251±417 Non Indian 3,030±407	9.3‡	Hass et al., 1980
Santa Cruz	400	3,396		Haas et al., 1982
La Paz	3,600	3,013		Haas et al., 1982
Low Altitude	<1,525	3,297		Jensen & Moore, 1997
High Altitude	>2,744	3,056		Jensen & Moore 1997
Lowland	<500	~3,500		Giussani et al., 2001
Highland	>3,500	~3,400		Giussani et al., 2001
Santa Cruz	400			Zamudio et al., 2007
• Andean		3,553±21		Zamudio et al., 2007
• European		3,414±32		Zamudio et al., 2007
La Paz	3,600			Zamudio et al., 2007
• Andean		3,317±34		Zamudio et al., 2007
• European		2,995±32		Zamudio et al., 2007
High Altitude • Andean	3,600	3,148±15		Soria et al., 2013
• Mestizo	3,600	3,081±6		Soria et al., 2013
• European	3,600	2,957±32		Soria et al., 2013
Santa Cruz	416	3,365±780		Julian et al., 2007
Cochabamba	2,500	3,306±944		Julian et al., 2007
La Paz	~3,700	3,101±739		Julian et al., 2007
Mexico				
(Santa Cruz, Bolivia)	400	3,328±540	12 to 13	Haas et al., 1987
Mexico City	2,240	3,035±503	9 to 10	Haas et al., 1987

Table 2. (Continued)

Location	Elevation (m)	Birthweight (gm)	Neonatal Death Rate	Reference
Asia, Himalayas				
Lhasa, Tibet	3,658	3,307±110		Moore, 1990
• Tibetan	>3,000		43† 123†	Moore et al., 2001
• Han Chinese	<3,000		415† 217†	Moore et al., 2001
Lhasa	3,658	3,307		Zamudio et al., 1993
• Tibetan		3,029±553	46‡	Yangzom et al., 2008
• Non-Tibetan		2,861±515	30‡	Yangzom et al., 2008
India, Himalayas				
Ladakh	~3,600	2,764	144‡	Wiley, 1994
Leh	3,534			Wiley, 1994

Note: Neonatal mortality rate: death within first 28 days after birth
†Infant mortality rate; death within first year after birth per 1,000 live births; ‡Postnatal mortality rate; duration of time after delivery not available given in text. Values for elevation are those given by author.

In a follow up study for the years 1950 to 1957 of almost one million live births in the USA, again the mountain states and Lake County, CO stood out for both their high rates of "prematurity" and neonatal deaths (Grahn and Kratchman, 1963) (see http://www.cdc.gov/ nchs/products/vsus/vsus_1939_1964.htm for Vital Statistics of the United States). Notable in this review was the association of these variables with high altitude, with minimal association with exposure to terrestrial irradiation. The authors concluded, "The weight of the evidence – historical, experimental, and clinical – strongly suggests that the reduced partial pressure of oxygen is responsible for the reduced fetal growth and subsequently increased neonatal death rate" (Grahn and Kratchman, 1963, p. 350) (Table 2).

A more recent analysis was conducted of all live births and infant deaths in the state of Colorado for the years 1978 to 1981 (Yip, 1987). After adjusting for socioeconomic factors, a modest association was noted between altitude and the percentage of preterm births of infants weighing <2,500 gm. This association was much stronger, however, for term births with BW <2,500 gm (Yip, 1987). Among comparable subpopulations of infants with gestational ages of at least 37 weeks, the lower BW at high altitude held for each BW distribution at differing altitudes (Yip, 1987). In terms of BW, one might ask about the extent to which it really matters, and what is its relation to morbidity rates. We are unaware of comparative morbidity rates, a fruitful area to explore. In terms of neonatal mortality, the studies from Lake County have been highly valuable.

Studies from South America

As has been noted, some anecdotal evidence by Peruvian doctors had suggested that newborn infants in the highlands were relatively small, while their placentas were "very large." In the mid 1960s, a rather serendipitous encounter occurred between Jean McClung, a

Radcliffe College graduate student interested in anthropological aspects of human adaptations to high altitude and Professor Paul Thornell Baker (1927-2007) (later a member of the National Academy of Sciences) of Pennsylvania State University, who headed an investigation of the physical anthropology of high altitude populations in the highlands of Peru (Garruto et al., 2009). With his wide knowledge of various anthropological relationships led Professor Baker to suggest to Ms. McClung that this might be a fruitful area to explore. This was at the time that Richard B. Mazess, one of Baker's graduate students at Penn State, published his survey of neonatal mortality in Peru (Mazess, 1965). In an analysis of neonatal mortality from the Peruvian census of 1958 and 1959, Mazess discovered that neonatal mortality in the highland departments was ~52, about double that in the lowland, 28.4 (Mazess, 1965) (Table 2). These values were about 40% higher to double comparable to figures in the USA. In this report, the post-neonatal death rates (deaths from 29 days to 1 year per 1,000 live births) also were much greater in the highlands (Mazess, 1965). Mazess has reviewed *in extenso* aspects of the human adaptations to high altitude (Mazess, 1975).

Subsequently, McClung was awarded a fellowship for such studies from the Committee on Latin American Studies of Harvard University. Following proper education in examination of the placenta and training in some of the fine points of measuring various features of the placenta and newborn infant, McClung embarked for Peru to conduct her studies at the *Hospital Regional* in Cuzco (3,416 m) and the *Maternidad* in Lima (203 m). This, in an attempt to differentiate the premature infant from that which is strictly growth restricted, and hopefully to test the hypothesis that the growth restriction seen at high altitude is a consequence of hypoxia *per se*, rather than other factors.

Indeed as anticipated at Cuzco, with the decrease in mean birthweights of 213 gm (6.4%), the placental to fetal weight ratio increased 13% (from 0.15 to 0.17 and 0.18) (McClung, 1969) (Table 3). No significant changes were noted in infant total length or crown-rump length, head circumference, thoracic circumference, arm length, skin-fold thickness, or other measures of nutrition. This decrease in mean BW in the Cuzco high altitude group was highly significant statistically, showing no interaction with other factors. A minor caveat is that the patient numbers were only 73 in Cuzco and 88 in Lima, although elsewhere she gives values of 100 each (McClung, 1969).

An additional feature of the McClung studies showed that when Cuzco-born women gave birth in Lima the infant's BW did not differ from those women native to Lima. Also of importance, this study confirmed the almost 50% increase in neonatal mortality, as well as mortality during the first two years of life, in the hypoxic high altitude environment, and the need for further investigation to deepen our understanding of the fundamental causes of hypoxic-induced FGR (McClung, 1969).

Although her data on infant mortality is not as definitive as one might like, McClung noted,

> ... the data showed a significant increase in child mortality at high altitude. Thirty-three (16.7 percent) of the 198 children live-born to Cuzco women had died before age two; the percentage for Lima women was 12.5 percent (37/295). The difference between these percentages is highly significant (P=.01). This .... Agrees with Mazess' finding[s] based on vital statistics, of significantly higher neonatal mortality in the highland[s] of Peru. [Mazess, 1966] ... Within the study samples themselves, three of the 100 Cuzco infants died before leaving the hospital (birth weights: 700, 1,720, 2,750) and one of the Lima infants died (birth weight: 1,000). No information on mortality was available from

hospital records in Lima, but Cuzco records showed that 27 (5.7 percent) of the 470 lower class infants born in 1965 had died before leaving the hospital. Seventeen of these 27 infants were of low birth weight; thus, 46 percent (17/37) of all low birth weight infants born in 1965 died before leaving the hospital. Of the 27 infants who died in the hospital, 21 (78 percent) were males ... the data indicate that the increased neonatal mortality at high altitude is significant and is associated with very high mortality among the increased percentage of infants of low birth weight.

(McClung, 1969, p. 102)

Table 3. Placental Weights and Placental Index at High Altitude

Location	Elevation (m)	Birth-weight (g)	Placental Weight (g)	Placental Index	Reference
USA					
Colorado					
Denver	1,600	3,359±336	542	0.20	Tissot van Patot et al., 2003
Leadville	3,100	3,123±489	605	0.16	Tissot van Patot et al., 2003
South America					
Peru					
Lima	203	3,297±511	550±87	0.15	Sánchez Kong, 1963
Cerro de Pasco	4,340	2,730±350	568±94	0.20	Sánchez Kong, 1963
Lima	203			0.15	McClung, 1969
Cuzco	3,416			0.17	McClung, 1969
Lima	152	3,489	501	0.14	Krüger & Arias-Stella, 1970
Rio Pallinga	4,602	2,946	561	0.19	Krüger & Arias-Stella, 1970
Bolivia					
Santa Cruz	400	3,415	454	0.13	Jackson et al., 1987a, 1987b
La Paz	3,600				Jackson et al., 1987a, 1987b
• Aymara & Quechua	3,155	480		0.15	Jackson et al., 1987a, 1987b
• European & Mestizo	2,925	457		0.15	Jackson et al., 1987a, 1987b
Santa Cruz	400	3,251±340	480±58	0.147	Montesinos, 1990
La Paz	3,600	2,994±241	459±55	0.153	Montesinos, 1990
Santa Cruz					
• Aymara	400	3,553±21	466±13	0.13	Zamudio et al., 2007
• European		3,414±32	473±15	0.14	Zamudio et al., 2007
La Paz					
• Aymara	3,600	3,317±34	497±17	0.15	Zamudio et al., 2007
• European		2,995±32	478±20	0.16	Zamudio et al., 2007
Saudi Arabia					
Mohayel City	500	3,330±480	524±76	0.16	Ali et al., 1996
Abha City	>3,000	2,940±570	429±107	0.15	Ali et al., 1996
Mohayel City	500	3,400	552	0.16	Khalid et al., 1997
Abha City	3,100	3,000	429	0.14	Khalid et al., 1997

Note: Placenta Index; ratio of weight of placenta to that of fetus. Values for elevation are those given by author.

In her 150 page thesis with several hundred references, McClung presented her studies with a historical review of the literature (McClung, 1969). Although not commonly cited, it is clear that this seminal report laid the groundwork for many of the studies during following several decades. In a subsequent report, McClung reviewed many of her findings (Goodwin, 1974).

In accounting for the significant decreases in birthweight observed at high altitude, a number of questions arose in regards to confounding variables. In an attempt to address these issues, a group at Cornell University, Ithaca, New York examined the role of ethnic background, nutritional status, and sex of newborn infant in the highlands and lowlands of Peru (Haas et al., 1977), Bolivia (Haas et al., 1982, Hass et al., 1980 [should be Haas et al., 1980]), and Mexico (Haas et al., 1987). In their original study from Puno (3,870 m), Arequipa (2,363 m), and Tacna (568 m), Southern Peru, infants delivered in hospital at ~2.5 days of age weighed 3,175, 3,263, and 3,443 gm, respectively. No mortality rates were given, but the infant weight data followed the trend of previous workers (Haas et al., 1977) (Table 2). In the Indian group at La Paz, the BWs of both sexes exceeded those for non-Indians, for both groups these were significantly less than that of Santa Cruz (400 m), and at high altitude male newborns were affected to a greater degree than females (Table 2). Neither socioeconomic nor nutritional status differed significantly among specific groups (Hass et al., 1980 [should be Haas et al., 1980]). In a subsequent study in Bolivia, Haas and his coworkers continued to document the effects of high altitude on birthweight (Table 2), as well as on the rate of growth during the first year of life. Despite their lighter BW, the highland infants showed significantly greater triceps and subscapular skin fold thickness and fat accumulation. The possible causes of the greater fat accumulation in the highland group (Haas et al., 1982) may relate to significant alterations in leptin metabolism (see below). Further, in a study in which they compared anthropomorphic measurements in two distinct Latin American populations Mexico City (elevation 2,134 m), and Santa Cruz, Bolivia, the Haas group found similar high altitude effects on birthweight and other parameters (Haas et al., 1987).

In a study from Peru of the critical barometric pressure below which birthweight at high altitude decreases, the authors concluded that 590 mmHg is that value, corresponding to ~2,500 m elevation (Mortola et al., 2000). From Bolivia shortly thereafter, Dino A. Giussani's group reported that in contrast to the effect of altitude, socioeconomic status played no important role in the lower infant birthweights at La Paz (3,649 m), as compared to those born in the lowlands (<500 m), and that the FGR phenotype was associated with high altitude LTH *per se* (Table 2) (Giussani et al., 2001).

Overall in humans, several studies have documented that, on average, above 2,000 m the weight of near-term newborns decreases ~100 gm per 1,000 m of elevation, independently from other factors, and that several times as many newborns show FGR for their gestational age, compared to low altitude controls (Jensen and Moore, 1997, Julian et al., 2007, Krampl, 2002, Moore, 2003; Moore et al., 2011) (see Table 2). This slowing of growth commenced after about 31 week gestation (Unger et al., 1988), although at altitudes at or above 4,300 m, this declining growth rate began at 25 to 29 weeks gestation (Krampl et al., 2000; Mortola et al., 2000).

The Relation of Birthweight to Gestational Age

A decade and a half following the early Colorado studies, and, in part, motivated by those findings, Lula O. Lubchenco and colleagues at the University of Colorado first described the relation of birthweight to gestational age during the third trimester (Lubchenco et al., 1963).

Although this study was conducted at moderately high altitude (Denver, CO, 1,609 m, 5,280 ft), it set a new standard for evaluation of the newborn infant, and the "Lulagram" developmental growth chart became used world-wide. For infants whose growth patterns lie outside normal developmental profiles, the terms small-, appropriate-, and large- for gestational age were introduced on the basis of weight, length, head circumference, and weight-length ratio (ponderal index) (Battaglia and Lubchenco, 1967, Lubchenco, 1970, Lubchenco et al., 1966, 1972). Although the term "low-birth weight" was introduced in the early sixties to replace the word "premature" for infants under 2,500 gm at birth, its acceptance was markedly facilitated by Lubchenco's popularization of matching birthweight with gestational age. Too long had the designation for term and premature been based on BW above and below 2,500 gm without awareness of two distinct populations for each weight group. A study by the University of California Berkeley biostatistician Jacob Yerushalmy (1904-1973) and coworkers showed that there were as many term as preterm infants born weighing under 2,500 gm in the United States, and surprisingly more preterm infants weighing above than below that figure (Yerushalmy et al., 1965).

Translational Studies of Pregnancy at High Altitude

Continuing in the Colorado tradition, in a series of enlightened studies, the physical anthropologist Lorna Grindlay Moore, of the University of Colorado, has described a number of important variables and adaptive mechanisms in both the pregnant mother and their fetus at high altitude. These include studies in Leadville (3,100 m), the Andean *alto plano* of Peru (4,300 m), and the Tibetan plateau (3,658 m) (Moore, 1990). Among other parameters these reports compare the infant birthweights and mortality rates among several groups (Moore, 1990, 2003, Moore et al., 1998, 2001, 2004) (Table 2). For instance, using pulsed-wave gated Doppler ultrasound, they compared birthweight to the uterine blood flow in Denver and Leadville measured a month earlier at 36 weeks gestation. At 40 weeks gestation, BWs of the high altitude group were reduced 8%, in part reflecting the decrease in the uterine artery fraction of common iliac blood flow seen at 36 weeks gestation. The authors concluded that this decrease in birthweights was a consequence of the combined effect of the smaller uterine artery diameter (27%) seen at 36 weeks gestation, smaller percentage of common iliac flow (36%), and reduced volumetric flow to the placenta (35%). This despite the high altitude associated increase in blood flow of the uterine artery *per se* (Zamudio et al., 1995) (Table 4).

In a subsequent study of 150 women of Andean or European ancestry in La Paz (>3,600 m) and Santa Cruz, Bolivia, Zamudio and colleagues demonstrated in both ancestry groups slight to modest decreases in both uterine artery diameter and mean blood flow velocity at high altitude, but with the increase in hematocrit slightly greater increase in uterine O_2 delivery in those of Andean ancestry (Zamudio et al., 2007). The altitude-associated decrement in BW was 418 gm in European, as opposed to 236 gm in the Andean women. The authors conclude that a deficit in maternal O_2 transport to the placenta is not likely to be causally related to the decreased birthweight (Zamudio et al., 2007). In an editorial commentary on this report, Giussani referred to these and related findings as "the Andean curse on the Conquistadors" (Giussani, 2007).

As a corollary, these investigators showed that DNA synthesis significantly decreased in the guinea pig uteroplacental vasculature at high altitude (Rockwell et al., 2000). Another of their studies from the highlands of Bolivia (3,600 to 4,100 m) demonstrated that uterine vascular high-end arteriolar resistance restricts fetal growth in those patients with preeclampsia, the incidence of which is higher at high altitude (Browne et al., 2011). As an aside, their other studies also suggested that the decrease in neonatal mortality seen at altitude reflect, in part, regionalization of healthcare delivery, with more infants at risk of being born and cared for in tertiary care centers (Unger et al., 1988).

In regards to diet, it has been suggested that impaired transplacental glucose transport also plays a role in high altitude associated FGR (Zamudio, 2003; see below). Of additional interest, in humans Doppler ultrasonic measurements of fetal arterial circulatory responses at 4,300 m have shown a lack of flow redistribution, as would be seen in acute hypoxia (Krampl et al., 2001b). Paradoxically, in some of these fetuses, the velocity of arterial blood flow was significantly less than that measured at low altitude (Krampl et al., 2001b), presumably because of the LTH increase in blood viscosity associated with increased erythrocyte concentration (Ballew and Haas, 1986). In light of the above, with the use of ultrasonography, to avoid the over-diagnosis of FGR, it probably is appropriate to use altitude-specific biometry charts to assess fetal dimensions during the third trimester of pregnancy (Krampl et al., 2000, 2002).

On the Bolivian *alto plano*, birth records by ethnic group of Andean, Mestizo (mixed ethnicity), or European ancestry, the duration of highland ancestry partially protected against the effects of altitude (Julian et al., 2007). In a subsequent study by this group this data was confirmed (Andean = 3,148±15 gm, Mestizo = 3,081±6 gm, European = 2,957±32 gm, p<0.001 for trend) (Soria et al., 2013) (Table 2). As noted, for reasons that remain to be elucidated, the degree of growth restriction may reflect, in part, in an inverse fashion the number of generations of ancestors who lived in a given location (Zamudio et al., 1993). Additionally, BW correlates positively with the vigor of the maternal ventilatory response to the hypoxic stress (Moore et al., 1986). Decrements in uteroplacental blood flow, as determined by ultrasonography (Julian et al., 2008), as well as ethnic ancestry (Julian et al., 2007) also may serve as a fetal protective mechanism in this regard.

For reasons unknown, the decrements in BW and increases in infant mortality are greater in individuals of the Peruvian Andes than in the Himalayas. Specifically, as compared to a number of near sea level studies that give control birthweights of ~3.4±0.3 kg, the birthweights at Leadville, Cerro de Pasco, Peru, and Lhasa, Tibet were 3.2±0.1, 2.9±0.1, and 3.3±0.1 kg, respectively (Moore, 1990) (see Table 2). Also in Tibet, in comparing indigenous Tibetan versus Han Chinese at 3,000 to 4,000 m, the Han experienced a much greater BW reduction and their postnatal mortality rate was almost twice that of Tibetans (Moore et al., 2001). In another study which compared BW and infant mortality between native Tibetans with non-Tibetans (Han Chinese and Hui Muslims) in Lhasa, birthweights were significantly lower (5.5%) and neonatal mortality was significantly decreased (~35%, a change the authors deemed to be non-significant) in the non-Tibetans (Table 2) (Yangzom et al., 2008). Of related interest, in separate studies genome-wide scans showed that Tibetans positively selected haplotypes of *Egln1* and *PPPARA* were associated with decreased hemoglobin phenotype unique to this highland population (Simonson et al., 2010). In a related study, the *Egln1* gene was identified as contributing to natural selection in Andeans as well as Tibetans

(Bigham et al., 2010), and a number of hypoxia-inducible factor-1α (HIF1α) pathway genes (but not HIF1α itself) were upregulated in the Andeans (Bigham et al., 2009).

Table 4. Fetal Physiologic Responses to High Altitude, Long-Term Hypoxia

Physiologic Variable	Normoxic Control	High Altitude Hypoxic	% Change	References
Arterial Blood Gas and Other				
PO$_2$ (Torr)	23±1	19±1*	-17.2	Kamitomo et al., 1993 Kitanaka et al., 1989a
[HbO$_2$] (%)	59±3	50±3†	-15.9	Kamitomo et al., 1993 Kitanaka et al., 1989a
[Hb] (g·dl^{-1})	10.1±0.7	12.6±0.6*	24.7	Kamitomo et al., 1993 Kitanaka et al., 1989a
O$_2$ content (ml·dl^{-1})	7.7±0.5	7.8±0.5	1.0	Kamitomo et al., 1993
P$_{CO2}$ (Torr)	42±1	38±1*	-9.5	Kamitomo et al., 1993
pH	7.36±0.01	7.37±0.01	0.1	Kamitomo et al., 1993
Lactate (mg·dl^{-1})	13.1±0.7	14.4±1	9.9	Kamitomo et al., 1993
Breathing Incidence (min·hr^{-1})	25	25	-	Koos et al., 1988
Uterine Artery Blood Flow				
Human uterine artery blood flow at 36 weeks gestation (ml·min^{-1})	312±22	203±48	-34.9	Zamudio et al., 1995
Uterine artery fraction of common iliac blood flow (% at 36 weeks gestation)	74±6	46±7	-36.3	Zamudio et al., 1995
Cardiac Function				
Heart Rate (beats·min^{-1})	168±5	165±5	-1.6	Kamitomo et al., 1992, 1993
Arterial Pressure (mmHg)	44±1	52±1*	18.1	Kamitomo et al., 1992, 1993
Right Ventricular Output (ml·min^{-1}·kg^{-1})	276±10	183±10*	-33.6	Kamitomo et al., 1992, 1993
Left Ventricular Output (ml·min^{-1}·kg^{-1})	166±16	142±16	-14.5	Kamitomo et al., 1992, 1993
Right Stroke Volume (ml·kg^{-1})	1.66±0.05	1.11±0.05 *	-33.1	Kamitomo et al., 1992, 1993
Left Stroke Volume (ml·kg^{-1})	0.97±0.09	0.84±0.08	-13.4	Kamitomo et al., 1992, 1993
Combined Ventricular Output (ml·min^{-1}·kg^{-1})	441±23	335±28†	-24.1	Kamitomo et al., 1992, 1993
Cerebral Artery Structure and Composition				
Vessel resting inside luminal diameter (mm)	0.94±0.07	1.30±0.04	39*	Henderson & Longo, 2003
Media Thickness, μm	21±1	30±6	42*	Henderson & Longo, 2003
Media Cross-Sectional Area (μm^2·10^{-3})	67±7	124±22	85*	Henderson & Longo, 2003
Number of Layers of SMC in media	5.6±0.2	11.5±2.1	105†	Henderson & Longo, 2003

Physiologic Variable	Normoxic Control	High Altitude Hypoxic	% Change	References
Base-Soluble Protein (%dry wt)	24.5±2.2	30.0±4.1	22*	Longo et al., 1993
Cranial Artery Contractile Proteins				
Flk-1 (protein $\cdot 10^{-6}$ total protein)	2.0±0.6	5±1	170↑	Adeoye et al., 2013
Flt-1 (protein $\cdot 10^{-6}$ total protein)	0.4±0.1	3.0±1.0	780↑	Adeoye et al., 2013
Myosin light chain kinase (protein $\cdot 10^{-6}$ total protein)	0.6±0.1	0.07±0.02	90↓	Adeoye et al., 2013
Myosin light chain$_{20}$ (protein $\cdot 10^{-6}$ total protein)	0.4±0.1	0.63±0.10	61↑	Adeoye et al., 2013
Cerebral Artery Electromechanical Coupling				
K^+ max tension (g)	1.0±0.06	1.1±0.1	10	Long et al., 2002
K^+ stress (10^{-6} dyn$\cdot$cm^{-2})	0.41±0.05	0.44±0.05	7	Longo et al., 1993
L-type Ca^{2+} Channel (% Inhibition tension by nifedipine)	100±10	100±10	-	Zhao et al., 2004
K_{ATP} channel (%inhibition tension by pinacidil)	5.2±0.1	4.7±0.1	10†	Long et al., 2002
K_{ca} channel (% inhibition tension by NS-1619)	100±10	41±5	-59†	Long et al., 2002
Membrane potential (mV)	-26.1±1.4	-42.0±5.2	61†	
BK Channel Current Density (pA$\cdot$pF^{-1})	57.9±6.6	75.1±4.8	30*	Lin et al., 2005 Tao et al., 2014
Calcium set point (10^{-6} M)	4.7	3.0	-36*	Lin et al., 2005
Right shift by dephosphorylation state (mV)	52.3±8.1	11.1±5.6	-79†	Lin et al., 2005
$V_{1/2}$ of dephosphorylated channels (mV)	64.1±4.8	23.6±5.2	-63†	Lin et al., 2005
Endogenous PKA shift (mV)	30.9±4.7	23.0±3.7	-26*	Lin et al., 2005
Cerebral Artery Pharmacomechanical Coupling				
Amine-induced tension, g (10^{-5} M serotonin and 2 X 10^{-5} M histamine)	2.0±0.2	1.5±0.2	-26	Longo et al., 1993
Amine/K^+ max (%max)	85±5	75±5	-12	Longo et al., 1993
NE-induced tension (g)	1.4±0.1	1.4±0.1		Long et al., 2002
NE/K^+ max (%max)	140±12	127±10	-9	
Total α_1-AR density (fmol$\cdot$mg protein^{-1})	47±4	11±1	-77†	Goyal et al., 2014
Ins(1,4,5)P$_3$ basal	40±10	42±7		Ueno et al., 1997
Ins(1,4,5)P$_3$ response (%basal)	345±27	225±30	-35*	Ueno et al., 1997
Ins(1,4,5)P$_3 \cdot \alpha_1$-AR^{-1}	5.2±1	11.7±1	125†	Ueno et al., 1997
Ins(1,4,5)P$_3$-receptor density (fmol$\cdot$mg protein^{-1})	115±15	22±3	-80†	Zhou et al., 1997
ERK1/2–total (%control)	1.0	0.9±0.1	-10	Zhao et al., 2004
-Phosphorylated	1.0	2.5±0.4	150†	

Table 4. (Continued)

Physiologic Variable	Normoxic Control	High Altitude Hypoxic	% Change	References
MLC_{20}–total (%control)	1.0	5.5±1.0	450†	Zhao et al., 2004
-Phosphorylated	1.0	0.8±0.2	-20	
CPI-17–total (%control)	1.0	1.9±0.2	90†	Zhao et al., 2004
-Phosphorylated	1.0	1.1±0.2	10	
Cerebral Artery Perivascular Innervation				
Basal NE release $(10^{-9}g \cdot 10^{-9}g \text{ content}^{-1})$	4.7±0.5	8.2±0.7	74*	Buchholz & Duckles, 2001
Stimulation-evoked fractional NE release after uptake blockade	0.52±0.05	0.69±.10	33*	Buchholz & Duckles, 2001
Stimulation-induced adrenergic contractions (%K_{max} at 8Hz)	0.5±0.1	8±2	>1,500†	Pearce, 1995
Cerebral Vasorelaxation Pathways				
A-23187-induced relaxation (%)	35	24	-31	Longo et al., 1993
sGC $(10^{-9}M \text{ GMP} \cdot 10^{-3}M \text{ protein} \cdot min^{-1})$	0.43±0.03	0.13±0.02	-70	Williams et al., 2006
sGC $(10^{-12} gm \cdot 10^{-3} \text{ protein})$	7.1±0.9	6.0±0.5	-15	Williams et al., 2006
cGMP $(10^{-9}M \cdot 10^{-3}gm \text{ protein} \cdot min^{-1})$	29.5±5.6	84.5±16.4	186	Williams et al., 2006
cGMP, $(10^{-9}M \cdot 10^{-3}gm \text{ soluble protein}^{-1})$	0.35±0.1	0.25±0.1	-28*	Williams et al., 2006
cGMP, $(10^{-9}M \cdot sGC^{-1} (10^{-6}gm) \cdot min^{-1})$	145±20	105±20	-28*	Williams et al., 2006
Max eNOS specific activity slope, NO $(10^{-12}M) \cdot eNOS^{-1}$ $10^{-6}gm \cdot min^{-1}$	3.8±0.5	1.5±0.3	-61†	Williams et al., 2006
Cranial Artery Gene Regulation				
38 genes upregulated	>2-fold			Goyal et al., 2013
9 genes downregulated	>2-fold			Goyal et al., 2013
Fetal HPA Axis Regulation				
CYP11A and CYP17				Myers & Ducsay, 2012
ACTH-Receptor				Myers et al., 2005
ACTH Response to AVP increased				Myers et al., 2005
Hormonal				
Norepinephrine (pg·ml^{-1})	553±55	635±65	14.8	
Epinephrine (pg·ml^{-1})	81±19	113±12	39.5†	
ACTH (pg·ml^{-1})	66±8	60±9	-10	
Cortisol (ng·ml^{-1})	47±3	50±1	6.4	
Erythropoietin (mU·ml^{-1})	23±2	31±17	35	
Some Placental Cellular Parameters				
Placental Nuclear Functions				
90 genes upregulated		-		Gheorghe et al., 2007
73 genes downregulated		-		Gheorghe et al., 2007
Mitochondrial DNA content•	455	698	35*	Lattuada et al., 2008

Values are mean ±SE; *p<0.01; † p<0.05 from normoxic control values; •Human FGR studies

Overall, because of its implications for pregnant women, high altitude needs to be added to the list of risk factors to be taken into account when considering pregnancy, or when comparing BW with gestational age distributions, or in preparing so-called "standard" BW for gestational age charts. Others have challenged the validity of BW for gestational age charts, this in view of the wide variation in race/ethnicity, socioeconomic status, parity, altitude, and other factors (Macfarlane, 1987). Figure 2 depicts some of the maternal acclimatization responses to high altitude associated long-term hypoxia. These include both adaptive responses such as: hyperventilation, increased red cell mass and hemoglobin concentration, changes in the placenta to promote transplacental oxygen flux, and others. Maternal maladaptive changes that may result in fetal growth restriction include: reduced diameter of iliac and uterine arteries, increased blood viscosity, and perhaps reduced uteroplacental blood flow.

Studies of Prolonged Hypoxia in Rodents

As a "model" for almost every aspect of reproduction, rodents have been used to explore antenatal maternal hypoxia and its sequelae for the mother, fetus, and offspring as an adult. These include the most vulnerable period of gestation, the degree of hypoxia, and its duration. Based on an analysis of 19 studies in rats and 5 in mice that met criteria of having appropriate controls and stringent statistical analysis (Jang et al., 2014), it is clear that, in addition to the factors given above, the species/breed studied is important and that these variables interact. For instance, in the rat 7 days or more and in the mouse 3 days or more of hypoxia at 14% or less O_2 concentration during the third (in some cases second) trimester of pregnancy are required to produce FGR. In both rodent species, overall analysis suggests that a newborn pup weight reduction of 22% is required to meet the human FGR definitions of below the 10th percentile (Jang et al., 2014). In the rabbit, uteroplacental ischemia produced by ligation of 50% of blood vessels on day 25 (of a 30 day gestation), produced a number of fetal cerebral neurostructural abnormalities associated with functional impairments (Illa et al., 2013).

A major factor in the determination of the tolerance to hypoxia in mammals would appear to be the affinity of hemoglobin for oxygen. Many reports have explored the role of fetal hypoxia in increasing hemoglobin concentration and some of the cellular and molecular mechanisms by which this occurs (Longo, 1987). For instance, in a number of species fetal and neonatal mice, rats, rabbits, and puppies exposed up to 20 hr·day^{-1} to a degree of hypoxia that did not inhibit growth increased their production of hemoglobin F and tolerance to hypoxia as determined by righting reflex times (Barker, 1957). As an aside, when incubated *in vitro* with zero percent O_2 for 1 to 4 hrs reticulocyte-rich suspension of human umbilical cord erythrocytes showed a striking increase in Hgb F synthesis (Allen and Jandl, 1960). The blood O_2 affinity studies also "… appear to involve a plasma transported substance, its production or activity being regulated by O_2 tension" (Barker, 1957, p. 289). This led later to the recognition of 2,3-diphosphoglycerate (2,3-DPG).

In the following decade it was discovered that the organic phosphate in greatest concentration in the erythrocyte is 2,3-diphosphoglycerate (Benesch and Benesch, 1967, Chanutin and Curnish, 1967; also called 2,3-bisphosphoglycerate). By cross-linking the beta chains with stabilization of the quaternary structure of deoxyhemoglobin, 2,3-DPG decreases hemoglobin O_2 affinity. In fetal erythrocytes with alpha/gamma chain dimers, such binding is minimized, resulting in increased O_2 affinity (Bauer et al., 1968, 1969, Delivoria-Papadopoulos et al., 1971a, Salhany et al., 1971). During the latter third of gestation, the fetal erythrocyte concentration of 2,3-DPG (called by some during the late 1960s and 1970s, the "Direct Path to Grants") rises to adult levels at term ($\sim$5mM$\cdot$L^{-1}). During the first year of life this increase continues, in concert with a decrease in hemoglobin F, before decreasing again to adult levels (Delivoria-Papadopoulos et al., 1971b). (For review see Delivoria-Papadopoulos and McGowan, 2011).

In a series of studies at the White Mountain Research Station, Bishop, California (elevation 3,801 m, 12,470 ft), Paola S. Timiras (1923-2008) of the University of California Berkeley explored the altitude effects in Long Evans rats. Although the majority of this work was in adult males, the F_1 offspring and F_2 descendants also were included (Timiras, 1964). For instance, compared to sea level controls, birthweight and body weight of F_2 generation offspring were and remained lower throughout life (up to 8 months). The mortality rate of the F_2 rats also was considerably higher, and only 27% of these reached this age (Timiras et al., 1957). The hypothesis that metabolic disturbances account for this growth restriction was supported by the observation that following descent to sea level the F_2 young adult body weights remained below normal over a 3 month period (Timiras et al., 1957). Of the organs studied, the heart showed the most change with pronounced hypertrophy (90%) as a constant and predominant finding in the F_2 descendants (Vaughan and Pace, 1956). The adrenal glands also demonstrated considerable enlargement, while weights of the target organs (thymus and spleen) decreased. These changes also were associated with an increase in skeletal muscle myoglobin, and a decrease in glycogen content of the liver and heart (Vaughan and Pace, 1956).

High Altitude, Long-Term Hypoxia in Sheep

As is well known, for an understanding of the biology and physiology of the fetus, that of the sheep *Ovis aries* is widely used. This, because of its relatively large size, accessibility and tranquility of the ewe, reliability of chronic catheterization and instrumentation for studies under physiologic conditions, and cost. As noted, because the arterial O_2 tension of the normoxic fetus at sea level approximates that of an adult at $\sim$5,000 m, one would anticipate that the PO_2 values of a fetus at high altitude would be much lower than sea level control. As has been demonstrated in a number of studies, surprisingly, such is not the case (Kamitomo et al., 1993, Kitanaka et al., 1989a, 1989b, Longo, 1987). Nonetheless, it is instructive to examine these blood gas values at several altitudes because those values for the unacclimatized animal differ considerably from those acclimatized for 6 weeks or more.

Based on increasing interest in the effects of high altitude hypoxia on various aspects of mammalian reproduction, shortly after mid-century Donald Henry Barron (1905-1993) and the Yale University group commenced a series of classic studies at the *Instituto de Biologia Andina*, Morococha, Peru (Barron et al., 1964). Over a series of seasons at high altitude, in Merino stock sheep they explored a number of questions relating to the biology and physiology of maternal and fetal acclimatization responses. For example, in the pregnant ewe the hematocrit and blood O_2 capacity were increased significantly, while arterial oxyhemoglobin saturation values were considerably less (~95% and ~67% at sea level and high altitude, respectively) (Metcalfe et al., 1962a). The high altitude animals showed no significant difference in blood O_2 affinity, however (Meschia et al., 1961). Newborn weight at birth and crown-rump length showed little significant difference from their Dorset sheep near sea level in New Haven, Connecticut (Metcalfe et al., 1962b). Although plasma volume was similar in the two groups, red cell mass and thus blood O_2 capacity were significantly greater in the high altitude animals (Prystowsky et al., 1960). Of interest, their measurement of umbilical blood gas values did not differ significantly (Metcalfe et al., 1962a), although this may have been the combined result of variance in values and small sample size. Striking as these studies were, and indeed they represent a milestone in both the physiology of high altitude and fetal physiology in general, they present a problem. Unfortunately, this series of investigations were conducted prior to the Barron group's introduction of the technique of chronic catheterization of the fetus *in utero* (Meschia, 2006, Meschia et al., 1965, 1969-1970). Thus, the experiments had the drawback of all such studies in acutely anesthetized preparations, e.g., effect of anesthesia *per se*, acute stress of a surgical procedure, and availability of single measurements in a given fetus, so that the altitude effects may have been too subtle or labile to be detected under their experimental conditions.

Along this line, under standard conditions (38°C, PCO_2=40Torr, pH=7.4) these investigators had observed a significant difference in the O_2 affinity and electrophoretic mobility and chromatographic separation of sheep blood (Naughton et al., 1963). In essence, two hemoglobin types could be distinguished: fast-moving (type A) and slow moving (type B) with PO_2 half-saturation values of 27.7 and 37.8 Torr, respectively (Naughton et al., 1963). These differences also were evident in the high altitude animals and the Barron group used these in an attempt to calculate maternal to fetal transplacental PO_2 gradients (Barron et al., 1964). Further, in a study of the maternal and fetal llama, the bloods of which also showed a high O_2 affinity (21.9 and 18.0 Torr, respectively) these workers concluded that the PO_2 gradients were similar despite the llama placenta having an additional membrane layer. These findings suggested that the transplacental O_2 gradient was a function of the number of cell membrane layers and/or thickness (that is, with increasing number of placental cell layers and thickness, the fetal umbilical venous (arterialized blood) O_2 tension would be lower) as being without foundation (Meschia et al., 1960).

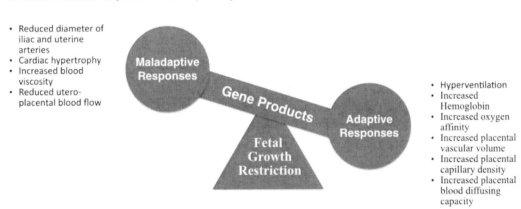

Figure 2. Maternal acclimatization responses to high altitude associated long-term hypoxia.

A question of relevance at this time was the extent to which the fetus produces hemoglobin in a maximal manner, or hemoglobin synthesis might be increased in response to hypoxia or other stress. In an effort to address this issue, from the University of Illinois and University of Minnesota, in one of the first studies to make use of a high altitude decompression chamber, at about 0.64 gestation (95 days versus 149 days term), 4 ewes were exposed to diminished ambient pressure at 385 mmHg (5,400 m simulated altitude) and 4 ewes were exposed to 345 mmHg (6,100 m) for 10 days. Then under analgesia and local anesthesia, the ewes' uterine arteries and veins were isolated, as were the fetal umbilical vein and artery. At the higher barometric pressure-lower equivalent altitude, all fetuses survived. This was in contrast to findings in the lower pressure-higher altitude group in which one ewe and two fetuses died. In the surviving fetus umbilical PO_2 plummeted to ~7 Torr in this extremely diminished O_2 state (Kaiser et al., 1958).

The author's contended that the hematologic response seen in this study suggested that indeed, hypoxia such as that observed at high altitude is of importance in this regard. The mean hemoglobin values in the ewe and fetus at the lower simulated altitude were 11.1 and 10.3 gm · dl^{-1}, respectively. In turn, these values at the more elevated altitude were 17.4 and 9.4 gm · dl^{-1}, respectively (Kaiser et al., 1958). Normoxic control values for the various parameters were not included, although these values (except that of the single fetus at high altitude) appear to be greater than that reported by ourselves and others (Longo, 1987). Also of interest, lyophilized maternal plasma from several of these ewes showed erythropoietic activity (Kaiser et al., 1958).

At the University of Florida, Gainesville, FL, one pregnant Nubian goat and three Dorset sheep were chronically catheterized in one uterine vein and one each femoral artery and vein (Cotter et al., 1967). Then following several weeks for recovery, decompression was initiated (rate = 1,000 ft · min^{-1}) to 5,000 and 10,000 ft (3 animals) and 15,000 (2 animals) at which level they were maintained for 30 min before withdrawing blood for hemoglobin, hematocrit, respiratory gases, and pH. At 10 and 15 thousand feet, arterial oxyhemoglobin saturation values fell from sea level control of 96±3% to 83±3% and 53±10%, respectively. Comparable oxyhemoglobin saturation values for the uterine venous blood were 79±4%, 68±6%, and 44±5%. No obvious trends were noted in either CO_2 tension or bicarbonate levels, and pH values did not change significantly (Cotter et al., 1967). In the goat, the estimated decrease in PO_2 (the only value reported) fell from sea level control of 29 to 24 Torr, again with no significant changes in CO_2, bicarbonate, or pH values. The authors concluded that despite the acute fall in uterine venous O_2 values at 10,000 feet, the decrease in umbilical venous (and presumably transplacental O_2 tension gradient) were far less (Cotter et al., 1967). In a follow up study using this facility with near-term ungulates (5 goats and one sheep) blood gas values were measured at 1,524 m (5,000 ft), 3,048 m (10,000 ft), and 4,592 m (15,000 ft) (Blechner et al., 1968). At these simulated elevations, compared to sea level values, maternal arterial PO_2 values were ~75 (control), 64, 47, and 34 Torr, respectively. Uterine venous PO_2 values averaged 39 (control), 36, 31, and 26 Torr, respectively. Those values for fetal umbilical venous (arterialized) blood were 20 (control), 18, 15, and 13 Torr, respectively. Finally, for the umbilical arterial (venous) blood the values were 16 (control), 17, 11 and 9 Torr, respectively. This was the first such study demonstrating that at high altitude the decreases in fetal blood respiratory gas values were considerably less than one would expect based on decrements of PO_2 values in the mother (Blechner et al., 1968).

At about the same time, the University of Colorado group conducted a study in which 6 third trimester ewes and their fetuses underwent chronic catheterization in Denver, after which they were transported to Mt. Evans (elevation 4,346 m, 14,260 ft) where they were studied for 10 to 18 days. They then were returned to Denver for an additional 18 days of continued investigation (Makowski et al., 1968). Although the duration of time at high altitude was insufficient for full acclimatization to occur, the investigators witnessed the beginnings of a hematologic response as evidenced by increased blood O_2 capacity (hemoglobin and hematocrit values were not reported) in response to decreased PO_2 and oxyhemoglobin saturation values, and a response in these variables upon return to Denver (Makowski et al., 1968). As a high altitude comparison, in acclimatized humans at Cerro de Pasco, Peru (4,200 m) fetal scalp PO_2 averaged 19 Torr, a value only slightly less than sea level control of 22 Torr (Sobrevilla et al., 1971). Thus, from mid-century onward, with the use of both hypobaric chambers and studies at altitude, an understanding of certain aspects of fetal oxygenation at high altitude was achieved slowly.

Studies at the White Mountain Research Station

In an effort to understand some of the fundamental cellular and molecular mechanisms associated with the fetal and adult physiologic acclimatization responses to prolonged hypoxia, we have developed a "model" using pregnant and non-pregnant sheep. The ewes are transported to high altitude at the White Mountain Research Station at ~30 days gestation where they are kept until the latter stages of gestation near term, e.g., ~140 days. At this altitude, the adult arterial PO_2 falls from a normoxic control value of 95±5 Torr to 60±3 Torr, and fetal arterial PO_2 falls from 25±3 to 19±2 Torr (Kitanaka et al., 1989a, 1989b). Although arterial PCO_2 falls slightly in both fetus (from 35 to 29 Torr) and adult (from 49 to 40 Torr), arterial pH remains unchanged. As may be clear, sheep are of value for such studies in light of their length of gestation, the relative large size of fetus, relative ease of chronic instrumentation for prolonged periods of time, and the similarity of physiologic organ systems in terms of their tissue, cellular, and subcellular response mechanisms.

Of note, in the sheep acclimatized to altitude at the White Mountain Research Station, despite long-term reduction in arterial PO_2, we have observed no reduction in body or organ weights of the term fetus, ~ 4.1±0.7 kg compared to sea level controls 3.9±0.6 kg (Harvey et al., 1993, Kamitomo et al., 1992; also our unpublished data for 5 years, n ~230 each group). This agrees with data from the studies at Morococha (~4,270 m) on the *alto plano* of Peru of Donald H. Barron (1905-1993) and colleagues (Metcalfe et al., 1962a, 1962b, Prystowsky et al., 1960). Even at that level of high altitude-induced hypoxemia, despite compensatory acclimatization responses in a number of systems (see below), the ability of the sheep fetus to defend itself in terms of growth restriction is remarkable, and may be of value in considering the basic physiologic mechanisms involved. In contrast to these observations, at 3,589 m (Parraguez et al., 2005) on the Chilean *alto plano*, the near-term lamb weights were decreased 24% from sea level controls of 4.2±0.03 kg to 3.2±0.8 kg (Parraguez et al., 2005) (Table 4). In a subsequent report, the BWs were 3.3±0.2 kg, as compared to normoxic sea level controls 4.4±0.2 kg, a 26% decrease (Parraguez et al., 2011) (Table 4). At 6 to 11 days following birth at 3,600m, the lamb weights were reported to be 3.8±0.3 kg and 7.0±0.4 kg respectively, a

43% difference (Herrera et al., 2010). Of interest but of unknown significance, in the 3,589 m group, the length of gestation was greater being 153.2±4.3 days at altitude, compared to 145.0±3.0 near sea level, a 6% increase (Parraguez et al., 2005).

From an experimental standpoint, in laboratory species fetal hypoxia with resultant FGR can be induced by several means. These include: maternal hypoxia (Giussani et al., 1994a, 1994b, Kitanaka et al., 1989b), maternal hyperthermia (Thureen et al., 1992), restricting maternal uterine blood flow (Baserga et al., 2009, 2010, Challis et al., 1989, Phillips et al., 1996, Wilkening and Meschia, 1983), reducing fetal umbilical blood flow (Giussani et al., 1997, Ueno et al., 1997), placental embolization (Boyle et al., 1984, Bubb et al., 2007, Clapp et al., 1980, Gagnon et al., 1997), and maternal uterine carunclectomy prior to mating (which restricts the number of placentomes; Alexander, 1964, Dyer et al., 2009, Phillips et al., 1996, Robinson et al., 1979). Details of many aspects of these approaches with their strengths and weaknesses, as well as similarities and differences in fetal physiologic responses, have been reviewed by others (Morrison, 2008). As a caveat, despite many similarities in the responses to these stresses, these several methodologies are associated with differing degrees of acidemia, hypoglycemia, and/or nutrient deprivation.

Fetal Cardiovascular Responses to Long-Term Hypoxia

In response to acute hypoxia, the fetus experiences redistribution of cardiac output from the peripheral circulation to maintain circulation of the brain, heart, and adrenal glands (Cohn et al., 1974, Lorijn and Longo, 1980, Peeters et al., 1979). Such redistribution has been shown to be mediated by a carotid body chemoreflex (Giussani et al., 1993) in concert with the release of catecholamines (Jones and Robinson, 1975), arginine vasopressin (Perez et al., 1989), neuropeptide Y (Fletcher et al., 2000), nitric oxide (NO) (Morrison et al., 2003), and other vasoactive factors. Reactive oxygen species also play a role in this response (Thakor et al., 2010).

As noted, prolonged fetal hypoxia, as a consequence of any of the factors noted above can result in cardiovascular changes (Kamitomo et al., 1993) with significant FGR (Giussani et al., 2001; Moore et al., 2011). In our "model" of high altitude acclimatized LTH in fetal sheep, combined right and left ventricular cardiac output was significantly reduced (-24%) compared to the normoxic fetuses (Kamitomo et al., 1992, 1993) (Table 4). Although heart rate was unchanged, fetal arterial blood pressure increased 18%. This decrease in ventricular output was similar to that observed following only two weeks of normobaric hypoxia in the near term sheep fetus (Alonso et al., 1989; Kamitomo et al., 1994). Despite prolonged hypoxia, blood flow to the brain and heart were maintained at near normal low altitude levels in these fetuses. This, coupled with an increase in hemoglobin concentration (from 10.1±0.7 to 12.6±0.6 $g \cdot dl^{-1}$), resulted in normal oxygen delivery to these organs (Kamitomo et al., 1993). Nonetheless, the distribution of cardiac output was altered in a striking manner, with blood flow and oxygen delivery to the kidneys, gastrointestinal tract, and carcass (skin, muscle, and bone) being significantly decreased (Kamitomo et al., 1993). Of importance to the LTH fetus, despite cardiac output already being redistributed to favor the brain and heart, when subjected to an additional bout of superimposed hypoxia (with further reduction of fetal arterial PO_2 from 19±2 Torr to 11±1 Torr), cardiac output was redistributed to even a greater extent to maintain oxygen delivery to the brain and heart at the expense of organs in the trunk and extremities (Kamitomo et al., 1993). In addition to alterations in cardiac contractility, the mechanisms for these cardiovascular changes include those of structure and function of blood vessels in the several vascular beds.

Mechanisms potentially responsible for the reduction in cardiac output in the LTH sheep fetus appear to involve extrinsic factors that alter cardiac output, such as afterload (mean arterial blood pressure), preload (atrial pressure), and heart rate. Although the long-term hypoxic fetus showed a significant 18% elevation of arterial blood pressure, compared to control (from 44±2 mmHg to 52±1 mmHg), this increase in afterload could account for only a small fraction of the reduction in cardiac output (Kamitomo et al., 1992). No differences were observed in right or left atrial pressures (preload) between the hypoxic (4.1±0.1 mmHg for each) and control values (4.1±0.1 mmHg for each ventricle), nor in heart rate (165±6 bpm for each) that could account for a decrease in cardiac output. Thus, mechanisms responsible for the reduction in cardiac contraction appear to be intrinsic to the heart. In fetal sheep subjected to 1 hour of hypoxemia (9% O_2 with 5% CO_2) at several ages during the third trimester of pregnancy (125 to 130, 135 to 140, and >140 days gestational age) cardiac chemoreflex function and a battery of vasoconstrictor hormones were measured. Fetal bradycardia increased in magnitude and persistence, as did the increase in femoral vascular resistance in concert with the near term rise in plasma cortisol concentration, as well as that for catecholamines, NPY, AVP, and ACTH (Fletcher et al., 2006). These findings demonstrate the near term changes in pattern and magnitude of fetal cardiovascular defense to hypoxemia, and some of their in parallel neural and endocrinologic mechanisms.

Papillary muscles isolated from LTH fetal sheep, studied *in vitro* in a well oxygenated (95% O_2 + 5% CO_2) bath system in which electrical stimulation parameters could be optimized, demonstrated development of reduced maximum tension (T_{max}) in response to increasing concentrations of external calcium, reduced maximum rate of tension development ($+dT \cdot dt_{max}^{-1}$), and reduced rate of relaxation ($-dT \cdot dt_{max}^{-1}$) compared to controls (Browne et al., 1997a). Although the reduction in T_{max} was the same in papillary muscle from both ventricles, the reduction in $+dT \cdot dt_{max}^{-1}$ was larger in the right than in the left ventricle. Of interest, when acute hypoxia was imposed in the bath (20% or 40% O_2, PO_2 ~3 and 7 Torr, respectively), papillary muscles from LTH fetal hearts maintained T_{max}, $+dT \cdot dt_{max}^{-1}$, and $-dT \cdot dt_{max}^{-1}$ at significantly higher values than papillary muscle from control fetuses (Ohtsuka et al., 1997). In addition, LTH fetal hearts displayed elevated levels of lactate dehydrogenase and citrate synthase (but not pyruvate kinase) activities, changes that may enhance aerobic energy production during hypoxia (Ohtsuka and Gilbert, 1995). Overall, there appeared to be no decrement in the calcium-induced-calcium-release mechanism in the LTH fetal heart. Rather, at least in the right ventricle, there was a greater dependence on SR released Ca^{2+} for contraction. This suggests a potential adaptive process to increase contractile function.

In addition to the reduction in cardiac output in the LTH fetus compared to normoxic control, there was also a reduced augmentation of cardiac output by stimulation of cardiac β_1-adrenergic receptors (β_1-AR) with the agonist isoproterenol (Kamitomo et al., 1995). Isoproterenol stimulation of isolated, well oxygenated papillary muscles resulted in significantly less augmentation of T_{max}, $+dT \cdot dt_{max}^{-1}$, and $-dT \cdot dt_{max}^{-1}$ in papillary muscles from both ventricles of LTH fetal hearts, compared to normoxic controls (Browne et al., 1997b). Although in the LTH fetal heart, the β_1-adrenergic receptor pathway, β_1-AR number (B_{max})

did not change in the left ventricle, the right ventricle showed a 55% increase in β_1-AR number (Browne et al., 1997a). These findings contrast with the downregulation of β_1-adrenergic receptors found in the hearts of the adult rat exposed to LTH (Kacimi et al., 1992) and, in addition to species, may result from differences in circulating catecholamine levels in the hypoxic adult versus the fetus (Harvey et al., 1993).

For the intracellular cyclic AMP second messenger system, although resting levels in either right or left ventricle of LTH ventricles showed no difference compared to controls, stimulation with a maximal dose of the agonist isoproterenol increased cAMP several-fold higher in the ventricles than in controls. Stimulation with forskolin, which acts directly on adenylyl cyclase to increase cAMP levels, resulted in reduced contractile responses in both ventricles of LTH fetuses, but 3-fold higher cAMP levels (Browne et al., 1997b). Thus, the reduced augmentation of contraction in both ventricles of the LTH fetal sheep heart cannot be explained by a downregulation of β_1-adrenergic receptors, nor of decreased adenylyl cyclase nor cAMP production. The elevated levels of cAMP generated by β_1-adrenergic receptor stimulation may have resulted in a higher than normal phosphorylation of troponin I by protein kinase A. This would result in decreased Ca^{2+} binding to troponin C which would reduce the β_1-AR stimulation responses, as has been reported in the spontaneously hypertensive adult rat (McConnell et al., 1998). In other studies in the placental embolized FGR sheep fetus, the incidence of left ventricular cardiomyocyte binucleation was significantly less, suggestive of retarded cardiomyocyte maturation (Bubb et al., 2007).

At the level of the contractile proteins, the isoform composition of myosin, actin, troponin T, or troponin I did not change in the LTH fetal heart (Kamitomo et al., 2002). In the hypoxic right ventricle (but not the left); however, there was a significant reduction in the activity of Mg^{2+}-activated myofibrillar ATPase (a contractile-associated enzyme involved in regulation of both the rate and strength of contraction) with no change in Ca^{2+}-activated ATPase activity (Kamitomo et al., 2002). The fall in myofibrillar Mg^{2+}-activated ATPase activity may be partially responsible for the decrease in contractility in the right ventricle of LTH fetal hearts. Overall, these findings contribute to the concept of FGR myocardial changes playing a major role in decreased contractility and, in some instances, having lifelong consequences.

Fetal asymmetric growth restriction and cardiovascular dysfunction also have been demonstrated in the rat (Herrera et al., 2012, Williams et al., 2005a, 2005b). Also in the guinea pig, Thompson and his group have demonstrated several cardiovascular sequelae including increased cardiac production of endothelial nitric oxide synthase (NOS) (Dong and Thompson, 2006, Thompson et al., 2000) with increased NO in such dysfunction (Thompson et al., 2009).

In the rat, antenatal chronic hypoxia also has been shown to affect fetal myocardial expression of cardioprotective enzymes such as protein kinase C epsilon (PKCε) with programming of an increase in cardiac susceptibility to ischemia and reperfusion injury in male offspring (Li et al., 2003, Patterson et al., 2010, Xue and Zhang, 2009). Presumably the result of ROS, studies also have demonstrated increased methylation of the promoter of the *PKCε* gene, an epigenetic change which could be prevented by administration of an inhibitor of DNA methylation (Patterson et al., 2012). The adult offspring of dams subjected to antenatal hypoxia also displayed cardiac structural and functional changes including: increased expression of collagen type I and III, and the ratio of beta to alpha myosin heavy chains (Xu et al., 2006), as well as increased left ventricular end diastolic pressure (Rueda-

Clausen et al., 2009), and decreased myocardial metabolism (Rueda-Clausen et al., 2011b). Further studies have demonstrated decreased beta 1 receptor and increased muscarinic receptor responses in adult offspring of rats so subjected to LTH (Giussani et al., 2012). Also of clinical relevance, cardiovascular disease in adults has been associated with elevated sympathetic and decreased parasympathetic reactivity. Thus, overall studies from several species support the idea of antenatal hypoxia resulting in cardiomyopathy in the adult offspring. Provocatively, many of these antenatal hypoxic-mediated changes show gender specificity for many complications, with males being more susceptible than females (Hemmings et al., 2005).

Studies in the Chick Embryo

To explore aspects of growth and the developing cardiovascular system independently from those influences of maternal physiologic responses, the chicken embryo also has been used to advantage. Several groups have demonstrated the effect of hypoxia in causing asymmetric embryonic/fetal growth as well as the growth of specific organs (Giussani et al., 2007, Lindgren and Altimiras, 2011, Miller et al., 2002, Ruijtenbeek et al., 2003a, 2003b, Sharma et al., 2006). The reported changes include aortic hypertrophy and left ventricular dysfunction (Rouwet et al., 2002), with enlargement of both ventricles (Villamor et al., 2004), and cardiomyopathy (Salinas et al., 2010). Such cardiovascular changes are associated with altered endothelial reactivity (Ruijtenbeek et al., 2003a, 2003b), and sympathetic hyperinnervation of peripheral arteries (Rouwet et al., 2002, Ruijtenbeek et al., 2000). As in the fetal lamb, in the chick embryo LTH decreased ventricular $+dT \cdot dt_{max}^{-1}$, peak pressure and ventricular ejection fraction (Sharma et al., 2006). In a critical study of fertilized eggs from hens acclimatized to either sea level or high altitude (3,600 m), and incubated at either condition of oxygenation (5 groups: eggs laid at sea level and incubated at either sea level or high altitude, eggs laid at high altitude and incubated at either sea level or high altitude, and eggs laid at sea level but incubated at high altitude with O_2 supplementation to mimic sea level values, percent O_2 not given). As expected, embryo weight was restricted in the high altitude incubated groups (45% in the eggs from sea level and 22% in those from high altitude) (Giussani et al., 2007). In the group of chick embryos at high altitude in which supplemental O_2 was administered, the LTH-induced asymmetric growth restriction and cardiac remodeling were not seen (Giussani et al., 2007, Salinas et al., 2010). Of importance, these studies isolated the effects of alterations in embryonic/fetal oxygenation on growth and development independent of maternal nutrition or other factors associated with high altitude.

Fetal Adaptive and Maladaptive Responses to Hypoxia

Figure 3 diagrams a few of the fetal acclimatization responses to high altitude associated long-term hypoxia. As detailed here and below, adaptive responses include increased hemoglobin with maintenance of blood flow to the brain, heart, and adrenal glands. Maladaptive responses that may lead to fetal growth restriction include: generalized increase in systemic vascular resistance with an increase in blood pressure and decreased cardiac output, reduced blood flow to the kidneys, gastrointestinal tract, and other organs, and reduced cardiomyocyte maturation.

Other studies have reported adult sequelae of antenatal hypoxia. For instance, following hypoxic incubation as chicks the femoral arteries of adult chickens showed increased sensitivity to both pharmacologic and electrical stimulation of periarterial sympathetic nerves, as well as decreased NO-dependent vasodilatation (Ruijtenbeek et al., 2003a, 2003b). Other investigators also have demonstrated NO-mediated endothelial dysfunction following antenatal hypoxia in the adult rat (Hemmings et al., 2005, Morton et al., 2010, 2011, Williams et al., 2005a, 2005b), and sheep (Giussani et al., 2012). Along this line, FGR offspring show evidence of endothelial dysfunction as manifest by high resolution ultrasound in both 9 to 11 year old children (Leeson et al., 1997), and in early adult life (Leeson et al., 2001). Also as is well documented, prolonged fetal hypoxemia is associated with elevated pulmonary arterial pressure and a number of vascular changes associated with pulmonary hypertension in the newborn infant (for instance, see Herrera et al., 2007, 2008, 2010, Llanos et al., 2012). Discussion of these changes in the newborn are beyond the limits of this chapter, however.

Fetal Coronary Vascular Responses

In terms of histomorphometry of the LTH fetal heart, no change was observed in ventricular capillary volume density, capillary-to-fiber ratio, or capillary anisotropy coefficient (Lewis et al., 1999). Nonetheless, the LTH heart showed significant changes in coronary artery activity and responses (Table 3). The maximum tension (T_{max}) response to 90 mM KCl was significantly lowered about 50% in isolated segments of left circumflex, left anterior descending, and right coronary arteries, compared to controls (Garcia et al., 2000a). Nitric oxide (NO) played no role in these responses. The sensitivity to U-46619 (a thromboxane A_2 receptor agonist), but not the T_{max} response, was significantly reduced in these artery segments. Relaxation responses to adenosine also were unaltered. In permeabilized coronary artery segments, the maximum Ca^{2+}-activated T_{max} (determined from a dose-response curve to Ca^{2+}) was significantly decreased in the left circumflex and left anterior descending coronary arteries of these hearts (Garcia et al., 2000b).

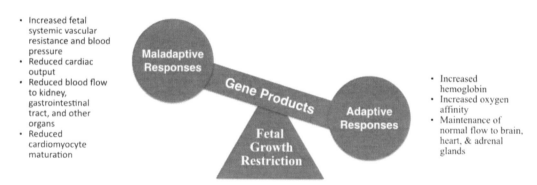

Figure 3. Fetal acclimatization responses to high altitude associated long-term hypoxia.

The reduced vascular Ca^{2+} responsiveness may partially explain the reduced contractile response of the coronary artery segments to KCl. However, the effects of LTH on the intracellular Ca^{2+} regulatory mechanisms involved in coronary artery smooth muscle contraction required examination, as these reduced contractile responses may play a role in the maintenance of coronary flow at normal levels in the LTH fetal heart. In other studies in the near-term placental-embolized FGR ovine fetus, the coronary arteries showed enhanced contractility to the vasoconstrictors angiotensin II and the thromboxane analog U-46619 (Bubb et al., 2007). In contrast, endothelin-dependent and –independent relaxation did not differ between the FGR fetus and control (Bubb et al., 2007). These investigators also reported increased glutathione levels in the liver and γ-glytamyl cysteine synthetase in lung, liver, and kidney (Oh et al., 2008). The guinea pig coronary vasculature showed a LTH-mediated increase in eNOS and NO (Thompson et al., 2000). Thus, characterization of contractile responses in all microdomains of the coronary vasculature is required for a comprehensive understanding of coronary vascular control during long-term hypoxia, its relation to FGR and lifelong cardiovascular consequences.

Fetal Cerebrovascular Responses to Long-Term Hypoxia

In the fetus, acute hypoxia can increase cerebral blood flow (CBF) several-fold (Ashwal et al., 1980; Peeters et al., 1979). In contrast, following acclimatization to long-term hypoxia CBF has returned to near normal, despite significant decreases in cardiac output and blood flow to the abdominal viscera and skeletal muscles (Kamitomo et al., 1993, Peña et al., 2007, Tomimatsu et al., 2006). Similarly, in adults who have been acclimatized to high altitude CBF also is relatively normal (Huang et al., 1987, Severinghaus et al., 1966). These findings support the concept for the cerebral circulation that while a number of physiologic changes, in part, mediated by HIF-1α and cascade of events that follow, produce profound responses in the signal transduction pathways, when that stress is prolonged, as in LTH, cerebrovascular compensatory alterations act to return CBF and O_2 delivery to a relatively normal state of homeostasis. The identity of these mechanisms, however, remains unclear, as does the extent to which, in response to LTH, vascular resistance is altered in the brain or other organs. Because the cerebrovascular system, with maintenance of homeostasis of the brain, is so critical in both health and disease we have used this in the sense of a "case study" to explore a number of facets of vascular biology.

As noted, with hypoxic acclimatization CBF is maintained despite a steady-state decrease in cardiac output, thus basal cerebrovascular resistance would appear to decrease. One possible contribution to a decrease in cerebrovascular resistance could be a shift in the structure and/or composition of the cerebral arteries favoring larger diameters and reduced hydraulic resistance. Consistent with this possibility in terms of composition and structure, is that unstressed inside diameters of the middle cerebral arteries (MCA) showed a 39% increase from the normoxic to hypoxic fetuses. Chronic hypoxia also demonstrated a 42% increase in artery wall (media) thicknesses, a 85% increase in media cross-sectional area and a doubling of the number of layers of smooth muscle cells in the media (from 5.6±0.2 to 11.5±2.1) (Henderson and Longo, 2003) (Table 4). In addition, LTH significantly increased base soluble protein content, which includes cytosolic and enzymatic but not structural, proteins, in both carotid and cerebral arteries (Longo and Pearce, 1998). Together, these results demonstrate that LTH had a significant effect on artery size and structure with an increase in protein composition (Longo and Pearce, 1998, 2005), which appears to be mediated, in part, by VEGF (Pearce et al., 2011, Silpanisong and Pearce, 2013). This could have major effects on cerebrovascular contractility.

In addition, cerebral arteries from the LTH fetus showed a large (2 to 3x) increase in perivascular innervation, the nature of which remains to be defined (Henderson and Longo, 2003, Pearce, 1995). These changes were accompanied by a modest decrease in cerebral artery NE content (Pearce, 1995). They also were accompanied by a large increase in basal norepinephrine (NE) release (74%) and stimulation-evoked fractional NE release following blockade of re-uptake mechanisms (33%; Buchholz and Duckles, 2001). Evidence from a study of cocaine-sensitive NE uptake, a sensitive measure of NE containing nerve terminals, supports the idea of hypoxia-induced NE uptake and nerve density in the common carotid, basilar, and posterior communicating arteries, but not the MCA (Pearce, 1995). As is appreciated, neuronal NE content is the product of both the tissue nerve density and mean NE content in each nerve fiber. Of course, NE content is decreased in those nerves that fire frequently, as opposed to those that are quiescent. Together with the huge increase in hypoxia-induced transmural stimulation-induced adrenergic mechanisms (>1,500; Pearce, 1995), these findings suggest intense neurogenic-mediated cerebrovascular vasomotion in the regulation of the acclimatized fetal brain. This concept is supported further by evidence of increased co-release of NPY with NE in the hypoxic fetal cranial arteries (Pearce, 1995). Regarding the effects of chronic hypoxia on perivascular peptidergic influences, the only transmitter studied to date is neuropeptide Y. Following depletion of NE from fetal MCA adrenergic nerve terminals by 1 µM guanethidine, LTH hypoxia dramatically enhanced stimulation-induced contractions (Pearce, 1995). Whereas this result may be explained by reduced synaptic cleft widths and/or generalized acceleration of maturation of the neuromuscular apparatus, many other mechanisms also are possible. These include changes in the intravesicular ratio of neuropeptide Y to NE, the postsynaptic density and coupling of neuropeptide Y receptors, and pathways for disposition of NPY. Each of these mechanisms remain potentially fruitful topics of investigation.

Hypoxia also may attenuate presynaptic inhibition of electrical stimulation-induced NE release. Blockade of prejunctional alpha-2 adrenoceptors with idazoxan increased electrical stimulation-induced NE release by blocking presynaptic inhibition, this increase being attenuated by LTH. Thus, long-term hypoxia attenuated both NO-mediated facilitation of NE release (see below), as well as alpha-2 adrenoceptor mediated inhibition of NE release through mechanisms that were prominent in adult, but not in fetal, cranial arteries. These effects of LTH in fetal arteries cannot be explained by the modest effects of chronic hypoxia on fetal artery NE release, and instead suggests that hypoxia may accelerate maturation of the neuromuscular junction, perhaps by decreasing synaptic cleft width (Pearce et al., 1999).

In terms of adrenergic regulation of fetal cerebral vascular tone as referred to above, in acclimatized sheep LTH is associated with significant increases in basal levels of both NE and epinephrine (Longo and Pearce, 1998, 2005). Paradoxically, despite these increased catecholamine levels, we recorded a 20% reduction in MCA contractile response to NE and to phenylephrine (PHE; Goyal et al., 2014). In LTH CA we examined the effects of specific α_1-AR subtype blockade on contractility responses. Whereas the α_{1A}-AR protein expression was unchanged in response to LTH acclimatization, the α_{1B}-AR increased 20 to 30%, and the α_{1D}-AR subtype expression decreased ~30% (Goyal et al., 2014). In addition to LTH effects on the fetal CA α_1-AR subtype *per se*, we have shown that the α_{1B}-AR subtype plays a major role in regulation of the mitogen-activated protein kinase (MAPK)-extracellular regulated kinase (ERK) negative feedback regulation of phenylephrine-induced contractility (Goyal et al., 2014). Thus overall, in ovine fetal cerebrovasculature, acclimatization to prolonged hypoxia was accompanied by profound effect on α_1-AR subtype expression and function. Fetal LTH acclimatized superior cervical ganglia sympathetic neurons (which govern Ca^{2+} release), also demonstrated a loss of Ca^{2+}-induced Ca^{2+} release, an important component of their function (Behringer et al., 2009).

Another important influence on cerebrovascular resistance is the release of vasoactive neurohormones from perivascular nerves. Cranial arteries receive abundant perivascular innervation that includes adrenergic, cholinergic, and peptidergic components (MacKenzie and Scatton, 1987). Consistent with the observations above, and despite the fact that nitric oxide plays a prominent role in hypoxic-mediated cerebral vasodilatation (Hunter et al., 2001), preliminary measurements of shear-stress-induced NO release suggest that it is elevated in chronically hypoxic adult carotid arteries. On the other hand, responses to exogenous NO released from s-nitroso-N-acetylpenicilamine (an NO donor), were not significantly different in normoxic and hypoxic middle cerebral arteries from adult sheep, suggesting that the enhanced vasodilator responses to A-23187 observed in hypoxic adult arteries reflect greater release of, but not greater sensitivity to, endothelium-derived NO. In addition, although in fetal MCA LTH had no significant effect on vasodilator responses to A-23187, on shear-stress-induced NO release, or on responses to exogenous NO, it is clear that the acclimatization-associated depressed cerebrovascular resistance must involve other mechanisms.

In studies of electrical stimulation-induced norepinephrine (NE) release, LTH was associated with decreased stimulation-evoked NE release and a 20 to 30% decrease in vessel NE content, while basal NE release increased (Buchholz et al., 1999). Because this inhibition of NO synthesis with 10 μM L-NAME (N^w-nitro-L-arginine methyl ester) significantly depressed electrical stimulation-induced NE release in normoxic fetal MCA, basal NO release appears to facilitate NE release. In arteries from hypoxic acclimatized animals this effect was abolished, possibly due to the ability of LTH to significantly reduce the relative abundance of neuronal NO synthase in these vessels (Mbaku et al., 2003).

In terms of vasorelaxation pathways, increased vasodilator release potentially could contribute to the decreased cerebrovascular resistance characteristic of hypoxic acclimatization. Most prominent among possible vasodilator influences are the endothelium-dependent vasorelaxant factors, which include nitric oxide, endothelium-derived hyperpolarization factor, prostacyclin, and numerous different vasoactive growth factors such as vascular endothelial growth factor (VEGF) (Zachary, 2001). In experiments designed to assess maximum endothelial vasodilator capacity, although the receptor-independent calcium ionophore A-23187 at 1μM produced endothelium-dependent relaxation in cranial arteries from LTH adult sheep, this had no effect in the fetus (Longo et al., 1993, Pearce, 1995). Other studies by the Pearce group reveal that long-term hypoxic inhibition by NO-induced vasodilation can be attributed to attenuation of soluble guanylate cyclase activity, but does not involve significant changes in its abundance or the activity of cyclic GMP (Pearce et al., 2009).

In the fetal cerebrovasculature, while long-term hypoxia is associated with reduced endothelial NO release, there occurs upregulation of some component of the NO-cGMP-Protein Kinase G vasodilatory pathway which tends to preserve endothelium-dependent vasodilatation in the LTH acclimatized vessel (Williams and Pearce, 2006). Of note, in response to acetylcholine (10^{-5}M) the fetal common carotid and middle cerebral arteries showed enhanced relaxation (Pearce, 1995). Prostanoids, metabolites of cyclooxygenase enzyme activity, also have potent effects on vascular tone in the fetus; however, their role in mediating fetal CBF responses to hypoxia is only indirect (Nishida et al., 2006).

When all perivascular neuronal peptides are released by treatment with capsaicin, the net effect in normoxic arteries is vasodilatation, the magnitude of which is much greater in fetal than in adult arteries. This observation indicates that perivascular peptidergic nerves are predominantly vasodilator in nature. Following LTH acclimatization, the responses to capsaicin are modestly attenuated, which suggests that hypoxic enhancement of vasodilator peptide release probably contributes little to the observed reduced cerebrovascular resistance. The effects of chronic hypoxia on perivascular cholinergic innervations remain unexamined. In the adult, however, the available evidence indicates that NE release is attenuated by perivascular nerves. This is not the case for fetal arteries. Although this effect is significant, it is probably not sufficient to explain the bulk of the effect of chronic hypoxia on basal cerebrovascular resistance, which in turn indicates that by other mechanisms hypoxia must directly affect the cerebral artery smooth muscle *per se*.

Electromechanical coupling describes the relation between membrane potential and contractile tone that is an intrinsic feature of all excitable smooth muscle. The single most important component of this coupling is the L-type calcium channel, which by virtue of its voltage-dependent conductivity, directly couples changes in membrane potential to changes in the rate of Ca^{2+} influx (Xiong and Sperelakis, 1995). For many artery types, including those of the brain (McCalden and Bevan, 1981), Ca^{2+} entry through calcium channels constitutes the main fraction of contractile Ca^{2+}, owing to sparse or poorly developed sarcoplasmic reticulum. This is particularly true for immature cerebral arteries, which are almost completely dependent upon Ca^{2+} influx through the calcium channels for contraction (Akopov et al., 1998, Long et al., 1999, 2000).

A common approach to assess electromechanical coupling is to monitor the contractions produced by depolarization with high concentrations of extracellular potassium (K^+). With this method, K^+-induced tensions were generally decreased by chronic hypoxia (Longo et al., 1993), these measurements possibly reflecting changes in L-channel function, however. In fetal arteries, when tensions were normalized relative to artery wall cross-sectional area, potassium-induced stress was decreased significantly, suggesting a hypoxia-induced change in L-type Ca^{2+} channel function. Because the L-type Ca^{2+} channel density is much greater in immature than mature cerebral arteries (Blood et al., 2002), LTH may depress L-type Ca^{2+} channel density, consistent with the accelerated maturation effect of hypoxia discussed above. Arguing against this possibility in fetal MCA, however, is the finding that LTH had no effect on potassium-induced increases in cytosolic Ca^{2+} (Long et al., 2002). This latter observation suggests that L-type Ca^{2+} channel function may be preserved in hypoxia-acclimatized fetuses, and that hypoxic changes in K^+-induced contractile force is a function of decreased calcium sensitivity. Compared to the adult, myofilament Ca^{2+} sensitivity is greatly upregulated in fetal cerebral arteries (Akopov et al., 1998, Geary et al., 2004, Long et al., 2000, Longo and Goyal,

2013), thus hypoxic downregulation of myofilament Ca^{2+} sensitivity would be consistent with hypoxia-induced accelerated maturation.

Yet another important component of electromechanical coupling includes the plasma membrane K^+ channels that largely determine the smooth muscle electrical responses to physiological stimuli, including basal stretch that governs myogenic tone (Nelson and Quayle, 1995). Hypoxia appears to modulate the activity of at least some types of K^+ channels, as suggested by the finding that sensitivity to the ATP-sensitive potassium channel opener pinacidil was decreased significantly in hypoxic fetal MCA (Long et al., 2002). This effect suggests that LTH decreases either the density of these channels, or their affinity for pinacidil. Similarly, activation of the big Ca^{2+}-sensitive K^+ (BK) channels with NS-1619 also yielded less inhibition of tension in the fetal, compared to adult, arteries. This suggests that LTH decreased either the density of these channels, or their Ca^{2+} sensitivity (Long et al., 2002). Certainly, a clear interpretation of these results requires detailed measurements of potassium channel densities and their current-voltage relations.

In this regard, we tested the hypothesis that during LTH acclimatization, basilar arteries (BA) in the near-term fetus would show increased smooth myocyte BK channel activity. In isolated fetal BA myocytes we used both whole-cell and inside-out patch-clamp techniques, flow cytometry, and confocal microscopy to study BK channel activity, expression, and cell surface distribution. We identified several functional features that distinguish BK channels of LTH acclimatized vessels from normoxic controls (Tao et al., 2014). These included: 1) BK channel Ca^{2+} set points for fetal LTH BA were significantly lower. 2) Fetal BA BK channels were relatively dephosphorylated in LTH compared to normoxic controls, presumably as a result of increased Ca^{2+} BK channel affinity. 3) BK channel half-activating voltages of LTH animals were left shifted 30 to 40 mV independently of phosphorylation state. 4) BK channel open or "dwell" times from LTH animals were generally longer and more sensitive to changes in phosphorylation state. In addition, in the perforated-patch mode the LTH fetus exhibited 2- to 3-fold upregulation of the BK β-1 subunit surface expression and 2-fold increased BK channel clustering with increased "coupling" to Ca^{2+} sparks and increased BK current density (Tao et al., 2014). These findings suggest increased BK channel to Ca^{2+} spark coupling in the LTH fetus to maintain decreased cerebral vascular resistance.

As opposed to electromechanical coupling, which governs the relations between membrane potential and contraction, pharmacomechanical coupling involves the relations between membrane receptor activation and changes in contractile tone. This coupling, in turn, is highly specialized for each of the many receptor types present in the vasculature. One pharmacomechanical pathway modulated by chronic hypoxia is that activated by the binding of the sympathetic neurotransmitter norepinephrine to adrenergic receptors. As indicated by studies of NE-induced contractility, in fetal MCA LTH only slightly attenuated (3%) NE's ability to induce contraction, as compared to a greater extent (18%) in adult (Long et al., 2002). Some of this effect in the LTH acclimatized fetus may be attributable to a 39% downregulation of alpha-2 adrenergic receptor density (Ueno et al., 1997), although as noted above, the α_{1B}-AR was upregulated 20 to 30% (Goyal et al., 2014). Because the magnitudes of the decreases in alpha-1 receptor density were much greater than the corresponding decrease in contractility, these results suggest either a substantial receptor reserve (Zhu, 1993) that is ablated by LTH, and/or that this stress also affects components of the pharmacomechanical coupling pathway downstream from the receptor. Consistent with the first possibility, NE-induced responses of inositol 1,4,5-trisphosphate (IP3) mobilization following alpha-1 receptor activation were decreased only 35% in fetal LTH arteries (Ueno et al., 1997). Given that the ratio of the NE-induced IP3 signals to alpha-1 receptor density was increased by chronic hypoxia in fetal (but not adult) arteries, the results suggest further that the size of the receptor reserve for alpha-1 adrenoceptors must be relatively large in these vessels. It is also clear, however, that chronic hypoxia affects multiple components of the alpha1-adrenergic receptor and other signal transduction pathways in an age-dependent manner. In addition, whereas LTH decreased basal IP3 levels 30% in the adult they remained unchanged in the fetus (Ueno et al., 1997). Nonetheless, in fetal arteries, LTH significantly decreased (80%) IP3 receptor density (Zhou et al., 1997).

The net effect of these fetal vascular changes was that NE-induced no significant increase in cytosolic Ca^{2+}, (despite being decreased 21% in adult arteries). Here again, the finding that LTH decreased the magnitudes of both the NE-induced IP3 signal and IP3 receptor density to a much greater extent than it affected contractility, suggests that hypoxia probably eliminated receptor reserve for alpha-1 adrenergic and IP3 receptors. In the fetus, some of the effect of reduced receptor densities may have been offset by corresponding relatively high Ca^{2+} sensitivity (Long et al., 2002). The increase in LTH myofilament Ca^{2+} sensitivity is associated with an increased ability of phosphorylated myosin to increase this sensitivity (Nauli et al., 2005). Altogether, these findings indicate that LTH reduces fetal artery densities for these receptors. Because receptor reserve appears to be high for both receptor types in the fetal arteries, hypoxia affects have relatively little influence on NE-induced fetal artery contractile responses. This complex pattern of hypoxic effects reveals that alpha1-adrenergic receptor pharmacomechanical coupling is regulated closely by multiple physiological mechanisms.

Although in carotid arteries acclimatization to long-term hypoxia is accompanied by no significant increases in vascular endothelial growth factor *per se*, its receptors Flk-1 and Flt-1 increase 171 and 786 percent, respectively (Adeoye et al., 2013). In turn, LTH decreased myosin light chain kinase ~90% while increasing the abundance of myosin light chain$_{20}$ ~60%. In this study, LTH also increased the colocalization of myosin light chain kinase with myosin light chain$_{20}$ with several other intracellular proteins. These results support the idea that VEGF plays a critical role in hypoxic-mediated vascular remodeling. Whether by changes in gene expression, in efficiency of message translation, through post-translational modifications, or by turnover of key signaling proteins, these mechanisms remain unknown. Obviously, this is a most promising target for future investigation, given that these pathways and proteins are critical for cardiovascular development and regulation in the embryo and fetus of both mammalian (Crossley and Altimiras, 2000) and non-mammalian species (Mulder et al., 2001).

As noted, fetal cerebral arteries show striking differences in signal transduction mechanisms compared to the adult, and these differences are magnified in response to high-altitude LTH. Because PKC plays a key role in regulating CA contractility, we tested the hypothesis that LTH differentially regulates the PKC-mediated Ca^{2+} sensitization pathways and contractility (Goyal et al., 2010). In fetal normoxic and hypoxic sheep, we examined several hypotheses in relation to responses of CA tension and intracellular Ca^{2+} concentration and measured levels of several cellular proteins. In both oxygenation groups, the PKC activator phorbol 12, 13-dibutyrate (PDBu) produced robust CA contractions. In the presence of a mitogen activated extracellular kinase (MEK) inhibitor (U-0126), the PDBu-induced contractions were increased a further 20 to 30%. Furthermore, in fetal CA PDBu lead to increased phosphorylation of extracellular regulated kinase (ERK2) but not ERK1. PDBu-stimulated ERK2 phosphorylation also was significantly greater in hypoxic than normoxic CA. Although RhoA/Rho kinase played a significant role in PDBu-mediated contractions of the normoxic fetal vessels, this was not the case in the LTH group. In addition, in contrast to adult the 17 kDa, PKC-potentiated myosin phosphatase inhibitor (CPI-17) played no significant role in fetal CA contractility (Goyal et al., 2010). Overall, this study demonstrated several important maturational and LTH acclimatization changes in PKC-induced contractile responses and downstream pathways. The latter may play a key role in pathophysiologic disorders associated with prolonged hypoxia.

Another important pharmacomechanical coupling pathway in CA is that activated by the binding of serotonin (5-hydroxytryptamine, 5HT) to 5HT2a receptors. In ovine cranial arteries, the 5HT2a subtype is the dominant 5HT receptor and hypoxia has no effect on the subtype expression for serotonergic receptors in this model (Teng et al., 1998). Nonetheless, hypoxia appears to modulate the signaling pathway initiated by the 5HT2a receptor in a manner distinct from that observed for the alpha-1 adrenergic pathway. Most importantly, in fetal ovine MCA, LTH does not appear to depress 5HT-induced contractions, despite hypoxia-induced decreases in 5HT2a receptor density of 49%. Correspondingly in fetal (but not adult) carotid arteries, LTH decreased the size of the 5HT-induced IP3 signal. Thus, as for the adrenergic system, the findings that LTH has little effect of 5HT-induced contractility, despite large age-dependent decreases in receptor density and IP3 signal, again suggests that this stress eliminated receptor reserve for serotonergic receptors, and that hypoxia affects multiple components of the serotonergic pathway. Among these, LTH reduces the ability of protein kinase G (PKG) to phosphorylate its target proteins, which attenuates its ability to induce vasorelaxation (Thorpe et al., 2013). Also, although the abundance of PKG is relatively high in fetal cranial arteries, in 5-HT contracted vessels pre-treatment with an inhibitor of the BK channel failed to attenuate the vasorelaxation induced by a PKG agonist as occurs in normoxic arteries (Thorpe et al., 2013). These findings support the idea that LTH attenuates the vasorelaxant effects of PKG by suppression of its ability to activate the BK channel. Given that this pathway plays a critical role in hemostasis, it also may be involved in the development of cerebral vasospasm following intracranial hemorrhage (Szabo et al., 1992), and also may play a role in coupling perfusion and metabolism via serotonergic perivascular innervation (Bonvento et al., 1991).

With the vital importance of gene regulation, to identify the signal transduction pathways and critical molecules which may be involved in acclimatization to high altitude, we conducted microarray with advanced bioinformatics analysis on carotid arteries from the normoxic near-term ovine fetus at sea-level and those acclimatized to high altitude for 110+ days. In response to LTH acclimatization, in fetal CA we identified mRNA from 38 genes upregulated > 2 fold and 9 genes downregulated > 2-fold (P<0.05 for each) (Goyal et al., 2013). The major genes with upregulated mRNA were SLC1A3, Insulin-like growth factor (IGF) binding protein 3, IGF type 2 receptor, transforming growth factor (TGF) Beta-3, and genes involved in the AKT and BCL2 signal transduction networks. Most genes with upregulated mRNA have a common motif for Pbx/Knotted homeobox in the promoter region, and Sox family binding sites in the 3' untranslated region. Genes with downregulated mRNA included those involved in the P53 pathway and 5-lipoxygenase activating proteins. The promoter region of all genes with downregulated mRNA, had a common 49 bp region with a binding site for DOT6 and TOD6, components of the RPD3 histone deacetylase complex RPD3C(L). We also identified miRNA complementary to a number of the altered genes.

Thus, this study identified molecules in the ovine fetus which may play an important role in the acclimatization response to high-altitude associated LTH (Goyal et al., 2013). In some respects, these results in the LTH fetus suggest that stress-induced changes can be regarded as advancing developmental maturation. Such a concept has been described in human FGR newborns that show decreased perinatal mortality, compared with those that are age-matched normally grown; although this concept has been negated by others (Bernstein et al., 2000). Figure 4 presents some of the chief molecular acclimatization responses to high altitude long-term hypoxia, with emphasis on epigenetic mechanisms.

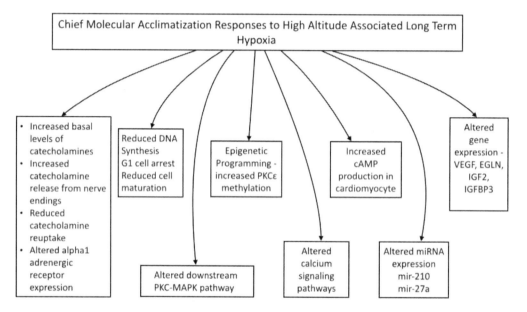

Figure 4. Chief molecular acclimatization responses to high altitude associated long-term hypoxia.

Some Aspects of Cardiovascular Function in the Llama Fetus

As a species native to high altitude, several South American investigators have conducted investigations in the llama (*Lama glama*) on the *alto plano*, which illustrates successful adaptation to a rather inhospitable environment. As with other species at altitude, the llama fetus faces the inherent double threat of a relatively low arterial PO_2 as well as the stress of superimposed high altitude hypobaric hypoxemia. In contrast to sheep and other lowland species, the llama employs a number of differing cardiovascular mechanisms in response to both acute and prolonged hypoxemia, and many of these have been reviewed (Giussani et al., 1994b, 1996, Llanos et al., 2003) (See Table 5 with comparisons to sheep). For instance, under basal control conditions the fetal llama has lower cardiac output and organ blood flows, with greater peripheral resistance than the sheep, showing more efficient O_2 extraction (Benavides et al., 1989, Llanos et al., 1995, 1998, Perez et al., 1989). Also in contrast to the sheep, acute continuous or graded hypoxemia (arterial PO_2=12 to 16 Torr) in the llama fetus is accompanied by intense peripheral vasoconstriction with no or little increase in cerebral blood flow (Giussani et al., 1996, 1999, Llanos et al., 1995, 2002). This lack of increase in CBF with no increase in brain O_2 extraction was accompanied by a decrease in O_2 consumption with hypometabolism (Llanos et al., 2002, 2003). As in the sheep, hypoxia in the llama fetus was accompanied by decrease in the high voltage, low frequency electroencephalographic state, as compared to the low voltage high frequency state (Blanco et al., 1997). However, in contrast to the sheep fetus which develops seizure activity with flattening of the ECoG activity, seizures do not occur in the fetal llama (Llanos et al., 2003). Despite its role in chemoreflex activity, carotid sinus denervation failed to modify the fetal llama vasoconstriction. Nonetheless, the increase in plasma AVP concentration was several-fold greater than that of sheep (Giussani et al., 1996). Surprisingly, administration of a V_1 AVP-receptor antagonist did not modify this vasoconstriction (Giussani et al., 1999, Herrera et al., 2000) (Table 5). In marked contrast, α_1-AR blockade in the hypoxemic fetal llama produced a profound decrease in systemic arterial pressure as well as carotid and femoral blood flows. In both the llama and sheep, this blockade led to cardiovascular collapse with fetal death (Giussani et al., 1999), indicating the vital role of the α_1-AR-mediated responses in maintaining homeostasis in response to hypoxia. This response supports evidence from other studies that the α_1-adrenergic system plays a critical role in fetal survival in response to hypoxia (Airede and Weerasinghe, 1995, Block et al., 1984, Giussani et al., 1999). In addition, an increase in femoral vascular resistance in the newborn llama was associated with increased expression of mRNA for the α_{1B}-AR, but lower expression for that of the α_{1A}-AR (although confirmatory Western immunoblots were not presented) (Moraga et al., 2011). This robust vasoconstrictor activity probably, in part, occurred in association with significantly higher plasma concentration of catecholamines (Fletcher et al., 2003).

Table 5. Fetal Sheep and Fetal Llama: A Comparison of Some Cardiovascular Functions and Responses to Acute Hypoxia

Physiologic Function	Sheep	Reference	Relative Value	Llama	Reference
Normoxia Control					
Gestational length (days)	147±3		<	350±5*	Fowler, 1989
Fetal weight (kg)	4.4±3		<	11±1*	Fowler, 1989
Mean Arterial blood pressure (mm Hg)	44±1	Kamitomo et al., 1992, 1993	=	48±2†	Llanos et al., 1995
Heart rate (beats·min⁻¹)	168±5 156±5	Kamitomo et al., 1992, 1993	>	124±5 113±6 122±6	Benavides et al., 1989 Llanos et al., 1995, 1998 Giussani et al., 1996
Hemoglobin concentration (gm·dl)	11±1 12±1	Benavides et al., 1989	>	10±1* 16±1	Benavides et al., 1989 †Moraga et al., 2011
P₅₀ (Torr)	17.0	Meschia et al., 1961 Longo, 1987		18.0	Meschia et al., 1960
Arterial PO₂ (Torr)	23±1 24±1	Kamitomo et al., 1993 Kitanaka et al., 1989a	=	25±1	Llanos et al., 1995

Table 5. (Continued)

Physiologic Function	Sheep	Reference	Relative Value	Llama	Reference
		Giussani et al., 1999 Moraga et al., 1996			
Combined ventricular output (ml·min⁻¹·kg⁻¹)	465±17	Benavides et al., 1989	>	238±18 250±13 113±11	Benavides et al., 1989 Giussani et al., 1996 Llanos et al., 2002
Umbilical blood flow (ml·min⁻¹·kg⁻¹)				82±10	
Carotid blood flow (ml·min⁻¹·kg⁻¹)				22.8±4	Giussani et al., 1996
Femoral blood flow (ml·min⁻¹·kg⁻¹)	6.1±0.4	†Moraga et al., 2011	>	4.6±0.6*	†Moraga et al., 2011
Oxygen consumption (ml O₂·min⁻¹·kg⁻¹)	~8		>	~4.2	Llanos et al., 2003
Acute Hypoxia **Cardiac Output and Blood Flows**					
Arterial blood pressure (mm Hg)	81±1		<	51±3	Llanos et al., 1995, 1998
Arterial PO₂ (Torr)	17±2	Hunter et al., 2003 Peña et al., 2007		12 to 16	Giussani et al., 1999 Llanos et al., 1998, 2002
Heart rate (beats·min⁻¹)	120±5	Peña et al., 2007		95±7	Llanos et al., 1998
Combined ventricular output (ml·min⁻¹·kg⁻¹)					
Umbilical blood flow (ml·min⁻¹·kg⁻¹)				82±10	
Cerebral blood flow	~40%↑	Hunter et al., 2003 Peña et al., 2007 Llanos et al., 2002, 2003	>	0 to 5%↑	
Coronary blood flow (Percent change)	~60%↑	Llanos et al., 2002, 2003	<	2 to 3-fold↑	Llanos et al., 1995, 1998, 2002, 2003
Adrenal blood flow (Percent change)	~160%↑	Llanos et al., 2002, 2003	>	~100%↑	Llanos et al., 1995, 1998, 2002, 2003
Kidney and other blood flow (Percent change)	~20%↓	Llanos et al., 2002, 2003	<	~80%↓	Llanos et al., 1995, 1998, 2003
Femoral blood flow (ml·min⁻¹·kg⁻¹)	5.2±0.4		>	3.7±0.8	Moraga et al., 2011
Circulating Hormones					
Cortisol					Llanos et al., 2003 Riquelme et al., 1998, 2002
ACTH				% ↑	Llanos et al., 2003 Riquelme et al., 1998, 2002
Catecholamines	2-fold↑				Llanos et al., 2003 Riquelme et al., 1998, 2002

Physiologic Function	Sheep	Reference	Relative Value	Llama	Reference
Arginine vasopressin	2-fold↑		<	2 to 3-fold↑	Herrera et al., 2000
Neuropeptide Y			<	2 to 3-fold↑	Giussani et al., 1996, 1999
Angiotensin II			>	-	Giussani et al., 1996, 1999
Interventions					
α1-AR Blockade	Vascular collapse		=	Vascular Collapse	Giussani et al., 1999 Moraga et al., 2011 Reuss et al., 1982
AVP-R Blockade					Giussani et al., 1993, 1999 Llanos et al., 2003 Perez et al., 1989
Nitric oxide synthase blockade			<		Giussani et al., 1999 Llanos et al., 2003
Carotid Sinus Denervation			>	-	Giussani et al., 1994a, 1994b, 1996
Other Changes					
Electrocorticogram	ECoG flattens, may develop seizure			ECOG flattens, but no seizure activity	Llanos et al., 2003

*P<0.05; †Newborn.

Subsequently, these workers demonstrated the vital role of NO in the maintenance of fetal llama cerebral and femoral artery tone in both normoxia and hypoxia (Giussani et al., 1999, Llanos et al., 2003). However, in addition during hypoxemia other vasodilator factors play an important role (Riquelme et al., 1998, Sanhueza et al., 2005). The relative increase in NO and its vasodilatory effects may serve as a mechanism to counteract the robust α-adrenergic mechanisms. Strikingly, and in agreement with the absence of an acute hypoxic-induced increase in CBF in the llama fetus, nitric oxide synthase levels in both cerebral cortex and cerebellum (chiefly in mitochondria, but also in microsomes and cytosol) did not increase significantly in response to 24 hours of acute hypoxia (~15 Torr) (Galleguillos et al., 2001). In addition, during acute hypoxemia, blockade of Endothelin A receptor ablated the hypoxic-induced increase in peripheral vascular resistance (Llanos et al., 2003).

Overall, the response to acute hypoxemia in the llama fetus suggest either a stronger endocrine/autocrine vasoconstrictor response and/or weaker vasodilator mechanisms (Llanos et al., 2003). Evidence also suggests that, as with the Quechua Indians, who over many generations have acclimatized to their relatively hypoxic environment (Hochachka et al., 1994), the fetal llama can employ a state of hypometabolism with a rate of O_2 consumption that is ~50% of control, with decreased $Na^+ K^+$ pump activity and no increase in cell death (Giussani et al., 2001) in its defense against hypoxia (Llanos et al., 2003, 2007). Of importance would be to discover the genes that have been selected in the llama to express the enzymes and other proteins that withstand hypoxic conditions. One can only imagine the implications of such knowledge for the prevention/treatment of human disease.

Long-Term Hypoxia and the Fetal Hypothalamic-Pituitary-Adrenal Axis

In light of its marked response to acute hypoxia, one might predict that the HPA axis would mount a substantial response to prolonged hypoxia. Perhaps surprisingly, initially this was not evident. In the near-term LTH fetus described above, basal levels of immunoreactive (IR) adrenocorticotropic hormone (ACTH) and cortisol were similar to that of normoxic controls (Adachi et al., 2004, Ducsay et al., 2009, Imamura et al., 2004). Nonetheless, LTH was associated with an increase in the ACTH precursor proopiomelanocortin (POMC) (Myers et al., 2005). Significantly, in response to the superimposed stress of hypotension (Adachi et al., 2004) or umbilical occlusion (Imamura et al., 2004), cortisol concentrations were elevated despite IR-ACTH remaining normal. In addition, in contrast to normoxic controls, adrenal denervation of the LTH fetus failed to alter cortisol production (Kato et al., 2003). In response to the secondary stress of umbilical cord occlusion, both ACTH (and to a lesser extent its precursors) were elevated (Myers et al., 2004). Also, despite elevated IR-ACTH expression in the LTH fetus, paradoxically the expression of two enzymes that mediate cortisol synthesis, cytochrome P450, family 11, sub family A, polypeptide 1 (CYP11A1 and CYP17); monooxygenases localized to the inner mitochondrial membrane that catalyze many reactions, including the synthesis of steroids) were decreased significantly, as was the ACTH-receptor (Myers et al., 2005) (Table 4). In addition, in the LTH fetus corticotropin releasing hormone (CRH) mRNA and arginine vasopressin (AVP) mRNA were upregulated in the hypothalamic parvocellular division of the paraventricular nucleus, as were levels of anterior pituitary AVP receptor expression (both mRNA and protein), and the ACTH release response to AVP (Myers and Ducsay, 2012). These complex findings suggest a LTH-mediated shift from CRH to AVP in regulation of the HPA axis.

In further studies, the Ducsay-Myers group have demonstrated the intra-adrenal regulatory mechanisms in the LTH fetal lamb have increased expression of endothelial nitric oxide synthase (NOS) (Monau et al., 2009) and nitric oxide release. This latter has been shown to inhibit ACTH-induced cortisol production (Monau et al., 2010). In addition, in LTH fetal perirenal adipose tissue these investigators demonstrated increased expression of leptin, associated with markedly elevated plasma leptin concentrations (Ducsay et al., 2006). Additionally, a 4 day infusion of leptin antagonist resulted in restored expression of both CYP11A1 and CYP17 to normoxic control values (Ducsay et al., 2013). These findings emphasize an important role of leptin in mediating the LTH adrenal response with CYP expression.

As observed by Myers and Ducsay, the functional changes in the HPA axis in response to LTH may be considered "adaptive" (Myers and Ducsay, 2012). Such changes are of critical importance in terms of LTH not precipitating prematurely the normal late gestation cortisol rise associated with the initiation of parturition. That is, in view of its normal relatively low fetal arterial PO_2, which is exacerbated by LTH, with elevated leptin levels modulating the HPA response, the organism can grow and develop in an optimal a manner to prepare it for its neonatal existence. As noted, acute secondary stress superimposed on that of LTH can result in premature maturation of the adrenal cortex with elevated production of cortisol and other stress hormones that contribute to the genesis of FGR.

Fetal Metabolic Responses to LTH

Perhaps surprisingly, despite the plethora of studies on the systems noted above and, despite what is known about programming of the fetus to disease later in life, relatively little investigation has addressed metabolic and endocrinologic issues (For instance see review Styne, 2011). Relatively early studies in several systems have demonstrated the role of mitochondrial oxidative metabolism with alteration in enzymatic pathways in preferentially producing the high energy phosphate bonds of adenosine triphosphate (ATP; Reynafarje, 1962). As noted, the hypoxic-mediated redistribution of cardiac output to the brain and heart occurs at the expense of the liver and other organs (Kiserud et al., 2006, Nathanielsz and Hanson, 2003, Peeters et al., 1979). Early work in the mid-twentieth century established the role of hematopoiesis in the acclimatization responses for both adults and infants (Reynafarje, 1957, 1959).

Chronic hypoxia has been shown to impair carbohydrate metabolism (Regnault et al., 2010), and insulin signaling (Thorn et al., 2009) in the fetal liver, and program insulin resistance in the offspring (Camm et al., 2011). In the rat liver, fetal FGR also has been shown to modify the epigenetic histone code of the *IGF2* gene (Fu et al., 2009). In livers of the near-term guinea pig, prolonged hypoxia (10.5% O_2 for 14 days; term=65 days), produced evidence of severe oxidative stress as evidenced by cellular damage, generation of elevated malondialdehyde (an index of peroxidation) and DNA fragmentation. These changes were attenuated by administration of the antioxidant *N*-acetylcysteine (Hashimoto et al., 2012). In humans at 4,300 m on the *alto plano* of Peru, maternal serum insulin-like growth factor binding proteins (IGFBP) were increased significantly during the second half of pregnancy (Krampl et al., 2002). By decreasing the circulatory levels of insulin-like growth factor, this could contribute significantly to FGR. In cultured bovine aortic and pulmonary artery endothelial cells, hypoxia (0% O_2 for 24 to 72h) has been shown to lower IGF-1 protein but up-regulate several of the IGFBP proteins. This suggests that these may be dominant paracrine regulators of endothelial cell proliferation (Tucci et al., 1998).

In the adult rat, both hepatic and skeletal muscle insulin signaling have been shown to be impaired following antenatal hypoxia (Camm et al., 2011). Such stress combined with a postnatal lipid obesogenic diet also has been shown to result in adult increases in intra-abdominal fat and adipocyte size with elevated levels of leptin, triglycerides, and free fatty acids, with elevated triglycerides and ceramides in liver and skeletal muscle, and evidence of insulin resistance (Rueda-Clausen et al., 2011a). To a great extent these changes can be ameliorated by postnatal administration of the mammalian target of rapamycin (mTOR) antagonist resveratrol (Dolinsky et al., 2011).

In addition to antenatal maternal hypoxia leading to FGR, studies suggest that LTH can play an important role in the genesis of idiopathic pulmonary hypertension of both newborn infant and adult. Because these also may be a consequence of alterations in the local pulmonary renin-angiotensin system (RAS), we tested the hypothesis that LTH is associated with alterations in gene and protein expression of the pulmonary renin-angiotensin system. In mice, we studied messenger RNA (mRNA) and protein expression, as well as promoter DNA methylation and microRNA (miRNA) levels in response to 48 hours hypoxia (10.5% O_2) at 15.5 days post conception (DPC) (Goyal et al., 2011a). In response to hypoxia, the pulmonary mRNA levels of angiotensin-converting enzyme (ACE) 1.2, ACE-2, and angiotensin II type

1b (AT-1b) receptors were increased significantly, as compared to controls. In addition, pulmonary protein levels of renin and ACE-2 were increased, whereas ACE-1 protein expression was reduced. In fetal lungs, we also observed reduced expression of the miRNAs: mmu-mir-199b, -27b, -200b, and -468 that putatively increase the translation of renin, ACE-1, ACE-2, and AT-1 receptors, respectively. Of note, promoter methylation of ACE was unchanged. We conclude that antenatal maternal hypoxia leads to significant changes in expression of pulmonary RAS of fetal mice (Goyal et al., 2011a). The possible implications of these changes for the regulation of pulmonary vascular contractility in later life remain to be explored. Many other aspects of metabolic changes in the growth restricted fetus (Battaglia, 2011), and sequelae in the adult such as metabolic syndrome, type 2 diabetes, and related disorders (Chernausek, 2012) have been reviewed.

Hypoxia-Mediated FGR and Neuropsychological Correlates

The correlation of cerebral neuroanatomical and neuropsychological changes with fetal growth restriction has been described by numerous investigators. Chronic hypoxia *per se* or hypoxia-ischemia as a consequence of prolonged reduction in uteroplacental blood flow can have invidious short-term and long-term consequences for the developing brain (Rees et al., 2008). For instance, an association of FGR with poor neurobehavioral and cognitive performance has been reported in neonates (Figueras et al., 2009). Some neurobehavioral impairment appears to be even more pronounced in preterm, as compared to near term, FGR infants (Rees et al., 2008), although these differences were not observed over a long time period of life (Bassan et al., 2011). Nonetheless, long-term follow-up studies have demonstrated significant neurodevelopmental delays persisting into adolescence (Aarnoudse-Moens et al., 2009, Feldman and Eidelman, 2006). Other investigators have reported cognitive impairment and learning deficiencies observed in school being related to a characteristic pattern of altered short-term memory, attention span and anxiety (Feldman and Eidelman, 2006, Geva et al., 2006a, 2006b, Leitner et al., 2007), and in some cases an increased risk of outright attention deficit disorders (Geva et al., 2006a, 2006b, Heinonen et al., 2010). These behavioral disturbances have been suggested to serve as indices of specific neurological changes such as in the anterior hippocampal-prefrontal cortical network, the parahippocampal complex, the striatum thalamus, and other structures (Cubillo et al., 2012, Eichenbaum et al., 2007, Geva et al., 2006a, 2006b).

A number of studies have reported that in developed nations, FGR is associated with consequential neurodevelopmental/neurocognitive outcomes later in life (Frisk et al., 2002, Leitner et al., 2007, Paz et al., 1995, Strauss, 2000, Sung et al., 1993, Zubrick et al., 2000). In an attempt to discover the mechanistic basis for this association, Robert H. Lane and colleagues at the University of Utah have explored several aspects of developmental neurogenesis in laboratory animals. In addition to significant changes in composition of the neuronal *N*-methyl-D-aspartate receptor subunits, which are critical for synaptogenesis, the alterations showed gender specificity (Schober et al., 2009).

In terms of structural changes in the brain of the FGR fetus and newborn infant, magnetic resonance imaging (MRI) has demonstrated a number of such changes (Sanz-Cortés et al.,

2013), including the cerebral cortex (Dubois et al., 2008) and hippocampus (Lodygensky et al., 2008). Rather than gross tissue destruction, FGR is believed to be associated with more subtle disruption of normal neurodevelopment (Rees et al., 2011). To date, we know of no long-term studies that have evaluated the correlation of functional impairments with the underlying neurological anomalies, however.

High Altitude and the Placenta

In human high altitude pregnancy, reports vary as to the size of the placenta; however, almost all such studies report a modest increase in relation to that of the fetus. For instance in her turn of the century review "The Placenta at High Altitude", Stacy Zamudio tabulated ten reports of placental and fetal weights and placental index (the ratio of placental to fetal weight) at altitudes ranging from 2,000 to 4,300 m (Zamudio, 2003). For normoxic control subjects at low altitude (347±60 m) the placental index equaled 0.15±0.01. In contrast, at high altitude (3550±620 m) this value was 0.17±0.01 (Table 3). As Zamudio noted, a *caveat* is that the total sample size for this comparison was less than 100 subjects (Zamudio, 2003). However, a later report from her group substantiated these findings among both Andean natives and those of European ancestry in Bolivia (Zamudio et al., 2007) (Table 3). On the basis of other reports, it is apparent that these placental index ratios of 0.15 and 0.17 for pregnancies from low and high altitude, respectively, are reasonable (Hass et al., 1980 [should be Haas et al., 1980], Khalid et al., 1997, Krüger and Arias-Stella, 1970) (Table 3). This, in concert with placental morphometric (Chabes et al., 1968) and other vascular changes, must work to optimize the exchange of O_2 and other nutrients under the stress of pregnancy at altitude (Mayhew et al., 1990). Thus, a fetal to placental weight ratio of >0.15 may serve as an index of growth restriction independent of fetal weight. In addition, Zamudio has emphasized that in the human placenta at altitude the most consistent morphometric findings were increased villous terminal capillary branching with increased villous vascularization/angiogenesis (capillary density and capillary diameter), thinning of the villous membranes, and proliferation of the villous cytotrophoblast with trophoblastic bridges and syncytial knots (Ali et al., 1996, Espinoza et al., 2001, Khalid et al., 1997, Zamudio, 2003). Along this line, in 13 patients with normal pregnancies at Leadville, CO, stereologic analysis disclosed significant remodeling of the decidual ends of the more than two-fold increase numbers of uteroplacental arteries, as well as an increase in fetal capillary density (Tissot van Patot et al., 2003). This fits with the well known finding that angiogenesis with neovascularization is a robust response to chronic hypoxia.

A related response to high altitude hypoxia is decreased impedance of uteroplacental arteries (Krampl et al., 2001a). Along this line, circulating plasma nitrate, a stable metabolite of nitric oxide, is significantly elevated in pregnant sheep acclimatized to high altitude (Zhang et al., 1998). As noted above, in pregnant women at high altitude, both uterine artery diameter and blood flow were decreased significantly, and the levels of NO metabolites were lower, so that the ratio of endothelin-1, which remained unchanged, to NO metabolites was greater. At 20 and 30 weeks of gestation this change accounted for 45% and 32%, respectively of the BW decrement at altitude (Julian et al., 2008). Yet to be understood are the factors that account for uteroplacental blood flow being decreased significantly in normal non-high altitude cases of FGR. For instance, in a study of 8 patients with FGR 113 Indium was used to quantitate this flow, which was reduced a profound 30 to 60% (Lunell et al., 1979).

To explore various mechanistic facets of these findings in the human placenta at high altitude, a number of studies have examined aspects of placental structure and function in laboratory animals. To test the hypothesis that placental structural anatomy and diffusing capacity were altered in response to LTH, we subjected guinea pigs to 12 to 14% O_2 from DPC 15 to near term (64 days). Placental blood vascular volume increased 12±3%, and despite a small decrease in tissue volume, the mean diffusion distance between maternal and fetal circulations decreased 18±4%, with an increase in diffusing capacity of 27±7% (Bacon et al., 1984). Again, teleologically these changes suggest changes to maintain or increase the efficiency of transplacental exchange. Nonetheless, in regards to transplacental exchange, despite the ability of the FGR infant to increase glucose uptake (Marconi et al., 1996), it has been suggested that impaired transplacental glucose transport play an important role in high altitude associated FGR (Zamudio, 2003). Also in guinea pigs, as demonstrated by quantifying DNA synthesis, uterine artery growth was shown to be decreased significantly at high altitude (Rockwell et al., 2000).

In sheep, we quantified the gross morphology of ovine placental cotyledons to examine the extent to which these are altered in response to LTH acclimatization. In comparison to the distribution of the four cotyledon types in sea level singleton controls (Type A=76±4%; B=22±3%; C=1±2%; D=1±1%), those at high altitude showed a markedly different distribution (Type A=33±4%; B=50±3%; C=10±7%; D=7±1%) (Penninga and Longo, 1998). Further, by use of corrosion casts and histological sections of these placentas, marked differences were seen in both the size and arrangement of maternal and fetal vessels. Specifically, in comparison to controls, the LTH group demonstrated significant increases in the percentage of vessels of the fetal placentome and luminal size per cross section, with a decrease in number of vascular cross sections and frequent branching of stem vessels (Krebs et al., 1997), changes similar to those seen in the human. (Unfortunately, as yet we do not know the correlation of vascular changes with cotyledon type). Overall with FGR, severe villous maldevelopment may represent the extreme of a spectrum of distorted angiogenesis.

In keeping with the observations on the human placenta at high altitude, on the *alto plano* of Chile, in conjunction with a longer gestation (see above), ovine placental weight was increased 40% (396±80 gm versus 280±40 gm) in ewes bred at high altitude (Parraguez et al., 2005) (Table 3). Of interest, among lowland sheep transported to high altitude (as in our studies) this placental weight increase was only 8% (303±64 gm versus 280±40 gm) (Parraguez et al., 2005). Again, these findings suggest that the high altitude, acclimatized placenta develops a significant increase in materno-fetal contiguous area to optimize O_2 and nutrient exchange. As a caveat, recent evidence suggests that even among those individuals living at low altitudes, variations in placental morphology can predict a wide range of disorders in the adult offspring (Barker and Thornburg, 2013).

In a further attempt to understand the mechanistic basis of some of the LTH-associated FGR changes noted above, in our mouse "model" of FGR, we tested the hypothesis that the placental response to hypoxic stress is associated with important gene expression changes. We quantified such expression in response to 48 hours of hypoxia near term (Gheorghe et al., 2007). Pregnant mice at 15.5 DPC were exposed to 48 hours of hypoxia (10.5% O_2), after which the Affymetrix Mouse 430A_2.0 array was used to measure gene expression changes (Gheorghe et al., 2007). 171 probe sets, corresponding to 163 genes, were regulated by hypoxia (P<0.01). Ninety of these genes were upregulated, and 73 were downregulated. We annotated the regulated genes and examined overrepresented functional categories. Among these we observed several overrepresented functional categories. Upregulated genes included those involved in metabolism, oxygen transport, proteolysis, cell death, metabolism of reactive oxygen species, and DNA methylation. Genes involved in transcription, cell cycle regulation, and cell structure were downregulated. The observation that hypoxia upregulates ROS metabolism, in conjunction with DNA methylation enzymes, suggest that in addition to the placenta, hypoxia may contribute to long-term epigenetic changes in stressed fetal tissues and organs (Gheorghe et al., 2007). In the human FGR placenta, microarray gene expression confirmed by real-time polymerase chain reaction studies demonstrated several-fold increased expression of a number of genes, including those for soluble endothelial growth factor receptor, human chorionic gonadotropin, HIF-2α, follistatin-like 3, and leptin. These changes suggest active placental angiogenesis (McCarthy et al., 2007).

We also tested the hypothesis that antenatal maternal hypoxic stress leads to alterations in the placental renin-angiotensin system genes (Goyal et al., 2011b). In this same murine placental "model", we observed: (1) angiotensinogen (AT) mRNA was undetectable; however, AGT protein increased significantly. (2) Although renin mRNA was reduced, protein expression increased in association with decreased microRNA (miRNA) 199b, which can lead to increased renin translation. (3) Also, angiotensin converting enzyme (ACE)-1 mRNA was unaltered; however, protein expression increased significantly, in association with decreased miRNA 27a, which can result in increased ACE-1 translation. (4) ACE-2 mRNA was reduced significantly, whereas protein expression was significantly greater, in association with reduced miRNA 429. (5) Angiotensin II type (AT)-1a receptor mRNA expression was unaltered while AT-1b receptor mRNA was undetectable in both groups. Moreover, AT-1 receptor protein expression was unchanged. (6) AT-2 receptor mRNA and proteins were undetectable in both groups. We conclude that the normal murine placenta not only possesses several components of RAS, but that in response to antenatal maternal stress several of these elements undergo important changes. In addition, differential expression of RAS mRNA, miRNA and protein, indicate post-transcriptional regulatory mechanisms involved with hypoxic stress, and necessitate further investigation (Goyal et al., 2011b).

As noted, in the mouse 48hr of hypoxia at 15 to 17 days post conception results in marked deviations in the pattern of gene expression in the placenta (Gheorghe et al., 2007, 2010), accompanied by significant alterations in the placental renin-angiotensin system (Goyal et al., 2011b) as well as the fetal lung (Goyal et al., 2011a).

In a rat bilateral uterine artery ligation FGR "model", the renal expression of 11β-hydroxysteroid dehydrogenase type 2 (11β-HSD2) mRNA and protein were significantly decreased (Baserga et al., 2007). This occurred in association with increased corticosteroid levels at the time of birth as well as at day 21 of life (Baserga et al., 2005). This enzyme plays a key role in the regulation of renal steroid sensitivity, catabolizing glucocorticoids to an inactive form in the kidney and other aldosterone target tissues, its deficiency being an important mechanism that can lead to hypertension. This FGR "model" also has been demonstrated to be associated with decreased binding of the transcription enhancers specificity protein 1 and NF-κB p65, with increased transcriptional repressors early growth response factor NF-κB p50 to the 11β-HSD2 promoter in males. Some of these changes were more predominant in females. In addition, DNA CpG methylation occurred in a sex specific manner (Baserga et al., 2010).

In a series of studies attempting to uncover aspects of the mechanistic basis for high altitude-FGR-associated placental and energy-demanding activities such as alterations in protein synthesis, compared to sea level controls in the placentas of women residing at Leadville, CO (3,100 m), Burton's group demonstrated marked alterations in endoplasmic reticulum (ER) cisternae with increased phosphorylation of eukaryotic initiation factor 2 subunit α, reduced phosphorylation of AKT, and increased 4E-binding protein (Yung et al., 2012). As noted by the authors, these findings suggest ER stress with inhibition of protein synthesis. In these studies hypoxia (1% O_2) also reduced the proliferation of several placental cell types, changes that suggest reduced villous volume and the likelihood of similar changes in fetal cells (Yung et al., 2012). In further studies in high altitude placental cells, this group demonstrated hypoxia altered mitochondrial function with suppression and compromise of electron transport chain complexes I and IV and thus energy metabolism, as well as increased expression of the HIF responsive microRNA-210 (Colleoni et al., 2013).

Conclusions with Perspectives

As is evident, pregnancy at high altitude is fraught with problems beyond those of the fetus/newborn showing growth restriction. While chiefly being a function of altitude *per se*, this FGR can vary with ethnicity and geographic location, the latter of which reflects the number of generations that a given group has lived at that environment. Also evident, the syndrome of fetal growth restriction, as seen at high altitude is a complex interplay of confounding variables that can present a variety of phenotypes. Beyond the phenomenology of having a birthweight below the 10th percentile, and beyond genetic- and environmental-epigenetic-mediated factors, a seemingly infinite mosaic of cellular, subcellular, and molecular alterations and mechanisms as a result of moderate to severe hypoxia.

Striking are the pronounced differences in response to hypoxia in the sheep and humans acclimatized to life at near sea level. In turn these acclimatization responses differ in many regards from those in the llama (and to a certain extent in human ethnic groups) acclimatized to high altitude for generations. In light of the host of evidence from both epidemiologic studies in humans and experimental studies in laboratory animals, the role of antenatal hypoxia in the genesis of FGR has raised a number of questions in regards to the underlying mechanisms of signaling for the development of these major long-term sequelae. Additional questions pertain to means of possible preventative intervention. With the evidence of altered levels of many hormones, receptor-mediated signaling, NO-mediated oxidative stress and many epigenetic factors playing a role in the pathophysiology of this syndrome, such interventions have been explored by several groups. Additionally, several investigators have exposed the possibility of postnatal treatment to rescue the FGR newborn from long-term sequelae (Giussani and Davidge, 2013). A further consideration is the use of potential biomarkers to identify those pregnancies characterized by adaptive as opposed to maladaptive acclimatization responses.

Oxygen being an essential requirement for aerobic metabolism and life, prolonged residence at high altitude, or other causes of hypoxemia with cellular hypoxia, pose significant challenges for survival. Fortunately, cardiovascular, endocrinologic, metabolic, and other acclimatization responses to LTH mitigate that risk and work to preserve oxygen homeostasis at the organismal level. Nonetheless, the responses to hypobaric hypoxia of pregnancy at high altitude or as a consequence of other conditions are complex. Thus, long-term hypoxia can serve as a useful "model" to explore the physiologic mechanisms of acclimatization, as well as to study the genetic adaptations borne out over multiple generations.

The acclimatization responses may be adaptive or maladaptive in terms of their role in leading to appropriate fetal growth and tissue and cellular function as opposed to fetal growth restriction. Physiologic responses in the mother include increased ventilation and O_2 transport capacity, and compensatory changes in uteroplacental blood flow. Placental function also is optimized with greater capillary blood volume and shorter transcapillary diffusion distance. For the fetus, a number of metabolites, growth factors, and other molecules may influence its tissue protein synthesis to constrain growth in an attempt to survive limited O_2 availability. In this regard, because of its potent influence on central nervous system function, the pathophysiology of cerebral hypoxia, the regulation of cerebral blood flow, and the mechanisms involved in development of and responses to cerebral edema and ischemia are of profound importance. As noted by Andrew J. Murray, when the oxygen supply becomes restricted, the fetus and placenta respond by altering its blood flow delivery and metabolism to optimize its allocation between the competing demands; thus these issues lie beyond a question of supply and demand (Murray, 2012).

Nonetheless, several caveats are in order. In terms of studies in LTH high altitude sheep, while some showed significant fetal weight decrements, others report no significant decrease in the high altitude animals. Nonetheless, although perhaps not constituting a strict "model" for FGR, the studies may be of value in consideration of successful acclimatization responses to LTH. Also, the significant differences in cellular responses of the fetus to LTH, in contrast to the adult (Longo and Goyal, 2014), reflect much more than maturational differences. In part, this is because the degrees of both relative and absolute hypoxia differ in the fetus as compared to adult. Presently, one can only speculate to what extent this may have compounded the maturational differences reported.

Under normal conditions the developing fetus has an arterial O_2 tension (but not that for CO_2) simulating "Mt Everest *in utero*" (Eastman, 1954, Longo, 1987), and severe hypoxia of more than momentary duration can pose particular peril. In turn, the mechanisms by which the fetus "acclimatizes" in response to LTH are of more than passing interest. Thus, the basic hypoxic-mediated cardiovascular, metabolic, neuropsychiatric, and other cellular and subcellular signal transduction mechanisms, and their role in the dysregulation of protein synthesis in the pathogenesis of growth restriction and functional dysregulation in the developing fetus, are of great clinical relevance.

In the present Chapter, in part, we have used the fetal cerebrovasculature as a case study for these responses. That is, that different elements of the adrenergic- and other-mediated perivascular contraction and relaxation mechanisms should be independently regulated, and show differing responses to LTH, should come as no surprise. This truism is even more so in comparing responses in the fetus and adult, and only furthers the view that physiological stresses differ considerably in immature and mature animals, as are the homeostatic responses to these stresses. Whereas cellular hypoxia is perhaps the most important primary stimulus, multiple secondary responses in levels of circulating catecholamines, cortisol or other stress-related hormones, the multiple growth factors, cytokines and other cellular responses including the synthesis of proteins are clearly critical to the hypoxic acclimatization process.

As noted, despite a number of studies to explore the fundamental hypoxic-mediated mechanisms that account for FGR at high altitude, there remain enormous gaps in our understanding. Whereas, to some degree, the changes in the fetal environment are "buffered" by maternal homeostatic mechanisms, it also is clear that under conditions of prolonged hypoxia or other invidious environmental factors, the fetus constitutes a stress for the mother. From this perspective, it would enhance the survival mechanisms for both the mother and conceptus if the latter were to mature more quickly. Whereas this hypothesis has some attraction, it remains highly speculative and in need of definitive experimental verification.

In particular, identification of the signals whereby cells sense limited O_2 or other nutrient availability remains a critical unknown. How, and by what tissues, the "prime mover" responses to hypoxia are mounted is a fascinating question that has been pursued for decades. Recent advances are promising in that they point the direction for the focus of more cellular and molecular investigation of gene regulation to elucidate their role in cellular protein synthesis and related process, and the mechanisms by which they are activated. The rapidly growing diversity and power of new, powerful technology offers unprecedented opportunity and great promise for furthering our understanding.

Our challenge today is to promote a new generation of studies of the mosaic of hypoxic- and other mediator-induced gene regulation and/or metabolomics that will yield the key clues to the origins of FGR at high altitude. Discovery of the genes that promote successful acclimatization and/or prevent high altitude associated disease may have profound implications for human well-being. Let us not delay to make these discoveries

Acknowledgment

Supported by USPHS NIH grants HD-03807 and HD-031226 to LDL. We thank Jimin Suh for her highly professional assistance in preparing this manuscript.

References

Aarnoudse-Moens, C. S., Weisglas-Kuperus, N., van Goudoever, J. B. & Oosterlaan, J. (2009). Meta-analysis of neurobehavioral outcomes in very preterm and/or very low birth weight children. *Pediatrics, 124,* 717-28.

Adachi, K., Umezaki, H., Kaushal, K. M. & Ducsay, C. A. (2004). Long-term hypoxia alters ovine fetal endocrine and physiological responses to hypotension. *Am J Physiol Regul Integr Comp Physiol, 287,* R209-17.

Adeoye, O. O., Butler, S. M., Hubbell, M. C., Semotiuk, A., Williams, J. M. & Pearce, W. J. (2013). Contribution of increased VEGF receptors to hypoxic changes in fetal ovine carotid artery contractile proteins. *Am J Physiol Cell Physiol, 304,* C656-65.

Airede, A. I. & Weerasinghe, H. D. (1995). Birth asphyxia: a review. *East Afr Med J, 72,* 252-7.

Akopov, S. E., Zhang, L. & Pearce, W. J. (1998). Maturation alters the contractile role of calcium in ovine basilar arteries. *Pediatr Res, 44,* 154-160.

Alexander, G. (1964). Studies on the placenta of the sheep (Ovis aries L.). Effect of surgical reduction in the number of caruncles. *J Reprod Fertil*, *7*, 307-22.

Ali, K. Z., Burton, G. J., Morad, N. & Ali, M. E. (1996). Does hypercapillarization influence the branching pattern of terminal villi in the human placenta at high altitude? *Placenta*, *17*, 677-82.

Allen, D. W. & Jandl, J. H. (1960). Factors influencing relative rates of synthesis of adult and fetal hemoglobin in vitro. *J Clin Invest*, *39*, 1107-13.

Alonso, J. G., Okai, T., Longo, L. D. & Gilbert, R. D. (1989). Cardiac function during long-term hypoxemia in fetal sheep. *Am J Physiol*, *257*, H581-9.

Ashwal, S., Majcher, J. S., Vain, N. & Longo, L. D. (1980). Patterns of fetal lamb regional cerebral blood flow during and after prolonged hypoxia. *Pediatr Res*, *14*, 1104-10.

Bacon, B. J., Gilbert, R. D., Kaufmann, P., Smith, A. D., Trevino, F. T. & Longo, L. D. (1984). Placental anatomy and diffusing capacity in guinea pigs following long-term maternal hypoxia. *Placenta*, *5*, 475-87.

Ballew, C. & Haas, J. D. (1986). Hematologic evidence of fetal hypoxia among newborn infants at high altitude in Bolivia. *Am J Obstet Gynecol*, *155*, 166-9.

Barcroft, J. (1927). Physiology of life in the high Andes. (Wilde Memorial Lecture). *Mem Proc Manch Lit Philos Soc*, *71*, xvii-xviii.

Barcroft, J., Binger, C. A., Bock, A. V., Doggart, J. H., Forbes, H. S., Harrop, G., et al. (1923). Observations upon the effect of high altitude on the physiological processes of the human body, carried out in the Peruvian Andes, chiefly at Cerro de Pasco. *Philos Trans R Soc Lond B*, *211*, 351-480.

Barker, D. J. & Thornburg, K. L. (2013). Placental programming of chronic diseases, cancer and lifespan: a review. *Placenta*, *34*, 841-5.

Barker, J. N. (1957). Role of hemoglobin affinity and concentration in determining hypoxia tolerance of mammals during infancy, hypoxia, hyperoxia and irradiation. *Am J Physiol*, *189*, 281-9.

Barron, D. H., Metcalfe, J., Meschia, G., Huckabee, W., Hellegers, A. & Prystowsky, H. (1964). Adaptations of pregnant ewes and their fetuses to high altitude. In: *The physiological effects of high altitude*. Weihe, W. H. (Ed). Oxford: Pergamon Press, p. 115-129.

Baserga, M., Bares, A. L., Hale, M. A., Callaway, C. W., McKnight, R. A., Lane, P. H. et al. (2009). Uteroplacental insufficiency affects kidney VEGF expression in a model of IUGR with compensatory glomerular hypertrophy and hypertension. *Early Hum Dev*, *85*, 361-7.

Baserga, M., Hale, M. A., McKnight, R. A., Yu, X., Callaway, C. W. & Lane, R. H. (2005). Uteroplacental insufficiency alters hepatic expression, phosphorylation, and activity of the glucocorticoid receptor in fetal IUGR rats. *Am J Physiol Regul Integr Comp Physiol*, *289*, R1348-53.

Baserga, M., Hale, M. A., Wang, Z. M., Yu, X., Callaway, C. W., McKnight, R. A., et al. (2007). Uteroplacental insufficiency alters nephrogenesis and downregulates cyclooxygenase-2 expression in a model of IUGR with adult-onset hypertension. *Am J Physiol Regul Integr Comp Physiol*, *292*, R1943-55.

Baserga, M., Kaur, R., Hale, M. A., Bares, A., Yu, X., Callaway, C. W., et al. (2010). Fetal growth restriction alters transcription factor binding and epigenetic mechanisms of renal

11beta-hydroxysteroid dehydrogenase type 2 in a sex-specific manner. *Am J Physiol Regul Integr Comp Physiol, 299*, R334-42.

Bassan, H., Stolar, O., Geva, R., Eshel, R., Fattal-Valevski, A., Leitner, Y., et al. (2011). Intrauterine growth-restricted neonates born at term or preterm: how different? *Pediatr Neurol, 44*, 122-130.

Battaglia, F. C. (2011). Circulatory and metabolic changes accompanying fetal growth restriction. In: *Fetal and neonatal physiology.* Polin, R. A., Fox, W. W. & Abman, S. H. (Eds). 4th edn, Vol 1. Philadelphia: Elsevier/Saunders, p. 302-10.

Battaglia, F. C. & Lubchenco, L. O. (1967). A practical classification of newborn infants by weight and gestational age. *J Pediatr, 71*, 159-63.

Battaglia, F. C. & Meschia, G. (1978). Principal substrates of fetal metabolism. *Physiol Rev, 58*, 499-527.

Bauer, C., Ludwig, I. & Ludwig, M. (1968). Different effects of 2,3 diphosphoglycerate and adenosine triphosphate on the oxygen affinity of adult and foetal human haemoglobin. *Life Sci, 7*, 1339-43.

Bauer, C., Ludwig, M., Ludwig, I. & Bartels, H. (1969). Factors governing the oxygen affinity of human adult and foetal blood. *Respir Physiol, 7*, 271-277.

Beall, C. M. (1981). Optimal birthweights in Peruvian populations at high and low altitudes. *Am J Phys Anthropol, 56*, 209-16.

Behringer, E. J., Leite, L. D., Buchholz, N. E., Keeney, M. G., Pearce, W. J., Vanterpool, C. K., et al. (2009). Maturation and long-term hypoxia alters Ca2+-induced Ca2+ release in sheep cerebrovascular sympathetic neurons. *J Appl Physiol, 107*, 1223-34.

Benavides, C. E., Pérez, R., Espinoza, M., Cabello, G., Riquelme, R., Parer, J. T., et al. (1989). Cardiorespiratory functions in the fetal llama. *Respir Physiol, 75*, 327-34.

Benesch, R. & Benesch, R. E. (1967). The effect of organic phosphates from the human erythrocyte on the allosteric properties of hemoglobin. *Biochem Biophys Res Commun, 26*, 162-7.

Bernstein, M., Horbar, J. D., Badger, G. J., Ohlsson, A. & Golan, A. (2000). Morbidity and mortality among very-low-birth-weight neonates with intrauterine growth restriction. The Vermont Oxford Network. *Am J Obstet Gynecol, 182*, 198-206.

Bert, P. (1878). *La pression barométrique. Recherches de physiologie expérimentale.* Paris: G. Masson.

Bigham, A., Bauchet, M., Pinto, D., Mao, X., Akey, J. M., Mei, R., et al. (2010). Identifying signatures of natural selection in Tibetan and Andean populations using dense genome scan data. *PLoS Genet, 6*, e1001116.

Bigham, A. W., Mao, X., Mei, R., Brutsaert, T., Wilson, M. J., Julian, C. G., et al. (2009). Identifying positive selection candidate loci for high-altitude adaptation in Andean populations. *Hum Genomics, 4*, 79-90.

Blanco, C. E., Giussani, D. A., Riquelme, R. A., Hanson, M. A. & Llanos, A. J. (1997). Carotid blood flow changes with behavioral states in the late gestation llama fetus in utero. *Brain Res Dev Brain Res, 104*, 137-41.

Blechner, J. N., Cotter, J. R., Hinkley, C. M. & Prystowsky, H. (1968). Observations on pregnancy at altitude. II. Transplacental pressure differences of oxygen and carbon dioxide. *Am J Obstet Gynecol, 102*, 794-805.

Block, B. S., Llanos, A. J. & Creasy, R. K. (1984). Responses of the growth-retarded fetus to acute hypoxemia. *Am J Obstet Gynecol, 148*, 878-85.

Blood, A. B., Zhao, Y., Long, W., Zhang, L. & Longo, L. D. (2002). L-type Ca2+ channels in fetal and adult ovine cerebral arteries. *Am J Physiol Regul Integr Comp Physiol, 282*, R131-8.

Bonvento, G., MacKenzie, E. T. & Edvinsson, L. (1991). Serotonergic innervation of the cerebral vasculature: relevance to migraine and ischaemia. *Brain Res Brain Res Rev, 16*, 257-263.

Boyle, J. W., Lotgering, F. K. & Longo, L. D. (1984). Acute embolization of the uteroplacental circulation: uterine blood flow and placental CO diffusing capacity. *J Dev Physiol, 6*, 377-86.

Browne, V. A., Stiffel, V. M., Pearce, W. J., Longo, L. D. & Gilbert, R. D. (1997a). Cardiac beta-adrenergic receptor function in fetal sheep exposed to long-term high-altitude hypoxemia. *Am J Physiol, 273*, R2022-31.

Browne, V. A., Stiffel, V. M., Pearce, W. J., Longo, L. D. & Gilbert, R. D. (1997b). Activator calcium and myocardial contractility in fetal sheep exposed to long-term high-altitude hypoxia. *Am J Physiol, 272*, H1196-204.

Browne, V. A., Toledo-Jaldin, L., Davila R. D., Lopez, L. P., Yamashiro, H., Cioffi-Ragan, D., et al. (2011). High-end arteriolar resistance limits uterine artery blood flow and restricts fetal growth in preeclampsia and gestational hypertension at high altitude. *Am J Physiol Regul Integr Comp Physiol, 300*, R1221-9.

Bubb, K. J., Cock, M. L., Black, M. J., Dodic, M., Boon, W. M., Parkington, H. C., et al. (2007). Intrauterine growth restriction delays cardiomyocyte maturation and alters coronary artery function in the fetal sheep. *J Physiol, 578*, 871-81.

Buchholz, J. & Duckles, S. P. (2001). Chronic hypoxia alters prejunctional alpha(2)-receptor function in vascular adrenergic nerves of adult and fetal sheep. *Am J Physiol Regul Integr Comp Physiol, 281*, R926-34.

Buchholz, J., Edwards-Teunissen, K. & Duckles, S. P. (1999). Impact of development and chronic hypoxia on NE release from adrenergic nerves in sheep arteries. *Am J Physiol, 276*, R799-808.

Burton, G. J. (2009). Oxygen, the Janus gas; its effects on human placental development and function. *J Anat, 215*, 27-35.

Burton, G. J. & Jauniaux, E. (2011). Oxidative stress. *Best Pract Res Clin Obstet Gynecol, 25*, 287-99.

Camm, E. J., Martin-Gronert, M. S., Wright, N. L., Hansell, J. A., Ozanne, S. E. & Giussani, D. A. (2011). Prenatal hypoxia independent of undernutrition promotes molecular markers of insulin resistance in adult offspring. *FASEB J, 25*, 420-7.

Chabes, A., Pereda, J., Hyams, L., Barrientos, N., Perez, J., Campos, L., et al. (1968). Comparative morphometry of the human placenta at high altitude and at sea level. *Obstet Gynecol, 31*, 178-85.

Challis, J. R., Fraher, L., Oosterhuis, J., White, S. E. & Bocking, A. D. (1989). Fetal and maternal endocrine responses to prolonged reductions in uterine blood flow in pregnant sheep. *Am J Obstet Gynecol, 160*, 926-32.

Chanutin, A. & Curnish, R. R. (1967). Effect of organic and inorganic phosphates on the oxygen equilibrium of human erythrocytes. *Arch Biochem Biophys, 121*, 96-102.

Chernausek, S. D. (2012). Update: consequences of abnormal fetal growth. *J Clin Endocrinol Metab, 97*, 689-95.

Clapp, J. F., 3rd, Szeto, H. H., Larrow, R., Hewitt, J. & Mann, L. I. (1980). Umbilical blood flow response to embolization of the uterine circulation. *Am J Obstet Gynecol, 138*, 60-7.

Cohn, H. E., Sacks, E. J., Heymann, M. A. & Rudolph, A. M. (1974). Cardiovascular responses to hypoxemia and academia in fetal lambs. *Am J Obstet Gynecol, 120*, 817-24.

Colleoni, F., Padmanabhan, N., Yung, H. W., Watson, E. D., Cetin, I., Tissot van Patot, M. C., et al. (2013). Suppression of mitochondrial electron transport chain function in the hypoxic human placenta: a role for miRNA-210 and protein synthesis inhibition. *PLoS One, 8*, e55194.

Cotter, J. R., Blechner, J. N. & Prystowsky, H. (1967). Observations on pregnancy at altitude. I. The respiratory gases in maternal arterial and uterine venous blood. *Am J Obstet Gynecol, 99*, 1-8.

Crossley, D. II & Altimiras, J. (2000). Ontogeny of cholinergic and adrenergic cardiovascular regulation in the domestic chicken (Gallus gallus). *Am J Physiol Regul Integr Comp Physiol, 279*, R1091-8.

Cubillo, A., Halari, R., Smith, A., Taylor, E. & Rubia, K. (2012). A review of fronto-striatal and fronto-cortical brain abnormalities in children and adults with Attention Deficit Hyperactivity Disorder (ADHD) and new evidence for dysfunction in adults with ADHD during motivation and attention. *Cortex, 48*, 194-215.

Delivoria-Papadopoulos, M., Morrow, G., 3rd, & Oski, F. A. (1971a). Exchange transfusion in the newborn infant with fresh and "old" blood: the role of storage on 2,3-diphosphoglycerate, hemoglobin-oxygen affinity, and oxygen release. *J Pediatr, 79*, 898-903.

Delivoria-Papadopoulos, M., Roncevic, N. P. & Oski, F. A. (1971b). Postnatal changes in oxygen transport of term, premature, and sick infants: the role of red cell 2,3-diphosphoglycerate and adult hemoglobin. *Pediatr Res, 5*, 235-45.

Delivoria-Papadopoulos, M. & McGowan, J. E. (2011). Oxygen transport and delivery. In: *Fetal and neonatal physiology.* Polin, R. A., Fox, W. W. & Abman, S. H. (Eds). 4th Edn., Vol. 1. Philadelphia, PA: Saunders, 970-9.

Dolinsky, V. W., Rueda-Clausen, C. F., Morton, J. S., Davidge, S. T. & Dyck, J. R. (2011). Continued postnatal administration of resveratrol prevents diet-induced metabolic syndrome in rat offspring born growth restricted. *Diabetes, 60*, 2274-84.

Dong, Y. & Thompson, L. P. (2006). Differential expression of endothelial nitric oxide synthase in coronary and cardiac tissue in hypoxic fetal guinea pig hearts. *J Soc Gynecol Investig, 13*, 483-90.

Douglas, C. G., Haldane, J. S., Henderson, Y., Schneider, E. C., Webb, G. B. & Richards, J. (1913). Physiological observations made on Pike's Peak, Colorado, with special reference to adaptation to low barometric pressures. *Philos Trans R Soc Lond B Biol Sci, 203*, 185-318.

Dubois, J., Benders, M., Borradori-Tolsa, C., Cachia, A., Lazeyras, F., Ha-Vinh Leuchter, R., et al. (2008). Primary cortical folding in the human newborn: an early marker of later functional development. *Brain, 131*, 2028-41.

Ducsay, C. A., Furuta, K., Vargas, V. E., Kaushal, K. M., Singleton, K., Hyatt, K., et al. (2013). Leptin receptor antagonist treatment ameliorates the effects of long-term maternal hypoxia on adrenal expression of key steroidogenic genes in the ovine fetus. *Am J Physiol Regul Integr Comp Physiol, 304*, R435-42.

Ducsay, C. A., Hyatt, K., Mlynarczyk, M., Kaushal, K. M. & Myers, D. A. (2006). Long-term hypoxia increases leptin receptors and plasma leptin concentrations in the late-gestation ovine fetus. *Am J Physiol Regul Integr Comp Physiol*, *291*, R1406-13.

Ducsay, C. A., Mlynarczyk, M., Kaushal, K. M., Hyatt, K., Hanson, K. & Myers, D. A. (2009). Long-term hypoxia enhances ACTH response to arginine vasopressin but not corticotropin-releasing hormone in the near-term ovine fetus. *Am J Physiol Regul Integr Comp Physiol*, *297*, R892-9.

Dyer, J. L., McMillen, I. C., Warnes, K. E. & Morrison, J. L. (2009). No evidence for an enhanced role of endothelial nitric oxide in the maintenance of arterial blood pressure in the IUGR sheep fetus. *Placenta*, *30*, 705-10.

Eastman, N. J. (1954). Mount Everest in utero. *Am J Obstet Gynecol*, *67*, 701-11.

Eichenbaum, H., Yonelinas, A. P. & Ranganath, C. (2007). The medial temporal lobe and recognition memory. *Annu Rev Neurosci*, *30*, 123-52.

Espinoza, J., Sebire, N. J., McAuliffe, F., Krampl, E. & Nicolaides, K. H. (2001). Placental villus morphology in relation to maternal hypoxia at high altitude. *Placenta*, *22*, 606-8.

Feldman, R. & Eidelman, A. I. (2006). Neonatal state organization, neuromaturation, mother-infant interaction, and cognitive development in small-for-gestational-age premature infants. *Pediatrics*, *118*, e869-78.

Figueras, F., Oros, D., Cruz-Martinez, R., Padilla, N., Hernandez-Andrade, E., Botet, F., et al. (2009). Neurobehavior in term, small-for-gestational age infants with normal placental function. *Pediatrics*, *124*, e934-41.

Fletcher, A. J., Edwards, C. M., Gardner, D. S., Fowden, A. L. & Giussani, D. A. (2000). Neuropeptide Y in the sheep fetus: effects of acute hypoxemia and dexamethasone during late gestation. *Endocrinology*, *141*, 3976-82.

Fletcher, A. J., Gardner, D. S., Edwards, C. M., Fowden, A. L. & Giussani, D. A. (2003). Cardiovascular and endocrine responses to acute hypoxaemia during and following dexamethasone infusion in the ovine fetus. *J Physiol*, *549*, 271-87.

Fletcher, A. J., Gardner, D. S., Edwards, C. M., Fowden, A. L. & Giussani, D. A. (2006). Development of the ovine fetal cardiovascular defense to hypoxemia towards full term. *Am J Physiol Heart Circ Physiol*, *291*, H3023-34.

Fowler, M. E. (1989). *Medicine and surgery of South American camelids: llama, alpaca, vicuña, guanaco*. Ames: Iowa State University Press.

Frisk, V., Amsel, R. & Whyte, H. E. (2002). The importance of head growth patterns in predicting the cognitive abilities and literacy skills of small-for-gestational-age children. *Dev Neuropsychol*, *22*, 565-93.

Fu, Q., Yu, X., Callaway, C. W., Lane, R. H. & McKnight, R. A. (2009). Epigenetics: intrauterine growth retardation (IUGR) modifies the histone code along the rat hepatic IGF-1 gene. *FASEB J*, *23*, 2438-49.

Gagnon, R., Murotsuki, J., Challis, J. R., Fraher, L. & Richardson, B. S. (1997). Fetal sheep endocrine responses to sustained hypoxemic stress after chronic fetal placental embolization. *Am J Physiol*, *272*, E817-23.

Galleguillos, M., Valenzuela, M. A., Riquelme, R., Sanhueza, E., Sanchez, G., Figueroa, J. P., et al. (2001). Nitric oxide synthase activity in brain tissues from llama fetuses submitted to hypoxemia. *Comp Biochem Physiol A Mol Integr Physiol*, *129*, 605-14.

Garcia, F. C., Stiffel, V. M. & Gilbert, R. D. (2000a). Effects of long-term high-altitude hypoxia on isolated fetal ovine coronary arteries. *J Soc Gynecol Investig*, *7*, 211-7.

Garcia, F. C., Stiffel, V. M., Pearce, W. J., Zhang, L. & Gilbert, R. D. (2000b). Ca(2+) sensitivity of fetal coronary arteries exposed to long-term, high-altitude hypoxia. *J Soc Gynecol Investig*, *7*, 161-6.

Garruto, R. M., James, G. D. & Little, M. A. (2009). *Biographical Memoir. Paul Thornell Baker 1927-2007*. Washington, D. C. : National Academy of Sciences.

Geary, G. G., Osol, G. J. & Longo, L. D. (2004). Development affects in vitro vascular tone and calcium sensitivity in ovine cerebral arteries. *J Physiol*, *558*, 883-96.

Geva, R., Eshel, R., Leitner, Y., Fattal-Valevski, A. & Harel, S. (2006a). Memory functions of children born with asymmetric intrauterine growth restriction. *Brain Res*, *1117*, 186-94.

Geva, R., Eshel, R., Leitner, Y., Valevski, A. F. & Harel, S. (2006b). Neuropsychological outcome of children with intrauterine growth restriction: a 9-year prospective study. *Pediatrics*, *118*, 91-100.

Gheorghe C. P., Goyal, R., Mittal, A. & Longo, L. D. (2010). Gene expression in the placenta: maternal stress and epigenetic responses. *Int J Develop Biol*, *54*, 507-23.

Gheorghe, C. P., Mohan, S., Oberg, K. & Longo, L. D. (2007). Gene expression patterns in the hypoxic murine placenta: a role in epigenesis? *Reprod Sci*, *14*, 223-33.

Giordano, F. J. (2005). Oxygen, oxidative stress, hypoxia, and heart failure. *J Clin Invest*, *115*, 500-8.

Giussani, D. A. (2007). Hypoxia, fetal growth and early origins of disease: the Andean curse on the Conquistadors. *J Physiol*, *582*, 472.

Giussani, D. A., Camm, E. J., Niu, Y., Richter, H. G., Blanco, C. E., Gottschalk, R., et al. (2012). Developmental programming of cardiovascular dysfunction by prenatal hypoxia and oxidative stress. *PLoS One*, *7*, e31017.

Giussani, D. A. & Davidge, S. T. (2013). Developmental programming of cardiovascular disease by prenatal hypoxia. *J Dev Orig Health Dis*, *4*, 328-37.

Giussani, D. A., McGarrigle, H. H., Spencer, J. A., Moore, P. J., Bennet, L. & Hanson, M. A. (1994a). Effect of carotid denervation on plasma vasopressin levels during acute hypoxia in the late-gestation sheep fetus. *J Physiol*, *477*, 81-7.

Giussani, D. A., Phillips, P. S., Anstee, S. & Barker, D. J. (2001). Effects of altitude versus economic status on birth weight and body shape at birth. *Pediatr Res*, *49*, 490-4.

Giussani, D. A., Riquelme, R. A., Moraga, F. A., McGarrigle, H. H., Gaete, C. R., Sanhueza, E. M., et al. (1996). Chemoreflex and endocrine components of cardiovascular responses to acute hypoxemia in the llama fetus. *Am J Physiol*, *271*, R73-83.

Giussani, D. A., Riquelme, R. A., Sanhueza, E. M., Hanson, M. A., Blanco, C. E. & Llanos, A. J. (1999). Adrenergic and vasopressinergic contributions to the cardiovascular response to acute hypoxaemia in the llama fetus. *J Physiol*, *515*, 233-41.

Giussani, D. A., Salinas, C. E., Villena, M. & Blanco, C. E. (2007). The role of oxygen in prenatal growth: studies in the chick embryo. *J Physiol*, *585*, 911-7.

Giussani, D. A., Spencer, J. A. & Hanson, M. A. (1994b). Fetal cardiovascular reflex responses to hypoxaemia. *Fetal Matern Med Rev*, *6*, 17-37.

Giussani, D. A., Spencer, J. A., Moore, P. J., Bennet, L. & Hanson, M. A. (1993). Afferent and efferent components of the cardiovascular reflex responses to acute hypoxia in term fetal sheep. *J Physiol*, *461*, 431-49.

Giussani, D. A., Unno, N., Jenkins, S. L., Wentworth, R. A., Derks, J. B., Collins, J. H., et al. (1997). Dynamics of cardiovascular responses to repeated partial umbilical cord compression in late-gestation sheep fetus. *Am J Physiol, 273*, H2351-60.

Goodwin, J. (1974). Altitude and maternal and infant capabilities. In: *Horizons in perinatal research: implications for clinical care.* Kretchmer, N. & Hasselmeyer, E. G. (Eds). New York: John Wiley & Sons, 84-93.

Goyal, R., Goyal, N., Chu, N., Van Wickle, J. & Longo, L. D. (2014). Cerebral artery α1-adrenergic receptor subtypes: high altitude long-term hypoxia responses. *PLoS One,* (In Review).

Goyal, R., Leitzke, A., Goyal, D., Gheorghe, C. P. & Longo, L. D. (2011a). Antenatal maternal hypoxic stress: epigenetic adaptations in fetal lung renin-angiotensin system. *Reprod Sci, 18*, 180-9.

Goyal, R., Lister, R. R., Goyal, D., Gheorghe, C. P. & Longo, L. D. (2011b). Antenatal maternal hypoxic stress: Adaptations of the placental renin-angiotensin system in the mouse. *Placenta, 32*, 134-9.

Goyal, R., Mittal, A., Chu, N., Arthur, R. A., Zhang, L. & Longo, L. D. (2010). Maturation and long-term hypoxia-induced acclimatization responses in PKC-mediated signaling pathways in ovine cerebral arterial contractility. *Am J Physiol Regul Integr Comp Physiol, 299*, R1377-86.

Goyal, R., Van Wickle, J., Goyal, D., Matei, N. & Longo, L. D. (2013). Antenatal maternal long-term hypoxia: acclimatization responses with altered gene expression in ovine fetal carotid arteries. *PLoS One, 8*, e82200.

Grahn, D. & Kratchman, J. (1963). Variation in neonatal death rate and birth weight in the United States and possible relations to environmental radiation, geology and altitude. *Am J Hum Genet, 15*, 329-52.

Haas, J. D., Baker, P. T. & Hunt, E. E., Jr. (1977). The effects of high altitude on body size and composition of the newborn infant in Southern Peru. *Hum Biol, 49*, 611-28.

Haas, J. D., Balcazar, H. & Caulfield, L. (1987). Variation in early neonatal mortality for different types of fetal growth retardation. *Am J Phys Anthropol, 73*, 467-73.

Haas, J. D., Moreno-Black, G., Frongillo, E. A., Jr., Pabon, J., Pareja, G., Ybarnegaray, J., et al. (1982). Altitude and infant growth in Bolivia: a longitudinal study. *Am J Phys Anthropol, 59*, 251-62.

Haldane, J. S. (1922). *Respiration.* New Haven: Yale University Press.

Harvey, L. M., Gilbert, R. D., Longo, L. D. & Ducsay, C. A. (1993). Changes in ovine fetal adrenocortical responsiveness after long-term hypoxemia. *Am J Physiol, 264*, E741-7.

Hashimoto, K., Pinkas, G., Evans, L., Liu, H., Al-Hassan, Y. & Thompson, L. P. (2012). Protective effect of *N*-acetylcysteine on liver damage during chronic intrauterine hypoxia in fetal guinea pig. *Reprod Sci, 19*, 1001-9.

Hass, J. D., Frongillo, E. A., Jr., Stepick, C. D., Beard, J. L. & Hurtado, L. (1980). Altitude, ethnic and sex difference in birth weight and length in Bolivia. *Hum Biol, 52*, 459-77.

Heinonen, K., Raikkonen, K., Pesonen, A. K., Andersson, S., Kajantie, E., Eriksson, J. G., et al. (2010). Behavioural symptoms of attention deficit/hyperactivity disorder in preterm and term children born small and appropriate for gestational age: a longitudinal study. *BMC Pediatr, 10*, 91.

Hemmings, D. G., Williams, S. J. & Davidge, S. T. (2005). Increased myogenic tone in 7-month-old adult male but not female offspring from rat dams exposed to hypoxia during pregnancy. *Am J Physiol Heart Circ Physiol*, *289*, H674-82.

Henderson, D. A. & Longo, L. D. (2003). Quantitative structural differences in media of middle cerebral arteries from hypoxic and normoxic near-term sheep fetuses: evidence for medial hyperplasia. *FASEB J*, *17*, A359.

Herrera, E. A., Camm, E. J., Cross, C. M., Mullender, J. L., Wooding, F. B. & Giussani, D. A. (2012). Morphological and functional alterations in the aorta of the chronically hypoxic fetal rat. *J Vasc Res*, *49*, 50-8.

Herrera, E. A., Pulgar, V. M., Riquelme, R. A., Sanhueza, E. M., Reyes, R. V., Ebensperger, G., et al. (2007). High-altitude chronic hypoxia during gestation and after birth modifies cardiovascular responses in newborn sheep. *Am J Physiol Regul Integr Comp Physiol*, *292*, R2234-40.

Herrera, E. A., Reyes, R. V., Giussani, D. A., Riquelme, R. A., Sanhueza, E. M., Ebensperger, G., et al. (2008). Carbon monoxide: a novel pulmonary artery vasodilator in neonatal llamas of the Andean *altiplano*. *Cardiovasc Res*, *77*, 197-201.

Herrera, E. A., Riquelme, R. A., Ebensperger, G., Reyes, R. V., Ulloa, C. E., Cabello, G., et al. (2010). Long-term exposure to high altitude chronic hypoxia during gestation induces neonatal pulmonary hypertension at sea level. *Am J Physiol Regul Integr Comp Physiol*, *299*, R1676-84.

Herrera, E. A., Riquelme, R. A., Sanhueza, E. M., Gajardo, C., Parer, J. T. & Llanos, A. J. (2000). Cardiovascular responses to arginine vasopressin blockade during acute hypoxemia in the llama fetus. *High Alt Med Biol*, *1*, 175-84.

Hochachka, P. W., Clark, C. M., Brown, W. D., Stanley, C., Stone, C. K., Nickles, R. J., et al. (1994). The brain at high altitude: hypometabolism as a defense against chronic hypoxia? *J Cereb Blood Flow Metab*, *14*, 671-9.

Howard, R. C., Bruns, P. D. & Lichty, J. A. (1957a). Studies on babies born at high altitudes. III. Arterial oxygen saturation and hematocrit values at birth. *AMA J Dis Child*, *93*, 674-8.

Howard, R. C., Lichty, J. A. & Bruns, P. D. (1957b). Studies on babies born at high altitude. II. Measurement of birth weight, body length and head size. *AMA J Dis Child*, *93*, 670-4.

Huang, S. Y., Moore, L. G., McCullough, R. E., McCullough, R. G., Micco, A. J., Fulco, C., et al. (1987). Internal carotid and vertebral arterial flow velocity in men at high altitude. *J Appl Physiol*, *63*, 395-400.

Hunter, C. J., Blood, A. B. & Power, G. G. (2003). Cerebral metabolism during cord occlusion and hypoxia in the fetal sheep: a novel method of continuous measurement based on heat production. *J Physiol*, *552*, 241-51.

Hunter, C. J., Blood, A. B., White, C. R., Pearce, W. J. & Power, G. G. (2001). Role of nitric oxide in hypoxic cerebral vasodilatation in the ovine fetus. *J Physiol*, *549*, 625-33.

Hurtado, A. (1955). Pathological aspects of life at high altitudes. *Mil Med*, *117*, 272-84.

Hurtado, A. (1960). Some clinical aspects of life at high altitudes. *Ann Intern Med*, *53*, 247-58.

Hurtado, A. (1964). Acclimatization to high altitudes. In: *The physiological effects of high altitude. Weihe*, W. H. (Ed). Oxford: Pergamon Press, 1-17.

Hutter, D., Kingdom, J. & Jaeggi, E. (2010). Causes and mechanisms of intrauterine hypoxia and its impact on the fetal cardiovascular system: a review. *Int J Pediatr*, *2010*, 401323.

Illa, M., Eixarch, E., Batalle, D., Arbat-Plana, A., Muñoz-Moreno, E., Figueras, F., et al. (2013). Long-term functional outcomes and correlation with regional brain connectivity by MRI diffusion tractography metrics in a near-term rabbit model of intrauterine growth restriction. *PLoS One, 8*, e76453.

Imamura, T., Umezaki, H., Kaushal, K. M. & Ducsay, C. A. (2004). Long-term hypoxia alters endocrine and physiologic responses to umbilical cord occlusion in the ovine fetus. *J Soc Gynecol Investig, 11*, 131-40.

Jackson, M. R., Mayhew, T. M. & Haas, J. D. (1987a). The volumetric composition of human term placentae: altitudinal, ethnic and sex differences in Bolivia. *J Anat, 152*, 173-87.

Jackson, M. R., Mayhew, T. M. & Haas, J. D. (1987b). Morphometric studies on villi in human term placentae and the effects of altitude ethnic grouping and sex of newborn. *Placenta, 8*, 487-95.

Jang, E. A., Longo, L. D. & Goyal, R. (2014). Antenatal maternal hypoxia and fetal growth restriction in rodents. *Reprod Sci,* (In Review).

Jensen, G. M. & Moore, L. G. (1997). The effect of high altitude and other risk factors on birthweight: independent or interactive effects? *Am J Public Health, 87*, 1003-7.

Jones, C. T. & Robinson, R. O. (1975). Plasma catecholamines in foetal and adult sheep. *J Physiol, 248*, 15-33.

Jourdanet, D. (1875). *Influence de la pression de l'air sur la vie de l'homme: climats d'altitude et climats de montagne*. Paris: G. Masson.

Julian, C. G., Galan, H. L., Wilson, M. J., Desilva, W., Cioffi-Ragan, D., Schwartz, J., et al. (2008). Lower uterine artery blood flow and higher endothelin relative to nitric oxide metabolite levels are associated with reductions in birth weight at high altitude. *Am J Physiol Regul Integr Comp Physiol, 295*, R906-15.

Julian, C. G., Vargas, E., Armaza, J. F., Wilson, M. J., Niermeyer, S. & Moore, L. G. (2007). High-altitude ancestry protects against hypoxia-associated reductions in fetal growth. *Arch Dis Child Fetal Neonatal Ed, 92*, F372-7.

Kacimi, R., Richalet, J. P., Corsin, A., Abousahl, I. & Crozatier, B. (1992). Hypoxia-induced downregulation of beta-adrenergic receptors in rat heart. *J Appl Physiol, 73*, 1377-82.

Kaiser, I. H., Cummings, J. N., Reynolds, S. R. & Marbarger, J. P. (1958). Acclimatization response of the pregnant ewe and fetal lamb to diminished ambient pressure. *J Appl Physiol, 13*, 171-8.

Kamitomo, M., Alonso, J. G., Okai, T., Longo, L. D. & Gilbert, R. D. (1993). Effects of long-term, high-altitude hypoxemia on ovine fetal cardiac output and blood flow distribution. *Am J Obstet Gynecol, 169*, 701-7.

Kamitomo, M., Longo, L. D. & Gilbert, R. D. (1992). Right and left ventricular function in fetal sheep exposed to long-term high-altitude hypoxemia. *Am J Physiol, 262*, H399-405.

Kamitomo, M., Longo, L. D. & Gilbert, R. D. (1994). Cardiac function in fetal sheep during two weeks of hypoxemia. *Am J Physiol, 266*, R1778-85.

Kamitomo, M., Ohtsuka, T. & Gilbert, R. D. (1995). Effects of isoproterenol on the cardiovascular system of fetal sheep exposed to long-term high-altitude hypoxemia. *J Appl Physiol, 78*, 1793-9.

Kamitomo, M., Onishi, J., Gutierrez, I., Stiffel, V. M. & Gilbert, R. D. (2002). Effects of long-term hypoxia and development on cardiac contractile proteins in fetal and adult sheep. *J Soc Gynecol Investig, 9*, 335-41.

Kato, A. H., Mlynarczyk, M., Kaushal, K. M., Gilbert, R. D., Longo, L. D. & Ducsay, C. A. (2003). Endocrine responses to umbilical cord occlusion following carotid sinus denervation in the long-term hypoxemic ovine fetus. *J Soc Gynecol Investig*, *10*, 235A.

Khalid, M. E., Ali, M. E. & Ali, K. Z. (1997). Full-term birth weight and placental morphology at high and low altitude. *Int J Gynaecol Obstet*, *57*, 259-65.

Kiserud, T., Kessler, J., Ebbing, C. & Rasmussen, S. (2006). Ductus venosus shunting in growth-restricted fetuses and the effect of umbilical circulatory compromise. *Ultrasound Obstet Gynecol*, *28*, 143-9.

Kitanaka, T., Alonso, J. G., Gilbert, R. D., Siu, B. L., Clemons, G. K. & Longo, L. D. (1989a). Fetal responses to long-term hypoxemia in sheep. *Am J Physiol*, *256*, R1348-54.

Kitanaka, T., Gilbert, R. D. & Longo, L. D. (1989b). Maternal responses to long-term hypoxemia in sheep. *Am J Physiol*, *256*, R1340-7.

Koos, B. J., Kitanaka, T., Matsuda, K., Gilbert, R. D. & Longo, L. D. (1988). Fetal breathing adaptation to prolonged hypoxaemia in sheep. *J Dev Physiol*, *10*, 161-6.

Krampl, E. (2002). Pregnancy at high altitude. *Ultrasound Obstet Gynecol*, *19*, 535-9.

Krampl, E., Espinoza-Dorado, J., Lees, C. C., Moscoso, G., Bland, J. M. & Campbell, S. (2001a). Maternal uterine artery Doppler studies at high altitude and sea level. *Ultrasound Obstet Gynecol*, *18*, 578-82.

Krampl, E., Kametas, N. A., McAuliffe, F., Cacho-Zegarra, A. M. & Nicolaides, K. H. (2002). Maternal serum insulin-like growth factor binding protein-1 in pregnancy at high altitude. *Obstet Gynecol*, *99*, 594-8.

Krampl, E., Lees, C., Bland, J. M., Espinoza Dorado, J., Moscoso, G. & Campbell, S. (2000). Fetal biometry at 4300m compared to sea level in Peru. *Ultrasound Obstet Gynecol*, *16*, 9-18.

Krampl, E., Lees, C., Bland, J. M., Espinoza Dorado, J., Moscoso, G. & Campbell, S. (2001b). Fetal Doppler velocimetry at high altitude. *Ultrasound Obstet Gynecol*, *18*, 329-34.

Krebs, C., Longo, L. D. & Leiser, R. (1997). Term ovine placental vasculature: comparison of sea level and high altitude conditions by corrosion cast and histomorphometry. *Placenta*, *18*, 43-51.

Krüger, H. & Arias-Stella, J. (1970). The placenta and the newborn infant at high altitudes. *Am J Obstet Gynecol*, *106*, 586-91.

Lattuada, D., Colleoni, F., Martinelli, A., Garretto, A., Magni, R., Radaelli, T., et al. (2008). Higher mitochondrial DNA content in human IUGR placenta. *Placenta*, *29*, 1029-33.

Leeson, C. P., Kattenhorn, M., Morley, R., Lucas, A. & Deanfield, J. E. (2001). Impact on low birth weight and cardiovascular risk factors on endothelial function in early adult life. *Circulation*, *103*, 1264-8.

Leeson, C. P., Whincup, P. H., Cook. D. G., Donald, A. E., Papacosta, O., Lucas, A., et al. (1997). Flow-mediated dilation in 9- to 11-year-old children: the influence of intrauterine and childhood factors. *Circulation*, *96*, 2233-8.

Leitner, Y., Fattal-Valevski, A., Geva, R., Eshel, R., Toledano-Alhadef, H., Rotstein, M., et al. (2007). Neurodevelopmental outcome of children with intrauterine growth retardation: a longitudinal, 10-year prospective study. *J Child Neurol*, *22*, 580-7.

Lewis, A. M., Mathieu-Costello, O., McMillan, P. J. & Gilbert, R. D. (1999). Effects of long-term, high-altitude hypoxia on the capillarity of the ovine fetal heart. *Am J Physiol*, *277*, H756-62.

Li, G., Xiao, Y., Estrella, J. L., Ducsay, C. A., Gilbert, R. D. & Zhang, L. (2003). Effect of fetal hypoxia on heart susceptibility to ischemia and reperfusion injury in the adult rat. *J Soc Gynecol Investig, 10*, 265-74.

Lichty, J. A., Ting, R. Y., Bruns, P. D. & Dyar, E. (1957). Studies of babies born at high altitudes. I. Relation of altitude to birth weight. *AMA J Dis Child, 93*, 666-9.

Lin, M. T., Longo, L. D., Pearce, W. J. & Hessinger, D. A. (2005). Ca2+-activated K+ channel-associated phosphatase and kinase activities during development. *Am J Physiol Heart Circ Physiol, 289*, H414-25.

Lindgren, I. & Altimiras, J. (2011). Sensitivity of organ growth to chronically low oxygen levels during incubation in Red Junglefowl and domesticated chicken breeds. *Poult Sci, 90*, 126-35.

Llanos, A. J., Ebensperger, G., Herrera, E. A., Reyes, R. V., Cabello, G., Díaz, M., et al. (2012). The heme oxygenase-carbon monoxide system in the regulation of cardiorespiratory function at high altitude. *Respir Physiol Neurobiol, 184*, 186-91.

Llanos, A. J., Riquelme, R. A., Herrera, E. A., Ebensperger, G., Krause, B., Reyes, R. V., et al. (2007). Evolving in thin air − Lessons from the llama fetus in the *altiplano. Respir Physiol Neurobiol, 158*, 298-306.

Llanos, A. J., Riquelme, R. A., Moraga, F. A., Cabello, G. & Parer, J. T. (1995). Cardiovascular responses to graded degrees of hypoxaemia in the llama fetus. *Reprod Fertil Dev, 7*, 549-52.

Llanos, A., Riquelme, R., Sanhueza, E., Gaete, C., Cabello, G. & Parer, J. (1998). Cardiorespiratory responses to acute hypoxemia in the chronically catheterized fetal llama at 0. 7-0. 9 of gestation. *Comp Biochem Physiol A Mol Integr Physiol, 119*, 705-9.

Llanos, A. J., Riquelme, R. A., Sanhueza, E. M., Hanson, M. A., Blanco, C. E., Parer, J. T., et al. (2003). The fetal llama versus the fetal sheep: different strategies to withstand hypoxia. *High Alt Med Biol, 4*, 193-202.

Llanos, A. J., Riquelme, R. A., Sanhueza, E. M., Herrera, E., Cabello, G., Giussani, D. A., et al. (2002). Regional brain blood flow and cerebral hemispheric oxygen consumption during acute hypoxaemia in the llama fetus. *J Physiol, 538*, 975-83.

Lodygensky, G. A., Seghier, M. L., Warfield, S. K., Tolsa, C. B., Sizonenko, S., Lazeyras, F., et al. (2008). Intrauterine growth restriction affects the preterm infant's hippocampus. *Pediatr Res, 63*, 438-43.

Long, W., Zhang, L. & Longo, L. D. (2000). Cerebral artery sarcoplasmic reticulum Ca(2+) stores and contractility: changes with development. *Am J Physiol Regul Integr Comp Physiol, 279*, R860-73.

Long, W., Zhang, L. & Longo, L. D. (2002). Fetal and adult cerebral artery K(ATP) and K(Ca) channel responses to long-term hypoxia. *J Appl Physiol, 92*, 1692-701.

Long, W., Zhao, Y., Zhang, L. & Longo, L. D. (1999). Role of Ca(2+) channels in NE-induced increase in [Ca(2+)](i) and tension in fetal and adult cerebral arteries. *Am J Physiol, 277*, R286-94.

Longo, L. D. (1984). Intrauterine growth retardation: a "mosaic" hypothesis of pathophysiology. *Semin Perinatol, 8*, 62-72.

Longo, L. D. (1987). Respiratory gas exchange in the placenta. In: *Handbook of Physiology. The Respiratory System. Gas Exchange.* (Sect. 3, vol. *IV*). Bethesda, MD: American Physiological Society, 351-401.

Longo, L. D. & Goyal, R. (2014). The stress of chronic hypoxia in fetal growth restriction: some physiological considerations. In: *Stress and developmental programming of health and disease: beyond phenomenology*. Zhang, L. & Longo, L. D. (Eds). New York, Nova Science Publishers, Inc.

Longo, L. D. & Goyal, R. (2013). Cerebral artery signal transduction mechanisms: developmental changes in dynamics and Ca2+ sensitivity. *Curr Vasc Pharmacol, 11,* 655-711.

Longo, L. D., Hull, A. D., Long, D. M. & Pearce, W. J. (1993). Cerebrovascular adaptations to high-altitude hypoxemia in fetal and adult sheep. *Am J Physiol, 264,* R65-72.

Longo, L. D. & Packianathan, S. (1997). Hypoxia-ischaemia and the developing brain: hypotheses regarding the pathophysiology of fetal-neonatal brain damage. *Br J Obstet Gynaecol, 104,* 652-62.

Longo, L. D. & Pearce, W. J. (1998). High altitude, hypoxic-induced modulation of noradrenergic-mediated responses in fetal and adult cerebral arteries. *Comp Biochem Physiol A Mol Integr Physiol, 119,* 683-94.

Longo, L. D. & Pearce, W. J. (2005). Fetal cerebrovascular acclimatization responses to high-altitude, long-term hypoxia: a model for prenatal programming of adult disease? *Am J Physiol Regul Integr Comp Physiol, 288,* R16-24.

Lorijn, R. H. & Longo, L. D. (1980). Norepinephrine elevation in the fetal lamb: oxygen consumption and cardiac output. *Am J Physiol, 239,* R115-22.

Lubchenco, L. O. (1970). Assessment of gestational age and development of birth. *Pediatr Clin North Am, 17,* 125-45.

Lubchenco, L. O., Hansman, C. & Boyd, E. (1966). Intrauterine growth in length and head circumference as estimated from live births at gestational ages from 26 to 42 weeks. *Pediatrics, 37,* 403-8.

Lubchenco, L. O., Hansman, C., Dressler, M. & Boyd, E. (1963). Intrauterine growth as estimated from liveborn birth-weight data at 24 to 42 weeks of gestation. *Pediatrics, 32,* 793-800.

Lubchenco, L. O., Searls, D. T. & Brazie, J. V. (1972). Neonatal mortality rate: relationship to birth weight and gestational age. *J Pediatr, 81,* 814-22.

Lunell, N. O., Sarby, B., Lewander, R. & Nylund, L. (1979). Comparison of uteroplacental blood flow in normal and in intrauterine growth-retarded pregnancy. Measurements with Indium-113m and a computer-linked gammacamera. *Gynecol Obstet Invest, 10,* 106-18.

Macfarlane, A. (1987). Altitude and birth weight: commentary. *J Pediatr, 111,* 842-4.

MacKenzie, E. T. & Scatton, B. (1987). Cerebral circulatory and metabolic effects of perivascular neurotransmitters. *CRC Crit Rev Clin Neurobiol, 2,* 357-419.

Maiti, P., Singh, S. B., Sharma, A. K., Muthuraju, S., Banerjee, P. K. & Ilavazhagan, G. (2006). Hypobaric hypoxia induces oxidative stress in rat brain. *Neurochem Int, 49,* 709-16.

Makowski, E. L., Battaglia, F. C., Meschia, G., Behrman, R. E., Schruefer, J., Seeds, A. E., et al. (1968). Effect of maternal exposure to high altitude upon fetal oxygenation. *Am J Obstet Gynecol, 100,* 852-61.

Marconi, A. M., Paolini, C., Buscaglia, M., Zerbe, G., Battaglia, F. C. & Pardi, G. (1996). The impact of gestational age and fetal growth on the maternal-fetal glucose concentration difference. *Obstet Gynecol, 87,* 937-42.

Maulik, D., Numagami, Y., Ohnishi, S. T., Mishra, O. P. & Delivoria-Papadopoulos, M. (1998). Direct measurement of oxygen free radicals during in utero hypoxia in the fetal guinea pig brain. *Brain Res, 798*, 166-172.

Mayhew, T. M., Jackson, M. R. & Haas, J. D. (1990). Oxygen diffusive conductances of human placentae from term pregnancies at low and high altitudes. *Placenta, 11*, 493-503.

Mazess, R. B. (1965). Neonatal mortality and altitude in Peru. *Am J Phys Anthropol, 23*, 209-13.

Mazess, R. B. (1975). Human adaptation to high altitude. In: *Physiological anthropology*. Damon, E. (Ed). New York: Oxford University Press, 167-209.

Mbaku, E. M., Zhang, L., Pearce, W. J., Duckles, S. P. & Buchholz, J. (2003). Chronic hypoxia alters the function of NOS nerves in cerebral arteries of near-term fetal and adult sheep. *J Appl Physiol, 94*, 724-32.

McCalden, T. A. & Bevan, J. A. (1981). Sources of activator calcium in rabbit basilar artery. *Am J Physiol, 241*, H129-33.

McCarthy, C., Cotter, F. E., McElwaine, S., Twomey, A., Mooney, E. E., Ryan, F., et al. (2007). Altered gene expression patterns in intrauterine growth restriction: potential role of hypoxia. *Am J Obstet Gynecol, 196*, 70. e1-6.

McClung, J. (1969). *Effects of high altitude on human birth. Observations on mothers, placentas, and the newborn in two Peruvian populations*. Cambridge, MA: Harvard University Press.

McConnell, B. K., Moravec, C. S. & Bond, M. (1998). Troponin I phosphorylation and myofilament calcium sensitivity during decompensated cardiac hypertrophy. *Am J Physiol, 274*, H385-96.

McCullough, R. E. & Reeves, J. T. (1977). Fetal growth retardation and increased infant mortality at high altitude. *Arch Environ Health, 32*, 36-9.

McCullough, R. E., Reeves, J. T. & Liljegren, R. L. (1977). Fetal growth retardation and increased infant mortality at high altitude. *Obstet Gynecol Surv, 32*, 596-8.

Meschia, G. (2006). Indwelling plastic catheters in developmental physiology. *Am J Obstet Gynecol, 194*, 1197-9.

Meschia, G., Cotter, J. R., Breathnach, C. S. & Barron, D. H. (1965). The hemoglobin, oxygen, carbon dioxide and hydrogen ion concentrations in the umbilical bloods of sheep and goats as sampled via indwelling plastic catheters. *Q J Exp Physiol Cogn Med Sci, 50*, 185-95.

Meschia, G., Hellegers, A., Prystowsky, H., Huckabee, W., Metcalfe, J. & Barron, D. H. (1961). Oxygen dissociation of the bloods of adult and fetal sheep at high altitude. *Q J Exp Physiol Cogn Med Sci, 46*, 156-60.

Meschia, G., Makowski, E. L. & Battaglia, F. C. (1969-1970). The use of indwelling catheters in the uterine and umbilical veins of sheep for a description of fetal acid-base balance and oxygenation. *Yale J Biol Med, 42*, 154-65.

Meschia, G., Prystowsky, H., Hellegers, A., Huckabee, W., Metcalfe, J. & Barron, D. H. (1960). Observations on the oxygen supply to the fetal llama. *Q J Exp Physiol Cogn Med Sci, 45*, 284-91.

Metcalfe, J., Meschia, G., Hellegers, A., Prystowsky, H., Huckabee, W. & Barron, D. H. (1962a). Observations on the placental exchange of the respiratory gases in pregnant ewes at high altitude. *Q J Exp Physiol Cogn Med Sci, 47*, 74-92.

Metcalfe, J., Meschia, G., Hellegers, A., Prystowsky, H., Huckabee, W. & Barron, D. H. (1962b). Observations on the growth rates and organ weights of fetal sheep at altitude and sea level. *Q J Exp Physiol Cogn Med Sci, 47*, 305-13.

Miller, S. L., Green, L. R., Peebles, D. M., Hanson, M. A. & Blanco, C. E. (2002). Effects of chronic hypoxia and protein malnutrition on growth in the developing chick. *Am J Obstet Gynecol, 186*, 261-7.

Monau, T. R., Vargas, V. E., King, N., Yellon, S. M., Myers, D. A. & Ducsay, C. A. (2009). Long-term hypoxia increases endothelial nitric oxide synthase expression in the ovine fetal adrenal. *Reprod Sci, 16*, 865-74.

Monau, T. R., Vargas, V. E., Zhang, L., Myers, D. A. & Ducsay, C. A. (2010). Nitric oxide inhibits ACTH-induced cortisol production in near-term, long-term hypoxic ovine fetal adrenocortical cells. *Reprod Sci, 17*, 955-62.

Monge, C. (1948). *Acclimatization in the Andes; historical confirmations of "climatic aggression" in the development of Andean man.* Baltimore, MD: Johns Hopkins Press.

Monge, C. (1960). *Aclimatación en los Andes: extractos de investigaciones sobre biología de altitude.* Lima: [Universidad Nacional Mayor de San Marcos].

Monge, M. & Monge, C. (1966). *High-altitude disease; mechanisms and management.* Springfield, IL: Charles C. Thomas.

Montesinos, D. C. (1990). Estudio morfometrico de la placenta termino en las grandes alturas. *Patologia, 28*, 79-87.

Moore, L. G. (1990). Maternal O_2 transport and fetal growth in Colorado, Peru, and Tibet high-altitude residents. *Am J Hum Biol, 2*, 627-37.

Moore, L. G. (2003). Fetal growth restriction and maternal oxygen transport during high altitude pregnancy. *High Alt Med Biol, 4*, 141-56.

Moore, L. G., Brodeur, P., Chumbe, O., D'Brot, J., Hofmeister, S. & Monge, C. (1986). Maternal hypoxic ventilatory response, ventilation, and infant birth weight at 4,300m. *J Appl Physiol, 60*, 1401-6.

Moore, L. G., Charles, S. M. & Julian, C. G. (2011). Humans at high altitude: hypoxia and fetal growth. *Respir Physiol Neurobiol, 178*, 181-90.

Moore, L. G., Niermeyer, S. & Zamudio, S. (1998). Human adaptation to high altitude: regional and life-cycle perspectives. *Am J Phys Anthropol, Suppl, 27*, 25-64.

Moore, L. G., Shriver, M., Bemis, L., Hickler, B., Wilson, M., Brutsaert, T., et al. (2004). Maternal adaptation to high-altitude pregnancy: an experiment of nature – a review. *Placenta*, 25 Suppl A, S60-71.

Moore, L. G., Young, D., McCullough, R. E., Droma, T. & Zamudio, S. (2001). Tibetan protection from intrauterine growth restriction (IUGR) and reproductive loss at high altitude. *Am J Hum Biol, 13*, 635-44.

Moraga, F., Monge, C., Riquelme, R. & Llanos, A. J. (1996). Fetal and maternal blood oxygen affinity: a comparative study in llamas and sheep. *Comp Biochem Physiol A Physiol, 115*, 111-5.

Moraga, F. A., Reyes, R. V., Herrera, E. A., Riquelme, R. A., Ebensperger, G., Pulgar, V. M., et al. (2011). Role of the α-adrenergic system in femoral vascular reactivity in neonatal llamas and sheep: a comparative study between highland and lowland species. *Am J Physiol Regul Integr Comp Physiol, 301*, R1153-60.

Morrison, J. L. (2008). Sheep models of intrauterine growth restriction: fetal adaptations and consequences. *Clin Exp Pharmacol Physiol, 35*, 730-43.

Morrison, S., Gardner, D. S., Fletcher, A. J., Bloomfield, M. R. & Giussani, D. A. (2003). Enhanced nitric oxide activity offsets peripheral vasoconstriction during acute hypoxaemia via chemoreflex and adrenomedullary actions in the sheep fetus. *J Physiol, 547*, 283-91.

Mortola, J. P., Frappell, P. B., Aguero, L. & Armstrong, K. (2000). Birth weight and altitude: A study in Peruvian communities. *J Pediatr, 136*, 324-9.

Morton, J. S., Rueda-Clausen, C. F. & Davidge, S. T. (2010). Mechanisms of endothelium-dependent vasodilation in male and female, young and aged offspring born growth restricted. *Am J Physiol Regul Integr Comp Physiol, 298*, R930-8.

Morton, J. S., Rueda-Clausen, C. F. & Davidge, S. T. (2011). Flow-mediated vasodilation is impaired in adult rat offspring exposed to prenatal hypoxia. *J Appl Physiol, 110*, 1073-82.

Mosso, A. (1897). *Fisiologia dell'uomo sulle Alpi: Studii fatti sul Monte Rosa.* Milano: Frat. Treves.

Mosso, A. (1899). *Der Mensch auf den Hochalpen.* Leipzig: Veit.

Mulder, A. L., van Goor, C. A., Giussani, D. A. & Blanco, C. E. (2001). Alpha-adrenergic contribution to the cardiovascular response to acute hypoxemia in the chick embryo. *Am J Physiol Regul Integr Comp Physiol, 281*, R2004-10.

Murray, A. J. (2012). Oxygen delivery and fetal-placental growth: beyond a question of supply and demand? *Placenta, 33*, Suppl 2, e16-22.

Myers, D. A., Bell, P. A., Hyatt, K., Mlynarczyk, M. & Ducsay, C. A. (2005). Long-term hypoxia enhances proopiomelanocortin processing in the near-term ovine fetus. *Am J Physiol Regul Integr Comp Physiol, 288*, R1178-84.

Myers, D. A., Bell, P., Mlynarczyk, M. & Ducsay, C. A. (2004). Long term hypoxia alters plasma ACTH 1-39 and ACTH precursors in response to acute cord occlusion in the ovine fetus. *J Soc Gynecol Investig, 11*, 249A.

Myers, D. A. & Ducsay, C. A. (2012). Adrenocortical and adipose responses to high-altitude-induced, long-term hypoxia in the ovine fetus. *J Pregnancy, 2012*, 681306.

Nathanielsz, P. W. & Hanson, M. A. (2003). The fetal dilemma: spare the brain and spoil the liver. *J Physiol, 548*, 333.

Naughton, M. A., Meschia, G., Battaglia, F. C., Hellegers, A., Hagopian, H. & Barron, D. H. (1963). Hemoglobin characteristics and the oxygen affinity of the bloods of Dorset sheep. *Q J Exp Physiol Cogn Med Sci, 48*, 313-23.

Nauli, S. M., Williams, J. M., Gerthoffer, W. T. & Pearce, W. J. (2005). Chronic hypoxia modulates relations among calcium, myosin light chain phosphorylation, and force differently in fetal and adult ovine basilar arteries. *J Appl Physiol, 99*, 120-7.

Neerhof, M. G. & Thaete, L. G. (2008). The fetal response to chronic placental insufficiency. *Semin Perinatol, 32*, 201-5.

Nelson, M. T. & Quayle, J. M. (1995). Physiological roles and properties of potassium channels in arterial smooth muscle. *Am J Physiol, 268*, C799-822.

Nishida, N., Blood, A. B., Hunter, C. J., Bragg, S., Williams, J., Pearce, W. J., et al. (2006). Role of prostanoids in the regulation of cerebral blood flow during normoxia and hypoxia in the fetal sheep. *Pediatr Res, 60*, 524-9.

Oh, C., Dong, Y., Harman, C., Mighty, H. E., Kopelman, J. & Thompson, L. P. (2008). Chronic hypoxia differentially increases glutathione content and gamma-glutamyl cysteine synthetase expression in fetal guinea pig organs. *Early Hum Dev, 84*, 121-7.

Ohtsuka, T., Browne, V. A. & Gilbert, R. D. (1997). Oxygen dose-response curve of cardiac papillary muscle from fetal and nonpregnant adult sheep exposed to long-term, high-altitude hypoxemia. *J Soc Gynecol Investig, 4*, 197-202.

Ohtsuka, T. & Gilbert, R. D. (1995). Cardiac enzyme activities in fetal and adult pregnant and nonpregnant sheep exposed to high-altitude hypoxemia. *J Appl Physiol, 79*, 1286-9.

Parraguez, V. H., Atlagich, M., Araneda, O., Garcia, C., Munoz, A., De Los Reyes, M., et al. (2011). Effects of antioxidant vitamins on newborn and placental traits in gestations at high altitude: comparative study in high and low altitude native sheep. *Reprod Fertil Dev, 23*, 285-96.

Parraguez, V. H., Atlagich, M., Diaz, R., Bruzzone, M. E., Behn, C. & Raggi, L. A. (2005). Effect of hypobaric hypoxia on lamb intrauterine growth: comparison between high- and low-altitude native ewes. *Reprod Fertil Dev, 17*, 497-505.

Patterson, A. J., Chen, M., Xue, Q., Xiao, D. & Zhang, L. (2010). Chronic prenatal hypoxia induces epigenetic programming of PKC{epsilon} gene repression in rat hearts. *Circ Res, 107*, 365-73.

Patterson, A. J., Xiao, D., Xiong, F., Dixon, B. & Zhang, L. (2012). Hypoxia-derived oxidative stress mediates epigenetic repression of PKCε gene in foetal rat. *Cardiovasc Res, 93*, 302-10.

Paz, I., Gale, R., Laor, A., Danon, Y. L., Stevenson, D. K. & Seidman, D. S. (1995). The cognitive outcome of full-term small for gestational age infants at late adolescence. *Obstet Gynecol, 85*, 452-6.

Pearce, W. J. (1995). Cerebrovascular development at altitude. In: *Hypoxia and the brain.* Sutton, J. R., Houston, C. S. & Coates, G. (Eds). Proceedings of the 9th International Hypoxia Symposium at Lake Louise, Canada. Burlington: Queen City Printers, p. 125-141.

Pearce, W. J., Butler, S. M., Abrassart, J. M. & Williams, J. M. (2011). Fetal cerebral oxygenation: the homeostatic role of vascular adaptations to hypoxic stress. *Adv Exp Med Biol, 701*, 225-32.

Pearce, W. J., Duckles, S. P. & Buchholz, J. (1999). Effects of maturation on adrenergic neurotransmission in ovine cerebral arteries. *Am J Physiol, 277*, R931-7.

Pearce, W. J., Williams, J. M., White, C. R. & Lincoln, T. M. (2009). Effects of chronic hypoxia on soluble guanylate cyclase activity in fetal and adult ovine cerebral arteries. *J Appl Physiol, 107*, 192-9.

Peeters, L. L., Sheldon, R. E., Jones, M. D. Jr., Makowski, E. L. & Meschia, G. (1979). Blood flow to fetal organs as a function of arterial oxygen content. *Am J Obstet Gynecol, 135*, 637-46.

Peña, J. P., Tomimatsu, T., Hatran D. P., McGill, L. L. & Longo, L. D. (2007). Cerebral blood flow and oxygenation in ovine fetus: responses to superimposed hypoxia at both low and high altitude. *J Physiol, 578*, 359-70.

Penninga, L. & Longo, L. D. (1998). Ovine placentome morphology: effect of high altitude, long-term hypoxia. *Placenta, 19*, 187-93.

Peréz, R., Espinoza, M., Riguelme, R., Parer, J. T. & Llanos, A. J. (1989). Arginine vasopressin mediates cardiovascular responses to hypoxemia in fetal sheep. *Am J Physiol, 256*, R1011-8.

Phillips, I. D., Simonetta, G., Owens, J. A., Robinson, J. S., Clarke, I. J. & McMillen, I. C. (1996). Placental restriction alters the functional development of the pituitary-adrenal axis in the sheep fetus during late gestation. *Pediatr Res*, *40*, 861-6.

Pringle, K. G., Kind, K. L., Sferruzzi-Perri, A. N., Thompson, J. G. & Roberts, C. T. (2010). Beyond oxygen: complex regulation and activity of hypoxia inducible factors in pregnancy. *Hum Reprod Update*, *16*, 415-31.

Prystowsky, H., Hellegers, A., Meschia, G., Metcalfe, J., Huckabee, W. & Barron, D. H. (1960). The blood volume of fetuses carried by ewes at high altitude. *Q J Exp Physiol Cogn Med Sci*, *45*, 292-7.

Rees, S., Harding, R. & Walker, D. (2008). An adverse intrauterine environment: implications for injury and altered development of the brain. *Int J Dev Neurosci*, *26*, 3-11.

Rees, S., Harding, R. & Walker, D. (2011). The biological basis of injury and neuroprotection in the fetal and neonatal brain. *Int J Dev Neurosci*, *29*, 551-63.

Regnault, T. R., Teng, C., de Vrijer, B., Galan, H. L., Wilkening, R. B. & Battaglia, F. C. (2010). The tissue and plasma concentration of polyols and sugars in sheep intrauterine growth retardation. *Exp Biol Med*, 235, 999-1006.

Reuss, M. L., Parer, J. T., Harris, J. L. & Krueger, T. R. (1982). Hemodynamic effects of alpha-adrenergic blockade during hypoxia in fetal sheep. *Am J Obstet Gynecol*, *142*, 410-5.

Reynafarje, C. (1957). The influence of high altitude on erythropoietic activity. *Brookhaven Symp Biol*, *10*, 132-46.

Reynafarje, C. (1959). Bone marrow studies in the newborn infant at high altitudes. *J Pediatr*, *54*, 152-61.

Reynafarje, C. (1962). Myoglobin content and enzymatic activity of muscle and altitude adaptation. *J Appl Physiol*, *17*, 301-5.

Riquelme, R. A., Llanos, J. A., McGarrigle, H. H., Sanhueza, E. M., Hanson, M. A. & Giussani, D. A. (1998). Chemoreflex contribution to adrenocortical function during acute hypoxemia in the llama fetus at 0. 6 and 0. 7 of gestation. *Endocrinology*, *139*, 2564-70.

Riquelme, R. A., Sánchez, G., Liberona, L., Sanhueza, E. M., Giussani, D. A., Blanco, C. E., et al. (2002). Nitric oxide plays a role in the regulation of adrenal blood flow and adrenocorticomedullary functions in the llama fetus. *J Physiol*, *544*, 267-76.

Robinson, J. S., Kingston, E. J., Jones, C. T. & Thorburn, G. D. (1979). Studies on experimental growth retardation in sheep. The effect of removal of a endometrial caruncles on fetal size and metabolism. *J Dev Physiol*, *1*, 379-98.

Rockwell, L. C., Keyes, L. E. & Moore, L. G. (2000). Chronic hypoxia diminishes pregnancy-associated DNA synthesis in guinea pig uteroplacental arteries. *Placenta*, *21*, 313-9.

Rouwet, E. V., Tintu, A. N., Schellings, M. W., van Bilsen, M., Lutgens, E., Hofstra, L., et al. (2002). Hypoxia induces aortic hypertrophic growth, left ventricular dysfunction, and sympathetic hyperinnervation of peripheral arteries in the chick embryo. *Circulation*, *105*, 2791-6.

Rueda-Clausen, C. F., Dolinsky, V. W., Morton, J. S., Proctor, S. D., Dyck, J. R. & Davidge, S. T. (2011a). Hypoxia-induced intrauterine growth restriction increases the susceptibility of rats to high-fat diet-induced metabolic syndrome. *Diabetes*, *60*, 507-16.

Rueda-Clausen, C. F., Morton, J. S. & Davidge, S. T. (2009). Effects of hypoxia-induced intrauterine growth restriction on cardiopulmonary structure and function during adulthood. *Cardiovasc Res, 81*, 713-22.

Rueda-Clausen, C. F., Morton, J. S., Lopaschuk, G. D. & Davidge, S. T. (2011b). Long-term effects of intrauterine growth restriction on cardiac metabolism and susceptibility to ischaemia/reperfusion. *Cardiovasc Res, 90*, 285-94.

Ruijtenbeek, K., Kessels, C. G., Janssen, B. J., Bitsch, N. J., Fazzi, G. E., Janssen, G. M. et al. (2003a). Chronic moderate hypoxia during in ovo development alters arterial reactivity in chickens. *Pflugers Arch, 447*, 158-67.

Ruijtenbeek, K., Kessels, L. C., De Mey, J. G. & Blanco, C. E. (2003b). Chronic moderate hypoxia and protein malnutrition both induce growth retardation, but have distinct effects on arterial endothelium-dependent reactivity in the chicken embryo. *Pediatr Res, 53*, 573-9.

Ruijtenbeek, K., le Noble, F. A., Janssen, G. M., Kessels, C. G., Fazzi, G. E., Blanco, C. E., et al. (2000). Chronic hypoxia stimulates periarterial sympathetic nerve development in chicken embryo. *Circulation, 102*, 2892-7.

Salhany, J. M., Mizukami, H. & Eliot, R. S. (1971). The deoxygenation kinetic properties of human fetal hemoglobin: effect of 2,3-diphosphoglycerate. *Biochem Biophys Res Commun, 45*, 1350-6.

Salinas, C. E., Blanco, C. E., Villena, M., Camm, E. J., Tuckett, J. D., Weerakkody, R. A., et al. (2010). Cardiac and vascular disease prior to hatching in chick embryos incubated at high altitude. *J Dev Orig Health Dis, 1*, 60-6.

Sánchez Kong, R. A. (1963). *Estudio macroscopic de 100 placentes en el hospital "Esperanza" de Cerro de Pasco*. Lima: Universidad Nacional Mayor de San Marcos, Facultad de Medicina.

Sanhueza, E. M., Riquelme, R. A., Herrera, E. A., Giussani, D. A., Blanco, C. E., Hanson, M. A., et al. (2005). Vasodilator tone in the llama fetus: the role of nitric oxide during normoxemia and hypoxemia. *Am J Physiol Regul Integr Comp Physiol, 289*, R776-83.

Sanz-Cortés, M., Figueras, F., Bonet-Carne, E., Padilla, N., Tenorio, V., Bargalló, N., et al. (2013). Fetal brain MRI texture analysis identifies different microstructural patterns in adequate and small for gestational age fetuses at term. *Fetal Diagn Ther, 33*,122-9.

Schober, M. E., McKnight, R. A., Yu, X., Callaway, C. W., Ke, X. & Lane, R. H. (2009). Intrauterine growth restriction due to uteroplacental insufficiency decreased white matter and altered NMDAR subunit composition in juvenile rat hippocampi. *Am J Physiol Regul Integr Comp Physiol, 296*, R681-92.

Severinghaus, J. W., Chiodi, H., Eger, E. I. 2nd, Brandstater, B. & Hornbein, T. F. (1966). Cerebral blood flow in man at high altitude. Role of cerebrospinal fluid pH in normalization of flow in chronic hypocapnia. *Circ Res, 19*, 274-82.

Shapiro, S., Unger, J., U. S. Public Health Service & National Center for Health Statistics (U. S.). (1954). *Weight at birth and its effect on survival of the newborn in the United States, early 1950*. Vital Statistics-Special Reports, Selected Studies, Vol. *39*, No. 1. Rockville, MD: U. S. Dept. of Health, Education, and Welfare, Public Health Service.

Sharma, S. K., Lucitti, J. L., Nordman, C., Tinney, J. P., Tobita, K. & Keller, B. B. (2006). Impact of hypoxia on early chick embryo growth and cardiovascular function. *Pediatr Res, 59*, 116-20.

Silpanisong, J. & Pearce, W. J. (2013). Vasotrophic regulation of age-dependent hypoxic cerebrovascular remodeling. *Curr Vasc Pharmacol*, *11*, 544-63.

Simonson, T. S., Yang, Y., Huff, C. D., Yun, H., Qin, G., Witherspoon, D. J., et al. (2010). Genetic evidence for high-altitude adaptation in Tibet. *Science*, *329*, 72-5.

Sobrevilla, L. A., Cassinelli, M. T., Carcelen, A. & Malaga, J. M. (1971). Human fetal and maternal oxygen tension and acid-base status during delivery at high altitude. *Am J Obstet Gynecol*, *111*, 1111-8.

Sobrevilla, L. A., Romero, I., Moncloa, F., Donayre, J. & Guerra-Garcia, R. (1967). Endocrine studies at high altitude. III. *Acta Endocrinol*, *56*, 369-75.

Soria, R., Julian, C. G., Vargas, E., Moore, L. G. & Giussani, D. A. (2013). Graduated effects of high-altitude hypoxia and highland ancestry on birth size. *Pediatr Res*, *74*, 633-8.

Strauss, R. S. (2000). Adult functional outcome of those born small for gestational age: twenty-six-year follow-up of the 1970 British Birth Cohort. *JAMA*, *283*, 625-32.

Styne, D. M. (2011). Endocrine factors affecting neonatal growth. In: *Fetal and neonatal physiology*. Polin, R. A., Fox, W. W. & Abman, S. H. (Eds). 4th Edn, Vol *1*. Philadelphia: Elsevier/Saunders, p. 310-23.

Sung, I. K., Vohr, B. & Oh, W. (1993). Growth and neurodevelopmental outcome of very low birth weight infants with intrauterine growth retardation: comparison with control subjects matched by birth weight and gestational age. *J Pediatr*, *123*, 618-24.

Szabo, C., Emilsson, K., Hardebo, J. E., Nystedt, S. & Owman, C. (1992). Uptake and release of serotonin in rat cerebrovascular nerves after subarachnoid hemorrhage. *Stroke*, *23*, 54-61.

Tao, X., Lin, M. T., Thorington, G. U., Wilson, L. D. & Hessinger, D. A. (2014). Acclimatization to long-term hypoxia in adult and fetal ovine basilar arteries: The role of increased Ca^{2+}-activated K^+ (BK) channel activity. (Submitted)

Teng, G. Q., Williams, J., Zhang, L., Purdy, R. & Pearce, W. J. (1998). Effects of maturation, artery size, and chronic hypoxia on 5-HT receptor type in ovine cranial arteries. *Am J Physiol*, *275*, R742-53.

Thakor, A. S., Richter, H. G., Kane, A. D., Dunster, C., Kelly, F. J., Poston, L., et al. (2010). Redox modulation of the fetal cardiovascular defence to hypoxaemia. *J Physiol*, *588*, 4235-47.

Thompson, L. P., Aguan, K., Pinkas, G. & Weiner, C. P. (2000). Chronic hypoxia increases the NO contribution of acetylcholine vasodilation of the fetal guinea pig heart. *Am J Physiol Regul Integr Comp Physiol*, *279*, R1813-20.

Thompson, L. P., Dong, Y. & Evans, L. (2009). Chronic hypoxia increases inducible NOS-derived nitric oxide in fetal guinea pig hearts. *Pediatr Res*, *65*, 188-92.

Thorn, S. R., Regnault, T. R., Brown, L. D., Rozance, P. J., Keng, J., Roper, M., et al. (2009). Intrauterine growth restriction increases fetal hepatic gluconeogenic capacity and reduces messenger ribonucleic acid translation initiation and nutrient sensing in fetal liver and skeletal muscle. *Endocrinology*, *150*, 3021-30.

Thorpe, R. B., Stockman, S. L., Williams, J. M., Lincoln, T. M. & Pearce, W. J. (2013). Hypoxic depression of PKG-mediated inhibition of serotonergic contraction in ovine carotid arteries. *Am J Physiol Regul Integr Comp Physiol*, *304*, R734-43.

Thureen, P. J., Trembler, K. A., Meschia, G., Makowski, E. L. & Wilkening, R. B. (1992). Placental glucose transport in heat-induced fetal growth retardation. *Am J Physiol*, *263*, R578-85.

Timiras, P. S. (1964). Comparison of growth and development of the rat at high altitude and at sea level. In: *The physiological effects of high altitude*. Weihe, W. H. (Ed). Oxford: Pergamon Press, p. 21-31.

Timiras, P. S., Krum, A. A. & Pace, N. (1957). Body and organ weights of rats during acclimatization to an altitude of 12,470 feet. *Am J Physiol, 191*, 598-604.

Tissot van Patot, M., Grilli, A., Chapman, P., Broad, E., Tyson, W., Heller, D. S., et al. (2003). Remodelling of uteroplacental arteries is decreased in high altitude placentae. *Placenta, 24*, 326-35.

Tomimatsu, T., Pereyra Pena, J., Hatran, D. P. & Longo, L. D. (2006). Maternal oxygen administration and fetal cerebral oxygenation: studies on near-term fetal lambs at both low and high altitude. *Am J Obstet Gynecol, 195*, 535-41.

Tucci, M., Nygard, K., Tanswell, B. V., Farber, H. W., Hill, D. J. & Han, V. K. (1998). Modulation of insulin-like growth factor (IGF) and IGF binding protein biosynthesis by hypoxia in cultured vascular endothelial cells. *J Endocrinol, 157*, 13-24.

Ueno, N., Zhao, Y., Zhang, L. & Longo, L. D. (1997). High altitude-induced changes in alpha 1-adrenergic receptors and Ins(1,4,5)P3 responses in cerebral arteries. *Am J Physiol, 272*, R669-74.

Unger, C., Weiser, J. K., McCullough, R. E., Keefer, S. & Moore, L. G. (1988). Altitude, low birth weight, and infant mortality in Colorado. *JAMA, 259*, 3427-32.

Vaughan, B. E. & Pace, N. (1956). Changes in myoglobin content of the high altitude acclimatized rat. *Am J Physiol, 185*, 549-56.

Villamor, E., Kessels, C. G., Ruijtenbeek, K., van Suylen, R. J., Belik, J., de Mey, J. G., et al. (2004). Chronic in ovo hypoxia decreases pulmonary arterial contractile reactivity and induces biventricular cardiac enlargement in the chicken embryo. *Am J Physiol Regul Integr Comp Physiol, 287*, R642-51.

Weihe, W. H. (1964). *The physiological effects of high altitude; proceedings of a symposium held at Interlaken, September 18-22, 1962*. Oxford: Pergamon Press.

West, J. B. (2002). Highest permanent human habitation. *High Alt Med Biol, 3*, 401-7.

Wiley, A. S. (1994). Neonatal and maternal anthropometric characteristics in a high altitude population of the Western Himalaya. *Am J Hum Biol, 6*, 499-510.

Wilkening, R. B. & Meschia, G. (1983). Fetal oxygen uptake, oxygenation, and acid-base balance as a function of uterine blood flow. *Am J Physiol, 244*, H749-55.

Williams, J. M. & Pearce, W. J. (2006). Age-dependent modulation of endothelium-dependent vasodilatation by chronic hypoxia in ovine cranial arteries. *J Appl Physiol, 100*, 225-32.

Williams, J. M., White, C. R., Chang, M. M., Injeti, E. R., Zhang, L. & Pearce, W. J. (2006). Chronic hypoxia decreases in soluble guanylate cyclase protein and enzyme activity are age dependent in fetal and adult ovine carotid arteries. *J Appl Physiol, 100*, 1857-66.

Williams, S. J., Campbell, M. E., McMillen, I. C. & Davidge, S. T. (2005a). Differential effects of maternal hypoxia or nutrient restriction on carotid and femoral vascular function in neonatal rats. *Am J Physiol Regul Integr Comp Physiol, 288*, R360-7.

Williams, S. J., Hemmings, D. G., Mitchell, J. M., McMillen, I. C. & Davidge, S. T. (2005b). Effects of maternal hypoxia or nutrient restriction during pregnancy on endothelial function in adult male rat offspring. *J Physiol, 565*, 125-35.

Xiong, Z. & Sperelakis, N. (1995). Regulation of L-type calcium channels of vascular smooth muscle cells. *J Mol Cell Cardiol, 27*, 75-91.

Xu, Y., Williams, S. J., O'Brien, D. & Davidge, S. T. (2006). Hypoxia or nutrient restriction during pregnancy in rats leads to progressive cardiac remodeling and impairs postischemic recovery in adult male offspring. *FASEB J, 20*, 1251-3.

Xue, Q. & Zhang, L. (2009). Prenatal hypoxia causes a sex-dependent increase in heart susceptibility to ischemia and reperfusion injury in adult male offspring: role of protein kinase C epsilon. *J Pharmacol Exp Ther, 330*, 624-32.

Yangzom, Y., Qian, L., Shan, M., La, Y., Meiduo, D., Hu, X., et al. (2008). Outcome of hospital deliveries of women living at high altitude: a study from Lhasa in Tibet. *Acta Paediatr, 97*, 317-21.

Yerushalmy, J., van den Berg, B. J., Erhardt, C. L. & Jacobziner, H. (1965). Birth weight and gestation as indices of "immaturity": neonatal mortality and congenital anomalies of the "immature". *Am J Dis Child, 109*, 43-57.

Yip, R. (1987). Altitude and birth weight. *J Pediatr, 111*, 869-76.

Yung, H. W., Cox, M., Tissot van Patot, M. & Burton, G. J. (2012). Evidence of endoplasmic reticulum stress and protein synthesis inhibition in the placenta of non-native women at high altitude. *FASEB J, 26*, 1970-81.

Zachary, I. (2001). Signaling mechanisms mediating vascular protective actions of vascular endothelial growth factor. *Am J Physiol Cell Physiol, 280*, C1375-86.

Zamudio, S. (2003). The placenta at high altitude. *High Alt Med Biol, 4*, 171-91.

Zamudio, S., Droma, T., Norkyel, K. Y., Acharya, G., Zamudio, J. A., Niermeyer, S. N., et al. (1993). Protection from intrauterine growth retardation in Tibetans at high altitude. *Am J Phys Anthropol, 91*, 215-24.

Zamudio, S., Palmer, S. K., Droma, T., Stamm, E., Coffin, C. & Moore, L. G. (1995). Effect of altitude on uterine artery blood flow during normal pregnancy. *J Appl Physiol, 79*, 7-14.

Zamudio, S., Postigo, L., Illsley, N. P., Rodriguez, C., Heredia, G., Brimacombe, M., et al. (2007). Maternal oxygen delivery is not related to altitude- and ancestry-associated differences in human fetal growth. *J Physiol, 582*, 883-95.

Zhang, L., Xiao, D. & Bouslough, D. B. (1998). Long-term high-altitude hypoxia increases plasma nitrate levels in pregnant ewes and their fetuses. *Am J Obstet Gynecol, 179*, 1594-8.

Zhao, Y., Zhang, L., & Longo, L. D. (2004). Regulation of long-term hypoxia (LTH)-induced changes in norepinephrine (NE)-induced contraction and Ca^{2+} sensitivity in ovine cerebral arteries. *FASEB J, 18*, A1010.

Zhou, L., Zhao, Y., Nijland, R., Zhang, L. & Longo, L. D. (1997). Ins(1,4,5)P3 receptors in cerebral arteries: changes with development and high-altitude hypoxia. *Am J Physiol, 272*, R1954-9.

Zhu, B. T. (1993). The competitive and noncompetitive antagonism of receptor-mediated drug actions in the presence of spare receptors. *J Pharmacol Toxicol Methods, 29*, 85-91.

Zubrick, S. R., Kurinczuk, J. J., McDermott, B. M., McKelvey, R. S., Silburn, S. R. & Davies, L. C. (2000). Fetal growth and subsequent mental health problems in children aged 4 to 13 years. *Dev Med Child Neurol, 42*, 14-20.

In: Stress and Developmental Programming …
Editors: Lubo Zhang and Lawrence D. Longo

ISBN: 978-1-63321-836-9
© 2014 Nova Science Publishers, Inc.

Chapter 6

The Developing Brain: What is the Role of Antenatal Stress-Mediated Epigenetics?

Lawrence D. Longo[1,2,], Lubo Zhang[1] and Ravi Goyal[1]*

[1]Center for Perinatal Biology, Departments of Physiology, Loma Linda, CA, US
[2]Obstetrics and Gynecology, Loma Linda University School of Medicine,
Loma Linda, CA, US

Abstract

The human brain develops following a complex, highly orchestrated series of histogenic events that depend upon exquisite regulation of gene expression. As knowledge of human development increases, it is becoming evident that the foundations for much of our life are established prior to birth. Early life experiences long have been believed to be associated with long-lasting consequences including neuropsychiatric disease in the adult. From a combination of epidemiologic studies in humans and investigation in laboratory animals, has emerged the concept of *in utero* "programming" or the "fetal origins of adult disease." This phenomenon is believed to occur by complex interactions between genetic heritage and the intrauterine environment. These stress-induced epigenetic changes that occur in the embryo or fetus can eventuate in a number of chronic clinical conditions in the adult offspring. These include: hypertension, coronary artery disease, metabolic syndrome, type 2 diabetes, and some malignancies. Associated neuropsychiatric disorders include schizophrenia, bipolar disorder, and a host of other syndromes. Of vital importance, antenatal stress such as maternal nutritional deprivation, hypoxia, environmental toxins, and other invidious factors can play a crucial role in mediating the epigenetic regulation/dysregulation of gene transcription, as well as influencing post-transcriptional mechanisms. These epidemiological associations raise the question of the mechanism(s) by which adverse early life experiences become integrated at the cellular-subcellular level into the architecture of the developing brain and other organs. Mechanistically, rather than genomic mutations in the DNA nucleotide

* E-mail: llongo@llu.edu, Tel: 909 558 4325.

sequence *per se*, environmental stress has been shown to alter epigenetic regulation of transcription by a "mosaic" of multifactorial mechanisms. These include: methylation of DNA nucleotide cytosine residues, methylation, acetylation, or other changes of the nucleosome core histone proteins, altered short RNA/transcription factor complexes (such as microRNAs), transcriptional splice variation, mitochondrial nuclear disorders, and/or other mechanisms. In short, these epigenetic-mediated molecular changes can play a major role not only in the genesis of many clinical disorders, but they even may have transgenerational effects. Beyond descriptive phenomenology, this Chapter will explore both population based epidemiologic and laboratory animal studies that support (and a few that argue against) the role of developmental epigenetics in adult disease. Importantly, we attempt to elucidate their fundamental cellular and molecular mechanisms, an understanding of which may allow for the implementation of antenatal maternal and early life interventions and/or targeted approaches to reprogram expression during development, and possibly later in life. Finally of considerable clinical relevance, we consider the relation of epigenetic changes in the developing organism to national and global health issues, and what we as basic scientists, obstetrician-gynecologists, pediatricians or other clinicians may do to help mitigate the associated pandemic of disease.

Keywords: Gene regulation, Microarray, Development, DNA Methylation, Histone modification, miRNA, Nutrition, Behavior, Neuropsychiatric Disorders

Abbreviations

5-HT	5-hydroxy tryptamine, serotonin
ACE	angiotensin converting enzyme
ACTH	adrenocorticotropic hormone
Akt	protein kinase B (PKB) serine/threonine-specific protein kinase
AMPD	antenatal maternal protein deprivation
Ang	angiotensin
APP	amyloid precursor protein
ART	assisted reproduction technology
AT1- and 2-	angiotensin II-type 1 and 2
ATR-X	Alpha-thalassemia mental retardation, X-linked
AVP	arginine vasopressin
bHLH	basic-helix-loop-helix
cAMP	cyclic adenosine monophosphate
CREB	cAMP response element binding protein
CpG	cytosine phosphodiester guanine
cDNA	complementary DNA
CSS	chronic social stress
DNA	deoxyribonucleic acid
DOHaD	developmental origins of adult health and disease
DPC	day post conception
E	embryonic day
ERK	extracellular regulated kinase
FGR	fetal growth restriction

FMR	fragile X mental retardation
GABA	gamma aminobutyric acid
GWAS	genome wide array (or association) study
H	histone
HAT	histone acetyl transferase
HDAC	histone deacetylase
HDM	histone demethylase
HIF	hypoxic inducible factor
HMT	histone methyl transferase
HSP	heat shock protein
HPA	hypothalamic pituitary axis
IAP	intracisternal A particle
IGF	insulin-like growth factor
IL	interleukin
IQ	intelligence quotient
LINE-1	long interspersed nuclear element-1
LPD	low protein diet
MAPK	mitogen-activated protein kinase
miRNA	micro RNA
mRNA	messenger RNA
mTOR	mammalian target of rapamycin
ncRNA	non-coding RNA
NFκB	nuclear factor kappa B
NMDA	N-methyl-D- aspartate
NSC	neural stem cells
PcG	Polycomb group
PVZ	periventricular zone
RAS	renin angiotensin system
ROCK	Rho kinase
siRNA	small interfering RNA
SIRT	sirtuin
SNP	single nucleotide polymorphism
SVZ	subventricular zone
TrxG	Trithorax group
UTR	untranslated region

Introduction

The human brain develops following a complex, highly stereotyped series of histogenic events that depend upon exquisite regulation of gene expression. As knowledge of human development increases, the sobering reality is becoming evident that the foundations for much of our life as adults, including our state of mind, are established prior to birth in our mother's womb. Antenatal existence thus encompasses a universally critical phase of development, so that disruption can result in a wide range of devastating consequences. Although our knowledge of some details of this highly orchestrated process is considerable, our deep understanding is only elementary. Thus, studies aimed at understanding the manner in which antenatal influences including stress in its various forms, play a role in defining the course of later life may illuminate mechanisms of fundamental importance to developmental neuroscience. Importantly, they also have vast and vital public health implications. Thus, one might ask, what do we as basic scientists, obstetricians, pediatricians, and other "healers" have to do with whether the infants delivered will grow up to be healthy adults? What is our role in lifestyle medicine? Although such questions apply to any or all organs and bodily functions, this Chapter will focus on the brain.

In the Western world, the leading causes of morbidity and mortality include cardiovascular disease with hypertension, coronary artery disease, and cerebrovascular accidents with their sequelae. Perhaps self evident, these pathobiological events may have a profound influence on cerebral function. Although the virtual pandemic of cardiovascular disease and metabolic disease is associated with a number of important risk factors (smoking, sedentary lifestyle, less than optimal nutrition, high body mass index), many individuals who develop these conditions do not have these risk factors. Thus, it is clear that as yet unrecognized and underappreciated elements must be considered in the genesis of their pathology. Despite remarkable advances in science, technology, and many other areas of life, cognitive and neuropsychiatric disturbances, mood disorders, and related problems are far too common. These include: autism, bipolar disorder, depression, schizophrenia, addiction disorders, learning and neurodevelopmental abnormalities, as well as other psychological and psychiatric conditions (Blumberg et al., 2004, Ham and Tronick, 2006, Hulshoff et al., 2000, Lewis et al., 2004, 2005, St. Clair et al., 2005). With increasing human lifespan, the number of individuals who suffer cognitive impairment is escalating; however, for the most part, neuropsychiatric problems are of occult origin.

Growth and development of the brain, the most complex organ not only in the body, but probably in the universe, and which determines our life and behavior, is unique in many respects. As with other cells, those in the central nervous system have identical genomic DNA sequences (the template of our heredity and thus the instruction sets for gene expression); however, they develop into strikingly different and unique phenotypes. Neurons, the cells responsible for signaling, conduction, and communication, convert a variety of stimuli into control of consciousness, short- and long-term memory, cognition, and behavior. By late-gestation in the developing fetus, neuron number is established during a "brain growth spurt", with little postnatal neurogenesis other than in several specialized regions. Development of the supporting neuroglia (astrocytes and microglia) follows a similar time course, with a delay of one to two weeks, while maturation of oligodendrocytes with myelin formation follows a later time course. In view of the complexity of orchestrated neurogenesis, with axon and dendrite formation, specialized cell type differentiation, migration, synaptogenesis, neurotransmitters with the connectivity of literally billions of synapses, and selective cell death (apoptosis), as may be imagined the brain is exquisitely sensitive to factors that may alter and interfere with its normal pattern of growth and development.

During the past decade or so, an expanding body of evidence has highlighted the role of environmental factors that mediate epigenetic mechanisms, e.g., those that can modulate gene expression in the absence of changes in DNA sequence. Morphologic, biochemical, and molecular brain development, and subsequent behavior emerge as a consequence of numerous interacting genetic and environmental factors. As is well recognized, compromised cerebral development of the conceptus can have both short- and long-term consequences for neurobehavioral function as an adult (Lewis, 1986, Rees et al., 2008).

Classically, biologists have viewed inheritance and development to be a consequence of our chromosomal heritage, with discreet genes determining the manner in which phenotypic traits and diseases pass from one generation to another. We now know that this relation of genotype to phenotype is only partially valid. A rapidly increasing body of evidence suggests that a number of cognitive, as well as cardiovascular and metabolic disorders have an epigenetic basis, and this evidence grows daily (Paul, 2010). In his monumental volume *The physiology and pathology of exposure to stress*, the McGill University and *Université de Montreal* endocrinologist, Hans Selye (1907-1982), observed that stress to the organism, in essentially any of its forms -- dietary, environmental, disease, and others -- could result in cellular, hormonal, and related damage, with the body mounting a response. He termed this the "General-Adaptation-Syndrome" (Selye, 1950). Writing years before many of the nuances of cellular biochemical and molecular mechanisms were established, and before the phenomenon of epigenesis was appreciated, Selye envisioned an orchestrated brain to tissue system-wide biological defensive response to the challenge of stress of whatever origin. (Subsequent investigation has clarified that while stress of relatively short duration may be followed by successful adaptation, that of longer duration and/or repeated insult may result in cell damage and death (Bale et al., 2010, McEwen, 2004)).

Along this line, stress can originate from multiple sources physical, chemical, and psychological. The ability to adapt to the stress of a changing environment is resilience, a response known as allostasis [Greek, other + standing still], e.g., maintenance of stability or homeostasis by making changes in response to challenge. For decades developmental psychologists have explored this ability to adapt and crucial survival mechanism, a facet of the "Nature versus Nurture" debate (Sameroff, 2010). As an outgrowth of the paradox that the prevalence of cardiovascular disease and metabolic disease increases with the prosperity of nations, while those that are less prosperous also suffer high rates of disease, the concept of antenatal "programming" of the developmental origins of adult health and disease (DOHaD) has received increasing attention (see below and Barker, 1990, 1991, 1992, 1994, 2001, 2007, Barker et al., 1989a, 1989b, 1993, Barker and Osmond, 1986a, 1986b, Bennet and Gunn, 2006, Bilbo and Schwarz, 2009, Giussani, 2011, Joseph and Kramer, 1996, Sayer et al., 1998, Ward et al., 2004). The interpretation of these relationships has been based on the association of neonatal deaths with low birthweight, the role of antenatal versus postnatal environment, the seemingly paradoxical increase in coronary artery disease with affluence, and related factors. These reflect "... variations in nutrition in early life, which are expressed pathologically on exposure to later dietary influences" (Barker and Osmond, 1986b, p. 108).

Among neurologists, psychiatrists, pediatricians, and others this issue has attracted considerable interest in terms of the role that early life stress and/or lifetime events can play in the etiology of mood, affective, and cognitive disorders – so-called "Life Course" or "Lifestyle Medicine" (see below and Lupien et al., 2009, Lynch and Davey Smith, 2005, Tsankova et al., 2007). In addition to antenatal stress, that during postnatal life also is a major consideration in this regard. An example of the latter is that of neglect during childhood, of which a considerable body of evidence has associated detrimental effects on neural development early in life (Hedges and Woon, 2011, Kaufman and Charney, 2001). Psychiatric disorders such as depression and schizophrenia that become evident as one ages also may follow (Morgan and Fisher, 2007).

In terms of lifestyle medicine, special features of such antenatal programming of DOHaD include: the intensity of the stressor, the stage of life or critical periods of vulnerability, failure or unsatisfactory completion of specific developmental milestones, association with functional defects, the permanent nature of such sequelae, and its heritability for several generations (Kuh and Ben-Shlomo, 1997, Kuh and Hardy, 2002, Kuh et al., 2003). Some would argue that the protective or allosteric changes become maladaptive later in life, due to hormonal or other alterations in the body and brain's homeostatic mechanisms. This, leading to vulnerability rather than to resilience (Larbi et al., 2008, McEwen, 2012). Also, it would appear that stressors that occur at vulnerable times during development appear to have greater and more enduring effects than those that occur later in life (Zannas and West, 2014). Figure 1 illustrates some interrelations of genetic (Mendelian) factors and environmental epigenetic factors within the context of the maternal-placental-fetal complex.

The epigenetic basis of the neurobehavioral and psychiatric disease also is becoming well recognized. For instance, in a study of 3,600 infants born in 1946 in the United Kingdom, birthweight was associated positively with cognitive ability at age 8, and subsequently up to age 26, as well as with the level of education achieved (Richards et al., 2001). Although caveats have been raised by a number of authors (Anonymous, 1989, Ben-Shlomo and Davey Smith, 1991, Elford et al., 1991, Paneth and Susser, 1995), supporting evidence for this idea has been provided by a series of epidemiologic studies from a number of cultures and countries.

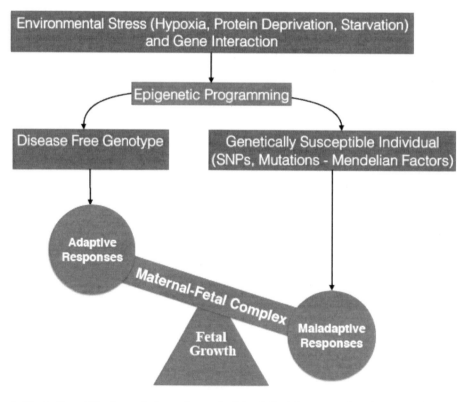

Figure 1. Illustration of the interrelations of genetic (Mendelian) factors and environmental factors in the epigenetic programming within the context of the maternal-placental-fetal complex, and resultant adaptive or maladaptive responses.

In association with effects of maternal nutritional deprivation on the developing fetus *per se*, placental growth and development also may be altered, thus disturbing the hormonal milieu. Again, these may eventuate in subsequent behavioral and hormonal consequences in the adult (Barker, 1992, 1994, 2003, Barker et al., 1989a, Gluckman and Hanson, 2006, Gluckman et al., 2008). These include cortisol secretion (Reynolds et al., 2007, Tu et al., 2007) and immune dysfunction (Götz et al., 2007, Merlot et al., 2008) later in life.

Several hypotheses have been proposed to account for the phenomena of genetic and epigenetic factors influencing fetal/adult cerebral growth, development, and long-term sequelae (Bateson et al., 2004). Originally, the "thrifty genotype" hypothesis was proposed to explain the origin of type 2 (non-insulin-dependent) diabetes among people as they become acculturated, adapting western style diets, so that calories could be stored more efficiently in times of plenty (Neel, 1962, 1976). In the early 1990s, the "thrifty phenotype" hypothesis was postulated; e.g., that impairment of nutritional supply in early life results in permanent changes in tissue/organ structure and function to conserve glucose, and prioritize development of the brain, heart, and other vital organs in infants who experience intrauterine growth restriction (Billack et al., 2012, Hales and Barker, 1992, 2001, Ong and Dunger, 2000, Prentice et al., 2005, Stöger, 2008). This phenotype, however, increases the risk of metabolic syndrome, obesity, hypertension, and associated disorders (Billack et al., 2012). Related hypotheses propose that epigenetic alterations in gene expression can be heritable, and may be reversible (Holness and Sugden, 2006).

In laboratory animals, numerous studies have demonstrated a relation between intrauterine stress to the fetus (particularly that of antenatal maternal protein deprivation (AMPD), excess caloric intake, hypoxia, and/or emotional trauma), and disease in the adult (Chmurzynska, 2010, Gheorghe et al., 2010, Gluckman et al., 2008, Gluckman and Hanson, 2006, Goyal et al., 2009, 2010, Hanson and Gluckman, 2005, Jansson and Powell, 2007). These stresses may "program" the embryonic and fetal brain and other organs; "Programming", being a general process whereby a stimulus or insult at a critical period of development has lasting or life-long consequences. Although a considerable body of phenomenological observations has been amassed, the fundamental cellular and molecular mechanisms of "programming" and its effects are largely unknown.

In this Chapter, for the developing brain, we survey and attempt to integrate the role of epigenetic influences mediated by maternal diet, hypoxia, and related stress during the antenatal period, that may result in life-long phenotypic and behavioral consequences with neuropsychiatric sequelae. We also examine the current state of knowledge of epigenetic-regulated gene expression in the developing brain, and responses to antenatal maternal stress. These include: protein deficiency or hypoxia and their potential sequelae in terms of lifestyle medicine (we make no attempt to review the entire field of developmental origins of adult health and disease, as these topics have been presented *in extenso* elsewhere) (Barker, 1992, 2004, 2007, Billack et al., 2012, Cutfield et al., 2007, Gluckman and Hanson, 2006, Gluckman et al., 2008, Godfrey et al., 2007, Green and Hanson, 2004, Harding, 2001, Waterland and Michels, 2007). Importantly, beyond mere description, we would propose a "mosaic" hypothesis to place these epidemiologic and laboratory phenomena into a framework of the biochemical signaling pathways and molecular mechanisms, by which stresses to the maternal organism can result in alterations of great neurobiologic and epigenetic importance to the conceptus. Under each subheading and in closing, we consider questions that probe the limits of our understanding for future investigation.

Epigenetics: What are Some Historical Perspectives?

In its broadest sense, epigenetic [from Greek, above, upon, over, or beyond conventional genetic] mechanisms constitute an aspect of cellular/molecular "memory" of stable, heritable, self-perpetuating, and reversible modifications of chromatin, that, without alterations in the genomic DNA sequence *per se*, modulate the state of gene expression (Bonasio et al., 2010, Devaskar and Raychaudhuri, 2007). Discovery of the phenomenon of epigenetics has added several layers of complexity to our understanding of the regulation of gene transcription, translation, and has changed the way in which we consider gene expression and inheritance (Berger et al., 2009, LaSalle et al., 2013, Ptashne, 2013). During the course of life and reproduction, cells store information handed down from their ancestors which, in turn, will be transmitted to their descendents. For the most part, this "memory" of heritable genetic information is encoded in the nucleic acid sequence that comprises the genomic DNA. From generation to generation, this genotype or entire complement of genes provides stable and accurate heritability.

Within the eukaryotic nucleus, the basic repeating unit of DNA consists of about 146 nucleic acid base pairs wrapped around a core histone octamer. This constitutes the nucleosome, which is compacted into chromatin. DNA compaction plays a critical role in the regulation of gene expression. Those regions of the genome that are transcriptionally active (euchromatin) have an open, loosely wound DNA structure that allows binding of transcription factors. In contrast, those inactive regions (heterochromatin) remain more tightly wound and condensed, inhibiting such binding. In addition, chromatin condensation and thus transcription status, are influenced by phenomena such as DNA folding, nucleosome positioning, and the formation of higher order structure without change in nucleotide sequence (Misteli, 2007). For the most part, genetics and the environment interact in the coding and promoter regions of genes.

In addition, cells can inherit and transmit information that is not a part of the genomic sequence. This "hidden" heritability of epigenetic processes acts in a cell specific, temporally-regulated manner to direct phenotypic development, differentiation, and related processes. As a metaphor, some have compared epigenetic mechanisms to the software that orchestrates and/or modulates expression of the genomic DNA hardware. During maturational development a complex of signal transduction networks operate by genetic and epigenetic mechanisms to orchestrate transcription and translation, so that uncommitted stem cells differentiate into specific cell types (Bernstein et al., 2007). Traditionally, lineage commitment and cellular differentiation have been considered to be unidirectional and irreversible. This view has been challenged by the discovery that a cell can be reprogrammed to pluripotency (Cowan et al., 2005) and that transcription factor based reprogramming may generate induced pluripotent stem cells (Ladewig et al., 2013, Takahashi and Yamanaka, 2006).

From an historical context, the pioneer Edinburgh geneticist and developmental biologist Conrad Hal Waddington (1905-1975), coined the term epigenetics for the study of how a wide variety of individual cellular phenotypes arise from a given genotype, i.e., those events that could not be explained from the principles of genetics, as seen in embryonic development (Waddington, 1939, 1940, 1942). Waddington later developed the concept of an "epigenetic landscape" to represent the process of phenotypic decision making that allowed development from a single embryonic cell to a number of differentiated cell types (Waddington, 1957). As noted, based on discoveries of interconversion of induced pluripotent stem cells and direct cell fate conversion (or transdifferation), it has been proposed that a non-hierarchical "epigenetic disc" model may be more appropriate to describe cell fate (Ladewig et al., 2013). Subsequent to Waddington, an attempt was made to distinguish two types of cellular regulatory systems. These are the primary genetic material DNA, which replicates by a Watson-Crick base-pairing template mechanism, and the auxiliary independent, modulatory, homeostatic, epigenetic systems (Nanney, 1958). Epigenesis has been redefined as the study of mitotically and/or meiotically heritable changes in gene function without a change in DNA sequence (Dolinoy et al., 2007a, 2007b, Russo et al., 1996), or more specifically "the structural adaptation of chromosomal regions so as to register, signal or perpetuate altered activity states" (Bird, 2007). A field, "epigenetic epidemiology," has been defined "... as the study of the associations between epigenetic variation and risk of disease" (Waterland and Michels, 2007, p. 368). These definitions encompass aspects such as DNA repair, cell-cycle phases, and those stable changes maintained from generation to generation. A major mediator of epigenetic mechanisms is: methylation and other covalent chemical DNA modifications (Holliday, 1987, Holliday and Pugh, 1975, Riggs, 1975). Other epigenetic mechanisms that alter gene expression include methylation, acetylation, and other changes in the histone protein core, and the influence of microRNAs (miRNA), long non-coding RNA (lncRNA), and other factors (see below). One must be clear, however. It is not epigenetic modifications that activate gene expression. Rather, that is the function of specific transcription factor regulatory proteins. In their several waves and combinations, these bind specific DNA sequences in the gene promoter to activate or repress that gene to transcribe messenger RNA (mRNA) (Ptashne, 2013).

Importantly, environmental influences not only may have profound effects on gene expression during development, but may be retained through mitosis. Also, while affecting development, in the mature brain these changes can regulate neuronal responses (Borrelli et al., 2008, Cooney et al., 2002, Franklin and Mansuy, 2010, LaSalle et al., 2013, Nanney, 1958, Sweatt, 2009).

A number of historical aspects of antenatal epigenetics have been reviewed (Gheorghe et al., 2010, Razin and Shemer, 1995, Reik et al., 2001). In particular, early embryonic development is a crucial period during which epigenetic marks are established (Reik et al., 2001), and a time when nutritional environment can affect the earliest stages of mammalian development (Doherty et al., 2000, Morgan et al., 2008). Of note, several lines of evidence indicate that, in addition to immediate maternal to fetal transfer, epigenetic modifications may be inherited across generations (Anway and Skinner 2006, Anway et al., 2005, Crews et al., 2007, Goldberg et al., 2007, Lane et al., 2003, Morgan et al., 1999, Pembrey et al., 2006, Rakyan et al., 2003). Thus, the epigenome (a prenatal archive of which is available, Heijmans et al., 2009), refers to the ensemble of coordinated epigenetic marks that govern accessibility of the machinery driving DNA transcription, with specific DNA methylation, histone modifications, and/or miRNA reciprocally regulating whether inaccessible genes are silenced and accessible genes can be actively transcribed. Thus, the overall epigenetic state of a cell, constitutes an interface between genes and the environment, allowing nutritional and other factors to affect transgenerational adaptation. Several reviews have detailed some of the vital issues and questions regarding the regulatory mechanisms in this rapidly evolving field. (Bernstein et al., 2007, Fagiolini et al., 2009, Feng et al., 2007, Goldberg et al., 2007, Reik et al., 2001, Wadhwa et al., 2009).

What are some Important Aspects of Gene Expression in Cerebral Development?

Commencing shortly following earliest embryonic differentiation, and continuing through the third decade of life, development of the brain with its consequent function and behavior is an enormously complex process, far beyond the limits of this review. Several fundamental observations may be in order, however. Brain development, with the main cell lineages being neurons and glia (including oligodendrocytes, astrocytes (astroglia), and microglia), accompanied by spatial and temporal regulation of specific gene expression patterns, is crucial for optimal growth and maturation. This with cognitive maturation reciprocally influence and reinforce one another, and may be divided into prenatal and postnatal periods.

During the late 1960s and 1970s, John Dobbing (1922-1999) and colleagues of the University of Manchester studied brain growth in a number of mammals, demonstrating that when fetal and neonatal weight is plotted against age, the brain grows in a sigmoid trajectory, the transitory period of rapid growth being the "brain growth spurt" (Dobbing, 1974, Dobbing and Sands, 1973, 1979). Timing of this growth spurt varies widely among species. In precocial species (guinea pig, monkey, sheep) this growth spurt occurs prenatally, while in non-precocial species (rat, rabbit, pig) it occurs following birth. In humans, following the first trimester during which the gross brain shape is determined, this growth spurt with neurogenesis is intermediate or perinatal, occurring during late gestation and early neonatal life (Altman and Das, 1965, Bayer, 1989, Dobbing and Sands, 1973, 1979, Rakic, 1975, 2003, 2005). Because the growth spurt encompasses an enormous number of specific anatomic, metabolic, neurochemical, and other physiologic events, each with their individual behavioral associations which vary dramatically with cell type, this "critical" period of developmental plasticity is believed to be associated with enhanced vulnerability to stress. When comparing or extrapolating from one species to another, this important factor must be taken into consideration (Altman et al., 1970, Dobbing, 1974, Dobbing and Smart, 1974).

As emphasized in more recent studies, the concept of the brain "growth spurt" may be somewhat misleading, as each brain region with specific cellular units has a unique period of neurogenesis, neural migration, synaptogenesis, and gliogenesis. These events, occurring "… prior to the major growth spurt cannot be ignored since this … cell division growth spurt, is a transient window of neurogenesis for the total macroneuronal population, which is ultimately responsible for the development of the larger circuit formations and for the basic architectonic organization of the brain" (Morgane et al., 1993, p. 98). In the developing brain neurogenesis is particularly active in the periventricular zone (PVZ), with progenitor regions in the subventricular zone (SVZ). In adult brain, stem cell, e.g., progenitor cell-derived, neurogenesis continues in the subventricular zone (Reynolds and Weiss, 1992, Richards et al., 1992), and in the subgranular zone of the dentate gyrus of the hippocampus (Gage et al., 1995, Kuwabara et al., 2009, Palmer et al., 1997, Suh et al., 2007, Zhao et al., 2008). The extracellular matrix, its proteins, and integrin cell surface receptors also play a critical role in neurogenesis and axonal guidance (Garcion et al., 2001, Rønn et al., 1998). Also of consideration in terms of cortical lamination, during fetal life transient patterns develop below and above the cortical plate that play a role in developmental plasticity. As a corollary of these changes, growth of the developing brain is not only extremely rapid but highly plastic (Toga et al., 2006), with an estimated 250,000 cells being formed each minute (Cowan,

1979), each with their multitude of synapses. A review of this development includes many aspects of nerve cell biology, neural generation and migration, interactions between neurons and target cells, the role of function in determining connections, and others (Gaze, 1970, 1974, Jacobson, 1970, Lund, 1978, Southwell et al., 2014). As an aside, a review of cerebral malformations includes a detailed summary of specific developmental events in the human brain (Williams, 1989).

In humans at the time of birth, the brain weighs ~350g (about 10 percent of body weight), but accounts for about one-quarter of basal metabolic rate (Holliday, 1971, Williams and Herrup, 1988). In proportion to whole body mass and metabolism, the brain of the fetus is relatively large, comprising about 27 percent of adult brain weight, with its mass continuing to increase in the infant and child, chiefly as a result of myelin deposition (Davison and Dobbing, 1966, Dobbing and Sands, 1973, 1979). With its high energy requirements compared to its low energy reserves, the brain is rendered particularly vulnerable to hypoxic stress. Because a number of physiologic adaptations tend to protect the developing brain, in the infant with fetal growth restriction (FGR) due to nutritional deprivation or other causes, in relation to body size and girth "brain sparing" preserves the brain and head size (Dobbing, 1981). In humans, the cerebral cortex constitutes six laminated layers of neurons with arrays of intersecting radial columns.

During embryogenesis, these vertically oriented radial columns arise from migration of excitatory projection neurons that originate from the proliferative periventricular zone or subventricular zone of the embryonic cerebral vesicles along elongated radial fibers (Mountcastle, 1997, Szentágothai, 1978, Torii et al., 2009). Cerebral cortical neurons migrate in a unique inside-out pattern, in which the newest neurons must travel through layers of existing neurons until they reach the outermost, pial surface. Of fundamental importance in terms of development, and providing scaffolding and guidance for neuronal migration and terminal location, are cortical radial glial cells, a distinct cell class which display unique features in each species studied (Rakic, 1972, 1975, 2003). Such neural development and diversity is determined by several major factors which can vary considerably, including: the number of stem or precursor cells from which the population is derived, the duration of the regional proliferative period, and the cell cycle duration (McConnell, 1991, Sur and Rubenstein, 2005, Williams, 1989).

As can be imagined, cerebral cortical development with its many nuclei, tracts, and other structures must proceed in a precisely orchestrated progression of production of neurons, glia, and the several other cell types, cell migration and differentiation, and the beginnings of molecular differentiation and synaptogenesis with the complement of neurons being relatively complete at the time of birth. Astroglia continue to develop at a more leisurely pace (Takizawa et al., 2001). By two years of age, brain volume has achieved 80 to 90 percent of its lifetime maximum (Pfefferbaum et al., 1994), with increasing myelination continuing beyond young adulthood (Sowell et al., 2004). The perinatal period also sees the emergence of unique cellular patterns, cytoarchitecture, and neurochemical maturation. Further neuronal growth, differentiation, and circuit organization with synaptogenesis follows through adolescence (Levitt, 2003).

Importantly, astroglial cell number appears to be adjusted proportionally to match the neuron population (Williams and Herrup, 1988). A recent study supports the hypothesis that in humans during the last trimester of pregnancy rapid neuronal growth in the cerebral, so called, "resting state networks" (as determined by functional magnetic radiation imaging for the several visual, auditory, somatosensory, motor, and other systems), become mature although this is prior to experiencing and being a consequence of related cognitive functions (Doria et al., 2010).

Despite the remarkable advances of contemporary neuroscience during the 1990s "Decade of the Brain" (Goldstein, 1994) and beyond, we are only in the infancy of understanding nuances of cerebral development and function (Aguirre et al., 2010, Bota et al., 2003, Edlund and Jessell, 1999, Guillemot et al., 2006, Jessell and Sanes, 2000, Price et al., 2006). As an aside, the recently announced (2013) U.S. Government Brain Research through Advancing Innovative Neurotechnologies (BRAIN) Initiative (Church, 2013), and the European Commission on Human Brain Project (HBP) give promise of obtaining a deeper understanding of the nuances of brain growth and development. A site of value is the Brain Span Atlas of the Developing Brain (http://brainspan.org) via the Allen Brain Atlas data portal (http:///www.brain-map.org). These resources include aspects of neurogenesis, synaptogenesis, the regulation of glial function, the regulation of neuronal-glial interactions, and the manner in which these are integrated to effect cognition, memory, and other cerebral functions. With the use of these resources a mesoscale connectome of the mouse brain recently has been presented (Oh et al., 2014).

At mid-century, "adaptability" or "plasticity" of the developing brain was postulated to be accomplished by "strengthening synapses" in the absence of structural reorganization (Hebb, 1949). Also at this time, a "chemoaffinity" theory was proposed in which "the establishment and maintenance of synaptic associations were conceived to be regulated by highly specific cytochemical affinities that arise systematically among the different types of neurons involved via self-differentiation, induction through terminal contacts, and embryonic gradient effects ..." to establish "... the developmental pattern of central nervous organization" (Sperry, 1963, pp. 703-704). Continued neurogenesis in the adult brain with structured plasticity also was proposed (Altman, 1962). In support of Sperry's hypothesis of neural cytochemical affinities, studies during the past decade are establishing the role of Down syndrome cell adhesion molecule and related proteins, in determining specific neural connections (Matthews et al., 2007, Schmucker et al., 2000, Wojtowicz et al., 2007). A galaxy of Down syndrome cell adhesion molecule isoforms are essential for a robust system of orchestrating the complexity of self-avoidance and normal axonal and dendritic patterning (Hattori et al., 2009, Zipursky, 2010). Environmental-mediated interference of lamination of the cerebral cortex has profound implications for cognitive function later in life (Kostovic and Judas, 2007). Many elements of neurogenesis in developing and adult brain, and their regulation by cell intrinsic transcription programs and cell external cues, have been reviewed by others (Cohen and Greenberg, 2008, Gage, 2000, Kintner, 2002, Miller et al., 2014, Rakic, 2003).

What is the Role of Epigenetics in Developing Brain Gene Expression?

Because early life events can exert a profound influence on brain development, the question arises as to the role of stress-mediated epigenetics in molding fundamental neural architecture and its behavioral sequelae. Now established from many lines of evidence, the timing and quality of early experience plays a critical role in brain development (Fox et al., 2010, Hammock and Levitt, 2006, Knudsen, 2004, Shonkoff and Levitt, 2010, Szyf et al.,

2008, Taylor, 2010, Thompson and Levitt, 2010). As noted, epigenetic changes in the brain play a key role in normal cellular function, as well as the development and differentiation of neurons and the several glial cell types (Bale et al., 2010, Borrelli et al., 2008, Drake and Walker, 2004, Gupta et al., 2009, Jablonka and Lamb, 2002, Jiang et al., 2008, Kawase-Koga et al., 2009, LaSalle et al., 2013, Levenson and Sweatt, 2005, Meaney, 2010, Monk, 1988, Murrell et al., 2005, O'Leary et al., 2007, Rahnama et al., 2006, Reik, 2007, Reul et al., 2009, Sanosaka et al., 2009, Tsankova et al., 2007, Valadkhan and Nilsen, 2010, Van Eldik and Wainwright, 2003, Yakovlev et al., 2010). Examples include X-chromosome inactivation in female mammals, and genomic imprinting in which one parental allele is altered resulting in parent-of-origin, or random modification of gene transcription (Willard et al., 1993) (see below). A critical issue is that of the role of epigenetic signals in neural stem cell biology, and may be illustrated in the role of epigenetic factors in regulation of the Notch signaling pathway (Martinez et al., 2009). For instance, during mitosis stem cells divide asymmetrically giving rise to one self-renewing cell and a cell that differentiates (Morrison and Kimble, 2006). Asymmetric partitioning of epigenetic signals, as proposed in the "silent sister" hypothesis may, in part, account for these cell fate decisions (Lansdorp, 2007). Presently, it is well established that cellular differentiation and functional regulation during health and disease are achieved by epigenetic modifications. These may be associated with several distinct sequelae: abnormal cell proliferation, cell dysfunction and/or loss, and alteration of cell state. The regulation of these phenomenon, however, are poorly defined (Johnstone and Baylin, 2010). The dentate gyrus of the hippocampus is particularly important in this regard, with dynamic and reversible DNA methylation regulating neurogenesis (Covic et al., 2010, Miller and Sweatt, 2007). This is in contrast to more static, irreversible methylation in other regions. The difference in meaning of these two mechanisms and their relation to brain function and memory formation are as yet unclear (Dulac, 2010, Si et al., 2004).

As noted, epigenetic modifications alter gene expression by mechanisms apart from germline mutations of the coding and promoter regions of genes or single nucleotide polymorphisms (SNPs). These epigenetic changes play a major role in the development and differentiation of various cell types as well as in normal neuronal function (Drake and Walker, 2004, Monk, 1988, Rahnama et al., 2006). Evidence from our laboratory and other investigators indicates that the epigenetic state can be disrupted by antenatal maternal environmental influences such as hypoxia (Gheorghe et al., 2007), protein deprivation (Gheorghe et al., 2010), caloric excess, and so forth, which alter DNA methylation, modify histones, or change miRNA expression (Gheorghe et al., 2010, Goyal et al., 2010).

For neurons and other brain cells (which are among the most sophisticated in the body), despite the differentiation signal having been experienced only once during the earliest development, cell identities may be maintained for a lifetime (Ringrose and Paro, 2004). Much of this developmental gene switching on and off in the transition from a single fertilized cell to fully formed organism is orchestrated and modulated in an elegant manner by epigenetic mechanisms (Bale et al., 2010, Borrelli et al., 2008, Jiang et al., 2008). For the major brain cells, deviation in the normal pattern of gene expression from neural progenitor cell to mature neuron or astroglia may lead to altered phenotype, and from a behavioral perspective such altered gene expression may be evidenced by neuropsychiatric disorders in humans, as well as in laboratory animals (the latter of which include numerous lethal embryonic null mutants). As can be appreciated, because of the complexity and specificity of neural regulatory circuits, in the distinct brain regions, classical analysis of individual genes in whole brain samples, or many of its composite parts, is of questionable value.

During the past several decades, studies in the mouse, which possesses many cell lineages and genes similar to the human, have revealed a number of fundamental molecular mechanisms with the proneural and other genes required underlying brain development. These include: aspects of cell differentiation with neural induction from precursor cells in the neural plate, regionalization of the neural tube along the dorsoventral and anteroposterior axes, neurogenesis with generation of the several cell types from multipotent progenitor stem cells located in the ventricular zone of the embryonic neural tube. The regulation of selective neuronal survival and apoptosis, neural cell migration with patterning and guidance to site of function, the acquisition of differentiated features, the formation of synapses among appropriate neurons with development of circuitry, and others, these all are of fundamental importance. The cerebral cortex is composed of two main neuronal populations. Projection or pyramidal neurons are glutamatergic and excitatory utilizing N-methyl-D-aspartate (NMDA) receptors. In contrast, inhibitory interneurons utilize the neurotransmitter gamma-aminobutyric acid (GABA) and its receptors (Guillemot et al., 2006, Jessell and Sanes, 2000, Price et al., 2006, Smith and Greenfield, 2003). GABA also plays a critical role in the development of neural progenitor cells (Yuan, 2008). Because of the limitations in a review such as this, we cannot consider the specific interactions among genes, gene products, and small molecules responsible for the regulation of the myriad of cellular processes, including those of neuronal proliferation, differentiation, and survival.

In an attempt to unravel the complexities of functional genomics into molecular mechanisms of cell growth, development and migration, responses to stress, and numerous other processes, the quintessential tool microarray analysis, has provided considerable insight (Chu et al., 1998, Gasa et al., 2004, Iyer et al., 1999). Since their creation, genome wide associated studies (GWAS) of cDNA, promoter-methylation/demethylation, histone modifications, and miRNA have proven their power in the elucidation of gene expression patterns and discovery. Figure 2 outlines possible approaches in such study. Beyond the up- or down-regulatory changes in specific genes *per se*, pathway analysis aids in the discovery of the signaling networks involved in these modifications. Although viewed by some as merely "phenomenological", "descriptive", "discovery-based", and/or "correlative" and criticized for their absence of a hypothesis to be tested (Weinberg, 2010), microarray analysis and associated epigenetic studies are proving their worth in providing valuable insights into subcellular/molecular mechanisms of genetic/epigenetic regulation, and, in turn, fostering focused hypothesis-based investigation (Golub, 2010). Of relevance to the brain, microarray studies have proven their worth in exploring nuances of gene expression in development of the hippocampus (Mody et al., 2001), cerebellum (Lim et al., 2004), prefrontal cortex (Semeralul et al., 2006), ventral mesencephalon (Yin et al., 2009), and other regions of critical importance.

In human neuronal cell culture *in vitro*, a number of gene classes are strongly up-and down-regulated in the course of differentiation (Dabrowski et al., 2003). Although recent studies have begun to shed some light on this process, the numerous genes involved and details regarding their regulation remain to be discovered. In essence, the cellular/molecular basis of cerebral development is understood only in its most elementary sense. In addition, specifics of the interactions, interrelations, and effects of these genetic mechanisms are far from clear.

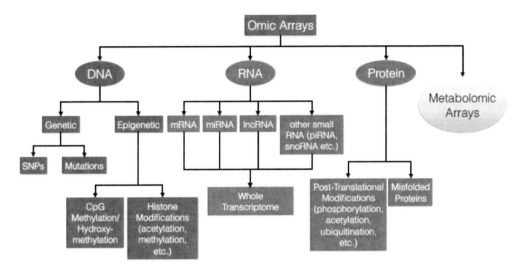

Figure 2. Available "omic" approaches to examine the complexities of developmental maturation.

To understand this process at a more fundamental level, investigators have used the developing rodent and other species to examine gene expression patterns in the brain at various pre- and post-natal ages, testing hypotheses regarding gene regulation and specific functional roles at several developmental ages (Semeralul et al., 2006). To examine specific aspects of gene clustering, functional pathway analysis, and the consequences of their interference during development, for the most part workers have focused on those genes most highly regulated. In the developing mouse hippocampus for instance, microarray analysis has shown significant increases of genes involved in neurogenesis, differentiation, and synapse formation up to postnatal day 30 (Mody et al., 2001). In mouse prefrontal cortex, the basic laminar structure is established *in utero* with extensive remodeling continuing into adolescence. During weeks 2 to 4 of postnatal life, messenger RNA (mRNA) transcripts that showed significant changes included those for cell growth, membrane expansion, and extracellular matrix modifications, specifically transcription factors, zinc finger proteins, DNA methylation, and translational regulation (Semeralul et al., 2006). In contrast, in developing cerebellum, the up-regulation of genes for ion transport channels, GABA and NMDA receptors, and synaptic components was shown to be particularly striking (Lim et al., 2004). At 2 to 4 weeks of age, several other functional categories have been demonstrated to be over-represented, including genes involved in angiogenesis, morphogenesis, and organogenesis, genes involved in lipid metabolism and transport, cell cycle control, and cell growth and maintenance. In the developing hindbrain of Pax6 homozygous mutant and wild type Sprague-Dawley rats, this transcription factor was shown to regulate anterior-posterior patterning via activation of several genes, including Cyp26b1, an enzyme that metabolizes retinoic acid, a key factor in neurogenesis (Numayama-Tsuruta et al., 2010).

In view of its importance to neural memory formation and other functions, development of the hypothalamus has received particular attention. The hormone leptin, originating in adipocytes, directs hypothalamic projections from the arcuate nucleus, affecting both the anorexigenic pro-opiomelanocortin and orexigenic neuropeptide Y neurons (Simerly, 2008). The paraventricular nuclei and lateral hypothalamus, targets of these neurons, contain cell types with widespread regulatory function, and, in turn, probably are regulated by numerous other factors. Another important aspect of epigenetic regulation is that of the immune system and neural development (Baharnoori et al., 2009). For instance, in addition to being an important modulator of immune responses, the cytokine interleukin (IL)-18 has been shown to play a critical role in neural development, as well as homeostasis and neuroinflammatory and neurodegenerative processes (Alboni et al., 2010). As emphasized by multiple lines of evidence, the several epigenetic regulatory mechanisms play extremely vital roles in individual neural gene expression (Feng et al., 2007, Hirabayashi and Gotoh, 2010).

For the majority of autosomal genes, expression from alleles is contributed by both parents. A special case of epigenetic-regulated gene expression in the brain is that of "imprinting", in which gene expression is monoallelic, and regulated by instruction imprints, e.g., those laid down in parental germ cells being specifically parent-of-origin dependent. Non-Mendelian in origin, genomic imprinting does not involve alterations in DNA sequence, but rather is regulated by differential DNA methylation and/or histone alteration of imprint control elements. These are read by an epigenetic initiator that silences genes in surrounding imprinted gene clusters. Such imprinting can play a major role in neurogenesis (Wilkinson et al., 2007) and the development of disease in the adult (Isles and Wilkinson, 2000, Waterland and Garza, 1999). Although expressed in the placenta, many imprinted genes such as insulin-like growth factors, play a vital role in not only the regulation of embryonic/fetal brain growth and development, but also in neural function and behavior following birth (Reik and Walter, 2001, Reik et al., 2001, Tycko, 2006). Prior to embryonic development, imprinted genes of maternal or paternal origin may be transmitted through meiosis and gamete formation (Brennecke et al., 2008, Hammoud et al., 2009, Razin and Shemer, 1995). Embryonic reprogramming also may be a factor contributing to the clustering of imprinted genes (Constância et al., 2002, Reik et al., 2001). For instance, in the pleiotropic insulin-like growth factor (IGF: IGF-I and –II) pathway, which has a major influence in mediating fetal growth and development as well as that of brain neurogenesis and synaptogenesis (D'Ercole and Ye, 2008, Niblock et al., 2000, O'Kusky et al., 2000), two oppositely functioning imprinted genes *Igf2* (a growth promoting factor expressed from the paternal allele) and *Igf2r* (a growth inhibiting factor expressed from the maternal allele) are subject to epigenetic regulation and programming (Smith et al., 2006). An important locus for these relatively cell specific genes is the hippocampus (Davies et al., 2005). Imprinted expression also can be lost during differentiation in a tissue specific manner. For example, in brain post-mitotic neurons, imprinted expression of *Igf2r* is lost and expression is from both alleles (Yamasaki et al., 2005). In addition, only neurons display imprinted expression of the *Ube3A* gene, while glial cells have biallelic expression (Yamasaki et al., 2003). In genetically identical uniparental mice, a complex pattern of paternal transmission of anxiety-related behaviors and growth suggest gender specific transgenerational epigenetic effects (Alter et al., 2009).

Somewhat similar complex effects have been described in Swedish probands who experienced varying degrees of nutritional deprivation during their period of slow growth (age 8 to 12), prior to the prepubertal peak (Kaati et al., 2007). To a great extent, this emerging concept of the brain being especially sensitive to epigenetic influences has derived from analysis of parental origin-specific gene expression in the mouse brain (Gregg et al., 2010a, 2010b). In fact, brain genomic imprinting appears to be extensive. For instance, in high-resolution genome wide array study of parent-of-origin allelic expression, more than 1,300 loci were identified, with marked differences in transcript isoforms and brain region. Importantly, this may illustrate the concept of the brain, rather than being a single organ, consists of many separate organs in close approximation. The developing brain displays preferential maternally imprinted gene expression, while the adult brain shows a bias in paternal contributions (Gregg et al., 2010b). Neural systems enriched in expression of imprinted genes include the major monoaminergic brain nuclei with dopaminergic, noradrenergic, or serotonergic neurons (general neurotransmission), the arcuate nucleus (feeding behavior), and pre-optic area of the hypothalamus (social behavior). Also in female, but not male, mice, the maternal allele of Interleukin-18 was expressed preferentially (Gregg et al., 2010a).

The health consequences of aberrant genomic imprinting, with the protection afforded by diploidy being lost, may be disastrous with monoallelic expression giving rise to the genesis of oncogenes (Plass and Soloway, 2002). Nongenotoxic environmental agents such as insufficiency of dietary factors or O_2, may lead to dysregulation of epigenetic regulatory mechanisms that maintain the functionally haploid state of these genes, giving rise to increased susceptibility to neurobehavioral disorders and other diseases (Dolinoy et al., 2007a). As described below, neural disorders including both Angelman and Prader-Willi Syndromes involve abnormal imprinted gene expression. As a caveat, beyond the phenomenology of specific genomic transcriptional responses to a particular nutritional event or environmental insult, the epigenomic mapping and regulation of fetal neuronal cells during normal gestation is unknown. For example, mice embryos implanted into the mothers of different strain (e.g., prenatal cross-fostering) retained their parental phenotype. When tested at 3 months of age, however, they displayed characteristic behavioral features of the adopted dam strain into which they had been implanted. These behaviors included: open field exploration, relative time in the open arms of a plus maze, latency to find the hidden platform of a Morris water maze, and acoustic startle pre-pulse inhibition (Francis et al., 2003). This illustrates the complex and dynamic interaction among genetic and epigenetic mechanisms, and that the prenatal environment interacts with the postnatal environment to affect select behaviors in complex manners. In addition, while chronic or prolonged stress, such as that considered in this review, can account for deleterious epigenetic sequelae, some modest acute or short-term stress may precondition the response to effect resilience (Bale et al., 2010).

As noted, the normal or basal epigenetic state can be disrupted by maternal environmental influences such as protein deprivation, caloric restriction or excess, hypoxia, and so forth; stresses that can alter the epigenetic mechanisms noted. Importantly, a wide variety of environmental toxins, including low dose radiation and psychological stress, also are important in activating epigenetic mechanisms (Dolinoy et al., 2007b, Feinberg, 2007, Hertz-Picciotto et al., 2008, Jirtle and Skinner, 2007, Pryce et al., 2002, Reuhl and Lowndes, 1992, Szyf et al., 2007). For instance, embryologically at a subcellular/molecular level, the extracellular matrix glycoprotein reelin is vital to cortical development including migration of immature neurons to laminated structures. And in the adult, reelin is involved in neurotransmission and synaptic plasticity displaying epigenetic regulation (Chen et al., 2002, Dong et al., 2005, Fatemi, 2005, Hawthorne, 2014, Kundakovic et al., 2009, Sibbe et al., 2009, Tremolizzo et al., 2002, Weeber et al., 2002, Zhao et al., 2004, 2007) (See Table 2). This is of particular importance as reelin dysregulation has been implicated in the pathogenesis of autism (Andres, 2002, Zhang et al., 2002), schizophrenia (Costa et al., 2002, Dong et al., 2005, Fatemi et al., 2001, Impagnatiello et al., 1998), and Alzheimer's disease (Durakoglugil et al., 2009) among other disorders. Epigenetic reelin promoter DNA methylation with lower mRNA level regulation has been shown in patients with schizophrenia and psychotic bipolar disorder (Veldic et al., 2005).

An additional example of the role of environmental-mediated epigenetic mechanisms in neurogenesis, is that of the retrotransposition (e.g. "jumping gene") long interspersed nuclear element-1 (LINE-1 or L1) (Muotri et al., 2005, 2007). In the neurogenic region of the hippocampal dentate gyrus this contributes to neuronal plasticity (Muotri et al., 2009). In cultured cells of mouse embryo, with suppression of DNA methylation the LINE-1 retrotransposition is increased in the absence of the methyl-CpG-binding protein 2 (Muotri et al., 2010).

The first demonstration of the dynamic nature of DNA methylation in the brain, was that in the hippocampal CA1 region and its role in memory consolidation in the mouse. In studies of fear-conditioned training, reelin gene demethylation occurred within 1 hour with increased reelin expression and formation of memory. Several hours following the training, reelin gene methylation returned to the initial level (Miller and Sweatt, 2007). Another example of epigenetic regulation is that of brain-derived neurotrophic factor, a neurotrophin that promotes neural precursor proliferation, with maturation and integration of seizure-induced newly generated granular cell layer, dentate gyrus, and hippocampal neurons (Scharfman, 2004). Decreased brain-derived neurotrophic factor promoter methylation with increased transcription follows *in vitro* depolarization (Chen et al., 2003, Martinowich et al., 2003), as well as hippocampal neurogenesis with memory consolidation (Lubin et al., 2008, Ma et al., 2009). In the developing brain, DNA methylation also is a critical cell-intrinsic determinant of glial fibrillary acidic protein expression and astrocyte differentiation (Condorelli et al., 1994, Takizawa et al., 2001). Increasingly, epigenetic changes are being recognized as being of importance in ageing and the development of cancer and other diseases (Jones and Baylin, 2007). Thus, in determining what and who we are, epigenetics with its role in augmenting plasticity is being hailed as the basis for information far beyond that of the genome *per se*. Nonetheless, despite the general understanding that DNA methylation, and/or histone and/or miRNA modifications play major roles in the pathogenesis of epigenesis, little is known of the molecular mechanisms whereby these biochemical/molecular reactions/changes are regulated, much less how they are transmitted between generations (Bird, 2007).

As may be assumed, a provocative area of recent investigation has been that of the epigenetic regulatory interrelations of brain development and neurocognitive outcome. One study suggests that even subtle normal variations in the intrauterine environment may precipitate recognizable differences in postnatal brain structure and cognitive function. Specifically, a longitudinal study of "normal" birthweight monozygotic twins from early childhood to 30 years of age demonstrated significant correlations among birthweight, brain volume and cortex surface area (but not cortical thickness), and cognitive function (intelligence quotient) (Raznahan et al., 2012). Such relations are associated with significant differences in fetal brain cellular and laminar neurogenesis and composition (Petanjek and Kostovic, 2012). Other studies have shown relations of brain weight at birth to the incidence of schizophrenia and other mental disorders (Abel et al., 2010) (see below). Another provocative report has demonstrated the role of perturbed neural activity produced by sensory overstimulation in the neonatal mouse in disrupting angiogenesis (Whiteus et al., 2014). This phenomenon, with feedback effects of disturbed angiogenesis, may alter further developmental neurogenesis. Quite obviously these findings have great implications for individual as well as for public health.

In regard to the myriad of processes by which the brain develops, a number of fundamental questions require exploration. A few of these include the following. By which mechanism(s) is the complexity of development of the brain encoded in the genome? By what manner are the several regulatory controls exerted upon the genome? By what mechanisms are the genetic and epigenetic information translated into the characteristic phenotypic and functional features of the neuron and other cell types? By what mechanisms are the growth and directionality of axons and dendrites regulated? What are the molecular mechanisms of terminal differentiation, and to what extent might the cellular switch from hyperplastic to hypertrophic be regulated? By what mechanisms are selective programmed cell death (apoptosis) regulated? To what extent do gene expression patterns in the developing brain reflect such expression in other tissues/organs? In the adult brain, what regulatory mechanism(s) account for continued neurogenesis from stem cells in the subventricular zone and subgranular zone of the hippocampus, but not in other brain regions? Other questions of relevance include: how are the complex interactions among genetics, epigenetics, and the environment regulated to determine neuronal or other cell phenotype? In nervous system stem cells, what role do epigenetic signals play in determining phenotypic cell fate? How is it that specific and individual gene expression is associated with different epigenetic regulatory mechanisms? By what approaches can we meet the challenge to identify those portions of the genome particularly vulnerable to epigenetic modification which underlie states of mental and other health and disease? Another will be to understand the mechanisms by which these changes occur. Yet another, what is the extent to which normal and abnormal brain function and memory formation involve epigenetic signals?

To What Extent is Gene Expression in the Developing Brain Altered by Maternal Dietary Restriction? Epidemiologic Studies in Humans

Evidence from a number of species demonstrate that, in general, caloric restriction plays an important role in the extension of lifespan (Fontana et al., 2010), and is beneficial in the maintenance of cognitive function (Gillette-Guyonnet and Vellas, 2008). In contrast, several epidemiologic studies in humans and numerous experiments in laboratory animals have shown that nutritional deprivation of the pregnant mother may have deleterious consequences for the progeny (Bale et al., 2010, Barker, 1995, Delisle, 2008, Dobbing and Smart, 1974, Gillman et al., 2008, Goyal et al., 2009, 2010, McMillen and Robinson, 2005, Morley and Lucas, 1997, Rush, 1989, Walker and Marlow, 2008, Wu et al., 2004, and others). Quite obviously, these studies vary considerably as to specific type of malnutrition, its severity, duration, and the neurodevelopmental period at which it occurred. Nonetheless, many authors agree that the period of intrauterine gestation is the single-most vulnerable period for the affects of antenatal maternal nutritional restriction on brain development (Leathwood, 1978, Lewis, 1990, Morgane et al., 1993, Smart, 1986, Smart and Dobbing, 1971a, 1971b, Winick and Rosso, 1975, Zamenhof and van Marthens, 1978). Of course, malnutrition in general is widely recognized to play a lead role in a number of disorders and diseases (Scrimshaw et al., 1968).

Of monumental historic importance, a shocking "experiment" in humans is that which occurred during World War II, *de Hongerwinter* [the "Hunger Winter"] in Western Holland. This mainly urbanized region of the Netherlands' six largest cities (Amsterdam, Den Hague, Haarlem, Leiden, Rotterdam, Utrecht), which included 4 million people (one half the population of the country). The famine commenced in late September 1944, reached its peak in February 1945 and continued until the Allied victory in early May of that year. Because this half-year of Nazi-inflicted-starvation occurred during one of the coldest winters on record, with the *Zuiderzee* and canals frozen so that food and fuel could not be moved by water, mortality rates among the general population more than doubled, accounting for more than 20,000 deaths, either directly from malnutrition or associated infections (Burger et al., 1948, Stein et al., 1975, Susser et al., 1998). (This number does not include the approximately 110,000 Jews deported to concentration camps, never to return (Trienekens, 2000)). This tragedy, with the subsequent "Dutch Famine Study" (Stein et al., 1975), has provided a number of lessons on the effects of caloric restriction/malnutrition, not only on fetal development, but on disease prevalence in adulthood (Schulz, 2010, Slager et al., 1985). These studies are summarized in Table 1. During the six month period in which the German occupation army interdicted food supplies for all groups in society, the caloric ration fell from about 1800 to 2000 calories per day to 400 to 800 calories per day, less than 25% of the recommended intake for adults (Roseboom et al., 2006). The survival diet included sugar beets and tulip bulbs, but little protein (Trienekens, 2000). Although children, and to some extent pregnant and lactating women, received extra rations during the early part of this disastrous famine, they too suffered starvation (Lumey and van Poppel, 1994, Roseboom et al., 2001a, 2006, Smith, 1947b, Stein and Susser, 1975c, Stein et al., 1972, 1975, Susser and Stein, 1994).

Because of the well organized Dutch health system, local registries remained functioning, and individuals exposed to this famine have been traced with careful follow-up for almost seven decades. In addition, the period of starvation was clearly defined, and food rations documented. The cohort profile has been described (Allied Forces Supreme Headquarters, 1948, Boerema, 1947, Burger et al., 1948, Lumey et al., 2007), and a consideration of the overall food supply, both during the early part of World War II with German Occupation, as well as during the famine itself, has been documented (Trienekens, 1985, 1995, 2000).

Among starved women, fertility (as reflected in births nine months later) was halved (Stein and Susser, 1975a), and weight gain during pregnancy was abnormally small or negative (Lumey and van Poppel, 1994, Stein et al., 1995). Of importance, this tragedy has helped to provide valuable insights into the long-term consequences to an individual in terms of whether the nutritional starvation occurred during the three trimesters of gestation. Although infants subjected to decreased nutrition during the first trimester had normal birthweights (Roseboom et al., 2006), birthweights were significantly lower in those exposed during the second and third trimesters (Lumey, 1992, Smith, 1947a, 1947b). The rates of stillbirths also were highest in this cohort (Stein and Susser, 1975a, 1975b, 1976, Stein et al., 1975).

Infant mortality doubled from ~39.5 to 79.7 deaths per 1,000 live-born children (Trienekens, 2000). Particularly striking, is the fact that those normal weight infants whose mothers experienced starvation only during the first trimester of gestation, when exposed after birth to plentiful nutrition, developed higher rates of obesity as adults (Ravelli et al.,

1976), a phenomenon noted especially in women (Ravelli et al., 1999, Roseboom et al., 2006).

Surviving infants who were exposed during the third trimester of pregnancy tended to be small throughout their lives. However, in concert with the prosperity that followed the war, upon reaching adulthood, this cohort demonstrated a significantly greater prevalence of cardiovascular disease, and an earlier onset of both coronary artery disease (47 years versus 50 year in controls) (Painter et al., 2006c) and type II diabetes (Kyle and Pichard, 2006, Painter et al., 2005a, Roseboom et al., 2000b, 2001a, 2001b, 2006, Stein et al., 1975, 2004).

Table 1. Health Sequelae of Dutch "Hunger Winter" by Gestational Age at Exposure

Condition	First Trimester	Second Trimester	Third Trimester	Reference
Female Fertility				Stein et al., 1975
Birthweight Decreased		X	X	de Rooij et al., 2010 Lumey, 1992 Lumey and van Poppel, 1994 Roseboom et al., 2006 Smith, 1947a, 1947b Stein and Susser, 1975a; 1975b
Newborn Head Circumference Decreased		X	X	de Rooij et al., 2010
Infant Mortality (2-fold increase)				Lumey and van Poppel, 1994 Stein et al., 1975 Trienekens, 2000
Metabolic				
IGF-2 gene hypomethylation	X			Heijmans et al., 2008 Tobi et al., 2009
Decreased Glucose Tolerance			X	de Rooij et al., 2006 Ravelli et al., 1998 Roseboom et al., 2006
Type II Diabetes				Kyle and Pichard, 2006 Painter et al., 2005a Roseboom et al., 2001b; 2001c
Obesity in young men	X	X		Ravelli et al., 1976
Obesity in women	X			Ravelli et al., 1999 Roseboom et al., 2006
Cardiovascular				
Atherogenic lipid profile (LDL/HDL)	X			Roseboom et al., 2000a, 2006
Decreased coagulation factors (Fibrinogen, Factor VII)	X			Roseboom et al., 2000c

Table 1. (Continued)

Condition	First Trimester	Second Trimester	Third Trimester	Reference
Coronary Artery Disease (2-fold increase)	X			Painter et al., 2006c Roseboom et al., 2000b; 2006
Stroke				
Microalbuminuria		X		Painter et al., 2005b Roseboom et al., 2006
Hypertension (Decreased ratio of Protein to Carbohydrate)			X	Roseboom et al., 1999; 2001a; 2006
Pulmonary				
Bronchitis and Pulmonary Disease				Lopuhaa et al., 2000
Obstructive airway disease		X		Roseboom et al., 2006
Renal				
Markers of reduced function		X		Roseboom et al., 2006
Breast Cancer (5-fold increase)	X			Painter et al., 2006a Roseboom et al., 2006
Neurodevelopment				
Anencephaly, Hydrocephaly Neural Tube Defects Cerebral Palsy				Brown and Susser, 1997 Stein et al., 1975 Stein and Susser, 1976 Susser et al., 1996; 1998
Head Circumference after age 56 Reduced		X	X	de Rooij et al., 2010
Neuropsychiatric				
Schizophrenia (2- to 3-fold; increase)		X	X	Brown and Susser, 2008 Hoek et al., 1998 Hulshoff Pol et al., 2000 International Schizophrenia Consortium, 2009 Susser and Lin, 1992 Susser and Stein, 1994 Susser et al., 1996
Schizophrenia with white matter hyperintensity	X			Hulshoff Pol et al., 2000
Affective mood and antisocial personality				Brown et al., 1995 Godfrey, 1998 Hoek et al., 1996 Neugebauer et al., 1999
Drug addiction	X			Franzek et al., 2008

Condition	First Trimester	Second Trimester	Third Trimester	Reference
Cognitive function after age 56 Decreased	X			de Rooij et al., 2010
Mortality	X			Ekamper et al., 2013
			X	Lumey and van Poppel, 1994 Painter et al., 2005a Roseboom et al., 2001a; 2001b
Also increased in F2 generation				Lumey, 1992 Painter et al., 2005a

In contrast, those exposed during the first trimester demonstrated atherogenic lipid profiles (Roseboom et al., 2000a, 2006) and a decrease in coagulation factors (Roseboom et al., 2000c). Although overall, no increase in the prevalence of hypertension was observed (Roseboom et al., 1999), those individuals who demonstrated fetal growth restriction at birth had higher blood pressures later in life. In offspring, an elevation of blood pressure in later life was shown to be related to lowered maternal intake of protein in relation to carbohydrate during the third trimester of pregnancy. This suggests a link to macronutrient ingestion (Roseboom et al., 1999, 2001c, 2001d, 2006). Those infants exposed to maternal caloric restriction in mid-gestation developed a much greater incidence of bronchitis and other pulmonary disease (Lopuhaa et al., 2000), and renal disease as evidenced by microalbuminuria (Painter et al., 2005c, Roseboom et al., 2006). In women exposed during early pregnancy, breast cancer (Painter et al., 2006a, Roseboom et al., 2006) also was increased significantly (See Table 1).

A series of sub-studies of the Dutch Famine Study have focused on neurodevelopmental and cognitive defects (Mook et al., 1997). In an initial report of 18 year old men at the time of compulsory military induction, no evidence was detected of mental impairment (Stein et al., 1972). However, notable among survivors of the most severe period of this intrauterine famine was a significant increased prevalence of neurodevelopmental anomalies of the central nervous system, including: hydrocephaly, neural tube defects, and spina bifida (Table 1). Because the perinatal mortality was doubled in this cohort, the prevalence of these neurologic disorders may in fact have been much greater (Stein and Susser, 1976). The prevalence of cerebral palsy also was elevated (Stein et al., 1975, Susser et al., 1996). In a study that revisited this data, and that used more narrow definitions of famine exposure and outcomes, the prenatal famine effect on the incidence of spina bifida was observed only in males (in which the relative risk of death was 2.62), suggesting gender specific nutritional effects (Brown and Susser, 1997). These studies also suggested an opposite sex difference for other disorders, females demonstrating a significantly higher incidence of cerebral palsy, spastic diplegia, and epilepsy (Brown and Susser, 1997, Susser et al., 1998).

At age 56 and above, both sexes showed a significant decrease in head circumference and cognitive ability and performed poorly on a selective attention task (de Rooij et al., 2010). This led the authors to speculate that these cognitive declines may be an early manifestation of an accelerated aging process (De Groot et al., 2011, de Rooij et al., 2010). Also importantly, surviving men and women showed a 2- to 3-fold increase in schizophrenia

(Brown and Susser, 2008, Hulshoff Pol et al., 2000, Susser and Lin, 1992, Susser and Stein, 1994, Susser et al., 1996), schizophrenia spectrum personality disorders (Hoek et al., 1998), other affective mood and anti-social personality disorders (Brown et al., 1995, 2000, Godfrey, 1998, Hoek et al., 1996, Neugebauer et al., 1999), and drug addiction (Franzek et al., 2008). These changes also were associated with decreased intracranial volume, increased brain anomalies, and focal hyperintensities predominantly in white matter. This may reflect the loss of myelin (Hulshoff Pol et al., 2000) (Table 1). Also of importance, a more recent study of men and women in the "Dutch Famine Birth Cohort", age 56 to 59 who experienced deprivation during the first trimester disclosed decreased cognitive function, including: motor-learning, and a selective attention ability e.g., Stroop-like task. These neurologic findings also were associated with a significant decrease in head circumference (de Rooij et al., 2010). Several of these observations, including that of altered cognitive ability (Stein et al., 1972) and decreased head circumference, had not been observed in these subjects as younger adults (Ravelli et al., 1999), although the reasons for these differences are not clear.

In terms of growth, one of the best-characterized epigenetically regulated and maternally imprinted gene locus is insulin-like growth factor II (IGF-2) (Smith et al., 2006). In the blood of periconceptional (but not late gestation) exposed survivors in the sixth decade following the "Hunger Winter", DNA methylation of the IGF-2 gene was decreased significantly, as compared to unexposed, same sex siblings (Heijmans et al., 2008) (Table 2). These reports are the first evidence in humans that transient environmental conditions early in gestation can result in persistent changes in epigenetic profile. As noted, an apparent paradox of these studies is that the epigenetic differences were observed in individuals exposed to famine early in gestation, but who had a normal birthweight, while those exposed later in gestation (when the fetus undergoes rapid growth), experienced a significant decrease in birthweight, but demonstrated little or no epigenetic changes (Heijmans et al., 2008). Transgenerational effects of intrauterine starvation also were noted. Despite being well fed as they were growing into adulthood, infants of the survivors (the F_2 generation) also showed significantly lower birthweights (Susser and Stein, 1994) and greater mortality as adults (Lumey, 1992, Pembrey et al., 2006). Noteworthy is that the Hunger Winter occurred at a well defined time and place, the scope and severity of the famine has been described carefully, and the health effects of birth cohorts exposed to famine at various times during gestation documented. Thus, the "Dutch Famine Study" has developed into a classic epidemiologic investigation of public health (Stein et al., 1975, Susser et al., 1998).

Earlier during WWII (November 1941 to late spring 1942), a similar experience of severe dietary restriction due to interdiction of food supplies by the German forces was subjected upon the people of St. Petersburg and surrounding area of Russia. Again, children born under these conditions were not only small for gestational age, but also developed health problems later in life (Neugebauer et al., 1999). Unfortunately, because records of the long-term sequelae of these individuals are not as clear as those in Holland, clear epidemiologic associations are not possible (Lind, 1984, Ravelli et al., 1976, Sparén et al., 2004). In central eastern China, as a consequence of one of the most severe and devastating famines in recorded history, from 1959 to 1961 precipitated by social turmoil of the "Great Leap Forward" in the Wuhu region of Anhui Province (Chen and Zhou, 2007, Dikötter, 2010, Peng, 1987, Smil, 1999), the risk of schizophrenia was doubled in adult offspring of starved mothers (St. Clair et al., 2005, Song et al., 2009, Xu et al., 2009). Although some have questioned the relation of antenatal food deprivation to subsequent disease in the offspring, given the markedly different circumstances, the similarity of findings as a consequence of the famine in China and that in The Netherlands, has helped to reinforce the concept that schizophrenia may develop as a consequence of dietary imbalance, rather than that of culture, ethnicity, or other factors (Neugebauer, 2005).

As is self evident, in contemporary society features of human malnutrition during pregnancy vary world-wide, with the most prevalent being a lack of dietary protein that is of a chronic and transgenerational nature. That withstanding, this is a vital issue, particularly because of governmental policies and "state sponsored" starvation in some developing nations. As observed by one author, "The reluctance of wealthy nations (together with governmental inaction in some affected countries) to support adequate measures to impede this expanding and deepening epidemic represents an abysmal failure of compassion and conscience.

Table 2. Antenatal Maternal Diet and Epigenetic Regulation of Genes in the Developing Brain

Species	Stress	Gene	Reference
Human	Starvation	Decreased methylation of imprinted Insulin-like growth factor II	Heijmans et al., 2008
Baboon	30% Nutritional Restriction	Differential Gene Regulation	Antonow-Schlorke et al., 2011
Mouse	Protein Deprivation	Angiotensinogen	Goyal et al., 2010
		Angiotensin Converting Enzyme 1 Increased mRNA Decreased protein	
		Angiotensin 2-Receptor Decreased mRNA and protein Upregulated miRNA mmu-mir 27a and 27b Downregulated miRNA mmu-mir 330	
	Methionine administration	Reelin	Dong et al., 2005 Noh et al., 2005
		Reelin promoter	Dong et al., 2007
		67-kDa glutamic acid decarboxylase promoter	Dong et al., 2007
Rat	Choline Deprivation		Albright et al., 1999a, 1999b
	Protein Deprivation	Hypomethylation of Angiotensin II type 1b Biogenic amines	Bogdarina et al., 2007 Resnick et al., 1979 Resnick and Morgane, 1984

It is important not to forget that the occasional ability to reap knowledge from the whirlwind is no exemption from the daily obligation to condemn human suffering and the political mendacity that creates it or permits it to continue unabated" (Neugebauer, 2005, p. 623).

As described, both antenatal and postnatal nutrition have profound effects on the development of brain structure and function. For instance, a study from Great Britain of preterm infants demonstrated in male (but not female) children (7.7 ± 0.5 years) fed a "standard" diet for 4 weeks, a significant deficiency in verbal IQ and a higher incidence of cerebral palsy, as compared to those who received the high-nutrient diet (Lucas et al., 1998). Among this same group, several years later as adolescents (15.7 ± 1.5 years), those fed the high-nutrient diet demonstrated a significantly larger caudate nucleus volume. Again, this correlated with verbal IQ scores (Isaacs et al., 2008). This and other studies suggest that during the early postnatal stage of brain growth, the male and female brain structure and function differ in terms of susceptibility to nutrition and other environmental influences. Quite obviously, a more complete understanding of the role of embryonic, prenatal, and postnatal nutrition on brain development and function is of critical importance to the future health of society (Hüppi, 2008). A complicating factor is that of prematurity *per se*, when birth occurs prior to the third trimester (~ 27 weeks), at which time for optimal development the infant should be *in utero*. This in itself is a hazard to neural development and cognitive outcome (Marlow, 2004, Walker and Marlow, 2008).

Among deficiencies with epigenetic-associated neurodevelopmental anomalies, a related consideration of importance is that of micronutrient (such as folate, iodine, and/or iron) deficiency for the developing brain (Olness, 2003). Studies of folate (the anionic form of folic acid) supplementation have provided compelling evidence for the role of micronutrients in epigenetic-mediated gene regulation (see below). Additional evidence from several randomized, controlled, clinical trials, supports the finding that periconceptual/antenatal folate supplementation greatly diminishes the incidence of neural tube defects (Czeizel and Dudás, 1992, Laurence et al., 1981, Wald and Sneddon, 1991, Wehby and Murray, 2008). Presumably this occurs, in part, by supplying methyl donors to silence some genes involved in regulating neurodevelopment (Waterland and Jirtle, 2004, Waterland et al., 2006). Rat offspring whose mothers were fed a folate deficient diet low in protein during gestation, showed significantly less DNA methylation of both the glucocorticoid receptor and peroxisomal proliferatory-activated genes, each with elevated protein expression.

Folate dietary supplementation prevented these changes (Lillycrop et al., 2005). These methylation changes also may be relevant to the increased insulin resistance observed in small for gestational age infants (Ruzzin et al., 2005). In sheep, restriction of dietary B_{12} and folate also resulted in DNA hypomethylation of genes related to metabolism and blood pressure regulation, with modified health-related phenotypes (Sinclair et al., 2007). Citing evidence from meta-analysis of over a decade of research for the prevention of neural tube defects, in 2009 the U.S. Preventive Services Task Force of the Agency for Healthcare Research and Quality updated its 1996 recommendations, stating that "… all women planning or capable of pregnancy take a daily supplement containing … folic acid", as "… folate is necessary for the regulation of DNA synthesis and function, and … probably affects important events in embryogenesis" (U.S. Preventive Task Force, 2009, p. 626-631).

As must be evident, the topic of micronutrients and their role in neural development is enormously complex and requires further exploration (Breimer and Nilsson, 2012,

Bygren, 2013). As an example, in the rat, vitamin D deficiency during pregnancy impacts behavior in adult offspring (O'Loan et al., 2007). Additionally, the vitamin D metabolite, 1,25-dihydroxyvitamin D_3, stimulates the secretion of neurological neurotropin, as well as acting on hippocampal neurons to down-regulate L-type calcium channel expression, thereby to protect these neurons against excitotoxic injury (Brewer et al., 2001).

Studies also have demonstrated the relation of nutrition during the fetal and/or newborn period to achievement later in life (Dobbing, 1987). For instance, from Pune, India a nutrition study demonstrated a strong association between a pregnant mother's abnormally low plasma vitamin B_{12} concentration at 28 weeks gestation, and the cognitive function (sustained attention and executive function and short-term working memory) of her offspring at 9 years of age (no significant differences in general intelligence were observed, however) (Bhate et al., 2008). From Bristol, United Kingdom, a longitudinal study assessed possible benefits/hazards of maternal seafood intake during pregnancy on offspring cognitive development. The children of mothers who ingested less than 340 g seafood (white fish, dark or oily fish, and shellfish) per week were in the lowest quartile for verbal intelligence quotient, and demonstrated suboptimum outcomes for prosocial behavior, fine motor skills, and communication and social development scores (Hibbeln et al., 2007). Also of relevance, a randomized, double-blind, controlled clinical trial demonstrated a positive link between maternal erythrocyte membrane levels of the omega-3, long-chain, polyunsaturated fatty acid of cell membranes, docosahexaenoic acid (particularly in brain perisynaptic membranes and retina photoreceptor and synaptic membranes), with accelerated attention span development and cognitive function in their infant cohort (Colombo et al., 2004). An additional consideration is the recognition of as yet unknown factors in FGR-associated brain development. For example, data on 18 year old military conscripts in Norway demonstrated an association (albeit not strong) between size (both weight and length) at birth and intellectual performance (Eide et al., 2007). As is evident, nutritional stress during critical time windows plays a vital role in optimal development of the brain and other organs. Clearly, however, the mechanisms of these *in utero* "programming" effects on the brain, other organs, and metabolism remain unknown. That is, by what mechanisms do developing or other cells sense that they are calorie, protein, and/or micronutrient deprived? What strategies can be employed to ameliorate invidious effects and long-term sequelae?

Antenatal Nutritional Deprivation, Hypoxia, and Brain Development: Studies in Laboratory Animals

Of importance in establishing associations and determining fundamental biologic mechanisms, epidemiologic studies in humans must be supplemented with well designed nutritional studies in laboratory animals. From an historical perspective, the earliest studies examined the relation of ante- or post-natal caloric/protein restriction to anatomic/morphologic and functional alterations in offspring (Smart, 1986, 1987).

An early such study of long-term sequelae, that of the effects of low maternal protein diet in the rat, demonstrated growth retardation, increased mortality, and, as evaluated by the Hebb-Williams test, a decrement in intelligence. Interpretation of this study is somewhat complicated however, as low protein diet was administered not only during preconception and gestation, but also following birth to 35 days of age (Cowley and Griesel, 1959).

Combined protein and caloric deficiency during and following gestation in beagle dogs resulted in pups with abnormal gait, athetoid movements of the head and neck, an abnormal electroencephalogram, and instances of convulsive seizures (Platt and Stewart, 1968). In terms of transgenerational effects, a study in the rat disclosed decreased body weight, as well as that of many organs through twelve generations (Stewart et al., 1975, 1980).

In regards to antenatal nutrition and fetal brain development, several hypotheses have been examined. These include: Dobbin's thesis of vulnerable periods during growth spurts (Dobbing, 1968), the hyperplasia/hypertrophy hypothesis of Winick and Noble (Winick and Noble, 1965, 1966), and the functional isolation hypothesis of behavioral development (Levitsky and Barnes, 1972). By examining the relation of antenatal maternal diet to the offspring's neural and metabolic phenotype, many human epidemiologic observations have been confirmed in animal models, leading to insights into the cellular mechanisms, timing, and dose-response relations of these associations (Armitage et al., 2004, Hoet and Hanson, 1999). Evidence demonstrates that neurons, neuroglia, and other brain cells that undergo rapid mitosis and early commitment are particularly vulnerable to amino acid deprivation or other nutritional insult. Because the several tissues and organ systems undergo critical, often brief, periods of growth and development during embryonic and fetal life (Dobbing and Sands, 1979, Morgane et al., 1993, Winick and Noble, 1966), "programming" as a consequence of maternal stress should not be unexpected, as such insults to the developing organism may have profound consequences later in life.

Commencing over a generation ago, studies in the commonly used rodent "model" demonstrated the role of maternal undernutrition/protein deprivation on many aspects of development of the brain, neurogenesis and cell numbers, migration, and transgenerational effects (Bresler et al., 1975, Cowley and Griesel, 1966, Debassio and Kemper, 1985, Lewis, 1990, Morgane et al., 1978, 1992, 1993, Winick and Noble, 1965, 1966, Zamenhof and van Marthens, 1978, 1982, Zamenhof et al., 1971). Rats subjected to maternal low protein diet during gestation delivered pups with significantly lowered weights of both body and brain, the latter of which showed reduced levels of DNA and protein. Despite relatively normal nutrition following birth, these findings persisted in the F_2 generation (Zamenhof et al., 1971). Second-generation offspring with low birthweight, also matured at a slower rate, and displayed poor cognitive performance in the Hebb-Williams maze (Cowley and Griesel, 1966).

Of particular vulnerability to AMPD are aspects of neurogenesis and synaptogenesis (Jones, 1976), as well as development of the cerebral cortical plate and matrix layer of neuronal cells, with significantly prolonged generation times (Shimada et al., 1977). Similarly, nutritional deprivation was shown to result in a significant decrease in hippocampal cell numbers (although their theta wave rhythm was unaffected; Jordan et al., 1982). In many studies, moderate nutritional and/or protein deprivation demonstrated significant alterations in brain or other organ composition in the absence of decrease in birthweight (Antonow-Schlorke et al., 2011, Levitsky and Strupp, 1995, Morgane et al., 1993). For myelin deposition, as well as neurogenesis in general, there is no basis for believing that these arrests of development are reversible (Miller, 1990, Morgane et al., 1993).

Behavioral studies in offspring of dams which experienced 50% gestational dietary deprivation, displayed considerable developmental delay and abnormal activity (Simonson et al., 1969), as well as less exploratory activity and neuromotor abnormalities (Simonson and Chow, 1970). Other nutritional deprivation studies in rats disclosed delayed appearance of certain reflexes and exploratory responses (Smart and Dobbing, 1971a, 1971b), associated with significantly decreased forebrain DNA (Smart et al., 1973). In another behavioral study in AMPD rats, in addition to retarded growth of offspring was their subpar ability to problem solve (Cowley and Griesel, 1966). Similar behavioral studies in mice following protein deprivation noted poor avoidance performance (Bush and Leathwood, 1975). As a function of specific dietary manipulation in mice, e.g., whether caloric restriction, protein deprivation, or low iron intake, behavioral assessment also demonstrated differences in both memory and hippocampal structure responses (Ranade et al., 2008).

In terms of timing of antenatal stress, maternal malnutrition begun prior to mating, and continued throughout pregnancy, produced more severe effects than that seen during the period of gestation alone (Rosso, 1990, Zamenhof and van Marthens, 1978). In addition, feeding a AMPD diet only during the preimplantation period (days post conception (DPC)), prior to return to control diet during the remainder of pregnancy, induced programming in blastocyst of reduced cell number of both inner cell mass (DPC 4) and trophectoderm (DPC 4.25). Birthweight also was reduced. By 12 weeks of age these offspring showed increased postnatal growth rate, increased systolic blood pressure, and altered organ to body weight ratios (Kwong et al., 2000). In the mouse, protein deprivation during oocyte maturation, also has been shown to result in behavioral and cardiovascular abnormalities in adult offspring (Watkins et al., 2008).

Antenatal malnutrition also has been shown to result in a number of neurophysiologic changes in offspring. These include: increased brain 5-hydroxytryptamine (5-HT, serotonin) turnover (Smart et al., 1976), and increased magnitude and duration of interneuron-mediated inhibition of dentate gyrus granule cell excitability (Austin et al., 1992). Presumably altered GABA metabolism resulted in a relative denervation of granule cell connections in the dendritic plexus (Diáz-Cintra et al., 1991), with altered circuit modulation (Bronzino et al., 1991a, 1991b), and altered vigilance state-dependent gating of information inflow into the hippocampus (Austin et al., 1992). Offspring of rats subjected to 50% caloric restriction during DPC 10 to 20 showed evidence of impaired neuronal progenitor cell division and migration, and reduced *in vitro* neuronal and astrocyte proliferation and differentiation (Desai et al., 2011). That optimal nutrition following birth does not reverse these neurobiologic effects, has been documented in several studies. For instance, at 3 to 4 months of age rats subjected to AMPD and then following birth cross-fostered to control lactating dams, displayed significant alterations in several measures of kindling-induced dentate gyrus granule cell excitability (Bronzino et al., 1991a, 1991b). Many other neurophysiologic changes have been reported. These studies are confounded, however, as they include postnatal as well as antenatal nutritional deprivation (for review see Morgane et al., 1993).

An important question is the extent to which these observed responses result from overall caloric restriction, as opposed to a qualitative component in the diet. Although every dietary nutrient is vital, a number of studies demonstrate that a major factor in these defects is protein deprivation *per se*. For example in the rat, growth reducing effects of AMPD could be reversed only by an increase in dietary protein, while vitamin supplements and caloric increases through carbohydrates failed to negate the observed effects (Hsueh et al., 1967). Another study in rats subjected to 50% AMPD demonstrated significant differences in maternal weight gain, birthweights, and the development of hypertension at 4 weeks of age, as a consequence of differences in the oils and carbohydrate composition of the diet (Langley-Evans, 2000). Other studies demonstrate dietary amino acid balance as a key mediator of some of the cardiovascular and metabolic effects observed in response to AMPD (Boujendar et al., 2003). For instance, deprivation of the methyl donor choline (mediated by S-adenosylmethionine), may result in abnormalities of the developing hippocampus (Albright et al., 1999b, Niculescu et al., 2006) and other brain structures (Albright et al., 1999a, Blusztajn, 1998). As noted earlier, folate and vitamin B_{12} deficiency also have been implicated in such defects.

The brains of Sprague-Dawley rat offspring from 10 to 90 days old, whose mothers had been subjected to AMPD (8% casein versus 25% in controls) demonstrated a number of significant changes. These included: structural anatomic (reduced cortical and subcortical dendritic branching), physiologic (altered sleep pattern maturation and seizure threshold), biochemical (increased biogenic amines, altered tryptophan metabolism), and behavioral (altered response to adverse stimulation) (Resnick et al., 1979). When the same low-protein, isocaloric diet was given to the second generation, alterations in brain levels of serotonin, tryptophan, and 5-hydroxyindoleacetic acid were even more severe (Resnick and Morgane, 1984). Of importance, these changes were not restored by giving the pups a normal diet following birth (Stern et al., 1984). Similarly, in rats subjected to AMPD with 50% casein, decreases in DNA methylation of several genes were more pronounced in the F_2 generation (Burdge et al., 2007). In terms of epigenetic-mediated changes of neurotransmitter function, several studies have demonstrated AMPD-associated lowered expression of dopamine-related molecules within the mesocorticolimbic neurons, associated with decreased dopamine-dependent reward-related behaviors (Palmer et al., 2008, Zambrano et al., 2006). Cerebral cortex vesicular density and forebrain DNA concentration also were significantly lower in offspring of protein deprived (8% versus 20%) dams (Bennis-Taleb et al., 1999). In addition to nutrition during embryonic and fetal development being of importance, that during the entire periconceptual period is vital (Oliver et al., 2005).

In adult mice, administration of L-methionine, an essential amino acid and methyl group donor, hypermethylates the reelin promoter and several other genes to reduce mRNA levels. Of significance, mice so treated demonstrate altered learning and memory, as well as altered sociability, amplifying further the importance of this protein and its signaling pathway in learning and behavior (Chen et al., 2002, Dong et al., 2005, Tremolizzo et al., 2002). Reelin expression in the adult mouse brain can be manipulated by pharmacologic intervention (see below and Dong et al., 2007, Noh et al., 2005). Overall, numerous studies have confirmed the role of antenatal nutritional deprivation (and protein restriction in particular) in producing deleterious long-term neurobehavioral sequelae that extend into adulthood. A 1986 review of sixteen studies during gestation on the effects of nutritional deprivation on learning ability (chiefly in the rat), concluded that the effects could of considerable significance, particularly in the male (Smart, 1986). In such studies, although working memory performance has been shown to be relatively unaffected, susceptibility to interference and extinction (Tonkiss and Galler, 1990) and acquisition of differential reinforcement (Tonkiss et al., 1990) may be altered significantly.

Of great relevance to the human condition, 30% maternal nutritional restriction during the first one-half of pregnancy in the baboon (*Papio hamadryas*) demonstrated a profound effect on fetal brain development at gestational day 90 (term = 185 DPC) (Antonow-Schlorke et al., 2011). In this study, although neither fetal body nor brain weights were decreased significantly, nutritional deprivation induced major changes in development of the cerebral cortex and subventricular zone. For instance in the SVZ, thickness decreased 44%, while the number of proliferating cells increased 43% and the number of apoptotic cells increased 119%. Immunohistochemical analysis showed a significant decrease in markers for several cell types, and expression of growth factors and regulatory proteins of cerebral development. Of interest, the whole-genome expression profile of the cortical plate showed differential expression of 318 genes (157 up- and 161 down-regulated) (Antonow-Schlorke et al., 2011) (Table 2). Attributable to complex alterations in major signaling pathways, this study emphasizes the complexity of cerebral development, and critical role of optimal nutrition and epigenetic-mediated mechanisms in its successful outcome. Along this line, several neuro-developmental disorders have been suggested to be a consequence of a "double whammy" effect, with a "first hit" by antenatal insult and a "second hit" occurring in adulthood (Woods, 1998). As noted repeatedly, the fundamental mechanisms whereby antenatal stress such as AMPD alters cerebral vasculogenesis, neurogenesis, synaptogenesis, and related functions are essentially unknown.

Yet another example of the manner in which moderate AMPD alters expression of genes in the brain, is that of proteins in the renin-angiotensin system (RAS). While the existence of renin-angiotensin cascade as a systemic pathway is well recognized, it also functions independently in individual tissues and organ systems, including the brain. The RAS cascade commences with cleavage of angiotensinogen into the decapeptide angiotensin-I (Ang I) by the action of renin. Angiotensin converting enzyme (ACE) then converts Ang I into the octapeptide and active moiety angiotensin II (Ang II), which by its two receptors angiotensin-II type 1 (AT1) (subdivided into AT1a and AT1b) appears to mediate most RAS effects (Timmermans et al., 1993), and angiotensin-II Type 2 (AT2) which mediates others. The first of these (AT1) include activation of sympathetic tone, blood pressure increase by vasoconstriction, vasopressin release, behavioral effects, and so forth. Several studies have shown the presence of all components of the renin-angiotensin system in brain (Goyal et al., 2010, Lavoie and Sigmund, 2003, Lenkei et al., 1997, McKinley et al., 2003, Nguyen et al., 2002), and their alterations in disorders such as depression, neurodegenerative disease, Alzheimer disease, hypertension, and stroke (Savaskan, 2005, Susser et al., 1996). Also established is the role of various components of the RAS in learning, memory, behavior, osmoregulation, and thermoregulation (McKinley et al., 2003, Savaskan, 2005). For instance, in the spontaneously hypertensive rat, increase in brain angiotensinogen mRNA has been shown to precede the development of hypertension (Tamura et al., 1996). Transgenic mice with small interfering RNA (siRNA)-mediated alterations of the various components of the RAS demonstrated changes in blood pressure, suggesting a causal role of this system in the pathogenesis of hypertension (He et al., 2008, 2009, Zhang et al., 2006). Protein-deprived rats showed hypomethylation of the promoter region of angiotensin II type 1b receptors in the adrenals, leading to increased protein expression of the AT1 gene (Bogdarina et al., 2007).

To increase further our understanding of these issues regarding the RAS system at E17.5 in mice we compared gene expression in brains of normal controls, in contrast to pregnancies in which the mothers were exposed to seven days of 50% protein deprivation, e.g., maternal low protein diet, i.e., $10g \cdot 100g^{-1}$ protein by weight versus the $20g \cdot 100g^{-1}$ of normal chow from E10.5 to E17.5 (Goyal et al., 2010). Brains from AMPD fetuses showed significantly increased mRNA levels of angiotensinogen; however, this was not reflected in protein expression levels, which did not differ significantly from control. Although in AMPD fetal brains, the ACE-1 mRNA levels were increased significantly, ACE-1 protein expression was decreased ~50%. Also in these brains, as compared to control, the mRNA levels and protein expression of AT2 receptors were reduced significantly. In addition with nutritional deprivation, mRNA and protein levels of renin, ACE-2, and AT1 receptors did not vary significantly from control. Importantly, analysis of 20 CpG sites in the fetal brain ACE-1 promoter showed significant hypomethylation at several positions. For instance, of the total 208 CpGs in the promoter region of ACE-1, 167 (80%) were methylated in the control, whereas only 88 (42%) were methylated in AMPD (P < 0.05; all sites considered together). This could account for the observed increased ACE-1 mRNA (Goyal et al., 2010). In this study, the microRNAs mmu-mir-27a and mmu-mir-27b, which regulate ACE-1 translation, were significantly upregulated, and of the three miRNA examined which regulate AT2 receptor translation, only one, mmu-mir-330, was found to be downregulated significantly (Table 2). Of importance, this study demonstrates that antenatal AMPD may lead to selective fetal brain alterations in angiotensinogen, ACE-1, and AT2 receptors at both transcriptional and translational levels. Furthermore, this study also demonstrates changes in promoter methylation and miRNA levels (Goyal et al., 2010), changes in the brain RAS expression with this degree of protein deprivation which previously were unknown.

Regarding the mechanisms by which brain RAS leads to elevated blood pressure and other neural-related changes, several signal transduction pathways may operate. Chiefly, stimulation of circumventricular or brainstem Ang II receptors elicits blood pressure increase, attenuation of the baroreceptor reflex, increased dypsogenic response, release of pituitary hormones such as vasopressin, oxytocin, and ACTH, and natriuresis (Gyurko et al., 1993, Nishimura et al., 1992, Steckelings et al., 1992, Tamura et al., 1996).

Figure 3 summarizes the findings of the mouse brain RAS study noted, and compares the effects of AMPD on the systemic RAS. During the second half of pregnancy protein restriction leads to epigenetic transcriptional and post-transcriptional changes, along with alterations in mRNA and proteins of several brain RAS genes. A transcriptional mechanism such as DNA hypomethylation is evident in the fetal brains, and may be the cause for increased mRNA expression (Goyal et al., 2010). In other studies in fetal mice subjected to similar stress, we have demonstrated significant changes in the expression of both the systemic RAS (Goyal et al., 2009), lung (Goyal et al., 2011a), and placenta (Goyal et al., 2011b).

These studies indicate several other changes in the developing fetal brain and systemic RAS with AMPD. Of note, these modifications can persist lifelong, leading to manifestation of hypertension and other disorders later in adult life. Because post-transcriptional mechanisms such as miRNA-mediated regulation finally determine the expression of proteins from mRNA, discrepancies in mRNA and protein levels may result of programming at the transcriptional and post-transcriptional level.

Thus, even though these genes become programmed in fetal life, they may be responsible for manifestation of disorders at a later age. Evidence that disturbed maternal nutrition may result in differential programming of gene and protein expression in the offspring is a critical issue that demands a deeper mechanistic understanding, as well as appreciation of its social implications.

Other studies in rodents have shown similar effects. In rats, AMPD triggered hypertension in the pups in adulthood (Langley and Jackson, 1994), probably by augmentation of the pups' renin-angiotensin system. Another hormonal alteration in nutritionally deprived rat pups, was an increase in somatostatin expression in the periventricular nucleus. This led to much lower levels of growth hormone expression, and showed deleterious effects on the pups' growth following birth (Huizinga et al., 2000). Fetal undernourishment may lead to other neuronal sequelae, such as under-development of the facial motor nucleus, resulting in decrease in the ability of pups to suckle and chew (Perez-Torrero et al., 2001).

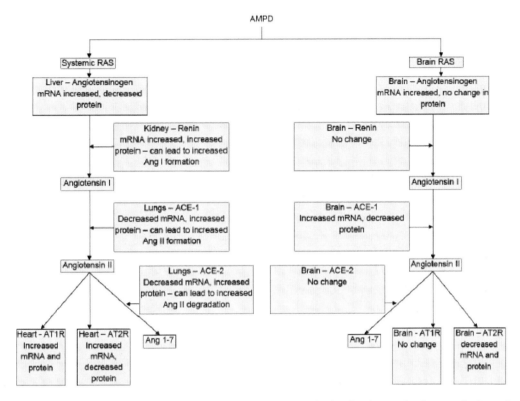

Figure 3. Comparative findings of the antenatal maternal protein deprivation on fetal mouse brain renin-angiotensin system, as compared to the systemic renin-angiotensin system.

In a contrasting series of studies in mice, antenatal maternal high fat diet was associated with a significant increase in offspring body length as well as reduced insulin sensitivity. These epigenetic sequelae persisted for at least two generations, and were shown to be transmitted via both maternal and paternal lineage (Dunn and Bale, 2009).

Of relevance, further studies have examined the extent to which gene expression in the developing brain is altered by a less than optimal supply of oxygen (O_2), e.g., hypoxia. A major stressor in development, hypoxia is believed to be a contributing factor in the genesis of fetal growth restriction (FGR), that may contribute to several problems for the newborn such as severe neurologic disorders (Longo, 1977, 1980, 1984, 1987) and persistent pulmonary hypertension (Gao and Raj, 2010). As with all other cell types, oxygen is a critical regulator of neuronal development. Acting through aryl receptor nuclear transporter and hypoxia-inducible factor-1_α (HIF1α), oxygen may regulate cell phenotype and gene expression (Adelman et al., 2000). For instance, hypoxic stress can lead to neuronal cell death, as well as dysregulation of vasculogenesis with development of the cerebral vascular bed. In a rat uterine artery ligation model of intrauterine ischemia/hypoxia, histone acetylation was dramatically altered, decreasing expression of those genes associated with hormonal neurotrophic factors as well as decreased development of the pancreas (Pinney and Simmons, 2010, Simmons et al., 2001). Although not hypoxia *per se*, a rat model of bilateral uterine artery ligation to produce ischemia/hypoxia FGR, profoundly altered expression of hippocampal NMDA receptor subunits (both mRNA and protein), which are critical for synaptogenesis and learning. In addition, the male offspring showed decreased ratio of myelin basic protein to neuronal nuclei in the CA1 and CA3 regions and dentate gyrus of the hippocampus (Schober et al., 2009). A further study using this experimental approach demonstrated significantly altered glucocorticoid receptor gene expression, an important receptor of HPA axis activity, and a factor underlying HPA axis reprogramming of neural activity (Ke et al., 2010). These studies emphasize the role of multiple trophic inputs to neural development, most of which are as yet unknown. In addition, they emphasize the sobering fact that essentially nothing is known about the fundamental molecular bases of these changes. A review of hypoxia/ischemia-mediated neuronal sequelae is beyond the scope of this review.

A number of other studies have highlighted the diverse manner in which developing brain cells respond to hypoxic stress, and many have examined gene expression changes in response to hypoxia at the global level. One study catalogued the hypoxic-induced responses in the rat embryo to hypoxic exposure for both 24 hours and 11 days. Glycolysis-related genes, calcium homeostasis-related genes, and inflammatory genes (particularly those related to oxidative stress) were upregulated, while cell growth-related genes were downregulated (Huang et al., 2004). In general, the murine brain appears to respond to hypoxia through several mechanisms, including upregulation of genes associated with erythropoiesis, increases in heme and iron metabolism, and in genes involved in proteolysis and peptidolysis. These varied responses suggest that, in general, the body responds by increasing its oxygen carrying capacity and increasing metabolic and antioxidant responses, and with the brain initiating angiogenesis with tissue growth, turnover, and remodeling. As noted, little is understood regarding the fundamental mechanisms of these changes. Epigenetic-mediated changes in extracellular matrix remodeling, altered cellular metabolism and transcriptional regulation, and modulation of apoptosis all appear to be crucial steps in the physiological responses to consider. In terms of stress-induced epigenetic responses some questions include: what determines the individual patterns of expression, as opposed to the up- or downregulation of those genes common to all stressors? By what signal transduction mechanisms are these genes regulated? What are the critical developmental stages/times of neuronal or other brain cell vulnerability to environmental, nutritional, hypoxic, or other stress? What are some of the most important environmental factors that alter the epigenome in a deleterious manner, and what are their dose-response relations? Can we define the roles of specific nutrients and micronutrients in epigenetic-mediated neurodevelopmental disorders?

Not to be excluded, is the role of postnatal early life experience in affecting epigenetic-mediated mechanisms. For instance, several studies implicate the hypothalamic-pituitary-adrenal (HPA) axis, a major component of the body's stress response system that leads to increased responsivity in adulthood. Consistent with this concept, depressed patients with a history of childhood abuse or neglect may be characterized by hyperactivity of the HPA axis (Heim and Nemeroff, 2002). In mice, the stress of infant-mother separation for 3 hours·day[-1] from postnatal day 1 to 10 resulted in life-long elevated glucocorticosteroid secretion, elevated endocrine responsiveness to subsequent stressors, and disruption of HPA homeostatic mechanisms which affect cognition as well as mood (Holsboer, 2000, Pariante and Lightman, 2008). A considerable body of evidence associates HPA hormones with mood and cognitive disorders, thus making their receptors potential targets for psychopharmacological intervention (Bao and Swaab, 2010).

In the infant-maternal separation model, within the parvocellular sub-division of the hypothalamic paraventricular nucleus, such stress also resulted in a significant reduction in DNA methylation at a downstream enhancer of the *Avp* gene (Murgatroyd and Spengler, 2011). Not surprisingly, this epigenetic change was accompanied by persistent elevation of arginine vasopressin mRNA and protein expression with sustained (> 1yr) hyperactivity of the HPA axis (Murgatroyd and Spengler, 2011). In addition, this change was associated with site-specific phosphorylation of the translation factor MeCP2 by calmodulin kinase II. In addition, disturbed MeCP2 activity altered several histone acetylases to increase gene expression (Murgatroyd and Spengler, 2011). The paradigm of chronic social stress in the newborn rodent displayed multiple long-term effects in regards to the neuroendocrinology of their maternal care and nursing of offspring as adult dams (Murgatroyd and Nephew, 2013, Nephew and Bridges, 2011).

Overall, these findings in humans, rodents, and other species that have been studied, strongly support the concept of antenatal as well as postnatal dietary and other environmental factors, acting via epigenetic mechanisms to influence (in most cases adversely) the developing brain. Of particular and sobering note, is the role of behavioral epigenetics and its role in early life programming of neuropsychiatric disorders. Again in caution, while studies in laboratory animals provide considerable information and insights, because of the hazards in extrapolating between species, and subtleties of behavioral manifestations, undoubtedly the findings do not represent in their entirety those epigenetic phenomena that occur in humans. As noted below, a number of critical questions concern the fundamental mechanisms of these changes.

By What Biochemical and Molecular Mechanisms are Epigenetic Changes in Developing Brain Gene Expression Mediated?

As noted, epigenetic-mediated DNA methylation, histone alterations, and microRNA, and related molecular mechanisms, play an important role in almost every biological process, including development of the brain (Jiang et al., 2008, MacDonald and Roskams, 2009). As with most phenomena of biology and life, the exceedingly complex molecular mechanisms whereby genes are repressed or activated in a stable manner (Berger, 2007, Kouzarides, 2007, Lister and Ecker, 2009, Lister et al., 2009), are beyond the limits of this review. In addition, because the several epigenetic mechanisms are reviewed in other Chapters of this volume, they will be described only briefly here.

The most extensively studied of the epigenetic modifications is that of DNA methylation/hydromethylation (Holliday and Pugh, 1975, Riggs, 1975). Recognized to be a dynamic process that varies from minutes to hours, this is catalyzed by a family of DNA methyltransferases that involves the 5′-carbon of cytosine residues followed by a guanine residue, i.e., "CpG methylation." As is becoming appreciated, these modifications would appear to play a key role in neurogenesis, dendritic and synapse formation, memory formation and storage, and in other neuronal functions (Day and Sweatt, 2010, Dulac, 2010, Wu and Sun, 2009). DNA methylation induces gene repression or "a silent chromatin state"

(The "p" in the dinucleotide CpG refers to the phosphodiester bond between cytosine and guanine). Methylation of CpG "islands", i.e., clusters of greater than 500 base pairs in the DNA promoter, directly inhibits the binding of specific DNA transcription factors, and/or indirectly inhibits transcription by recruiting methyl-CPG binding proteins, with their associated repressive chromatin-remodeling activities (Li et al., 2007a, Razin, 1998, Razin and Riggs, 1980, Turek-Plewa and Jagodziński, 2005). Both intrinsic factors and environmental/nutritional factors can modulate the activity of the several methyltransferases and demethylases upon which this phenomenon is dependent (Bestor, 2000).

For instance, folate deficiency (see above) can affect DNA stability via hypomethylation with altered gene expression, and/or by affecting its synthesis and repair (Duthie et al., 2002). A wealth of data supports the concept of DNA hyper- methylation (which incidentally governs allelic imprinting) or hypo-methylation of specific genes decreasing or increasing, respectively, mRNA expression (Bogdarina et al., 2004, 2007). Because of the requirement for a high DNA synthesis rate during the course of gametogenesis, early embryogenesis, and fetal development, considerable activity in DNA methylation/demethylation patterning occurs, a time during which the cells are vulnerable to the influence of abnormal environmental/nutritional factors (Li et al., 2002, Mayer et al., 2000, Oswald et al., 2000). Of importance, such epigenetic changes in germ cells may be transmitted to future generations (Anway et al., 2005).

In addition to DNA methylation with transcriptional repression, there exists an additional world of factors that interact with histones to modify chromatin structure and thus gene expression. As is becoming appreciated, the biochemical organization of histones in the nucleosomes, around which DNA is wrapped, contributes an additional layer of complexity of profound importance in the regulation of transcription (Jiang et al., 2008, Lee et al., 2010, Zhou et al., 2011). Post-translational covalent modifications of histones include: acetylation, methylation, phosphorylation, ADP-ribosylation, ubiquitination and/or sumoylation alone, or in combination. These chemical modifications occur on the amino acids that constitute the histone N-terminal tails, and modify their interaction with DNA and/or other nuclear proteins. Histone methylation (Dambacher et al., 2010) is catalyzed by two families of proteins that regulate homeotic genes. These are Polycomb group of proteins (PcG), which via complex regulatory mechanisms (Xu et al., 2010), in general repress transcription through local heterochromatin formation. In contrast, the Trithorax group (TrxG) of proteins are associated with transcriptional activation (Bonasio et al., 2010, Cedar and Bergman, 2009, Covic et al., 2010, Ringrose and Paro, 2004). Enzymes critically associated with these nucleosomal modifications include: histone acetyltransferases (HAT), histone deacetylases (HDAC), histone methyltransferases (HMT), histone demethylases (HDM), and others (Dodd et al., 2007, Klose et al., 2006, Riccio, 2010). In the developing brain, in modulating the chromatin activity state, HDAC-1 and -2 regulate synapse development, maturation, and function (Akhtar et al., 2009). As noted, antenatal methyl supplements can increase DNA methylation in offspring (Waterland et al., 2006).

In the mouse, impairment of hippocampal chromatin plasticity, learning, and memory are associated with deregulation of histone H4 lysine 12 (H4K12) acetylation, which upon restoration reinstates the expression of genes leading to recovery of cognitive abilities (Peleg et al., 2010). This suggests an interplay of histone acetylation and DNA methylation (Dong et al., 2007, Noh et al., 2005, Tremolizzo et al., 2005). These interactions are supported by a study of the effect of choline deficiency during intrauterine development on altered neural gene expression. In addition to decreased progenitor cell proliferation and increased apoptosis in hippocampal cells, a number of behavioral alterations have been observed (Mehedint et al., 2010). Also in the developing brain, epigenetic-mediated histone deacetylation plays a key role in the timing of oligodendrocyte progenitor cell differentiation and myelin formation (Shen et al., 2005). In addition, the potential role of histone deacetylase inhibitors in neuroprotection has been demonstrated (Jiang et al., 2008). A host of other histone associated changes play major roles in neurodevelopment.

In addition, an entirely new vista in genomic regulation has been revealed by the appreciation that both relatively small (micro or miRNA) and long non-coding RNA (lncRNA) molecules (the stuff of so-called "junk" DNA), play critical roles in gene expression. These RNAs are capable of base pairing with mRNA, and fine-tuning promoters/repressors of gene expression. In addition, during development and differentiation they influence proximate genes without changes in the nucleic acid code *per se* (Martin and Zhang, 2005, Wolffe and Matzke, 1999). The use of miRNA microarrays in both rat and monkey has demonstrated a temporal wave of expression of sequential classes of miRNAs with brain development (Miska et al., 2004). Specifically, miRNA-124 has been shown to regulate several aspects of neuronal growth and differentiation, including the cytoskeletal elements actin and tubulin (Yu et al., 2008). miRNA-219 has been shown to modulate NMDA glutamate receptors which, in turn, regulate neurotransmission and synaptic plasticity, and are implicated in a number of neuropsychiatric disorders (Kocerha et al., 2009). Both miRNA-9 (Leucht et al., 2008, Lukiw, 2007) and miRNA-124 (Cheng et al., 2009; Visvanathan et al., 2007; Yoo et al., 2009) also play critical roles in embryonic neural development, while miRNA-219 and miRNA-338 are important in differentiation of oligodendrocytes with myelin formation (Zhao et al., 2010). In the highly expressed fetal neural stem cells, transcription factor Hmga2 is targeted by the miRNA let-7b, contributing to decline in neural stem cell function with advancing age (Nishino et al., 2008). In turn, in the dentate gyrus of the adult hippocampus miRNA-132 regulates dendritic growth and arborization of newly born neurons in response to signaling by the cAMP response element binding protein (CREB) (Magill et al., 2010). Other classes of regulatory RNAs include small interfering RNA, and others. As may be evident, the dynamic remodeling of neuronal stem cells to mature differentiated neurons requires a host of epigenetic events (Singh et al., 2009). A number of reviews on epigenetic molecular regulation of these mechanisms during embryogenesis and fetal development are available (Bird, 2007, Jaenisch, 1997, Jaenisch and Bird, 2003, Jones and Takai, 2001, Molfese, 2011, Paulsen et al., 2008, Santos et al., 2005, Tost, 2008a, 2008b).

By combining both genetic and epigenetic information (the so-called "epigenome" or "epigenotype"), more accurate and insightful information can be obtained with regards to gene expression regulation and ultimately biological phenotype. Several additional epigenetic mechanisms of importance in the brain have been described (Bowman, 2010, Kouzarides, 2007, Riccio, 2010, Sandovici et al., 2011, Yoo and Crabtree, 2009). As a caveat, the extent to which histone modifications, non-coding RNAs, and other epigenetic mechanisms are self-perpetuating and heritable is debated by some (For instance see Bourc'his and Voinnet, 2010).

As with other topics, vital questions regarding these epigenetic mechanisms include: by what mechanisms are cerebral and other patterns of these biochemical/molecular events regulated? By what mechanisms are long-term neurodevelopmental decisions regulated? By what mechanism(s) are these inherited through cell division? During cell differentiation and development, in a defined cell lineage, how is stability maintained while flexibility is allowed? To what extent can one use the findings of stress-induced gene expression responses, to gain an understanding of the phenomenon of epigenesis and its various manifestations?

By What Mechanisms Might the Signal of Amino Acid Deficiency or other Stress be Transduced to Developing Brain Cells

As discussed, an imbalance in the maternal diet or actual moderate to severe caloric and/or protein deficiency during pregnancy have been linked to fetal growth restriction, as well as to a number of pathologies including cognitive impairment, schizophrenia, and other neuropsychiatric diseases in the adult offspring. The question arises, however, by what mechanism(s) can a stressor during antenatal life be linked to the serious disorders in the adult? Embryonic cells and tissues with altered "programming" manifest themselves as different clinical disorders in the adult, based on the precise timing and severity of the antenatal stress. For instance, changes in availability of dietary amino acids which participate in methylation can affect the remethylation process either directly or through regulators of amino acid transporters, metabolism, cellular growth, differentiation, and signaling pathways. Whereas a decade or two ago, one viewed cellular/subcellular signaling as occurring via one of several discreet pathways, it now is appreciated that such signaling occurs via a network with interactions among a dozen or more such pathways, a number of which interconnect into complex networks. To name just a few, these include: protein kinase B, serine/threonine-specific protein kinase (AKT), cyclic adenosine monophosphate (cAMP), mitogen-activated protein kinase (MAPK), extracellular regulated kinase (ERK), mammalian target of rapamycin (mTOR), nuclear factor kappa B (NFκB), and others. The manner in which several of these may be involved in amino acid signaling is illustrated in Figure 4. In essence, the molecular mechanisms for programming of such disorders, cellular specific amino acid deprivation would be sensed by mTOR. Low protein diet has been implicated in reducing activity of the protein/kinase mTOR, which further reduces the patterns of cellular growth and differentiation. mTOR also possesses histone deacetylase activity, thus, its modulation as a consequence of AMPD adds complexity to embryonic epigenome regulation. These signals then regulate cell growth and differentiation via the epigenetic mechanisms described, which provide post-transcriptional and/or translational control.

What Are Some of the Human Correlates on the Role of Epigenetics in Mental Health and Disease?

Throughout the world, the burden of neuropsychiatric problems such as depressive disorders, schizophrenia, bipolar disorders, autism, and many others, is enormous. These take a staggering toll on health, accounting for enormous misery and heartbreak, as well as stress on the economy. With remarkable advances in molecular genetics, for the past decade or more the hope that has filled the hearts of neuroscientists and clinicians is that of discovering the cellular/molecular basis of these myriad and complex disorders. Nonetheless, despite genome-wide association studies of a large number of patients, and the power of microarrays, and other advanced technologies, we are far from an understanding their fundamental basis.

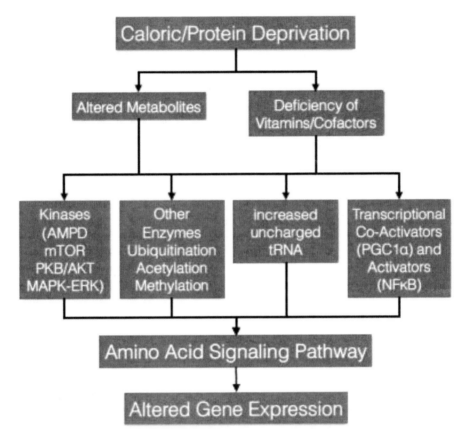

Figure 4. Overview of differing pathways involved in caloric/protein deprivation-mediated alteration of the Amino Acid Signaling.

In part, this is a consequence of the incredible complexity of the brain. Despite the enigmas presented, a number of these are being discovered to be associated with multiple gene polymorphisms. In addition, an increasing body of evidence from genome-wide association studies and other lines of investigation has supported the idea that epigenetic mechanisms play a critical role in neurodevelopmental disorders, including those of post-mitotic neurons (Dulac, 2010, Hsieh and Eisch, 2010).

A complicating factor of such analysis, however, is that for the most part, clinical diagnosis is based on subjective and inconsistent criteria rather than cellular and molecular markers. Thus, the search goes on. What follows is a synthesis of some of what is known and not known regarding the epigenetic genesis of selected neuropsychiatric disorders. Many, but not all, of these may follow antenatal stress *in utero*. Nonetheless, on a cautionary note, because almost all clinical studies on the neuropsychiatric disorders are performed in tissue samples from the brains of individuals in an advanced state of disease, the extent to which the epigenetic changes noted represent a cause or consequence of the disease remains unclear (Chouliaras et al., 2010).

As noted, both genetic mutations in DNA sequences, and epigenetic alteration (DNA methylation and/or histone modifications, and/or miRNAs), play a vital role in the genesis of many neuropsychiatric diseases (Abel and Zukin, 2008, Nelson and Jeste, 2008, Urdinguio et al., 2009) (See Table 3).

Table 3. Neuro-Psychiatric Disorders and Altered Genetic and Epigenetic Associations

Neuro-Psychiatric Disorder	Genetic and Epigenetic Alterations	Reference
Fragile X syndrome	FMR1 and FMR2 expansion of promoter CGG triplet repeats with DNA Methylation	Pietrobono et al., 2002 Wang et al., 2010
	Associated histone deacetylation	Coffee et al., 1999
Immunodeficiency-centromeric instability-facial anomalies syndrome	DNMT 3B methyltransferase mutations, with hypomethylation at centromeres of chromosome 1, 9, and 16	Ausio et al., 2003 Dittrich et al., 1996 Hansen et al., 1999, 2000 Jeanpierre et al., 1993 Tiepolo et al., 1979 Xu et al., 1999
Prader-Willi syndrome	Imprinting defect. DNA methylation of paternal copy of imprinted chromosomal region 15q11-q13	Cassidy et al., 2000 Davies et al., 2005 Dittrich et al., 1996 Goldstone, 2004 Horsthemke and Wagstaff, 2008 Knoll et al., 1989 Nicholls et al., 1998 Suttcliffe et al., 1994
Angelman syndrome	Imprinting defect. DNA methylation of maternal copy of imprinted chromosomal region 15q11-q13	Cassidy et al., 2000 Knoll et al., 1989 Nicholls et al., 1998
Beckwith-Wiedemann Syndrome	Imprinting defect. Loss of function on maternal allele of chromosome 11p15.5, containing IGF2-H19 locus	Li et al., 1998 Maher and Reik, 2000 Sparago et al., 2004
B-W Syndrome increased several-fold following assisted reproductive technology	Aberrant methylation of *H19* and *LIT1*	DeBaun et al., 2003
Coffin-Lowry syndrome	Crebbp – Rsk 2 histone phosphorylation	Ausio et al., 2003 Hanauer and Young, 2002
Rubinstein-Taybi syndrome	CREB binding protein histone acetylation	Ausio et al., 2003 Das et al., 2009 Petrij et al., 1995
Autism and Autism spectrum disorders	BCL2 and RA-OR with DNA Methylation	Nguyen et al., 2010

Neuro-Psychiatric Disorder	Genetic and Epigenetic Alterations	Reference
	CNTNAP 2 gene	Alarcón et al., 2008 Arking et al., 2008 Scott-Van Zeeland et al., 2010
	Elevated amyloid β precursor protein	Lahiri et al., 2013
Rett syndrome	Mutation in x-linked gene encoding methyl-CpG-binding protein 2	Adachi et al., 2009 Amir et al., 1999 Chahrour et al., 2008 Guy et al., 2007 Moretti and Zoghbi, 2006
	Above by miRNA dysregulation	Wu et al., 2010
	SIRT1 alpha secretase (Mouse Model)	Mattson, 2004
	Duplication of MECP2 region	Van Esch et al., 2005
	Alpha secretase ADAM10 (Mouse Model)	Donmez et al., 2010
	ROCK1 inhibit alpha secretase (Mouse Model)	Qin et al., 2006
ATR-X syndrome	Hypo- and/or hypermethylation of ATRX gene	Gibbons et al., 1995; 2000
Schizophrenia	The major histocompatibility complex and polygenic component	International Schizophrenia Consortium, 2009
	Polymorphism of [$Val^{108/158}$ Met genotype] in catechol-o-methyl transferase (COMT) gene val allele	Egan et al., 2001
	MTHFR gene C677T polymorphism and folate metabolism	Lewis et al., 2005
	Disruption-in-Schizophrenia 1 (DISC1) gene	Hikida et al., 2007
	GSK 3β/β-catenin by (DISC1) gene	Mao et al., 2009 Millar et al., 2000
	Elevated levels of miRNA-219	Coyle, 2009
	Elevated levels of miRNA-181b	Beveridge et al., 2008
	Dysregulation of DNA methylation and histone modification	Veldic et al., 2005
	Neuregulin 1 (NRG1) pathway epistatic changes	Nicodemus et al., 2010
Bipolar disorder	Dysregulation of DNA methylation and histone modification	Veldic et al., 2005
Alzheimer's disease	APP demethylation alpha secretase	Chouliaras et al., 2010 Marques et al., 2010

Table 3. (Continued)

Neuro-Psychiatric Disorder	Genetic and Epigenetic Alterations	Reference
	APP promoter hypomethylation	Tohgi et al., 1999a, 1999b West et al., 1995
	SIRT1 alpha secretase (Mouse Model)	Mattson, 2004
	ROCK1 inhibition of alpha secretase (Mouse Model)	Qin et al., 2006
	Alpha secretase ADAM10 (Mouse Model)	Donmez et al., 2010
	Increased methylation of *Sorbs3* Gene	Wang et al., 2008
	Decreased methylation of *S100A2* Gene	Wang et al., 2008
	Elevated HDAC 6	Ding et al., 2008
	Decreased acetylation of H3K18/K23	Zhang et al., 2012
	Elevated levels of miRNA-9 and -128	Lukiw, 2007
Parkinson's disease	Alpha-synuclein binding to histones to reduce HACT	Kontopoulos et al., 2006

For example, the most common heritable disorder causing mental retardation, fragile X syndrome (severe mental retardation with high forehead, enlarged jaws, ears, and testes in males, mild menstrual retardation in heterozygous females), is a consequence of CGG triplet repeat sequence expansion in the promoter (5'-untranslated) region of the fragile X mental retardation gene (*Fmr1*) in brain cells (Jacquemont et al., 2011, Verkerk et al., 1991). From the normal 50 or so triplet repeats, these may increase to up to several thousand, many of which are methylated resulting in gene silencing (Pietrobono et al., 2002, Wang et al., 2010). Associated histone deacetylation leads to absence of FMR1 protein (Coffee et al., 1999). In an *Fmr* knockout mouse model, both neuronal morphology and behavioral phenotype have been rescued by selective therapy (de Vrij et al., 2008).

A host of other neuropsychiatric syndromes including Alpha-thalassemia mental retardation syndrome, Coffin-Lowry syndrome, and Rubinstein-Taybi syndrome also show chromatin remodeling with epigenetic modifications (Ausio et al., 2003). Some of these syndromes with mild to moderate mental retardation are a consequence of mutations in genes that encode regulators of epigenetic mechanisms. Other examples show epigenetic chromatin remodeling. These include the autosomal recessive disorder immunodeficiency-centromeric instability-facial (ICF) anomalies syndrome (with facial abnormalities, immunoglobulin deficiencies, and centromeric heterochromatin instability) (Ausio et al., 2003, Hansen et al., 2000, Maraschio et al., 1988, Tiepolo et al., 1979, Xu et al., 1999), associated with pronounced DNA hypomethylation (Jeanpierre et al., 1993). Another example is Prader-Willi syndrome (characterized by neonatal hypotonia, facial dysmorphia, hypogonadism, reduced secretion of growth hormone with short stature), which results from a lack of transcripts expressed by the paternal copy of the imprinted chromosome region 15q11.13 (Davies et al., 2005, Knoll et al., 1989, Tsankova et al., 2007). Angelman syndrome (Davies et al., 2005), also is associated with an epigenetic imprinted gene anomaly, a deletion in the same region of chromosome 15, but the maternal copy (Cassidy et al., 2000, Horsthemke and Wagstaff, 2008, Knoll et al., 1989). Beckwith-Wiedemann syndrome (characterized by variable degrees of giantism, exomphalos, macroglossia, and mental retardation; Kent et al., 2008) has been recognized to result from epigenetic alteration of the imprinted chromosome 11p15 region. Overexpression of insulin-like growth factor 2 (*Igf2*) may, in part, account for the associated overgrowth features (Li et al., 1998, Maher and Reik, 2000). Although the prevalence has been reported to be increased in offspring conceived by assisted reproduction technologies (ART) (Arnaud and Feil, 2005), and this is associated with abnormal methylation of the genes *H19* and *Lit1* (DeBaun et al., 2003) (See Table 3). Questions remain regarding the significance of this association (see below).

Discovery of these epigenetic-associated mental retardation syndromes, has promoted exploration of the role of epigenetics in other neurologic disorders with as yet undefined etiologies. An example in which prolonged stress in early life is believed to be a factor is that of the autism-spectrum disorders. These syndromes are characterized by impairment of reciprocal social interactions, verbal and non verbal communication, and capacity for other activities and interests, hypo- or hyperreactivity to certain stimuli, lack of coordination of gaze, facial expression, and gesture, repetitive movements, stereotypic behavior and mannerisms, and other problems. With onset usually early in life, and occurring several times more frequently in males, autistic features are displayed in a broad range of phenotypes with both genetic and epigenetic origins in their pathogenesis (Schanen, 2006, Urdinguio et al., 2009, Wang et al., 2010). A recent report has demonstrated dysregulation of cerebral cortical neuronal layer formation, with focal patches representing disruption of laminar architecture in the prefrontal and temporal cortex of children ages 2 to 15 who presented with autism (Stoner et al., 2014). Although suggestive of antenatal epigenetic-based neurodevelopmental regulation, this was not established. In addition, a number of microstructural and growth abnormalities have been described, particularly in the frontal and temporal, cerebral regions, associated with higher order social, emotional, language, and cognitive functions (Courchesne et al., 2005).

Specifically, these changes have been shown to be associated with altered DNA methylation of genes vital to neuronal development, such as *BCL2* and the retinoic acid-related orphan receptor in both lymphoblastoid cell lines and the brain itself (Nguyen et al., 2010). Several genes, *Met* (Eagleson et al., 2011, Judson et al., 2011) and *Plaur* with a duplication in chromosomal 15q11.13 (Nakatani et al., 2009) have been implicated to impact cerebral cortical differential development (Eagleson et al., 2011). Postsynaptic cell adhesion receptors for neurexins, the neuroligins, also may be involved with this disorder (Flint and Shifman, 2008). Additionally, as demonstrated with functional neuroimaging, variants in the autism risk gene contactin-associated-protein-like 2 (CNTNAP2) are associated with altered functional connectivity in frontal lobe circuits. An additional consideration is the finding that the Alzheimer's disease associated amyloid-β precursor protein (APP), and especially its neuroprotective processing product secreted APPα, is significantly elevated in individuals with autism (Lahiri et al., 2013). This has led to the "anabolic hypothesis" in the etiology of autism, as neuronal overgrowth in the brain results in interneuronal misconceptions that may underlie multiple autism symptoms (Lahiri et al., 2013). The above noted changes confirm that some cases of autism, and probably other neuropsychiatric disorders, may have an epigenetic basis (Alarcón et al., 2008, Arking et al., 2008, Haglund and Källén, 2011, Scott-Van Zeeland et al., 2010). This scenario is complicated however, as autism may, in fact, encompass several biologically distinct, albeit related, disorders (Courchesne et al., 2005, Happé et al., 2006).

Rett syndrome, a progressive developmental autism-spectrum disorder in females, becomes apparent at 6 to 18 months of age, and is characterized by autistic behavior, ataxia, dementia, seizures, and loss of purposeful movement of hands. This syndrome is associated with cerebral atrophy, particularly cortical gray matter, mild hyperammonemia, and decreased levels of biogenic amines; and has been termed a "Rosetta Stone" for understanding the molecular pathogenesis of autism (LaSalle et al., 2005). This occurs as a consequence of loss of function mutations in the X-linked gene encoding the epigenetic-related methyl CpG binding protein 2 (MeCP2) that links DNA methylation to chromatin complexes. Thus, the up- or down-expression of many other genes may be involved (Adachi et al., 2009, Amir et al., 1999, Ausio et al., 2003, Chahrour et al., 2008, Guy et al., 2007, Hagberg et al., 1983, Moretti and Zoghbi, 2006) (Table 3). MeCP2 is believed to play a critical role in neural function, and mice with genetic *MeCP2* deletion display features of Rett syndrome at about six weeks of age, and dying prematurely at about 12 weeks (Chen et al., 2003, Guy et al., 2001, 2007). Induced pluripotent stem cells from patients with Rett syndrome demonstrated smaller than normal soma size, fewer synapses, reduced spine density, as well as altered calcium signaling with electrophysiological anomalies (Marchetto et al., 2010). Murine models with decreased MeCP2 activity also demonstrate deficits in neuronal maturation, synaptogenesis, and establishment of neural circuits (Dani et al., 2005, Wood et al., 2009). Rett syndrome also is associated with dysregulation/upregulation of multiple miRNAs (Wu et al., 2010) (Table 3). Genetic *MeCP2* mutations also have been reported in females with syndromes of mild learning disabilities, and following neonatal encephalopathy in males, autism, and other neuropsychiatric disorders (Moretti and Zoghbi, 2006). These studies of epigenetic regulation modulating the expression of a number of genes, is an important illustration of the complexity of the problem.

ATR-X syndrome also is associated with dysregulation of DNA methylation, with the *Atrx* gene localized to pericentromeric heterochromatin during interphase and mitosis. Among other features this is characterized by severe mental retardation and facial dysmorphism. Its mutations also are associated with alterations in the DNA methylation patterns of a number of sequences (Gibbons et al., 1995, 2000).

As noted earlier in reference to the Dutch "Hunger Winter" of 1944-1945 (Brown and Susser, 2008, International Schizophrenia Consortium, 2009, Susser et al., 1996, 2008) (see Table 1), and the Wuhu, China famine of 1959-1961 (St. Clair et al., 2005, Xu et al., 2009), studies on survivors have demonstrated a significant increase in the prevalence of schizophrenia. This complex syndrome is manifest with so-called positive symptoms (hallucinations and paranoid or bizarre delusions), and negative symptoms (significant social withdrawal, apathy, and occupational dysfunction) (Tandon et al., 2009). Importantly, many of these symptoms have been related to epigenetic mechanisms (Egger et al., 2004, Ptak and Petronis, 2008). Schizophrenia also has been associated with FGR and thinness during childhood (as well as low body mass of the mother) (Wahlbeck et al., 2001), and is the subject of epigenetic profiling (Iwamoto and Kato, 2009). Also as noted earlier, these findings have profound social and public health implications, and emphasize the importance of optimizing the conditions for growth and function of the developing brain. Of note in relation to schizophrenia, another major epidemiologic study showed a significant association between stress to the mother (death or diagnosis of grave disease in a near relative) during the first trimester of pregnancy and schizophrenia in adult male offspring (Khashan et al., 2008).

Schizophrenia later in life also has been linked to antenatal stresses such as exposure to maternal infection (Brown and Derkits, 2010, Brown and Susser, 2002, Messias et al., 2007, Westergaard et al., 1999), influenza (Brown et al., 2004, Kendell and Kemp, 1989, Mednick et al., 1988, Penner and Brown, 2007) and poliomyelitis (Suvisaari et al., 1999). Among other factors, this association with infection has been postulated to be a consequence of hyperthermia-induced stochastic events during early development (Woolf, 1997). Immune system hyperactivation with elevated levels of IgG and IgA also has been implicated (Buka et al., 2001, Oh-Nishi et al., 2010, Ozawa et al., 2006, Patterson, 2009, Zuckerman et al., 2003), as have hypoxia/ischemia (Cannon et al., 2002, Zornberg et al., 2000). Dysregulation of glutamate may account for excessive dopamine in some parts of the brain (such as the nucleus accumbens) with too little in others (such as prefrontal cortex), and, in part, may account for hallucinations in the former instance to anxiety and social withdrawal in the latter (Elert, 2014). Also of consequence, postnatal cerebral structural changes have been demonstrated to follow some of these antenatal stresses. The neurostructural abnormalities, such as increased volume of the hypothalamus associated with schizophrenia appear to be established during fetal development. These are gender-specific with increased incidence in females (Goldstein, 2006, Goldstein et al., 2007). Of related importance, these findings suggest neural-associated mechanisms for the increased incidence of endocrine disorders in schizophrenia.

Characterized by its symptoms rather than by biologic/biochemical markers, the molecular/cellular basis of schizophrenia is poorly understood, and the development and use of laboratory animal models has presented a major challenge (Kellendonk et al., 2009). Translocation of the disruption-in-schizophrenia 1 (*Disc1*) gene has been reported as a strong contender for the abnormal brain circuits seen with this condition (Hikida et al., 2007, Koike et al., 2006, Li et al., 2007b, Mao et al., 2009, Millar et al., 2000, Ross and Margolis, 2009). Also of epigenetic relevance, the role of miRNAs in schizophrenia and other neurobehavioral dysfunctions is suggested by the finding that miRNA-219, which modulates NMDA receptors (Kocerha et al., 2009), is elevated (Coyle, 2009) as is miRNA-181b (Beveridge et al., 2009) (Table 3). By use of genome-wide single nucleotide polymorphism arrays, patients with rare copy number variations with deletions of 1q21.1, 15q11.2, and 15q13.3 showed an association with schizophrenia (Stefansson et al., 2008). Multiple, individually rare mutations, each with possible epigenetic constructs, also have been demonstrated to contribute to this disorder (Walsh et al., 2008). Additionally, alterations in the hippocampus, particularly the CA1 subfield, have been demonstrated to play a role in the disease's pathophysiology (Schobel et al., 2009). On a neuropathologic basis, a genetic Df(16)A$^{+/-}$ mouse model of schizophrenia demonstrated impaired prefrontal-hippocampal-prefrontal synchrony (Sigurdsson et al., 2010). And in rat's prefrontal cortex-hippocampal pyramidal neurons demonstrated morphologic abnormalities in response to antenatal immune challenge (Baharnoori et al., 2009). Again, a problem here is that schizophrenia-related research has lacked strong hypothesis-based investigation (Flint and Shifman, 2008; for exception see Crow, 2007b). Thus, some caution must be exercised in the interpretation of the results quoted above, as a strong association of copy number mutations has been shown with some (Xu et al., 2008), but not all (Burmeister et al., 2008) forms of schizophrenia.

An associated epigenetic consideration in schizophrenia is that of its relation to maternal antenatal folate deficiency. As noted, several studies have indicated the developmental importance of folic acid as a dietary factor *in utero*, and the manner in which it modulates disease risks later in life (McKay et al., 2004, Torrens et al., 2006). The *MTHFR* gene *C677T* polymorphism influences folate metabolism, and therefore intracellular folate and homocysteine availability with DNA and histone methylation. A meta-analysis of six studies demonstrated that individuals homozygous for the *MTHFR C667T TT* genotype and who had low folate levels, were at significantly greater risk of developing schizophrenia (Lewis et al., 2005). Also as observed, the risk of schizophrenia associated with antenatal maternal dietary deficiency may be mediated by an increased rate of *de novo* mutations, a component of which may be folate deficiency (McClellan et al., 2006).

So-called affective disorders, including major depressive disorders that occur several times more frequently in females, also have been associated with intrauterine stress (Bale, 2009, Goel and Bale, 2009, Van Os and Jones, 1999). These stresses include food deprivation (Brown et al., 1995, 2000). Again, in many instances these neuropsychiatric disorders are gender specific, with males and females demonstrating significant differences in prevalence, depending upon the stress (Goel and Bale, 2009). In addition, a neural mechanism for epigenetic vulnerability to, or protection against, depression has been demonstrated by functional magnetic resonance imaging of amygdala and hippocampus, combined with genotype identification of a variant of the serotonin receptor (Canli et al., 2006). In regards to depression, Figure 5 illustrates proposed mechanisms of the hypothalamic-pituitary-axis and its role in the stress-mediated increase in arginine vasopressin and related hormones.

In another study, the role of antenatal stress in altering hormonal levels with subsequent development of psychological/psychiatric problems is illustrated in the 11 September 2001 attack on and collapse of New York City's World Trade Center. Many, but not all, pregnant women who experienced this trauma developed Post-traumatic Stress Disorder (Simeon et al., 2008, Yehuda et al., 2005, 2009). The full extent to which the offspring of these women showed neurologic pathologies is as yet unknown; however, in one study at nine months of age the infants showed greater distress to novelty, as compared to controls (Brand et al., 2006). Others have suggested antenatal stress as playing a role in the genesis of Attention-Deficit Hyperactivity Disorder (Mill et al., 2008, Mill and Petronis, 2008). An additional line of evidence of epigenetic factors in the genesis of neuropsychiatric disorders, is that in monozygotic twins, in which the concordance rate for both twins to experience an affective disorder is much greater than that of dizygotic twins or sibling pairs (Gross and Hen, 2004, Petronis et al., 2003, Ptak and Petronis, 2008). In the Stanley Foundation brain collection and Neuropathology Consortium (Torrey et al., 2000), a study of brains of patients with schizophrenia and bipolar disorder demonstrated significant epigenetic changes in a number of neurochemical markers including those for GABA receptors and developmental synaptic systems and reelin (Torrey et al., 2005). For bipolar disorder and circadian rhythms, the genes that constitute the molecular clock also have been implicated. For instance, mice with a mutation of *Clock* gene display a behavioral profile similar to that seen in this disorder, and this can be rescued by expression of the CLOCK protein (Roybal et al., 2007).

Of increasing prevalence in our aging society, Alzheimer's disease, characterized by progressive neural dysfunction and cognitive dementia associated with accumulation of neurofibrillary tangles and beta amyloid plaques, also may demonstrate an epigenetic basis in its genesis. Affecting nearly 2 percent of the population in industrialized countries, the risk increases dramatically beyond age 65, and some predict that the incidence will increase three-fold within the next several decades (http://www.alz.org). With ageing, the amyloid precursor protein (*APP*) gene is believed to become demethylated.

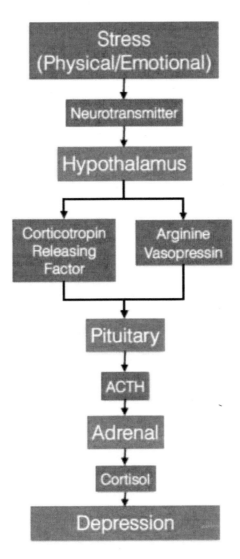

Figure 5. Illustration of proposed mechanisms of the hypothalamic-pituitary-adrenal-axis, and its role in the stress-mediated increase in arginine vasopressin.

This leads to excessive APP production, which generates beta-amyloid peptides that aggregate to form plaques (Chouliaras et al., 2010, Marques et al., 2010, Mattson, 2004). In an Alzheimer-like mouse model, increased or decreased expression of the histone deacetylase sirtuin 1 (SIRT1), has been shown to decrease or increase, respectively, beta amyloid deposition. By deacetylation, SIRT1 may activate the alpha-secretase *ADAM10* gene with co-activation of the retinoic acid receptor and, in turn, induce the Notch pathway, essential to the repair of neuronal damage (Donmez et al., 2010). SIRT1-mediated deacetylase activity also may activate the serine/threonine RHO kinase, ROCK1, to inhibit alpha-secretase processing of amyloid precursor protein (Qin et al., 2006). Other reports testify to the role of histone deacetylation (H3K18/K23) in the brains of patients with Alzheimer's disease (Zhang et al., 2012). MicroRNA-9 and -128 have been shown to be increased markedly in the hippocampus of patients with Alzheimer's disease (Lukiw, 2007) (Table 3). In addition, in neural cell cultures a subset of miRNAs is increased in response to reactive oxygen species (Lukiw and Pogue, 2007). As noted, microRNAs also have been implicated in several other neurodegenerative disorders (Nelson et al., 2008). Again, because for the most part studies performed on these epigenetic relations are on tissues from patients in the late stage of disease, the extent to which these represent cause or effect is unclear (Chouliaras et al., 2010).

The progressive neurodegenerative disorder Parkinson's disease, which affects about 1 percent of the population over age 65, also may have a combined epigenetic and genetic basis (Gasser, 2001). In terms of alpha-synuclein, studies have demonstrated that targeting it to the cell nucleus promotes neurotoxicity, whereas its sequestration in cytoplasm is neuroprotective. This neurotoxicity appears to be a consequence of alpha-synuclein binding to histones, thereby reducing histone acetyltransferase (HACT)-mediated acetylation of histone H3, with subsequent neurodegeneration (Table 3). On a positive note, administration of histone deacetyltransferase inhibitors may reduce alpha-synuclein-induced toxicity (Kontopoulos et al., 2006). A theme common to each of these neurodegenerative disorders is the idea that intraneuronal protein aggregates decrease transcriptional activity with consequent anomalous signaling and cognition (Abel and Zukin, 2008).

The Role of Antenatal Inflammation, Chorioamnionitis, and Other Stress

Schizophrenia later in life also has been linked to antenatal stresses such as exposure to maternal infection (Brown and Derkits, 2010, Brown and Susser, 2002, Messias et al., 2007, Westergaard et al., 1999), influenza (Brown et al., 2004, Kendell and Kemp, 1989, Mednick et al., 1988, Penner and Brown, 2007) and poliomyelitis (Suvisaari et al., 1999). Associated with inflammation, neuroimmune factors are recognized to be critically involved in brain development and the genesis of neuropsychiatric disorders with life-long consequences (Bale et al., 2010, Bilbo and Schwarz, 2009, Meyer et al., 2011). Of particular relevance, many of these studies document the impact of antenatal maternal infection in the genesis of autistic spectrum disorders (Libbey et al., 2005), in particular maternal viral infection in the first trimester and bacterial infection during the second trimester (Atladóttir et al., 2010). Perinatal inflammation/infection has been suggested to contribute to the pathogenesis of both the autism spectrum disorders and schizophrenia, disorders with markedly different characteristics but with some shared features may be "pieces of the same puzzle" (Meyer et al., 2011). In fact, because these disorders overlap at multiple behavioral levels, autism has been referred to as "schizophrenia syndrome of childhood" (Kolvin, 1971, Kolvin et al., 1971).

Among other factors, these associations with infection have been postulated to be a consequence of hyperthermia-induced stochastic events during early development (Woolf, 1997). Immune system hyperactivation with elevated levels of IgG and IgA also has been implicated (Buka et al., 2001, Oh-Nishi et al., 2010, Ozawa et al., 2006, Patterson, 2009, Zuckerman et al., 2003), as have hypoxia/ischemia (Cannon et al., 2002, Zornberg et al., 2000). In fact, hypoxia and inflammation may be regarded as "two sides of the same coin" (Bartels et al., 2013, Scholz et al., 2013). Dysregulation of glutamate may account for excessive dopamine in some parts of the brain (such as the nucleus accumbens) with too little in others (such as prefrontal cortex), and, in part, may account for hallucinations in the former instance to anxiety and social withdrawal in the latter (Elert, 2014).

Table 4. Effects of Early Life Stress on Maternal Neuroendocrinology and Behavior

Hormone	Effects following Chronic Socio-Stress
Oxytocin	Maternal Care and Attachment
	Maternal Aggression
	Post Partum Depression
	Changes reflected in Offspring
Prolactin	Maternal Behavior
	Post Partum Depression
Arginine Vasopressin	Maternal Care
	Maternal Aggression
	Depression
Corticosteroid Releasing Hormone	Decreased Maternal Care
	Stress-Induced Mood Disorders

Modified from Murgatroyd, C.A. and Nephew, B.C. (2013), Effects of early life social stress on maternal behavior and neuroendocrinology. *Psychoneuroendocrinology* 38:219-228 and others.

For both schizophrenia and autism, a host of studies suggest a "cytokine hypothesis" in their pathogenesis (Atladóttir et al., 2010, Bilbo and Schwarz, 2009, Meyer et al., 2011). With their crucial role in neurogenesis, synaptogenesis, and other aspects of normal brain development, it is not surprising that neuropoietic cytokines may play an important role in the pathogenesis of abnormal brain development in response to inflammation/infection (Benveniste, 1998, Cai et al., 2000, Pang et al., 2003). Cytokines and chemokines are synthesized within the central nervous system by both glial cells and neurons, and modulate these cell functions via interaction with specific cell surface receptors (Benveniste, 1998). A number of aspects of the signaling pathways and molecular mechanisms by which cytokines may produce its effects have been reviewed (Bauer et al., 2007, Benveniste, 1998). For instance, concentrations of interleukin-1β (IL-1β), IL-6, leukemia inhibitory factor IL-27, ciliary neurotrophic factor, and tumor necrosis factor (TNF) are elevated in infants with inflammatory complications (Bauer et al., 2007, Miller et al., 1990). Children with meningitis also have increased levels of IL-6 that correlate strongly with the occurrence of neurologic disorders (Mustafa et al., 1989); and increased IL-6 in amniotic fluid has been suggested as a useful marker for the increased risk of neurologic disorders and morbidity (Yoon et al., 1995).

Also of consequence, postnatal cerebral structural changes have been demonstrated to follow some of these antenatal stresses. The neurostructural abnormalities, such as increased volume of the hypothalamus associated with schizophrenia appear to be established during fetal development. These are gender-specific with increased incidence in females (Goldstein, 2006, Goldstein et al., 2007). Of related importance, these findings suggest neural-associated mechanisms for the increased incidence of endocrine disorders in schizophrenia. Intrauterine inflammation and infection with subsequent development of cerebral palsy has been associated with damage to white matter (Dammann and Leviton, 1997, 2000, Leviton et al., 2010). This association is suggested strongly by a meta-analysis of histological as well as clinical chorioamnionitis (Shatrov et al., 2010), and supports the findings of such an analysis a decade earlier (Wu and Colford, 2000).

In laboratory animals, several "models" have been developed to explore the cellular-molecular-epigenetic mechanisms of neuropsychiatric disorders (Brown and Derkits, 2010, Hodgson et al., 2001, Patterson, 2009, Rees and Inder, 2005, Wang et al., 2006). In terms of species, the two main groups studied include the mouse (both BALB/c and C57BL/6 mice), which include those to investigate viral infection such as influenza in the pregnant mother (Patterson, 2002, Shi et al., 2003). Other workers have used the Lewis rat, which injected intracerebrally shortly before birth with the Borna virus display stereotypic behaviors typical of autism with neuronal apoptosis and mRNA transcripts for several cytokines in multiple brain regions (Hornig et al., 1999). Others used this model to demonstrate deficits that suggest autism in play behavior and other social interaction (Pletnikov et al., 1999). Other virus including those for rubella, rubeola, herpes simplex virus, and mumps have been associated with autism (Libbey et al., 2005).

In a number of laboratory animal studies, Lipopolysaccharide (LPS), a cell wall component of gram-negative bacteria has been used to mimic infection as it initiates a rapid and well-characterized immune response (Hodgson et al., 2001, Shanks et al., 2000, Vaccarino and Ment, 2004, Wang et al., 2006). LPS induces a robust expression of cytokines in the immature rat brain, and may play a role in the pathophysiology of white matter injury in cerebral palsy (Cai et al., 2000, Fidel et al., 1994, Urakubo et al., 2001). LPS also induces a number of behavioral changes (Bilbo and Schwarz, 2009). Of importance, the strong association between inflammation and developmental disorders spans a diverse array of bacterial and viral agents that suggest a common mechanism such as the release of excessive cytokines (Bilbo and Schwarz, 2009). Rabbits (Yoon et al., 1997), as well as sheep (Dalitz et al., 2003, Duncan et al., 2002) also have been used for such studies.

Other Antenatal Influences and Neuropsychiatric Disease

In the early twentieth century, the field of neuroendocrinology arose from the discovery of hormones (Bayliss and Starling, 1904, Starling, 1905). Subsequently, the first half of the century witnessed numerous studies demonstrating the role of the ovary (Doisy et al., 1924), testes (Butenandt, 1931), and adrenal glands (Kendall et al., 1936, Mason et al., 1936), not only as endocrine organs in their own right, but also in regulating functions of the hypothalamus and pituitary gland (Harris, 1964). During the course of antenatal development, hormones play a major role in the genesis of cerebral neural function as well as gender differences in brain development and behavior (Cohen-Bendahan et al., 2005, Crews, 2008, 2010, Crews et al., 2006). In addition to the gonadal hormones *per se*, stress-induced increases in hypothalamic-pituitary hormones and glucocorticoids also are potent modulators of synaptic plasticity and thus neural function (Goel and Bale, 2009). The role of endocrine disruption in neuropsychiatric disorders is emphasized by the reality that antenatal maternal nutrition deprivation in general, or AMPD specifically, results in altered glucose metabolism with a host of hormonal changes, including those of insulin, leptin, prolactin, and estrogen (Fernandez-Twinn et al., 2003), as well as insulin resistance (Petry et al., 2001). One example is the role of altered maternal fatty acid metabolism, with elevated beta-hydroxybutyrate levels being associated with decreased infant mental-development index scores (intelligence quotient) (Rizzo et al., 1991).

Because the brain displays numerous aspects of sexual dimorphism and, as noted, a number of neuropsychiatric disorders have a gender basis in their presentation, age of onset, and/or response to therapy, an important consideration is that of neuroendocrine and neuroimmune influences. Thus, in determining the state of cerebral well being, the idea of the interaction of Genes, Environment, and Development (G x E x D) has been expanded to include sex (e.g., G x E x D x S) (Bale, 2009). Other studies have emphasized the importance of sexual differentiation of the brain to neuropsychiatric disorders (For instance see Cohen-Bendahan et al., 2005, Koshibu and Levitt, 2008, Krishnan et al., 2009).

As demonstrated by a multitude of studies, an optimal uterine environment is essential for establishment and maintenance of embryonic and fetal epigenetic patterns (Vickaryous and Whitelaw, 2005). Because embryo culture and manipulation are employed in contemporary assisted reproductive technologies, the question arises as to the extent to which ART or related procedures induce epigenetic changes in the developing organism (Brar et al., 2001, Feil, 2006, Khosla et al., 2001a, 2001b, Vickaryous and Whitelaw, 2005). Normally DNA methylation is confined to only one of the two parent alleles, thus imprinted gene loci allow minor alterations to be detected. A number of the epigenetic imprinting disorders noted above have been associated with assisted reproductive technology (Arnaud and Feil, 2005). For instance, following ART, Beckwith-Wiedemann Syndrome, with epigenetic alterations in DNA methylation of *H19* and *Lit1*, has been reported to be increased significantly in offspring (DeBaun et al., 2003). Thus, issues of great importance are the extent to which the chemical composition of culture medium, the duration of culture, or other factors in ART, may play a role in effecting changes in epigenetic mechanisms (Doherty et al., 2000, Khosla et al., 2001a, 2001b, Mann et al., 2004, Young et al., 2001). Under these conditions, the embryonic pre-implantation growth environment (e.g., commercial human *in vitro* fertilization media) can affect postnatal expression of epigenetically sensitive alleles (Morgan et al., 2008). Nonetheless, a major review of ART concluded that most children born appear developmentally normal and the risks are low (Owen and Segars, 2009). In view of the large number of variables involved, it follows that well designed prospective studies are needed to examine possible ART-associated long-term effects.

An additional epigenetic consideration of importance is the role of antenatal and postnatal exposure to environmental toxins and their timing in relation to birth, severity of stress, and duration, are issues with profound implications for health and disease as an adult (Agin, 2010, Landrigan et al., 2004, Lerner, 2010), drugs (Friedler and Wheeling, 1979) such as narcotics, or other factors (Diamond, 2009), in producing alterations in the nucleosome with adverse consequences. An obvious example from the mid-twentieth century is the ingestion of the estrogen-receptor agonist diethylstilbestrol by women in an attempt to reduce the risk of spontaneous abortion. In offspring, antenatal administration of diethylstilbestrol was followed by vaginal clear cell carcinoma (Swan, 2000), and altered limb development (phocomelia) in the first generation, and deafness in the second generation (Stoll et al., 2003). Anticancer drugs and other environmental compounds also may alter expression of specific genes, as well as the stress-related chaperone heat shock protein (HSP)-90, which has been shown to play a role in histone modifications (Feil, 2006, Rutherford and Lindquist, 1998). Fetal alcohol syndrome (Grossman et al., 2003), also has been attributed to epigenetic causes. A host of environmental contaminants including metals (mercury, lead, copper, and others) (Bakulski et al., 2012), organic phosphates, and others may lead to epigenetic changes with their long-term effects. Endocrine-disrupting chemicals also are known to demonstrate epigenetic effects on the germ line, and promote disease across several generations (Crews et al., 2007; Parodi et al., 2006). Beyond this, the wide scope of developmental toxicology is beyond the limits of this Chapter, as are other aspects of the interrelations of genetic and epigenetic factors in determining the state of brain health. Hopefully, the NIH-induced National Children's Study (http://www.nationalchildrensstudy.gov) initiated in 2000, which aims to recruit 100,000 pregnant women and track every aspect of their babies' health as they mature, including dietary patterns, chemical exposure, and socio-economic factors, will bring to light many aspects of neuronal and other development.

Figure 6 summarizes some of the epigenetic-mediated molecular mechanisms whereby environmental factors may alter neuronal gene expression, thereby resulting in neurologic disorder and/or other lifestyle healthcare considerations. During the past several decades, laboratory animals have provided an immense resource for pursuing questions as to the role of specific stressors in neurodevelopmental disorders. These have contributed considerable insight into genetic and epigenetic mechanisms of neuropathology. Nonetheless, the subjective nature of many symptoms (delusions, hallucinations, guilt, sadness) cannot be ascertained in animals, and because of the absence of biomarkers and/or objective diagnostic tests, the extrapolation from animal models to human disease presents limits (Nestler and Hyman, 2010). As a consequence, interpretation of experimental findings must meet well defined criteria (Fisch, 2007, Flint and Shifman, 2008, Insel, 2007, McKinney and Bunney, 1969).That being said, in laboratory animals a host of data has and is continuing to provide evidence on the role of sustained stress in the genesis of neuropsychiatric disorders, and the neurologic changes associated with depression, chronic anxiety disorders, and minimal brain dysfunction (Altman, 1986, 1987). For instance, early studies in Wistar rats examined the role of antenatal stress (changes in the rat's living conditions) on pup development and behavioral depression in the adult (Secoli and Teixeira, 1998, Wilner, 1997, Wilner et al., 1987). From these experiments, only generalizations were possible, however. In rats, a period of immobilization restraint for six hours per day for three weeks, was associated with an initial elevation in plasma corticosterone levels. Then, within several days these returned to normal. In terms of neuroanatomical changes, pyramidal neurons in the CA-3 region and dentate gyrus of the hippocampus demonstrated attenuated dendritic length and synaptic branching, with the opposite findings in basolateral amygdala and medial prefrontal cortex (Magarinos et al., 1997, Mitra et al., 2005, Vyas et al., 2002). Because of the role of these neurons in excitatory amino acid (aspartate and glutamate) release with action on NMDA receptors, these findings have substantial implications in terms of not only learning and memory, but also behavior (Mitra et al., 2005, Wood et al., 2003), and these appear to be gender-dependent (Luine et al., 2007). In addition, in male offspring of mice (Mueller and Bale, 2008) and guinea pigs (Kapoor et al., 2008), antenatal stress may result in increased behavioral stress sensitivity, a hallmark of many neuropsychiatric disorders including depression (Nestler et al., 2002).

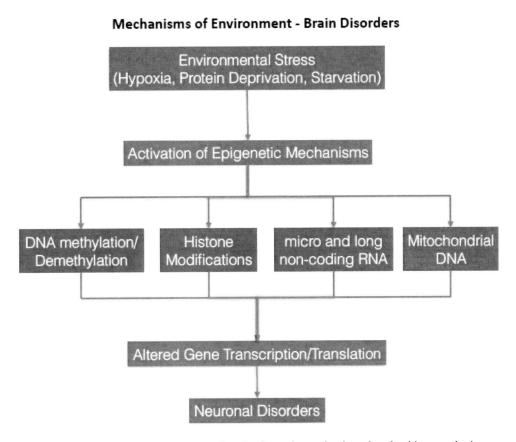

Mechanisms of Environment - Brain Disorders

Figure 6. Some of environmental factor-mediated epigenetic mechanisms involved in neurologic disorders and/or lifestyle healthcare consideration.

These phenomena are associated with changes in corticotrophin-releasing factor and glucocorticoid receptor (Mueller and Bale, 2008, Nemeroff, 1992). In terms of pathogenesis, an increase in maternal corticosteroids, with their transfer across the placenta, may account for gene specific epigenetic-mediated programming of the conceptus (Seckl and Holmes, 2007). During the neonatal period, variations in maternal care in the newborn also can affect permanently "Context-Dependent" (Crews, 2008, 2010) epigenetic changes (Meaney, 2001, Meaney and Szyf, 2005). Such epigenetic programming can remain active and dynamic throughout life (Szyf et al., 2007). For instance, Bonnet macaques (*Macaca radiata*) subjected to stress in early life demonstrated persistent significantly elevated cerebrospinal fluid levels of the adenohypophysis endogenous neuropeptide corticotropin releasing factor (Coplan et al., 1996). Although this stress occurred in infancy, this suggests an additional potential neurobiologic mechanism for psychopathology in the adult.

As described, discovering the genes and epigenetic changes responsible for various neuropsychiatric disorders has presented considerable challenge. In part, this is because of disagreement whether the various neuropathological diagnoses are truly separate diseases with unique underlying molecular alterations. In fact, some neuroscientists suggest abandoning conventional clinical definitions, and focusing on brain structure, wiring, and function of "intermediate phenotypes", somewhere between the risk genes evident and the clinically diagnosed neuropathology (Abbott, 2008). As an example of the caution required, one study of almost 750 patients diagnosed with schizophrenia, included analysis of about half a million SNPs. Not one gene, however, met the statistical requirements of a risk factor (Sullivan et al., 2008). Although disorders, including schizophrenia, bipolar disorder, and autism, appear to be heritable, identifying their genetic basis has presented problems, including failure to replicate given changes. Thus "psychiatric genetics" exhibits complexity at several levels including: allelic and phenotypic heterogeneity, phenotypic pleiotropy, and environmental-mediated epigenetic disorders. With the small individual effect sizes of the identified risk variants, and the complexity of genetic/epigenetic risk factors (either rare alleles or large effect or common alleles of modest effect) and phenotypes, some question whether biomarkers or genetic tests for individual diagnosis will be of great value in the foreseeable future (Burmeister et al., 2008, Craddock et al., 2007, Crow, 2007a, 2007b, McClellan et al., 2007). Given the complexity of the brain and its circuitry, discovering the fundamental pathophysiologic mechanisms that result in neuropsychiatric dysregulation presents monumental challenges. This will necessitate an enormous commitment of resources, both scientific and financial (Akil et al., 2010).

With this background, a major challenge for the future is to develop strategies to negate the long-term consequences of epigenetic basis of dysregulation of gene expression, as demonstrated in neural development (Canli et al., 2006, Collins and Barker, 2007, Ke et al., 2006), metabolic syndrome with insulin resistance (Lane et al., 1996), cancer (Esteller, 2007, 2008), and other disorders (Pembrey, 2002). Rather than isolated instances, epigenetic mechanisms may be a major factor in the seemingly increasing and intractable pandemic of these diseases (Gal-Yam et al., 2008, Palii and Robertson, 2007). Regarding the extent to which changes in epigenetic labels and pathways are the cause or the effect of a given disorder, the fundamental question remains. In essence, what is the role of epigenetic modification in neurodegenerative disorders, and to what extent might methylation patterns, miRNA, or other molecular related interventions be of therapeutic value?

Not to be overlooked, is that although the present review focuses on antenatal influences on epigenetic mechanisms, a considerable body of evidence supports the importance of the postnatal, early life environment in this regard (Bale et al., 2010, Krishnan and Nestler, 2010, Mathews and Janusek, 2011). As noted, a major issue in regards to the role of adverse biological and/or social stress in early life in the development of neuropsychiatric or other disease in the adult is the so-called "Life Course" approach to DOHaD (Ben-Shlomo and Kuh 2002). For instance, maternal mood disorders such as chronic anxiety and depression can affect adversely the lives of mothers and their offspring. In turn, chronic social stress (CSS) during the period of lactation can affect growth of both the dam and offspring, and increase maternal aggression (Nephew and Bridges, 2011). In addition, CSS during early life can have adverse effects on the maternal behavior in regards to their reduced maternal care and lactating efficiency, as well as post partum care and anxiety upon exposure to a male intruder (Murgatroyd and Nephew, 2013). A considerable body of evidence on these and related aspects of "The future is now: early life events preset adult behaviour" has been reported (Patchev et al., 2014).

In recognition of the importance of these vital issues, several recent National Institutes of Health initiatives, as part of its "Roadmap" program, seek applications to understand the "Epigenomics of Human Health and Disease" (Jones and Martienssen, 2005). Several other of the major national initiatives for brain development noted above include: the Decade of the Brain (1990-2000) (Goldstein, 1994), the National Institute of Mental Health Twin Study, the European Commission Human Brain Project (HBR; 2013-2023) (Schwartz, 2013), and the U.S. Government Brain Research through Advancing Innovated Neurotechnologies (BRAIN) initiative (2013) (Church, 2013). Although the goals and many aspects of these programs remain to be defined, without question they place emphasis on the vital nature of neuroscience and advanced computing methodologies in solving many mysteries of the brain. Hopefully, with advanced methodologies by collaborations among the nations and the world's scientists and engineers, striking advances will be made in our understanding the brain, its development, and how to eliminate so many maladies that plague mankind.

Summary and Overall Perspective

To recapitulate, during intrauterine existence, successful development of the embryonic and fetal brain with its myriad nuclei, tracts, and other structures is crucial for optimal maturation, survival, and function into adulthood. Clearly, for one's long-term well-being the several developmental periods are critical for the physical and mental health that we celebrate. In addition, this success results from the life-long adaptations to stress dictated by our genetic endowment as well as epigenetic-mediated responses to environmental factors. Inhibition or alteration of this highly ordered process at key time points may have grave, long-term, poorly predictable consequences. Response to the multitude of stressors lead to biological imbedding in brain structure and neurohormonal responses, that, in turn, impact our ability to respond to stresses as adults. Although once believed to be permanent, the processes of epigenetic responses including neuronal plasticity, have been shown to be amenable to positive environmental changes.

As with other tissues and organ systems, a true understanding of cerebral development and its response to stress remain *terra incognita*. Both epidemiologic studies in humans and a plethora of studies in laboratory animals, have demonstrated the profound invidious influence of antenatal maternal stress, of nutrition, oxygenation, and the intrauterine environment on the regulation and dysregulation of neuronal function and life. This includes behavioral disorders and neuropsychiatric diseases to which one is subject as an adult. Far from encompassing a comprehensive picture, the present Chapter depicts but a fraction of specific reactions and interactions of what we know and what we need to know. This to understand more completely the complexity of the cellular and molecular regulation of cerebral development, and to lessen the ravages of dysregulation. As is evident, at the present time a certain degree of confusion reigns. Although we know a great deal, we understand little. Thus, in terms of these issues we face enormous challenges.

An "experiment" on the invidious effects of antenatal famine/malnutrition, the Dutch "Hunger Winter" of 1944-1945, provided sobering evidence of the role of timing and severity of nutritional stress on subsequent developmental profiles as an adult. Other epidemiologic studies have contributed to this knowledge base. Nonetheless, to examine issues of epigenetic-mediated cerebral gene expression in a controlled manner, and in an attempt to determine fundamental mechanisms in a species in which the genome has been sequenced, most of these reported laboratory studies have been performed in rodents, both mice and rats. While in many respects, such studies have provided mechanistic insights, for the most part, much of their relevance to the human condition remains to be demonstrated. As our understanding of cellular and molecular mechanisms of gene regulation has increased, we are beginning to tease apart the genetic and epigenetic pathways and regulation that determine given responses. Although individual maternal stressors are characterized by up- or down-regulation of specific genes, functional analysis reveals some patterns of expression common to the several stressors. Individual gene expression also may be associated with differing epigenetic mechanisms. Thus, the debate of a former era, that of "nature versus nurture" has been superseded by an appreciation of the complementarity and complex interactions of Mendelian genomic heritage and environmental influences. In addition to overt behavioral dysfunction and learning disabilities, of particular relevance are cases of suboptimal brain development and function, resulting in an inability to attain ones full genetic potential.

During the past several decades, neuroscience has advanced enormously providing a plethora of experimental data and information, much of which is of value towards gaining an understanding of the genesis of several neuropathologic disorders. Nonetheless, our understanding of the mechanisms whereby neural architecture is created, and the manner by which cellular and molecular mechanisms are translated into memory and complex cognitive and behavioral responses, eludes us. Thus, we have but glimpses of understanding of the mechanisms by which these molecular/cellular changes are transferred into complex multicellular, multicompartmental processes such as long-term potentiation, hippocampal circuit stabilization, short- or long-term memory, and the nuances of behavior (Day and Sweatt, 2010). As demonstrated in many studies, the pathophysiology of many maternal stressors appears not to involve gross neural deformities, but rather irrecoverable distortions of pattern and alterations in chronological and developmentally-regulated sequences of neuronal and other cell development and their interactions in terms of neurotransmission, synaptic function, the orchestration of neurohormonal release and uptake, and related mechanisms. For the pregnant mother, whether a teenager or at any age, the stresses enumerated can effect profoundly her infant's developing brain.

In addition to those questions posed above, some of the most obvious follow. What is the role of epigenetic programming in normal brain development, and in the etiology of disease? What are the roles of antenatal epigenetic changes in the genesis of problems manifest in infancy or childhood such as cerebral palsy, mental retardation, seizure disorders, or others? Under many conditions, epigenetic changes during embryonic/fetal life do not become manifest for decades in the adult. What mechanisms regulate this phenomenon of delayed manifestation? Considerable evidence demonstrates a combination of genetic and epigenetic mechanisms operative in the programming of long-term sequelae. What is their relative importance, and to what degree can they be manipulated? Increasingly, a number of molecular signatures/adducts/biomarkers are associated with specific conditions. The question remains, however, to what extent can we use these to detect invidious interactions or disease at an early stage? What is the role of non-chromatin or even non-nuclear epigenetic mechanisms in neurodevelopmental regulation? To what extent can an understanding of these issues and mechanisms provide us effective means to contain or counteract their influence and consequences, and possibly even treat various neuropathologies? For instance, might it be possible to identify potential windows for timely interventions in DNA, histone, miRNA memory-mediated states to alter the course of the several diseases? By what mechanisms is epigenetic memory transmitted through cell division and/or from generation to generation? With contemporary "-omic" technology, humongous data sets can be generated. In their analysis, integration, and functional interpretation, how can we meet the future challenges? These are but a few of the vital issues that must be addressed in our pursuit to improve the lives and well being of mothers and infants, and the latter's life as an adult. As biomedical scientists dedicated to betterment of the human condition, can we do less?

In closing, we would propose a "mosaic" multifactorial hypothesis of epigenetic origins, with the combined insults of both overall and micronutrient nutritional deprivation, hypoxia, inflammation, and other stresses, modifying a variety of genes by DNA methylation, histone modifications, non-coding RNA, mitochondrial DNA methylation, and/or other regulatory mechanisms in gene regulation. These epigenetic changes involve cell cycle regulation, neurogenesis, synaptogenesis, neuronal plasticity, and global pathways of great relevance to the developmental origins of adult health and disease. One must be cautious, however. Despite our identification of a number of altered epigenetic phenomena, and the enzymes and other proteins that activate these processes, the cellular and molecular gene regulatory mechanisms are extraordinarily complex and elusive. The basic mechanisms of these changes and the control of transcription are only in the earliest stages of understanding.

As noted by many, we live in an age of uncertainty with threats of major disruptions in global climate, supply of foodstuffs, and the prevalence of disease. Each of these has enormous biological, psychological, and sociological consequences. In both developed and developing countries, of the various types of malnutrition, that during gestation is of critical importance. Too often, however, this is underappreciated. Of enormous clinical import, given the prevalence of nutritional deficiencies in pregnant women throughout the world, one cannot overestimate the need to ensure proper nutrition or the absence of other stress in the prevention of neuropsychological sequelae. As is all too evident, the challenges presented regarding the role of nutrition and other environmental factors on brain development and the global epidemic of the toll in neuropsychiatric sequelae, are many (Galler et al., 1984, Morgane et al., 1992, 1993, Olness, 2003, van Gelder et al., 1990).

To ensure the intellectual and social development of the next and future generations, our responsibility and challenge is to ensure that every pregnant mother is provided with optimal nutrition for her growing child. As cautioned by one group, "… for the millions of children around the world who begin their lives in adverse circumstances, we should be mindful of what is known about sensitive periods and act with alacrity to improve the lives of these children before neural circuits become well established and, thus, difficult to modify" (Fox et al., 2010, p. 316).

In essence, our responsibility and challenge is to gain an understanding of the "mosaic" of mechanisms by which stress during early development alters normal epigenetic regulation and health that we may point to new avenues to optimize health and to prevent disease to ensure that "… every uterus is a center for excellence."

Acknowledgment

We thank Jimin Suh for her highly professional assistance in the preparation of this manuscript.

References

[Anonymous] (1989). Editorial. Thrifty genotype rendered detrimental by progress? *Lancet*, 334, 839-40.

Abbott, A. (2008). Psychiatric genetics: The brains of the family. Does the difficulty in finding the genes responsible for mental illness reflect the complexity of the genetics or the poor definitions of psychiatric disorders? *Nature*, 454, 154-7.

Abel, K. M., Wicks, S., Susser, E. S., Dalman, C., Pedersen, M. G., Mortensen, P. B., et al. (2010). Birth weight, schizophrenia, and adult mental disorder: is risk confined to the smallest babies? *Arch. Gen. Psychiatry*, 67, 923-30.

Abel, T. and Zukin, R. S. (2008). Epigenetic targets of HDAC inhibition in neurodegenerative and psychiatric disorders. *Curr. Opin. Pharmacol.*, 8, 57-64.

Adachi, M., Autry, A. E., Covington III, H. E. and Monteggia, L. M. (2009). MeCP2-mediated transcription repression in the basolateral amygdala may underlie heightened anxiety in a mouse model of Rett syndrome. *J. Neurosci.*, 29, 4218-27.

Adelman, D. M., Gertsenstein, M., Nagy, A., Simon, M. C. and Maltepe, E. (2000). Placental cell fates are regulated in vivo by HIF-mediated hypoxia responses. *Genes Dev.*, 14, 3191-203.

Agin, D. P. (2010). More than genes: what science can tell us about toxic chemicals, development, and the risk to our children. Oxford: Oxford University Press.

Aguirre, A., Rubio, M. E. and Gallo, V. (2010). Notch and EGFR pathway interaction regulates neural stem cell number and self-renewal. *Nature*, 467, 323-7.

Akhtar, M. W., Raingo, J., Nelson, E. D., Montgomery, R. L., Olson, E. N., Kavalali, E. T., et al. (2009). Histone deacetylases 1 and 2 form a developmental switch that controls excitatory synapse maturation and function. *J. Neurosci.*, 29, 8288-97.

Akil, H., Brenner, S., Kandel, E., Kendler, K. S., King, M. C., Scolnick, E., et al. (2010). Medicine. The future of psychiatric research: genomes and neural circuits. *Science*, 327, 1580-1.

Alarcón, M., Abrahams, B. S., Stone, J. L., Duvall, J. A., Perederiy, J. V., Bomar, J. M., et al. (2008). Linkage, association, and gene-expression analyses identify CNTNAP2 as an autism-susceptibility gene. *Am. J. Hum. Genet.*, 82, 150-9.

Alboni, S., Cervia, D., Sugama, S. and Conti, B. (2010). Interleukin 18 in the CNS. *J. Neuroinflammation*, 7, 9.

Albright, C. D., Friedrich, C. B., Brown, E. C., Mar, M. H. and Zeisel, S. H. (1999a). Maternal dietary choline availability alters mitosis, apoptosis and the localization of TOAD-64 protein in the developing fetal rat septum. *Brain Res. Dev. Brain Res.*, 115, 123-9.

Albright, C. D., Tsai, A. Y., Friedrich, C. B., Mar, M. H. and Zeisel, S. H. (1999b). Choline availability alters embryonic development of the hippocampus and septum in the rat. *Brain Res. Dev. Brain Res.*, 113, 13-20.

[Allied Forces Supreme Headquarters. Netherlands Mission] (1948). Malnutrition and starvation in western Netherlands, September, 1944 [to] July 1945. The Hague: General State Printing Office.

Alter, M. D., Gilani, A. I., Champagne, F. A., Curley, J. P., Turner, J. B. and Hen, R. (2009). Paternal transmission of complex phenotypes in inbred mice. *Biol. Psychiatry*, 66, 1061-6.

Altman, J. (1962). Are new neurons formed in the brains of adult mammals? *Science*, 135, 1127-8.

Altman, J. (1986). An animal model of minimal brain dysfunction. In: Learning disabilities and prenatal risk. Lewis, M. (Ed). Urbana: University of Illinois Press, p. 241-304.

Altman, J. (1987). Morphological and behavioral markers of environmentally induced retardation of brain development: an animal model. *Environ. Health Perspect.*, 74, 153-68.

Altman, J. and Das, G. D. (1965). Post-natal origin of microneurones in the rat brain. *Nature*, 207, 953-6.

Altman, J., Das, G. D. and Sudarshan, K. (1970). The influence of nutrition on neural and behavioral development. I. Critical review of some data on the growth of the body and the brain following dietary deprivation during gestation and lactation. *Dev. Psychobiol.*, 3, 281-301.

Amir, R. E., Van den Veyver, I. B., Wan, M., Tran, C. Q., Francke, U. and Zoghbi, H. Y. (1999). Rett syndrome is caused by mutations in X-linked MECP2, encoding methyl-CpG-binding protein 2. *Nat. Genet.*, 23, 185-8.

Andres, C. (2002). Molecular genetics and animal models in autistic disorder. *Brain Res. Bull.*, 57, 109-19.

Antonow-Schlorke, I., Schwab, M., Cox, L. A., Li, C., Stuchlik, K., Witte, O. W., et al. (2011). Vulnerability of the fetal primate brain to moderate reduction in maternal global nutrient availability. *Proc. Natl. Acad. Sci. U S A*, 108, 3011-6.

Anway, M. D., Cupp, A. S., Uzumcu, M. and Skinner, M. K. (2005). Epigenetic transgenerational actions of endocrine disruptors and male fertility. *Science*, 308, 1466-9.

Anway, M. D. and Skinner, M. K. (2006). Epigenetic transgenerational actions of endocrine disruptors. *Endocrinology*, 147, S43-9.

Arking, D. E., Cutler, D. J., Brune, C. W., Teslovich, T. M., West, K., Ikeda, M., et al. (2008). A common genetic variant in the neurexin superfamily member CNTNAP2 increases familial risk of autism. *Am. J. Hum. Genet.*, 82, 160-4.

Armitage, J. A., Khan, I. Y., Taylor, P. D., Nathanielsz, P. W. and Poston, L. (2004). Developmental programming of the metabolic syndrome by maternal nutritional imbalance: how strong is the evidence from experimental models in mammals? *J. Physiol.*, 561, 355-77.

Arnaud, P. and Feil, R. (2005). Epigenetic deregulation of genomic imprinting in human disorders and following assisted reproduction. *Birth Defects Res. (Part C)*, 75, 81-97.

Atladóttir, H. Ó., Thorsen, P., Østergaard, L., Schendel, D. E., Lemcke, S., Abdallah, M., et al. (2010). Maternal infection requiring hospitalization during pregnancy and autism spectrum disorders. *J. Autism. Dev. Disord.*, 40, 1423-30.

Ausió, J., Levin, D. B., De Amorim, G. V., Bakker, S. and Macleod, P. M. (2003). Syndromes of disordered chromatin remodeling. *Clin. Genet.*, 64, 83-95.

Austin, K. B., Beiswanger, C., Bronzino, J. D., Austin-LaFrance, R. J., Galler, J. R. and Morgane, P.J. (1992). Prenatal protein malnutrition alters behavioral state modulation of inhibition and facilitation in the dentate gyrus. *Brain Res. Bull.*, 28, 245-55.

Baharnoori, M., Brake, W. G. and Srivastava, L. K. (2009). Prenatal immune challenge induces developmental changes in the morphology of pyramidal neurons of the prefrontal cortex and hippocampus in rats. *Schizophr. Res.*, 107, 99-109.

Bakulski, K. M., Rozek, L. S., Dolinoy, D. C., Paulson, H. L. and Hu, H. (2012). Alzheimer's disease and environmental exposure to lead: the epidemiologic evidence and potential role of epigenetics. *Curr. Alzheimer Res.*, 9, 563-73.

Bale, T. L. (2009). Neuroendocrine and immune influences on the CNS: it's a matter of sex. *Neuron*, 64, 13-16.

Bale, T. L., Baram, T. Z., Brown, A. S., Goldstein, J. M., Insel, T. R., McCarthy, M. M., et al. (2010). Early life programming and neurodevelopmental disorders. *Biol. Psychiatry*, 68, 314-9.

Bao, A. M. and Swaab, D. F. (2010). Corticotropin-releasing hormone and arginine vasopressin in depression: focus on the human postmortem hypothalamus. *Vitam. Horm.*, 82, 339-65.

Barker, D. J. (1990). The fetal and infant origins of adult disease. *BMJ*, 301, 1111.

Barker, D. J. (1991). The intrauterine origins of cardiovascular and obstructive lung disease in adult life. The Marc Daniles Lecture 1990. *J. R. Coll. Physicians Lond.*, 25, 129-33.

Barker, D. J. (1992). Fetal and infant origins of adult disease. London: BMJ Publishing.

Barker, D. J. (1994). Mothers, babies, and health in later life. Edinburgh: Churchill Livingstone. (2nd Ed. Churchill Livingstone, Edinburgh, 1998).

Barker, D. J. (1995). Fetal origins of coronary heart disease. *BMJ*, 311, 171-4.

Barker, D. J. (2001). Fetal origins of cardiovascular and lung disease. New York: M. Dekker.

Barker, D. J. (2003). The midwife, the coincidence, and the hypothesis. *BMJ*, 327, 1428-30.

Barker, D. J. (2004). The developmental origins of chronic adult disease. *Acta. Paediatr. Suppl.*, 93, 26-33.

Barker, D. J. (2007). The origins of the developmental origins theory. *J. Intern. Med.*, 261, 412-7.

Barker, D. J., Forsén, T., Uutela, A., Osmond, C. and Eriksson, J. G. (2001). Size at birth and resilience to effects of poor living conditions in adult life: longitudinal study. *BMJ*, 323, 1-5.

Barker, D. J., Gluckman, P. D., Godfrey, K. M., Harding, J. E., Owens, J. A. and Robinson, J. S. (1993). Fetal nutrition and cardiovascular disease in adult life. *Lancet*, 341, 938-41.

Barker, D. J. and Osmond, C. (1986a). Diet and coronary heart disease in England and Wales during and after the second World War. *J. Epidemiol. Community Health*, 40, 37-44.

Barker, D. J. and Osmond, C. (1986b). Infant mortality, childhood nutrition, and ischaemic heart disease in England and Wales. *Lancet*, 1, 1077-81.

Barker, D. J., Osmond, C., Golding, J., Kuh, D. and Wadsworth, M. E. (1989a). Growth *in utero*, blood pressure in childhood and adult life, and mortality from cardiovascular disease. *BMJ*, 298, 564-7.

Barker, D. J., Winter, P. D., Osmond, C., Margetts, B. and Simmonds, S. J. (1989b). Weight in infancy and death from ischaemic heart disease. *Lancet*, 2, 577-80.

Bartels, K., Grenz, A. and Eltzschig, H. K. (2013). Hypoxia and inflammation are two sides of the same coin. *Proc. Natl. Acad. Sci. U S A*, 110, 18351-2.

Bateson, P., Barker, D., Clutton-Brock, T., Deb, D., D'Udine, B., Foley, R. A., et al. (2004). Developmental plasticity and human health. *Nature*, 430, 419-21.

Bauer, S., Kerr, B. J. and Patterson, P. H. (2007). The neuropoietic cytokine family in development, plasticity, disease and injury. *Nat. Rev. Neurosci.*, 8, 221-32.

Bayer, S. A. (1989). Cellular aspects of brain development. *Neurotoxicology*, 10, 307-20.

Bayliss, W. M. and Starling, E. H. (1904). The chemical regulation of the secretory process. *Proc. R. Soc. London*, 73, 310-22.

Bennet, L. and Gunn, A. J. (2006). The fetal origins of adult mental illness. In: Early life origins of health and disease. Owens, J. A. and Wintour, E. M. (Eds). New York: Springer Science + Business Media.

Bennis-Taleb, N., Remacle, C., Hoet, J. J. and Reusens, B. (1999). A low-protein isocaloric diet during gestation affects brain development and alters permanently cerebral cortex blood vessels in rat offspring. *J. Nutr.*, 129, 1613-9.

Ben-Shlomo, Y. and Davey Smith, G. (1991). Deprivation in infancy or in adult life: which is more important for mortality risk? *Lancet*, 337, 530-4.

Ben-Shlomo, Y. and Kuh, D. (2002). A life course approach to chronic disease epidemiology: conceptual models, empirical challenges and interdisciplinary perspectives. *Int. J. Epidemiol.*, 31, 285-93.

Benveniste, E. N. (1998). Cytokine actions in the central nervous system. *Cytokine. Growth Factor Rev.*, 9, 259-75.

Berger, S. L. (2007). The complex language of chromatin regulation during transcription. *Nature*, 447, 407-12.

Berger, S. L., Kouzarides, T., Shiekhattar, R. and Shilatifard, A. (2009). An operational definition of epigenetics. *Genes. Dev.*, 23, 781-3.

Bernstein, B. E., Meissner, A. and Lander, E. S. (2007). The mammalian epigenome. *Cell*, 128, 669-81.

Bestor, T. H. (2000). The DNA methyltransferases of mammals. *Hum. Mol. Genet.*, 9, 2395-402.

Beveridge, N. J., Tooney, P. A., Carroll, A. P., Gardiner, E., Bowden, N., Scott, R. J., et al. (2008). Dysregulation of miRNA 181b in the temporal cortex in schizophrenia. *Hum. Mol. Genet.*, 17, 1156-68.

Bhate, V., Deshpande, S., Bhat, D., Joshi, N., Ladkat, R., Watve, S., et al. (2008). Vitamin B_{12} status of pregnant Indian women and cognitive function in their 9-year-old children. *Food Nutr. Bull.*, 29, 249-54.

Bilbo, S. D. and Schwarz, J. M. (2009). Early-life programming of later-life brain and behavior: a critical role for the immune system. *Front Behav. Neurosci.*, 3, 14.

Billack, B., Serio, R., Silva, I. and Kinsley, C. H. (2012). Epigenetic changes brought about by perinatal stressors: a brief review of the literature. *J. Pharmacol. Toxicol. Methods*, 66, 221-31.

Bird, A. (2007). Perceptions of epigenetics. *Nature*, 447, 396-8.

Blumberg, H. P., Kaufman, J., Martin, A., Charney, D. S., Krystal, J. H. and Peterson, B. S. (2004). Significance of adolescent neurodevelopment for the neural circuitry of bipolar disorder. *Ann. N Y Acad. Sci.*, 1021, 376-83.

Blusztajn, J. K. (1998). Choline, a vital amine. *Science*, 281, 794-5.

Boerema, I. (Ed) (1947). Medische ervaringen in Nederland tijdens de bezetting, 1940-1945. Groningen: Wolters.

Bogdarina, I., Murphy, H. C., Burns, S. P. and Clark, A. J. (2004). Investigation of the role of epigenetic modification of the rat glucokinase gene in fetal programming. *Life Sci.*, 74, 1407-15.

Bogdarina, I., Welham, S., King, P. J., Burns, S. P. and Clark, A. J. (2007). Epigenetic modification of the renin-angiotensin system in the fetal programming of hypertension. *Circ. Res.*, 100, 520-6.

Bonasio, R., Tu, S. and Reinberg, D. (2010). Molecular signals of epigenetic states. *Science*, 330, 612-6.

Borrelli, E., Nestler, E. J., Allis, C. D. and Sassone-Corsi, P. (2008). Decoding the epigenetic language of neuronal plasticity. *Neuron*, 60, 961-74.

Bota, M., Dong, H. W. and Swanson, L. W. (2003). From gene networks to brain networks. *Nat. Neurosci.*, 6, 795-9.

Boujendar, S., Arany, E., Hill, D., Remacle, C. and Reusens, B. (2003). Taurine supplementation of a low protein diet fed to rat dams normalizes the vascularization of the fetal endocrine pancreas. *J. Nutr.*, 133, 2820-5.

Bourc'his, D. and Voinnet, O. (2010). A small-RNA perspective on gametogenesis, fertilization, and early zygotic development. *Science*, 330, 617-22.

Bowman, G. D. (2010). Mechanisms of ATP-dependent nucleosome sliding. *Curr. Opin. Struct. Biol.*, 20, 73-81.

Brand, S. R., Engel, S. M., Canfield, R. L. and Yehuda, R. (2006). The effect of maternal PTSD following *in utero* trauma exposure on behavior and temperament in the 9-month-old infant. *Ann. NY Acad. Sci.*, 1071, 454-8.

Brar, A. K., Handwerger, S., Kessler, C. A. and Aronow, B. J. (2001). Gene induction and categorical reprogramming during in vitro human endometrial fibroblast decidualization. *Physiol. Genomics*, 7, 135-48.

Breimer, L. H. and Nilsson, T. K. (2012). Has folate a role in the developing nervous system after birth and not just during embryogenesis and gestation? *Scand. J. Clin. Lab. Invest.*, 72, 185-91.

Brennecke, J., Malone, C. D., Aravin, A. A., Sachidanandam, R., Stark, A. and Hannon, G. J. (2008). An epigenetic role for maternally inherited piRNAs in transposon silencing. *Science*, 322, 1387-92.

Bresler, D. E., Ellison, G. and Zamenhof, S. (1975). Learning deficits in rats with malnourished grandmothers. *Dev. Pyschobiol.*, 8, 315-23.

Brewer, L. D., Thibault, V., Chen, K. C., Langub, M. C., Landfield, P. W. and Porter, N. M. (2001). Vitamin D hormone confers neuroprotection in parallel with downregulation of L-type calcium channel expression in hippocampal neurons. *J. Neurosci.*, 21, 98-108.

Bronzino, J. D., Austin-LaFrance, R. J., Morgane, P. J. and Galler, J. R. (1991a). Effects of prenatal protein malnutrition on kindling-induced alterations in dentate granule cell excitability. I. Synaptic transmission measures. *Exp. Neurol.*, 112, 206-15.

Bronzino, J. D., Austin-LaFrance, R. J., Morgane, P. J. and Galler, J. R. (1991b). Effects of prenatal protein malnutrition on kindling-induced alterations in dentate granule cell excitability. II. Paired-pulse measures. *Exp. Neurol.*, 112, 216-23.

Brown, A. S., Begg, M. D., Gravenstein, S., Schaefer, C. A., Wyatt, R. J., Bresnahan, M., et al. (2004). Serologic evidence of prenatal influenza in the etiology of schizophrenia. *Arch. Gen. Psychiatry*, 61, 774-80.

Brown, A. S. and Derkits, E. J. (2010). Prenatal infection and schizophrenia: a review of epidemiologic and translational studies. *Am. J. Psychiatry*, 167, 261-80.

Brown, A. S. and Susser, E. S. (1997). Sex differences in prevalence of congenital neural defects after periconceptional famine exposure. *Epidemiology*, 8, 55-8.

Brown, A. S. and Susser, E. S. (2002). In utero infection and adult schizophrenia. *Ment. Retard. Dev. Disabil. Res. Rev.*, 8, 51-7.

Brown, A. S. and Susser, E. S. (2008). Prenatal nutritional deficiency and risk of adult schizophrenia. *Schizophr. Bull.*, 34, 1054-63.

Brown, A. S., Susser, E. S., Lin, S. P., Neugebauer, R. and Gorman, J. M. (1995). Increased risk of affective disorders in males after second trimester prenatal exposure to the Dutch hunger winter of 1944-45. *Br. J. Psychiatry*, 166, 601-6.

Brown, A. S., van Os, J., Driessens, C., Hoek, H. W. and Susser, E. S. (2000). Further evidence of relation between prenatal famine and major affective disorder. *Am. J. Psychiatry*, 157, 190-5.

Buka, S. L., Tsuang, M. T., Torrey, E. F., Klebanoff, M. A., Bernstein, D. and Yolken, R. H. (2001). Maternal infections and subsequent psychosis among offspring. *Arch. Gen. Psychiatry*, 58, 1032-7.

Burdge, G. C., Slater-Jefferies, J., Torrens, C., Phillips, E. S., Hanson, M. A. and Lillycrop, K.A. (2007). Dietary protein restriction of pregnant rats in the F_0 generation induces altered methylation and hepatic gene promoters in the adult male offspring in the F_1 and F_2 generations. *Br. J. Nutr.*, 97, 435-9.

Burger, G. C. E., Drummond, J. C. and Sandstead, H. R. (Eds). (1948). Malnutrition and starvation in Western Netherlands, September 1944-July 1945. Parts I and II. The Hague, Netherlands: General State Printing Office.

Burmeister, M., McInnis, M. G. and Zöllner, S. (2008). Psychiatric genetics: progress amid controversy. *Nat. Rev. Genet.*, 9, 527-40.

Bush, M. and Leathwood, P. D. (1975). Effect of different regimens of early malnutrition on behavioural development and adult avoidance learning in Swiss white mice. *Br. J. Nutr.*, 33, 373-85.

Butenandt, A. F. J. (1931). Ueber die chemische Untersuchung der Sexualhormone. *Z. Angew. Chem.*, 44, 905-8.

Bygren, L. O. (2013). Intergenerational health responses to adverse and enriched environments. *Annu. Rev. Public. Health*, 34, 49-60.

Cai, Z., Pan, Z. L., Pang, Y., Evans, O. B. and Rhodes, P. G. (2000). Cytokine induction in fetal rat brains and brain injury in neonatal rats after maternal lipopolysaccharide administration. *Pediatr. Res.*, 47, 64-72.

Canli, T., Qiu, M., Omura, K., Congdon, E., Haas, B. W., Amin, Z., et al. (2006). Neural correlates of epigenesis. *Proc. Natl. Acad. Sci. U S A*, 103, 16033-8.

Cannon, T. D., van Erp, T. G., Rosso, I. M., Huttunen, M., Lönnqvist, J., Pirkola, T., et al. (2002). Fetal hypoxia and structural brain abnormalities in schizophrenic patients, their siblings, and controls. *Arch. Gen. Psychiatry*, 59, 35-41.

Cassidy, S. B., Dykens, E. and Williams, C. A. (2000). Prader-Willi and Angelman syndromes: sister imprinted disorders. *Am. J. Med. Genet.*, 97, 136-46.

Cedar, H. and Bergman, Y. (2009). Linking DNA methylation and histone modification: patterns and paradigms. *Nat. Rev. Genet.*, 10, 295-304.

Chahrour, M., Jung, S. Y., Shaw, C., Zhou, X., Wong, S. T., Qin, J., et al. (2008). MeCP2, a key contributor to neurological disease, activates and represses transcription. *Science*, 320, 1224-9.

Chen, W. G., Chang, Q., Lin, Y., Meissner, A., West, A. E., Griffith, E. C., et al. (2003). Derepression of BDNF transcription involves calcium-dependent phosphorylation of MeCP2. *Science*, 302, 885-9.

Chen, Y., Sharma, R. P., Costa, R. H., Costa, E. and Grayson, D. R. (2002). On the epigenetic regulation of the human reelin promoter. *Nucleic Acids Res.*, 30, 2930-9.

Chen, Y. and Zhou, L. A. (2007). The long-term health and economic consequences of the 1959-1961 famine in China. *J. Health Econ.*, 26, 659-81.

Cheng, L. C., Pastrana, E., Tavazoie, M. and Doetsch, F. (2009). miR-124 regulates adult neurogenesis in the subventricular zone stem cell niche. *Nat. Neurosci.*, 12, 399-408.

Chmurzynska, A. (2010). Fetal programming: link between early nutrition, DNA methylation, and complex diseases. *Nutr. Rev.*, 68, 87-98.

Chouliaras, L., Rutten, B. P. F., Kenis, G., Peerbooms, O., Visser, P. J., Verhey, F., et al. (2010). Epigenetic regulation in the pathophysiology of Alzheimer's disease. *Prog. Neurobiol.*, 90, 498-510.

Chu, S., DeRisi, J., Eisen, M., Mulholland, J., Botstein, D., Brown, P. O., et al. (1998). The transcriptional program of sporulation in budding yeast. *Science,* 282, 699-705.

Church, G. M. (2013). BRAIN: innovative neurotechnologies for imaging and therapeutics. *Dialogues Clin. Neurosci.*, 15, 241-3.

Coffee, B., Zhang, F., Warren, S. T. and Reines, D. (1999). Acetylated histones are associated with FMR1 in normal but not fragile X-syndrome cells. *Nat. Genet.*, 22, 98-101.

Cohen, S. and Greenberg, M. E. (2008). Communication between the synapse and the nucleus in neuronal development, plasticity, and disease. *Annu. Rev. Cell Dev. Biol.*, 24, 183-209.

Cohen-Bendahan, C. C., van de Beek, C. and Berenbaum, S. A. (2005). Prenatal sex hormone effects on child and adult sex-typed behavior: methods and findings. *Neurosci. Biobehav. Rev.*, 29, 353-84.

Collins, F. S. and Barker, A. D. (2007). Mapping the cancer genome. Pinpointing the genes involved in cancer will help chart a new course across the complex landscape of human malignancies. *Sci. Am.*, 296, 50-7.

Colombo, J., Kannass, K. N., Shaddy, D. J., Kundurthi, S., Maikranz, J. M., Anderson, C. J.,et al. (2004). Maternal DHA and the development of attention in infancy and toddlerhood. *Child. Dev.*, 75, 1254-67.

Condorelli, D. F., Nicoletti, V. G., Barresi, V., Caruso, A., Conticello, S., de Vellis, J., et al. (1994). Tissue-specific DNA methylation patterns of the rat glial fibrillary acidic protein gene. *J. Neurosci. Res.*, 39, 694-707.

Constância, M., Hemberger, M., Hughes, J., Dean, W., Ferguson-Smith, A., Fundele, R., et al. (2002). Placental-specific IGF-II is a major modulator of placental and fetal growth. *Nature*, 417, 945-8.

Cooney, C. A., Dave, A. A. and Wolff, G. L. (2002). Maternal methyl supplements in mice affect epigenetic variation and DNA methylation of offspring. *J. Nutr.*, 132, 2393S-2400S.

Coplan, J. D., Andrews, M. W., Rosenblum, L. A., Owens, M. J., Friedman, S., Gorman, J. M., et al. (1996). Persistent elevations of cerebrospinal fluid concentrations of corticotrophin-releasing factor in adult nonhuman primates exposed to early-life stressors: implications for the pathophysiology of mood and anxiety disorders. *Proc. Natl. Acad. Sci. U S A*, 93, 1619-23.

Costa, E., Chen, Y., Davis, J., Dong, E., Noh, J. S., Tremolizzo, L., et al. (2002). REELIN and schizophrenia: a disease at the interface of the genome and the epigenome. *Mol. Interv.*, 2, 47-57.

Courchesne, E., Redcay, E., Morgan, J. T. and Kennedy, D. P. (2005). Autism at the beginning: Microstructural and growth abnormalities underlying the cognitive and behavioral phenotype of autism. *Dev. Psychopathol.*, 17, 577-97.

Covic, M., Karaca, E. and Lie, D. C. (2010). Review. Epigenetic regulation of neurogenesis in the adult hippocampus. *Heredity*, 105, 122-34.

Cowan, C. A., Atienza, J., Melton, D. A. and Eggan, K. (2005). Nuclear reprogramming of somatic cells after fusion with human embryonic stem cells. *Science*, 309, 1369-73.

Cowan, W. M. (1979). The development of the brain. *Sci. Am.*, 241, 113-33.

Cowley, J. J. and Griesel, R. D. (1959). Some effects of a low protein diet on a first filial generation of white rats. *J. Genet. Psychol.*, 95, 187-201.

Cowley, J. J. and Griesel, R. D. (1966). The effect on growth and behaviour of rehabilitating first and second generation low protein rats. *Anim. Behav.*, 14, 506-17.

Coyle, J. T. (2009). MicroRNAs suggest a new mechanism for altered brain gene expression in schizophrenia. *Proc. Natl. Acad. Sci. U S A*, 106, 2975-6.

Craddock, N., O'Donovan, M. C. and Owen, M. J. (2007). Phenotypic and genetic complexity of psychosis. Invited commentary on ... Schizophrenia: a common disease caused by multiple rare alleles. *Br. J. Psychiatry*, 190, 200-3.

Crews, D. (2008). Epigenetics and its implications for behavioral neuroendocrinology. *Front Neuroendocrinol.*, 29, 344-57.

Crews, D. (2010). Epigenetics, brain, behavior, and the environment. *Hormones*, 9, 41-50.

Crews, D., Gore, A. C., Hsu, T. S., Dangleben, N. L., Spinetta, M., Schallert, T., et al. (2007). Transgenerational epigenetic imprints on mate preference. *Proc. Natl. Acad. Sci. U S A*, 104, 5942-6.

Crews, D., Lou, W., Fleming, A. and Ogawa, S. (2006). From gene networks underlying sex determination and gonadal differentiation to the development of neural networks regulating sociosexual behavior. *Brain Res.*, 1126, 109-21.

Crow, T. (2007a). Is DISC1 really a gene predisposing to psychosis? *Br. J. Psychiatry*, 190, 270.

Crow, T. (2007b). Genetic hypotheses for schizophrenia. *Br. J. Psychiatry*, 191, 180.

Cutfield, W. S., Hofman, P. L., Mitchell, M. and Morison, I. M. (2007). Could epigenetics play a role in the developmental origins of health and disease? *Pediatr. Res.*, 61, 68R-75R.

Czeizel, A. E. and Dudás, I. (1992). Prevention of the first occurrence of neural-tube defects by periconceptional vitamin supplementation. *N. Engl. J. Med.*, 327, 1832-5.

Dabrowski, M., Aerts, S., Van Hummelen, P., Craessaerts, K., De Moor, B., Annaert, W., et al. (2003). Gene profiling of hippocampal neuronal culture. *J. Neurochem.*, 85, 1279-88.

Dalitz, P., Harding, R., Rees, S. M. and Cock, M. L. (2003). Prolonged reductions in placental blood flow and cerebral oxygen delivery in preterm fetal sheep exposed to endotoxin: possible factors in white matter injury after acute infection. *J. Soc. Gynecol. Investig.*, 10, 283-90.

Dambacher, S., Hahn, M. and Schotta, G. (2010). Epigenetic regulation of development by histone lysine methylation. *Heredity*, 105, 24-37.

Dammann, O. and Leviton, A. (1997). Maternal intrauterine infection, cytokines, and brain damage in the preterm newborn. *Pediatr. Res.*, 42, 1-8.

Dammann, O. and Leviton, A. (2000). Role of the fetus in perinatal infection and neonatal brain damage. *Curr. Opin. Pediatr.*, 12, 99-104.

Dani, V. S., Chang, Q., Maffei, A., Turrigiano, G. G., Jaenisch, R. and Nelson, S. B. (2005). Reduced cortical activity due to a shift in the balance between excitation and inhibition in a mouse model of Rett syndrome. *Proc. Natl. Acad. Sci. U S A*, 102, 12560-5.

Das, C., Lucia, M. S., Hansen, K. C. and Tyler, J. K. (2009). CBP/p300-mediated acetylation of histone H3 on lysine 56. *Nature*, 459, 113-7.

Davies, W., Isles, A. R. and Wilkinson, L. S. (2005). Imprinted gene expression in the brain. *Neurosci. Biobehav. Rev.*, 29, 421-30.

Davison, A. N. and Dobbing, J. (1966). Myelination as a vulnerable period of brain development. *Br. Med. Bull.*, 22, 40-4.

Day, J. J. and Sweatt, J. D. (2010). DNA methylation and memory formation. *Nat. Neurosci.*, 13, 1319-23.

Debassio, W. A. and Kemper, T. L. (1985). The effects of protein deprivation on neuronal migration in rats. *Dev. Brain Res.*, 20, 191-6.

DeBaun, M. R., Niemitz, E. L. and Feinberg, A. P. (2003). Association of in vitro fertilization with Beckwith-Wiedemann syndrome and epigenetic alterations of *LIT1* and *H19*. *Am. J. Hum. Genet.*, 72, 156-60.

De Groot, R. H., Stein, A. D., Jolles, J., van Boxtel, M. P., Blauw, G. J., van der Bor, M., et al. (2011). Prenatal famine exposure and cognition at age 59 years. *Int. J. Epidemiol.*, 40, 327-37.

Delisle, H. F. (2008). Poverty. The double burden of malnutrition in mothers and the intergenerational impact. *Ann. NY Acad. Sci.*, 1136, 172-84.

D'Ercole, A. J. and Ye, P. (2008). Minireview: Expanding the mind: Insulin-like growth factor I and brain development. *Endocrinology*, 149, 5958-62.

De Rooij, S. R., Painter, R. C., Phillips, D. I., Osmond, C., Michels, R. P., Godsland, I. F., et al. (2006). Impaired insulin secretion after prenatal exposure to the Dutch famine. *Diabetes Care*, 29, 1897-901.

De Rooij, S. R., Wouters, H., Yonker, J. E., Painter, R. C. and Roseboom, T. J. (2010). Prenatal undernutrition and cognitive function in late adulthood. *Proc. Natl. Acad. Sci. U S A*, 107, 16881-6.

Desai, M., Li, T. and Ross, M. G. (2011). Hypothalamic neurosphere progenitor cells in low birth-weight rat newborns: Neurotrophic effects of leptin and insulin. *Brain Res.*, 1378, 29-42.

Devaskar, S. U. and Raychaudhuri, S. (2007). Epigenetics – a science of heritable biological adaptation. *Pediatr. Res.*, 61, 1R-4R.

De Vrij, F. M.., Levenga, J., van der Linde, H. C., Koekkoek, S. K., De Zeeuw, C. I., Nelson, D. L., et al. (2008). Rescue of behavioral phenotype and neuronal protrusion morphology in Fmr1 KO mice. *Neurobiol. Dis.*, 31, 127-32.

Diamond, A. (2009). The interplay of biology and the environment broadly defined. *Dev. Psychol.*, 45, 1-8.

Diáz-Cintra, S., Cintra, L., Galván, A., Aguilar, A., Kemper, T. and Morgane, P. J. (1991). Effects of prenatal protein deprivation on postnatal development of granule cells in the fascia dentata. *J. Comp. Neurol.*, 310, 356-64.

Dikötter, F. (2010). Mao's great famine. The history of China's most devastating catastrophe, 1958-1962. New York: Walker and Co.

Ding, H., Dolan, P. J. and Johnson, G. V. (2008). Histone deacetylase 6 interacts with the microtubule-associated protein tau. *J. Neurochem.*, 106, 2119-30.

Dittrich, B., Buiting, K., Korn, B., Rickard, S., Buxton, J., Saitoh, S., et al. (1996). Imprint switching on human chromosome 15 may involve alternative transcripts of the SNRPN gene. *Nat. Genet.*, 14, 163-70.

Dobbing, J. (1968). Vulnerable periods in developing brain. In: Applied Neurochemistry. Davison, A. N. and Dobbing, J. (Eds). Chapter 7. Philadelphia: F. A. Davis Company, p. 287-316.

Dobbing, J. (1974). The later development of the brain and its vulnerability. In: Scientific foundations of paediatrics. Davis, J. A. and Dobbing, J. (Eds). Philadelphia: W. B. Saunders Company, p. 565-77.

Dobbing, J. (1981). Maternal nutrition in pregnancy-eating for two? *Early Hum. Dev.*, 5, 113-5.

Dobbing, J. (1987). Early nutrition and later achievement. London: Academic Press.

Dobbing, J. and Sands, J. (1973). Quantitative growth and development of human brain. *Arch. Dis. Child*, 48, 757-67.

Dobbing, J. and Sands, J. (1979). Comparative aspects of the brain growth spurt. *Early Hum. Dev.*, 3, 79-83.

Dobbing, J. and Smart, J. L. (1974). Vulnerability of developing brain and behaviour. *Br. Med. Bull.*, 30, 164-8.

Dodd, I. B., Micheelsen, M. A., Sneppen, K. and Thon, G. (2007). Theoretical analysis of epigenetic cell memory by nucleosome modification. *Cell*, 129, 813-22.

Doherty, A. S., Mann, M. R., Tremblay, K. D., Bartolomei, M. S. and Schultz, R. M. (2000). Differential effects of culture on imprinted H19 expression in the preimplantation mouse embryo. *Biol. Reprod.*, 62, 1526-35.

Doisy, E. A., Ralls, J. O., Allen, E. and Johnston, C. G. (1924). The extraction and some properties of an ovarian hormone. *J. Biol. Chem.*, 61, 711-27.

Dolinoy, D. C., Das, R., Weidman, J. R. and Jirtle, R. L. (2007a). Metastable epialleles, imprinting, and the fetal origins of adult diseases. *Pediatr. Res.*, 61, 30R-37R.

Dolinoy, D. C., Weidman, J. R. and Jirtle, R. L. (2007b). Epigenetic gene regulation: Linking early developmental environment to adult disease. *Reprod. Toxicol.*, 23, 297-307.

Dong, E., Agis-Balboa, R. C., Simonini, M. V., Grayson, D. R., Costa, E. and Guidotti, A. (2005). Reelin and glutamic acid decarboxylase67 promoter remodeling in an epigenetic methionine-induced mouse model of schizophrenia. *Proc. Natl. Acad. Sci. U S A*, 102, 12578-83.

Dong, E., Guidotti, A., Grayson, D. R. and Costa, E. (2007). Histone hyperacetylation induces demethylation of reelin and 67-kDa glutamic acid decarboxylase promoters. *Proc. Natl. Acad. Sci. U S A*, 104, 4676-81.

Donmez, G., Wang, D., Cohen, D. E. and Guarente, L. (2010). SIRT1 suppresses β-amyloid production by activating the α-secretase gene ADAM10. *Cell*, 142, 320-32.

Doria, V., Beckmann, C. F., Arichi, T., Merchant, N., Groppo, M., Turkheimer, F. E., et al. (2010). Emergence of resting state networks in the preterm human brain. *Proc. Natl. Acad. Sci. U S A*, 107, 20015-20.

Drake, A. J. and Walker, B. R. (2004). The intergenerational effects of fetal programming: non-genomic mechanisms for the inheritance of low birth weight and cardiovascular risk. *J. Endocrinol.*, 180, 1-16.

Dulac, C. (2010). Brain function and chromatin plasticity. *Nature*, 465, 728-35.

Duncan, J. R., Cock, M. L., Scheerlinck, J. P., Westcott, K. T., McLean, C., Harding, R., et al. (2002). White matter injury after repeated endotoxin exposure in the preterm ovine fetus. *Pediatr. Res.*, 52, 941-9.

Dunn, G. A. and Bale, T. L. (2009). Maternal high-fat diet promotes body length increases and insulin insensitivity in second-generation mice. *Endocrinology*, 150, 4999-5009.

Durakoglugil, M. S., Chen, Y., White, C. L., Kavalali, E. T. and Herz, J. (2009). Reelin signaling antagonizes beta-amyloid at the synapse. *Proc. Natl. Acad. Sci. U S A*, 106, 15938-43.

Duthie, S. J., Narayanan, S., Brand, G. M., Pirie, L. and Grant, G. (2002). Impact of folate deficiency on DNA stability. *J. Nutr.*, 132, 2444S-2449S.

Eagleson, K. L., Campbell, D. B., Thompson, B. L., Bergman, M. Y. and Levitt, P. (2011). The autism risk genes *MET* and *PLAUR* differentially impact cortical development. *Autism. Res.*, 4, 68-83.

Edlund, T. and Jessell, T. M. (1999). Progression from extrinsic to intrinsic signaling in cell fate specification: a view from the nervous system. *Cell*, 96, 211-24.

Egan, M. F., Goldberg, T. E., Kolachana, B. S., Callicott, J. H., Mazzanti, C. M., Straub, R. E., et al. (2001). Effect of COMT Val[108/158] Met genotype on frontal lobe function and risk for schizophrenia. *Proc. Natl. Acad. Sci. U S A*, 98, 6917-22.

Egger, G., Liang, G., Aparicio, A., Jones P. A. (2004). Epigenetics in human disease and prospects for epigenetic therapy. *Nature*, 429, 457-63.

Eide, M. G., Øyen, N., Skjærven, R. and Bjerkedal, T. (2007). Associations of birth size, gestational age, and adult size with intellectual performance: evidence from a cohort of Norwegian men. *Pediatr. Res.*, 62, 636-42.

Ekamper, P., van Poppel, F., Stein, A. D. and Lumey, L. H. (2013). Independent and additive association of prenatal famine exposure and intermediary life conditions with adult mortality between age 18-63 years. *Soc. Sci. Med.*, [doi: 10.1016/ j.socscimed.2013.10.027].

Elert, E. (2014). Aetiology: searching for schizophrenia's roots. *Nature*, 508, S2-3.

Elford, J., Whincup, P. and Shaper, A. G. (1991). Early life experience and adult cardiovascular disease: longitudinal and case-control studies. *Int. J. Epidemiol.*, 20, 833-44.

Esteller, M. (2007). Cancer epigenomics: DNA methylomes and histone-modification maps. *Nat. Rev. Genet.*, 8, 286-98.

Esteller, M. (2008). Molecular origins of cancer. Epigenetics in cancer. *N. Engl. J. Med.*, 358, 1148-59.

Fagiolini, M., Jensen, C. L. and Champagne, F. A. (2009). Epigenetic influences on brain development and plasticity. *Curr. Opin. Neurobiol.*, 19, 207-12.

Fatemi, S. H. (2005). Reelin glycoprotein: structure, biology and roles in health and disease. *Mol. Psychiatry*, 10, 251-7.

Fatemi, S. H., Kroll, J. L. and Stary, J. M. (2001). Altered levels of Reelin and its isoforms in schizophrenia and mood disorders. *Neuroreport*, 12, 3209-15.

Feil, R. (2006). Environmental and nutritional effects on the epigenetic regulation of genes. *Mutation Res.*, 600, 46-57.

Feinberg, A. P. (2007). Phenotypic plasticity and the epigenetics of human disease. *Nature*, 447, 433-40.

Feng, J., Fouse, S. and Fan, G. (2007). Epigenetic regulation of neural gene expression and neuronal function. *Pediatr. Res.*, 61, 58R-63R.

Fernandez-Twinn, D. S., Ozanne, S. E., Ekizoglou, S., Doherty, C., James, L., Gusterson, B., et al. (2003). The maternal endocrine environment in the low-protein model of intra-uterine growth restriction. *Br. J. Nutr.*, 90, 815-22.

Fidel, P. L., Jr., Romero, R., Wolf, N., Cutright, J., Ramirez, M., Araneda, H., et al. (1994). Systemic and local cytokine profiles in endotoxin-induced preterm parturition in mice. *Am. J. Obstet. Gynecol.*, 170, 1467-75.

Fisch, G. S. (2007). Animal models and human neuropsychiatric disorders. *Behav. Genet.*, 37, 1-10.

Flint, J. and Shifman, S. (2008). Animal models of psychiatric disease. *Curr. Opin. Genet. Dev.*, 18, 235-40.

Fontana, L., Partridge, L. and Longo, V. D. (2010). Extending healthy life span – from yeast to humans. *Science*, 328, 321-6.

Fox, S. E., Levitt, P. and Nelson III, C. A. (2010). How the timing and quality of early experiences influence the development of brain architecture. *Child Dev.*, 81, 28-40.

Francis, D. D., Szegda, K., Campbell, G., Martin W. D. and Insel, T. R. (2003). Epigenetic sources of behavioral differences in mice. *Nat. Neurosci.*, 6, 445-6.

Franklin, T. B. and Mansuy, I. M. (2010). Epigenetic inheritance in mammals: Evidence for the impact of adverse environmental effects. *Neurobiol. Dis.*, 39, 61-5.

Franzek, E. J., Sprangers, N., Janssens, A. C., Van Duijn, C. M. and Van De Wetering, B. J. (2008). Prenatal exposure to the 1944-45 Dutch 'hunger winter' and addiction later in life. *Addiction*, 103, 433-8.

Friedler, G. and Wheeling, H. S. (1979). Behavioral effects in offspring of male mice injected with opioids prior to mating. *Pharmacol. Biochem. Behav. (Suppl.)*, 11, 23-8.

Gage, F. H. (2000). Mammalian neural stem cells. *Science*, 287, 1433-8.

Gage, F. H., Coates, P. W., Palmer, T. D., Kuhn, H. G., Fisher, L. J., Suhonen, J. O., et al. (1995). Survival and differentiation of adult neuronal progenitor cells transplanted to the adult brain. *Proc. Natl. Acad. Sci. U S A*, 92, 11879-83.

Galler, J. R., Ramsey, F. and Solimano, G. (1984). The influence of early malnutrition on subsequent behavioral development. III. Learning disabilities as a sequel to malnutrition. *Pediatr. Res.*, 18, 309-13.

Gal-Yam, E. N., Saito, Y., Egger, G. and Jones, P. A. (2008). Cancer epigenetics: modifications, screening, and therapy. *Annu. Rev. Med.*, 59, 267-80.

Gao, Y. and Raj, J. U. (2010). Regulation of the pulmonary circulation in the fetus and newborn. *Physiol. Rev.*, 90, 1291-335.

Garcion, E., Faissner, A. and ffrench-Constant, C. (2001). Knockout mice reveal a contribution of the extracellular matrix molecule tenascin-C to neural precursor proliferation and migration. *Development*, 128, 2485-96.

Gasa, R., Mrejen, C., Leachman, N., Otten, M., Barnes, M., Wang, J., et al. (2004). Proendocrine genes coordinate the pancreatic islet differentiation program in vitro. *Proc. Natl. Acad. Sci. U S A*, 101, 13245-50.

Gasser, T. (2001). Genetics of Parkinson's disease. *J. Neurol.*, 248, 833-40.

Gaze, R. M. (1970). The formation of nerve connections: a consideration of neural specificity modulation and comparable phenomena. New York: Academic Press.

Gaze, R. M. (1974). Neuronal specificity. *Br. Med. Bull.*, 30, 116-21.

Gheorghe, C. P., Mohan, S., Oberg, K. and Longo, L. D. (2007). Gene expression patterns in the hypoxic murine placenta: a role in epigenesis? *Reprod. Sci.*, 14, 223-33.

Gheorghe, C. P., Goyal, R., Mittal, A. and Longo, L. D. (2010). Gene expression in the placenta: maternal stress and epigenetic responses. *Int. J. Dev. Biol.*, 54, 507-23.

Gibbons, R. J., McDowell, T. L., Raman, S., O'Rourke, D. M., Garrick, D., Ayyub, H., et al. (2000). Mutations in ATRX, encoding a SWI/SNF-like protein, cause diverse changes in the pattern of DNA methylation. *Nat. Genet.*, 24, 368-71.

Gibbons, R. J., Picketts, D. J., Villard, L. and Higgs, D. R. (1995). Mutations in a putative global transcriptional regulator cause X-linked mental retardation with alpha-thalassemia (ATR-X syndrome). *Cell*, 80, 837-45.

Gillette-Guyonnet, S. and Vellas, B. (2008). Caloric restriction and brain function. *Curr. Opin. Clin. Nutr. Metab. Care*, 11, 686-92.

Gillman, M. W., Rifas-Shiman, S. L., Kleinman, K., Oken, E., Rich-Edwards, J. W. and Taveras, E. M. (2008). Developmental origins of childhood overweight: potential public health impact. *Obesity (Silver Spring)*, 16, 1651-6.

Giussani, D. A. (2011). The vulnerable developing brain. *Proc. Natl. Acad. Sci. U S A*, 108, 2641-2.

Gluckman, P. D. and Hanson, M. A. (2006). Mismatch: why our world no longer fits our bodies. Oxford: Oxford University Press.

Gluckman, P. D., Hanson, M. A., Cooper, C. and Thornburg, K. L. (2008). Effect of in utero and early-life conditions on adult health and disease. *N. Engl. J. Med.*, 359, 61-73.

Godfrey, K. M. (1998). Maternal regulation of fetal development and health in adult life. *Eur. J. Obstet. Gynecol. Reprod. Biol.*, 78, 141-50.

Godfrey, K. M., Lillycrop, K. A., Burdge, G. C., Gluckman, P. D. and Hanson, M. A. (2007). Epigenetic mechanisms and the mismatch concept of the developmental origins of health and disease. *Pediatr. Res.*, 61, 5R-10R.

Goel, N. and Bale, T. L. (2009). Examining the intersection of sex and stress in modeling neuropsychiatric disorders. *J. Neuroendocrinol.*, 21, 415-20.

Goldberg, A. D., Allis, C. D. and Bernstein, E. (2007). Epigenetics: A landscape takes shape. *Cell*, 128, 635-8.

Goldstein, J. M. (2006). Sex, hormones and affective arousal circuitry dysfunction in schizophrenia. *Horm. Behav.*, 50, 612-22.

Goldstein, J. M., Seidman, L. J., Makris, N., Ahern, T., O'Brien, L. M., Caviness, Jr., V. S., et al. (2007). Hypothalamic abnormalities in schizophrenia: sex effects and genetic vulnerability. *Biol. Psychiatry*, 61, 935-45.

Goldstein, M. (1994). Decade of the brain. An agenda for the nineties. *West. J. Med.*, 161, 239-41.

Goldstone, A. P. (2004). Prader-Willi syndrome: advances in genetics, pathophysiology and treatment. *Trends Endocrinol. Metab.*, 15, 12-20.

Golub, T. (2010). Counterpoint: Data first. *Nature*, 464, 679.

Goos, L. M. and Silverman, I. (2001). The influence of genomic imprinting on brain development and behavior. *Evol. Hum. Behav.*, 22, 385-407.

Götz, A. A., Wittlinger, S. and Stefanski, V. (2007). Maternal social stress during pregnancy alters immune function and immune cell numbers in adult male Long-Evans rat offspring during stressful life-events. *J. Neuroimmunol.*, 185, 95-102.

Goyal, R., Galffy, A., Field, S. A., Gheorghe, C. P., Mittal, A. and Longo, L. D. (2009). Maternal protein deprivation: changes in systemic renin-angiotensin system of the mouse fetus. *Reprod. Sci.*, 16, 894-904.

Goyal, R., Goyal, D., Leitzke, A., Gheorghe, C. P. and Longo, L. D. (2010). Brain renin-angiotensin system: fetal epigenetic programming by maternal protein restriction during pregnancy. *Reprod. Sci.*, 17, 227-38.

Goyal, R., Leitzke, A., Goyal, D., Gheorghe, C. P. and Longo, L. D. (2011a). Antenatal maternal hypoxic stress: adaptations in fetal lung renin-angiotensin system. *Reprod. Sci.*, 18, 180-9.

Goyal, R., Lister, R., Leitzke, A., Goyal, D., Gheorghe, C. P. and Longo, L. D. (2011b). Antenatal maternal hypoxic stress: adaptations of the placental renin-angiotensin system in the mouse. *Placenta*, 32, 134-9.

Green, L. R., Hanson, M. A. (2004). Programming of the fetal circulation. In: Fetal and Neonatal Physiology. Polin, R. A., Fox, W. W. and Abman, S. H. (Eds). 3rd Ed., Vol. 1. Philadelphia, PA: Saunders, p. 727-32.

Gregg, C., Zhang, J., Butler, J. E., Haig, D. and Dulac, C., (2010a). Sex-specific parent-of-origin allelic expression in the mouse brain. *Science*, 329, 682-5.

Gregg, C., Zhang, J., Weissbourd, B., Luo, S., Schroth, G. P., Haig, D., et al. (2010b). High-resolution analysis of parent-of-origin allelic expression in the mouse brain. *Science*, 329, 643-8.

Gross, C. and Hen, R. (2004). The developmental origins of anxiety. *Nat. Rev. Neurosci.*, 5, 545-52.

Grossman, A. W., Churchill, J. D., McKinney, B. C., Kodish, I. M., Otte, S. L. and Greenough, W.T. (2003). Experience effects on brain development: possible contributions to psychopathology. *J. Child Psychol. Psychiatry*, 44, 33-63.

Guillemot, F., Molnár, Z., Tarabykin, V. and Stoykova, A. (2006). Molecular mechanisms of cortical differentiation. *Eur. J. Neurosci.*, 23, 857-68.

Gupta, S. K., Gressens, P. and Mani, S. (2009). NRSF downregulation induces neuronal differentiation in mouse embryonic stem cells. *Differentiation*, 77, 19-28.

Guy, J., Gan, J., Selfridge, J., Cobb, S. and Bird, A. (2007). Reversal of neurological defects in a mouse model of Rett Syndrome. *Science*, 315, 1143-7.

Guy, J., Hendrich, B., Holmes, M., Martin, J. E. and Bird, A. (2001). A mouse Mecp2-null mutation causes neurological symptoms that mimic Rett syndrome. *Nat. Genet.*, 27, 322-6.

Gyurko, R., Wielbo, D. and Phillips, M. I. (1993). Antisense inhibition of AT1 receptor mRNA and angiotensinogen mRNA in the brain of spontaneously hypertensive rats reduces hypertension of neurogenic origin. *Regul. Pept.*, 49, 167-74.

Hagberg, B., Aicardi, J., Dias, K. and Ramos, O. (1983). A progressive syndrome of autism, dementia, ataxia, and loss of purposeful hand use in girls: Rett's syndrome: report of 35 cases. *Ann. Neurol.*, 14, 471-9.

Haglund, N. G. and Källén, K. B. (2011). Risk factors for autism and Apserger syndrome. Perinatal factors and migration. *Autism*, 15, 163-83.

Hales, C. N. and Barker, D. J. (1992). Type 2 (non-insulin-dependent) diabetes mellitus: the thrifty phenotype hypothesis. *Diabetologia*, 35, 595-601.

Hales, C. N. and Barker, D. J. (2001). The thrifty phenotype hypothesis. *Br. Med.* Bull., 60, 5-20.

Ham, J. and Tronick, E. (2006). Infant resilience to the stress of the still-face. Infant and maternal psychophysiology are related. *Ann. NY Acad. Sci.*, 1094, 297-302.

Hammock, E. A. D. and Levitt, P. (2006). The discipline of neurobehavioral development: the emerging interface of processes that build circuits and skills. *Hum. Dev.*, 49, 294-309.

Hammoud, S. S., Nix, D. A., Zhang, H., Purwar, J., Carrell, D. T. and Cairns, B. R. (2009). Distinctive chromatin in human sperm packages genes for embryo development. *Nature*, 460, 473-8.

Hanauer, A. and Young, I. D. (2002). Coffin-Lowry syndrome: clinical and molecular features. *J. Med. Genet.*, 39, 705-13.

Hansen, R. S., Stöger, R., Wijmenga, C., Stanek, A. M., Canfield, T. K., Luo, P., et al. (2000). Escape from gene silencing in ICF syndrome: evidence for advanced replication time as a major determinant. *Hum. Mol. Genet.*, 9, 2575-87.

Hansen, R. S., Wijmenga, C., Luo, P., Stanek, A. M., Canfield, T. K., Weemaes, C. M., et al. (1999). The DNMT3B DNA methyltransferase gene is mutated in the ICF immunodeficiency syndrome. *Proc. Natl. Acad. Sci. U S A*, 96, 14412-7.

Hanson, M. A. and Gluckman, P. D. (2005). Developmental processes and the induction of cardiovascular function: conceptual aspects. *J. Physiol. (Lond.)*, 565, 27-34.

Happé, F., Ronald, A. and Plomin, R. (2006). Time to give up on a single explanation for autism. *Nat. Neurosci.*, 9, 1218-20.

Harding, J. E. (2001). The nutritional basis of the fetal origins of adult disease. *Int. J. Epidemiol.*, 30, 15-23.

Harris, G. W. (1964). The Upjohn Lecture of the Endocrine Society. Sex hormones, brain development and brain function. *Endocrinology*, 75, 627-48.

Hattori, D., Chen, Y., Matthews, B. J., Salwinski, L., Sabatti, C., Grueber, W. B., et al. (2009). Robust discrimination between self and non-self neuritis requires thousands of Dscam1 isoforms. *Nature*, 461, 644-8.

Hawthorne, A. L. (2014). Repurposing Reelin: The new role of radial glia, Reelin and Notch in motor neuron migration. *Exp. Neurol.*, 256, 17-20.

He, J., Bian, Y., Gao, F., Li, M., Qiu, L., Wu, W., et al. (2009). RNA interference targeting the ACE gene reduced blood pressure and improved myocardial remodelling in SHRs. *Clin. Sci. (Lond.)*, 116, 249-55.

He, J. H., Xiao, C. S., Li, M. L. and Bian, Y. F. (2008). [Effects of RNA interference targeting angiotensin-converting enzyme on the blood pressure and myocardial remodeling in spontaneously hypertensive rats]. *Zhonghua Xin Xue Guan Bing Za Zhi*, 36, 249-53.

Hebb, D. O. (1949). The organization of behavior, a neuropsychological theory. New York: Wiley.

Hedges, D. W. and Woon, F. L. (2011). Early-life stress and cognitive outcome. *Psychopharmacology (Berl.)*, 214, 121-30.

Heijmans, B. T., Tobi, E. W., Lumey, L. H. and Slagboom, P. E. (2009). The epigenome: archive of the prenatal environment. *Epigenetics*, 4, 526-31.

Heijmans, B. T., Tobi, E. W., Stein, A. D., Putter, H., Blauw, G. J., Susser, E. S., et al. (2008). Persistent epigenetic differences associated with prenatal exposure to famine in humans. *Proc. Natl. Acad. Sci. U S A*, 105, 17046-9.

Heim, C. and Nemeroff, C. B. (2002). Neurobiology of early life stress: Clinical Studies. *Semin. Clin. Neuropsychiatry*, 7, 147-59.

Hertz-Picciotto, I., Park, H.-Y., Dostal, M., Kocan, A., Trnovec, T. and Sram, R. (2008). Prenatal exposures to persistent and non-persistent organic compounds and effects on immune system development. *Basic Clin. Pharmacol. Toxicol.*, 102, 146-54.

Hibbeln, J. R., Davis, J. M., Steer, C., Emmett, P., Rogers, I., Williams, C., et al. (2007). Maternal seafood consumption in pregnancy and neurodevelopmental outcomes in childhood (ALSPAC study): an observational cohort study. *Lancet*, 369, 578-85.

Hikida, T., Jaaro-Peled, H., Seshadri, S., Oishi, K., Hookway, C., Kong, S., et al. (2007). Dominant-negative DISC1 transgenic mice display schizophrenia-associated phenotypes detected by measures translatable to humans. *Proc. Natl. Acad. Sci. U S A*, 104, 14501-6.

Hirabayashi, Y. and Gotoh, Y. (2010). Epigenetic control of neural precursor cell fate during development. *Nat. Rev. Neurosci.*, 11, 377-88.

Hodgson, D. M., Knott, B. and Walker, F. R. (2001). Neonatal endotoxin exposure influences HPA responsivity and impairs tumor immunity in Fischer 344 rats in adulthood. *Pediatr. Res.*, 50, 750-5.

Hoek, H. W., Brown, A. S. and Susser, E. (1998). The Dutch Famine and schizophrenia spectrum disorders. *Soc. Psychiatry Psychiatr. Epidemiol.*, 33, 373-9.

Hoek, H. W., Susser, E., Buck, K. A., Lumey, L. H., Lin, S. P. and Gorman, J. M. (1996). Schizoid personality disorder after prenatal exposure to famine. *Am. J. Psychiatry*, 153, 1637-9.

Hoet, J. J. and Hanson, M. A. (1999). Intrauterine nutrition: its importance during critical periods for cardiovascular and endocrine development. *J. Physiol. (Lond.)*, 514, 617-27.

Holliday, M. A. (1971). Metabolic rate and organ size during growth from infancy to maturity and during late gestation and early infancy. *Pediatrics*, 47, 169-79.

Holliday, R. (1987). The inheritance of epigenetic defects. *Science*, 238, 163-70.

Holliday, R. and Pugh, J. E. (1975). DNA modification mechanisms and gene activity during development. *Science*, 187, 226-32.

Holsboer, F. (2000). The corticosteroid receptor hypothesis of depression. *Neuropsychopharmacology*, 23, 477-501.

Holness, M. J. and Sugden, M. C. (2006). Epigenetic regulation of metabolism in children born small for gestational age. *Curr. Opin. Clin. Nutr. Metab. Care*, 9, 482-8.

Hornig, M., Weissenböck, H., Horscroft, N. and Lipkin, W. I. (1999). An infection-based model of neurodevelopmental damage. *Proc. Natl. Acad. Sci. U S A*, 96, 12102-7.

Horsthemke, B. and Wagstaff, J. (2008). Mechanisms of imprinting of the Prader-Willi/Angelman region. *Am. J. Med. Genet. A.*, 146A, 2041-52.

Hsieh, J. and Eisch, A. J. (2010). Epigenetics, hippocampal neurogenesis, and neuropsychiatric disorders: Unraveling the genome to understand the mind. *Neurobiol. Dis.*, 39, 73-84.

Hsueh, A. M., Agustin, C. E. and Chow, B. F. (1967). Growth of young rats after differential manipulation of maternal diet. *J. Nutr.*, 91, 195-200.

Huang, S. T., Vo, K. C., Lyell, D. J., Faessen, G. H., Tulac, S., Tibshirani, R., et al. (2004). Developmental response to hypoxia. *FASEB J.*, 18, 1348-65.

Huizinga, C. T., Oudejans, C. B., Steiner, R. A., Clifton, D. K. and Delemarre-van de Waal, H. A. (2000). Effects of intrauterine and early postnatal growth restriction on hypothalamic somatostatin gene expression in the rat. *Pediatr. Res.*, 48, 815-20.

Hulshoff Pol, H. E., Hoek, H. W., Susser, E., Brown, A. S., Dingemans, A., Schnack, H. G., et al. (2000). Prenatal exposure to famine and brain morphology in schizophrenia. *Am. J. Psychiatry*, 157, 1170-2.

Hüppi, P. S. (2008). Nutrition for the brain: commentary on the article by Isaacs et al. on page 308. *Pediatr. Res.*, 63, 229-31.

Impagnatiello, F., Guidotti, A. R., Pesold, C., Dwivedi, Y., Caruncho, H., Pisu, M. G., et al. (1998). A decrease of reelin expression as a putative vulnerability factor in schizophrenia. *Proc. Natl. Acad. Sci. U S A*, 95, 15718-23.

Insel, T. R. (2007). From animal models to model animals. *Biol. Psychiatry*, 62, 1337-9.

[International Schizophrenia Consortium] (2009). Common polygenic variation contributes to risk of schizophrenia and bipolar disorder. *Nature*, 460, 748-52.

Isaacs, E. B., Gadian, D. G., Sabatini, S., Chong, W. K., Quinn, B. T., Fischl, B. R., et al. (2008). The effect of early human diet on caudate volumes and IQ. *Pediatr. Res.*, 63, 308-14.

Isles, A. R. and Wilkinson, L. S. (2000). Imprinted genes, cognition and behaviour. *Trends Cogn. Sci.*, 4, 309-18.

Iwamoto, K. and Kato, T. (2009). Epigenetic profiling in schizophrenia and major mental disorders. *Neuropsychobiology*, 60, 5-11.

Iyer, V. R., Eisen, M. B., Ross, D. T., Schuler, G., Moore, T., Lee, J. C., et al. (1999). The transcriptional program in the response of human fibroblasts to serum. *Science*, 283, 83-7.

Jablonka, E. and Lamb, M. J. (2002). The changing concept of epigenetics. *Ann. NY Acad. Sci.*, 981, 82-96.

Jacobson, M. (1970). Developmental neurobiology. New York: Holt, Rinehart and Winston, Inc. (2nd Ed., New York: Plenum Press, 1978).

Jacquemont, S., Curie, A., des Portes, V., Torrioli, M. G., Berry-Kravis, E., Hagerman, R. J., et al. (2011). Epigenetic modification of the *FMR1* gene in fragile X syndrome is associated with differential response to the mGluR5 antagonist AFQ056. *Sci. Transl. Med.*, 3, 64ra1.

Jaenisch, R. (1997). DNA methylation and imprinting: Why bother? *Trends Genet.*, 13, 323-9.

Jaenisch, R. and Bird, A. (2003). Epigenetic regulation of gene expression: how the genome integrates intrinsic and environmental signals. *Nat. Genet.*, 33 Suppl., 245-54.

Jansson, T. and Powell, T. L. (2007). Role of the placenta in fetal programming: underlying mechanisms and potential interventional approaches. *Clin. Sci.*, 113, 1-13.

Jeanpierre, M., Turleau, C., Aurias, A., Prieur, M., Ledeist, F., Fischer, A., et al., (1993). An embryonic-like methylation pattern of classical satellite DNA is observed in ICF syndrome. *Hum. Mol. Genet.*, 2, 731-5.

Jessell, T. M. and Sanes, J. R. (2000). The decade of the developing brain. *Curr. Opin. Neurobiol.*, 10, 599-611.

Jiang, Y., Langley, B., Lubin, F. D., Renthal, W., Wood, M. A., Yasui, D. H., et al. (2008). Epigenetics in the nervous system. *J. Neurosci.*, 28, 11753-9.

Jirtle, R. L. and Skinner, M. K. (2007). Environmental epigenomics and disease susceptibility. *Nat. Rev. Genet.*, 8, 253-62.

Johnstone, S. E. and Baylin, S. B. (2010). Stress and the epigenetic landscape: a link to the pathobiology of human diseases? *Nat. Rev. Genet.*, 11, 806-12.

Jones, D. G. (1976). The vulnerability of the brain to undernutrition. *Sci. Prog.*, 63, 483-502.

Jones, P. A. and Baylin, S. B. (2007). The epigenomics of cancer. *Cell*, 128, 683-92.

Jones, P. A. and Martienssen, R. (2005). A blueprint for a Human Epigenome Project: the AACR Human Epigenome Workshop. *Cancer Res.*, 65, 11241-6.

Jones, P. A. and Takai, D. (2001). The role of DNA methylation in mammalian epigenetics. *Science*, 293, 1068-70.

Jordan, T. C., Howells, K. F., McNaughton, N. and Heatlie, P. L. (1982). Effects of early undernutrition on hippocampal development and function. *Res. Exp. Med.*, 180, 201-7.

Joseph, K. S. and Kramer, M. S. (1996). Review of the evidence on fetal and early childhood antecedents of adult chronic disease. *Epidemiol. Rev.*, 18, 158-74.

Judson, M. C., Amaral, D. G. and Levitt, P. (2011). Conserved subcortical and divergent cortical expression of proteins encoded by orthologs of the autism risk gene MET. *Cereb. Cortex.*, 21, 1613-26.

Kaati, G., Bygren, L. O., Pembrey, M. and Sjöström, M. (2007). Transgenerational response to nutrition, early life circumstances and longevity. *Eur. J. Hum. Genet.*, 15, 784-90.

Kapoor, A., Leen, J. and Matthews, S. G. (2008). Molecular regulation of the hypothalamic-pituitary-adrenal axis in adult male guinea pigs after prenatal stress at different stages of gestation. *J. Physiol.*, 586, 4317-26.

Kaufman, J. and Charney, D. (2001). Effects of early stress on brain structure and function: implications for understanding the relationship between child maltreatment and depression. *Dev. Psychopathol.*, 13, 451-71.

Kawase-Koga, Y., Otaegi, G. and Sun, T. (2009). Different timings of Dicer deletion affect neurogenesis and gliogenesis in the developing mouse central nervous system. *Dev. Dyn.*, 238, 2800-12.

Ke, X., Lei, Q., James, S. J., Kelleher, S. L., Melnyk, S., Jernigan, S., et al. (2006). Uteroplacental insufficiency affects epigenetic determinants of chromatin structure in brains of neonatal and juvenile IUGR rats. *Physiol. Genomics*, 25, 16-28.

Ke, X., Schober, M. E., McKnight, R. A., O'Grady, S., Caprau, D., Yu, X., et al. (2010). Intrauterine growth retardation affects expression and epigenetic characteristics of the rat hippocampal glucocorticoid receptor gene. *Physiol. Genomics*, 42, 177-89.

Kellendonk, C., Simpson, E. H. and Kandel, E. R. (2009). Modeling cognitive endophenotypes of schizophrenia in mice. *Trends Neurosci.*, 32, 347-58.

Kendall, E. C., Mason, H. L., Myers, C. S. and Allers, W. D. (1936). A physiologic and chemical investigation of the suprarenal cortex. *J. Biol. Chem.*, 114, lvii-lviii.

Kendell, R. E. and Kemp, I. W. (1989). Maternal influenza in the etiology of schizophrenia. *Arch. Gen. Psychiatry*, 46, 878-82.

Kent, L., Bowdin, S., Kirby, G. A., Cooper, W. N. and Maher, E. R. (2008). Beckwith Weidemann syndrome: a behavioral phenotype-genotype study. *Am. J. Med. Genet. B. Neuropsychiatr. Genet.*, 147B, 1295-7.

Khashan, A. S., Abel, K. M., McNamee, R., Pedersen, M. G., Webb, R. T., Baker, P. N., et al. (2008). Higher risk of offspring schizophrenia following antenatal maternal exposure to severe adverse life events. *Arch. Gen. Psychiatry*, 65, 146-52.

Khosla, S., Dean, W., Reik, W. and Feil, R. (2001a). Culture of pre-implantation embryos and its long-term effects on gene expression and phenotype. *Hum. Reprod. Update*, 7, 419-27.

Khosla, S., Dean, W., Brown, D., Reik, R. and Feil, R. (2001b). Culture of pre-implantation mouse embryos affects fetal development and the expression of imprinted genes. *Biol. Reprod.*, 64, 918-26.

Kintner, C. (2002). Neurogenesis in embryos and in adult neural stem cells. *J. Neurosci.*, 22, 639-43.

Klose, R. J., Kallin, E. M. and Zhang, Y. (2006). JmjC-domain-containing proteins and histone demethylation. *Nat. Rev. Genet.*, 7, 715-27.

Knoll, J. H., Nicholls, R. D., Magenis, R. E., Graham, J. M., Jr., Lalande, M. and Latt, S. A. (1989). Angelman and Prader-Willi syndromes share a common chromosome 15 deletion but differ in parental origin of the deletion. *Am. J. Med. Genet.*, 32, 285-90.

Knudsen, E. I. (2004). Sensitive periods in the development of the brain and behavior. *J. Cogn. Neurosci.*, 16, 1412-25.

Kocerha, J., Faghihi, M. A., Lopez-Toledano, M. A., Huang, J., Ramsey, A. J., Caron, M. G., et al. (2009). MicroRNA-219 modulates NMDA receptor-mediated neurobehavioral dysfunction. *Proc. Natl. Acad. Sci. U S A*, 106, 3507-12.

Koike, H., Arguello, P. A., Kvajo, M., Karayiorgou, M. and Gogos, J. A. (2006). Disc1 is mutated in the 129S6/SvEv strain and modulates working memory in mice. *Proc. Natl. Acad. Sci. U S A*, 103, 3693-7.

Kolvin, I. (1971). Studies in the childhood psychoses. I. Diagnostic criteria and classification. *Br. J. Psychiatry*, 118, 381-4.

Kolvin, I., Ounsted, C., Humphrey, M. and McNay, A. (1971). Studies in the childhood pyschoses. II. The phenomenology of childhood psychoses. *Br. J. Psychiatry*, 118, 385-95.

Kontopoulos, E., Parvin, J. D. and Feany, M. B. (2006). α-synuclein acts in the nucleus to inhibit histone acetylation and promote neurotoxicity. *Hum. Mol. Genet.*, 15, 3012-23.

Koshibu, K. and Levitt, P. (2008). Gene x environment effects: stress and memory dysfunctions caused by stress and gonadal factor irregularities during puberty in control and TGF-alpha hypomorphic mice. *Neuropsychopharmacology*, 33, 557-65.

Kostović, I. and Judaš, M. (2007). Transient patterns of cortical lamination during prenatal life: Do they have implications for treatment? *Neurosci. Biobehav. Rev.*, 31, 1157-68.

Kouzarides, T. (2007). Chromatin modifications and their function. *Cell*, 128, 693-705.

Krishnan, S., Intlekofer, K. A., Aggison, L. K. and Petersen, S. L. (2009). Central role of TRAF-interacting protein in a new model of brain sexual differentiation. *Proc. Natl. Acad. Sci. U S A*, 106, 16692-7.

Krishnan, V. and Nestler, E. J. (2010). Linking molecules to mood: new insight into the biology of depression. *Am. J. Psychiatry*, 167, 1305-20.

Kuh, D. and Ben-Shlomo, Y. (Eds). (1997). A life course approach to chronic disease epidemiology. Oxford: Oxford University Press.

Kuh, D., Ben-Shlomo, Y., Lynch, J., Hallqvist, J. and Power, C. (2003). Life course epidemiology. *J. Epidemiol. Community Health*, 57, 778-83.

Kuh, D. and Hardy, R. (Eds). (2002). A life course approach to women's health. Oxford: Oxford University Press.

Kundakovic, M., Chen, Y., Guidotti, A. and Grayson, D. R. (2009). The reelin and GAD67 promoters are activated by epigenetic drugs that facilitate the disruption of local repressor complexes. *Mol. Pharmacol.*, 75, 342-54.

Kuwabara, T., Hsieh, J., Muotri, A., Yeo, G., Warashina, M., Lie, D. C., et al. (2009). Wnt-mediated activation of NeuroD1 and retro-elements during adult neurogenesis. *Nat. Neurosci.*, 12, 1097-105.

Kwong, W. Y., Wild, A. E., Roberts, P., Willis, A. C. and Fleming, T. P. (2000). Maternal undernutrition during the preimplantation period of rat development causes blastocyst abnormalities and programming of postnatal hypertension. *Development*, 127, 4195-202.

Kyle, U. G. and Pichard, C. (2006). The Dutch Famine of 1944-1945: a pathophysiological model of long-term consequences of wasting disease. *Curr. Opin. Clin. Nutr. Metab. Care*, 9, 388-94.

Ladewig, J., Koch, P. and Brustle, O. (2013). Leveling Waddington: the emergence of direct programming and the loss of cell fate hierarchies. *Nat. Rev. Mol. Cell Biol.*, 14, 225-36.

Lahiri, D. K., Sokol, D. K., Erickson, C., Ray, B., Ho, C. Y. and Maloney, B. (2013). Autism as early neurodevelopmental disorder: evidence for an sAPPα-mediated anabolic pathway. *Front Cell Neurosci.*, 7, 94.

Landrigan, P. J., Kimmel, C. A., Correa, A. and Eskenazi, B. (2004). Children's health and the environment: public health issues and challenges for risk assessment. *Environ. Health Perspect*, 112, 257-65.

Lane, N., Dean, W., Erhardt, S., Hajkova, P., Surani, A., Walter, J., et al. (2003). Resistance of IAPs to methylation reprogramming may provide a mechanism for epigenetic inheritance in the mouse. *Genesis*, 35, 88-93.

Lane, R. H., Flozak, A. S., Ogata, E. S., Bell, G. I. and Simmons, R. A. (1996). Altered hepatic gene expression of enzymes involved in energy metabolism in the growth-retarded fetal rat. *Pediatr. Res.*, 39, 390-4.

Langley, S. C. and Jackson, A. A. (1994). Increased systolic blood pressure in adult rats induced by fetal exposure to maternal low protein diets. *Clin. Sci. (Lond.)*, 86, 217-22; discussion 121.

Langley-Evans, S. C. (2000). Critical differences between two low protein diet protocols in the programming of hypertension in the rat. *Int. J. Food Sci. Nutr.*, 51, 11-7.

Lansdorp, P. M. (2007). Immortal strands? Give me a break. *Cell*, 129, 1244-7.

Larbi, A., Franceschi, C., Mazzatti, D., Solana, R., Wikby, A. and Pawelec, G. (2008). Aging of the immune system as a prognostic factor for human longevity. *Physiology*, 23, 64-74.

LaSalle, J. M., Hogart, A. and Thatcher, K. N. (2005). Rett syndrome: a rosetta stone for understanding the molecular pathogenesis of autism. *Intl. Rev. Neurobiol.*, 71, 131-65.

LaSalle, J. M., Powell, W. T. and Yasui, D. H. (2013). Epigenetic layers and players underlying neurodevelopment. *Trends Neurosci.*, 36, 460-70.

Laurence, K. M., James, N., Miller, M. H., Tennant, G. B. and Campbell, H. (1981). Double-blind randomized controlled trial of folate treatment before conception to prevent recurrence of neural-tube defects. *BMJ*, 282, 1509-11.

Lavoie, J. L. and Sigmund, C. D. (2003). Minireview: overview of the renin-angiotensin system – an endocrine and paracrine system. *Endocrinology*, 144, 2179-83.

Leathwood, P. (1978). Influence of early undernutrition on behavioral development and learning in rodents. In: Early influences. Gottlieb, G. (Ed). Volume 4. New York: Academic Press, p. 187-209.

Lee, J. S., Smith, E. and Shilatifard, A. (2010). The language of histone crosstalk. *Cell*, 142, 682-5.

Lenkei, Z., Palkovits, M., Corvol, P. and Llorens-Cortès, C. (1997). Expression of angiotensin type-1 (AT1) and type-2 (AT2) receptor mRNAs in the adult rat brain: a functional neuroanatomical review. *Front Neuroendocrinol.*, 18, 383-439.

Lerner, S. (2010). Sacrifice zones. The front lines of toxic chemical exposure in the United States. Cambridge, MA: The MIT Press.

Leucht, C., Stigloher, C., Wizenmann, A., Klafke, R., Folchert, A. and Bally-Cuif, L. (2008). MicroRNA-9 directs late organizer activity of the midbrain-hindbrain boundary. *Nat. Neurosci.*, 11, 641-8.

Levenson, J. M. and Sweatt, J. D. (2005). Epigenetic mechanisms in memory formation. *Nat. Rev. Neurosci.*, 6, 108-18.

Leviton, A., Allred, E. N., Kuban, K. C., Hecht, J. L., Onderdonk, A. B., O'shea, T. M., et al. (2010). Microbiologic and histologic characteristics of the extremely preterm infant's placenta predict white matter damage and later cerebral palsy. The ELGAN study. *Pediatr. Res.*, 67, 95-101.

Levitsky, D. A. and Barnes, R. H. (1972). Nutritional and environmental interactions in the behavioral development of the rat: long-term effects. *Science*, 176, 68-71.

Levitsky, D. A. and Strupp, B. J. (1995). Malnutrition and the brain: changing concepts, changing concerns. *J. Nutr.*, 125, 2212S-2220S.

Levitt, P. (2003). Structural and functional maturation of the developing primate brain. *J. Pediatr.*, 143, S35-45.

Lewis, D. A., Cruz, D., Eggan, S. and Erickson, S. (2004). Postnatal development of prefrontal inhibitory circuits and the pathophysiology of cognitive dysfunction in schizophrenia. *Ann. N Y Acad. Sci.*, 1021, 64-76.

Lewis, M. (Ed). (1986). Learning disabilities and prenatal risk. Urbana: University of Illinois.

Lewis, P. D. (1990). Nutrition and anatomical development of the brain. In: (Mal)nutrition and the infant brain: proceedings of an international symposium held in Montréal, Québec, Canada, May 11-12, *1989*. van Gelder, N. M., Butterworth, R. F. and Drujan, B. D. (Eds). New York: Wiley-Liss, p. 89-109.

Lewis, S. J., Zammit, S., Gunnell, D. and Smith, G. D. (2005). A meta-analysis of the MTHFR C677T polymorphism and schizophrenia risk. *Am. J. Med. Genet. Part B.*, 135B, 2-4.

Li, B., Carey, M. and Workman, J. L. (2007a). The role of chromatin during transcription. *Cell*, 128, 707-19.

Li, M., Squire, J. A. and Weksberg, R. (1998). Overgrowth syndromes and genomic imprinting: from mouse to man. *Clin. Genet.*, 53, 165-70.

Li, W., Zhou, Y., Jentsch, J. D., Brown, R. A., Tian, X., Ehninger, D., et al. (2007b). Specific developmental disruption of disrupted-in-schizophrenia-1 function results in schizophrenia-related phenotypes in mice. *Proc. Natl. Acad. Sci. U S A*, 104, 18280-5.

Li, Y. H., Liu, R. H., Jiao, L. H. and Wang, W. H. (2002). Synergetic effects of epidermal growth factor and estradiol on cytoplasmic maturation of porcine oocytes. *Zygote*, 10, 349-54.

Libbey, J.E., Sweeten, T. L., McMahon, W. M. and Fujinami, R. S. (2005). Autistic disorder and viral infections. *J. Neurovirol.*, 11, 1-10.

Lillycrop, K. A., Phillips, E. S., Jackson, A. A., Hanson, M. A. and Burdge, G. C. (2005). Dietary protein restriction of pregnant rats induces and folic acid supplementation prevents epigenetic modification of hepatic gene expression in the offspring. *J. Nutr.*, 135, 1382-6.

Lim, C. R., Fukakusa, A. and Matsubara, K. (2004). Gene expression profiling of mouse postnatal cerebellar development using cDNA microarrays. *Gene*, 333, 3-13.

Lind, T. (1984). Would more calories per day keep low birthweight at bay? *Lancet*, 1, 501-2.

Lister, R. and Ecker, J. R. (2009). Finding the fifth base: genome-wide sequencing of cytosine methylation. *Genome Res.*, 19, 959-66.

Lister, R., Pelizzola, M., Dowen, R. H., Hawkins, R. D., Hon, G., Tonti-Filippini, J., et al. (2009). Human DNA methylomes at base resolution show widespread epigenomic differences. *Nature*, 462, 315-22.

Longo, L. D. (1977). The biological effects of carbon monoxide on the pregnant woman, fetus, and newborn infant. *Am. J. Obstet. Gynecol.*, 129, 69-103.

Longo, L. D. (1980). Environmental pollution and pregnancy: Risks and uncertainties for the fetus and infant. *Am. J. Obstet. Gynecol.*, 137, 162-73.

Longo, L. D. (1984). Intrauterine growth retardation: A "mosaic" hypothesis of pathophysiology. *Semin. Perinatol.*, 8, 62-72.

Longo, L. D. (1987). Respiratory gas exchange in the placenta. In: Handbook of physiology. Section 3: The Respiratory System, Vol. IV, Gas Exchange. Fishman, A. P., Farhi, L. E. and Tenney, S. M. (Eds). Washington, D.C.: American Physiological Society, p. 351-401.

Lopuhaa, C. E., Roseboom, T. J., Osmond, C., Barker, D. J., Ravelli, A. C., Bleker, O. P., et al. (2000). Atopy, lung function, and obstructive airways disease after prenatal exposure to famine. *Thorax*, 55, 555-61.

Lubin, F. D., Roth, T. L. and Sweatt, J. D. (2008). Epigenetic regulation of *BDNF* gene transcription in the consolidation of fear memory. *J. Neurosci.*, 28, 10576-86.

Lucas, A., Morley, R. and Cole, T. J. (1998). Randomised trial of early diet in preterm babies and later intelligence quotient. *BMJ*, 317, 1481-7.

Luine, V. N., Beck, K. D., Bowman, R. E., Frankfurt, M. and MacLusky, N. J. (2007). Chronic stress and neural function: accounting for sex and age. *J. Neuroendocrinol.*, 19, 743-51.

Lukiw, W. J. (2007). Micro-RNA speciation in fetal, adult and Alzheimer's disease hippocampus. *NeuroReport*, 18, 297-300.

Lukiw, W. J. and Pogue, A. I. (2007). Induction of specific micro RNA (miRNA) species by ROS-generating metal sulfates in primary human brain cells. *J. Inorg. Biochem.*, 101, 1265-9.

Lumey, L. H. (1992). Decreased birthweights in infants after maternal in utero exposure to the Dutch famine of 1944-1945. *Paediatr. Perinat. Epidemiol.*, 6, 240-53.

Lumey, L. H., Stein, A. D., Kahn, H. S., van der Pal-de Bruin, K. M., Blauw, G. J., Zybert, P. A., et al. (2007). Cohort Profile: The Dutch Hunger Winter families study. *Intl. J. Epidemiol.*, 36, 1196-204.

Lumey, L. H. and Van Poppel, F. W. A. (1994). The Dutch Famine of 1944-45: mortality and morbidity in past and present generations. *Soc. Hist. Med.*, 7, 229-46.

Lund, R. D. (1978). Development and plasticity of the brain: an introduction. New York: Oxford University Press.

Lupien, S. J., McEwen, B. S., Gunnar, M. R. and Heim, C. (2009). Effects of stress throughout the lifespan on the brain, behviour and cognition. *Nat. Rev. Neurosci.*, 10, 434-45.

Lynch, J. and Davey Smith, G. (2005). A life course approach to chronic disease epidemiology. *Annu. Re.v Public Health*, 26, 1-35.

Ma, D. K., Jang, M. H., Guo, J. U., Kitabatake, Y., Chang, M. L., Pow-Anpongkul, N., et al. (2009). Neuronal activity-induced Gadd45b promotes epigenetic DNA demethylation and adult neurogenesis. *Science*, 323, 1074-7.

MacDonald, J. L. and Roskams, A. J. (2009). Epigenetic regulation of nervous system development by DNA methylation and histone deacetylation. *Prog. Neurobiol.*, 88, 170-83.

Magariños, A. M., Verdugo, J. M. and McEwen, B. S. (1997). Chronic stress alters synaptic terminal structure in hippocampus. *Proc. Natl. Acad. Sci. U S A*, 94, 14002-8.

Magill, S. T., Cambronne, X. A., Luikart, B. W., Lioy, D. T., Leighton, B. H., Westbrook, G. L., et al. (2010). microRNA-132 regulates dendritic growth and arborization of newborn neurons in the adult hippocampus. *Proc. Natl. Acad. Sci. U S A*, 107, 20382-7.

Maher, E. R. and Reik, W. (2000). Beckwith-Wiedemann syndrome: imprinting in clusters revisited. *J. Clin. Invest.*, 105, 247-52.

Mann, M. R., Lee, S. S., Doherty, A. S., Verona, R. I., Nolen, L. D., Schultz, R. M., et al. (2004). Selective loss of imprinting in the placenta following pre-implantation development in culture. *Development*, 131, 3727-35.

Mao, Y., Ge, X., Frank, C. L., Madison, J. M., Koehler, A. N., Doud, M. K., et al. (2009). Disrupted in schizophrenia 1 regulates neuronal progenitor proliferation via modulation of GSK3β/β-catenin signaling. *Cell*, 136, 1017-31.

Maraschio, P., Zuffardi, O., Fior, T. D. and Tiepolo, L. (1988). Immunodeficiency, centromeric heterochromatin instability of chromosomes 1, 9, and 16, and facial anomalies: the ICF syndrome. *J. Med. Genet.*, 25, 173-80.

Marchetto, M. C., Carromeu, C., Acab, A., Yu, D., Yeo, G. W., Mu, Y., et al. (2010). A model for neural development and treatment of Rett syndrome using human induced pluripotent stem cells. *Cell*, 143, 527-39.

Marlow, N. (2004). Neurocognitive outcome after very preterm birth. *Arch. Dis. Child Fetal Neonatal Ed.*, 89, F224-8.

Marques, S. C., Oliveira, C. R., Outeiro, T. F. and Pereira, C. M. (2010). Alzheimer's disease: The quest to understand complexity. *J. Alzheimers Dis.*, 21, 373-83.

Martin, C. and Zhang, Y. (2005). The diverse functions of histone lysine methylation. *Nat. Rev. Mol. Cell Biol.*, 6, 838-49.

Martinez, A. M., Schuettengruber, B., Sakr, S., Janic, A., Gonzalez, C. and Cavalli, G. (2009). Polyhomeotic has a tumor suppressor activity mediated by repression of Notch signaling. *Nat. Genet.*, 41, 1076-82.

Martinowich, K., Hattori, D., Wu, H., Fouse, S., He, F., Hu, Y., et al. (2003). DNA methylation-related chromatin remodeling in activity-dependent BDNF gene regulation. *Science*, 302, 890-3.

Mason, H. L., Myers, C. S. and Kendall, E. C. (1936). The chemistry of crystalline substances isolated from the suprarenal gland. *J. Biol. Chem.*, 114, 613-31.

Mathews, H. L. and Janusek, L. W. (2011). Epigenetics and psychoneuroimmunology: mechanisms and models. *Brain Behav. Immun.*, 25, 25-39.

Matthews, B. J., Kim, M. E., Flanagan, J. J., Hattori, D., Clemens, J. C., Zipursky, S. L., et al. (2007). Dendrite self-avoidance is controlled by Dscam. *Cell*, 129, 593-604.

Mattson, M. P. (2004). Pathways towards and away from Alzheimer's disease. *Nature*, 430, 631-9.

Mayer, W., Niveleau, A., Walter, J., Fundele, R. and Haaf, T. (2000). Demethylation of the zygotic paternal genome. *Nature*, 403, 501-2.

McClellan, J. M., Susser, E. and King, M. C. (2006). Maternal famine, *de novo* mutations, and schizophrenia. *JAMA*, 296, 582-4.

McClellan, J. M., Susser, E. and King, M. C. (2007). Schizophrenia: a common disease caused by multiple rare alleles. *Br. J. Psychiatry*, 190, 194-9.

McConnell, S. K. (1991). The generation of neuronal diversity in the central nervous system. *Annu. Rev. Neurosci.*, 14, 269-300.

McEwen, B. S. (2004). Protection and damage from acute and chronic stress: allostasis and allostatic overload and relevance to the pathophysiology of psychiatric disorders. *Ann. N Y Acad. Sci.*, 1032, 1-7.

McEwen, B. S. (2012). Brain on stress: how the social environment gets under the skin. *Proc. Natl. Acad. Sci. U S A*, 109, 17180-5.

McKay, J. A., Williams, E. A. and Mathers, J. C. (2004). Folate and DNA methylation during in utero development and aging. *Biochem. Soc. Trans.*, 32, 1006-7.

McKinley, M. J., Albiston, A. L., Allen, A. M., Mathai, M. L., May, C. N., McAllen, R. M., et al. (2003). The brain renin-angiotensin system: location and physiological roles. *Int. J. Biochem. Cell Biol.*, 35, 901-18.

McKinney, W. T. and Bunney, W. E., Jr. (1969). Animal model of depression. I. Review of evidence: implications for research. *Arch. Gen. Psychiatry*, 21, 240-8.

McMillen, I. C. and Robinson, J. S. (2005). Developmental origins of the metabolic syndrome: prediction, plasticity, and programming. *Physiol. Rev.*, 85, 571-633.

Meaney, M. J. (2001). Maternal care, gene expression, and the transmission of individual differences in stress reactivity across generations. *Ann. Rev. Neurosci.*, 24, 1161-92.

Meaney, M. J. (2010). Epigenetics and the biological definition of gene x environment interactions. *Child Dev.*, 81, 41-79.

Meaney, M. J. and Szyf, M. (2005). Environmental programming of stress responses through DNA methylation: life at the interface between a dynamic environment and a fixed genome. *Dialogues Clin. Neurosci.*, 7, 103-23.

Mednick, S. A., Machon, R. A., Huttunen, M. O. and Bonett, D. (1988). Adult schizophrenia following prenatal exposure to an influenza epidemic. *Arch. Gen. Psychiatry*, 45, 189-92.

Mehedint, M. G., Craciunescu, C. N. and Zeisel, S. H. (2010). Maternal dietary choline deficiency alters angiogenesis in fetal mouse hippocampus. *Proc. Natl. Acad. Sci. U S A*, 107, 12834-9.

Merlot, E., Couret, D. and Otten, W. (2008). Prenatal stress, fetal imprinting and immunity. *Brain Behav. Immun.*, 22, 42-51.

Messias, E. L., Chen, C. Y. and Eaton, W. W. (2007). Epidemiology of schizophrenia: review of findings and myths. *Psychiatr. Clin. North Am.*, 30, 323-38.

Meyer, U., Feldon, J. and Dammann, O. (2011). Schizophrenia and autism: both shared and disorder-specific pathogenesis via perinatal inflammation? *Pediatr. Res.*, 69, 26R-33R.

Mill, J. and Petronis, A. (2008). Pre- and peri-natal environmental risks for attention-deficit hyperactivity disorder (ADHD): the potential role of epigenetic processes in mediating susceptibility. *J. Child Psychol. Psychiatry*, 49, 1020-30.

Mill, J., Tang, T., Kaminsky, Z., Khare, T., Yazdanpanah, S., Bouchard, L., et al. (2008). Epigenomic profiling reveals DNA-methylation changes associated with major psychosis. *Am. J. Hum. Genet.*, 82, 696-711.

Millar, J. K., Wilson-Annan, J. C., Anderson, S., Christie, S., Taylor, M. S., Semple, C. A., et al. (2000). Disruption of two novel genes by a translocation co-segregating with schizophrenia. *Hum. Mol. Genet.*, 9, 1415-23.

Miller, C. A. and Sweatt, J. D. (2007). Covalent modification of DNA regulates memory formation. *Neuron*, 53, 857-69.

Miller, J. A., Ding, S. L., Sunkin, S. M., Smith, K. A., Ng, L., Szafer, A., et al. (2014). Transcriptional landscape of the prenatal human brain. *Nature*, 508, 199-206.

Miller, L. C., Isa, S., LoPreste, G., Schaller, J. G. and Dinarello, C. A. (1990). Neonatal interleukin-1 beta, interleukin-6, and tumor necrosis factor: cord blood levels and cellular production. *J. Pediatr.*, 117, 961-5.

Miller, S. L. (1990). Effects of undernutrition on myelin deposition. In: *(Mal)nutrition and the infant brain: proceedings of an international symposium held in Montréal, Québec, Canada, May 11-12, 1989.* van Gelder, N.M., Butterworth, R.F. and Drujan, B.D. (Eds). New York:Wiley-Liss, p. 175-190.

Miska, E. A., Alvarez-Saavedra, E., Townsend, M., Yoshii, A., Šestan, N., Rakic, P., et al. (2004). Microarray analysis of microRNA expression in the developing mammalian brain. *Genome Biol.*, 5, R68.

Misteli, T. (2007). Beyond the sequence: cellular organization of genome function. *Cell*, 128, 787-800.

Mitra, R., Jadhav, S., McEwen, B. S., Vyas, A. and Chattarji, S. (2005). Stress duration modulates the spatiotemporal patterns of spine formation in the basolateral amygdala. *Proc. Natl. Acad. Sci. U S A*, 102, 9371-6.

Mody, M., Cao, Y., Cui, Z., Tay, K. Y., Shyong, A., Shimizu, E., et al. (2001). Genome-wide gene expression profiles of the developing mouse hippocampus. *Proc. Natl. Acad. Sci. U S A*, 98, 8862-7.

Molfese, D. L. (2011). Advancing neuroscience through epigenetics: molecular mechanisms of learning and memory. *Dev. Neurpsychol.*, 36, 810-27.

Monk, M. (1988). Genomic imprinting. *Genes Dev.*, 2, 921-5.

Mook, J., Schreuder, B. J., van der Ploeg, H. M., Bramsen, I., van Tiel-Kadiks, G. W. and Feenstra, W. (1997). Psychological complaints and characteristics in postwar children of

Dutch World War II victims: those seeking treatment as compared with their siblings. *Psychother. Psychosom.*, 66, 268-75.

Moretti, P. and Zoghbi, H. Y. (2006). MeCP2 dysfunction in Rett syndrome and related disorders. *Curr. Opin. Genet. Dev.*, 16, 276-81.

Morgan, C. and Fisher, H. (2007). Environment and schizophrenia: environmental factors in schizophrenia: childhood trauma – a critical review. *Schizophr. Bull.*, 33, 3-10.

Morgan, H. D., Jin, X. L., Li, A., Whitelaw, E. and O'Neil, C. (2008). The culture of zygotes to the blastocyst stage changes the postnatal expression of an epigenetically labile allele, agouti viable yellow, in mice. *Biol. Reprod.*, 79, 618-23.

Morgan, H. D., Sutherland, H. G., Martin, D. I. and Whitelaw, E. (1999). Epigenetic inheritance at the agouti locus in the mouse. *Nat. Genet.*, 23, 314-8.

Morgane, P. J., Austin-LaFrance, R., Bronzino, J., Tonkiss, J., Díaz-Cintra, S., Cintra, L., et al. (1993). Prenatal malnutrition and development of the brain. *Neurosci. Biobehav. Rev.*, 17, 91-128.

Morgane, P. J., Austin-LaFrance, R. J., Bronzino, J. D., Tonkiss, J. and Galler, J. R. (1992). Malnutrition and the developing central nervous system. In: Isaacson, R. L. and Jensen, K. F. (Eds). The vulnerable brain and environmental risks. Volume 1, Malnutrition and hazard assessment. New York: Plenum Press, p. 3-44.

Morgane, P. J., Miller, M., Kemper, T., Stern, W., Forbes, W., Hall, R., et al. (1978). The effects of protein malnutrition on the developing central nervous system in the rat. *Neurosci. Biobehav. Rev.*, 2, 137-230.

Morley, R. and Lucas, A. (1997). Nutrition and cognitive development. *Br. Med. Bull.*, 53, 123-34.

Morrison, S. J. and Kimble, J. (2006). Asymmetric and symmetric stem-cell divisions in development and cancer. *Nature*, 441, 1068-74.

Mountcastle, V. B. (1997). The columnar organization of the neocortex. *Brain*, 120, 701-22.

Mueller, B. R. and Bale, T. L. (2008). Sex-specific programming of offspring emotionality after stress early in pregnancy. *J. Neurosci.*, 28, 9055-65.

Muotri, A. R., Chu, V. T., Marchetto, M. C., Deng, W., Moran, J. V. and Gage, F. H. (2005). Somatic mosaicism in neuronal precursor cells mediated by L1 retrotransposition. *Nature*, 435, 903-10.

Muotri, A. R., Marchetto, M. C., Coufal, N. G. and Gage, F. H. (2007). The necessary junk: new functions for transposable elements. *Hum. Mol. Genet.*, 16, R159-67.

Muotri, A. R., Marchetto, M. C., Coufal, N. G., Oefner, R., Yeo, G., Nakashima, K., et al. (2010). L1 retrotransposition in neurons is modulated by MeCP2. *Nature*, 468, 443-6.

Muotri, A. R., Zhao, C., Marchetto, M. C. and Gage, F. H. (2009). Environmental influence on L1 retrotransposons in the adult hippocampus. *Hippocampus*, 19, 1002-7.

Murgatroyd, C. A. and Nephew, B. C. (2013). Effects of early life social stress on maternal behavior and neuroendocrinology. *Psychoneuroendocrinology*, 38, 219-28.

Murgatroyd, C. A. and Spengler, D. (2011). Epigenetic programming of the HPA axis : Early life decides. *Stress*, 14, 581-9.

Murrell, A., Rakyan, V. K. and Beck, S. (2005). From genome to epigenome. *Hum. Mol. Genet.*, 14 Spec. No 1, R3-R10.

Mustafa, M. M., Lebel, M. H., Ramilo, O., Olsen, K. D., Reisch, J. S., Beutler, B., et al. (1989). Correlation of interleukin-1 beta and cachectin concentrations in cerebrospinal fluid and outcome from bacterial meningitis. *J. Pediatr.*, 115, 208-13.

Nakatani, J., Tamada, K., Hatanaka, F., Ise, S., Ohta, H., Inoue, K., et al. (2009). Abnormal behavior in a chromosome-engineered mouse model for human 15q11-13 duplication seen in autism. *Cell*, 137, 1235-46.

Nanney, D. L. (1958). Epigenetic control systems. *Proc. Natl Acad. Sci. U S A*, 44, 712-7.

Neel, J. V. (1962). Diabetes mellitus: a "thrifty" genotype rendered detrimental by "progress"? *Am. J. Hum. Genet.*, 14, 353-62.

Neel, J. V. (1976). Towards a better understanding of the genetic basis of diabetes mellitus. In: The genetics of diabetes mellitus. Creutzfeldt, W., Kobberling, J. and Neel, J. V. (Eds). Berlin: Springer Verlag, p. 240-4.

Nelson, C. and Jeste, S. (2008). Neurobiological perspectives on developmental psychopathology. In: Rutter's child and adolescent psychiatry. Rutter, M., Bishop, D. V. M., Pine, D. S., Scott, S., Stevenson, J., Taylor, E. and Thapar, A. (Eds). Fifth Edition. Oxford: Blackwell Publishing, p. 145-59.

Nelson, P. T., Wang, W.-X. and Rajeev, B. W. (2008). MicroRNAs (miRNAs) in neurodegenerative diseases. *Brain Pathol.*, 18, 130-8.

Nemeroff, C. B. (1992). The role of neuropeptides in the pathophysiology of affective disorders. *Clin. Neuropharmacol.*, 15 Suppl., 6A-7A.

Nephew, B. C. and Bridges, R. S. (2011). Effects of chronic social stress during lactation on maternal behavior and growth in rats. *Stress*, 14, 677-84.

Nestler, E. J., Gould, E., Manji, H., Buncan, M., Duman, R. S., Greshenfeld, H. K., et al. (2002). Preclinical models: status of basic research in depression. *Biol. Psychiatry*, 52, 503-28.

Nestler, E. J. and Hyman, S. E. (2010). Animal models of neuropsychiatric disorders. *Nat. Neurosci.*, 13, 1161-9.

Neugebauer, R. (2005). Accumulating evidence for prenatal nutritional origins of mental disorders. *JAMA*, 294, 621-3.

Neugebauer, R., Hoek, H. W. and Susser, E. (1999). Prenatal exposure to wartime famine and development of antisocial personality disorder in early adulthood. *JAMA*, 282, 455-62.

Nguyen, G., Delarue, F., Burcklé, C., Bouzhir, L., Giller, T. and Sraer, J. D. (2002). Pivotal role of the renin/prorenin receptor in angiotensin II production and cellular responses to renin. *J. Clin. Invest.*, 109, 1417-27.

Nguyen, A., Rauch, T. A., Pfeifer, G. P. and Hu, V. W. (2010). Global methylation profiling of lymphoblastoid cell lines reveals epigenetic contributions to autism spectrum disorders and a novel autism candidate gene, RORA, whose protein product is reduced in autistic brain. *FASEB J.*, 24, 3036-51.

Niblock, M. M., Brunso-Bechtold, J. K. and Riddle, D. R. (2000). Insulin-like growth factor I stimulates dendritic growth in primary somatosensory cortex. *J. Neurosci.*, 20, 4165-76.

Nicholls, R. D., Saitoh, S. and Horsthemke, B. (1998). Imprinting in Prader-Willi and Angelman syndromes. *Trends Genet.*, 14, 194-200.

Nicodemus, K. K., Law, A. J., Radulescu, E., Luna, A., Kolachana, B., Vakkalanka, R., et al. (2010). Biological validation of increased schizophrenia risk with NRG1, ERBB4, and AKT1 epistasis via functional neuroimaging in healthy controls. *Arch. Gen. Psychiatry*, 67, 991-1001.

Niculescu, M. D., Craciunescu, C. N. and Zeisel, S. H. (2006). Dietary choline deficiency alters global and gene-specific DNA methylation in the developing hippocampus of mouse fetal brains. *FASEB J.*, 20, 43-9.

Nishimura, M., Milsted, A., Block, C. H., Brosnihan, K. B. and Ferrario, C. M. (1992). Tissue renin-angiotensin systems in renal hypertension. *Hypertension*, 20, 158-67.

Nishino, J., Kim, I., Chada, K. and Morrison, S. J. (2008). Hmga2 promotes neural stem cell self-renewal in young but not old mice by reducing p16^{Ink4a} and p19^{Arf} expression. *Cell*, 135, 227-39.

Noh, J. S., Sharma, R. P., Veldic, M., Salvacion, A. A., Jia, X., Chen, Y., et al. (2005). DNA methyltransferase 1 regulates reelin mRNA expression in mouse primary cortical cultures. *Proc. Natl. Acad. Sci. U S A*, 102, 1749-54.

Numayama-Tsuruta, K., Arai, Y., Takahashi, M., Sasaki-Hoshino, M., Funatsu, N., Nakamura, S., et al. (2010). Downstream genes of Pax6 revealed by comprehensive transcriptome profiling in the developing rat hindbrain. *BMC Dev. Biol.*, 10, 6.

Oh, S. W., Harris, J. A., Ng, L., Winslow, B., Cain, N., Mihalas, S., et al. (2014). A mesoscale connectome of the mouse brain. *Nature*, 508, 207-14.

Oh-Nishi, A., Obayashi, S., Sugihara, I., Minamimoto, T. and Suhara, T. (2010). Maternal immune activation by polyriboinosinic-polyribocytidilic acid injection produces synaptic dysfunction but not neuronal loss in the hippocampus of juvenile rat offspring. *Brain Res.*, 1363, 170-9.

O'Kusky, J. R., Ye, P. and D'Ercole, A. J. (2000). Insulin-like growth factor-I promotes neurogenesis and synaptogenesis in the hippocampal dentate gyrus during postnatal development. *J. Neurosci.*, 20, 8435-42.

O'Leary, D. D., Chou, S. J. and Sahara, S. (2007). Area patterning of the mammalian cortex. *Neuron*, 56, 252-69.

Oliver, M. H., Hawkins, P. and Harding, J. E. (2005). Periconceptional undernutrition alters growth trajectory and metabolic and endocrine responses to fasting in late-gestation fetal sheep. *Pediatr. Res.*, 57, 591-8.

Olness, K. (2003). Effects on brain development leading to cognitive impairment: a worldwide epidemic. *J. Dev. Behav. Pediatr.*, 24, 120-30.

O'Loan, J., Eyles, D. W., Kesby, J., Ko, P., McGrath, J. J. and Burne, T. H. (2007). Vitamin D deficiency during various stages of pregnancy in the rat; its impact on development and behaviour in adult offspring. *Psychoneuroendocrinology*, 32, 227-34.

Ong, K. K. and Dunger, D. B. (2000). Thrifty genotypes and phenotypes in the pathogenesis of type 2 diabetes mellitus. *J. Pediatr. Endocrinol. Metab.*, 13 (Suppl. 6), 1419-24.

Oswald, J., Engemann, S., Lane, N., Mayer, W., Olek, A., Fundele, R., et al. (2000). Active demethylation of the paternal genome in the mouse zygote. *Curr. Biol.*, 10, 475-8.

Owen, C. M. and Segars Jr., J. H. (2009). Imprinting disorders and assisted reproductive technology. *Semin. Reprod. Med.*, 27, 417-28.

Ozawa, K., Hashimoto, K., Kishimoto, T., Shimizu, E., Ishikura, H. and Iyo, M. (2006). Immune activation during pregnancy in mice leads to dopaminergic hyperfunction and cognitive impairment in the offspring: a neurodevelopmental animal model of schizophrenia. *Biol. Psychiatry*, 59, 546-54.

Painter, R. C., de Rooij, S. R., Bossuyt, P. M., Osmond, C., Barker, D. J., Bleker, O. P., et al. (2006a). A possible link between prenatal exposure to famine and breast cancer: a preliminary study. *Am. J. Hum. Biol.*, 18, 853-6.

Painter, R. C., de Rooij, S. R., Bossuyt, P. M., Phillips, D. I., Osmond, C., Barker, D. J., et al. (2006b). Blood pressure response to psychological stressors in adults after prenatal exposure to the Dutch famine. *J. Hypertens.*, 24, 1771-8.

Painter, R. C., de Rooij, S. R., Bossuyt, P. M., Simmers, T. A., Osmond, C., Barker, D. J., et al. (2006c). Early onset of coronary artery disease after prenatal exposure to the Dutch famine. *Am. J. Clin. Nutr.*, 84, 322-7.

Painter, R. C., Roseboom, T. J. and Bleker, O. P. (2005a). Prenatal exposure to the Dutch famine and disease in later life: An overview. *Reprod. Toxicol.*, 20, 345-52.

Painter, R. C., Roseboom, T. J., Bossuyt, P. M., Osmond, C., Barker, D. J. and Bleker, O. P. (2005b). Adult mortality at age 57 after prenatal exposure to the Dutch famine. *Eur. J. Epidemiol.*, 20, 673-6.

Painter, R. C., Roseboom, T. J., van Montfrans, G. A., Bossuyt, P. M., Krediet, R. T., Osmond, C., et al. (2005c). Microalbuminuria in adults after prenatal exposure to the Dutch famine. *J. Am. Soc. Nephrol.*, 16, 189-94.

Palii, S. S. and Robertson, K. D. (2007). Epigenetic control of tumor suppression. *Crit. Rev. Eukaryot. Gene Expr.*, 17, 295-316.

Palmer, A. A., Brown, A. S., Keegan, D., Siska, L. D., Susser, E., Rotrosen, J., et al. (2008). Prenatal protein deprivation alters dopamine-mediated behaviors and dopaminergic and glutamatergic receptor binding. *Brain Res.*, 1237, 62-74.

Palmer, T. D., Takahashi, J. and Gage, F. H. (1997). That adult hippocampus contains primordial neural stem cells. *Mol. Cell Neurosci.*, 8, 389-404.

Paneth, N. and Susser, M. (1995). Early origin of coronary heart disease (the "Barker hypothesis"). *BMJ*, 310, 411-2.

Pang, Y., Cai, Z. and Rhodes, P. G. (2003). Disturbance of oligodendrocyte development, hypomyelination and white matter injury in the neonatal rat brain after intracerebral injection of lipopolysaccharide. *Brain Res. Dev. Brain Res.*, 140, 205-14.

Pariante, C. M. and Lightman, S. L. (2008). The HPA axis in major depression: classical theories and new developments. *Trends Neurosci.*, 31, 464-8.

Parodi, A., Neasham, D. and Vineis, P. (2006). Environment, population, and biology. A short history of modern epidemiology. *Perspect. Biol. Med.*, 49, 357-68.

Patchev, A. V., Rodrigues, A. J., Sousa, N., Spengler, D. and Almeida, O. F. (2014). The future is now: early life events preset adult behaviour. *Acta. Physiol. (Oxf.)*, 210, 46-57.

Patterson, P. H. (2002). Maternal infection: window on neuroimmune interactions in fetal brain development and mental illness. *Curr. Opin. Neurobiol.*, 12, 115-8.

Patterson, P. H. (2009). Immune involvement in schizophrenia and autism: etiology, pathology and animal models. *Behav. Brain Res.*, 204, 313-21.

Paul, A. M. (2010). *Origins*. How the nine months before birth shape the rest of our lives. New York: Free Press.

Paulsen, M., Tierling, S. and Walter, J. (2008). DNA methylation and the mammalian genome. In: Epigenetics. Tost, J. (Ed). Norfolk, UK: Caister Academic Press, p. 1-21.

Peleg, S. Sananbenesi, F., Zovoilis, A., Burkhardt, S., Bahari-Javan, S., Agis-Balboa, R. C., et al. (2010). Altered histone acetylation is associated with age-dependent memory impairment in mice. *Science*, 328, 753-6.

Pembrey, M. E. (2002). Time to take epigenetic inheritance seriously. *Eur. J. Hum. Genet.*, 10, 669-71.

Pembrey, M. E., Bygren, L. O., Kaati, G., Edvinsson, S., Northstone, K., Sjöström, M., et al. (2006). Sex-specific, male-line transgenerational responses in humans. *Eur. J. Hum. Genet.*, 14, 159-66.

Peng, X. (1987). Demographic consequences of the Great Leap Forward in China's provinces. *Popul. Dev. Rev.*, 13, 639-70.

Penner, J. D. and Brown, A. S. (2007). Prenatal infectious and nutritional factors and risk of adult schizophrenia. *Expert Rev. Neurotherapeutics*, 7, 797-805.

Perez-Torrero, E., Torrero, C. and Salas, M. (2001). Effects of perinatal undernourishment on neuronal development of the facial motor nucleus in the rat. *Brain Res.*, 905, 54-62.

Petanjek, Z. and Kostovic, I. (2012). Epigenetic regulation of fetal brain development and neurocognitive outcome. *Proc. Natl. Acad. Sci. U S A*, 109, 11062-3.

Petrij, F., Giles, R. H., Dauwerse, H. G., Saris, J. J., Hennekam, R. C., Masuno, M., et al. (1995). Rubinstein-Taybi syndrome caused by mutations in the transcriptional co-activator CBP. *Nature*, 376, 348-51.

Petronis, A., Gottesman, I. I., Kan, P., Kennedy, J. L., Basile, V. S., Paterson, A. D., et al. (2003). Monozygotic twins exhibit numerous epigenetic differences: clues to twin discordance? *Schizophr. Bull.*, 29, 169-78.

Petry, C. J., Dorling, M. W., Pawlak, D. B., Ozanne, S. E. and Hales, C. N. (2001). Diabetes in old male offspring of rat dams fed a reduced protein diet. *Int. J. Exp. Diabetes Res.* 2, 139-43.

Pfefferbaum, A., Mathalon, D. H., Sullivan, E. V., Rawles, J. M., Zipursky, R. B. and Lim, K. O. (1994). A quantitative magnetic resonance imaging study of changes in brain morphology from infancy to late adulthood. *Arch. Neurol.*, 51, 874-87.

Pietrobono, R., Pomponi, M. G., Tabolacci, E., Oostra, B., Chiurazzi, P. and Neri, G. (2002). Quantitative analysis of DNA demethylation and transcriptional reactivation of the *FMR1* gene in fragile X cells treated with 5-azadeoxycytidine. *Nucleic. Acids Res.*, 30, 3278-3285.

Pinney, S. E. and Simmons, R. A. (2010). Epigenetic mechanisms in the development of type 2 diabetes. *Trends Endocrinol. Metab.*, 21, 223-9.

Plass, C. and Soloway, P. D. (2002). DNA methylation, imprinting and cancer. *Eur. J. Hum. Genet.*, 10, 6-16.

Platt, B. S. and Stewart, R. J. (1968). Effects of protein-calorie deficiency on dogs. 1. Reproduction, growth and behaviour. *Dev. Med. Child Neurol.*, 10, 3-24.

Pletnikov, M. V., Rubin, S. A., Vasudevan, K., Moran, T. H. and Carbone, K. M. (1999). Developmental brain injury associated with abnormal play behavior in neonatally Borna disease virus-infected Lewis rats: a model of autism. *Behav. Brain Res.*, 100, 43-50.

Prentice, A. M., Rayco-Solon, P. and Moore, S. E. (2005). Insights from the developing world: Thrifty genotypes and thrifty phenotypes. *Proc. Nutr. Soc.*, 64, 153-61.

Price, D. J., Kennedy, H., Dehay, C., Zhou, L., Mercier, M., Jossin, Y., et al. (2006). The development of cortical connections. *Eur. J. Neurosci.*, 23, 910-20.

Pryce, C. R., Ruedi-Bettschen, D., Dettling, A. C. and Feldon, J. (2002). Early life stress: Long-term physiological impact in rodents and primates. *News Physiol. Sci.*, 17, 150-5.

Ptak, C. and Petronis, A. (2008). Epigenetics and complex disease: from etiology to new therapeutics. *Annu. Rev. Pharmacol. Toxicol.*, 48, 257-76.

Ptashne, M. (2013). Epigenetics: core misconcept. *Proc. Natl. Acad. Sci. U S A*, 110, 7101-3.

Qin, W., Yang, T., Ho, L., Zhao, Z., Wang, J., Chen, L., et al. (2006). Neuronal SIRT1 activation as a novel mechanism underlying the prevention of Alzheimer disease amyloid neuropathology by calorie restriction. *J. Biol. Chem.*, 281, 21745-54.

Rahnama, F., Shafiei, F., Gluckman, P. D., Mitchell, M. D. and Lobie, P. E. (2006). Epigenetic regulation of human trophoblastic cell migration and invasion. *Endocrinology*, 147, 5275-83.

Rakic, P. (1972). Mode of cell migration to the superficial layers of fetal monkey neocortex. *J. Comp. Neurol.*, 145, 61-83.

Rakic, P. (1975). Cell migration and neuronal ectopias in the brain. *Birth Defects Orig. Artic. Ser.*, 11, 95-129.

Rakic, P. (2003). Developmental and evolutionary adaptations of cortical radial glia. *Cereb. Cortex*, 13, 541-9.

Rakic, P. (2005). Less is more: progenitor death and cortical size. *Nat. Neurosci.*, 8, 981-2.

Rakyan, V. K., Chong, S., Champ, M. E., Cuthbert, P. C., Morgan, H. D., Luu, K. V., et al. (2003). Transgenerational inheritance of epigenetic states at the murine $Axin^{Fu}$ allele occurs after maternal and paternal transmission. *Proc. Natl. Acad. Sci. U S A*, 100, 2538-43.

Ranade, S. C., Rose, A., Rao, M., Gallego, J., Gressens, P. and Mani, S. (2008). Different types of nutritional deficiencies affect different domains of spatial memory function checked in a radial arm maze. *Neuroscience*, 152, 859-66.

Ravelli, A. C., van der Meulen, J. H., Michels, R. P., Osmond, C., Barker, D. J., Hales, C. N., et al. (1998). Glucose tolerance in adults after prenatal exposure to famine. *Lancet*, 351, 173-7.

Ravelli, A. C., van der Meulen, J. H., Osmond, C., Barker, D. J. and Bleker, O. P. (1999). Obesity at the age of 50 y in men and women exposed to famine prenatally. *Am. J. Clin. Nutr.*, 70, 811-6.

Ravelli, G. P., Stein, Z. A. and Susser, M. W. (1976). Obesity in young men after famine exposure in utero and early infancy. *N. Engl. J. Med.*, 295, 349-53.

Razin, A. (1998). CpG methylation, chromatin structure and gene silencing – a three-way connection. *EMBO J.*, 17, 4905-8.

Razin, A. and Riggs, A. D. (1980). DNA methylation and gene function. *Science*, 210, 604-10.

Razin, A. and Shemer, R. (1995). DNA methylation in early development. *Hum. Mol. Genet.*, 4, 1751-5.

Raznahan, A., Greenstein, D., Lee, N. R., Clasen, L. S. and Giedd, J. N. (2012). Prenatal growth in humans and postnatal brain maturation into late adolescence. *Proc. Natl. Acad. Sci. U S A*, 109, 11366-71.

Rees, S., Harding, R. and Walker, D. (2008). An adverse intrauterine environment: implications for injury and altered development of the brain. *Int. J. Dev. Neurosci.*, 26, 3-11.

Rees, S. and Inder, T. (2005). Fetal and neonatal origins of altered brain development. *Early Hum. Dev.*, 81, 753-61.

Reik, W. (2007). Stability and flexibility of epigenetic gene regulation in mammalian development. *Nature*, 447, 425-32.

Reik, W., Dean, W. and Walter, J. (2001). Epigenetic reprogramming in mammalian development. *Science*, 293, 1089-93.

Reik, W. and Walter, J. (2001). Genomic imprinting: parental influence on the genome. *Nat. Rev. Genet.*, 2, 21-32.

Resnick, O., Miller, M., Forbes, W., Hall, R., Kemper, T., Bronzino, J., et al. (1979). Developmental protein malnutrition: influences on the central nervous system of the rat. *Neurosci. Biobehav. Rev.*, 3, 233-46.

Resnick, O. and Morgane, P. J. (1984). Generational effects of protein malnutrition in the rat. *Brain Res. Dev. Brain Res.*, 15, 219-27.

Reuhl, K. R. and Lowndes, H. E. (1992). Factors influencing morphological expression of neurotoxicity. In: Neurotoxicology. Tilson, H. A. and Mitchell, C. L. (Eds). New York: Raven Press, p. 67-81.

Reul, J. M., Hesketh, S. A., Collins, A. and Mecinas, M. G. (2009). Epigenetic mechanisms in the dentate gyrus act as a molecular switch in hippocampus-associated memory formation. *Epigenetics*, 4, 434-9.

Reynolds, B. A. and Weiss, S. (1992). Generation of neurons and astrocytes from isolated cells of the adult mammalian central nervous system. *Science*, 255, 1707-10.

Reynolds, R. M., Godfrey, K. M., Barker, M., Osmond, C. and Phillips, D. I. (2007). Stress responsiveness in adult life: influence of mother's diet in late pregnancy. *J. Clin. Endocrinol. Metab.*, 92, 2208-10.

Riccio, A. (2010). New endogenous regulators of class I histone deacetylases. *Sci. Signal*, 3, pe1.

Richards, L. J., Kilpatrick, T. J. and Bartlett, P. F. (1992). De novo generation of neuronal cells from the adult mouse brain. *Proc. Natl. Acad. Sci. U S A*, 89, 8591-5.

Richards, M., Hardy, R., Kuh, D. and Wadsworth, M. E. (2001). Birth weight and cognitive function in the British 1946 birth cohort: longitudinal population based study. *BMJ*, 322, 199-203.

Riggs, A. D. (1975). X inactivation, differentiation, and DNA methylation. *Cytogenet. Cell Genet.*, 14, 9-25.

Ringrose, L. and Paro, R. (2004). Epigenetic regulation of cellular memory by the polycomb and trithorax group proteins. *Annu. Rev. Genet.*, 38, 413-43.

Rizzo, T., Metzger, B. E., Burns, W. J. and Burns, K. (1991). Correlation between antepartum maternal metabolism and intelligence of offspring. *N. Engl. J. Med.*, 325, 911-6.

Rønn, L. C., Hartz, B. P. and Bock, E. (1998). The neural cell adhesion molecular (NCAM) in development and plasticity of the nervous system. *Exp. Gerontol.*, 33, 853-64.

Roseboom, T., de Rooij, S. and Painter, R. (2006). The Dutch famine and its long-term consequences for adult health. *Early Hum. Dev.*, 82, 485-91.

Roseboom, T. J., van der Meulen, J. H., Osmond, C., Barker, D. J., Ravelli, A. C. and Bleker, O. P. (2000a). Plasma lipid profiles in adults after prenatal exposure to the Dutch famine. *Am. J. Clin. Nutr.*, 72, 1101-6.

Roseboom, T. J., van der Meulen, J. H., Osmond, C., Barker, D. J., Ravelli, A. C. and Bleker, O.P. (2001a). Adult survival after prenatal exposure to the Dutch famine 1944-45. *Paediatr. Perinat. Epidemiol.*, 15, 220-5.

Roseboom, T. J., van der Meulen, J. H., Osmond, C., Barker, D. J., Ravelli, A. C., Schroeder-Tanka, J.M., et al. (2000b). Coronary heart disease after prenatal exposure to the Dutch famine, 1944-1945. *Heart*, 84, 595-8.

Roseboom, T. J., van der Meulen, J. H., Ravelli, A. C., Osmond, C., Barker, D. J. and Bleker, O. P. (2000c). Plasma fibrinogen and factor VII concentrations in adults after prenatal exposure to famine. *Br. J. Haematol.*, 111, 112-7.

Roseboom, T. J., van der Meulen, J. H., Ravelli, A. C., Osmond, C., Barker, D. J. and Bleker, O. P. (2001b). Effects of prenatal exposure to the Dutch famine on adult disease in later life: an overview. *Mol. Cell Endocrinol.*, 185, 93-8.

Roseboom, T. J., van der Meulen, J. H., Ravelli, A. C., Osmond, C., Barker, D. J. and Bleker, O. P. (2001c). Effects of prenatal exposure to the Dutch famine on adult disease in later life: an overview. *Twin Res.*, 4, 293-8.

Roseboom, T. J., van der Meulen, J. H., Ravelli, A. C., van Montfrans, G. A., Osmond, C., Barker, D. J., et al. (1999). Blood pressure in adults after prenatal exposure to famine. *J. Hypertens.*, 17, 325-30.

Roseboom, T. J., van der Meulen, J. H., van Montfrans, G. A., Ravelli, A. C., Osmond, C., Barker, D. J., et al. (2001d). Maternal nutrition during gestation and blood pressure in later life. *J. Hypertens.*, 19, 29-34.

Ross, C. A. and Margolis, R. L. (2009). Schizophrenia. A point of disruption. *Nature*, 458, 976-7.

Rosso, P. R. (1990). Prenatal nutrition and brain growth. In: *(Mal)nutrition and the infant brain: proceedings of an international symposium held in Montréal, Québec, Canada, May 11-12, 1989.* van Gelder, N.M., Butterworth, R.F. and Drujan, B.D. (Eds). New York: Wiley-Liss, p. 25-40.

Roybal, K., Theobold, D., Graham, A., DiNieri, J. A., Russo, S. J., Krishnan, V., et al. (2007). Mania-like behavior induced by disruption of CLOCK. *Proc. Natl. Acad. Sci. U S A*, 104, 6406-11.

Rush, D. (1989). Effects of changes in maternal energy and protein intake during pregnancy, with special reference to fetal growth. In: Fetal growth. Sharp, F., Fraser, R. B. and Milner, R. D. B. (Eds). London: Springer-Verlag, p. 203-29.

Russo, V. E., Martienssen, R. A. and Riggs, A. D. (Eds). (1996). Epigenetic mechanisms of gene regulation. Woodbury, NY: Cold Spring Harbor Laboratory Press.

Rutherford, S. L. and Lindquist, S. (1998). Hsp90 as a capacitor for morphological evolution. *Nature*, 396, 336-42.

Ruzzin, J., Wagman, A. S. and Jensen, J. (2005). Glucocorticoid-induced insulin resistance in skeletal muscles: defects in insulin signalling and the effects of a selective glycogen synthase kinase-3 inhibitor. *Diabetologia*, 48, 2119-30.

St. Clair, D., Xu, M., Wang, P., Yu, Y., Fang, Y., Zhang, F., et al. (2005). Rates of adult schizophrenia following prenatal exposure to the Chinese famine of 1959-1961. *JAMA*, 294, 557-62.

Sameroff, A. (2010). A unified theory of development: a dialectic integration of nature and nurture. *Child Dev.*, 81, 6-22.

Sandovici, I., Smith, N. H., Nitert, M. D., Ackers-Johnson, M., Uribe-Lewis, S., Ito, Y., et al. (2011). Maternal diet and aging alter the epigenetic control of promoter-enhancer interaction at the *Hnf4a* gene in rat pancreatic islets. *Proc. Natl. Acad. Sci. U S A*, 108, 5449-54.

Sanosaka, T., Namihira, M. and Nakashima, K. (2009). Epigenetic mechanisms in sequential differentiation of neural stem cells. *Epigenetics*, 4, 89-92.

Santos, K. F., Mazzola, T. N. and Carvalho, H. F. (2005). The prima donna of epigenetics: the regulation of gene expression by DNA methylation. *Braz. J. Med. Biol. Res.*, 38, 1531-41.

Savaskan, E. (2005). The role of the brain renin-angiotensin system in neurodegenerative disorders. *Curr. Alzheimer Res.*, 2, 29-35.

Sayer, A. A., Cooper, C., Evans, J. R., Rauf, A., Wormald, R. P., Osmond, C., et al. (1998). Are rates of ageing determined in utero? *Age Ageing*, 27, 579-83.

Schanen, N. C. (2006). Epigenetics of autism spectrum disorders. *Hum. Mol. Genet.*, 15, R138-50.

Scharfman, H. E. (2004). Functional implications of seizure-induced neurogenesis. *Adv. Exp. Med. Biol.*, 548, 192-212.

Schmucker, D., Clemens, J. C., Shu, H., Worby, C. A., Xiao, J., Muda, M., et al. (2000). Drosophila Dscam is an axon guidance receptor exhibiting extraordinary molecular diversity. *Cell*, 101, 671-84.

Schobel, S. A., Lewandowski, N. M., Corcoran, C. M., Moore, H., Brown, T., Malaspina, D., et al. (2009). Differential targeting of the CA1 subfield of the hippocampus formation by schizophrenia and related psychotic disorders. *Arch. Gen. Psychiatry*, 66, 938-46.

Schober, M. E., McKnight, R. A., Yu, X., Callaway, C. W., Ke, X. and Lane, R. H. (2009). Intrauterine growth restriction due to uteroplacental insufficiency decreased white matter and altered NMDAR subunit composition in juvenile rat hippocampi. *Am. J. Physiol. Regul. Integr. Comp. Physiol.*, 296, R681-92.

Scholz, C. C., Cavadas, M. A., Tambuwala, M. M., Hams, E., Rodriguez, J., von Kriegsheim, A., et al. (2013). Regulation of IL-1β-induced NF-κB by hydroxylases links key hypoxic and inflammatory signaling pathways. *Proc. Natl. Acad. Sci. U S A*, 110, 18490-5.

Schulz, L. C. (2010). The Dutch Hunger Winter and the developmental origins of health and disease. *Proc Natl Acad Sci U S A*, 107, 16757-8.

Schwartz, A. (2013). First volley in the brain race? Europe's human brain project the first to the starting line – will U.S. brain initiative catch up? *Ann. Neurol.*, 73, A7.

Scott-Van Zeeland, A. A., Abrahams, B. S., Alvarez-Retuerto, A. I., Sonnenblick, L. I., Rudie, J. D., Ghahremani, D., et al. (2010). Altered functional connectivity in frontal lobe circuits is associated with variation in the autism risk gene CNTNAP2. *Sci. Transl. Med.*, 2, 56ra80.

Scrimshaw, N. S., Taylor, C. E. and Gordon, J. E. (1968). Interactions of nutrition and infection. Geneva: World Health Organization.

Secoli, S. R. and Teixeira, N. A. (1998). Chronic prenatal stress affects development and behavioral depression in rats. *Stress*, 2, 273-80.

Seckl, J. R. and Holmes, M. C. (2007). Mechanisms of disease: glucocorticoids, their placental metabolism and fetal 'programming' of adult pathophysiology. *Nat. Clin. Pract. Endocrinol. Metab.*, 3, 479-88.

Selye, H. (1950). The physiology and pathology of exposure to stress. A treatise based on the concepts of the general-adaptation-syndrome and the diseases of adaptation. Montreal: Acta Inc. Semeralul, M. O., Boutros, P. C., Likhodi, O., Okey, A. B., Van Tol, H. H. and Wong, A. H. (2006). Microarray analysis of the developing cortex. *J. Neurobiol.*, 66, 1646-58.

Shanks, N., Windle, R. J., Perks, P. A., Harbuz, M. S., Jessop, D. S., Ingram, C. D., et al. (2000). Early-life exposure to endotoxin alters hypothalamic-pituitary-adrenal function and predisposition to inflammation. *Proc. Natl. Acad. Sci. U S A*, 97, 5645-50.

Shatrov, J. G., Birch, S. C., Lam, L. T., Quinlivan, J. A., McIntyre, S. and Mendz, G. L. (2010). Chorioamnionitis and cerebral palsy: a meta-analysis. *Obstet. Gynecol.*, 116, 387-92.

Shen, S., Li, J. and Casaccia-Bonnefil, P. (2005). Histone modifications affect timing of oligodendrocyte progenitor differentiation in the developing rat brain. *J. Cell Biol.*, 169, 577-89.

Shi, L., Fatemi, S. H., Sidwell, R. W. and Patterson, P. H. (2003). Maternal influenza infection causes marked behavioral and pharmacological changes in the offspring. *J. Neurosci.*, 23, 297-302.

Shimada, M., Yamano, T., Nakamura, T., Morikawa, Y. and Kusunoki, T. (1977). Effect of maternal malnutrition on matrix cell proliferation in the cerebrum of mouse embryo: an autoradiographic study. *Pediatr. Res.*, 11, 728-31.

Shonkoff, J. P. and Levitt, P. (2010). Neuroscience and the future of early childhood policy: moving from why to what and how. *Neuron*, 67, 689-91.

Si, K., Lindquist, S. and Kandel, E. (2004). A possible epigenetic mechanism for the persistence of memory. *Cold Spring Harb. Symp. Quant. Biol.*, 69, 497-8.

Sibbe, M., Förster, E., Basak, O., Taylor, V. and Frotscher, M. (2009). Reelin and Notch1 cooperate in the development of the dentate gyrus. *J. Neurosci.*, 29, 8578-85.

Sigurdsson, T., Stark, K. L., Karayiorgou, M., Gogos, J. A. and Gordon, J. A. (2010). Impaired hippocampal-prefrontal synchrony in a genetic mouse model of schizophrenia. *Nature*, 464, 763-7.

Simeon, D., Yehuda, R., Knutelska, M. and Schmeidler, J. (2008). Dissociation versus posttraumatic stress: Cortisol and physiological correlates in adults highly exposed to the World Trade Center attack on 9/11. *Pyschiatry Res.*, 161, 325-9.

Simerly, R. B. (2008). Hypothalamic substrates of metabolic imprinting. *Physiol. Behav.*, 94, 79-89.

Simmons, R. A., Templeton, L. J. and Gertz, S. J. (2001). Intrauterine growth retardation leads to the development of type 2 diabetes in the rat. *Diabetes*, 50, 2279-86.

Simonson, M. and Chow, B. F. (1970). Maze studies on progeny of underfed mother rats. *J. Nutr.*, 100, 685-90.

Simonson, M., Sherwin, R. W., Anilane, J. K., Yu, W. Y. and Chow, B. F. (1969). Neuromotor development in progeny of underfed mother rats. *J. Nutr.*, 98, 18-24.

Sinclair, K. D., Allegrucci, C., Singh R., Gardner, D. S., Sebastian, S., Bispham, J., et al. (2007). DNA methylation, insulin resistance, and blood pressure in offspring determined by maternal periconceptional B vitamin and methionine status. *Proc. Natl. Acad. Sci. U S A*, 104, 19351-6.

Singh, R. P., Shiue, K., Schomberg, D. and Zhou, F. C. (2009). Cellular epigenetic modifications of neural stem cell differentiation. *Cell Transplant.*, 18, 1197-211.

Slager, K., Feis, N. and van der Gaag, P. (1985). Hongerwinter: verhalen om te onthouden. Amsterdam, The Netherlands: Link Publ.

Smart, J. L. (1986). Undernutrition, learning and memory: review of experimental studies. In: Proceedings of the XIII International Congress of Nutrition. Taylor, T. G. and Jenkins, N. K. (Eds). London: John Libbey, p. 74-78.

Smart, J. L. (1987). The need for and the relevance of animal studies of early undernutrition. In: Early nutrition and later achievement. Dobbing, J. (Ed). London: Academic Press, p. 50-85.

Smart, J. L. and Dobbing, J. (1971a). Vulnerability of developing brain. II. Effects of early nutritional deprivation on reflex ontogeny and development of behaviour in the rat. *Brain Res.*, 28, 85-95.

Smart, J. L. and Dobbing, J. (1971b). Vulnerability of developing brain. VI. Relative effects of foetal and early postnatal undernutrition on reflex ontogeny and development of behaviour in the rat. *Brain Res.*, 33, 303-14.

Smart, J. L., Dobbing, J., Adlard, B. P., Lynch, A. and Sands, J. (1973). Vulnerability of developing brain: relative effects of growth restriction during the fetal and suckling periods on behavior and brain composition of adult rats. *J. Nutr.*, 103, 1327-38.

Smart, J. L., Tricklebank, M. D., Adlard, B. P. and Dobbing, J. (1976). Nutritionally small-for-dates rats: their subsequent growth, regional brain 5-hydroxytryptamine turnover, and behavior. *Pediatr. Res.*, 10, 807-11.

Smil, V. (1999). Education and debate. China's great famine: 40 years later. *BMJ*, 319, 1619-21.

Smith, C. A. (1947a). Effects of maternal undernutrition upon the newborn infant in Holland (1944-1945). *J. Pediatr.*, 30, 229-43.

Smith, C. A. (1947b). The effect of wartime starvation in Holland upon pregnancy and its product. *Am. J. Obstet. Gynecol.*, 53, 599-608.

Smith, F. M., Garfield, A. S. and Ward, A. (2006). Regulation of growth and metabolism by imprinted genes. *Cytogenet. Genome Res.*, 113, 279-91.

Smith, L. and Greenfield, A. (2003). DNA microarrays and development. *Hum. Mol. Genet.*, 12 Spec. No 1, R1-8.

Song, S., Wang, W. and Hu, P. (2009). Famine, death, and madness: schizophrenia in early adulthood after prenatal exposure to the Chinese Great Leap Forward Famine. *Soc. Sci. Med.*, 68, 1315-21.

Southwell, D. G., Nicholas, C. R., Basbaum, A. I., Stryker, M. P., Kriegstein, A. R., Rubenstein, J. L., et al. (2014). Interneurons from embryonic development to cell-based therapy. *Science*, 344, 1240622.

Sowell, E. R., Thompson, P. M., Leonard, C. M., Welcome, S. E., Kan, E. and Toga, A. W. (2004). Longitudinal mapping of cortical thickness and brain growth in normal children. *J. Neurosci.*, 24, 8223-31.

Sparago, A., Cerrato, F., Vernucci, M., Ferrero, G. B., Silengo, M. C. and Riccio, A. (2004). Microdeletions in the human H19 DMR result in loss of IGF2 imprinting and Beckwith-Wiedemann syndrome. *Nat. Genet.*, 36, 958-60.

Sparén, P., Vågerö, D., Shestov, D. B., Plavinskaja, S., Parfenova, N., Hoptiar, V., et al. (2004). Long term mortality after severe starvation during the siege of Leningrad: prospective cohort study. *BMJ*, 328, 11-5.

Sperry, R. W. (1963). Chemoaffinity in the orderly growth of nerve fiber patterns and connections. *Proc. Natl. Acad. Sci. U S A*, 50, 703-10.

Starling, E. H. (1905). The Croonian Lectures on the chemical correlation of the functions of the body. *Lancet*, 2, 339-41; 423-5; 501-3; 579-83.

Steckelings, U., Lebrun, C., Qadri, F., Veltmar, A. and Unger, T. (1992). Role of brain angiotensin in cardiovascular regulation. *J. Cardiovasc. Pharmacol.*, 19 Suppl. 6, S72-9.

Stefansson, H., Rujescu, D., Cichon, S., Pietiläinen, O. P., Ingason, A., Steinberg, S., et al. (2008). Large recurrent microdeletions associated with schizophrenia. *Nature*, 455, 232-6.

Stein, A. D., Ravelli, A. C. and Lumey, L. H. (1995). Famine, third-trimester pregnancy weight gain, and intrauterine growth: The Dutch Famine Birth Cohort Study. *Hum. Biol.*, 67, 135-50.

Stein, A. D., Zybert, P. A., van de Bor, M. and Lumey, L. H. (2004). Intrauterine famine exposure and body proportions at birth: the Dutch Hunger Winter. *Int. J. Epidemiol.*, 33, 831-6.

Stein, Z. and Susser, M. (1975a). Fertility, fecundity, famine: food rations in the Dutch Famine 1944/5 have a causal relation to fertility, and probably to fecundity. *Hum. Biol.*, 47, 131-54.

Stein, Z. and Susser, M. (1975b). The Dutch Famine, 1944-1945, and the reproductive process. I. Effects on six indices at birth. *Pediatr. Res.*, 9, 70-6.

Stein, Z. and Susser, M. (1975c). The Dutch Famine, 1944-1945, and the reproductive process. II. Interrelations of caloric rations and six indices at birth. *Pediatr. Res.*, 9, 76-83.

Stein, Z. and Susser, M. (1976). Maternal starvation and birth defects. In: Birth defects. Risks and consequences. Kelly, S., Hook, E.B., Janerich, D.T. and Porter, I.H. (Eds). New York: Academic Press, Inc, p. 205-20.

Stein, Z., Susser, M., Saenger, G. and Marolla, F. (1972). Nutrition and mental performance. Prenatal exposure to the Dutch famine of 1944-1945 seems not related to mental performance at age 19. *Science*, 178, 708-13.

Stein, Z., Susser, M., Saenger, G. and Marolla, F. (1975). Famine and human development. The Dutch Hunger Winter of 1944-1945. New York: Oxford University Press.

Stern, W. C., Pugh, W. W., Resnick, O. and Morgane, P. J. (1984). Developmental protein malnutrition in the rat: effects on single-unit activity in the frontal cortex. *Brain Res.*, 306, 227-34.

Stewart, R. J., Preece, R. F. and Sheppard, H. G. (1975). Twelve generations of marginal protein deficiency. *Br. J. Nutr.*, 33, 233-53.

Stewart, R. J., Sheppard, H., Preece, R. and Waterlow, J. C. (1980). The effect of rehabilitation at different stages of development of rats marginally malnourished for ten to twelve generations. *Br. J. Nutr.*, 43, 403-12.

Stöger, R. (2008). The thrifty epigenotype: An acquired and heritable predisposition for obesity and diabetes? *Bioessays*, 30, 156-66.

Stoll, C., Alembik, Y. and Dott, B. (2003). Limb reduction defects in the first generation and deafness in the second generation of intrauterine exposed fetuses to diethylstilbestrol. *Ann. Genet.*, 46:459-465.

Stoner, R., Chow, M. L., Boyle, M. P., Sunkin, S. M., Mouton, P. R., Roy, S., et al. (2014). Patches of disorganization in the neocortex of children with autism. *N. Engl. J. Med.*, 370, 1209-19.

Suh, H., Consiglio, A., Ray, J., Sawai, T., D'Amour, K. A. and Gage, F. H. (2007). In vivo fate analysis reveals the multipotent and self-renewal capacities of Sox2[+] neural stem cells in the adult hippocampus. *Cell Stem Cell*, 1, 515-28.

Sullivan, P. F., Lin, D., Tzeng, J. Y., van den Oord, E., Perkins, D., Stroup, T. S., et al. (2008). Genomewide association for schizophrenia in the CATIE study: results of stage 1. *Mol. Psychiatry*, 13, 570-84.

Sur, M. and Rubenstein, J. L. (2005). Patterning and plasticity of the cerebral cortex. *Science*, 310, 805-10.

Susser, E., Hoek, H. W. and Brown, A. (1998). Neurodevelopmental disorders after prenatal famine. The story of the Dutch Famine Study. *Am. J. Epidemiol.*, 147, 213-6.

Susser, E., Neugebauer, R., Hoek, H. W., Brown, A. S., Lin, S., Labovitz, D., et al. (1996). Schizophrenia after prenatal famine. Further evidence. *Arch. Gen. Psychiatry*, 53, 25-31.

Susser, E., St. Clair, D. and He, L. (2008). Latent effects of prenatal malnutrition on adult health. The example of schizophrenia. *Ann. N Y Acad. Sci.*, 1136, 185-92.

Susser, E. S. and Lin, S. P. (1992). Schizophrenia after prenatal exposure to the Dutch Hunger Winter of 1944-1945. *Arch. Gen. Psychiatry*, 49, 983-8.

Susser, M. and Stein, Z. (1994). Timing in prenatal nutrition: a reprise of the Dutch Famine Study. *Nutr. Rev.*, 52, 84-94.

Sutcliffe, J. S., Nakao, M., Christian, S., Orstavik, K. H., Tommerup, N., Ledbetter, D. H., et al. (1994). Deletions of a differentially methylated CpG island at the SNRPN gene define a putative imprinting control region. *Nat. Genet.*, 8, 52-8.

Suvisaari, J., Haukka, J., Tanskanen, A., Hovi, T. and Lonnqvist, J. (1999). Association between prenatal exposure to poliovirus infection and adult schizophrenia. *Am. J. Psychiatry*, 156, 1100-2.

Swan, S. H. (2000). Intrauterine exposure to diethylstilbestrol: Long-term effects in humans. *APMIS*, 108, 793-804.

Sweatt, J. D. (2009). Experience-dependent epigenetic modifications in the central nervous system. *Biol. Psychiatry*, 65, 191-7.

Szentágothai, J. (1978). The Ferrier Lecture, 1977. The neuron network of the cerebral cortex: a functional interpretation. *Proc. R. Soc. Lond. B. Biol. Sci.*, 201, 219-48.

Szyf, M., McGowan, P. and Meaney, M. J. (2008). The social environment and the epigenome. *Environ. Mol. Mutagen.*, 49, 46-60.

Szyf, M., Weaver, I. and Meaney, M. (2007). Maternal care, the epigenome and phenotypic differences in behavior. *Reprod. Toxicol.*, 24, 9-19.

Takahashi, K. and Yamanaka, S. (2006). Induction of pluripotent stem cells from mouse embryonic and adult fibroblast cultures by defined factors. *Cell*, 126, 663-76.

Takizawa, T., Nakashima, K., Namihira, M., Ochiai, W., Uemura, A., Yanagisawa, M., et al. (2001). DNA methylation is a critical cell-intrinsic determinant of astrocyte differentiation in the fetal brain. *Dev. Cell*, 1, 749-58.

Tamura, K., Umemura, S., Nyui, N., Yamakawa, T., Yamaguchi, S., Ishigami, T., et al. (1996). Tissue-specific regulation of angiotensinogen gene expression in spontaneously hypertensive rats. *Hypertension*, 27, 1216-23.

Tandon, R., Nasrallah, H. A. and Keshavan, M. S. (2009). Schizophrenia, "just the facts" 4. Clinical features and conceptualization. *Schizophr. Res.*, 110, 1-23.

Taylor, S. E. (2010). Mechanisms linking early life stress to adult health outcomes. *Proc. Natl. Acad. Sci. U S A*, 107, 8507-12.

Thompson, B. L. and Levitt, P. (2010). The clinical-basic interface in defining pathogenesis in disorders of neurodevelopmental origin. *Neuron*, 67, 702-12.

Tiepolo, L., Maraschio, P., Gimelli, G., Cuoco, C., Gargani, G. F. and Romano, C. (1979). Multibranched chromosome 1, 9, and 16 in a patient with combined IgA and IgE deficiency. *Hum. Genet.*, 51, 127-37.

Timmermans, P. B., Wong, P. C., Chiu, A. T., Herblin, W. F., Benfield, P., Carini, D. J., et al. (1993). Angiotensin II receptors and angiotensin II receptor antagonists. *Pharmacol. Rev.*, 45, 205-51.

Tobi, E. W., Lumey, L. H., Talens, R. P., Kremer, D., Putter, H., Stein, A. D., et al. (2009). DNA methylation differences after exposure to prenatal famine are common and timing- and sex-specific. *Hum. Mol. Genet.*, 18, 4046-53.

Toga, A. W., Thompson, P. M. and Sowell, E. R. (2006). Mapping brain maturation. *Trends Neurosci.*, 29, 148-59.

Tohgi, H., Utsugisawa, K., Nagane, Y., Yoshimura, M., Genda, Y. and Ukitsu, M. (1999a). Reduction with age in methylcytosine in the promoter region -224 approximately -101 of the amyloid precursor protein gene in autopsy human cortex. *Brain Res. Mol. Brain Res.*, 70, 288-92.

Tohgi, H., Utsugisawa, K., Nagane, Y., Yoshimura, M., Ukitsu, M. and Genda, Y. (1999b). The methylation status of cytosines in a tau gene promoter region alters with age to downregulate transcriptional activity in human cerebral cortex. *Neurosci. Lett.*, 275, 89-92.

Tonkiss, J. and Galler, J. R. (1990). Prenatal protein malnutrition and working memory performance in adult rats. *Behav. Brain Res.*, 40, 95-107.

Tonkiss, J., Galler, J. R., Formica, R. N., Shukitt-Hale, B. and Timm, R. R. (1990). Fetal protein malnutrition impairs acquisition of a DRL task in adult rats. *Physiol. Behav.*, 48, 73-7.

Torii, M., Hashimoto-Torii, K., Levitt, P. and Rakic, P. (2009). Integration of neuronal clones in the radial cortical columns by EphA and ephrin-A signaling. *Nature*, 461, 524-8.

Torrens, C., Brawley, L., Anthony, F. W., Dance, C. S., Dunn, R., Jackson, A. A., et al. (2006). Folate supplementation during pregnancy improves offspring cardiovascular dysfunction induced by protein restriction. *Hypertension*, 47, 982-7.

Torrey, E. F., Barci, B. M., Webster, M. J., Bartko, J. J., Meador-Woodruff, J. H. and Knable, M. B. (2005). Neurochemical markers for schizophrenia, bipolar disorder, and major depression in postmortem brains. *Biol. Psychiatry*, 57, 252-60.

Torrey, E. F., Webster, M., Knable, M., Johnston, N. and Yolken, R. H. (2000). The Stanley Foundation brain collection and Neuropathology Consortium. *Schizophr. Res.*, 44, 151-5.

Tost, J. (Ed). (2008a). Epigenetics. Norfolk, UK: Caister Academic Press.

Tost, J. (2008b). Methods for the genome-wide and gene-specific analysis of DNA methylation levels and patterns. In: Epigenetics. Tost, J. (Ed). Norfolk, UK: Caister Academic Press, p. 63-103.

Tremolizzo, L., Carboni, G., Ruzicka, W. B., Mitchell, C. P., Sugaya, I., Tueting, P., et al. (2002). An epigenetic mouse model for molecular and behavioral neuropathologies related to schizophrenia vulnerability. *Proc. Natl. Acad. Sci. U S A*, 99, 17095-100.

Tremolizzo, L., Doueiri, M. S., Dong, E., Grayson, D. R., Davis, J., Pinna, G., et al. (2005). Valproate corrects the schizophrenia-like epigenetic behavioral modifications induced by methionine in mice. *Biol. Psychiatry*, 57, 500-9.

Trienekens, G. (2000). The food supply in The Netherlands during the Second World War. In: Food, science, policy and regulation in the twentieth century. International and comparative perspectives. Smith, D.F. and Phillips, J. (Eds). London: Routledge, p. 117-33.

Trienekens, G. M. T. (1985). Tussen ons volk en de honger: de voedselvoorziening, 1940-1945. Utrecht: Matrijs.

Trienekens, G. M. T. (1995). Voedsel en honger in oorlogstijd 1940-1945: misleading, mythe en werkelijkheid. Utrecht: Kosmos-ZandK Uitgevers.

Tsankova, N., Renthal, W., Kumar, A. and Nestler, E. J. (2007). Epigenetic regulation in psychiatric disorders. *Nat. Rev. Neurosci.*, 8, 355-67.

Tu, M. T., Grunau, R. E., Petrie-Thomas, J., Haley, D. W., Weinberg, J. and Whitfield, M. F. (2007). Maternal stress and behavior modulate relationships between neonatal stress, attention, and basal cortisol at 8 months in preterm infants. *Dev. Psychobiol.*, 49, 150-64.

Turek-Plewa, J. and Jagodziński, P. P. (2005). The role of mammalian DNA methyltransferases in the regulation of gene expression. *Cell Mol. Biol. Lett.*, 10, 631-47.

Tycko, B. (2006). Imprinted genes in placental growth and obstetric disorders. *Cytogenet. Genome Res.*, 113, 271-8.

U.S. Preventive Services Task Force (2009). Folic acid for the prevention of neural tube defects: U.S. Preventive Services Task Force recommendation statement. *Ann. Intern. Med.*, 150, 626-31.

Urakubo, A., Jarskog, L. F., Lieberman, J. A. and Gilmore, J. H. (2001). Prenatal exposure to maternal infection alters cytokine expression in the placenta, amniotic fluid, and fetal brain. *Schizphr. Res.*, 47, 27-36.

Urdinguio, R. G., Sanchez-Mut, J. V. and Esteller, M. (2009). Epigenetic mechanisms in neurological diseases: genes, syndromes, and therapies. *Lancet Neurol.*, 8, 1056-72.

Vaccarino, F. M. and Ment, L. R. (2004). Injury and repair in developing brain. *Arch. Dis. Child Fetal Neonatal. Ed.*, 89, F190-2.

Valadkhan, S. and Nilsen, T. W. (2010). Reprogramming of the non-coding transcriptome during brain development. *J. Biol.*, 9, 5.

Van Eldik, L. J. and Wainwright, M. S. (2003). The Janus face of glial-derived S100B: beneficial and detrimental functions in the brain. *Restor. Neurol. Neurosci.*, 21, 97-108.

Van Esch, H., Bauters, M., Ignatius, J., Jansen, M., Raynaud, M., Hollanders, K., et al. (2005). Duplication of the MECP2 region is a frequent cause of severe mental retardation and progressive neurological symptoms in males. *Am. J. Hum. Genet.*, 77, 442-53.

Van Gelder, N. M., Butterworth, R. F., Drujan, B. D. (Eds). (1990). *(Mal)nutrition and the infant brain. Proceedings of an International Symposium held in Montréal, Québec, Canada, May 11-12, 1989.* New York: Wiley-Liss.

Van Os, J. and Jones, P. B. (1999). Early risk factors and adult person-environment relationships in affective disorder. *Psychol. Med.*, 29, 1055-67.

Veldic, M., Guidotti, A., Maloku, E., Davis, J. M. and Costa, E. (2005). In psychosis, cortical interneurons overexpress DNA-methyltransferase 1. *Proc. Natl. Acad. Sci. U S A*, 102, 2152-7.

Verkerk, A. J., Pieretti, M., Sutcliffe, J. S., Fu, Y. H., Kuhl, D. P., Pizzuti, A., et al. (1991). Identification of a gene (FMR-1) containing a CGG repeat coincident with a breakpoint cluster region exhibiting length variation in fragile X syndrome. *Cell*, 65, 905-14.

Vickaryous, N. and Whitelaw, E. (2005). The role of early embryonic environment on epigenotype and phenotype. *Reprod. Fertil Dev.*, 17, 335-40.

Visvanathan, J., Lee, S., Lee, B., Lee, J. W. and Lee, S. K. (2007). The microRNA miR-124 antagonizes the anti-neural REST/SCP1 pathway during embryonic CNS development. *Genes. Dev.*, 21, 744-9.

Vyas, A., Mitra, R., Rao, B. S. and Chattarji, S. (2002). Chronic stress induces contrasting patterns of dendritic remodeling in hippocampal and amygdaloid neurons. *J. Neurosci.*, 22, 6810-8.

Waddington, C. H. (1939). Preliminary notes on the development of the wings in normal and mutant strains of *drosophila*. *Proc. Natl. Acad. Sci. U S A*, 25, 299-307.

Waddington, C. H. (1940). Organisers and Genes. Cambridge: Cambridge University Press.

Waddington, C. H. (1942). The epigenotype. *Endeavour*, 1, 18-20.

Waddington, C. H. (1957). The Strategy of the Genes. London: Allen and Unwin.

Wadhwa, P. D., Buss, C., Entringer, S. and Swanson, J. M. (2009). Developmental origins of health and disease: brief history of the approach and current focus on epigenetic mechanisms. *Semin. Reprod. Med.*, 27, 358-68.

Wahlbeck, K., Forsen, T., Osmond, C., Barker, D. J. and Eriksson, J. G. (2001). Association of schizophrenia with low maternal body mass index, small size at birth, and thinness during childhood. *Arch. Gen. Psychiatry*, 58, 48-52.

Wald, N. and Sneddon, J. (1991). Prevention of neural tube defects: Results of the Medical Research Council Vitamin Study. *Lancet* 338, 131-7.

Walker, D. M. and Marlow, N. (2008). Neurocognitive outcome following fetal growth restriction. *Arch. Dis. Child Fetal Neonatal. Ed.*, 93, F322-5.

Walsh, T., McClellan, J. M., McCarthy, S. E., Addington, A. M., Pierce, S. B., Cooper, G. M., et al. (2008). Rare structural variants disrupt multiple genes in neurodevelopmental pathways in schizophrenia. *Science*, 320, 539-43.

Wang, L. W., Berry-Kravis, E. and Hagerman, R. J. (2010). Fragile X: leading the way for targeted treatments in autism. *Neurotherapeutics*, 7, 264-74.

Wang, S. C., Oelze, B. and Schumacher, A. (2008). Age-specific epigenetic drift in late-onset Alzheimer's disease. *PLoS One*, 3, e2698.

Wang, X., Rousset, C. I., Hagberg, H. and Mallard, C. (2006). Lipopolysaccharide-induced inflammation and perinatal brain injury. *Semin. Fetal Neonatal Med.*, 11, 343-53.

Ward, A. M., Moore, V. M., Steptoe, A., Cockington, R. A., Robinson, J. S. and Phillips, D. I. (2004). Size at birth and cardiovascular responses to psychological stressors: evidence for prenatal programming in women. *J Hypertens*, 22, 2295-301.

Waterland, R. A., Dolinoy, D. C., Lin, J. R., Smith, C. A., Shi, X. and Tahiliani, K. G. (2006). Maternal methyl supplements increase offspring DNA methylation at *Axin. Fused. Genesis*, 44, 401-6.

Waterland, R. A. and Garza, C. (1999). Potential mechanisms of metabolic imprinting that lead to chronic disease. *Am. J. Clin. Nutr.*, 69, 179-97.

Waterland, R. A. and Jirtle, R. L. (2004). Early nutrition, epigenetic changes at transposons and imprinted genes, and enhanced susceptibility to adult chronic diseases. *Nutrition*, 20, 63-8.

Waterland, R. A. and Michels, K. B. (2007). Epigenetic epidemiology of the developmental origins hypothesis. *Annu. Rev. Nutr.*, 27, 363-88.

Watkins, A. J., Wilkins, A., Cunningham, C., Perry, V. H., Seet, M. J., Osmond, C., et al. (2008). Low protein diet fed exclusively during mouse oocyte maturation leads to behavioural and cardiovascular abnormalities in offspring. *J. Physiol. (Lond.)*, 586, 2231-44.

Weeber, E. J., Beffert, U., Jones, C., Christian, J. M., Forster, E., Sweatt, J. D., et al. (2002). Reelin and ApoE receptors cooperate to enhance hippocampal synaptic plasticity and learning. *J. Biol. Chem.*, 277, 39944-52.

Wehby, G. L. and Murray, J. C. (2008). The effects of prenatal use of folic acid and other dietary supplements on early child development. *Matern. Child Health J.*, 12, 180-7.

Weinberg, R. (2010). Point: Hypotheses first. *Nature*, 464, 678.

West, R. L., Lee, J. M. and Maroun, L. E. (1995). Hypomethylation of the amyloid precursor protein gene in the brain of an Alzheimer's disease patient. *J. Mol. Neurosci.*, 6, 141-6.

Westergaard, T., Mortensen, P. B., Pedersen, C..B., Wohlfahrt, J. and Melbye, M. (1999). Exposure to prenatal and childhood infections and the risk of schizophrenia: suggestions from a study of sibship characteristics and influenza prevalence. *Arch. Gen. Psychiatry*, 56, 993-8.

Whiteus, C., Freitas, C. and Grutzendler, J. (2014). Perturbed neural activity disrupts cerebral angiogenesis during a postnatal critical period. *Nature*, 505, 407-11.

Wilkinson, L. S., Davies, W. and Isles, A. R. (2007). Genomic imprinting effects on brain development and function. *Nat. Rev. Neurosci.*, 8, 832-43.

Willard, H. F., Brown, C. J., Carrel, L., Hendrich, B. and Miller, A. P. (1993). Epigenetic and chromosomal control of gene expression: molecular and genetic analysis of X chromosome inactivation. *Cold Spring Harb. Symp. Quant Biol.*, 58, 315-22.

Williams, R. S. (1989). Cerebral malformations arising in the first half of gestation. In: Developmental neurobiology. Evrard, P. and Minkowski, A. (Eds). New York: Raven Press, p. 11-20.

Williams, R. W. and Herrup, K. (1988). The control of neuron number. *Annu. Rev. Neurosci.*, 11, 423-53.

Willner, P. (1997). Validity, reliability and utility of the chronic mild stress model of depression: a 10-year review and evaluation. *Pyschopharmacology*, 134, 319-29.

Willner, P., Towell, A., Sampson, D., Sophokleous, S. and Muscat, R. (1987). Reduction of sucrose preference by chronic unpredictable mild stress, and its restoration by a tricyclic antidepressant. *Psychopharmacology*, 93, 358-64.

Winick, M. and Noble, A. (1965). Quantitative changes in DNA, RNA, and protein during prenatal and postnatal growth in the rat. *Dev. Biol.*, 12, 451-66.

Winick, M. and Noble, A. (1966). Cellular response in rats during malnutrition at various ages. *J. Nutr.*, 89, 300-6.

Winick, M. and Rosso, P. (1975). Malnutrition and central nervous system development. In: Brain function and malnutrition. Neuropsychological methods of assessment. Prescott, J. W., Read, M. S. and Coursin, D. B. (Eds). New York: John Wiley and Sons, p. 41-51.

Wojtowicz, W. M., Wu, W., Andre, I., Qian, B., Baker, D. and Zipursky, S. L. (2007). A vast repertoire of Dscam binding specificities arises from modular interactions of variable Ig domains. *Cell*, 130, 1134-45.

Wolffe, A. P. and Matzke, M. A. (1999). Epigenetics: regulation through repression. *Science*, 286, 481-6.

Wood, G. E., Young, L. T., Reagan, L. P. and McEwen, B. S. (2003). Acute and chronic restraint stress alter the incidence of social conflict in male rats. *Horm. Behav.*, 43, 205-13.

Wood, L., Gray, N. W., Zhou, Z., Greenberg, M. E. and Shepherd, G. M. (2009). Synaptic circuit abnormalities of motor-frontal layer 2/3 pyramidal neurons in an RNA interference model of methyl-CpG-binding protein 2 deficiency. *J. Neurosci.*, 29, 12440-8.

Woods, B. T. (1998). Is schizophrenia a progressive neurodevelopmental disorder? Toward a unitary pathogenetic mechanism. *Am. J. Psychiatry*, 155, 1661-70.

Woolf, C. M. (1997). Does the genotype for schizophrenia often remain unexpressed because of canalization and stochastic events during development? *Psychol. Med.*, 27, 659-68.

Wu, G., Baser, F. W., Cudd, T. A., Meininger, C. J. and Spencer, T. E. (2004). Maternal nutrition and fetal development. *J. Nutr.*, 134, 2169-72.

Wu, H. and Sun, Y. E. (2009). Reversing DNA methylation: new insights from neuronal activity-induced Gadd45b in adult neurogenesis. *Sci. Signal*, 2, pe17.

Wu, H., Tao, J., Chen, P. J., Shahab, A., Ge, W., Hart, R. P., et al. (2010). Genome-wide analysis reveals methyl-CpG-binding protein 2-dependent regulation of microRNAs in a mouse model of Rett syndrome. *Proc. Natl. Acad. Sci. U S A*, 107, 18161-6.

Wu, Y. W. and Colford, J. M., Jr. (2000). Chorioamnionitis as a risk factor for cerebral palsy: a meta-analysis. *JAMA*, 284, 1417-24.

Xu, B., Roos, J. L., Levy, S., van Rensburg, E. J., Gogos, J. A. and Karayiorgou, M. (2008). Strong association of *de novo* copy number mutations with sporadic schizophrenia. *Nat. Genet.*, 40, 880-5.

Xu, G. L., Bestor, T. H., Bourc'his D., Hsieh, C. L., Tommerup, N., Bugge, M., et al. (1999). Chromosome instability and immunodeficiency syndrome caused by mutations in a DNA methyltransferase gene. *Nature*, 402, 187-91.

Xu, M. Q., Sun, W. S., Liu, B. X., Feng, G. Y., Yu, L., Yang, L., et al. (2009). Prenatal malnutrition and adult schizophrenia: further evidence from the 1959-1961 Chinese famine. *Schizophr. Bull.*, 35, 568-76.

Yakovlev, A., Khafizova, M., Abdullaev, Z., Loukinov, D. and Kondratyev, A. (2010). Epigenetic regulation of caspase-3 gene expression in rat brain development. *Gene*, 450, 103-8.

Yamasaki, K., Joh, K., Ohta, T., Masuzaki, H., Ishimaru, T., Mukai, T., et al. (2003). Nuerons but not glial cells show reciprocal imprinting of sense and antisense transcripts of Ube3a. *Hum. Mol. Genet.*, 12, 837-47.

Yamasaki, Y., Kayashima, T., Soejima, H., Kinoshita, A., Yoshiura, K., Matsumoto, N., et al. (2005). Neuron-specific relaxation of Igf2r imprinting is associated with neuron-specific histone modifications and lack of its antisense transcript Air. *Hum. Mol. Genet.*, 14, 2511-20.

Yehuda, R., Cai, G., Golier, J. A., Sarapas, C., Galea, S., Ising, M., et al. (2009). Gene expression patterns associated with posttraumatic stress disorder following exposure to the World Trade Center attacks. *Biol. Psychiatry*, 66, 708-11.

Yehuda, R., Engel, S. M., Brand, S. R., Seckl, J., Marcus, S. M. and Berkowitz, G. S. (2005). Transgenerational effects of posttraumatic stress disorder in babies of mothers exposed to the World Trade Center attacks during pregnancy. *J. Clin. Endocrinol. Metab.*, 90, 4115-8.

Yin, M., Liu, S., Yin, Y., Li, S., Li, Z., Wu, X., et al. (2009). Ventral mesencephalon-enriched genes that regulate the development of dopaminergic neurons in vivo. *J. Neurosci.*, 29, 5170-82.

Yoo, A. S. and Crabtree, G. R. (2009). ATP-dependent chromatin remodeling in neural development. *Curr. Opin. Neurobiol.*, 19, 120-6.

Yoo, A. S., Staahl, B. T., Chen, L. and Crabtree, G. R. (2009). MicroRNA-mediated switching of chromatin-remodelling complexes in neural development. *Nature*, 460, 642-6.

Yoon, B. H., Kim, C. J., Romero, R., Jun, J. K., Park, K. H., Choi, S. T., et al. (1997). Experimentally induced intrauterine infection causes fetal brain white matter lesions in rabbits. *Am. J. Obstet. Gynecol.*, 177, 797-802.

Yoon, B. H., Romero, R., Kim, C. J., Jun, J. K., Gomez, R., Choi, J. H., et al. (1995). Amniotic fluid interleukin-6: a sensitive test for antenatal diagnosis of acute inflammatory lesions of preterm placenta and prediction of perinatal morbidity. *Am. J. Obstet. Gynecol.*, 172, 960-70.

Young, L. E., Fernandes, K., McEvoy, T. G., Butterwith, S. C., Gutierrez, C. G., Carolan, C., et al. (2001). Epigenetic changes in *IGF2R* is associated with fetal overgrowth after sheep embryo culture. *Nat. Genet.*, 27, 153-4.

Yu, J. Y., Chung, K. H., Deo, M., Thompson, R. C. and Turner, D. L. (2008). MicroRNA miR-124 regulates neurite outgrowth during neuronal differentiation. *Exp. Cell Res.*, 314, 2618-33.

Yuan, T. F. (2008). GABA effects on neurogenesis: an arsenal of regulation. *Sci. Signal*, 1, jc1.

Zambrano, E., Bautista, C. J., Deás, M., Martinez-Samayoa, P. M., González-Zamorano, M., Ledesma, H., et al. (2006). A low maternal protein diet during pregnancy and lactation has sex- and window of exposure-specific effects on offspring growth and food intake, glucose metabolism and serum leptin in the rat. *J. Physiol. (Lond.)*, 571, 221-30.

Zamenhof, S. and van Marthens, E. (1978). Nutritional influences on prenatal brain development. In: *Early influences*. Gottlieb, G. (Ed). New York: Academic Press, p. 149-186.

Zamenhof, S. and van Marthens, E. (1982). Chronic undernutrition for 10 generations: differential effects on brain and body development among neonatal rats. *Nutr. Rep. Int.*, 26, 703-9.

Zamenhof, S., van Marthens, E. and Grauel, L. (1971). DNA (cell number) in neonatal brain: second generation (F_2) alteration by maternal (F_0) dietary protein restriction. *Science*, 172, 850-1.

Zannas, A. S. and West, A. E. (2014). Epigenetics and the regulation of stress vulnerability and resilience. *Neuroscience*, 264, 157-170.

Zhang, H., Liu, X., Zhang, C., Mundo, E., Macciardi, F., Grayson, D. R., et al. (2002). Reelin gene alleles and susceptibility to autism spectrum disorders. *Mol. Psychiatry*, 7, 1012-7.

Zhang, J. Q., Sun, H. L., Ma, Y. X. and Wang, D. W. (2006). [Effects of RNA interference targeting angiotensin 1a receptor on the blood pressure and cardiac hypertrophy of rats with 2K1C hypertension]. *Zhonghua Yi Xue Za Zhi*, 86, 1138-43.

Zhang, K., Schrag, M., Crofton, A., Trivedi, R., Vinters, H. and Kirsch, W. (2012). Targeted proteomics for quantification of histone acetylation in Alzheimer's disease. *Proteomics*, 12, 1261-8.

Zhao, C., Deng, W. and Gage, F. H. (2008). Mechanisms and functional implications of adult neurogenesis. *Cell*, 132, 645-60.

Zhao, S., Chai, X., Förster, E. and Frotscher, M. (2004). Reelin is a positional signal for the lamination of dentate granule cells. *Development*, 131, 5117-25.

Zhao, S., Chai, X. and Frotscher, M. (2007). Balance between neurogenesis and gliogenesis in the adult hippocampus: role for reelin. *Dev. Neurosci.*, 29, 84-90.

Zhao, X., He, X., Han, X., Yu, Y., Ye, F., Chen, Y., et al. (2010). MicroRNA-mediated control of oligodendrocyte differentiation. *Neuron*, 65, 612-26.

Zhou, V. W., Goren, A. and Bernstein, B. E. (2011). Charting histone modifications and the functional organization of mammalian genomes. *Nat. Rev. Genet.*, 12, 7-18.

Zipursky, S. L. (2010). Driving self-recognition. *Scientist*, 24, 41-5.

Zornberg, G. L., Buka, S. L. and Tsuang, M. T. (2000). Hypoxic-ischemia-related fetal/neonatal complications and risk of schizophrenia and other nonaffective psychoses: a 19-year longitudinal study. *Am. J. Psychiatry*, 157, 196-202.

Zuckerman, L., Rehavi, M., Nachman, R. and Weiner, I. (2003). Immune activation during pregnancy in rats leads to a postpubertal emergence of disrupted latent inhibition, dopaminergic hyperfunction, and altered limbic morphology in the offspring: a novel neurodevelopmental model of schizophrenia. *Neuropsychopharmacology*, 28, 1778-89.

In: Stress and Developmental Programming ...
Editors: Lubo Zhang and Lawrence D. Longo

ISBN: 978-1-63321-836-9
© 2014 Nova Science Publishers, Inc.

Chapter 7

Maternal Cardiovascular Adaptation and Uterine Circulation: Physiology and Pathophysiology

Ronald R. Magness[1] and Stephen P. Ford[2]*

[1]Departments of Ob/Gyn, Pediatrics, and Animal Sciences,
University of Wisconsin, Madison, WI, US
[2]Department of Animal Sciences, Center for the Study of Fetal Programming,
University of Wyoming, Laramie, WY, US

Abstract

In order to ensure a successful pregnancy with a normally grown fetus and newborn, the maternal cardiovascular system must undergo a plethora of uterine and systemic changes. The greatest changes are seen in the uterine vasculature since the uterine wall is in intimate contact with the feto-placental unit which produces many hormones (e.g. estrogen and progesterone) and angiogenic growth factors (e.g. VEGF and bFGF) that are thought to drive these hemodynamic adaptations. Furthermore, this chapter summarizes the systemic peripheral maternal cardiovascular adaptations seen during pregnancy that are characterized by minor decreases in blood pressure, substantial falls in systemic vascular resistance, associated with increases in cardiac output, heart rate and stroke volume. Normal gestation is also associated with a dramatic expansion of the intravascular compartment, characteristic rises in blood and plasma volume as well as compositional shifts in body fluids with increases in red blood cell mass and decreases in viscosity. These local uterine and systemic peripheral and cardiac adaptations are thought to be crucial in order to meet the metabolic needs of the rapidly growing fetus. In this chapter we comprehensively review these changes in a temporal fashion throughout gestation making inclusive species comparisons where appropriate. We also integrate physiological principles to allow better interpretation of the interaction of local uterine,

* Address correspondence to: Ronald R. Magness, PhD, Department of Obstetrics and Gynecology, Perinatal Research Laboratories, Atrium B Meriter Hospital, 202 S. Park Street, Madison, WI, 53715. Phone: (608) 417-6314. Fax: (608) 257-1304. E-mail: rmagness@wisc.edu.

systemic peripheral, and cardiac changes during gestation. The clinical relevance of these maternal cardiovascular adaptations is highlighted by the fact that many of these alterations are partly or completely abrogated in gestational disorders such as preeclampsia.

Keywords: Estrogen, maternal cardiovascular system, preeclampsia, pregnancy, progesterone, uterine vasculature

Introduction

During normal gestation, numerous maternal systemic and uterine hemodynamic adaptations are seen which function to meet the developmental and metabolic demands of the rapidly growing fetus. These cardiovascular adaptations include an initial fall in systemic vascular tone, followed by an increase the cardiac output and expansion of maternal blood volume (Atkins et al., 1981, Capeless and Clapp, 1991, Clapp et al., 1988, Cunningham et al., 1989, Duvekot and Peeters, 1994, Gilson et al., 1992, Hansen and Ueland, 1974, Hoversland et al., 1974, Hytten and Leitch, 1971, Irgens et al., 2001, Lees et al., 1967, Magness, 1998, Metcalfe and Parer, 1966, Metcalfe and Ueland, 1974, Palmer and Walker, 1949, Robson et al., 1989b, Stock and Metcalfe, 1994). There are also a significant number of local changes taking place within the uterine vascular bed itself, which first function to facilitate generalized growth and development of the conceptus (placenta and embyro), and later to allow the placenta to support the exponential fetal growth seen during the third trimester of gestation (Clapp, 1978, Dowell and Kauer, 1997, Greiss, 1982, Johnson et al., 1985, Lees et al., 1971, Magness et al., 1998, Magness and Rosenfeld, 1986, Magness et al., 1992; Magness and Zheng, 1996, Rosenfeld, 1977, 1984, Rosenfeld and Naden, 1989, Rosenfeld et al., 1974, 1996, Spitz et al., 1998). Systemic and/or local uterine vascular maladaptations during pregnancy appear to lead to gestational hypertension and preeclampsia with intrauterine growth restriction (IUGR) and also other negative pregnancy outcomes (Gaillard et al., 2011, Moutquin et al., 1985, Palmer et al., 1992, Sprague et al., 2009). As has been well characterized in a wide range of mammalian species including rodents, sheep, non-human primates and women, uterine arterial blood flow increases markedly and progressively from nonpregnant levels during the course of pregnancy, with flows being directed increasingly away from the uterine wall to the feto-placental interface (Dowell and Kauer, 1997, Greiss, 1982, Lees et al., 1971, Magness, 1998, Palmer et al., 1992, Rosenfeld, 1989, Rosenfeld et al., 1974). This is consistent with the hypothesis that there are changes in vessel compliance and reactivity that begin at the smaller caliber vessels in the vicinity of the placenta, and progress to the larger caliber vessels in the uterine wall, finally reaching the main uterine artery (Cipolla and Osol, 1994, Osol and Mandala, 2009). The end result of these changes in vessel compliance is that uterine blood flow during gestation increases to levels 30-70 fold greater than that of nonpregnant uterine flows (Kulandavelu et al., 2012, Magness, 1998, Mu and Adamson, 2006, Rosenfeld, 1989, Venditti et al., 2013). Vessel compliance is also associated with a doubling or tripling of uterine arterial diameters, also known as outward remodeling (Adamson et al., 2002, Cross et al., 2002, Osol and Mandala, 2009, Osol and Moore, 2014), as well as substantial increases in arterial length, i.e. radial and axial remodeling, respectively, by the third trimester (Annibale et al., 1990, Cipolla and Osol,

1994, Griendling et al., 1985, Guenther et al., 1988, Moll, 2003, Moll and Gotz, 1985, Osol and Mandala, 2009, Sprague et al., 2009, van der Heijden et al., 2005). As will be discussed below, this progressively increasing blood flow capacity of the uterine arterial vasculature during pregnancy appears to result not only from the remodeling of components within the vessel wall itself, but also from altered responsiveness to local and systemic vasoactive agents (Magness, 1998, Sledek et al., 1997). The importance of these changes is further underscored by the observation that failure of the uterine vasculature to undergo these developmental changes during pregnancy results in placental under-perfusion and pathologies such as preeclampsia with IUGR. This review will attempt to integrate the pregnancy-associated changes in the maternal cardiovascular system with local changes in the uterine arterial composition, growth, and vasoactivity to clarify their impacts on successful pregnancy outcome.

Physical Changes in the Uterine Arterial Wall during Pregnancy

A significant number of studies have suggested a role for the female sex steroids estrogen and progesterone in uteroplacental vascular adaptations during pregnancy. Estrogen has been shown to reduce uterine vascular resistance in sheep with a resultant increase in uterine arterial vasodilation (Evans et al., 1998, Magness, 1998, Magness and Rosenfeld, 1989a, 1989b, Magness et al., 1993, 1998, Reynolds et al., 1998a, 1998b, Sprague et al., 2009). Moll and Gotz (Moll and Gotz, 1985) reported that the pressure-diameter curves of uterine radial arteries were shifted towards wider diameters in pregnant, estrus, and estrogen treated guinea pigs, in the presence and absence of papaverine, a smooth muscle relaxant. These data suggest that long term changes in uterine arterial diameter during pregnancy may result in part from estrogens impact on nonmuscular elements of the arterial wall. Elevated local exposure of the uterine arterial vasculature to placental estrogen is probable due to the demonstrated transport of elevated estrogen concentrations in porous lymphatic vessels which run in close proximity to the uterine arterial vasculature (Magness and Ford, 1982, 1983).

Another potential mechanism mediating elevated estrogen concentrations around the uteroplacental vessels include veno-arterial transfer which is likely to be counter current in nature (Osol and Mandala, 2009, Osol and Moore, 2014). Long-term exposure to exogenous estrogen reduces the collagen to elastin ratio in the walls of rat systemic arteries (Cox and Fischer, 1978, Fischer and Swain, 1977). This reduced collagen to elastin ratio appears to be due solely to decreases in collagen content in the arterial wall, as estrogen has been shown to decrease collagen synthesis (Fischer, 1972) and increase degradation (Beldekas et al., 1981). Evidence for this hypothesis is the observation that the uterine arterial collagen to elastin ratio progressively declines with the advancement of pregnancy in the pig, as a result of decreased collagen content alone rather than any changes in vessel elastin content (Guenther et al., 1988). Similarly, in the late pregnant ewe decreases in the collagen to elastin ratio were reported (Griendling et al., 1985) and this is associated with reductions in local uterine artery elastic modulus and *in vivo* impedance (Sprague et al., 2009, Zhu et al., 2009). Furthermore, the progressive decrease in uterine arterial collagen during porcine gestation was highly correlated with circulating estrogen concentration and vessel diameter at physiological pressures (Guenther et al., 1988). Estrogen has also been linked to increased DNA synthesis in uterine radial arteries (Tabata et al., 1988), increased mitosis in the uterine arterial wall (Forbes and Glassen, 1972, Jobe et al., 2010, Keyes et al., 1996, 1997), and the stimulation of vascular smooth muscle cell migration in endometrial vessels during remodeling (Babischkin et al., 2009). While progesterone may play a role in remodeling of the uterine vasculature during pregnancy, this has not been critically evaluated (Ford, 1982, Gibson et al., 2004, Magness and Rosenfeld, 1989b, 1992, Rupnow et al., 2001, 2002).

Role of Angiogenesis in Gravid Uterine Vascular Development

Uterine arterial angiogenesis, defined as the formation of new blood vessels from preexisting vasculature, is critical for the progressively increasing growth of uterine and placental tissues, which support fetal growth and development (Borowicz et al., 2007, Reynolds and Redmer, 1998, Reynolds et al., 2010). During the estrous cycle, estrogen is a known to increase endometrial angiogenesis, blood flow and uterine growth (Jobe et al., 2010, 2011, Magness and Rosenfeld, 1989a, 1989b, Magness et al., 1998, Reynolds and Redmer, 2001, Reynolds et al., 2002), and during pregnancy, these same estrogen-induced uterotropic effects are known to facilitate conceptus growth and development (Hildebrandt et al., 2001, Reynolds et al., 1998a, 1998b, 2002, 2005). The impact of estrogen on uterine blood vessel growth and development are thought to function in part through increased expression of several major angiogenic factors and their receptors (Hyder and Stancel, 2000, Losordo and Isner, 2001, Millaway et al., 1989, Reynolds et al., 2002, 2005, Zheng et al., 1997, 2000), which are known to increase within hours of estrogen administration (Johnson et al., 2006). In addition, estrogen-induced vasodilation has been linked to the nitric oxide (NO)/extracellular regulated kinase (ERK) pathway (Chen et al., 2004). Nitric oxide is known to be an important positive regulator of blood flow to uterus in both the nonpregnant and pregnant state (Gibson et al., 2004, Magness, 1998, Rosenfeld et al., 1996, Sladek et al., 1997). In addition, eNOS and soluble Guanylate Cyclase (GUCY1B3), the enzyme in vascular smooth muscle that NO stimulates to increase its second messenger cGMP, are both elevated in uterine arteries during pregnancy (Itoh et al., 1998, Joyce et al., 2002, Magness et al., 2001, Rosenfeld et al., 1996, Vagnoni et al., 1998, Zheng et al., 2000). The resulting elevations in NO during gestation are responsible for the substantial secretion of cGMP into the uterine venous drainage being elevated by 38 fold in late ovine gestation (Magness et al., 2001, Rosenfeld et al., 1996, Sladek et al., 1997).

Placental angiogenesis occurs in all species studied to date including the human and sheep. In the ovine model Reynolds and Redmer (Magness and Zheng, 1996, Reynolds and Redmer, 1995) reported that angiogenesis is seen throughout gestation, but the site of synthesis of the growth factors stimulating angiogenesis (maternal or placental) appears to differ across gestation. These researchers suggested that there is important temporal developmental regulation and that this is intimately linked to the rises in uteroplacental growth and uterine perfusion. For example during the early first trimester, angiogenic activity, evaluated as endothelial cell proliferation, occurs primarily in the maternal portion (caruncle), but not the placental portion (cotyledon), of the ovine placentome (functional unit of feto-maternal exchange).

Angiogenesis in the placentome remains relatively unchanged during the second trimester, the time when blood flow per gram of tissue falls and then plateaus (Rosenfeld, 1977, 1984, 1989, Rosenfeld et al., 1974). During the third trimester of ovine pregnancy, however angiogenic activity, measured as conditioned media stimulated bovine aortic endothelial cells proliferation, is found primarily in the fetal cotyledonary rather than the maternal caruncular compartment of the placentome (Millaway et al., 1989, Zheng et al., 1997). The location of angiogenic activity within the placentome (maternal vs. placental) probably accounts for the observed differences in vascular growth patterns in individual placentomal tissues during the course of gestation. Increased angiogenic activity is highly correlated with increased vascular development in the maternal placenta (caruncle) during the first trimester and in the fetal placenta (cotyledon) during the last trimester. Although not yet fully characterized, this *ex vivo* angiogenic activity, is positively associated with concentrations of fibroblast growth factors (FGFs) (Zheng et al., 1997) and vascular endothelial growth factors (VEGFs) (Borowicz et al., 2007, Reynolds and Redmer, 2001, Reynolds et al., 2002, 2010). Both families of growth factors are implicated in the processes regulating placental vascular growth, including direct and specific stimulation of endothelial cell proliferation and migration. Additionally, the production of these growth factors also has been directly implicated in other functions within the placenta. Specifically, increased expression of VEGFs in the fetal placenta causes profound increases in microvascular permeability and both VEGF and bFGF directly stimulate vasodilator (e.g. NO and PGI2) production (Zheng et al., 1999, 2000). Furthermore, these angiogenic effects are important in modulating placental blood flows, especially during the accelerating fetal growth period in the third trimester. Indeed the elevated expression of VEGFs and/or FGFs within the ovine placental tissues appear to correlate with the increase in placental perfusion occurring during this period.

Growth and development of all body tissues requires the formation of new blood vessels, and vascular development is in general proportional to the growth of the other cellular components within tissues. In contrast, the ovine placentomes show substantial increases in vascular density expressed relative to cross-sectional area of tissue mass (Stegeman, 1974). During the early stages of ovine placentation, caruncular vascular density increases markedly by day 24 and is associated with a four- to six-fold increase in uterine blood flow, as well as a nearly two-fold increase in angiogenic activity (Magness and Zheng, 1996, Reynolds and Redmer, 1995). From day 40-80, caruncular vascular density doubles but remains relatively unchanged from day 80 to term (145-150 days). Changes observed in caruncular vascular density up to approximately 80 days of gestation are also associated with the changes in caruncular blood flow (ml/min) and total placentomal weight which become maximum between 90-95 days. Unlike the caruncular vascular growth, the cotyledonary vascular density remains relatively constant until around 80-90 days of gestation, when it increases dramatically through elevated angiogenesis. This dramatic increase in cotyledonary vascular density correlates with marked increases in placental blood flow during the third trimester. In contrast to the pronounced increases in cotyledonary angiogenesis during the last third of gestation, the caruncular blood vessels exhibit a marked increase in diameter through production of vasodilators, thus facilitating a parallel increase in blood flow through the cotyledonary and caruncular vascular beds with an acceleration of fetal growth. (Greiss, 1982, Magness, 1998, Magness and Zheng, 1996, Rosenfeld, 1977, 1984, 1989, Rosenfeld et al., 1974).

Overview of the Systemic Hemodynamic Adaptations during Gestation

In concert with the progressive and substantial changes in the uterine arterial vascular bed, there are numerous alterations in the systemic vasculature observed during the course of gestation (Dowell and Kauer, 1997, Gaillard et al., 2011, Irgens et al., 2001, Lees et al., 1971, Magness, 1998, Rosenfeld et al., 1974, Strevens et al., 2001). These include minor decreases in systemic arterial blood pressure, but quite substantial reductions in systemic vascular resistance. The latter, vascular resistance, is associated with increases in cardiac output due to rises in heart rate and stroke volume.

As the body senses this under filled state of vasodilatation there is a profound shift in fluid and electrolyte balance to increase plasma and blood volume (Magness, 1998, Metcalfe and Parer, 1966). It is noteworthy that although these gestational changes in systemic vascular function do not necessarily follow the same temporal pattern as blood concentrations of the ovarian and placental derived estrogen and progesterone, it is thought that long term exposures to these steroids impact directly or indirectly some of these adaptations observed during pregnancy (Magness et al., 1983). This however remains to be fully determined.

Arterial and Venous Blood Pressure and Vascular Resistance

In pregnant women, numerous studies have reported that hypotension commences around 8 weeks of gestation, but does not reach significance until 12 weeks which coincides with the time when many women suffer from dizziness and posture-induced and orthostatic syncope (Figure 1) (Cunningham et al., 1989, Duvekot and Peeters, 1994, Magness, 1998, Metcalfe and Parer, 1966, Robson et al., 1989b, Stock and Metcalfe, 1994). There is an observed nadir seen in blood pressure that plateaus around 20 weeks of gestation and remains low until 32-33 weeks (term = 38-40 wk).

It is noteworthy that after this time, blood pressure gradually returns to nonpregnant levels by term (Atkins et al., 1981, Cunningham et al., 1989, Duvekot and Peeters, 1994, Longo, 1983, Magness, 1998, Metcalfe and Parer, 1966, Robson et al., 1989b, Stock and Metcalfe, 1994). There has been much speculation about the mechanisms by which this reversal in hypotension occurs because it rises earlier, overshoots and is exacerbated in women with early onset preeclampsia. We propose herein that the *de facto* reason for the late gestational reversal of the initial hypotensive effects of pregnancy is a strategy designed to maintain uterine perfusion pressures (uterine hydrostatic pressure) and thus oxygen and nutrient delivery to the gravid uterus when the metabolic demands of the growing fetus are rising exponentially. Although, the exact mechanisms that drive this perfusion pressure reversal are unclear, we propose that they are likely to utilize a series of maternal endocrine and nervous system homeostatic mechanisms orchestrated by fetal and placental factors reacting to metabolic and hormonal alterations it senses at the maternal-fetal interface.

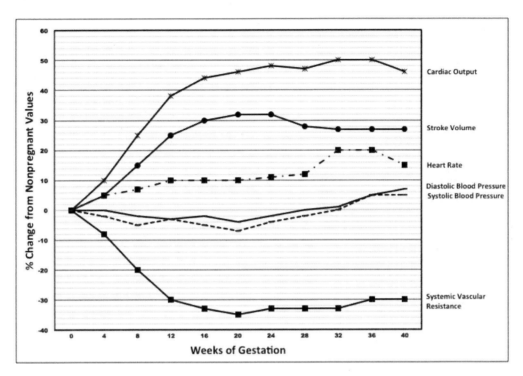

Figure 1. Blood pressure, cross-sectional echocardiographic, and Doppler results obtained longitudinally throughout gestation in women. Data were normalized as a percent change relative to the corresponding value measured during the nonpregnant state. (Adapted from Magness, 1998, Robson et al., 1989b).

Table 1. Systemic and Uterine Cardiovascular Measurements in Nonpregnant (n=28) and Late Pregnant (n=27; Days 115-135) Sheep

	Nonpregnant		Pregnant	% Δ
Mean arterial pressure (mmHg)	89 ± 1	**	81 ± 1	↓9
Heart rate (beats/min)	76 ± 2	**	109 ± 2	↑43
Cardiac output (mL/min)	5236 ± 84	**	7032 ± 161	↑34
Systemic vascular resistance (mmHg • min/L)	17.5 ± 0.4	**	11.9 ± 0.3	↓32
Uterine blood flow (mL/min)	22 ± 1.3	**	992 ± 103	↑4409
Uterine vascular resistance (mmHg • min/mL)	7.4 ± 0.3	**	0.12 ± 0.02	↓98

$**P < 0.01$ Nonpregnant vs. pregnant; Values are means ± SEM.

Regardless, because greater reductions in diastolic versus systolic pressures have been reported (Cunningham et al., 1989, Robson et al., 1989b),in gestation and it is generally thought that decreases in vascular tone in multiple reproductive and nonreproductive vascular beds must directly underlie these cardiovascular alterations in this dynamic vasodilated state. In ovine gestation, decreases in mean arterial pressure are also noted early in pregnancy, but unlike that observed in the woman, hypotension is maintained for the remainder of pregnancy (Clapp, 1978, 1985, Magness and Rosenfeld, 1986, 1988, 1989b, Magness et al., 1990, 1992, Metcalfe and Parer, 1966, Rosenfeld, 1989) (Table 1) unless the pregnant ewe is rendered hypertensive experimentally. Guinea pigs (Curran-Everett et al., 1991, Hariharan et al., 1987, Harrison and Moore, 1989, Hart et al., 1985, Morton et al., 1984, Myers and Tseng, 1985), rats (Conrad and Colpoys, 1986, Conrad and Russ, 1992, Danielson and Conrad, 1995, 1996, Gilson et al., 1992, Melone et al., 1991, Slangen et al., 1996, 1997), and mice (Burke et al., 2010, Butz and Davisson, 2001, Bytautiene et al., 2010, Falcao et al., 2009, Roghair et al., 2009, Van Vliet and Chafe, 2007) may also have moderate decreases in arterial blood pressure during gestation, however this is not a consistent finding. Following on from the suggestion that the placenta monitors and coordinates the need to maintain homeostatic levels of uterine perfusion pressure to maintain uteroplacental blood flows, it is also not known if these differential species responses relate to the different types of placentation epithelio-syndesmochorial (sheep and other ruminants) or hemochorial (humans and rodents), thus warranting a more comprehensive study of this question.

When considered on a relative percent basis only minor decreases in arterial blood pressure are seen during human gestation. By contrast, the relative increases in cardiac output which is the total systemic blood flow are much more substantial (Figure 1 and Table 1). These substantial elevations in cardiac output are associated with proportionally enormous falls in systemic vascular resistance in women (Bader et al., 1955, Capeless and Clapp, 1991, Clapp et al., 1988, Cunningham et al., 1989, Duvekot and Peeters, 1994, Duvekot et al., 1993, Easterling et al., 1990, 1991, Hansen and Ueland, 1974, Magness, 1998, Mashini et al., 1987, Metcalfe and Parer, 1966, Moutquin et al., 1985, Palmer and Walker, 1949, Robson et al., 1989b, Stock and Metcalfe, 1994, Vorys et al., 1961), sheep (Clapp, 1978, Evans et al., 1996, Greiss, 1982, Longo, 1983, Magness and Rosenfeld, 1986, 1988, Magness and Zheng, 1996, Magness et al., 1990, 1992, Metcalfe and Parer, 1966, Naden et al., 1984, Rosenfeld, 1977, 1989) (Table 1), goats (Hoversland et al., 1974), guinea pigs (Cha et al., 1992, Curran-Everett et al., 1991, Hariharan et al., 1987, Harrison and Moore, 1989, Hart et al., 1985, Morton et al., 1984, Myers and Tseng, 1985, Peeters et al., 1980), rats (Ahokas et al., 1983, Bruce, 1976, Gilson et al., 1992, Lundgren et al., 1979, Slangen et al., 1996), nonhuman primates (Lees et al., 1971, Phippard et al., 1986), and rabbits (Johnson et al., 1985). Therefore gestation should be classified as a physiologic state of profound systemic vasodilatation. Since systemic vascular resistance accounts for both moderate reductions in blood pressure, as well as the much more substantial increases in total systemic flows to all vascular beds (increased cardiac output), it is the best physiologic index of vasodilatation.

This relationship is described by the equation:

Systemic Vascular Resistance = Central Arterial Pressure - Central Venous Pressure/Cardiac Output

Because central venous pressure is generally very low (1-3 mmHg) this calculation has been estimated more easily as:

Systemic Vascular Resistance = Mean Arterial Pressure/Cardiac Output

In view of the 30-40 fold fall in systemic vascular resistance that occurs during gestation, there has been little attention paid to the question of why profound hypotension does not normally occur during pregnancy in such a vasodilated state. We therefore (Magness and Rosenfeld, 1988, Magness et al., 1998, Naden et al., 1984) reversed the above equation evaluating mean arterial blood pressure as the dependent variable, i.e.:

Mean Arterial Pressure = Systemic Vascular Resistance * Cardiac Output

This equation mathematically illustrates the relationship showing that as systemic vascular resistance falls, the profound gestational rises in cardiac output will be partly responsible for the maintenance of blood pressure. Another way to visualize this interesting equation is if the relative falls in mean arterial blood pressure and systemic vascular resistance were identical, this would yield a "line of identity" graphed on a linear plot. If this were the case, then this would mean cardiac output did not play a role in maintaining pressures which surely is not the case. Other mechanisms that are recruited and have been shown to be interrelated causing to rises in cardiac output during gestation are increases in blood volume (Baylis, 1980, Chesley, 1972, Chesley and Duffus, 1971, Del Valle, et al., 1993, Donovan et al., 1965, Hard and Anderson, 1982, Hart et al., 1985, Hoversland et al., 1974, Hytten, 1985, Hytten and Paintin, 1963, Longo, 1983, Phippard et al., 1986, Reynolds, 1953, Rovinsky and Jaffin, 1965, Taylor and Lind, 1979), activation of both the renin-angiotensin-aldosterone system (Blair-West et al., 1972, Conrad et al., 1989, Laragh, 1985, Mackanjee et al., 1991, Magness et al., 1994, Naden et al., 1984, 1985, Paller, 1984, Rosenfeld et al., 1995, Siddiqi et al., 1983) and the sympathetic division of the autonomic nervous system (Chesley et al., 1965, Conrad and Russ, 1992, Magness and Rosenfeld, 1988, Pan et al., 1990), which collectively all contribute to both maintaining blood pressure during this state of substantial vasodilation, and also to the positive chronotropism (increased heart rate) of pregnancy. In order to maintain blood pressure, both the renin-angiotensin and sympathetic division of the autonomic nervous systems also function peripherally by constricting vascular smooth muscle of various resistance vascular beds.

Redistribution of Cardiac Output during Pregnancy

During normal pregnancy, cardiac output is dramatically redistributed within the entire maternal cardiovascular system, such that by the end of the third trimester it predominantly, but not solely, reflects the growth and development of the uteroplacental and mammary gland vascular beds. It is noteworthy that all of these hemodynamic alterations are ephemeral such that during the postpartum period they return to the nonpregnant levels usually within 2-5 weeks after birth (Capeless and Clapp, 1991, Cunningham et al., 1989, Duvekot and Peeters, 1994, Metcalfe and Ueland, 1974, Robson et al., 1989b, Stock and Metcalfe, 1994, Walters et al., 1966). Moreover, during early gestation the major reductions in systemic vascular resistance that are noted due to rises in cardiac output occur with only minor falls in blood pressure (Figure 1) and are observed even prior to the time that the uterine vascular bed enlarges, full placentation occurs, or uterine vascular resistance has been reduced to its greatest extent. These early events are best exemplified by a study which demonstrated a 10-15% increase in cardiac output, a 5-7% rise in plasma volume, and a 30% decline in systemic vascular resistance during the luteal phase of the menstrual cycle immediately following conception. These changes may be universal since systemic vascular resistance falls in early-to mid-gestation mainly in association with increases in cardiac output in women (Atkins et al., 1981, Bader et al., 1955, Capeless and Clapp, 1989, Clapp et al., 1988, Cunningham et al., 1989, Duvekot and Peeters, 1994, Duvekot et al., 1993, Hunter and Robson, 1992, Katz et al., 1978, Lees et al., 1967, Mabie et al., 1994, Mashini et al., 1987, Metcalfe and Ueland, 1974, Robson et al., 1989a, 1989b, Rovinsky and Jaffin, 1965, Stock and Metcalfe, 1994, Ueland et al., 1969, Veille et al., 1985, Vered et al., 1991, Walters et al., 1966), sheep (Clapp, 1978, Evans et al., 1996, Greiss, 1982, Longo, 1983, Magness, 1998, Magness and Rosenfeld, 1986, 1988, Magness et al., 1990, 1992, Metcalfe and Parer, 1966, Naden et al., 1984, Rosenfeld, 1977, 1989), guinea pigs (Cha et al., 1992, Curran-Everett et al., 1991, Hariharan et al., 1987, Harrison and Moore, 1989, Hart et al., 1985, Magness, 1998, Morton et al., 1984, Myers and Tseng, 1985, Peeters et al., 1980, goats (Hoversland et al., 1974), rats (Ahokas et al., 1983, Bruce, 1976, Gilson et al., 1992, Lundgren et al., 1979, Magness, 1998, Slangen et al., 1996), and baboons (Phippard et al., 1986). We interpret these alterations in peripheral or systemic vasodilation and the rise in blood volume as "anticipating" the future major increases in uteroplacental perfusion, and setting the stage for the accelerated third trimester fetal growth and development. These results also dispel the much older misconceived theory that systemic alterations in pregnancy merely reflect the formation of a "uterine arteriovenous shunt" to account for the observed peripheral vasodilation and rise in cardiac output. An alternate model described in detail by Gilson and coworkers (Gilson et al., 1992) suggests that early in pregnancy there is the rise in blood flow to nonreproductive tissues, and in particular renal blood flow (Conrad, 1984, Danielson and Conrad, 1995, 1996, Metcalfe and Ueland, 1974, Stock and Metcalfe, 1994). Therefore because renal blood flow accounts for approximately 20% of cardiac output, these renal vascular changes more than likely contribute to the reduced systemic vascular resistance which sets into motion the cascade of events leading to and maintaining progressive increases in cardiac output during gestation.

Cardiac Adaptations during Pregnancy

Since reductions in the calculation of systemic vascular resistance primarily are reflective of the rises in cardiac output (Figure 1; Table 1), understanding the component factors associated with these increases in systemic blood flows is extremely important. During the course of normal gestation, cardiac output increases 25-60% in women (Atkins et al., 1981, Bader et al., 1955, Capeless and Clapp, 1989, Clapp et al., 1988, Cunningham et al., 1989, Duvekot et al., 1993, Duvekot and Peeters, 1994, Hunter and Robson, 1992, Katz et al., 1978, Lees et al., 1967, Mabie et al., 1994, Mashini et al., 1987, Metcalfe and Ueland, 1974, Robson et al., 1989a, 1989b, Rovinsky and Jaffin, 1965, Stock and Metcalfe, 1994, Ueland et al., 1969, Veille et al., 1985, Vered et al., 1991, Walters et al., 1966), sheep (Clapp, 1978, Evans et al., 1996, Greiss, 1982, Longo, 1983, Magness and Rosenfeld, 1986, 1988, Magness et al., 1990, 1992, Metcalfe and Parer, 1966, Naden et al., 1984, Rosenfeld, 1977, 1989) (Table 1), guinea pigs (Cha et al., 1992, Curran-Everett et al., 1991, Hariharan et al., 1987, Harrison and Moore, 1989, Hart et al., 1985, Morton et al., 1984, Myers and Tseng, 1985, Peeters et al., 1980), goats (Hoversland, et al., 1974), rats (Ahokas et al., 1983, Bruce, 1976, Gilson et al., 1992, Lundgren et al., 1979, Slangen et al., 1996), and baboons (Phippard et al., 1986). Specifically in pregnant women (Figure 1), cardiac output has been reported to be elevated from early- to mid-gestation (5-20 weeks, i.e. 1st to 2nd trimester) and then it reaches a plateau (Gilson et al., 1992, Lees et al., 1967, Robson et al., 1989a) to remain relatively unchanged (Lees et al., 1967, Robson et al., 1989a, Vered et al., 1991), or even to fall slightly during the third trimester (Gilson et al., 1992, Mashini et al., 1987, Robson et al., 1989a). Definitive information in women in the past has been somewhat elusive because of the difficulty in obtaining consistent measurements of cardiac output after the second trimester. This was a result of the increasing size of the gravid uterus, which often compresses or partially occludes both the vena cava and aorta thus causing transient reductions in cardiac output secondary to decreasing venous return (i.e. cardiac preload and thus end-diastolic volume). Several reports have shown that cardiac output may be 22% lower in the same women evaluated in the supine as compared to the lateral recumbent position (Hansen and Ueland, 1974, Metcalfe and Ueland, 1974, Ueland et al., 1969, Vorys et al., 1961). Very consistent and definitive data have been obtained from sheep and goats i.e. animal models which, being quadrupeds, does not have the uterus resting upon the "great vessels". Cardiac output increases progressively throughout the course of gestation in ovine (Greiss, 1982, Magness and Zheng, 1996, Magness 1998, Metcalfe and Parer, 1966, Rosenfeld, 1977, 1989), caprine (Hoversland et al., 1974), and rat (Gilson et al., 1992, Peeters et al., 1980), animal models (Rosenfeld, 1977, 1984, Rosenfeld et al., 1974). For example in the sheep, cardiac output increases from nonpregnant values of 74 ± 5 mL/ min • kg to 148 ± 2.4 mL/ min • kg by the end of gestation (145-150 days) (Rosenfeld, 1977, 1989). This has been confirmed in numerous studies using different techniques, e.g. dye-dilution, thermal dilution, radio-labeled microspheres, 2-D echocardiography and electromagnetic flow transducers (Clapp, 1978, Evans et al., 1996, Greiss, 1982, Longo, 1983, Magness and Rosenfeld, 1986, 1988, Magness et al., 1990, 1992, Metcalfe and Parer, 1966, Naden et al., 1984, Rosenfeld, 1977, 1989) (Table 1). In contrast to these species, in guinea pigs, the elevation in cardiac output during pregnancy reaches maximum values (~22% above nonpregnant levels) by 20 days, i.e. the end of the 1st trimester and remains elevated until term (65-68 d) (Cha et al., 1992, Curran-Everett et al., 1991, Hariharan et al., 1987, Harrison and Moore, 1989, Hart et al., 1985, Morton et al., 1984, Myers and Tseng, 1985, Peeters et al., 1980). It is not clear why the ovine, caprine, and rat animal models must have continuous increases in cardiac output and decreases in systemic vascular resistance throughout pregnancy whereas the human and guinea pig reach maximum values much earlier in pregnancy.

It is critical to better understand which of the components is responsible for the rises in cardiac output that are noted during normal gestation. We can evaluate this by the equation:

Cardiac Output = Heart Rate * Stroke Volume

In both women and sheep, relative percent increases in heart rate (tachycardia) of 20-30% have been reported (Figure 1; Table 1). The heart rate of women gradually rises from 4-8 weeks to 28-36 weeks of gestation, then reaches a plateau (Cunningham et al., 1989, Duvekot and Peeters, 1994, Hunter and Robson, 1992, Palmer and Walker, 1949, Robson et al., 1989b, Stock and Metcalfe, 1994, Ueland et al., 1969, Vered et al., 1991). This rise in heart rate is attributed to reciprocal alterations in both divisions of the autonomic nervous system (i.e. sympathetic increases and parasympathetic decreases) as well as to elevations in the placental steroids estrogen and/or progesterone; however, their specific roles in elevating heart rate and/or cardiac output during gestation or their interactions remain unclear. Because the elevation in heart rate is significant, but proportionately less than the relative rise in cardiac output in some but not all studies, this increase in cardiac output also reflect rises in stroke volume of 30-35% (Capeless and Clapp, 1989, Cunningham et al., 1989, Duvekot and Peeters, 1994, Robson et al., 1989b, Rosenfeld, 1989, Stock and Metcalfe, 1994, Ueland et al., 1969) by midpregnancy. There may be a slight decrease in cardiac output at term in women that reflects minor declines in stroke volume because heart rate is unchanged over this period of gestation (Robson et al., 1989b, Ueland et al., 1969). In detailed echocardiographic studies performed on women at different time points of normal gestation, left ventricular wall mass, left atrial dimension, and end-diastolic dimensions are all increased by the 12th week of pregnancy and continue to rise through 20-32 weeks, then remain elevated through term (Devereux and Reichek, 1977, Lees et al., 1967, Robson et al., 1989b). Furthermore, since rises in stroke volume are directly proportional to end-diastolic volume as well as ventricular diameter, these data imply that ventricular dilation may attenuate any dramatic change in the inotropic state of the myocardium during normal singleton pregnancies. Therefore because cardiac filling pressures do not greatly increase during gestation, this makes a strong case against Starling mechanisms fully controlling the changes in stroke volume. Starling mechanisms denotes a direct proportionality of venous return (cardiac preload) to increase the end diastolic filling volume by "stretching" the cardiac myocytes of the ventricles and thus a greater stroke volume is ejected with each cardiac cycle. However, in multifetal gestations the additional 20-30% rise in cardiac output and stroke volume occurs predominantly by increased inotropism as indexed by an increased fractional shortening of the ventricular diameter via true Starling mechanisms (Cunningham et al., 1989, Devereux and Reichek, 1977, Duvekot and Peeters, 1994, Giraud et al., 1993, Hart et al., 1986, Hunter and Robson, 1992, Katz et al., 1978, Longo, 1983, Metcalfe and Ueland, 1974, Robson et al., 1989a, 1989b, Rubler et al., 1977, Stock and Metcalfe, 1994, Veille et al., 1985). Similarly gestation associated left ventricular dimension enlargement has been reported in guinea pigs (Cha et al., 1992, Hart et al., 1985, Morton et al., 1984) and this is mimicked in guinea pigs and sheep treated chronically with estrogen (Giraud et al., 1993, Hart et al., 1985, Magness et al., 1993). Collectively these data suggest a decrease in "cardiac reserve" in normal pregnancy. In addition, the aorta has been observed to be larger and more compliant in pregnancy, which may in addition to the mild hypotension contribute to the decreased afterload on the heart during gestation (Easterling et al., 1991, Hart et al., 1986, Manalo-Estrella and Barker, 1967, Slangen et al., 1997).

Plasma and Blood Volume Changes during Gestation

Rises in cardiac output during pregnancy in concert with elevations in plasma and blood volume have been reported in women (Chesley, 1972, Chesley and Duffus, 1971, Cunningham et al., 1989, Del Valle et al., 1993, Donovan et al., 1965, Duvekot and Peeters, 1994, Hytten, 1985, Longo, 1983, Metcalfe and Ueland, 1974, Robson et al., 1989b, Rovinsky and Jaffin, 1965, Stock and Metcalfe, 1994, Taylor and Lind, 1979, Ueland, 1976), sheep (Longo, 1983), goats (Hoversland et al., 1974), cows (Reynolds, 1953), guinea pigs (Hart et al., 1985), pigs (Hard and Anderson, 1982), baboons (Phippard et al., 1986), and rats (Baylis, 1980, Del Valle et al., 1993, Ueland, 1976). These pregnancy associated blood volume and cardiac changes relate to rises in stroke volume. Specifically these important relationships derive from the direct proportionality between stroke volume, end-diastolic volume and blood volume which are thought to cause positive ionatrophy as described by Starlings law of the heart. However as described above, echocardio-graphic and cardiac dimension studies in humans (Robson et al., 1989b) and guinea pigs (Cha et al., 1992, Hart et al., 1985, Morton et al., 1984) have shown increases in ventricular chamber size and left ventricular end-diastolic dimensions of the heart in pregnancy (Capeless and Clapp, 1989, Giraud et al., 1993, Hart et al., 1986, Morton et al., 1984, Robson et al., 1989b, Vered et al., 1991). It would therefore be inappropriate, at least in singleton pregnancies, to "mix" these cardiac remodeling mechanisms responsible for increasing stroke volume with "true Starling mechanisms" which require elevations in cardiomyocyte stretch with elevation in pre-load. The degree of the rise in blood volume in gestation is dependent on both the species and on the presence of a singleton or multifetal pregnancy and varies from 10-50%. In ruminants such as the sheep (Longo, 1983), goat (Hoversland et al., 1974), and cow (Reynolds, 1953) blood volume expands by only 10-20% during gestation whereas in guinea pigs (Hart et al., 1985) and rats (Barron et al., 1984, Baylis, 1980, Del Valle et al., 1993) it increases 30-50%. During pregnancies carrying multiple fetuses (Chesley, 1972, Cunningham et al., 1989, Duvekot and Peeters, 1994, Longo, 1983) the increase in venous return are associated with greater rises in blood volume which are associated with a degree of positive inotropism. This concept also is suggestive that the cardiac dilation (remodeling) or hypertrophic mass theory (Cha et al., 1992, Devereux and Reichek, 1977, Duvekot et al., 1993, Hart et al., 1986, Robson et al., 1989b, Vered et al., 1991) of the ventricular wall has definite limits.

Reports showing temporal changes in plasma and blood volume during human gestation provide important clues for the role of blood volume expansion in healthy pregnancies. In women during normal gestation, elevations in plasma volume begin at about 6 weeks and plateau around 30-34 weeks of gestation (Chesley and Duffus, 1971, Hytten and Paintin, 1963). It was suggested that the fall in systemic vascular resistance in association with the rise seen in cardiac output precede the elevation in plasma volume by several weeks (Chesley and Duffus, 1971, Hytten and Paintin, 1963, Phippard et al., 1986, Robson et al., 1989b). However, Chapman et al. (Chapman et al., 1997) reported early declines in systemic vascular resistance, increases in cardiac output, with minor changes in plasma volume as early as the luteal phase of the menstrual cycle following conception. Thus, we interpret these observations as suggestive that early pregnancy initiates a cascade of events triggered by the presence of the conceptus and sensed by the maternal cardiovascular system as being "under filled" which requires rapid and prolonged homeostatic compensatory mechanisms. These include rises in renin, angiotensin II, and aldosterone in association with water and electrolyte retention. As the plasma volume expands there is an obligatory requirement for the balance of water and electrolyte retention to help drive these important processes. This supposition is borne out by empirical data, in that during the course of healthy human gestation, the renal system retains 500-900 mEq sodium, 300 mEq of potassium, and 30 g of calcium (Stock and Metcalfe, 1994). However, even in the face of substantial extra sodium retention, osmolality has been shown to drop because water retention is proportionately greater than sodium uptake as shown in women and rats, however this may not be the case in sheep. It is likely, but not totally substantiated, that sodium retention and expansion of plasma volume are driven by a rise in plasma renin activity which increases angiotensin II levels in order to elevate aldosterone secretion by the zona glomerulosa of the adrenal cortex (Magness et al., 1993, Phippard et al., 1986). It is likely that estrogen and progesterone play a primary role in controlling the renin angiotensin aldosterone system in pregnancy as these two hormones have been shown to increase plasma renin activity and aldosterone levels (Longo, 1983, Magness et al., 1993). An additional mechanism not well investigated may involve increased renal efferent sympathetic nerve activity (Aberdeen et al., 1992).

As the plasma volume expands there must be an obligatory increase in the whole blood elements and in particular the erythrocytes in order to maintain the oxygen carrying capacity of the blood. During gestation there is indeed a substantially enhanced erythropoiesis, which is associated with rises in erythropoietin levels (Beguin et al., 1991, Cotes et al., 1983, Del Valle et al., 1993, Gough et al., 1995, Manasc and Jepson, 1969, Widness et al., 1984, Zivny et al., 1982), that would serve to elevate total red blood cell volume sometime referred to as red blood cell mass. It is noteworthy however, that the rise in plasma volume in women (Chesley, 1972, Chesley and Duffus, 1971, Donovan et al., 1965, Hytten, 1985, Metcalfe and Ueland, 1974, Ueland, 1976) and possibly goats (Hoversland et al., 1974), but not sheep (Longo, 1983) or cows (Reynolds, 1953), generally exceeds the increase in red cell volume which explains the so called "physiologic anemia of pregnancy" or "hemodilutional anemia of pregnancy" as illustrated by the equation:

Blood Volume – Plasma Volume = Red Blood Cell Volume

The reason why there are disproportional rises in plasma volume versus red blood cell volume in some species (Chesley, 1972, Chesley and Duffus, 1971, Donovan et al., 1965, Hoversland et al., 1974, Hytten, 1985, Longo, 1983, Metcalfe and Ueland, 1974, Ueland, 1976) and not in others (Longo, 1983, Reynolds, 1953) remains unclear. What appears to be more certain is that because plasma and blood volume expansion during pregnancy are not proportionate in women (Chesley, 1972, Chesley and Duffus, 1971, Donovan et al., 1965, Hytten, 1985, Metcalfe and Ueland, 1974, Ueland, 1976) and possibly goats (Hoversland et al., 1974) this results in falls in hematocrit, which also decreases the viscosity of the blood. Because viscosity is inversely proportional to systemic vascular resistance, this is likely to be an additional mechanism contributing to the rise in systemic flows in pregnancy. In women and sheep, decreases in systemic vascular resistance, increases in cardiac output and expansion of blood volume are larger for multifetal than singleton pregnancies (Campbell and

Campbell, 1985, Cunningham et al., 1989, Duvekot and Peeters, 1994, Longo, 1983, Stock and Metcalfe, 1994). We interpret this to mean that the maternal hemodynamic adaptations seen in gestation are exacerbated by the greater mass of placental tissue and a much larger uteroplacental unit. In addition, the steroid hormones produced during gestation e.g. estrogen, progesterone, and/or aldosterone are produced in greater quantities because of the additional placental mass (Carnegie and Robertson, 1978, Ferrell and Ford, 1980, Ford, 1982, Magness et al., 1991, Pepe and Rothchild, 1974, Phippard et al., 1986, Robertson and King, 1979, Rosenfeld et al., 1980, Weems et al., 1994) and earlier blood volume expansion is in preparation for the tremendous metabolic demands of having multiple fetuses growing within the uterus. Regardless, in human twin pregnancies there are substantial increases in the incidence of pregnancy-induced hypertension/preeclampsia suggesting that these hemodynamic adaptations exceed the normal limits set by the maternal system as dictated by the presence of the fetoplacental units. Alternatively, the very large placenta is potentially subjected to ischemia/hypoxia during twin gestation which contributes to the higher incidence of pregnancy-induced hypertension/preeclampsia. Recently Bernstein et al. (Bernstein et al., 2001, 2003, 2009, Damron et al., 2004) has suggested that there are pathologic reductions in plasma and blood volume in the preeclamptic pregnancies which have a volume constrictive nature. It is not clear if it is the reduced adaptations of volume during preeclampsia that drive this or the loss of the attenuated vascular responses seen in response to infused vasoconstrictors which partly abrogate the normal expansion of blood volume.

Reductions in Vascular Reactivity to Vasoconstrictors during Gestation

A mechanism suggested to partly modulate the fall in blood pressure and systemic vascular resistance during gestation is the generalized attenuation of blood pressure responses to infused doses of various vasosoconstrictors such as angiotensin II (Berssenbrugge et al., 1980, Blair-West et al., 1972, Brown et al., 1990, Chesley et al., 1965, Conrad and Colpoys, 1986, Hariharan et al., 1987, Harrison and Moore, 1989, Ito et al., 1992, Lumbers, 1970, Magness and Gant, 1994, Magness and Zheng, 1996, Magness et al., 1992, 1994, Molnar and Hertelendy, 1992, Naden et al., 1984, 1985, Novak and Kaufman, 1991, Paller et al., 1984, Pan et al., 1990, Rosenfeld and Gant, 1981, Rosenfeld et al., 1995, Sanchez-Ramos et al., 1987, Siddiqi et al., 1983, Spitz et al., 1988) (Figure 2), adrenergic agonists (epinephrine, norepinephrine, phenylephrine) (Conrad and Colpoys, 1986, Harrison and Moore, 1990, Hines and Barron, 1992, Leduc et al., 1991, Magness and Rosenfeld, 1986, 1988, McLaughlin et al., 1989, Molnar and Hertelendy, 1992, Paller, 1984, Paller et al., 1989, Pan et al., 1990) arginine vasopressin (Hines and Barron, 1992) or even prostaglandin (PG) F_2a (Moore and Reeves, 1980). What is implicitly implied by the concept of "generalized attenuation" is that the mechanisms may be post-receptor i.e., affected by downstream stimulated signaling that is likely to be modulated by the environment of pregnancy. Candidate factors controlling this "generalized attenuation" in the systemic and uterine vasculature could be the substantial and prolonged exposure to the steroid hormones estrogen and progesterone (Byers et al., 2005, Evans et al., 1998, Jobe et al., 2013, Magness, 1991, Magness and Rosenfeld, 1989b, 1992, Magness et al., 1993, 1998, 2005, Rupnow et al.,

2001, 2002, Vagnoni et al., 1998) and growth factors (VEGF, bFGF, EGF) (Magness and Zheng, 1996, Reynolds and Redmer, 1995, Vonnahme et al., 2005, Zheng et al., 1997, 1999) or even alterations in the shear or frictional forces of the blood flowing through the vessels (Joyce et al., 2002, Li et al., 2003, 2004, 2005, Sprague et al., 2010) as cardiac output rises and blood volume expands. These reduced vasoconstrictor pressor responses also appear to be neither species nor agonist specific, however depending on the agonist used the mechanisms are likely to vary somewhat. Various mechanisms have been evaluated to collectively account for the pregnancy-mediated attenuated pressor responses, and many to this day remain controversial. For example: 1) Elevations in the arterial and/or possibly cardiac baroreceptor feedback control for elevations in blood pressure which appears to be the case for adrenergic agents (Conrad and Russ, 1992, Leduc et al., 1991, Lee et al., 1980, Lumbers, 1970, Magness and Rosenfeld, 1988, McLaughlin et al., 1989, Paller, 1984, Pan et al., 1990, Ramsay et al., 1992), but not angiotensin II (Lee et al., 1980, Naden et al., 1984, Ramsay et al., 1992); 2) Activation of the mechanisms responsible for the metabolic clearance rate of infused vasoactive agents in pregnancy (Ito et al., 1992, Magness et al., 1994, Naden et al., 1985, Rosenfeld et al., 1995), which was disproved during angiotensin II infusions (Magness et al., 1994, Rosenfeld et al., 1995) (Figure 2); 3) Down regulation of the number, affinity or functional signaling activity of vascular smooth muscle receptors (Annibale et al., 1989, Baker et al., 1992, Bird et al., 1997, Brown and Venuto, 1986, Cox et al., 1996, Mackanjee et al., 1991, Paller, 1984, Shaul et al., 1990), however this may not be supported in the case of angiotensin II (Aberdeen et al., 1992, Cotes et al., 1983, Hoversland et al., 1974); 4) Release of endothelium-derived vasodilators either under basal conditions or in response to vasoconstrictor agents (e.g., angiotensin II, norepinephrine, etc.) to locally antagonize pressor responses including vasodilator prostanoids (PGI_2, or PGE_2) (Brown et al., 1990, Conrad and Colpoys, 1986, Cox et al., 1996, Everett et al., 1978, Janowiak et al., 1998, Magness, 1991, Magness and Gant, 1994, Magness and Rosenfeld, 1993, Magness et al., 1985, 1990, 1992, 1994, 1996, Sanchez-Ramos et al., 1987, Spitz et al., 1988, Yoshimura et al., 1990, 1991), Nitric Oxide (Li et al., 1996, Magness, 1991, Magness et al., 1996, 1997, Molnar and Hertelendy, 1992, Nelson et al., 1995, Rosenfeld et al., 1996, Sladek et al., 1997, Tong and Eisenach, 1992, Weiner et al., 1989, 1991, 1994) or Endothelial Derived Hyperpolarizing Factor (EDHF) (Gerber et al., 1998, Gillham et al., 2003, 2007, Gokina et al., 2010, Morton and Davidge, 2013).

In this regard, we have demonstrated that the increases in vasodilator production by uterine or omental arteries treated with angiotensin II *ex vivo* (Magness and Rosenfeld, 1993, Magness et al., 1985, 1996) occurs in association with an 8-10-fold elevation of angiotensin II (AT1) receptors located on the uterine artery endothelium and a nearly two-fold increase on omental artery endothelium (Bird et al., 1997). Moreover, there is a large body of literature supporting the notion that increases in vascular vasodilators (e.g., PGI_2 and Nitric Oxide) in pregnancy (Magness, 1991, Magness and Rosenfeld, 1993, Magness et al., 1996, 1997, Sladek et al., 1997) are derived primarily from the endothelium and that these vasodilatory substances act to locally reduce vascular smooth muscle tone (Magness, 1991, Magness and Zheng, 1996, Molnar and Hertelendy, 1992, Nelson et al., 1995, Sladek et al., 1997, Weiner et al., 1989, 1991). These increases in PGI_2 and Nitric Oxide in uterine artery endothelium are regulated, in part, by increases in the expression (mRNA and/or protein) of phospholipase A2, prostaglandin-H synthase-1 (cyclooxygenase-1), prostacyclin synthase (PGIS), and endothelial cell Nitric Oxide synthase (eNOS or NOS III) (Janowiak et al., 1998,

Magness et al., 1992, Rupnow et al., 1992). However, it remains unclear which factors of pregnancy (e.g. estrogen, progesterone, growth factors, shear stress, etc.) increase expression of the enzymes responsible for elevating the production of these important endothelium-derived vasodilators (Cheung et al., 1995, Cockell and Poston, 1996, 1997, Kublickiene et al., 1997, Learmont and Poston, 1996, Magness, 1991, Magness and Gant, 1994, Magness and Rosenfeld, 1989a, 1989b, Magness and Zheng, 1996, Magness et al., 1993, Millaway et al., 1989, Reynolds and Redmer, 1995, Rubanyi et al., 1986, Zheng et al., 1997). Functional roles for Nitric Oxide in maintaining the blunted pressor responsiveness observed during pregnancy has been reported (Molnar and Hertelendy, 1992). The involvement of Nitric Oxide in regulating normal vascular alterations during gestation are further supported by studies in which inhibition of Nitric Oxide synthesis, using infusions of inhibitors such as L-NAME, during gestation causes hypertension and IUGR and that these effects can be reversed by co-infusion with L-arginine, the substrate for Nitric Oxide synthesis (Buhimschi et al., 1995, Edwards et al., 1996, Yallampalli and Garfield, 1993). A role for the second messenger of NO, cGMP, in modulating these effects derive from recent studies using the phosphodiesterase 5 inhibitor Sidenifil (Viagra) in order to maintain fetal growth in an ovine under nutrition IUGR model (Satterfield et al., 2010) or to reverse the preeclampsia like symptoms seen in Catechol-O-Methyl Transferase knock out mouse model (Stanley et al., 2012).

Change in Mean Arterial Pressure (mmHg)

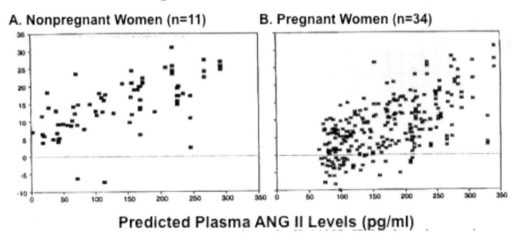

Figure 2. Relationship between the plasma angiotensin II *(ANG II)* levels and systemic pressor responses (change in mean arterial pressure) in (A) nonpregnant [n = 11] and (B) pregnant [n = 34] women, including all "stepwise" doses of infused angiotensin II. These concentration-dependent pressor response relationships were best defined by linear regression analysis *(P > 0.05* vs. quadratic regressions) and are different between groups. Nonpregnant: Delta-MAP = 0.06 [Concentration ANGII] + 6.97, *r* = 0.63 *(P< 0.001, n* = 84). Pregnant: Delta-MAP = 0.07 [Concentration ANGII − 4.11, *r* = 0.61 *(P < 0.001, n* =276). P < 0.001. y-intercept, Nonpregnant >. Pregnant. (Adapted from Magness et al., 1994).

Conclusion

There are numerous uterine and systemic peripheral and cardiac hemodynamic changes seen during gestation that are necessary for the development of the fetus culminating in the birth of a healthy offspring at term. In this chapter we have interpreted results from numerous studies reporting on these adaptations and integrated "classic" physiologic principles on how the maternal cardiovascular system responds to the presence of the conceptus (embryo and placenta). We, and others, have concluded that pregnancy is a state of profound progressive vasodilation that is not seen in any other physiologic state and this, in part, is regulated by the production to endothelial-derived vasodilators. It is clear that the uterine vascular changes are much greater than the systemic, peripheral and cardiac adaptations, most likely due to its close proximity to the feto-placental unit and the steroid hormones (estrogen and progesterone) and growth factors (VEGF, bFGF, EGF, etc.) that are produced. Moreover, in pathological pregnancies there is a loss or reversal of these local uterine and peripheral systemic vascular adaptations. For example, in preeclampsia there is hypertension, uterine endothelial and vascular remodeling defects, proteinuria related to renal dysfunctions (e.g. glomerular endotheliosis) and intrauterine growth restriction. As defined in this chapter, by better understanding the normal hemodynamic changes in gestation, we can better devise strategies to ameliorate the symptoms, or better yet, find causes that manifest in pathophysiologic pregnancies.

Acknowledgments

We thank Cindy Goss, Bryan C. Ampey, and Vladimir E. Vargas for their help in preparing and editing this book chapter and its' figures for publication.

Funding Sources:
NIH HL49210, HL87144, HD38843, HL117341 (RRM) and HD070096 (SPF)

Conflict(s) of Interest/Disclosure(s):
None.

References

Aberdeen, G.W., Cha, S.C., Mukaddam-Daher, S., Nuwayhid, B.S. & Quillen, E.W., Jr. (1992). Renal nerve effects on renal adaptation to changes in sodium intake during ovine pregnancy. *Am J Physiol*, 262, F823-9.

Adamson, S.L., Lu, Y., Whiteley, K.J., Holmyard, D., Hemberger, M., Pfarrer, C., et al. (2002). Interactions between trophoblast cells and the maternal and fetal circulation in the mouse placenta. *Dev Biol*, 250, 358-73.

Ahokas, R.A., Anderson, G.D. & Lipshitz, J. (1983). Cardiac output and uteroplacental blood flow in diet-restricted and diet-repleted pregnant rats. *Am J Obstet Gynecol*, 146, 6-13.

Annibale, D.J., Rosenfeld, C.R. & Kamm, K.E. (1989). Alterations in vascular smooth muscle contractility during ovine pregnancy. *Am J Physiol*, 256, H1282-8.

Annibale, D.J., Rosenfeld, C.R., Stull, J.T. & Kamm, K.E. (1990). Protein content and myosin light chain phosphorylation in uterine arteries during pregnancy. *Am J Physiol*, 259, C484-9.

Atkins, A.F., Watt, J.M., Milan, P., Davies, P. & Crawford, J.S. (1981). A longitudinal study of cardiovascular dynamic changes throughout pregnancy. *Eur J Obstet Gynecol Reprod Biol*, 12, 215-24.

Babischkin, J.S., Bonagura, T.W., Udoff, L.C., Vergara, C.O., Johnson, H.W., Atlas, R.O., et al. (2009). Estrogen stimulates the human endometrium to express a factor(s) that promotes vascular smooth muscle cell migration as an early step in microvessel remodeling. *Endocrine*, 35, 81-8.

Bader, R.A., Bader, M.E., Rose, D.F. & Braunwald, E. (1955). Hemodynamics at rest and during exercise in normal pregnancy as studies by cardiac catheterization. *J Clin Invest*, 34, 1524-36.

Baker, P.N., Broughton Pipkin, F. & Symonds, E.M. (1992). Changes in human platelet angiotensin ii binding sites associated with early pregnancy. *Am J Obstet Gynecol*, 166, 255-6.

Barron, W.M., Stamoutsos, B.A. & Lindheimer, M.D. (1984). Role of volume in the regulation of vasopressin secretion during pregnancy in the rat. *J Clin Invest*, 73, 923-32.

Baylis, C. (1980). The mechanism of the increase in glomerular filtration rate in the twelve-day pregnant rat. *J Physiol*, 305, 405-14.

Beguin, Y., Lipscei, G., Thoumsin, H. & Fillet, G. (1991). Blunted erythropoietin production and decreased erythropoiesis in early pregnancy. *Blood*, 78, 89-93.

Beldekas, J.C., Smith, B., Gerstenfeld, L.C., Sonenshein, G.E. & Franzblau, C. (1981). Effects of 17 beta-estradiol on the biosynthesis of collagen in cultured bovine aortic smooth muscle cells. *Biochemistry*, 20, 2162-7.

Bernstein, I.M., Damron, D., Schonberg, A.L. & Shapiro, R. (2009). The relationship of plasma volume, sympathetic tone, and proinflammatory cytokines in young healthy nonpregnant women. *Reprod Sci*, 16, 980-5.

Bernstein, I.M., Shapiro, R.E., Whitsel, A. & Schonberg, A.L. (2003). Relationship of plasma volume to sympathetic tone in nulliparous women. *Am J Obstet Gynecol*, 188, 938-42.

Bernstein, I.M., Ziegler, W. & Badger, G.J. (2001). Plasma volume expansion in early pregnancy. *Obstet Gynecol*, 97, 669-72.

Berssenbrugge, A.D., Goodfriend, T.L., Ball, D.L. & Rankin, J.H. (1980). The effect of pregnancy on the angiotensin II pressor response in the rabbit. *Am J Obstet Gynecol*, 136, 762-7.

Bird, I.M., Zheng, J., Cale, J.M. & Magness, R.R. (1997). Pregnancy induces an increase in angiotensin II type-1 receptor expression in uterine but not systemic artery endothelium. *Endocrinology*, 138, 490-8.

Blair-West, J.R., Coghlan, J.P., Denton, D.A., Scoggins, B.A. & Wintour, E.M. (1972). The pressor effect of angiotensin II in pregnant sheep. *Aust J Exp Biol Med Sci*, 50, 739-44.

Borowicz, P.P., Arnold, D.R., Johnson, M.L., Grazul-Bilska, A.T., Redmer, D.A. & Reynolds, L.P. (2007). Placental growth throughout the last two thirds of pregnancy in sheep: Vascular development and angiogenic factor expression. *Biol Reprod*, 76, 259-67.

Brown, C.E., Gant, N.F., Cox, K., Spitz, B., Rosenfeld, C.R. & Magness, R.R. (1990). Low-dose aspirin. II. Relationship of angiotensin II pressor responses, circulating eicosanoids, and pregnancy outcome. *Am J Obstet Gynecol*, 163, 1853-61.

Brown, G.P. & Venuto, R.C. (1986). Angiotensin II receptor alterations during pregnancy in rabbits. *Am J Physiol*, 251, E58-64.

Bruce, N.W. (1976). The distribution of blood flow to the reproductive organs of rats near term. *J Reprod Fertil*, 46, 359-62.

Buhimschi, I., Yallampalli, C., Chwalisz, K. & Garfield, R.E. (1995). Pre-eclampsia-like conditions produced by nitric oxide inhibition: Effects of l-arginine, d-arginine and steroid hormones. *Hum Reprod*, 10, 2723-30.

Burke, S.D., Barrette, V.F., Bianco, J., Thorne, J.G., Yamada, A.T., Pang, S.C., et al. (2010). Spiral arterial remodeling is not essential for normal blood pressure regulation in pregnant mice. *Hypertension*, 55, 729-37.

Butz, G.M. & Davisson, R.L. (2001). Long-term telemetric measurement of cardiovascular parameters in awake mice: A physiological genomics tool. *Physiol Genomics*, 5, 89-97.

Byers, M.J., Zangl, A., Phernetton, T.M., Lopez, G., Chen, D.B. & Magness, R.R. (2005). Endothelial vasodilator production by ovine uterine and systemic arteries: Ovarian steroid and pregnancy control of eralpha and erbeta levels. *J Physiol*, 565, 85-99.

Bytautiene, E., Lu, F., Tamayo, E.H., Hankins, G.D., Longo, M., Kublickiene, K., et al. (2010). Long-term maternal cardiovascular function in a mouse model of sflt-1-induced preeclampsia. *Am J Physiol Heart Circ Physiol*, 298, H189-93.

Campbell, D.M. & Campbell, A.J. (1985). Arterial blood pressure--the pattern of change in twin pregnancies. *Acta Genet Med Gemellol (Roma)*, 34, 217-23.

Capeless, E.L. & Clapp, J.F. (1989). Cardiovascular changes in early phase of pregnancy. *Am J Obstet Gynecol*, 161, 1449-53.

Capeless, E.L. & Clapp, J.F. (1991). When do cardiovascular parameters return to their preconception values? *Am J Obstet Gynecol*, 165, 883-6.

Carnegie, J.A. & Robertson, H.A. (1978). Conjugated and unconjugated estrogens in fetal and maternal fluids of the pregnant ewe: A possible role for estrone sulfate during early pregnancy. *Biol Reprod*, 19, 202-11.

Cha, S.C., Aberdeen, G.W., Nuwayhid, B.S. & Quillen, E.W., Jr. (1992). Influence of pregnancy on mean systemic filling pressure and the cardiac function curve in guinea pigs. *Can J Physiol Pharmacol*, 70, 669-74.

Chapman, A.B., Zamudio, S., Woodmansee, W., Merouani, A., Osorio, F., Johnson, A., et al. (1997). Systemic and renal hemodynamic changes in the luteal phase of the menstrual cycle mimic early pregnancy. *Am J Physiol*, 273, F777-82.

Chen, D.B., Bird, I.M., Zheng, J. & Magness, R.R. (2004). Membrane estrogen receptor-dependent extracellular signal-regulated kinase pathway mediates acute activation of endothelial nitric oxide synthase by estrogen in uterine artery endothelial cells. *Endocrinology*, 145, 113-25.

Chesley, L.C. (1972). Plasma and red cell volumes during pregnancy. *Am J Obstet Gynecol*, 112, 440-50.

Chesley, L.C. & Duffus, G.M. (1971). Posture and apparent plasma volume in late pregnancy. *J Obstet Gynaecol Br Commonw*, 78, 406-12.

Chesley, L.C., Talledo, E., Bohler, C.S. & Zuspan, F.P. (1965). Vascular reactivity to angiotensin II and norepinephrine in pregnant women. *Am J Obstet Gynecol*, 91, 837-42.

Cheung, C.Y., Singh, M., Ebaugh, M.J. & Brace, R.A. (1995). Vascular endothelial growth factor gene expression in ovine placenta and fetal membranes. *Am J Obstet Gynecol*, 173, 753-9.

Cipolla, M. & Osol, G. (1994). Hypertrophic and hyperplastic effects of pregnancy on the rat uterine arterial wall. *Am J Obstet Gynecol*, 171, 805-11.

Clapp, J.F. (1978). Cardiac output and uterine blood flow in the pregnant ewe. *Am J Obstet Gynecol*, 130, 419-23.

Clapp, J.F., 3rd. (1985). Maternal heart rate in pregnancy. *Am J Obstet Gynecol*, 152, 659-60.

Clapp, J.F., 3rd, Seaward, B.L., Sleamaker, R.H. & Hiser, J. (1988). Maternal physiologic adaptations to early human pregnancy. *Am J Obstet Gynecol*, 159, 1456-60.

Cockell, A.P. & Poston, L. (1996). Isolated mesenteric arteries from pregnant rats show enhanced flow-mediated relaxation but normal myogenic tone. *J Physiol*, 495, 545-51.

Cockell, A.P. & Poston, L. (1997). Flow-mediated vasodilatation is enhanced in normal pregnancy but reduced in preeclampsia. *Hypertension*, 30, 247-51.

Conrad, K.P. (1984). Renal hemodynamics during pregnancy in chronically catheterized, conscious rats. *Kidney Int*, 26, 24-9.

Conrad, K.P. & Colpoys, M.C. (1986). Evidence against the hypothesis that prostaglandins are the vasodepressor agents of pregnancy. Serial studies in chronically instrumented, conscious rats. *J Clin Invest*, 77, 236-45.

Conrad, K.P., Morganelli, P.M., Brinck-Johnsen, T. & Colpoys, M.C. (1989). The renin-angiotensin system during pregnancy in chronically instrumented, conscious rats. *Am J Obstet Gynecol*, 161, 1065-72.

Conrad, K.P. & Russ, R.D. (1992). Augmentation of baroreflex-mediated bradycardia in conscious pregnant rats. *Am J Physiol*, 262, R472-7.

Cotes, P.M., Canning, C.E. & Lind, T. (1983). Changes in serum immunoreactive erythropoietin during the menstrual cycle and normal pregnancy. *Br J Obstet Gynaecol*, 90, 304-11.

Cox, B.E., Rosenfeld, C.R., Kalinyak, J.E., Magness, R.R. & Shaul, P.W. (1996). Tissue specific expression of vascular smooth muscle angiotensin II receptor subtypes during ovine pregnancy. *Am J Physiol*, 271, H212-21.

Cox, R.H. & Fischer, G.M. (1978). Effects of sex hormones on the passive mechanical properties of rat carotid artery. *Blood Vessels*, 15, 266-76.

Cross, J.C., Hemberger, M., Lu, Y., Nozaki, T., Whiteley, K., Masutani, M., et al. (2002). Trophoblast functions, angiogenesis and remodeling of the maternal vasculature in the placenta. *Mol Cell Endocrinol*, 187, 207-12.

Cunningham, F.G., MacDonald, P.C. & Gant, N.F. (1989). Maternal adaptations to pregnancy. In: *Williams obstetrics*. Chapter 7, 18th edn. Norwalk, CT: Appleton and Lange.

Curran-Everett, D., Morris, K.G., Jr. & Moore, L.G. (1991). Regional circulatory contributions to increased systemic vascular conductance of pregnancy. *Am J Physiol*, 261, H1842-7.

Damron, D.P., Bouchard, B.A., Shapiro, R.E., Schonberg, A.L. & Bernstein, I.M. (2004). Platelet activation, sympathetic tone, and plasma volume in nulligravid women of reproductive age. *Obstet Gynecol*, 103, 931-6.

Danielson, L.A. & Conrad, K.P. (1995). Acute blockade of nitric oxide synthase inhibits renal vasodilation and hyperfiltration during pregnancy in chronically instrumented conscious rats. *J Clin Invest*, 96, 482-90.

Danielson, L.A. & Conrad, K.P. (1996). Prostaglandins maintain renal vasodilation and hyperfiltration during chronic nitric oxide synthase blockade in conscious pregnant rats. *Circ Res*, 79, 1161-6.

Del Valle, G.O., Mosher, M.D. & Conrad, K.P. (1993). Serum immunoreactive erythropoietin and red blood cell mass during pregnancy in conscious rats. *Am J Physiol*, 265, R399-403.

Devereux, R.B. & Reichek, N. (1977). Echocardiographic determination of left ventricular mass in man. Anatomic validation of the method. *Circulation*, 55, 613-8.

Donovan, J.C., Lund, C.J. & Hicks, E.L. (1965). Effect of lactation on blood volume in the human female. *Am J Obstet Gynecol*, 93, 588-9.

Dowell, R.T. & Kauer, C.D. (1997). Maternal hemodynamics and uteroplacental blood flow throughout gestation in conscious rats. *Methods Find Exp Clin Pharmacol*, 19, 613-25.

Duvekot, J.J., Cheriex, E.C., Pieters, F.A., Menheere, P.P. & Peeters, L.H. (1993). Early pregnancy changes in hemodynamics and volume homeostasis are consecutive adjustments triggered by a primary fall in systemic vascular tone. *Am J Obstet Gynecol*, 169, 1382-92.

Duvekot, J.J. & Peeters, L.L. (1994). Maternal cardiovascular hemodynamic adaptation to pregnancy. *Obstet Gynecol Surv*, 49 (12 Suppl), S1-14.

Easterling, T.R., Benedetti, T.J., Schmucker, B.C., Carlson, K. & Millard, S.P. (1991). Maternal hemodynamics and aortic diameter in normal and hypertensive pregnancies. *Obstet Gynecol*, 78, 1073-7.

Easterling, T.R., Benedetti, T.J., Schmucker, B.C. & Millard, S.P. (1990). Maternal hemodynamics in normal and preeclamptic pregnancies: A longitudinal study. *Obstet Gynecol*, 76, 1061-9.

Edwards, D.L., Arora, C.P., Bui, D.T. & Castro, L.C. (1996). Long-term nitric oxide blockade in the pregnant rat: Effects on blood pressure and plasma levels of endothelin-1. *Am J Obstet Gynecol*, 175, 484-8.

Evans, W., Capelle, S.C. & Edelstone, D.I. (1996). Lack of a critical cardiac output and critical systemic oxygen delivery during low cardiac output in the third trimester in the pregnant sheep. *Am J Obstet Gynecol*, 175, 222-8.

Evans, W., Phernetton, T.M. & Magness, R.R. (1998). 17beta-estradiol effect on critical cardiac output with reduction of cardiac output in oophorectomized sheep. *Am J Physiol*, 275, H57-64.

Everett, R.B., Worley, R.J., MacDonald, P.C. & Gant, N.F. (1978). Effect of prostaglandin synthetase inhibitors on pressor response to angiotensin ii in human pregnancy. *J Clin Endocrinol Metab*, 46, 1007-10.

Falcao, S., Stoyanova, E., Cloutier, G., Maurice, R.L., Gutkowska, J. & Lavoie, J.L. (2009). Mice overexpressing both human angiotensinogen and human renin as a model of superimposed preeclampsia on chronic hypertension. *Hypertension*, 54, 1401-7.

Ferrell, C.L. & Ford, S.P. (1980). Blood flow steroid secretion and nutrient uptake of the gravid bovine uterus. *J Anim Sci*, 50, 1113-21.

Fischer, G.M. (1972). In vivo effects of estradiol on collagen and elastin dynamics in rat aorta. *Endocrinology*, 91, 1227-32.

Fischer, G.M. & Swain, M.L. (1977). Effect of sex hormones on blood pressure and vascular connective tissue in castrated and noncastrated male rats. *Am J Physiol*, 232, H617-21.

Forbes, T.R. & Glassen, G. (1972). Steroid compounds and the dilatation of ovarian and uterine veins in the mouse. *Am J Obstet Gynecol*, 113, 678-80.

Ford, S.P. (1982). Control of uterine and ovarian blood flow throughout the estrous cycle and pregnancy of ewes, sows and cows. *J Anim Sci*, 55 Suppl 2, 32-42.

Gaillard, R., Bakker, R., Willemsen, S.P., Hofman, A., Steegers, E.A. & Jaddoe, V.W. (2011). Blood pressure tracking during pregnancy and the risk of gestational hypertensive disorders: the Generation R Study. *Eur Heart J*, 32, 3088-97.

Gerber, R.T., Anwar, M.A. & Poston, L. (1998). Enhanced acetylcholine induced relaxation in small mesenteric arteries from pregnant rats: An important role for endothelium-derived hyperpolarizing factor (EDHF). *Br J Pharmacol*, 125, 455-60.

Gibson, T.C., Phernetton, T.M., Wiltbank, M.C. & Magness, R.R. (2004). Development and use of an ovarian synchronization model to study the effects of endogenous estrogen and nitric oxide on uterine blood flow during ovarian cycles in sheep. *Biol Reprod*, 70, 1886-94.

Gillham, J.C., Kenny, L.C. & Baker, P.N. (2003). An overview of endothelium-derived hyperpolarising factor (EDHF) in normal and compromised pregnancies. *Eur J Obstet Gynecol Reprod Biol*, 109, 2-7.

Gillham, J.C., Myers, J.E., Baker, P.N. & Taggart, M.J. (2007). Regulation of endothelial-dependent relaxation in human systemic arteries by SKCa and IKCa channels. *Reprod Sci*, 14, 43-50.

Gilson, G.J., Mosher, M.D. & Conrad, K.P. (1992). Systemic hemodynamics and oxygen transport during pregnancy in chronically instrumented, conscious rats. *Am J Physiol*, 263, H1911-8.

Giraud, G.D., Morton, M.J., Davis, L.E., Paul, M.S. & Thornburg, K.L. (1993). Estrogen-induced left ventricular chamber enlargement in ewes. *Am J Physiol*, 264, E490-6.

Gokina, N.I., Kuzina, O.Y. & Vance, A.M. (2010). Augmented EDHF signaling in rat uteroplacental vasculature during late pregnancy. *Am J Physiol Heart Circ Physiol*, 299, H1642-52.

Gough, S.R., Mosher, M.D. & Conrad, K.P. (1995). Metabolism of erythropoietin in conscious pregnant rats. *Am J Physiol*, 268, R1117-20.

Greiss, F.C. (1982). Uterine blood flow in pregnancy: An overview. In: *Uterine and placental blood flow*. Moawad, A.H. & Lindheimer, M.D. (Eds). New York: Masson, p. 19-26.

Griendling, K.K., Fuller, E.O. & Cox, R.H. (1985). Pregnancy-induced changes in sheep uterine and carotid arteries. *Am J Physiol*, 248, H658-65.

Guenther, A.E., Conley, A.J., Van Orden, D.E., Farley, D.B. & Ford, S.P. (1988). Structural and mechanical changes of uterine arteries during pregnancy in the pig. *J Anim Sci*, 66, 3144-52.

Hansen, J.M. & Ueland, K. (1974). Maternal cardiovascular dynamics during pregnancy and parturition. *Clin Anesth*, 10, 21-36.

Hard, D.L. & Anderson, L.L. (1982). Interaction of maternal blood volume and uterine blood flow with porcine fetal development. *Biol Reprod*, 27, 79-90.

Hariharan, S., Tseng, H. & Myers, S.A. (1987). A comparison of the hemodynamic responses of systematic and uteroplacental vasculature to angiotensin in conscious guinea pigs. *Am J Perinatol*, 4, 235-9.

Harrison, G.L. & Moore, L.G. (1989). Blunted vasoreactivity in pregnant guinea pigs is not restored by meclofenamate. *Am J Obstet Gynecol*, 160, 258-64.

Harrison, G.L. & Moore, L.G. (1990). Systemic vascular reactivity during high-altitude pregnancy. *J Appl Physiol*, 69, 201-6.

Hart, M.V., Hosenpud, J.D., Hohimer, A.R. & Morton, M.J. (1985). Hemodynamics during pregnancy and sex steroid administration in guinea pigs. *Am J Physiol*, 249, R179-85.

Hart, M.V., Morton, M.J., Hosenpud, J.D. & Metcalfe, J. (1986). Aortic function during normal human pregnancy. *Am J Obstet Gynecol*, 154, 887-91.

Hildebrandt, V.A., Babischkin, J.S., Koos, R.D., Pepe, G.J. & Albrecht, E.D. (2001). Developmental regulation of vascular endothelial growth/permeability factor messenger ribonucleic acid levels in and vascularization of the villous placenta during baboon pregnancy. *Endocrinology*, 142, 2050-7.

Hines, T. & Barron, W.M. (1992). Effect of sinoaortic denervation on pressor responses in pregnant rats. *Am J Physiol*, 262, R1100-5.

Hoversland, A.S., Parer, J.T. & Metcalfe, J. (1974). Hemodynamic adjustments in the pygmy goat during pregnancy and early postpartum. *Biol Reprod*, 10, 578-88.

Hunter, S. & Robson, S.C. (1992). Adaptation of the maternal heart in pregnancy. *Br Heart J*, 68, 540-3.

Hyder, S.M. & Stancel, G.M. (2000). Regulation of vegf in the reproductive tract by sex-steroid hormones. *Histol Histopathol*, 15, 325-34.

Hytten, F. (1985). Blood volume changes in normal pregnancy. *Clin Haematol*, 14, 601-12.

Hytten, F.E. & Leitch, I. (1971). *The physiology of human pregnancy*. Oxford, Blackwell Scientific Publications.

Hytten, F.E. & Paintin, D.B. (1963). Increase in plasma volume during normal pregnancy. *J Obstet Gynaecol Br Emp*, 70, 402-7.

Irgens, H.U., Reisaeter, L., Irgens, L.M. & Lie, R.T. (2001). Long term mortality of mothers and fathers after pre-eclampsia: Population based cohort study. *BMJ*, 323, 1213-7.

Ito, M., Nakamura, T., Yoshimura, T., Koyama, H. & Okamura, H. (1992). The blood pressure response to infusions of angiotensin ii during normal pregnancy: Relation to plasma angiotensin ii concentration, serum progesterone level, and mean platelet volume. *Am J Obstet Gynecol*, 166, 1249-53.

Itoh, H., Bird, I.M., Nakao, K. & Magness, R.R. (1998). Pregnancy increases soluble and particulate guanylate cyclases and decreases the clearance receptor of natriuretic peptides in ovine uterine, but not systemic, arteries. *Endocrinology*, 139, 3329-41.

Janowiak, M.A., Magness, R.R., Habermehl, D.A. & Bird, I.M. (1998). Pregnancy increases ovine uterine artery endothelial cyclooxygenase-1 expression. *Endocrinology*, 139, 765-71.

Jobe, S.O., Fling, S.N., Ramadoss, J. & Magness, R.R. (2011). A novel role for an endothelial adrenergic receptor system in mediating catecholestradiol-induced proliferation of uterine artery endothelial cells. *Hypertension*, 58, 874-81.

Jobe, S.O., Ramadoss, J., Koch, J.M., Jiang, Y., Zheng, J. & Magness, R.R. (2010). Estradiol-17beta and its cytochrome p450- and catechol-o-methyltransferase-derived metabolites stimulate proliferation in uterine artery endothelial cells: Role of estrogen receptor-alpha versus estrogen receptor-beta. *Hypertension*, 55, 1005-11.

Jobe, S.O., Ramadoss, J., Wargin, A.J. & Magness, R.R. (2013). Estradiol-17beta and its cytochrome p450- and catechol-o-methyltransferase-derived metabolites selectively stimulate production of prostacyclin in uterine artery endothelial cells: Role of estrogen receptor-alpha versus estrogen receptor-beta. *Hypertension*, 61, 509-18.

Johnson, M.L., Grazul-Bilska, A.T., Redmer, D.A. & Reynolds, L.P. (2006). Effects of estradiol-17beta on expression of mrna for seven angiogenic factors and their receptors in the endometrium of ovariectomized (ovx) ewes. *Endocrine*, 30, 333-42.

Johnson, R.L., Gilbert, M., Meschia, G. & Battaglia, F.C. (1985). Cardiac output distribution and uteroplacental blood flow in the pregnant rabbit: A comparative study. *Am J Obstet Gynecol*, 151, 682-6.

Joyce, J.M., Phernetton, T.M., Shaw, C.E., Modrick, M.L. & Magness, R.R. (2002). Endothelial vasodilator production by uterine and systemic arteries. IX. eNOS gradients in cycling and pregnant ewes. *Am J Physiol Heart Circ Physiol*, 282, H342-8.

Katz, R., Karliner, J.S. & Resnik, R. (1978). Effects of a natural volume overload state (pregnancy) on left ventricular performance in normal human subjects. *Circulation*, 58, 434-41.

Keyes, L.E., Majack, R., Dempsey, E.C. & Moore, L.G. (1997). Pregnancy stimulation of DNA synthesis and uterine blood flow in the guinea pig. *Pediatr Res*, 41, 708-15.

Keyes, L.E., Moore, L.G., Walchak, S.J. & Dempsey, E.C. (1996). Pregnancy-stimulated growth of vascular smooth muscle cells: Importance of protein kinase c-dependent synergy between estrogen and platelet-derived growth factor. *J Cell Physiol*, 166, 22-32.

Kublickiene, K.R., Cockell, A.P., Nisell, H. & Poston, L. (1997). Role of nitric oxide in the regulation of vascular tone in pressurized and perfused resistance myometrial arteries from term pregnant women. *Am J Obstet Gynecol*, 177, 1263-9.

Kulandavelu, S., Whiteley, K.J., Qu, D., Mu, J., Bainbridge, S.A. & Adamson, S.L. (2012). Endothelial nitric oxide synthase deficiency reduces uterine blood flow, spiral artery elongation, and placental oxygenation in pregnant mice. *Hypertension*, 60, 231-8.

Laragh, J.H. (1985). Atrial natriuretic hormone, the renin-aldosterone axis, and blood pressure-electrolyte homeostasis. *N Engl J Med*, 313, 1330-40.

Learmont, J.G. & Poston, L. (1996). Nitric oxide is involved in flow-induced dilation of isolated human small fetoplacental arteries. *Am J Obstet Gynecol*, 174, 583-8.

Leduc, L., Wasserstrum, N., Spillman, T. & Cotton, D.B. (1991). Baroreflex function in normal pregnancy. *Am J Obstet Gynecol*, 165, 886-90.

Lee, W.B., Ismay, M.J. & Lumbers, E.R. (1980). Mechanisms by which angiotensin ii affects the heart rate of the conscious sheep. *Circ Res*, 47, 286-92.

Lees, M.H., Hill, J.D., Ochsner, A.J., 3rd, Thomas, C.L. & Novy, M.J. (1971). Maternal placental and myometrial blood flow of the rhesus monkey during uterine contractions. *Am J Obstet Gynecol*, 110, 68-81.

Lees, M.M., Taylor, S.H., Scott, D.B. & Kerr, M.G. (1967). A study of cardiac output at rest throughout pregnancy. *J Obstet Gynaecol Br Commonw*, 74, 319-28.

Li, P., Tong, C. & Eisenach, J.C. (1996). Pregnancy and ephedrine increase the release of nitric oxide in ovine uterine arteries. *Anesth Analg*, 82, 288-93.

Li, Y., Zheng, J., Bird, I.M. & Magness, R.R. (2003). Effects of pulsatile shear stress on nitric oxide production and endothelial cell nitric oxide synthase expression by ovine fetoplacental artery endothelial cells. *Biol Reprod*, 69, 1053-9.

Li, Y., Zheng, J., Bird, I.M. & Magness, R.R. (2005). Effects of pulsatile shear stress on signaling mechanisms controlling nitric oxide production, endothelial nitric oxide synthase phosphorylation, and expression in ovine fetoplacental artery endothelial cells. *Endothelium*, 12, 21-39.

Li, Y., Zheng, J., Bird, I.M. & Magness, R.R. (2004). Mechanisms of shear stress-induced endothelial nitric-oxide synthase phosphorylation and expression in ovine fetoplacental artery endothelial cells. *Biol Reprod*, 70, 785-96.

Longo, L.D. (1983). Maternal blood volume and cardiac output during pregnancy: A hypothesis of endocrinologic control. *Am J Physiol*, 245, R720-9.

Losordo, D.W. & Isner, J.M. (2001). Vascular endothelial growth factor-induced angiogenesis: Crouching tiger or hidden dragon? *J Am Coll Cardiol*, 37, 2131-5.

Lumbers, E.R. (1970). Peripheral vascular reactivity to angiotensin and noradrenaline in pregnant and non-pregnant women. *Aust J Exp Biol Med Sci*, 48, 493-500.

Lundgren, Y., Karlsson, K. & Ljungblad, U. (1979). Circulatory changes during pregnancy in spontaneously and renal hypertensive rats. *Clin Sci (Lond)*, 57 Suppl 5, 337s-339s.

Mabie, W.C., DiSessa, T.G., Crocker, L.G., Sibai, B.M. & Arheart, K.L. (1994). A longitudinal study of cardiac output in normal human pregnancy. *Am J Obstet Gynecol*, 170, 849-56.

Mackanjee, H.R., Shaul, P.W., Magness, R.R. & Rosenfeld, C.R. (1991). Angiotensin ii vascular smooth-muscle receptors are not down-regulated in near-term pregnant sheep. *Am J Obstet Gynecol*, 165, 1641-8.

Magness, R.R. (1991). Endothelium-derived vasoactive substances and uterine blood vessels. *Semin Perinatol*, 15, 68-78.

Magness, R.R. (1998). Maternal cardiovascular and other physiologic responses to the endocrinology of pregnancy. In: *The endocrinology of pregnancy*. Bazer, F.W. (Ed). Chapter 18. Totowa, NJ: Humana Press, p. 507-39.

Magness, R.R., Cox, K., Rosenfeld, C.R. & Gant, N.F. (1994). Angiotensin II metabolic clearance rate and pressor responses in nonpregnant and pregnant women. *Am J Obstet Gynecol*, 171, 668-79.

Magness, R.R. & Ford, S.P. (1982). Steroid concentrations in uterine lymph and uterine arterial plasma of gilts during the estrous cycle and early pregnancy. *Biol Reprod*, 27, 871-7.

Magness, R.R. & Ford, S.P. (1983). Estrone, estradiol-17 beta and progesterone concentrations in uterine lymph and systemic blood throughout the porcine estrous cycle. *J Anim Sci*, 57, 449-55.

Magness, R.R. & Gant, N.F. (1994). Control of vascular reactivity in pregnancy: The basis for therapeutic approaches to prevent pregnancy-induced hypertension. *Semin Perinatol*, 8, 45-69.

Magness, R.R., Mitchell, M.D. & Rosenfeld, C.R. (1990). Uteroplacental production of eicosanoids in ovine pregnancy. *Prostaglandins*, 39, 75-88.

Magness, R.R., Osei-Boaten, K., Mitchell, M.D. & Rosenfeld, C.R. (1985). In vitro prostacyclin production by ovine uterine and systemic arteries. Effects of angiotensin II. *J Clin Invest*, 76, 2206-12.

Magness, R.R., Parker, C.R., Jr. & Rosenfeld, C.R. (1993). Systemic and uterine responses to chronic infusion of estradiol-17 beta. *Am J Physiol*, 265, E690-8.

Magness, R.R., Phernetton, T.M., Gibson, T.C. & Chen, D.B. (2005). Uterine blood flow responses to ici 182 780 in ovariectomized oestradiol-17beta-treated, intact follicular and pregnant sheep. *J Physiol*, 565, 71-83.

Magness, R.R., Phernetton, T.M. & Zheng, J. (1998). Systemic and uterine blood flow distribution during prolonged infusion of 17beta-estradiol. *Am J Physiol*, 275, H731-43.

Magness, R.R. & Rosenfeld, C.R. (1986). Systemic and uterine responses to alpha-adrenergic stimulation in pregnant and nonpregnant ewes. *Am J Obstet Gynecol*, 155, 897-904.

Magness, R.R. & Rosenfeld, C.R. (1988). Mechanisms for attenuated pressor responses to alpha-agonists in ovine pregnancy. *Am J Obstet Gynecol*, 159, 252-61.

Magness, R.R. & Rosenfeld, C.R. (1989a). Local and systemic estradiol-17 beta: Effects on uterine and systemic vasodilation. *Am J Physiol*, 256, E536-42.

Magness, R.R. & Rosenfeld, C.R. (1989b). The role of steroid hormones in the control of uterine blood flow. In: *Reproductive and perinatal medicine*. Rosenfeld, C.R. (Ed). Ithaca, NY: Perinatology Press.

Magness, R.R. & Rosenfeld, C.R. (1992). Steroid control of blood vessel function. In: **Editors: N.S. Alexander and C. D'Arcangues - National Institutes of Health Meeting.** In: *Endometrial function and dysfunctional uterine bleeding*. Washington DC: American Assoc Adv Science Press;107-120.

Magness, R.R. & Rosenfeld, C.R. (1993). Calcium modulation of endothelium-derived prostacyclin production in ovine pregnancy. *Endocrinology*, 132, 2445-52.

Magness, R.R., Rosenfeld, C.R. & Carr, B.R. (1991). Protein kinase c in uterine and systemic arteries during ovarian cycle and pregnancy. *Am J Physiol*, 260, E464-70.

Magness, R.R., Rosenfeld, C.R., Faucher, D.J. & Mitchell, M.D. (1992). Uterine prostaglandin production in ovine pregnancy: Effects of angiotensin II and indomethacin. *Am J Physiol*, 263, H188-97.

Magness, R.R., Rosenfeld, C.R., Hassan, A. & Shaul, P.W. (1996). Endothelial vasodilator production by uterine and systemic arteries. I. Effects of ANG II on PGI2 and NO in pregnancy. *Am J Physiol*, 270, H1914-23.

Magness, R.R., Shaw, C.E., Phernetton, T.M., Zheng, J. & Bird, I.M. (1997). Endothelial vasodilator production by uterine and systemic arteries. II. Pregnancy effects on NO synthase expression. *Am J Physiol*, 272, H1730-40.

Magness, R.R., *Shideman, C.R., Habermehl, D.A. Sullivan, JA* and Bird., I.M. 2000. Endothelial vasodilator production by uterine and systemic arteries. V. Effects of ovariectomy, the ovarian cycle, and pregnancy on prostacyclin synthase expression. Prostaglandins and Other Lipid Mediators 60:103-118.

Magness, R.R., Sullivan, J.A., Li, Y., Phernetton, T.M. & Bird, I.M. (2001). Endothelial vasodilator production by uterine and systemic arteries. VI. Ovarian and pregnancy effects on eNOS and NO(x). *Am J Physiol Heart Circ Physiol*, 280, H1692-8.

Magness, R.R. & Zheng, J. (1996). *Maternal cardiovascular alterations during pregnancy*. London: Arnold Publishing.

Manalo-Estrella, P. & Barker, A.E. (1967). Histopathologic findings in human aortic media associated with pregnancy. *Arch Pathol*, 83, 336-41.

Manasc, B. & Jepson, J. (1969). Erythropoietin in plasma and urine during human pregnancy. *Can Med Assoc J*, 100, 687-91.

Mashini, I.S., Albazzaz, S.J., Fadel, H.E., Abdulla, A.M., Hadi, H.A., Harp, R., et al. (1987). Serial noninvasive evaluation of cardiovascular hemodynamics during pregnancy. *Am J Obstet Gynecol*, 156, 1208-13.

McLaughlin, M.K., Keve, T.M. & Cooke, R. (1989). Vascular catecholamine sensitivity during pregnancy in the ewe. *Am J Obstet Gynecol*, 160, 47-53.

Melone, P.J., Meis, P.J. & Blizard, D.A. (1991). Circadian rhythms of heart rate and mean arterial pressure in chronically instrumented pregnant rats. *Am J Obstet Gynecol*, 165, 758-63.

Metcalfe, J. & Parer, J.T. (1966). Cardiovascular changes during pregnancy in ewes. *Am J Physiol*, 210, 821-5.

Metcalfe, J. & Ueland, K. (1974). Maternal cardiovascular adjustments to pregnancy. *Prog Cardiovasc Dis*, 16, 363-74.

Millaway, D.S., Redmer, D.A., Kirsch, J.D., Anthony, R.V. & Reynolds, L.P. (1989). Angiogenic activity of maternal and fetal placental tissues of ewes throughout gestation. *J Reprod Fertil*, 86, 689-96.

Moll, W. (2003). Structure adaptation and blood flow control in the uterine arterial system after hemochorial placentation. *Eur J Obstet Gynecol Reprod Biol*, 110 Suppl 1, S19-27.

Moll, W. & Gotz, R. (1985). Pressure-diameter curves of mesometrial arteries of guinea pigs demonstrate a non-muscular, oestrogen-inducible mechanism of lumen regulation. *Pflugers Arch*, 404, 332-6.

Molnar, M. & Hertelendy, F. (1992). N omega-nitro-l-arginine, an inhibitor of nitric oxide synthesis, increases blood pressure in rats and reverses the pregnancy-induced refractoriness to vasopressor agents. *Am J Obstet Gynecol*, 166, 1560-7.

Moore, L.G. & Reeves, J.T. (1980). Pregnancy blunts pulmonary vascular reactivity in dogs. *Am J Physiol*, 239, H297-301.

Morton, J.S. & Davidge, S.T. (2013). Arterial endothelium-derived hyperpolarization: Potential role in pregnancy adaptations and complications. *J Cardiovasc Pharmacol*, 61, 197-203.

Morton, M., Tsang, H., Hohimer, R., Ross, D., Thornburg, K., Faber, J., et al. (1984). Left ventricular size, output, and structure during guinea pig pregnancy. *Am J Physiol*, 246, R40-8.

Moutquin, J.M., Rainville, C., Giroux, L., Raynauld, P., Amyot, G., Bilodeau, R., et al. (1985). A prospective study of blood pressure in pregnancy: Prediction of preeclampsia. *Am J Obstet Gynecol*, 151, 191-6.

Mu, J. & Adamson, S.L. (2006). Developmental changes in hemodynamics of uterine artery, utero- and umbilicoplacental, and vitelline circulations in mouse throughout gestation. *Am J Physiol Heart Circ Physiol*, 291, H1421-8.

Myers, S.A. & Tseng, H.Y. (1985). A longitudinal study of cardiac output in unstressed pregnant guinea pigs. *Am J Physiol*, 248, R698-701.

Naden, R.P., Coultrup, S., Arant, B.S. & Rosenfeld, C.R. (1985). Metabolic clearance of angiotensin ii in pregnant and nonpregnant sheep. *Am J Physiol*, 249, E49-55.

Naden, R.P., Gant, N.F., Jr. & Rosenfeld, C.R. (1984). The pressor response to angiotensin IIhe roles of peripheral and cardiac responses in pregnant and nonpregnant sheep. *Am J Obstet Gynecol*, 148, 450-7.

Nelson, S.H., Steinsland, O.S., Johnson, R.L., Suresh, M.S., Gifford, A. & Ehardt, J.S. (1995). Pregnancy-induced alterations of neurogenic constriction and dilation of human uterine artery. *Am J Physiol*, 268, H1694-701.

Novak, K. & Kaufman, S. (1991). Effects of pregnancy, estradiol, and progesterone on pressor responsiveness to angiotensin II. *Am J Physiol*, 261, R1164-70.

Osol, G. & Mandala, M. (2009). Maternal uterine vascular remodeling during pregnancy. *Physiology (Bethesda)*, 24, 58-71.

Osol, G. & Moore, L.G. (2014). Maternal uterine vascular remodeling during pregnancy. *Microcirculation*, 21, 38-47.

Paller, M.S. (1984). Mechanism of decreased pressor responsiveness to ang II, NE, and vasopressin in pregnant rats. *Am J Physiol*, 247, H100-8.

Paller, M.S., Douglas, J.G. & Linas, S.L. (1984). Mechanism of decreased vascular reactivity to angiotensin ii in conscious, potassium-deficient rats. *J Clin Invest*, 73, 79-86.

Paller, M.S., Gregorini, G. & Ferris, T.F. (1989). Pressor responsiveness in pseudopregnant and pregnant rats: Role of maternal factors. *Am J Physiol*, 257, R866-71.

Palmer, A.J. & Walker, A.H. (1949). The maternal circulation in normal pregnancy. *J Obstet Gynaecol Br Emp*, 56, 537-47.

Palmer, S.K., Zamudio, S., Coffin, C., Parker, S., Stamm, E. & Moore, L.G. (1992). Quantitative estimation of human uterine artery blood flow and pelvic blood flow redistribution in pregnancy. *Obstet Gynecol*, 80, 1000-6.

Pan, Z.R., Lindheimer, M.D., Bailin, J. & Barron, W.M. (1990). Regulation of blood pressure in pregnancy: Pressor system blockade and stimulation. *Am J Physiol*, 258, H1559-72.

Peeters, L.L., Grutters, G. & Martin, C.B., Jr. (1980). Distribution of cardiac output in the unstressed pregnant guinea pig. *Am J Obstet Gynecol*, 138, 1177-84.

Pepe, G.J. & Rothchild, I. (1974). A comparative study of serum progesterone levels in pregnancy and in various types of pseudopregnancy in the rat. *Endocrinology*, 95, 275-9.

Phippard, A.F., Horvath, J.S., Glynn, E.M., Garner, M.G., Fletcher, P.J., Duggin, G.G., et al. (1986). Circulatory adaptation to pregnancy--serial studies of haemodynamics, blood volume, renin and aldosterone in the baboon (papio hamadryas). *J Hypertens*, 4, 773-9.

Ramsay, M., Broughton Pipkin, F. & Rubin, P. (1992). Comparative study of pressor and heart rate responses to angiotensin ii and noradrenaline in pregnant and non-pregnant women. *Clin Sci (Lond)*, 82, 157-62.

Reynolds, L.P., Biondini, M.E., Borowicz, P.P., Vonnahme, K.A., Caton, J.S., Grazul-Bilska, A.T., et al. (2005). Functional significance of developmental changes in placental microvascular architecture. *Endothelium*, 12, 11-9.

Reynolds, L.P., Borowicz, P.P., Caton, J.S., Vonnahme, K.A., Luther, J.S., Buchanan, D.S., et al. (2010). Uteroplacental vascular development and placental function: An update. *Int J Dev Biol*, 54, 355-66.

Reynolds, L.P., Grazul-Bilska, A.T. & Redmer, D.A. (2002). Angiogenesis in the female reproductive organs: Pathological implications. *Int J Exp Pathol*, 83, 151-63.

Reynolds, L.P., Kirsch, J.D., Kraft, K.C., Knutson, D.L., McClaflin, W.J. & Redmer, D.A. (1998a). Time-course of the uterine response to estradiol-17beta in ovariectomized ewes: Uterine growth and microvascular development. *Biol Reprod*, 59, 606-12.

Reynolds, L.P., Kirsch, J.D., Kraft, K.C. & Redmer, D.A. (1998b). Time-course of the uterine response to estradiol-17beta in ovariectomized ewes: Expression of angiogenic factors. *Biol Reprod*, 59, 613-20.

Reynolds, L.P. & Redmer, D.A. (1995). Utero-placental vascular development and placental function. *J Anim Sci*, 73, 1839-51.

Reynolds, L.P. & Redmer, D.A. (1998). Expression of the angiogenic factors, basic fibroblast growth factor and vascular endothelial growth factor, in the ovary. *J Anim Sci*, 76, 1671-81.

Reynolds, L.P. & Redmer, D.A. (2001). Angiogenesis in the placenta. *Biol Reprod*, 64, 1033-40.

Reynolds, M. (1953). Measurement of bovine plasma and blood volume during pregnancy and lactation. *Am J Physiol*, 175, 118-22.

Robertson, H.A. & King, G.J. (1979). Conjugated and unconjugated oestrogens in fetal and maternal fluids of the cow throughout pregnancy. *J Reprod Fertil*, 55, 463-70.

Robson, S.C., Hunter, S., Boys, R.J. & Dunlop, W. (1989a). Hemodynamic changes during twin pregnancy. A doppler and m-mode echocardiographic study. *Am J Obstet Gynecol*, 161, 1273-8.

Robson, S.C., Hunter, S., Boys, R.J. & Dunlop, W. (1989b). Serial study of factors influencing changes in cardiac output during human pregnancy. *Am J Physiol*, 256, H1060-5.

Roghair, R.D., Segar, J.L., Volk, K.A., Chapleau, M.W., Dallas, L.M., Sorenson, A.R., et al. (2009). Vascular nitric oxide and superoxide anion contribute to sex-specific programmed cardiovascular physiology in mice. *Am J Physiol Regul Integr Comp Physiol*, 296, R651-62.

Rosenfeld, C.R. (1977). Distribution of cardiac output in ovine pregnancy. *Am J Physiol*, 232, H231-5.

Rosenfeld, C.R. (1984). Consideration of the uteroplacental circulation in intrauterine growth. *Semin Perinatol*, 8, 42-51.

Rosenfeld, C.R. (1989). Changes in uterine blood flow during pregnancy. In: *The uterine circulation*. Rosenfeld, C.R. (Ed). Reproductive and perinatal medicine, vol. 10. Ithaca, NY: Perinatology Press, p. 135-56.

Rosenfeld, C.R., Cox, B.E., Roy, T. & Magness, R.R. (1996). Nitric oxide contributes to estrogen-induced vasodilation of the ovine uterine circulation. *J Clin Invest*, 98, 2158-66.

Rosenfeld, C.R. & Gant, N.F., Jr. (1981). The chronically instrumental ewe: A model for studying vascular reactivity to angiotensin ii in pregnancy. *J Clin Invest*, 67, 486-92.

Rosenfeld, C.R., Gresores, A., Roy, T.A. & Magness, R.R. (1995). Comparison of ang ii in fetal and pregnant sheep: Metabolic clearance and vascular sensitivity. *Am J Physiol*, 268, E237-47.

Rosenfeld, C.R., Morriss, F.H., Jr., Makowski, E.L., Meschia, G. & Battaglia, F.C. (1974). Circulatory changes in the reproductive tissues of ewes during pregnancy. *Gynecol Invest*, 5, 252-68.

Rosenfeld, C.R. & Naden, R.P. (1989). Uterine and nonuterine vascular responses to angiotensin ii in ovine pregnancy. *Am J Physiol*, 257, H17-24.

Rosenfeld, C.R., Worley, R.J., Milewich, L., Grant, N.F., Jr. & Parker, C.R., Jr. (1980). Ovine fetoplacental sulfoconjugation and aromatization of dehydroepiandrosterone. *Endocrinology*, 106, 1971-9.

Rovinsky, J.J. & Jaffin, H. (1965). Cardiovascular hemodynamics in pregnancy. I. Blood and plasma volumes in multiple pregnancy. *Am J Obstet Gynecol*, 93, 1-15.

Rubanyi, G.M., Romero, J.C. & Vanhoutte, P.M. (1986). Flow-induced release of endothelium-derived relaxing factor. *Am J Physiol*, 250, H1145-9.

Rubler, S., Damani, P.M. & Pinto, E.R. (1977). Cardiac size and performance during pregnancy estimated with echocardiography. *Am J Cardiol*, 40, 534-40.

Rupnow, H.L., Phernetton, T.M., Modrick, M.L., Wiltbank, M.C., Bird, I.M. & Magness, R.R. (2002). Endothelial vasodilator production by uterine and systemic arteries. VIII. Estrogen and progesterone effects on cPLA2, COX-1, and PGIS protein expression. *Biol Reprod*, 66, 468-74.

Rupnow, H.L., Phernetton, T.M., Shaw, C.E., Modrick, M.L., Bird, I.M. & Magness, R.R. (2001). Endothelial vasodilator production by uterine and systemic arteries. VII. Estrogen and progesterone effects on enos. *Am J Physiol Heart Circ Physiol*, 280, H1699-705.

Sanchez-Ramos, L., O'Sullivan, M.J. & Garrido-Calderon, J. (1987). Effect of low-dose aspirin on angiotensin II pressor response in human pregnancy. *Am J Obstet Gynecol*, 156, 193-4.

Satterfield, M.C., Bazer, F.W., Spencer, T.E. & Wu, G. (2010). Sildenafil citrate treatment enhances amino acid availability in the conceptus and fetal growth in an ovine model of intrauterine growth restriction. *J Nutr*, 140, 251-8.

Shaul, P.W., Magness, R.R., Muntz, K.H., DeBeltz, D. & Buja, L.M. (1990). Alpha 1-adrenergic receptors in pulmonary and systemic vascular smooth muscle. Alterations with development and pregnancy. *Circ Res*, 67, 1193-200.

Siddiqi, T.A., Austin, J.E., Holroyd, J.C. & Clark, K.E. (1983). Modulation of angiotensin ii pressor responsiveness by circulating levels of angiotensin ii in pregnant sheep. *Am J Obstet Gynecol*, 145, 458-64.

Sladek, S.M., Magness, R.R. & Conrad, K.P. (1997). Nitric oxide and pregnancy. *Am J Physiol*, 272, R441-63.

Slangen, B.F., Out, I.C., Verkeste, C.M. & Peeters, L.L. (1996). Hemodynamic changes in early pregnancy in chronically instrumented, conscious rats. *Am J Physiol*, 270, H1779-84.

Slangen, B.F., van Ingen Schenau, D.S., van Gorp, A.W., De Mey, J.G. & Peeters, L.L. (1997). Aortic distensibility and compliance in conscious pregnant rats. *Am J Physiol*, 272, H1260-5.

Spitz, B., Magness, R.R., Cox, S.M., Brown, C.E., Rosenfeld, C.R. & Gant, N.F. (1988). Low-dose aspirin. I. Effect on angiotensin II pressor responses and blood prostaglandin concentrations in pregnant women sensitive to angiotensin II. *Am J Obstet Gynecol*, 159, 1035-43.

Sprague, B., Chesler, N.C. & Magness, R.R. (2010). Shear stress regulation of nitric oxide production in uterine and placental artery endothelial cells: Experimental studies and hemodynamic models of shear stresses on endothelial cells. *Int J Dev Biol*, 54, 331-9.

Sprague, B.J., Phernetton, T.M., Magness, R.R. & Chesler, N.C. (2009). The effects of the ovarian cycle and pregnancy on uterine vascular impedance and uterine artery mechanics. *Eur J Obstet Gynecol Reprod Biol*, 144 Suppl 1, S170-8.

Stanley, J.L., Andersson, I.J., Poudel, R., Rueda-Clausen, C.F., Sibley, C.P., Davidge, S.T., et al. (2012). Sildenafil citrate rescues fetal growth in the catechol-o-methyl transferase knockout mouse model. *Hypertension*, 59, 1021-8.

Stegeman, J.H.J. (1974). *Bijdragen tot de dierkunde (contrib zool)*.

Stock, M.K. & Metcalfe, J. (1994). Maternal physiology during gestation. In: *The physiology of reproduction*. Knobil, E. & Neill, J.D. (Eds). New York: Raven Press, p. 947-83.

Strevens, H., Wide-Swensson, D. & Ingemarsson, I. (2001). Blood pressure during pregnancy in a swedish population; impact of parity. *Acta Obstet Gynecol Scand*, 80, 824-9.

Tabata, M., Negishi, H., Yamaguchi, T., Makinoda, S., Fujimoto, S. & Moll, W. (1988). The effects of the proliferation of the radial arteries of the placenta on oxygen transport to the fetal guinea pig. *Adv Exp Med Biol*, 222, 675-81.

Taylor, D.J. & Lind, T. (1979). Red cell mass during and after normal pregnancy. *Br J Obstet Gynaecol*, 86, 364-70.

Tong, C. & Eisenach, J.C. (1992). The vascular mechanism of ephedrine's beneficial effect on uterine perfusion during pregnancy. *Anesthesiology*, 76, 792-8.

Ueland, K. (1976). Maternal cardiovascular dynamics. VII. Intrapartum blood volume changes. *Am J Obstet Gynecol*, 126, 671-7.

Ueland, K., Novy, M.J., Peterson, E.N. & Metcalfe, J. (1969). Maternal cardiovascular dynamics. Iv. The influence of gestational age on the maternal cardiovascular response to posture and exercise. *Am J Obstet Gynecol*, 104, 856-64.

Vagnoni, K.E., Shaw, C.E., Phernetton, T.M., Meglin, B.M., Bird, I.M. & Magness, R.R. (1998). Endothelial vasodilator production by uterine and systemic arteries. III. Ovarian and estrogen effects on no synthase. *Am J Physiol*, 275, H1845-56.

Van der Heijden, O.W., Essers, Y.P., Fazzi, G., Peeters, L.L., De Mey, J.G. & van Eys, G.J. (2005). Uterine artery remodeling and reproductive performance are impaired in endothelial nitric oxide synthase-deficient mice. *Biol Reprod*, 72, 1161-8.

Van Vliet, B.N. & Chafe, L.L. (2007). Maternal endothelial nitric oxide synthase genotype influences offspring blood pressure and activity in mice. *Hypertension*, 49, 556-62.

Veille, J.C., Morton, M.J. & Burry, K.J. (1985). Maternal cardiovascular adaptations to twin pregnancy. *Am J Obstet Gynecol*, 153, 261-3.

Venditti, C.C., Casselman, R., Murphy, M.S., Adamson, S.L., Sled, J.G. & Smith, G.N. (2013). Chronic carbon monoxide inhalation during pregnancy augments uterine artery blood flow and uteroplacental vascular growth in mice. *Am J Physiol Regul Integr Comp Physiol*, 305, R939-48.

Vered, Z., Poler, S.M., Gibson, P., Wlody, D. & Perez, J.E. (1991). Noninvasive detection of the morphologic and hemodynamic changes during normal pregnancy. *Clin Cardiol*, 14, 327-34.

Vonnahme, K.A., Wilson, M.E., Li, Y., Rupnow, H.L., Phernetton, T.M., Ford, S.P., et al. (2005). Circulating levels of nitric oxide and vascular endothelial growth factor throughout ovine pregnancy. *J Physiol*, 565, 101-9.

Vorys, N., Ullery, J.C. & Hanusek, G.E. (1961). The cardiac output changes in various positions in pregnancy. *Am J Obstet Gynecol*, 82, 1312-21.

Walters, W.A., MacGregor, W.G. & Hills, M. (1966). Cardiac output at rest during pregnancy and the puerperium. *Clin Sci*, 30, 1-11.

Weems, Y.S., Sasser, R.G., Vincent, D.L., Nusser, K.D., Tanaka, Y., Miller-Patrick, K., et al. (1994). Effects of prostaglandin F2 alpha (PGF2 alpha) on secretion of pregnancy specific protein B (PSPB) and placentome weights in intact or ovariectomized 90 to 100 day pregnant ewes. *Prostaglandins*, 48, 377-87.

Weiner, C., Liu, K.Z., Thompson, L., Herrig, J. & Chestnut, D. (1991). Effect of pregnancy on endothelium and smooth muscle: Their role in reduced adrenergic sensitivity. *Am J Physiol*, 261, H1275-83.

Weiner, C., Martinez, E., Zhu, L.K., Ghodsi, A. & Chestnut, D. (1989). In vitro release of endothelium-derived relaxing factor by acetylcholine is increased during the guinea pig pregnancy. *Am J Obstet Gynecol*, 161, 1599-605.

Weiner, C.P., Lizasoain, I., Baylis, S.A., Knowles, R.G., Charles, I.G. & Moncada, S. (1994). Induction of calcium-dependent nitric oxide synthases by sex hormones. *Proc Natl Acad Sci U S A*, 91, 5212-6.

Widness, J.A., Clemons, G.K., Garcia, J.F. & Schwartz, R. (1984). Plasma immunoreactive erythropoietin in normal women studied sequentially during and after pregnancy. *Am J Obstet Gynecol*, 149, 646-50.

Yallampalli, C. & Garfield, R.E. (1993). Inhibition of nitric oxide synthesis in rats during pregnancy produces signs similar to those of preeclampsia. *Am J Obstet Gynecol*, 169, 1316-20.

Yoshimura, T., Magness, R.R. & Rosenfeld, C.R. (1990). Angiotensin II and alpha-agonist. II. Effects on ovine fetoplacental prostaglandins. *Am J Physiol*, 259, H473-9.

Yoshimura, T., Rosenfeld, C.R. & Magness, R.R. (1991). Angiotensin II and alpha-agonist. III. In vitro fetal-maternal placental prostaglandins. *Am J Physiol*, 260, E8-13.

Zheng, J., Bird, I.M., Melsaether, A.N. & Magness, R.R. (1999). Activation of the mitogen-activated protein kinase cascade is necessary but not sufficient for basic fibroblast growth factor- and epidermal growth factor-stimulated expression of endothelial nitric oxide synthase in ovine fetoplacental artery endothelial cells. *Endocrinology*, 140, 1399-407.

Zheng, J., Li, Y., Weiss, A.R., Bird, I.M. & Magness, R.R. (2000). Expression of endothelial and inducible nitric oxide synthases and nitric oxide production in ovine placental and uterine tissues during late pregnancy. *Placenta*, 21, 516-24.

Zheng, J., Vagnoni, K.E., Bird, I.M. & Magness, R.R. (1997). Expression of basic fibroblast growth factor, endothelial mitogenic activity, and angiotensin IIype-1 receptors in the ovine placenta during the third trimester of pregnancy. *Biol Reprod*, 56, 1189-97.

Zhu, Y., Sprague, B.J., Phernetton, T.M., Magness, R.R. & Chesler, N.C. (2009). Transmission line models to simulate the impedance of the uterine vasculature during the ovarian cycle and pregnancy. *Eur J Obstet Gynecol Reprod Biol*, 144 Suppl 1, S184-91.

Zivny, J., Kobilkova, J., Neuwirt, J. & Andrasova, V. (1982). Regulation of erythropoiesis in fetus and mother during normal pregnancy. *Obstet Gynecol*, 60, 77-81.

In: Stress and Developmental Programming …
Editors: Lubo Zhang and Lawrence D. Longo

ISBN: 978-1-63321-836-9
© 2014 Nova Science Publishers, Inc.

Chapter 8

The Role of the Placenta in Fetal Programming

John R. G. Challis[1], Kent Thornburg[2] and Felice Petraglia[3]*

[1]University of Toronto, Dept of Obstetrics and Gynecology and Physiology, Toronto,
Ontario; Simon Fraser University, Faculty of Health Sciences,
Vancouver BC, Canada; and Dept of Obstetrics and Gynaecology,
University of Western Australia, Perth WA, Australia
[2]Oregon Health Sciences University, Department of Medicine,
Knight Cardiovascular Institute and Moore Institute for Nutrition
and Wellness, Portland, Oregon, US
[3]School of Reproductive Sciences,
Department of Obstetrics and Gynaecology,
University of Siena, Siena, Italy

Abstract

The rise in rates of non-communicable diseases that emerged over the past 20 years is without precedent. The causes of the epidemic remain enigmatic. The usual explanation, that disease is caused by poor genes or detrimental lifestyle choices are inadequate to explain the rapid time course. However, the work of David Barker and colleagues, published some 25 years ago, showed powerful relationships between low birthweight and risk for adult onset type 2 diabetes and offered new ways of thinking regarding the origins of chronic disease. It is now evident that (i) programming later life health or disease begins at conception or earlier, at different windows of developmental plasticity through altered structural or epigenetic responses; (ii) prenatal changes predispose to altered post natal environmental responses (epigenome x environment, E2, interaction) and (iii) the placenta has a central role in mediating these effects. While the placenta is known to be the conduit through which maternal nutrients reach the embryo and fetus, the mechanisms that underlie the transport of the vast number of nutrients is

---

* Corresponding Author: John R.G. Challis, University of Toronto, Department of Obstetrics and Gynecology and Physiology, Toronto, Ontario, j.challis@utoronto.ca; john.challis@uwa.edu.au

complex and includes, diffusion, active transport and vesicular transport. These transport systems are influenced by maternal body composition and physiological state. The predilection for various chronic diseases among adults is associated with placental size and shape. The physiological features of the maternal, fetal and placental units are important in regulating transport function of the placenta. Levels of 11β hydroxysteroid dehydrogenase influence the degree to which maternal cortisol reaches the fetal circulation. Maternal under and over-nutritional states affect the fetal HPA axis beyond birth. Five year old offspring of periconceptional undernourished ewes have reduced hypothalamic GR promoter methylation, increased levels of glucocorticoid receptor mRNA and protein and increased adiposity. Thus, the research task of the next generation will be to determine 1) the appropriate use of glucocorticoids in clinical practice balancing potential detrimental effects on offspring, 2) the roles of maternal nutritional state before and during pregnancy and their short term effects on placental function and long term effects on offspring and 3) the degree to which biomarkers associated with maternal conditions can predict disease in offspring.

Keywords: Birthweight, cortisol, glucocorticoids, maternal nutrition, non-comunicable disease, placenta, programming, undernutrition

Introduction

The world is facing an emerging epidemic of non-communicable diseases (NCD). For example, the proportion of adults in the USA who are obese (BMI greater than 30kg per m^2) or diagnosed with diabetes has increased dramatically over the last 15 years. It is projected that by 2050 one in three Americans will have diabetes. Already there are 360 million people worldwide with this disease; 90 million in China alone, showing that this is not just a condition of an affluent western society (Swinburn et al., 2011).

Our health potential in adult life has been ascribed in part to the food we ingest and by our level of physical activity superimposed on a particular genetic background. Over the past 20 years, however we have recognized that this picture is far more complicated. Early life events that affect development of the early embryo and the fetus during the course of pregnancy, program that individual towards certain kinds of later life disease and disease risk. Thus, the later life environmental influences play upon a particular genetic or epigenetic background predetermined by responses to the environment in utero and at the outset of pregnancy. This relationship has been described as the developmental origins of health and disease (DOHaD).

Understanding these relationships is of critical importance. An approach to applying this knowledge in health promotion is to consider different phases; Prevention I (intrauterine and immediate postnatal life or the first 1000 days), which leads into (predisposes towards) Prevention 2, adolescence and adult life, and finally, if prevention has failed, treatment (Gluckman, 2013).

The field was opened in the late 1980's by the pioneering studies of David Barker and his colleagues at the University of Southampton, UK. They showed a remarkable inverse relationship between weight of an individual at birth and the risk of death from coronary heart disease or development of high blood pressure in men and women aged 60 or more in later life (Barker et al., 1993, 2002). In the Hertfordshire study, Barker and his co-workers showed this same inverse relationship existed between birth weight and the appearance of type II diabetes in adult men and women. Birth weight and the relative risk of glucose intolerance and impaired pancreatic beta cell function were also inversely related. These findings have now been replicated by many groups in different populations worldwide. Subsequent studies have suggested that programming of the fetus may occur in response to different environmental factors during intra-uterine development. Most often studied has been the relationship between maternal undernutrition during pregnancy and postnatal type II diabetes, obesity, and heart disease (Pyhälä et al., 2009). Subsequently, studies have been extended to determine the relationships of nutritional status during pregnancy with later life responses to stress, appetite control, certain cancers and aspects of neurologic development. Exposure of the fetus to stress during pregnancy, either directly as a response to fetal hypoxemia or indirectly as a result of maternal stress and consequent excessive exposure to glucocorticoids in the fetus, produces many of the same responses (Edwards et al., 1993, Seckl and Holmes, 2007). This has led workers to suggest that while programming may occur directly in response to inappropriate maternal nutrition, the nutritional effects could also be mediated or influenced by inappropriate levels of glucocorticoids (see below).

More recently, it has been recognized that maternal conditions such as an underlying inflammation may affect pregnancy outcomes, including fetal growth and fetal programming (Blank et al., 2008, Challis et al., 2009).

An exaggerated maternal inflammatory response, particularly in the placenta, may be a common contributor to diseases of pregnancy such as preeclampsia and preterm birth which may be associated with intrauterine fetal growth restriction and later life programming. In turn, the process of programming may result in changes in an individual such as altered immune responsiveness, stem cell availability or inflammation that provide a common base to various adult disease conditions. More recently, the role of the maternal microbiome in developmental programming has gained importance, through its effects on maternal nutrient availability and through the production of a variety of factors, including cytokines, which may influence maternal responses and behaviour.

The key messages of this chapter are that: (i) Programming later life health or disease begins at conception or earlier, at different windows of developmental plasticity through altered structural or epigenetic responses; (ii) These prenatal changes predispose to altered post natal environmental responses (epigenome x environment, E^2, interaction); (iii) The placenta has a central role in mediating these effects.

The role of the placenta may be exerted in several ways (for detail see Barker et al., 2011, Braun et al., 2013a). First, the placenta is a critical regulator of nutrient transfer from the mother to the fetus. Second, the placenta produces hormones that directly affect fetal growth and development, or indirectly alter maternal metabolism during pregnancy, that in turn alters nutrient availability to the fetus. Third, the placenta produces a myriad of hormones that act locally or systemically to alter uterine blood flow in a manner that determines nutrient and oxygen availability to the fetus.

Finally, the placenta provides a metabolic barrier between the mother and fetus. For example, the placenta expresses a critical enzyme 11β hydroxysteroid dehydrogenase-2 (11βHSD2) that contributes to maintenance of the difference in cortisol concentration between the maternal and fetal compartments (Edwards et al., 1993, Holmes et al., 2006). While cortisol is necessary for normal fetal organ differentiation, excessive amounts of glucocorticoids are detrimental to fetal growth. In fact, many studies have shown the importance of placental 11βHSD2 in influencing the amount of cortisol that is transferred from the mother to the fetus during pregnancy and hence the maternal influence on fetal programming (see Braun et al., 2013a).

The Fetal Supply Line

Fetal nutrition is clearly far more complicated than simply being a product of what the mother eats or of her body composition. The fetal supply line (Harding, 2001) is of course affected by the level and type of maternal nutrition (under and over nutrition, the proportions of protein and fat, the micronutrient content), the maternal pre-pregnancy body composition, the maternal microbiome during pregnancy, and by factors that regulate maternal blood flow particularly to the uterus and placenta. At the level of the placenta, the activity of different placental transport proteins must be finely regulated, and evidence from gene deletion or mutation studies point to a balance between various transporter systems (Desforges et al., 2009, Kotelevtsev, 1997). Placental blood flow and the integrity of the trophoblast and vascular membrane structures between maternal and fetal blood are crucial. Some of these characteristics may be manifest in altered changes in placental shape and thickness, dimensions that themselves may predict fetal growth characteristics and later life predisposition to growth patterns and disease (Barker and Thornburg, 2013). The regulation of umbilical blood flow, especially in response to different autocrine vasoregulators, fetal circulatory responses, for example with hypoxemia, and the efficiency of nutrient uptake by fetal tissues are all important components of the fetal supply line. Furthermore, these vasoregulators modulate the loading conditions on the fetal organs and have profound influences on the development of the vasculature in brain and heart. Collectively these activities are regulated by hormones and by autocrines in a complex and interactive manner (Burton and Jauniaux, 2011).

The importance of placental transporter function is illustrated by studies of the placental System A amino acid transporter. This function is located on the syncytiotrophoblast, and transports small unbranched neutral amino acids from mother to fetus (Jansson and Powell, 2011).

The transporter consists of three isoforms; SNAT1, SNAT2 and SNAT4, each a different gene product. Various studies have shown that the SNAT isoforms localize to the syncytiotrophoblast of the human placenta and that the expression of different isoforms is regulated separately through the course of gestation. The activity of SNAT isoforms is reduced in the placenta of growth restricted fetuses, and in the rat, experimental inhibition of System A activity across gestation results in reductions in fetal weight.

In mice, we found that System A transport function and isoform expression increased progressively from mid to late gestation and was not influenced by the sex of the fetus (Audette et al., 2011). We further found that administration of synthetic glucocorticoid at day 13.5 and 14.5 (term 18.5 days) had no immediate effect on System A, but by day 18 the activity of this transporter was reduced by almost 50 percent. Of interest, the altered System A activity was not attributable to reduced expression of any one of the three different isoforms, raising the question of whether glucocorticoids might alter rates of translation or of incorporation of the isoforms into the syncytiotrophoblast membrane.

The Effects of Placental Hormones

The placenta also affects fetal growth and development through the production of different hormones and autocrine factors (Barker et al., 2011, Braun et al., 2013a). Placental lactogen (PL) production influences maternal metabolism to favour increased flow of substrate to the fetus during the course of pregnancy. In sheep, ovine placental lactogen is produced by the binucleate cells within the placental cotyledons and as in the human, PL output rises progressively throughout the course of gestation. Administration of glucocorticoids to sheep during the last one third of gestation decreases the numbers of binucleate cells in the placenta and the concentrations of placental lactogen in both maternal and fetal circulation, thereby recapitulating the decline in PL output associated with the normal prepartum rise in fetal cortisol values (Braun et al., 2007). When glucocorticoids were administered in early pregnancy to sheep, the effects on oPL were less dramatic, but it appears that there is a reduced expression of anti-apoptotic factors and a corresponding increase in factors that would promote apoptosis. However, application of this information to human pregnancy may be questionable. Ongoing studies have shown that glucocorticoid administration to women in the third trimester of pregnancy results in reductions in fetal growth that occur independently of changes in placental or circulating placental lactogen concentrations (Braun et al., 2013b).

The human placenta, through its interactions with the maternal and fetal adrenal glands produces increasing amounts of estrogen during the course of gestation. Estrogen in turn contributes to remodelling of the uterine vascular bed and increases utero-placental blood flow. Other hormones, for examples neuropeptides of the corticotrophin releasing hormone (CRH) family, directly regulate myometrial contractility and utero-placental blood flow (see Petraglia et al., 2010). CRH itself, produced locally within the human placenta increases placental blood flow, both directly and indirectly. Further studies are needed to identify the CRH receptor sub types responsible for these actions and the potential for therapeutic intervention. In addition, however, CRH upregulates placental aromatase activity and increases the potential for placental estrogen production (Imperatore et al., 2009). Thus CRH could affect placental blood flow through that pathway. Recently we have shown that the urocortin peptides, which have extensive homology with CRH, are also expressed in high amounts by first trimester human placental tissues. The expression of urocortin2 and urocortin3 is increased at the lower oxygen tensions which prevail in early gestation (Imperatore et al., 2010). Urocortins also increase placental aromatase activity and upregulate matrix metalloproteinase activity and expression by human placental explants maintained in tissue culture (Li and Challis, 2005). Ongoing studies suggest that the urocortins affect expression of peptides involved in apoptosis of trophoblast cells. The further regulation of their production in early gestation, in particular in relation to altered oxygen tensions may be important in relation to placental modelling and function in later gestation.

Regulation of CRH and urocortin peptides by the placenta is multifactorial (Petraglia et al., 2010). Altered output of CRH occurs in relation to changes in pro-and anti- inflammatory cytokines, prostaglandins and steroid hormones. Importantly glucocorticoids play a major role. Cortisol upregulates placental CRH gene expression and this response is antagonized by progesterone. Maternal plasma CRH concentrations rise progressively through the course of human pregnancy, associated in part with increasing levels of cortisol in the maternal circulation (see Petraglia et al., 2010). At the same time output of the inhibitory CRH binding protein is reduced and this pattern can be reproduced in vitro by treating trophoblast explants with glucocorticoid. Hence, glucocorticoids increase placental CRH output and biological activity and alterations in this relationship may have important influences on placental function and fetal growth (see Petraglia et al., 2010).

In the presence of infection or inflammation, placental function may be impaired. Recent work has shown that lipopolysaccharide (LPS) increases mRNA expression of CRH and urocortin2 by term trophoblast cells, while it decreases expression of urocortin and urocortin3. In turn, urocortin2 increases LPS-induced TNFα output, and the current view is that urocortin2 has a proinflammatory effect in the placenta via CRH-Receptor2 species (Torricelli et al., 2011). Conversely, urocortin3 has predominantly anti-inflammatory effects also mediated by CRH-Receptor2. Modulation of this receptor species and subtypes appears critical in determining placental inflammatory responsiveness. The effects of CRH-CRH-Receptor 2 must depend on the available ligand and post translational receptor signalling.

Increasing evidence related to inflammatory processes in the placenta suggest that the standard definitions of inflammation are too rigid for application to placental biology. For example, while full blown inflammation of the placenta, characterized by granulocyte accumulation is rare, more subtle forms that include placental expression of proinflammatory genes may be commonly found under different adverse conditions. The role of the CRH system in inflammation is an example (Barker et al., 2010a).

Placental 11β Hydroxysteroid Dehydrogenase

As described, expression of CRH family peptides by the placenta is modulated by agents that include cortisol. Cortisol can be derived from either the maternal or fetal circulation. The ability of maternal cortisol to reach placental cells and also to cross the placenta into the fetus is dictated in large part by the metabolizing enzyme 11βHSD2. This enzyme, which inactivates cortisol to cortisone is down regulated with maternal infection, hypoxemia, preeclampsia, and under nutrition (Alfaidy et al., 2002, Braun et al., 2013a, Nyirenda et al., 1998, Petraglia et al., 2010). Hence it is a critical enzyme in mediating many of the environmental and pathophysiologic factors which alter the effects of cortisol on the placenta and on the fetus. Its regulation has been studies extensively. For example, levels of 11βHSD2 mRNA in placental villous explants are reduced dramatically with lowered oxygen tension (Alfaidy et al., 2002). In sheep, periconceptional undernutrition of the mother reduced placental 11βHSD2 activity at days 50 and 85 during the first half of pregnancy (Connor et al., 2009). The ratio of cortisol: cortisone in the fetal circulation was significantly higher in undernourished sheep than in control pregnancies, presumably as a result of less placental cortisol metabolism and increased transfer of maternal cortisol to the fetus. Undernutrition of pregnant rats also reduces placental 11βHSD2, and in a preliminary study, Johnston et al. (Johnstone et al., 2005) showed that women who had dieted to lose weight before the start of pregnancy had lower 11βHSD2 protein expression in placental tissue collected at term.

Regulation of glucocorticoid concentrations in the fetus therefore results from complex interactions between mother, placenta and fetus and interplay with the environment including the maternal nutritional state. Maternal stress increases maternal glucocorticoid output. When placental 11βHSD2 is reduced, more maternal cortisol is available to act on the placenta and more cortisol crosses the placenta into the fetus. Decreases in uterine blood flow, umbilical blood flow, or placental insufficiency are all ways of provoking fetal "undernutrition" and hypoxemia. These affects are replicated at high altitude and provide potent stimulus to increased fetal adrenal cortisol activity and circulating fetal cortisol concentrations.

There is abundant evidence that glucocorticoids are potent regulators of fetal growth and development (Challis et al., 2001). Studies in sheep show that administration of synthetic betamethasone to the mother in late gestation reduces fetal and placental weights and affects growth and development of different fetal tissues that impact later health (Newnham et al., 1999, Sloboda et al., 2000). When betamethasone (0.5mg/kg) is given at weekly intervals in late pregnancy, fetal body organ and brain weights are decreased, skeletal maturation and myelination of the optic nerve are delayed, and brain structures are altered in a manner that might predict neuropathology in later life. Similar effects have been seen in other animal species, including rat, guinea pig, rhesus monkey and human (Sloboda et al., 2005). Administration of glucocorticoids in early or late gestation predisposes to post natal hypertension, glucose intolerance and insulin insensitivity which predict Type II diabetes in later life (Braun et al., 2009, Moss et al., 2001). These animals also show profoundly altered HPA axis responses after birth suggesting altered immune tolerance and inflammatory responsiveness with later maturity. Thus the placenta, in regulating bioactive cortisol concentrations reaching the fetus, has a critical role in determining these aspects of fetal development and post natal health.

Nutrition and Glucocorticoids

It is now clear that effects of undernutrition and excess glucocorticoid are interrelated. For example, periconceptual undernutrition of sheep preciously activates the fetal HPA axis, increases fetal cortisol concentrations in late gestation and results in preterm birth (Bloomfield et al., 2003, 2004). These fetuses are already exposed to elevated levels of cortisol in early pregnancy because of a reduction in placental 11βHSD2 (Connor et al., 2009). Term fetuses of mothers undernourished during the periconceptional period have altered expression of the glucocorticoid receptor (GR) in the hypothalamus. Underfed animals have decreased hypothalamic GR promoter methylation, reduced DNA methyltransferase activity and increased GR mRNA expression. Interestingly in twin pregnancies both control and underfed animals have the same reduced methylation and DNMT activity as underfed singletons, but there is no increase in GR mRNA expression (Begum et al., 2012, Stevens et al., 2010). These data suggest that the twin "control" animal may already exist in, and be responding to, a compromised intra-uterine environment. Importantly, these actions on the hypothalamic GR truly reflect a programming change that persists into later life. Adult (five year old) offspring of periconceptional undernourished mothers still have reduced GR promoter methylation in the hypothalamus, increased GR mRNA expression and levels of GR protein and increased adiposity (Begun et al., 2013, Jaquiery et al., 2012). In male offspring these changes are associated with a reduction in hypothalamic proopiomelanocortin (POMC) and increased NPY activity (Begum et al., 2013). These are neuropeptides that decrease and stimulate appetite respectively. In the rat, undernutrition during pregnancy increases appetite in the offspring (Vickers et al., 2005). In sheep these gene changes are associated with alterations in body composition consistent with increased food intake (Jaquiery et al., 2012). Hence, periconceptual undernutrition programs appetite regulating genes in male offspring after that have grown up as adult animals. These effects may be direct responses of the early developing brain to an altered nutrient supply, anticipating a lowered plane of nutrition but with later life mismatch. Alternatively, the responses may be mediated by altered glucocorticoid concentrations in fetal life, which in turn have been determined by changes in the placental metabolism of cortisol.

Maternal glucocorticoid treatment for prevention of respiratory distress of the newborn in women presenting in threatened preterm labor is a well-established procedure in human obstetric practice. However, there is now convincing evidence that inappropriate uses of excessive glucocorticoids may produce decreases in birth weight and have long term consequences for later health and disease including altered childhood neurodevelopment, and later hypertension, adiposity and diabetes (Lunghi et al., 2010, McKinlay et al., 2012). A recent study has shown that children of mothers treated with glucocorticoids for threatened preterm birth, but subsequently delivered at term, responded to a standard stress test at 6-11 years of age with significantly greater rises in salivary cortisol than controls (Alexander et al., 2012). Clearly a transient exposure to inappropriate glucocorticoid has long term consequences. At the present time, the importance of different times of exposure of glucocorticoids has not been resolved and the long term effects on cardiovascular, neurological and endocrine responses including diabetes remains unknown (Challis, 2012).

Final Thoughts

It will be important to resolve these issues concerning adverse effects of glucocorticoids on fetal growth and development and to balance them against the established beneficial effects of antenatal glucocorticoids on pulmonary development (Liggins and Howie, 1972). It will be necessary to determine the interactions with maternal nutritional state, sub-clinical infection and diseases of pregnancy such as preeclampsia. It is already clear that in each of these circumstances the normal functioning of the placenta is altered and likely impaired. Those alterations may be manifest in the changes in shape and dimension of the placenta that predict later health (Barker et al., 2010b).

Future research will need to establish appropriate biomarkers and relate these to known morphologic markers in the context of the physiologic events that we have described. We shall then be in a better position to intervene, potentially to influence placental function and apply that information in the prevention of later life disease.

References

Alexander, N., Rosenlocher, F., Stadler, T., Linke, J., Distler, W., Morgner, J., et al. (2012). Impact of antenatal synthetic glucorticoid exposure on endocrine stress reactivity in term-born children. *J. Clin. Endocrinol. Metab.*, 97, 3538-44.

Alfaidy, N., Gupta, S., DeMarco, C., Caniggia, I. & Challis, J.R. (2002). Oxygen regulation of placental 11 beta-hydroxysteroid dehydrogenase 2: Physiological and pathological implications. *J. Clin. Endocrinol. Metab.*, 87, 4797-805.

Audette, M.C., Challis, J.R., Jones, R.L., Sibley, C.P. & Matthews, S.G. (2011). Antenatal dexamethasone treatment in midgestation reduces system A-mediated transport in the late-gestation murine placenta. *Endocrinology*, 152, 3561-70.

Barker, D.J., Eriksson, J.G., Forsen, T. & Osmond, C. (2002). Fetal origins of adult disease: strength of effects and biological basis. *Int. J. Epidemiol.*, 31, 1235-9.

Barker, D.J. Hales, C.N., Fall, C.H., Osmond, C., Phipps, K., & Clark, P.M. (1993). Type 2 (non-insulin-dependent) diabetes mellitus, hypertension and hyperlipidaemia (syndrome X): relation to reduced fetal growth. *Diabetologia*, 36, 62-7.

Barker, D.J. & Thornburg, K.L. (2013). Placental programming of chronic diseases, cancer and lifespan: a review. *Placenta*, 34, 841-5.

Barker, D.J., Thornburg, K.L., Osmond, C., Kajantie, E. & Eriksson, J.G. (2010a). The prenatal origins of lung cancer. II. The placenta. *Am. J. Hum. Biol.*, 22, 512-16.

Barker, D.J., Thornburg, K.L., Osmond, C., Kajantie, E. & Eriksson, J.G. (2010b). The surface area of the placenta and hypertension in the offspring in later life. *Int. J. Dev. Biol.*, 54, 525-30.

Barker, D.J.P., Eriksson, J.G., Kajantie, E., Alwasel, S.H., Fall, C.H.D., Roseboom, T.J. & Osmond, C. (2011). Origins of chronic disease. In: *The placenta and human developmental programming*. Burton, P.J., Barker, D.J.P., Moffett, A. & Thornburg, K. (Eds). Cambridge: Cambridge University Press.

Begum, G., Davies, A., Stevens, A., Oliver, M., Jaquiery, A., Challis, J., et al. (2013). Maternal undernutrition programs tissue-specific epigenetic changes in the glucocorticoid receptor in adult offspring. *Endocrinology*, 154, 4560-9.

Begum, G., Stevens, A., Smith, E.B., Connor, K., Challis, J.R., Bloomfield, F., et al. (2012). Epigenetic changes in fetal hypothalamic energy regulating pathways are associated with maternal undernutrition and twinning. *FASEB J.*, 26, 1694-703.

Blank, V., Hirsch, E., Challis, J.R., Romero, R., & Lye, S.J. (2008). Cytokine signaling, inflammation, innate immunity and preterm labour- a workshop report. *Placenta*, 29 Suppl A, S102-4.

Bloomfield, F.H., Oliver, M.H., Hawkins, P., Campbell, M., Phillips, D.J., Gluckman, P.D., et al. (2003). A periconceptional nutritional origin for noninfectious preterm birth. *Science*, 300, 606.

Bloomfield, F.H., Oliver, M.H., Hawkins, P., Holloway, A.C., Campbell, M., Gluckman, P.D., et al. (2004). Periconceptional undernutrition in sheep accelerates maturation of the fetal hypothalamic-pituitary-adrenal axis in late gestation. *Endocrinology*, 145, 4278-85.

Braun, T., Challis, J.R., Newnham, J.P. & Sloboda, D.M. (2013a). Early-life glucocorticoid exposure: the hypothalamic-pituitary-adrenal axis, placental function, and long-term disease risk. *Endocr Rev*, 34, 885-916.

Braun, T., Husar, A., Challis, J.R., Dudenhausen, J.W., Henrich, W., Plagemann, A., et al. (2013b). Growth restricting effects of a single course of antenatal betamethasone treatment and the role of human placental lactogen. *Placenta*, 34, 407-15.

Braun, T., Li, S., Moss, T.J., Newnham, J.P., Challis, J.R., Gluckman, P.D., et al. (2007). Maternal betamethasone administration reduces binucleate cell number and placental lactogen in sheep. *J. Endocrinol.* 194, 337-47.

Braun, T., Li, S., Sloboda, D.M., Li, W., Audette, M.C., Moss, T.J., et al. (2009). Effects of maternal dexamethasone treatment in early pregnancy on pituitary-adrenal axis in fetal sheep. *Endocrinology*, 150, 5466-77.

Burton, G.J. & Jauniaux, E. (2011). The maternal circulation and placental shape. In: *The placenta and human developmental programming*. Burton, P.J., Barker, D.J.P., Moffett, A. & Thornburg, K. (Eds). Cambridge: Cambridge University Press.

Challis, J.R. (2012). Endocrine disorders in pregnancy: Stress responses in children after maternal glucocorticoids . *Nat. Rev. Endocrinol.*, 8, 629-30.

Challis, J.R., Lockwood, C.J., Myatt, L., Norman, J.E., Strauss, J.F., 3rd, & Petraglia, F. (2009). Inflammation and pregnancy. *Reprod. Sci.*, 16, 206-15.

Challis, J.R., Sloboda, D., Matthews, S.G., Holloway, A., Alfaidy, N., Patel, F.A., et al. (2001). The fetal placental hypothalamic-pituitary-adrenal (HPA) axis, parturition and post natal health. *Mol. Cell. Endocrinol.*, 185, 135-44.

Connor, K.L., Challis, J.R., van Zijl, P., Rumball, C.W., Alix, S., Jaquiery, A.L., et al. (2009). Do alterations in placental 11 β-hydroxysteroid dehydrogenase (11βHSD) activities explain differences in fetal hypothalamic-pituitary-adrenal (HPA) function following periconceptional undernutrition or twinning in sheep? *Reprod. Sci.*, 16, 1201-12.

Desforges, M., Mynett, K.J., Jones, R.L., Greenwood, S.L., Westwood, M., Sibley, C.P., et al. (2009). The SNAT4 isoform of the system A amino acid transporter is functional in human placental microvillous plasma membrane. *J. Physiol.*, 587, 61-72.

Edwards, C.R., Benediktsson, R., Lindsay, R.S. & Seckl, J.R. (1993). Dysfunction of placental glucocorticoid barrier: link between fetal environment and adult hypertension? *Lancet*, 341, 355-7.

Gluckman, P.D. (2013). Keynote address. 8th World Congress on Developmental Origins of Health and Disease. 17-20 November 2013, Singapore.

Harding, J.E. (2001). The nutritional basis of the fetal origins of adult disease. *Int J Epidemiol*, 30, 15-23.

Holmes, M.C., Abrahamsen, C.T., French, K.L., Paterson, J.M., Mullins, J.J. & Seckl, J.R. (2006). The mother or the fetus? 11 beta-hydroxysteroid dehydrogenase type 2 null mice provide evidence for direct fetal programming of behavior by endogenous glucocorticoids. *J. Neurosci.*, 26, 3840-4.

Imperatore, A., Li, W., Petraglia, F. & Challis, J.R. (2009). Urocortin 2 stimulates estradiol secretion from cultured human placental cells: an effect mediated by the type 2 corticotrophin-releasing hormone (CRH) receptor. *Reprod. Sci.*, 16, 551-8.

Imperatore, A., Rolfo, A., Petraglia, F., Challis, J.R. & Caniggia, I. (2010). Hypoxia and preeclampsia: increased expression of urocortin 2 and urocortin 3. *Reprod. Sci.*, 17, 833-43.

Jansson, T. & Powell, T. (2011). Placental amino acid transporters. In: *The placenta and human developmental programming*. Burton, P.J., Barker, D.J.P., Moffett, A. & Thornburg, K. (Eds). Cambridge: Cambridge University Press.

Jaquiery, A.L., Oliver, M.H., Honeyfield-Ross, M., Harding, J.E., & Bloomfield, F.H. (2012). Periconceptional undernutrition in sheep affects adult phenotype only in males. *J Nutr Metab*, 2012, 123610.

Johnstone, J.F., Bocking, A.D., Unlugedik, E. & Challis, J.R. (2005). The effects of chorioamnionitis and betamethasone on 11beta hydroxysteroid dehydrogenase types 1 and 2 and the glucocorticoid receptor in preterm human placenta. *J. Soc. Gynecol. Investig.*, 12, 238-45.

Kotelevtsev, Y., Holmes, M.C., Burchell, A., Houston, P.M., Schmoll, D., Jamieson, P., et al. (1997). 11beta-hydroxysteroid dehydrogenase type 1 knockout mice show attenuated glucocorticoid-inducible responses and resist hyperglycemia on obesity or stress. *Proc Natl. Acad. Sci. U S A*, 94, 14924-9.

Li, W. & Challis, J.R. (2005). Corticotropin-releasing hormone and urocortin induce secretion of matrix metalloproteinase-9 (MMP-9) without change in tissue inhibitors of MMP-1 by cultured cells from human placenta and fetal membranes. *J. Clin. Endocrinol. Metab.*, 90, 6569-74.

Liggins, G.C. & Howie, R.N. (1972). A controlled trial of antepartum glucocorticoid treatment for prevention of the respiratory distress syndrome in premature infants. *Pediatrics*, 50, 515-25.

Lunghi, L., Pavan, B., Biondi, C., Paolillo, R., Valerio, A., Vesce, F., et al. (2010). Use of glucocorticoids in pregnancy. *Curr. Pharm. Des.*, 16, 3616-37.

McKinlay, C.J., Crowther, C.A., Middleton, P. & Harding, J.E. (2012). Repeat antenatal glucocorticoids for women at risk of preterm birth: A Cochrane Systematic Review. *Am. J. Obstet. Gynecol.*, 206, 187-94.

Moss, T.J., Sloboda, D.M., Gurrin, L.C., Harding, R., Challis, J.R. & Newnham, J.P. (2001). Programming effects in sheep of prenatal growth restriction and glucocorticoid exposure. *Am. J. Physiol. Regul. Integr. Comp. Physiol.*, 281, R960-70.

Newnham, J.P., Evans, S.F., Godfrey, M., Huang, W., Ikegami, M. & Jobe, A. (1999). Maternal, but not fetal, administration of corticosteroids restricts fetal growth. *J. Matern. Fetal. Med.*, 8, 81-7.

Nyirenda, M.J., Lindsay, R.S., Kenyon, C.J., Burchell, A. & Seckl, J.R. (1998). Glucocorticoid exposure in late gestation permanently programs rat hepatic phosphoenolpyruvate carboxykinase and glucocorticoid receptor expression and causes glucose intolerance in adult offspring. *J. Clin. Invest.*, 101, 2174-81.

Petraglia, F., Imperatore, A. & Challis, J.R. (2010). Neuroendocrine mechanisms in pregnancy and parturition. *Endocr. Rev.*, 31, 783-816.

Pyhälä, R., Räikkönen, K., Feldt, K., Andersson, S., Hovi, P., Eriksson, J.G., et al. (2009). Blood pressure responses to psychological stress in young adults with very low birth weight: Helsinki study of very low birth weight adults. *Pediatrics*, 123, 731-4.

Seckl, J.R. & Holmes, M.C. (2007). Mechanisms of disease: glucocorticoids, their placental metabolism and fetal 'programming' of adult pathophysiology. *Nat. Clin. Pract. Endocrinol. Metab.*, 3, 479-88.

Sloboda, D.M., Challis, J.R., Moss, T.J. & Newnham, J.P. (2005). Synthetic glucocorticoids: antenatal administration and long-term implications. *Curr. Pharm. Des.*, 11, 1459-72.

Sloboda, D.M., Newnham, J.P. & Challis, J.R. (2000). Effects of repeated maternal betamethasone administration on growth and hypothalamic-pituitary-adrenal function of the ovine fetus at term. *J. Endocrinol.*, 165, 79-91.

Stevens, A., Begum, G., Cook, A., Connor, K., Rumball, C., Oliver, M., et al. (2010). Epigenetic changes in the hypothalamic proopiomelanocortin and glucocorticoid receptor genes in the ovine fetus after periconceptional undernutrition. *Endocrinology*, 151, 3652-64.

Swinburn, B.A., Sacks, G., Hall, K.D., McPherson, K., Finegood, D.T., Moodie, M.L., et al. (2011). The global obesity pandemic: shaped by global drivers and local environments. *Lancet*, 378, 804-14.

Torricelli, M., Novembri, R., Bloise, E., De Bonis, M., Challis, J.R. & Petraglia, F. (2011). Changes in placental CRH, urocortins and CRH-receptor mRNA expression associated with preterm delivery and chorioamnionitis. *J. Clin. Endocrinol. Metab.*, 96, 534-40.

Vickers, M.H., Gluckman, P.D., Coveny, A.H., Hofman, P.L., Cutfield, W.S., Gertler, A., et al. (2005). Neonatal leptin treatment reverses developmental programming. *Endocrinology*, 146, 4211-6.

In: Stress and Developmental Programming …
Editors: Lubo Zhang and Lawrence D. Longo

ISBN: 978-1-63321-836-9
© 2014 Nova Science Publishers, Inc.

Chapter 9

Stress and Maternal Response: Preeclampsia and Its Impact on Offspring Health

*Nicholas Parchim[1,3], Takayuki Iriyama[1],
Olaide Ashimi[2] and Yang Xia[1,3,•]*
[1]Department of Biochemistry and Molecular Biology,
University of Texas Medical School at Houston, Houston, US
[2]Department of Obstetrics and Gynecology and Reproductive Sciences,
The University of Texas, Houston Medical School, Houston, TX, US
[3]Graduate School of Biomedical Sciences, The University of Texas,
Houston, US

Abstract

Preeclampsia (PE) is a life-threatening pregnancy complication that affects approximately 8% of first pregnancies and accounts for more than 50,000 maternal deaths worldwide each year. The major features of PE are hypertension, proteinuria, and placenta and kidney damage. It is also a leading cause of intrauterine growth restriction (IUGR), a life-threatening condition that puts the fetus at risk for many long term cardiovascular disorders. Thus, PE is a leading cause of maternal and neonatal mortality and morbidity and has an acute and long-term impact on both moms and babies. A multitude of underlying conditions can contribute to PE. As reviewed here a growing body of evidence indicates that i) multiple preexisting maternal cardiovascular and metabolomic disorders including chronic hypertension, diabetics and obesity are risk factors for PE and fetal stress; ii) altered inflammatory responses, such as increased secretion of pro-inflammatory cytokine and immune mediator, are key components to induce impaired placental development, maternal disease development and fetal abnormality; iii) pathogenic autoantibodies exist in the circulation of patients with PE and contribute to disease development and IUGR. We highlight both human and animal

• E-mail: yang.xia@uth.tmc.edu.

evidence showing that PE is caused by multiple cellular and system alterations including imbalance of vasoactive systems, increased inflammatory responses and autoimmune components. Moreover, we integrate the maternal systemic stress associated with PE to abnormal fetal development and a long term impact on the health of their offspring. Overall, this chapter summarizes molecular and cellular mechanisms underlying the preexisting risk factors, inflammatory response and autoimmunity in PE and subsequent impact on offspring. Furthermore, the new insight revealed by current understanding of pathogenesis of PE and IUGR is important for developing new therapeutic strategies aimed at the interfering specific factors and signaling pathways detrimental to both moms and babies.

Keywords: Placenta, preeclampsia, autoantibody, hypertension, angiotensin receptor, intrauterine growth restriction

Introduction

PE is a life-threatening disease of late pregnancy characterized by hypertension and proteinuria (Granger et al., 2002, Redman and Sargent, 2005, Xia and Kellems, 2009). The condition affects approximately 8% of first pregnancies and accounts for over 80,000 premature births each year in the US (approximately 15% of total premature births), over \$4 billion in medical costs, and immeasurable human suffering. By conservative estimates, each year this disease is responsible for over 75,000 maternal deaths worldwide. PE is also associated with intrauterine growth restriction (IUGR), a dangerous condition that puts the fetus at risk for many long term cardiovascular disorders (Barker, 1998, Baum et al., 2003, Fernandez-Twinn et al., 2003, Godfrey and Barker, 2000). Thus, PE is a leading cause of maternal and neonatal mortality and morbidity and has an acute and long-term impact on both moms and babies. Despite intense research efforts, the underlying cause of PE remains poorly understood and the clinical management of PE is hampered by the lack of pre-symptomatic screening, reliable diagnostic tests and effective therapy. The only effective treatment is delivery of the fetus and placenta, often resulting in serious complications of prematurity for the neonate. The pathogenesis of PE is multifactorial, with different underlying mechanisms contributing to the disease.

Disease symptoms generally abate following delivery, suggesting that the placenta plays a central role in this disease. It is widely accepted that hypoxia is an initial trigger to induce placenta abnormalities, elevated secretion of toxic factors and subsequent maternal features (Saito and Sakai, 2003). This concept is strongly supported by animal studies showing that experimentally reduced uterine perfusion pressure (RUPP) in pregnant rats results in abnormal placentas, increased secretion of toxic factors and key preeclamptic features including hypertension and kidney damage (Granger et al., 2002). However, the past few years have provided compelling evidence that various factors other than uteroplacental hypoxia also promote placental abnormalities and disease progression: these include inflammatory cytokines (Lamarca, 2010), growth factors (Maynard et al., 2003), components of the complement cascade (Girardi et al., 2006), and autoantibodies (Zhou et al., 2008). Moreover, numerous human and animal studies indicate that chronic hypertension and metabolomic disorders are major risk factors for PE and have a detrimental role for fetal development. Here we review the impact of three major causative factors for PE including preexisting metabolomic and hypertensive disorders, increased inflammatory response and pathogenic autoantibodies, on fetal development and potential underlying mechanisms for detrimental impact on offspring health (Figure 1).

2. Maternal Risk Factors that Impact PE and Fetal Outcome

PE is a heterogeneous form of hypertension that is unique to pregnancy. The true etiology of PE remains unknown. However, multiple animal and human model studies have identified numerous clinical risk factors associated with PE. Among them, preexisting maternal cardiovascular and metabolomic disorders are highly associated with the increased morbidity and mortality of PE and impact on the outcome of the fetus. Below we review current understanding of the impacts of maternal chronic hypertension, diabetics and obesity on PE and fetal outcome.

2A. Chronic Hypertension

2A-1. Human Studies

Chronic hypertension is defined as blood pressure of 140/90 mm Hg before pregnancy or diagnosed before 20 weeks' gestation not attributable to gestational trophoblastic disease. It is also defined as hypertension first diagnosed after 20 weeks' gestation that continues to persist after 12 weeks postpartum. Superimposed PE is diagnosed in women with chronic hypertension if there is an exacerbated increase in blood pressure to the severe range (systolic pressure of 180 mm Hg or more or diastolic pressure of 110 mm Hg or more) (Buurma et al., 2012). A study conducted by Sibai et al. evaluated a large number of pregnant women and found that the presence of hypertension lasting at least four years (OR 1.6 with confidence interval 1.1-2.2), and diastolic blood pressure of at least 100 mm Hg early in pregnancy (OR 2.2 with confidence interval 1.3-5.0) were significantly associated with a higher rate of superimposed PE. Women who acquire superimposed PE during pregnancy pose an increase in the overall mortality and morbidity to their own perspective lives along with the life of their fetus. In a study done by Chappell et al., indices of maternal and perinatal morbidity and mortality were determined in women with chronic hypertension. This study represents one of the most comprehensive and contemporaneous prospective datasets of pregnant women with chronic hypertension and documents the clinically significant occurrences of adverse maternal and perinatal outcomes in this group. The study population consisted of 861 women with chronic hypertension recruited from 25 hospitals in the United Kingdom and 1 hospital in the Netherlands between August 2003 and June 2005. This prospective study found the incidence of superimposed PE was 22% (n=180). The study further found that early-onset PE ($\leq$34 weeks gestation) accounted for nearly half of the cases (42%). Finally, the studied revealed that delivering an infant <10th customized birth weight centile complicated 48% (87/180) of those with superimposed PE. The relative risk was 2.30; 95% confidence intervals [CI] 1.85 to 2.84.

This study highlighted the high prevalence of fetal growth restriction, suggesting that heightened surveillance strategies are needed in clinical practice.

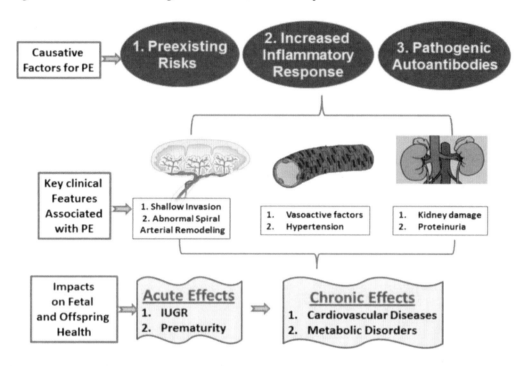

Figure 1. Causative factors for PE, IUGR and offspring health. Human and animal studies indicate that preexisting cardiovascular disease and metabolomic disorder, increased inflammatory response and pathogenic autoantibodies are major causative factors in PE. These three causative factors are not only associated with PE patients, but also have an acute effect on fetal growth restriction and long term impact on offspring health. Thus, better understanding the molecular basis for pathogenesis of PE and IUGR will provide new insight fetal development and potential underlying mechanisms for detrimental impact on offspring health.

A study done by Duckitt further supported this data by illustrating that those with superimposed PE had significantly higher rates of perinatal morbidity (odds ratio 8.8, 2.6 to 39.0), small for gestational age infants (5.6, 1.8 to 16.0), and delivery before 32 weeks (15.0, 5.7 to 38.0).

2A-2. Animal Studies

Given that the mechanisms underlying this disease are still poorly understood, animal models are of great use for elucidation. In a study done by Falcoa et al., transgenic mice that were overexpressed with human renin and angiotensinogen were found to develop de novo proteinuria during gestation and marked blood pressure elevation, which are hallmarks of superimposed PE. Abnormal placentation present in these mothers produced a significant decrease in pup and placental weight and was associated with an increased placental expression of soluble fms-like tyrosine kinase 1. Furthermore, cardiac hypertrophy was observed in these transgenic mice and was exacerbated by gestation. As a result, heart function was significantly decreased, and markers of pathological hypertrophy were increased. This animal model used in this study proved to be an excellent tool to better explain the molecular mechanisms triggering superimposed PE.

In conclusion, these studies all support that chronic hypertension is a predictive clinical risk factor for the development of superimposed PE and its severity can lead to detrimental fetal outcomes.

2B. Diabetes

2B-1. Human Evidence

Diabetes mellitus is a chronic metabolomic disorder that is characterized by either absolute or relative insulin deficiency resulting in increased glucose concentrations (Buurma et al., 2012). During pregnancy, classification of women with diabetes relies primarily on the White classification; a classification that was proposed in 1940 to better describe severity of diabetes in pregnancy (Table 1). This classification is based on factors such as age of onset, duration, as well as end organ involvement; i.e., retinal, cardiovascular, and renal. It is unquestioned that pre-gestational diabetes is a major clinical risk factor of acquiring PE in pregnancy. Hypertension that is induced or exacerbated in pregnancy is a major complication in diabetic women. The likelihood of successful outcomes with these two diseases is dependent on both the type of diabetes the mother has and the overall degree of glycemic control. Sibai et al. have determined the frequencies of PE among women with pre-gestational diabetes. The prospective observational study found that among 462 women with pregestational diabetes, 92 (20%) later had PE. The study also illustrated that PE frequency rose significantly with increasing severity of diabetes according to White classification (class B, 11%; class C, 22%; class D, 21%; class R plus class F, 36%; $P < .0001$).

Pre-gestational diabetes combined with PE has a significant impact on pregnancy outcome. More importantly there have been studies that have found that the underlying cardiovascular and renal disease decreases the likelihood of good pregnancies and fetal outcomes in diabetic women. In the same study done by Sibai et al., the frequency of preterm delivery at <35 weeks' gestation was increased in women with diabetes, and in addition it was found that the incidence of preterm delivery rose greatly with increasing severity of diabetes ($P = .00020$). Women with proteinuria at baseline were also significantly more likely to have small-for-gestational-age infants (14% vs 3%; odds ratio, 5.4; 95% confidence interval, 2.7-17.7). Research done by Garner et al., showed that the perinatal mortality rate is increased 20-fold in preeclamptic women with diabetes compared with that to those who remain normotensive. While diabetes in pregnancy is associated with increased obstetric risk compared with normal pregnancy, the overall future risk to the fetus remains large. The intrauterine environment is a key determinant of child and adult health, particularly of conditions associated with metabolic disturbances. Maternal and fetal concentrations of several growth factors, hormones and cytokines are altered in diabetes and may affect the placenta and the fetal development (Almasry et al., 2012). More recently, it has been suggested that environmental signals can alter the epigenetic state of specific genes and modulate their activity. It is possible that modulation of epigenetic states provides a possible mechanism by which maternal diabetes can mediate known long-term effects on risk for type 2 diabetes for the offspring. Studies have shown that the offspring of women with diabetes during pregnancy are also at higher risk of developing hypertension and other cardiovascular diseases later in life.

Table 1. Clinical Risk Factors for Preeclampsia and IUGR

Clinical Risk Factor for Preeclampsia	Maternal/Obstetrical Risk	Fetal Risk	Evidence from Human Studies	Evidence from Animal Studies
Chronic Hypertension	*Relative Risk of Superimposed Preeclampsia 1.38, 95% CI 1.01-1.87 (Duckitt and Harrington, 2005) *Preterm Delivery at <32 weeks(Duckitt and Harrington, 2005)	IUGR	*Early onset of preeclampsia in women with chronic hypertension (Sibai et al., 1998, Sibai, 1992)	*Mice over expressing both human angiotensinogen and human renin as a model of Superimposed Preeclampsia show abnormal placentation present in these mothers produced a significant decrease in pup weight (Franco et al., 2011)
Pregestational Diabetes	*Relative Risk of Preeclampsia 3.56%, 95% CI 2.54-4.99 (Duckitt and Harrington, 2005) *Preterm delivery at <35 weeks' gestation (Sibai et al., 1998, Sibai, 1992)	Small for gestational age (SGA)	*Perinatal mortality rate is increased 20-fold for preeclamptic women with diabetes (Luyckx et al., 2013)	*Maternal glycemia is directly associated with fetal development (Taki et al., 2012)
Obesity	Relative Risk of Preeclampsia 2.47, 95% CI 1.66-3.67 (Rowe et al., 2012)	Intrauterine fetal demise,	*Inflammation in the vasculature in obese women can increase the rate of developing preeclampsia (Irani et al., 2010)	*Dams put on high fat diet exhibited altered vascular development in the placenta along with increased hypoxia (Lorthongpanich et al., 2013)

2B-2. Animal Studies

Besides human studies, multiple animal studies not only confirm human findings, but also reveal how diabetes induces PE and impacts on fetal outcome. For example, Kiss et al. found that fetal growth were retarded in the pregnant rats with severe and mild diabetes. The study confirmed that maternal glycemia is directly associated with fetal development, specifically finding that newborns from severe diabetic mothers presented with intrauterine growth restriction. The study further highlighted that placental structure and function can be changed as a result of maternal diabetes. Although animal models have limitations and strengths, used together with clinical trials in humans, they are essential for research on the metabolic syndrome and for rapid progress in understanding the etiology and pathogenesis towards treatment and prevention of neonatal mortalities in these women. Specifically, diabetic pregnancies complicated by PE are of concern because of poor perinatal outcome. However, with improved maternal and fetal surveillance the impact of PE in diabetic pregnancies is declining (Luyckx et al., 2013).

2C. Obesity

2C-1. Human Evidence

As the world becomes more developed, obesity has become a major issue in women of child bearing age. Obesity is measured using the body mass index tool (BMI). BMI provides a simple numeric measure of a person's thickness or thinness, allowing health professionals to discuss overweight and underweight problems more objectively with their patients. The BMI of a patient is calculated using the individual's body mass divided by the square of their height - with the value universally being given in units of kg/m^2. As the numerical value increases, the individual is categorized as underweight, normal weight, overweight, obese, and morbidly obese (Table 2).

Previously, obese women typically were known to have issues with conception which may have been secondary to polycystic ovarian syndrome; however, with recent advances in assisted reproductive technologies (ART) obese women are now able to conceive. Although ART provides a great tool that physicians can use to assist these women in starting families, their pregnancies do pose as a risk. Pregnancies complicated with obesity have introduced several challenges for the maternal and the fetal system. Obesity is a definite risk factor for PE, and with the worldwide increase in obesity, there is likely to be a rise in the frequency of PE and poor fetal outcome (Buurma et al., 2012).

A study found that in comparison to women with a BMI 20 − 24.9, morbidly obese women (defined in this study as BMI > 35 Kg/m^2) faced the highest risk of PE {OR 7.2 (95% CI 4.7, 11.2)} and underweight women the lowest {OR 0.6 (95% CI 0.5, 0.7)}(Tjoa et al., 2003). It is not known why obesity is a risk factor for PE, but these conditions might be related through common features related to oxidative stress, inflammation and altered vascular function. Recently, extensive vascular infiltration of neutrophils and vascular inflammation has been reported in both preeclamptic and obese women. Evidence suggests that if the vasculature of obese women is inflamed, they could be at increased risk of developing PE when they become pregnant and are exposed to the additional burdens of pregnancy (Irani et al., 2010).

Table 2. Elevated Inflammatory Cytokines in PE and IUGR

CRP	Innate immune factor; assists complement in opsonization of foreign components	Contributes to vascular permeability (Hsuchou et al., 2012) Elevated CRP shown to cause renal damage (Pegues et al., 2013)	Contributes to direct endothelial damage (Kvehaugen et al., 2011) Shown elevated in mothers and children after birth; hypothesized to contribute to cardiac risk (Richani et al., 2005, Souwer et al., 2011)
Complement	Innate immune cascade involved in opsonization of foreign pathogens; causes direct cellular damage by pore necrosis	C5a is correlated to soluble VEGF and recurrent pregnancy loss (Denny et al., 2013b) Crry inhibitor resolves features of PE (Tincani et al., 2010) Paradoxically, C1q -/- mice exhibit PE features secondary to improper placentation (Agostinis et al., 2010)	C5a can be found in umbilical cords and amniotic fluid and correlates with pregnancy loss(Denny et al., 2013a, 2013b)
TNF-α	Key inflammatory mediator and acute phase reactant involved in direct cellular damage and recruitment of immune cells	TNF-α leads to PE features which can be blocked by specific antibody (Irani et al., 2010) Involved in B/T cell splenic compartmentalization at developmental stages(Milicevic et al., 2011) Causes vasoconstriction via nf-KB upregulation(Giorgi et al., 2012)	Genetic polymorphism results in greater TNF production (Mohajertehran et al., 2012) Inversely correlates to IQ in children (von Ehrenstein et al., 2012) Folic acid attenuates TNF increase in pregnancy (Araujo et al., 2013) Anti-TNF therapies during pregnancy have no effect on fetal development (Marchioni and Lichtenstein, 2013)

| IL-6 | Acute phase reactant thought to influence immune mediated type switching. | Increased IL-6 reduces murine litter size (Prins et al., 2012)

Complete IL-6 deficiency results in reduced implantation (Prins et al., 2012) | Patients exhibit higher bioactivity of IL-6 via trans-signaling (Rose-John, 2012)

Involved in CD8+ type switching in T cell regulation (Fujimoto et al., 2011)

Involved in increased autism risk and neurodevelopment in children (Parker-Athill and Tan, 2010) |

Inflammation is another feature of obesity relevant to cardiovascular disease. Adipose tissue produces several inflammatory mediators that can act to alter endothelial function. The role of inflammation in cardiovascular diseases is indicated by increased concentrations of inflammatory markers, and studies have shown that several of these markers are also increased in PE. C-reactive protein is an example of one of these inflammatory markers that is found to be higher in obesity and is also elevated in early pregnancy in women who later develop PE. Studies indicate that CRP could account for about one third of the relationship between BMI and the risk of PE (Kenny et al., 2010).

Research has confirmed that maternal obesity complicated with PE offers an altered genetic, hormonal and biochemical environment for the developing fetus and influences fetal growth and organ development. Furthermore, the offspring of obese mothers are subject to an increased risk of fetal demise, congenital anomalies and disrupted growth patterns, causing an increase in perinatal mortality. The impact of maternal obesity extends beyond intrauterine and neonatal life to childhood, into adolescence and adulthood (Lorthongpanich et al., 2013).

2C-2. Animal Studies

The exact mechanism by which obesity mediates poor health outcomes for fetus are far from clear. Knowledge gathered from epidemiological studies, experiments on animals and placenta models have helped to provide insight on this question. A study by Hayes et al. developed a rodent model of life-long maternal obesity to more clearly understand the mechanisms that contribute to adverse fetal outcomes in obese women. Female Sprague Dawley rats were fed a control diet (CON - 16% of calories from fat) or high fat diet (HF - 45% of calories from fat) from 3 to 19 weeks of age. Prior to pregnancy HF-fed dams exhibited significant increases in body fat, serum leptin and triglycerides. A subset of dams was sacrificed at gestational day 15 to evaluate fetal and placental development. The outcomes were associated with altered vascular development in the placenta, as well as increased hypoxia in the labyrinth. This animal model study illustrates that the placenta may play a key role in regulating the nutrient supply to the fetus and producing hormones that control fetal as well as maternal metabolism. The study also suggested that PE may be caused by the alterations in the placental vasculature. The critical alterations of placental function could induce programming of the fetus. The evidence is compelling that obesity increases the risk of PE and cardiovascular disease. Whether weight reduction prior to pregnancy or restricting weight gain during pregnancy will reduce the risk of PE is not established.

2D. Summary

The similarities between cardiovascular disease, metabolomic disorders and PE justify considering disease mechanisms established for cardiovascular and metabolomics disorders as potentially important contributors to the pathophysiology of PE. It is unlikely that these factors act independently but rather are very likely interactive. Formally establishing the relationship of these mechanisms to PE could provide targets for future therapy.

3. Elevated Inflammatory Mediators Play a Key Role in PE and Affect Fetal Outcome

Inflammation is defined as a pathophysiologic response to infection or tissue damage. In order to kill bacteria or remove damaged tissue, the innate immune systems launch a program to initially induce proliferation and migration of multiple immune cells including neutrophils and macrophages to the inflamed sites. Subsequently, activated inflammatory cells secret multiple cytokines to facilitate initial immune response to attack infection and prevent further tissue damage. Among all of the cytokines, TNF-α is the most studied and known to induce IL-6 production predominantly from macrophages via activation of its receptors. Elevated IL-6 facilitates proinflammaotry response on macrophage cells to activate IL-6 receptor (IL-6R) signaling cascade and multiple other non-IL-6R cells types to trans-activate gp130 by complex of IL-6 and soluble receptor (sIL-6) (Rose-John, 2012). Subsequently, IL-6 is a major cytokine to induce C-reactive protein (CRP) production from liver to cooperatively work complement signaling cascade to increase membrane perturbation, phagocytosis and inflammation. Thus, TNF-α-IL-6-CRP and activated complement components work coordinately and synergistically to maintain our normal immune network and regulate multi-organ functions (Figure 2). However, persistently elevated inflammatory cells secrete cytokines to the circulation and subsequent elevated CRP and activated complement that go beyond the local tissues, resulting in multi-systemic tissue damage and injury. A growing body of evidence indicates that an increased inflammatory response is associated with PE and contributes to disease (Granger et al., 2002, Lamarca, 2010, LaMarca et al., 2007). Both human and animal studies have shown that multiple circulating proinflammatory cytokines and mediators including TNF-α, IL-6, C-reactive protein (CRP) and activated complement components are increased in PE. *In vitro* and *in vivo* evidence indicates that elevated proinflammatory cytokines function via specific signaling pathways leading to shallow trophoblast invasion, trophoblast apoptosis (Allaire et al., 2000, Yu et al., 1999), and elevation of anti-angiogenic factors (Ahmad and Ahmed, 2004). All of which likely lead to impaired placentation, decreased uteroplacental perfusion and subsequent hypertension and kidney injury, hallmark features associated with PE, damage of the fetus, newborn, even leading into adulthood (Figure 2).

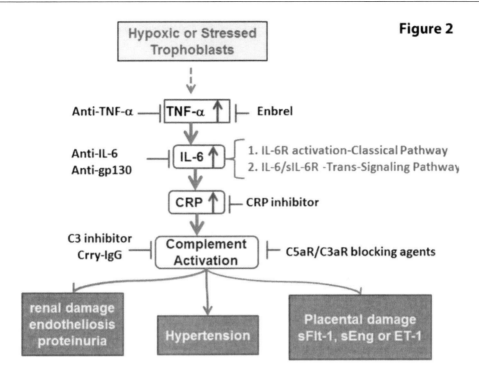

Figure 2. Multiple cytokines and immune mediators are elevated in PE patients and coordinately work together to promote disease progression and impact on fetal growth and offspring health. In response to trophoblast cell stress, TNF-□ is elevated and leads to subsequent IL-6 secretion from immune cells. IL-6 receptors (IL-6R) are expressed on neutrophils and hepatocytes. Elevated IL-6 signaling via its classical pathways activates IL-6R on hepatocytes to induce secretion of CRP. Additionally, elevated IL-6 can signal via trans-signaling by forming complex of IL-6/sIL-6R (soluble IL-6R) to activate other cell types with no or low abundance of IL-6R. Finally, elevated CRP work synergistically with activated complements to promote proinflammatory response and disease development. Multiple animal studies have shown the detrimental role of elevated cytokines and immune mediators in PE and IUGR. Moreover, preclinical studies have shown that reducing their elevated levels by neutralizing antibodies or interfering specific receptor activation successfully ameliorate PE features including hypertension, kidney damage, placental injury and anti-angiogenic factor secretion and IUGR. Thus, these studies provide new insight of pathogenesis of disease and novel therapies to treat PE, prevent IUGR and improve offspring health.

Significant amount studies demonstrate that reducing elevated TNF-α, IL-6, CRP or activated complements or interfering their specific receptor activation are effective in preclinical studies to treat PE in multiple animal models of PE (Figure 2). Below we highlight the essential role and molecular mechanisms of proinflammatory cytokines in PE and the impact on fetal growth and postnatal health.

3A. Important Role of Tumor Necrosis Factor-α in PE and Fetal Growth

A growing body of evidence indicates that increased TNF-α, a potent inflammatory cytokine, is associated with PE and may contribute to disease (Granger et al., 2002, Lamarca, 2010). Here, we summarize both human and animal studies to highlight the pathological role of TNF-α in PE and IUGR and the underlying mechanisms of disease pathogenesis.

3A-1. Human Studies-Elevated TNF-a Production and Polymorphism Associated with PE and Fetal Growth Restriction

Multiple human studies have provided strong evidence that elevated TNF-α correlates to onset of PE symptomology and to severity of disease (Lau et al., 2013). In the constellation of PE disease subtypes, TNF family members can also be elevated in women with hemolysis, elevated liver enzymes, and low platelets (HELLP) syndrome and chorioamnionitis (Carpentier et al., 2011, Murphy et al., 2013). Further data have characterized TNF-α polymorphisms in populations with PE. Promoter polymorphism at G308A is associated with increased TNF production (Mohajertehran et al., 2012). Besides elevation in maternal circulation in PE patients, TNF-α is also elevated in small for gestational age infants characterized with IQ deficits, suggesting that elevated TNF may impair neuronal development and network formation. These data are mirrored by studies which correlate reduced folic acid uptake with increased TNF-α (Araujo et al., 2013). Folic acid is critical during early development to ensure proper neural crest cell migration and neural tube formation. Failure during this stage can lead to severe fetal malformation and death. Similarly, a study by Almasry et al., found increased TNF-α deposition in the villous trophoblast cells of growth restricted infants (Almasry et al., 2012). Elevated deposition was found in trophoblast giant cells, responsible for placental invasion and maintenance. Studies have shown that TNF-α deposition can be toxic to these cells and directly damaging to developing endothelial cells. TNF-α mRNA expression was also increased in umbilical arteries of PE mothers compared to normal control (Almasry et al., 2012). It is thought that this elevation of TNF-α is contributory to placental damage and hypoxia via damage to the endothelial cellular structure.

3A-2. Molecular Basis Underlies TNF-a-Mediated Pathophysiology of PE and Fetal Growth Restriction

3A-2a) In vitro studies-Multiple *in vitro* studies demonstrated the important roles of TNF-α in PE. For example, previous *in vitro* studies showed that TNF-α induces trophoblast apoptosis.

Moreover, early *in vitro* studies indicated that TNF-α contributes to elevated secretion of sVEGFR1 (sFlt-1) from cultured human villous explants (Ahmad and Ahmed, 2004). As such, elevated sVEGFR1 (sFlt-1) likely leads to impaired placentation, decreased uteroplacental perfusion and subsequent hypertension and kidney injury.

3A-2b) In vivo animal studies- Accumulating animal studies have supported the pathogenic role of TNF-α in PE and fetal growth restriction. For instance, direct injection of TNF-α leads to hypertension and proteinuria and small fetus in pregnant rats (Alexander et al., 2002). Consistently, infusion of TNF-α induces PE features in pregnant baboons (Sunderland et al., 2011). Supporting these studies, circulating TNF-α is elevated in several other animal models of PE including restricted uterine perfusion pressure (RUPP) pregnant rats and angiotensin receptor type I agonistic autoantibody (AT1-AA)-infused pregnant mice (Irani et al., 2010, LaMarca et al., 2005). Neutralizing TNF-α antibody or interfering its receptor activation has significantly reduced PE features and increased baby sizes in both RUPP and AT1-AA animal models of PE (Irani et al., 2010, LaMarca et al., 2005). Thus, these animal studies indicate a general important role of elevated TNF-α in PE and restricted fetal growth.

Of note, in a model of inflammation and infection, lipopolysaccharide (LPS) injections in mid-pregnancy (embryonic day 12.5) leads to elevations of inflammatory molecules *via* toll like receptor (TLR) activation. The study concludes that the TNF-α receptor I is integral in this pathogenesis (Xu et al., 2006). Interestingly, LPS stimulations during this pregnancy midpoint influence many factors of fetal development, including neural progenitor cell proliferation and reactive oxygen species formation. Additionally, LPS injection resulted in reduced litter size and fetal loss. Indeed, TNF-α activation, due to its cytotoxic nature, is integral in inflammatory-based pregnancy loss and fetal damage. Further study also showed that this model was characterized by skeletal anomalies and developmental deficits in eye patterning (Carpentier et al., 2011, Liu et al., 2012, Murphy et al., 2013). This stated, TNF signaling is a double-edged sword. Studies have shown that the primary receptor, TNF receptor 1, is required for proper splenic development and B/T cell compartmentalization especially in adult life (Milicevic et al., 2011, Odaka et al., 2010). Therefore, complete blockade may be detrimental early in development. Despite the wide regard as a detrimental cytokine in fetal development and in pregnancy, it might be required for proper developmental events.

3B. Role of IL-6-Mediated Signaling Network in PE and Fetal Growth Restriction

IL-6 is a pro-inflammatory cytokine with multiple function predominantly secreted by T cells and macrophages (Rose-John, 2012). It is also produced by adipocytes which is consistent with elevated IL-6 in obese individuals (Scheller and Rose-John, 2012). Of note, IL-6 is involved in two signaling cascades, classical and trans-signaling pathways. Like other cytokines, classical IL-6 pathway refers to IL-6 activating the cell types containing IL-6 receptor (IL-6R) on the cell surface, such as inflammatory cells. Besides classical IL-6 pathway, recent studies demonstrate that IL-6 also functions via its trans-signaling pathway by soluble IL-6 (sIL-6R). Specifically, a soluble form of IL-6R (sIL-6R) comprising the extracellular portion of the receptor can bind IL-6 with a similar affinity as the membrane bound IL-6R. The sIL-6R forming complex with circulating IL-6 activates numerous cell types containing no IL-6R by trans-activating its membrane bound cofactor, gp130 (Rose-John, 2012). Thus, both classical and trans IL-6 pathways are involved in inflammation, clotting, hemodynamics, and oncogenesis signaling via the Jak/STAT pathways and gp130 receptor (Lau et al., 2013, Prins et al., 2012, Weiss et al., 2013). Moreover, elevated IL-6 is known to contribute to the development of hypertension in many disease states including metabolic syndrome, kidney injury, and autoimmune conditions (Weiss et al., 2013). Here, we highlight human and mouse studies about the role of elevated IL-6 in PE and maternal and fetal pathophysiology.

3B-1. Human Evidence-Circulating IL-6 Levels Is Elevated in PE and Associated with Disease Severity and IUGR

Numerous human studies have shown that elevated IL-6 has been closely associated with severity of PE (Prins et al., 2012). Most studies characterize elevated IL-6 by third trimester of pregnancy. Interestingly, IL-6 exerts most effects *via* the soluble IL-6 receptor and gp130 receptor (Prins et al., 2012). Recent studies indicate that in early-onset severe PE patients there is less circulating IL-6, but greater gp130, owing to a greater sensitivity to IL-6. Interestingly, Parker-Athill et al., reviewed that viral exposure and subsequent activation of the IL-6 cascade are integral in the development of autism spectrum disorders (Parker-Athill and Tan, 2010). Thus, elevated circulating IL-6 is associated with PE and fetal development.

3B-2. Animal Studies-Pathogenic Role of IL-6 in PE and IUGR

Numerous animal studies have demonstrated the important role of IL-6 in the pathophysiology of PE and fetal growth. A role for IL-6 in hypertension is evident from the fact that IL-6 deficient mice are resistant to angiotensin II induced hypertension (Zhang et al., 2012). Moreover, direct infusion of IL-6 into pregnant rats results in hallmark features of PE including hypertension, proteinuria and small babies (Lamarca et al., 2011a). Supporting this finding, circulating IL-6 is found to be induced in several other animal models of PE including restricted uterine perfusion pressure (RUPP) pregnant rats and angiotension receptor type I agonistic autoantibody (AT1-AA)-infused pregnant mice (Gadonski et al., 2006, Zhou et al., 2011). Interfering IL-6R activation has significantly reduced PE features and increased baby sizes in both RUPP and AT1-AA animal models of PE (Gadonski et al., 2006, Zhou et al., 2011). These animal studies demonstrate a general pathogenic role of elevated IL-6 in PE and restricted fetal growth. Supporting the detrimental role of elevated IL-6 in PE and fetal growth, as reviewed by Dixon, IL-6 and its soluble receptor may be integral in cardiac remodeling and cardiac fibroblast formation. For example, IL-6 knockout was shown to be cardioprotective and assisted in preserving cardiac function and reducing myocyte hypertrophy post-ischemia. Further, IL-6 trans signaling has been implicated in metabolic syndrome, endothelial dysfunction, and worsening atherosclerosis.

While most animal studies have shown the detrimental role of elevated IL-6 and sIL-6R in PE and IUGR, certain amounts of studies indicate that IL-6 may be required for successful maintenance of pregnancy. For instance, a CBA/J x DBA/2 mouse combination model is typically associated with a higher fetal resorption rate with less IL-6 secretion (Prins et al., 2012). Supplementation of IL-6 during pregnancy in this model partially rescues fetal litter size. IL-6 deficient mice, despite a lack of overt phenotype, have compromised implantation and increased incidence of fetal resorption. The IL-6 deficient model also has delayed parturition, but can be rescued by supplementation of IL-6 mid-gestation (Wei et al., 2013). Thus, these studies indicate balanced IL-6 levels are essential for normal pregnancy, fetal development, stress, and immunology (Dixon, 2010). Persistently elevated IL-6 and sIL-6 become detrimental to induce PE, IUGR and many other cardiovascular abnormalities.

3C. Pathogenic Role of C-Reactive Protein (CRP) in PE and Fetal Growth Restriction

CRP is an innate immune factor which is induced by IL-6 and elevated early in the inflammatory immune response. Involved in opsonization of foreign pathogens, it works with complement components to assist in the removal of these products. Because of its early rise in the inflammatory process, CRP is often considered important to stimulation of other cytokines in the process. In conditions such as cardiac risk prediction, CRP, along with troponin, is shown to be elevated in response to damaged tissue (Grad and Danenberg, 2013, Ridker, 2003). While it is largely thought to be nonspecific in its action and serves along the innate immune axis, recent evidence points to specific actions against host. Recruitment of nonspecific inflammatory mediators has been shown to be detrimental by damaging the host tissues or signaling inflammatory cells to the site of insult. Recent studies have closely tied CRP with renal dysfunction and atherosclerosis secondary to intimal arterial damage (Castellano et al., 2010, Grad and Danenberg, 2013, Grad et al., 2012, Labarrere and Zaloga, 2004). Further, persistently elevated CRP is correlated to progressive decline of kidney function in chronic kidney disease patients. Mechanisms postulated for its role in kidney dysfunction is due to deposition of CRP in the glomerulus and subsequent increase in oxidative stress. In this part, we will review recent human and animal studies in the understanding the roles of CRP in PE, fetal development, and offspring health.

3C-1. Human Evidence-Circulating CRP is Elevated in PE and Persistently Elevated in Moms and Babies Postpartum

Human studies have attempted to characterize importance of CRP in the maternal environment. Although no definitive connection has been tied to CRP and the role in immune activation or maternal-fetal damage, numerous reports have shown that circulating CRP is elevated in PE and its level is correlated to the severity of the disease (Boij et al., 2012, Catarino et al., 2012, Chakravarty et al., 2005). For example, early studies have shown an increase in CRP family member pentraxin 3, PTX3, correlated with PE severity (Castellano et al., 2010). Of note, several studies have identified that the elevation of circulating CRP is also correlated to multiple pathogenic factors including TNF-α, IL-6, excess complement production and soluble VEGF, implicating its role in endothelial dysfunction, uterine arterial constriction, macrophage activation, and arterial plaque formation (Rampersad et al., 2008). Supporting the possible long-term role of CRP for maternal and fetal pathophysiology in PE, a recent cohort study found circulating CRP is still elevated 5-8 years postpartum in mothers with PE and the presence of CRP in fetuses after birth (Kvehaugen et al., 2011). Additionally, this study also found the persistent presence of endothelial dysfunction in preeclamptic women postpartum and babies born from these mothers for years (Kvehaugen et al., 2011). These findings suggest that elevated CRP in PE may have a role in endothelial dysfunction in both moms and babies in their later life and could be a potential risk factor for future cardiac events (Kvehaugen et al., 2011, Richani et al., 2005, Souwer et al., 2011, Tincani et al., 2010).

3C-2. Animal Studies-CRP Contributes to Vascular Permeability, Renal Damage, and Alterations in Immunity

Although no animal studies are available about the role of CRP in pathophysiology of PE and fetal growth, multiple studies have shown the detrimental effects of CRP in kidney injury and vascular damage in non-pregnant animals. These studies could have ramifications for its role in pregnancy related hypertension and impact on fetal growth and postnatal health. For example, Pegues et al. demonstrated that overexpressing human CRP in transgenic mice results in increased proinflammatory response and acute kidney damage. This study further revealed that CRP is involved in switching the macrophage inflammatory balance to strongly proinflammatory, worsening kidney injury and creating a malicious cycle (Tron et al., 2008). Similarly, injection of CRP leads to increased blood brain permeability and neuro-inflammation in mouse models (Hsuchou et al., 2012). Previous studies have shown that CRP promotes M1 type macrophage differentiation and enhances inflammation by increasing inflammatory cytokines (Tron et al., 2008). The presence of proinflammatory cytokines indicates a self-reinforcing cycle and a potentially hostile fetal environment.

3D. Role of Activated Complement Cascades in PE and Fetal Growth Restriction

The complement cascades are tightly regulated effector pathways of innate immunity, communicating efficiently with CRP to assist with removal of foreign immune invaders (Ricklin et al., 2010). There are three main pathways through which complement can assist in removal of foreign pathogens: classical, alternative, and mannose-lectin binding pathway. Moreover, activation of the terminal complement components is necessary for formation of the membrane attack complex on the foreign pathogen. Each pathway is necessary for elimination of pathogenic components in the circulation and in tissues. While complement and CRP are known to assist in bacteria, fungal, and, occasionally, viral clearance, the systems can become harmful when directed toward self-tissues. Tight regulation, especially during pregnancy, is necessary for successful pregnancy maintenance. In this part, we summarize the role of activated complement components in PE and the impact on fetal growth.

3D-1. Human Evidence-Activated Complement Components in PE and the Association with IUGR

The multiple activated complement pathways are associated with PE. For instance, early studies showed extensive activation of the alternative complement pathway in the third trimester of pregnancy in the absence of maternal infection in PE. The upregulation of these complement split products is similar between patients with PE who exhibited term and preterm delivery. Furthermore, complement split products were detected in the fetal compartment although it was unclear whether the placenta or maternal vasculature was the site of activation of the complement system. Further investigation into the complement pathway has also implicated the role of the classical pathway in the influence of immunologic reactivity of PE. A recent study focused on classical complement components as potential causative factors in PE when deranged (Agostinis et al., 2010, Sjowall et al., 2007). Correlation of terminal complement components (TCC) with recurrent spontaneous abortion has been noted (Tincani et al., 2010). Further, complement components contribute to increased production of soluble-VEGFR which binds free VEGF and prevents activation of VEGFR1 and vascular growth. This soluble-VEGFR1 is instrumental in affecting fetal growth restriction and pregnancy loss (Castellano et al., 2010, Collard et al., 1999). A study by Buurma et al., found C4d, integral in the classical pathway to be a specific indicator of PE severity (Buurma et al., 2012). C4d staining and its mRNA expression are increased significantly in the placentas of PE patients (Buurma et al., 2012). However, co-localization of C4d to terminal components was not statistically significant compared to controls indicating that some regulation of complement activation is present in PE patients (Buurma et al., 2012). More recent studies showed that C3a deposition is significantly increased in the placentas of PE patients (Wang et al., 2012). Taken together, both classic and alternative complement cascades are activated in the placentas of women with PE. More troubling is the presence of complement components, especially C5a, at the maternal-fetal interface. Recently, Denny et al., have characterized the presence of anaphylotoxin C5a in the umbilical cord of women with PE (Denny et al., 2013a, 2013b). This is an early inciting element in priming the infant immune system toward inflammation. Similar studies showed that elevated C5a in amniotic fluid was significantly associated with spontaneous fetal loss. Richani et al. have hypothesized that this could be due to significant changes within the fetus, due to increased oxidative stress and rapid failure of vascular development (Richani et al., 2005).

3D-2. Animal Evidence- Role of Complements in PE and Fetal Immunity

Many studies have characterized problems with the complement system during pregnancy. Each complement component has very specific functions, but two of the most potent are C3a and C5a, both anaphylotoxins. They are integral in recruiting inflammatory cells (chemotaxis) and inducing vascular permeability. Recent mouse studies have linked the role of C5a to elevations of soluble VEGFR1 and the fall of placental growth factors (Denny et al., 2013a, Ehrnthaller et al., 2011). Interestingly, elevation of C5a is implicated in recurrent pregnancy loss and fetal morbidity. Treatment of C5a inhibitors, does however, lead to abatement of fetal morbidity, as well, as reversal of placental and vascular growth factor deficiencies. Other murine based complement models have shown insight into the role of the innate immune axis in pregnancy. Treatment with Crry, a murine complement regulatory protein, can prevent oxidative stress and placental dysfunction in CBA/J mice bred to induce global complement components. Treatment with Crry reduces soluble VEGFR1, oxidative stress, proteinuria, urea nitrogen and reduces features of PE (Java et al., 2013, Ricklin et al., 2010, Tincani et al., 2010). On the contrary, early complement components such as C1q have been hypothesized to be necessary for proper placentation and maintenance of a successful pregnancy. C1q $^{-/-}$ mice exhibit features of PE, presumably from improper placentation, but features resolve postpartum (Agostinis et al., 2010). This indicates that the complement cascade is in delicate balance and must be tightly regulated in order to have successful pregnancies and proper maternal fetal interface.

3D-3. Summary

In this part, we have reviewed and highlighted studies regarding the important role of inflammatory cytokines in PE, IUGR and impact on the health of offspring in their later life. It is important to realize that balanced inflammatory response is essential for normal pregnancy and fetal growth. Too much or too little turns out to be detrimental for normal pregnancy and has a long term impact on offspring's health.

4. Role of Autoimmune Conditions in PE, Fetal Development and Offspring Health

Autoimmune diseases are the major medical burden that affects approximately 5% of US population and the coexistence of pregnancy and autoimmune diseases is far from rare. The relationship between autoimmunity and pregnancy is represented by a bidirectional model. Autoimmune disease can be affected by pregnancy, in turn, pregnancy can also be affected by autoimmune disease from the early stage of gestation. Over the years, antiphospholipid syndrome (APS) and systemic lupus erythematosus (SLE) are two most well studied autoimmune diseases with multiple complications during the pregnancy. Potential adverse events include miscarriage, fetal loss, intrauterine fetal growth restriction (IUGR), and PE. Numerous recent studies over 14 years have demonstrated that PE patients develop the autoantibodies that can activate angiotensin II type1 receptor (termed AT1-AA) and contribute to the disease pathophysiology. Moreover, AT1-AA can cross placentas to fetal circulation leading to IUGR. Thus, these studies provide strong evidence that AT1-AA is a pathogenic autoantibody contributing to PE and IUGR. This evidence suggests the possibility that PE is a pregnancy-induced autoimmune condition. In this part, we will review recent studies and advances in the understanding of roles of pathogenic autoantibodies (AT1-AA) or autoimmune diseases including APS and SLE in PE, fetal development, and offspring health.

4A. Antiphospholipid Syndrome Causes Multiple Maternal Complications and Impacts Fetal Outcome

Antiphospholipid syndrome (APS) is an autoimmune disease characterized by vascular thrombosis and/or obstetrical complications in association with the presence of antiphospholipid antibodies (aPL-Abs). Like many autoimmune diseases, it is more common in women than in men, especially in reproductive ages. aPL-Abs are involved in vascular thrombosis as well as pregnancy-related complications such as miscarriage, stillbirth, preterm delivery, or PE (Meroni et al., 2011). The syndrome can be divided into primary (no underlying disease state) and secondary (in association with an underlying disease state) forms. APS also occurs in the context of other autoimmune diseases, such as systemic lupus erythematosus (SLE).

4A-1. Human Epidemiological Studies Indicate that APS Increases Risk of PE and Induces Fetal Abnormalities

In addition to clinical thrombotic events, several obstetric complications are associated with aPL-Abs, including fetal loss, PE, placental insufficiency-mediated IUGR, and preterm delivery (Irani et al., 2009). PE comprises one of the pregnancy-related maternal and fetal morbidities and mortalities seen in APS patients. In the United States, PE occurs in approximately 8% of pregnancies and 16.1% of maternal deaths are attributable to PE (Khan et al., 2006). The frequency of PE in pregnant women with APS can reach up to 50% (Zhou et al., 2007). Many studies have shown a positive association between aPL-Abs and PE, with a relative risk ranging 2 to 20 (Heilmann et al., 2011). For example, Cnossen JS et al. have conducted a systematic review on multiple maternal risk factors for PE that includes aPL-Abs. In this review five studies were selected, and meta-analysis of two cohort studies found a relative risk of 9.73 (Wang et al., 2012). Additional clinical studies report that aPL-Ab titer is correlated to the severity of PE. Yamada et al. reported a prospective evaluation of more than 1,000 women showing women with aPL-Abs had an increased risk of pregnancy-induced hypertension (OR 5.5) and this OR is higher in severe pregnancy-induced hypertension (OR 8.1) (Yamada et al., 2009). Additional studies document that 11 − 17% of women with PE will test positive for aPL-Abs, and the association is the strongest in women with severe preterm PE (less than 34 weeks of gestation) (Moodley et al., 1995, Thway et al., 2004).

aPL-Abs are also well-known to adversely affect the fetal development and offspring health resulting from recurrent embryonic or fetal loss and IUGR. Most studies have reported that 5-20% of women with recurrent pregnancy loss test positive for aPL-Abs (Irani et al., 2009). IUGR complicates pregnancies in APS patients, occurring in 15-30% in most reports (Cetin and Alvino, 2009, Irani et al., 2009). According to a recent systematic review and meta-analysis, lupus anticoagulant test has the strongest association with recurrent fetal losses (>10 weeks GA) (OR; 4.73) and IUGR (OR; 4.65) (Abou-Nassar et al., 2011).

4A-2. Pathogenic Mechanisms Underlie Antiphospholipid Antibodies-Mediated Impaired Pregnancy and Fetal Loss

It has been long speculated that most of these potentially pathogenic aPL-Abs should be absorbed at the placenta and should not be transferred to the fetus. Thus, most of the detrimental effects of aPL leading to these pregnancy complications are supposed to be induced at the maternal and placental levels. A number of studies have been conducted to elucidate the detrimental function of aPL-Abs in the pathogenesis of fetal loss. Limited number of reports link directly to PE or IUGR. However, evidence obtained from studies of fetal loss are invaluable for us to understand the pathogenesis of PE as well as IUGR, since the possible causative pathologic factors of fetal loss are thought to have a lot in common with impaired placentation, intraplacental thrombosis, and enhanced inflammation. Here we summarize causative mechanisms associated with the development of obstetrical complications seen in APS.

*4A-2a) Intraplacental thrombosis and defective placentation are key mechanism for abnormal pregnancy-*Among several pathogenic mechanisms hypothesized to explain the obstetrical complications related to APS, intraplacental thrombosis was traditionally suggested to be the main pathogenic event. This hypothesis is supported by a substantial body of histological findings of intervillous thrombosis, extensive villous fibrosis, or marked infarction in placentas from APS patients (Franco et al., 2011). An array of studies has demonstrated the ability of aPL-Abs to induce a general procoagulant state characterized by endothelial cell activation, inhibition of protein C/S system, increased thromboxane synthesis, tissue factor activation, and cytokine production (Wei et al., 2013). Moreover, recent investigations reported that Apl-Abs can displace annexin V from trophoblast surface where this protein carries out a potent anticoagulant activity based on its high binding affinity to anionic phospholipids (Rand et al., 1997).

However, a thrombophilic state alone cannot explain the pregnancy complications associated with APS. Besides thrombosis, evidence indicates that alternative aPL-mediated pathogenic mechanisms impede placentation that results from direct targeting of the invading trophoblasts by aPL-Abs. The failure in proper placental development is believed to be the main cause of PE as well as fetal loss and IUGR. These non-thrombotic mechanisms are thought to be caused by direct effects of anti-β2 glycoprotein I autoantibodies on the placenta. On the fetal side, the binding of aPL-Abs to β2 glycoprotein I expressed on trophoblast membranes might trigger membrane perturbation, resulting in modulation of several cell biological functions, cell injury and apoptosis, inhibition of proliferation, decreased production of human chorionic gonadotrophin, defective secretion of growth factors and impaired invasiveness (Meroni et al., 2011). All of these aPL-Ab-mediated effects might participate in causing defective placentation associated with the diseases.

*4A-2b) Increased Inflammatory response underlies fetal loss in APL-*PE is characterized as an excessive maternal inflammatory response, which results in the defective placentation, placental ischemia, vascular damage, and oxidative stress. A growing body of evidence indicates that enhanced inflammatory response such as increased inflammatory cytokines secretion (TNF-α, IL-6, IL-8, and IL-12), leukocyte proliferation, and complement activation is seen in PE patients and contributes to the disease (Cetin and Alvino, 2009). There have been no study directly linking the involvement of enhanced maternal inflammatory response in APS patients to PE, however, recent studies in the research field of fetal loss have provided compelling evidence indicating that the presence of an enhanced maternal inflammatory state contributes to the disease.

In the experimental model of fetal loss, repeated intraperitoneal injections of human IgG with aPL-Ab activity to pregnant mice after embryo implantation induces considerable placental inflammatory damage that results in fetal resorption. In this mouse placenta, the deposition of human IgG and mouse complement, neutrophil infiltration, and local TNF-α secretion are seen, in association with an increase in blood TNF-α levels (Holers et al., 2002, Irani and Xia, 2008).

Excessive deposition and activation of complement system are known to be observed in placentas of SLE patients (Shamonki et al., 2007). Several lines of evidence also support the involvement of complement systems in aPL-Ab-mediated fetal loss in this mouse model, as suggested by the protection that deficiency in complement components confers on the animals (Girardi et al., 2006, Thurman et al., 2005). The hypothesis that complement is involved in the fetal loss induced by aPL-Abs is further supported by the demonstration that the protective effect of heparin in the mouse model is related to the anticomplement, rather than to the anticoagulant, activity (Irani and Xia, 2008). These evidences described above are from fetal loss studies, however, it is possible that these mechanisms suggesting that aPL-Abs could induce maternal inflammatory response in mice might also link to the pathogenesis of PE.

4B. Systemic Lupus Erythematosus (SLE)

Systemic lupus erythematosus (SLE) is an autoantibody-mediated systemic autoimmune disease that primarily affects women in their reproductive age years. In the USA, about 4,500 pregnancies yearly occur in women complicated by SLE (Xia et al., 2007). This chronic disease is characterized by its multi-organ involvements; joints, hearts, lung, kidneys, and skin.

The general understanding of this disease encompasses autoantibody production and immune complex deposition, which causes the subsequent autoimmune phenomenon. SLE predominantly affects women of reproductive age; therefore, pregnancy in women with SLE is a common clinical problem. With treatment advances, the prognosis of pregnancy in women with SLE has been improved. However, SLE is still associated with poor obstetric outcomes including PE.

4B-1. Epidemiological Pregnancy-Related Risks in SLE Patients

Pregnancies in patients with SLE are associated with higher maternal and fetal morbidity and mortality. In a recent US study of 16.7 million pregnancies, 13,555 occurred in SLE patients and were associated with a 20-fold increase in maternal mortality and an increased likelihood of PE, IUGR, and preterm labor (OR of 3.0, 2.6, and 2.4 respectively) (Siddiqui et al., 2010). PE complicates 13–35% of lupus pregnancies, compared with 5–8% of pregnancies among the general US population (Chakravarty et al., 2005, Moroni and Ponticelli, 2003, Xia et al., 2007). From the recent nationwide inpatient samples for a 4-year period in US, SLE patients have a 3-fold increased risk of PE (OR; 3.0). This increased risks persisted when adjusted for maternal age (Siddiqui et al., 2010). Fetal morbidity and mortality in SLE pregnancies were recently reported in a systematic review and meta-analysis of case series from throughout the world. Among 29 observational studies with 2751 pregnancies, the rate of premature birth was 39.4%, spontaneous abortion 16%, intrauterine growth restriction (IUGR) 12.7%, stillbirth 3.6% and neonatal deaths 2.5% (Smyth et al., 2010).

In addition to these pregnancy-related complications, some autoantibodies seen in SLE patients are well-known to be transferred from mother to fetus and compromise the health of fetuses and neonates. Neonatal lupus erythematosus (NLE) occurs in some babies born from mothers with anti-Ro/SSA and/or anti-La/SSB antibody. Anti-Ro/SSA and anti-La/SSB are among the most frequently detected autoantibodies against extractable nuclear antigen and are associated with SLE and Sjogren's syndrome. The most serious complication of neonates is congenital heart block (CHB) which is seen in 1-5% pregnancies with these antibodies (Ruiz-Irastorza and Khamashta, 2008, Salmon et al., 2011, Xia et al., 2007).

4B-2. Mechanisms of SLE-Associated Obstetrical Complications

4B-2a) Antiphospholipid antibodies-Antiphospholipid antibodies (aPL-Abs) are present in about a quarter to a half of SLE patients (Lateef and Petri, 2012). As described in the section on antiphospholipid syndrome (APS), aPL-Abs are supposed to exert their detrimental effects on pregnancies with SLE by inducing intraplacental thrombosis, defective placentation, and excessive inflammatory response, which could be associated with obstetrical complications such as PE, fetal loss, and placental insufficiency-mediated IUGR.

4B-2b) Immunological Abnormality in Pregnancy Complicated by SLE

*4B-2b-i) Disturbance of cytokine production related to Th1/Th2 imbalance-*Multiple immunological adaptations occur during normal pregnancy to allow for maternal tolerance towards fetal alloantigens. These adaptations include alterations in cytokine profiles, changes in lymphocyte populations, production of complement inhibitors in the placenta, and regulation of the molecules expressed in trophoblast cells (Gill et al., 2007). As a cause of PE as well as fetal loss and placental insufficiency-associated IUGR, the disturbance of this process is hypothesized to be associated with the impairment of placentation, which leads to the development of diseases (Saito and Sakai, 2003). The most important changes include the T helper type 2 (Th2) cell polarization in maternal immune response.

Cytokines produced by CD4+ T helper (Th) cells have been traditionally classified into Th1 and Th2 repertoires. Th1 cytokines includes interleukin (IL)-1, IL-2, IL-12, TNF-α, and interferon (IFN) γ, which stimulate cellular immunity. Th2 cytokines, which includes IL-4, IL-5, IL-6, and IL-10, are involved in humoral immunity. Maternal tolerance toward fetal alloantigens has been explained by the predominant Th2-type immunity during pregnancy both at the systemic level and the feto-maternal interface, which overrules Th1-type immunity and thereby protects the fetus from maternal Th1-cell attack (Wegmann et al., 1993). Hormonal changes, including progressively increasing levels of estrogen, progesterone, glucocorticoids and prolactin, contribute to this shift in the cytokine balance. These immunological responses are known to be altered in pregnancies in patients with SLE. The serum level of multiple proinflammatory cytokines, such as interleukin (IL)-6, IL-10, IL-17, and TNF-α, are higher in pregnancies complicated by SLE compared with pregnancies in healthy women (Doria et al., 2012, Torricelli et al., 2011). However, the Th2 cell polarization does not occur with pregnancy progression in women with SLE, as much as it does in healthy pregnant women (Doria et al., 2012). This difference could be partially accounted for by the aberrant production and lower increase in estrogen and progesterone levels during pregnancy in SLE (Doria et al., 2002). In addition, disassociation between hormone and cytokine production has been reported in patients with the disease (Verthelyi et al., 2001).

*4B-2b-ii) Impairment of regulatory T cell function-*The regulatory T (Treg) cell is another important immunological player in feto-maternal adaptation. Treg cells are a subset of T lymphocytes that play a key role in the regulation of immune response and immunological self-tolerance (Tower et al., 2011). Treg cells are thought to be essential for successful placentation by ensuring fetal tolerance. During the pregnancy, the number of Treg cells in the maternal-fetal interface as well as in the circulation is dramatically increased during the second trimester, which coincides with the timing of maximal trophoblast cells invasion (Somerset et al., 2004). In the context of obstetrical complications, several lines of evidence suggest that the levels of Treg cells both in the decidua and maternal circulation are lower in pregnancies complicated by miscarriage or PE compared with normal pregnancies (Sasaki et al., 2004, 2007).

SLE is known to be partly associated with the impairment in Treg cell-mediated tolerance and the generation of antinuclear antibodies such as antibodies against double-stranded DNA and the Smith antigen, which has been shown in a number of human and animal studies (Tower et al., 2011). There have ever been no studies that directly link this defective Treg cell function in SLE patients to pregnancy complication such as PE. However, a tempting hypothesis is that the low levels of Treg cells in SLE patients might be associated with the defective capacity of Treg cells during pregnancy, which causes the breakdown of feto-maternal tolerance and proper placental development. This impaired responsiveness might be a causative factor which can explain the high rate of obstetrical complications seen in SLE patients.

*4B-2b-iii) Involvement of genetic disposition of PE in SLE patients-*The involvement of genetic predisposition for the development of PE remains controversial. However, several candidate genes have been reported to provide an increased susceptibility for PE, including those encoding angiotensinogen, the angiotensinogen receptors, factor V Leiden variant, methylene tetrahydrofolate reductase, nitric oxide synthase, liver X receptor-β, and TNF-α (Consortium, 2005, Mouzat et al., 2011). The PROMISSE study was the first report to look at specific genetic factors that may predispose SLE patients to develop PE (Salmon et al., 2011). The investigators hypothesized that impaired function to suppress excessive complement activation predisposes pregnant women complicated by SLE. The genes for three complement regulatory proteins were examined as candidates: membrane cofactor protein, complement factor H and complement factor I. In normal pregnant women, these regulatory proteins are highly expressed especially on trophoblast membranes and prevent excessive complement activation. Of the 40 patients who developed PE, seven (18%) were found to possess heterozygous mutations in membrane cofactor protein and complement factor I.

*4B-2b-iv) Direct detrimental effects of Anti-Ro/SSA, anti-La/SSB antibody on fetal heart-*Some evidence for a direct pathogenic role of Anti-Ro/SSA and anti-La/SSB antibodies can be found in studies of NLE. The fetal cardiac damage is related to the expression levels of Ro and La antigens in fetal hearts from 18 to 24 weeks of gestation which are particularly expressed on the surface of cardiomyocytes (Taylor et al., 1986). These antibodies can bind to apoptotic cardiocytes and induce impaired clearance of these cells from healthy cells during the physiological cell deletion process in embryogenesis, which is supposed to contribute to the pathogenesis of CHB (Irani et al., 2010, Lateef and Petri, 2012)

4C. Angiotensin II Type 1 Receptor Agonistic Autoantibodies in PE and IUGR

4C-1. Renin-Angiotensin System in PE

The renin-angiotensin-aldosterone (RAS) system has been implicated in the pathogenesis of PE for several decades (Allaire et al., 2000). Renin, a key enzyme which converts angiotensin precursor to angiotensin I, is a circulating volume sensor in response to the decreased blood pressure and/or perfusion to the kidney. Plasma renin activity in PE patients is known to be lower than that of women with normal pregnancy, which has been suggested to be associated with the compensatory response to hypertension in PE (Zhou et al., 2010). In addition, it is known that plasma angiotensin II (Ang II) levels are increased and vascular responsiveness to Ang II is decreased during normal pregnancy. In contrast, PE patients have the increased responsiveness to Ang II, whereas the circulating Ang II concentration is lower in PE patients compared with normal pregnancy (Abbasi et al., 2006). Supporting this evidence, the expression of AT1 receptor in the decidua as well as in the chorionic villi is higher in PE than in normal pregnancies, which is supposed to be associated with the increased responsiveness to Ang II (Fischer et al., 2008).

4C-2. Presence of Angiotensin II type 1 Receptor Agonistic Autoantibodies in PE Patients

In 1999, Wallukat et al. initially identified an agonistic autoimmune antibody against angiotensin II receptor type 1 (AT1-AA) in the circulation of PE patients but not in normal pregnant women (Wallukat et al., 1999). In this report, the authors detected the presence of AT1-AA which can bind and activate AT1 receptors. Additionally, the precise epitope recognized by these autoantibodies has been identified in the second loop of the AT1 receptor, which is comprised of the 7 amino-acids AFHYESQ. A growing body of evidence has suggested the presence of AT1-AA in PE patients (Herse et al., 2009, Siddiqui et al., 2010).

Approximately 70%-95% of PE patients have been reported to have the elevated AT1-AA and also to correlate with the disease severity. AT1-AA was also detectable in women with a history of PE up to 18 months of delivery (Hubel et al., 2007).

4C-3. Potential Pathogenic Mechanisms of AT1-AA

Numerous studies over the past 10 years have suggested that AT1-AA can activate AT1 receptor in various cell types and provoke pathophysiologically-related responses other than its direct vasopressor action through the AT1 receptor activation.

4C-3a) Evidence from in Vitro Studies

4C-3a-i) Hypercoagulation-Elevated expression of tissue factor (TF) that initiates the extrinsic pathway of coagulation is known to contribute to the hypercoagulation, which is associated with PE. AT1-AA can induce the increased TF expression through AT1 receptor activation in trophoblast cells, smooth vascular muscle cells, and monocytes (Dechend et al., 2000, Lamarca et al., 2007). Plasminogen activator inhibitor-1 (PAI-1), which inhibits the conversion of plasminogen to plasmin, is elevated in the maternal circulation of PE patients and is believed to be involved in the state of hypercoagulation and fibrinolytic imbalance associated with the disease. The activation of AT1 receptor by AT1-AA can induce the synthesis and secretion of PAI-1 in trophoblast cells, mesangial cells, and cardiomyocytes (Bobst et al., 2005, Caniggia and Winter, 2002). Thus, AT1-AA may contribute to hypercoagulation in two ways through elevation of TF and stimulation of the synthesis of PAI-1 resulting in the activation of coagulation pathway and the reduction of plasmin production and the degradation of fibrin clots.

4C-3a-ii) Effects on trophoblast invasion-Placental abnormalities seen in PE patients include the shallow trophoblast invasion. The ability of its invasion is partly dependent on the regulated synthesis of plasmin from plasminogen by plasmin activators. AT1-AA inhibits the trophoblast cell invasion ability through the synthesis and secretion of PAI-1 (Caniggia and Winter, 2002).

4C-3a-iii) Antiangiogenic factor production-Several antiangiogenic factors are elevated in PE patients. It is commonly believed that these factors secreted from placenta such as soluble fms-like tyrosine kinase-1 (sFlt-1) and soluble endoglin (sEng) are responsible for various features seen in PE (Irani et al., 2010, Maynard et al., 2003). AT1-AA can stimulate the production of sFlt-1 and sEng in human trophoblast cells and placental explants (Irani et al., 2010, Zhou et al., 2008).

4C-3b-iv) Reactive oxygen species (ROS) production-The oxidative stress caused by the excessive production of ROS has been believed to be associated with the PE development. AT1-AA contributes to the production of ROS through the activation of NADPH oxidase in trophoblast cells and vascular smooth muscle cells leading to the oxidative damage (LaMarca et al., 2005).

4C-3b) Evidence from Animal Studies

4C-3b-i) AT1-AA adoptive transfer experiment-As described above, AT1-AA has been shown to induce numerous biological effects on a variety of cell types that are relevant to PE, however, these studies were restricted to the *in vitro* cell and tissue explant systems. To directly address the involvement of AT1-AA to clinical features seen in PE, Zhou et al. conducted the adoptive transfer experiment of AT1-AA in pregnant mice and found that AT1-AA can induce the characteristic features of PE including hypertension, proteinuria, and kidney damage (Zhou et al., 2008).

Evidence from AT1-AA adoptive transfer model haselucidated the various disease contributing factors to PE induced by AT1-AA. These factors include antiangiogenic factors such as sFlt-1 and sEng, elevated inflammatory cytokines, endothelin-1 (ET-1), and compliment component C3a. The evidences of these factors as well as therapeutic possibilities targeting them that have been obtained from this animal model will be described in details below.

4C-3b-ii) Antiangiogenic factors-Soluble form of VEGF receptor-1 (also called sFlt-1) is significantly elevated during pregnancy complicated by PE and is thought to play a key role in disease pathophysiology by blocking VEGF signaling, which results in endothelial dysfunction and thereby hypertension and renal pathology (Maynard et al., 2003). These factors are known to be elevated in AT1-AA-treated pregnant mice or rats (Parrish et al., 2010, Siddiqui et al., 2011). Siddiqui et al. showed that AT1-AA can induce the elevated levels of sFlt-1 in the circulation of pregnant mice and the treatment of recombinant VEGF121, a relatively stable form of VEGF, attenuated AT1-AA-induced impaired placental angiogenesis and PE phenotypes (Siddiqui et al., 2011). Their results suggest not only the importance of sFlt-1 in AT1-AA-induced disease development but also the possibility of therapeutics targeting VEGF signaling.

Soluble endoglin (sEng), a soluble form of TGF-β receptor, is also known to be elevated in the circulation of PE patients and contribute to the disease (Bdolah et al., 2006, Venkatesha et al., 2006). AT1-AA can induce sEng production in pregnant mice through enhanced TNF-α signaling, which contributes to impaired placental angiogenesis and the disease development (Irani et al., 2010). The blockade of TNF-α reduced AT1-AA-mediated sEng production and disease phenotype.

4C-3b-iii) Inflammatory cytokines-Inflammatory cytokines such as TNF-α and IL-6 are known to be increased in the circulation of PE patients (Pegues et al., 2013). The involvement of these cytokines in disease development is supported by evidence that infusion of TNF-α or IL-6 into pregnant rodents can cause features seen in PE (Gutkowska et al., 2011, Parrish et al., 2010). TNF-α functions at the downstream of AT1-AA-mediated signaling to induce clinical features of PE in pregnant mice through the production of antiangiogenic factors such as sFlt-1 and sEng (Irani et al., 2010). In addition, IL-6 also plays a key role in AT1-AA-mediated Endothelin-1 (ET-1) production in pregnant mice through TNF-αsignaling (Zhou et al., 2011). The blockade of IL-6 is shown to be capable of attenuating the features of PE induced by AT1-AA in pregnant mice. These results suggest that TNF-α/IL-6 signaling is a key mechanism underlying AT1-AA-induced disease development and the inhibition of these cascades might possess the therapeutic possibilities.

4C-3b-iv) Complement activation-The complement cascade is activated during pregnancy, however, its excessive activation is thought to provoke a systemic inflammatory response leading to PE. Wang et al. found that C3 deposition is increased in placentas from PE patients and enhanced C3a signaling plays a detrimental role in AT1-AA-induced hypertension and proteinuria in pregnant mice (Liu et al., 2012). These phenotypes are shown to be prevented by a C3a receptor antagonist.

4C-4. Involvement of AT1-AA in Intrauterine Fetal Growth Restriction

Intrauterine fetal growth restriction (IUGR) is a key feature seen in PE. AT1-AAs exist in the cord blood of PE patients and are capable of activating AT1 receptors (Irani et al., 2009).

Using an adoptive transfer model, AT1-AA was shown to cross the placenta, enter the fetal circulation and cause placental damage and fetal growth restriction together with the impaired organ growth.

4C-5. Contributing Factors to AT1-AA Production

Recently, AT1-AA has been reported to be produced in some rodent models of PE (Firooz et al., 2011, Gutkowska et al., 2011, LaMarca et al., 2008a, Parrish et al., 2010). A rat model of placental ischemia caused by surgical reduction in uterine perfusion pressure (RUPP) is one of the well-accepted PE experimental models. Interestingly, RUPP rats were shown to develop AT1-AA that is associated with PE phenotypes (Gilbert et al., 2008). The production of AT1-AA in RUPP rats is inhibited by rituximab that blocks CD20 leading to B lymphocyte depletion and thereby suppressing production of antibodies (Gutkowska et al., 2011). In addition, adoptive transfer of CD4+ T lymphocytes can induce PE phenotypes in pregnant rats, which is mediated by the production and effects of AT1-AA (Parrish et al., 2010). As described above, the infusion of cytokines (TNF- α, IL-6, and IL-17) into pregnant rats can cause features of PE (LaMarca et al., 2008b, 2011a, 2011b). In these models, AT1-AA has been shown to be produced and contribute to the pathophysiology (LaMarca et al., 2008b, 2011a, 2011b).

Considering these findings, it is possible to hypothesize that generation of AT1-AA caused by RUPP model results from the secondary enhanced inflammatory response. The inflammatory changes may include elevated inflammatory cytokines and antigenic stimuli that lead to the activation of T and B lymphocytes and thereby the AT1-AA production. The specific immunologic mechanism for the production of AT1-AA has yet to be determined, however, the evidences from these animal studies might provide a clue leading to the understanding of the detailed molecular mechanisms responsible for its production.

4C-6. Summary of AT1-AA in PE

Evidence reviewed here indicates that PE is an autoimmune state characterized by the presence of autoantibody that can activate AT1 receptor (AT1-AA) and provoke various biological responses leading to disease development (Table 5). However, the immunologic basis for the production of AT1-AA has yet to be elucidated. In the coming years, we expect the further understanding of AT1-AA could make it possible to consider AT1-AA as biomarkers and therapeutic targets leading to the improved management for PE patients.

4D. Summary

As described, several mechanisms in the development of maternal and fetal complications associated with APS, SLE, and AT1-AA have in common with each other, such as defective placentation caused by failure in trophoblast cell functions, immunologic disturbance leading to the enhanced inflammatory response, hypercoagulation, and the direct detrimental effects of autoantibodies on fetuses (Table 3-5). A critical feature of the immune system is the ability to discriminate between self and non-self. Autoimmune diseases are characterized by the failure in the immunological control mechanisms maintaining this self-tolerance.

On the other hand, during pregnancy, women are exposed to fetal alloantigens and must establish immunological tolerance to these antigens to prevent the rejection of the fetus, which is achieved by various immunological changes leading to the generalized reduction of maternal immune responsiveness.

Table 3. Pathogenic role of aPL in PE, IUGR and offspring's health

Autoantibody	Proposed mechanism	Related obstetric disorder	Evidence from human subjects	Evidence from animal studies
aPL	Impaired placentation	Preeclampsia Fetal loss IUGR	Studies using 1st trimester placental explants or human trophoblast cells show that aPL can cause increased trophoblast apoptosis, reduced hCG production, and reduced trophoblast invasion (Meroni et al., 2011).	
	Aberrant inflammatory response	Preeclampsia Fetal loss IUGR	Increased complements deposition and activation shown in placentas from APS patients (Shamonki et al., 2007).	Studies using Fetal loss mouse model by the treatment of β2 glycoprotein I or aPL isolated from human sera show elevated placental and systemic TNF-α levels, neutrophil infiltration, and complement activation (Berman et al., 2005, Holers et al., 2002).
	Intraplacental thrombosis	Preeclampsia Fetal loss IUGR	Intravillous thrombosis, extensive villous fibrosis, or marked infarction in placentas from APS patients (Franco et al., 2011).	
		Fetal loss	Treatment of heparin or in combination with aspirin can reduce the miscarriage rate, but not the risk of preeclampsia or IUGR in APS patients (Committee on Practice Bulletins-Obstetrics and Gynecologists, 2012).	

Table 4. Detrimental role of autoantibodies of Systemic Lupus Erythematosus in PE, IUGR and offspring health

Autoantibody	Proposed mechanism	Related obstetric disorder	Evidence from human subjects	Evidence from animal studies
undetermined	Aberrant inflammatory response	Preeclampsia Fetal loss IUGR	The serum level of multiple proinflammatory cytokines are higher in pregnant women with SLE (Doria et al., 2012, Torricelli et al., 2011).	
		Preeclampsia Fetal loss IUGR	Th2 cell polarization does not occur with pregnancy progression in women with SLE, as much as it does in healthy pregnant women (Torricelli et al., 2011).	
		Preeclampsia Fetal loss IUGR	Pregnant women with SLE have decreased number of regulatory T cells (Somerset et al., 2004).	
		Preeclampsia	Some SLE patients who developed preeclampsia possess heterozygous mutations in complement regulatory proteins to suppress excessive complement activation (Salmon et al., 2011).	
anti-Ro/SSA anti-La/SSB	Impaired clearance of apoptotic fetal cardiomyocytes during embryogenesis	Congenital heart block		Binding of anti-Ro/SSA and La/SSB antibodies to fetal cardiomyocytes impairs phagocytic uptake of physiologically-induced apoptosis of cardiomyocytes during embryogenesis (Clancy et al., 2006).

Table 5. Human and animal studies about Angiotensin II Type 1 Receptor Agonistic Autoantibodies in PE, IUGR and offspring health

Autoantibody	Proposed mechanism	Related obstetric disorder	Evidence from human subjects	Evidence from animal studies
AT1-AA	Impaired placentation	preeclampsia	AT1-AA can inhibit the invasiveness of human trophoblasts (Xia et al., 2003)	
	Aberrant inflammatory response	preeclampsia	Positive correlation between levels of bioactivity of AT1-AA and TNF-α in preeclampsia patients (Irani et al., 2010).	TNF-α is increased in AT1-AA-treated mice and the blockade of TNF-α attenuates the PE features (Irani et al., 2010).
			AT1-AA can induce IL-6 from human placental explants (Zhou et al., 2011).	IL-6 is induced and contributes to PE features through endothelin-1 production in AT1-AA-treated mice (Zhou et al., 2011).
	Antiangiogenic factors	preeclampsia	AT1-AA can induce sFlt1 and sEng from human placental explants (Irani et al., 2010, Siddiqui et al., 2011).	sFlt-1 and sEng are induced in AT1-AA-treated pregnant mice contribute to PE phenotype (Irani et al., 2010, Siddiqui et al., 2011).
	ROS production	preeclampsia	AT1-AA can induce ROS production through the activation of NADPH oxidase in primary human trophoblasts (Dechend et al., 2003).	
	Increased apoptosis in placenta	IUGR	AT1-AA can induce apoptosis in human placental explants and trophoblasts (Irani et al., 2009).	Increased apoptosis was seen in placentas of AT1-AA-treated pregnant mice (Irani et al., 2009).
	Impaired fetal organ development	IUGR	AT1-AA can pass through placenta and retains bioactivities in fetal circulation (Irani et al., 2009).	Injected-AT1-AA to pregnant mice can enter the fetal circulation with its bioactivities and cause IUGR and impaired multiple organ development (Irani et al., 2009).

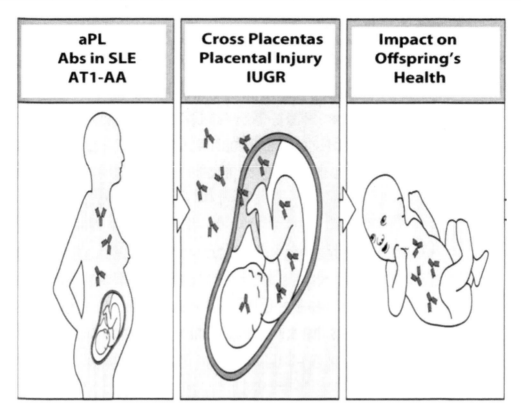

Figure 3. Autoimmunity, PE, IUGR and offspring health. aPL, SLE antibodies and AT1-AA are there pathogenic autoantibodies associated with PE and IUGR or pregnancy loss. Animal studies demonstrate that these autoantibodies not only contribute to multiple PE features in pregnant moms, but also have direct effects on placentas including shallow trophoblast invasion, trophoblast apoptosis and impaired placental vasculature. Moreover, these antibodies cross placentas and therefore have direct detrimental effects on fetal growth and likely have a long term impact on offspring health. As such, removing these pathogenic autoantibodies or interfering its downstream effects is likely effective therapies for PE under these conditions and thereby improving offspring health.

The disturbance of this feto-maternal tolerance leads to the impaired placentation that is highly associated with obstetrical complications such as PE, fetal loss, and IUGR.

Thus, failure of immunologic tolerance system is hypothesized to be a common key causative factor between autoimmune diseases and PE (Figure 3).

As described in the section of SLE, one plausible explanation to this hypothesis is the impairment of regulatory T cell functions seen both in SLE and PE patients. The breakdown of regulatory T cell function can affect the immunologic tolerance state, which is believed to be related to the pathogenesis in both diseases. In addition, the identification of AT1-AA as a contributing factor to develop PE opened up a new window on how PE may link to the autoimmunity. It is likely that further understanding of mechanisms associated with the immunological disturbance in autoimmune diseases might be a clue to uncover the pathophysiology of pregnancy complications that compromise the health of mother, fetus, and offspring.

Conclusion

Taken together, we have summarized current progress in understanding of pathogenesis of PE and subsequent IUGR and impact on offspring's health. In particular, we have focused on 1) multiple high risk factors including cardiovascular diseases and metabolomic disorders, 2) imbalanced inflammatory response and 3) pathogenic autoimmunity in PE and IUGR and impacts on offspring's health. It is important to integrate our current knowledge to preventative and therapeutic strategies to interfere specific detrimental signaling cascades to decrease PE and thereby preventing IUGR and impacts on offspring's health.

References

Abbasi, S., Lee, J. D., Su, B., Chen, X., Alcon, J. L., Yang, J., et al. (2006). Protein kinase-mediated regulation of calcineurin through the phosphorylation of modulatory calcineurin-interacting protein 1. *J. Biol. Chem.*, 281, 7717-26.

Abou-Nassar, K., Carrier, M., Ramsay, T. and Rodger, M. A. (2011). The association between antiphospholipid antibodies and placenta mediated complications: a systematic review and meta-analysis. *Thromb Res.*, 128, 77-85.

Agostinis, C., Bulla, R., Tripodo, C., Gismondi, A., Stabile, H., Bossi, F., et al. (2010). An alternative role of C1q in cell migration and tissue remodeling: contribution to trophoblast invasion and placental development. *J. Immunol.*, 185, 4420-9.

Ahmad, S. and Ahmed, A. (2004). Elevated placental soluble vascular endothelial growth factor receptor-1 inhibits angiogenesis in preeclampsia. *Circ. Res.*, 95, 884-91.

Alexander, B. T., Cockrell, K. L., Massey, M. B., Bennett, W. A. and Granger, J. P. (2002). Tumor necrosis factor-alpha-induced hypertension in pregnant rats results in decreased renal neuronal nitric oxide synthase expression. *Am. J. Hypertens.*, 15, 170-5.

Allaire, A. D., Ballenger, K. A., Wells, S. R., McMahon, M. J. and Lessey, B. A. (2000). Placental apoptosis in preeclampsia. *Obstet. Gynecol.*, 96, 271-6.

Almasry, S. M., Eldomiaty, M. A., Elfayomy, A. K. and Habib, F. A. (2012). Expression pattern of tumor necrosis factor alpha in placentae of idiopathic fetal growth restriction. *J. Mol. Histol.*, 43, 253-61.

Araujo, J. R., Correia-Branco, A., Moreira, L., Ramalho, C., Martel, F. and Keating, E. (2013). Folic acid uptake by the human syncytiotrophoblast is affected by gestational diabetes, hyperleptinemia, and TNF-alpha. *Pediatr. Res.*, 73, 388-94.

Barker, D. J. (1998). In utero programming of chronic disease. *Clin. Sci. (Lond.)*, 95, 115-28.

Baum, M., Ortiz, L. and Quan, A. (2003). Fetal origins of cardiovascular disease. *Curr. Opin. Pediatr.*, 15, 166-70.

Bdolah, Y., Palomaki, G. E., Yaron, Y., Bdolah-Abram, T., Goldman, M., Levine, R. J., et al. (2006). Circulating angiogenic proteins in trisomy 13. *Am. J. Obstet. Gynecol.*, 194, 239-45.

Berman, J., Girardi, G. and Salmon, J. E. (2005). TNF-alpha is a critical effector and a target for therapy in antiphospholipid antibody-induced pregnancy loss. *J. Immunol.*, 174, 485-90.

Bobst, S. M., Day, M. C., Gilstrap, L. C., 3rd, Xia, Y. and Kellems, R. E. (2005). Maternal autoantibodies from preeclamptic patients activate angiotensin receptors on human mesangial cells and induce interleukin-6 and plasminogen activator inhibitor-1 secretion. *Am. J. Hypertens.*, 18, 330-6.

Boij, R., Svensson, J., Nilsson-Ekdahl, K., Sandholm, K., Lindahl, T. L., Palonek, E., et al. (2012). Biomarkers of coagulation, inflammation, and angiogenesis are independently associated with preeclampsia. *Am. J. Reprod. Immunol.*, 68, 258-70.

Buurma, A., Cohen, D., Veraar, K., Schonkeren, D., Claas, F. H., Bruijn, J. A., et al. (2012). Preeclampsia is characterized by placental complement dysregulation. *Hypertension*, 60, 1332-7.

Caniggia, I. and Winter, J. L. (2002). Adriana and Luisa Castellucci Award lecture 2001. Hypoxia inducible factor-1: oxygen regulation of trophoblast differentiation in normal and pre-eclamptic pregnancies--a review. *Placenta*, 23 Suppl A, S47-57.

Carpentier, P. A., Dingman, A. L. and Palmer, T. D. (2011). Placental TNF-alpha signaling in illness-induced complications of pregnancy. *Am. J. Pathol.*, 178, 2802-10.

Castellano, G., Di Vittorio, A., Dalfino, G., Loverre, A., Marrone, D., Simone, S., et al. (2010). Pentraxin 3 and complement cascade activation in the failure of arteriovenous fistula. *Atherosclerosis*, 209, 241-7.

Catarino, C., Santos-Silva, A., Belo, L., Rocha-Pereira, P., Rocha, S., Patricio, B., et al. (2012). Inflammatory disturbances in preeclampsia: relationship between maternal and umbilical cord blood. *J. Pregnancy*, 2012, 684384.

Cetin, I. and Alvino, G. (2009). Intrauterine growth restriction: implications for placental metabolism and transport. A review. *Placenta,* 30 Suppl. A, S77-82.

Chakravarty, E. F., Colon, I., Langen, E. S., Nix, D. A., El-Sayed, Y. Y., Genovese, M. C., et al. (2005). Factors that predict prematurity and preeclampsia in pregnancies that are complicated by systemic lupus erythematosus. *Am. J. Obstet. Gynecol.*, 192, 1897-904.

Clancy, R. M., Neufing, P. J., Zheng, P., O'Mahony, M., Nimmerjahn, F., Gordon, T. P., et al. (2006). Impaired clearance of apoptotic cardiocytes is linked to anti-SSA/Ro and -SSB/La antibodies in the pathogenesis of congenital heart block. *J. Clin. Invest.*, 116, 2413-22.

Collard, C. D., Agah, A., Reenstra, W., Buras, J. and Stahl, G. L. (1999). Endothelial nuclear factor-kappaB translocation and vascular cell adhesion molecule-1 induction by complement : inhibition with anti-human C5 therapy or cGMP analogues. *Arterioscler. Thromb Vasc. Biol.*, 19, 2623-9.

Committee on Practice Bulletins-Obstetrics, American College of Obstetricians and Gynecologists. (2012). Practice Bulletin No. 132: Antiphospholipid syndrome. *Obstet. Gynecol.*, 120, 1514-21.

Consortium, G. (2005). Disentangling fetal and maternal susceptibility for pre-eclampsia: a British multicenter candidate-gene study. *Am. J. Hum. Genet.*, 77, 127-31.

Dechend, R., Homuth, V., Wallukat, G., Kreuzer, J., Park, J. K., Theuer, J., et al. (2000). AT(1) receptor agonistic antibodies from preeclamptic patients cause vascular cells to express tissue factor. *Circulation*, 101, 2382-7.

Dechend, R., Viedt, C., Muller, D. N., Ugele, B., Brandes, R. P., Wallikat, G., et al. (2003). AT1 receptor agonistic antibodies from preeclamptic patients stimulate NADPH oxidase. *Circulation*, 107, 1632-9.

Denny, K. J., Coulthard, L. G., Finnell, R. H., Callaway, L. K., Taylor, S. M. and Woodruff, T. M. (2013a). Elevated complement factor C5a in maternal and umbilical cord plasma in preeclampsia. *J. Reprod. Immunol.*, 97, 211-6.

Denny, K. J., Woodruff, T. M., Taylor, S. M. and Callaway, L. K. (2013b). Complement in pregnancy: a delicate balance. *Am. J. Reprod. Immunol.*, 69, 3-11.

Dixon, I. M. (2010). The soluble interleukin 6 receptor takes its place in the pantheon of interleukin 6 signaling proteins: phenoconversion of cardiac fibroblasts to myofibroblasts. *Hypertension*, 56, 193-5.

Doria, A., Cutolo, M., Ghirardello, A., Zampieri, S., Vescovi, F., Sulli, A., et al. (2002). Steroid hormones and disease activity during pregnancy in systemic lupus erythematosus. *Arthritis Rheum.*, 47, 202-9.

Doria, A., Cutolo, M., Ghirardello, A., Zen, M., Villalta, D., Tincani, A., et al. (2012). Effect of pregnancy on serum cytokines in SLE patients. *Arthritis Res. Ther.*, 14, R66.

Duckitt, K. and Harrington, D. (2005). Risk factors for pre-eclampsia at antenatal booking: systematic review of controlled studies. *BMJ*, 330, 565.

Ehrnthaller, C., Ignatius, A., Gebhard, F. and Huber-Lang, M. (2011). New insights of an old defense system: structure, function, and clinical relevance of the complement system. *Mol. Med.*, 17, 317-29.

Fernandez-Twinn, D. S., Ozanne, S. E., Ekizoglou, S., Doherty, C., James, L., Gusterson, B., et al. (2003). The maternal endocrine environment in the low-protein model of intra-uterine growth restriction. *Br. J. Nutr.*, 90, 815-22.

Firooz, N., Albert, D., Wallace, D., Ishimori, M., Berel, D. and Weisman, M. (2011). High-sensitivity C-reactive protein and erythrocyte sedimentation rate in systemic lupus erythematosus. *Lupus*, 20, 588-97.

Fischer, R., Dechend, R., Qadri, F., Markovic, M., Feldt, S., Herse, F., et al. (2008). Dietary n-3 polyunsaturated fatty acids and direct renin inhibition improve electrical remodeling in a model of high human renin hypertension. *Hypertension*, 51, 540-6.

Franco, C., Walker, M., Robertson, J., Fitzgerald, B., Keating, S., McLeod, A., et al. (2011). Placental infarction and thrombophilia. *Obstet. Gynecol.*, 117, 929-34.

Fujimoto, M., Nakano, M., Terabe, F., Kawahata, H., Ohkawara, T., Han, Y., et al. (2011). The influence of excessive IL-6 production in vivo on the development and function of Foxp3+ regulatory T cells. *J. Immunol.*, 186, 32-40.

Gadonski, G., LaMarca, B. B., Sullivan, E., Bennett, W., Chandler, D. and Granger, J. P. (2006). Hypertension produced by reductions in uterine perfusion in the pregnant rat: role of interleukin 6. *Hypertension*, 48, 711-6.

Gilbert, J. S., LaMarca, B. B. and Granger, J. P. (2008). ACE2 and ANG-(1-7) in the gravid uterus: the new players on the block. *Am. J. Physiol. Regul. Integr. Comp. Physiol.*, 294, R915-6.

Gill, R. M., Coleman, N. M. and Hunt, J. S. (2007). Differential cellular expression of LIGHT and its receptors in early gestation human placentas. *J. Reprod. Immunol.*, 74, 1-6.

Giorgi, V. S., Peracoli, M. T., Peracoli, J. C., Witkin, S. S. and Bannwart-Castro, C. F. (2012). Silibinin modulates the NF-kappab pathway and pro-inflammatory cytokine production by mononuclear cells from preeclamptic women. *J. Reprod. Immunol.*, 95, 67-72.

Girardi, G., Yarilin, D., Thurman, J. M., Holers, V. M. and Salmon, J. E. (2006). Complement activation induces dysregulation of angiogenic factors and causes fetal rejection and growth restriction. *J. Exp. Med.*, 203, 2165-75.

Godfrey, K. M. and Barker, D. J. (2000). Fetal nutrition and adult disease. *Am. J. Clin. Nutr.*, 71, 1344S-52S.

Grad, E. and Danenberg, H. D. (2013). C-reactive protein and atherothrombosis: Cause or effect? *Blood Rev.*, 27, 23-9.

Grad, E., Pachino, R. M., FitzGerald, G. A. and Danenberg, H. D. (2012). Role of thromboxane receptor in C-reactive protein-induced thrombosis. *Arterioscler. Thromb Vasc. Biol.*, 32, 2468-74.

Granger, J. P., Alexander, B. T., Llinas, M. T., Bennett, W. A. and Khalil, R. A. (2002). Pathophysiology of preeclampsia: linking placental ischemia/hypoxia with microvascular dysfunction. *Microcirculation*, 9, 147-60.

Gutkowska, J., Granger, J. P., Lamarca, B. B., Danalache, B. A., Wang, D. and Jankowski, M. (2011). Changes in cardiac structure in hypertension produced by placental ischemia in pregnant rats: effect of tumor necrosis factor blockade. *J. Hypertens.*, 29, 1203-12.

Heilmann, L., Schorsch, M., Hahn, T. and Fareed, J. (2011). Antiphospholipid syndrome and pre-eclampsia. *Semin. Thromb Hemost.*, 37, 141-5.

Herse, F., Verlohren, S., Wenzel, K., Pape, J., Muller, D. N., Modrow, S., et al. (2009). Prevalence of agonistic autoantibodies against the angiotensin II type 1 receptor and soluble fms-like tyrosine kinase 1 in a gestational age-matched case study. *Hypertension*, 53, 393-8.

Holers, V. M., Girardi, G., Mo, L., Guthridge, J. M., Molina, H., Pierangeli, S. S., et al. (2002). Complement C3 activation is required for antiphospholipid antibody-induced fetal loss. *J. Exp. Med.*, 195, 211-20.

Hsuchou, H., Kastin, A. J., Mishra, P. K. and Pan, W. (2012). C-reactive protein increases BBB permeability: implications for obesity and neuroinflammation. *Cell Physiol. Biochem.*, 30, 1109-19.

Hubel, C. A., Wallukat, G., Wolf, M., Herse, F., Rajakumar, A., Roberts, J. M., et al. (2007). Agonistic angiotensin II type 1 receptor autoantibodies in postpartum women with a history of preeclampsia. *Hypertension*, 49, 612-7.

Irani, R. A. and Xia, Y. (2008). The functional role of the renin-angiotensin system in pregnancy and preeclampsia. *Placenta*, 29, 763-71.

Irani, R. A., Zhang, Y., Blackwell, S. C., Zhou, C. C., Ramin, S. M., Kellems, R. E., et al. (2009). The detrimental role of angiotensin receptor agonistic autoantibodies in intrauterine growth restriction seen in preeclampsia. *J. Exp. Med.*, 206, 2809-22.

Irani, R. A., Zhang, Y., Zhou, C. C., Blackwell, S. C., Hicks, M. J., Ramin, S. M., et al. (2010). Autoantibody-mediated angiotensin receptor activation contributes to preeclampsia through tumor necrosis factor-alpha signaling. *Hypertension*, 55, 1246-53.

Java, A., Atkinson, J. and Salmon, J. (2013). Defective complement inhibitory function predisposes to renal disease. *Annu. Rev. Med.*, 64, 307-24.

Kenny, L. C., Broadhurst, D. I., Dunn, W., Brown, M., North, R. A., McCowan, L., et al. (2010). Robust early pregnancy prediction of later preeclampsia using metabolomic biomarkers. *Hypertension*, 56, 741-9.

Khan, K. S., Wojdyla, D., Say, L., Gulmezoglu, A. M. and Van Look, P. F. (2006). WHO analysis of causes of maternal death: a systematic review. *Lancet*, 367, 1066-74.

Kvehaugen, A. S., Dechend, R., Ramstad, H. B., Troisi, R., Fugelseth, D. and Staff, A. C. (2011). Endothelial function and circulating biomarkers are disturbed in women and children after preeclampsia. *Hypertension*, 58, 63-9.

Labarrere, C. A. and Zaloga, G. P. (2004). C-reactive protein: From innocent bystander to pivotal mediator of atherosclerosis. *Am. J. Med.*, 117, 499-507.

Lamarca, B. (2010). The role of immune activation in contributing to vascular dysfunction and the pathophysiology of hypertension during preeclampsia. *Minerva Ginecol.*, 62, 105-20.

LaMarca, B., Speed, J., Fournier, L., Babcock, S. A., Berry, H., Cockrell, K., et al. (2008a). Hypertension in response to chronic reductions in uterine perfusion in pregnant rats: effect of tumor necrosis factor-alpha blockade. *Hypertension*, 52, 1161-7.

LaMarca, B., Speed, J., Ray, L. F., Cockrell, K., Wallukat, G., Dechend, R., et al. (2011a). Hypertension in response to IL-6 during pregnancy: role of AT1-receptor activation. *Int. J. Infereron Cytokine. Mediator Res.*, 2011, 65-70.

LaMarca, B., Wallace, K., Herse, F., Wallukat, G., Martin, J. N., Jr., Weimer, A., et al. (2011b). Hypertension in response to placental ischemia during pregnancy: role of B lymphocytes. *Hypertension*, 57, 865-71.

LaMarca, B., Wallukat, G., Llinas, M., Herse, F., Dechend, R. and Granger, J. P. (2008b). Autoantibodies to the angiotensin type I receptor in response to placental ischemia and tumor necrosis factor alpha in pregnant rats. *Hypertension*, 52, 1168-72.

LaMarca, B. B., Bennett, W. A., Alexander, B. T., Cockrell, K. and Granger, J. P. (2005). Hypertension produced by reductions in uterine perfusion in the pregnant rat: role of tumor necrosis factor-alpha. *Hypertension*, 46, 1022-5.

LaMarca, B. D., Ryan, M. J., Gilbert, J. S., Murphy, S. R. and Granger, J. P. (2007). Inflammatory cytokines in the pathophysiology of hypertension during preeclampsia. *Curr. Hypertens. Rep.*, 9, 480-5.

Lateef, A. and Petri, M. (2012). Management of pregnancy in systemic lupus erythematosus. *Nat. Rev. Rheumatol.*, 8, 710-8.

Lau, S. Y., Guild, S. J., Barrett, C. J., Chen, Q., McCowan, L., Jordan, V., et al. (2013). Tumor necrosis factor-alpha, interleukin-6, and interleukin-10 levels are altered in preeclampsia: a systematic review and meta-analysis. *Am. J. Reprod. Immunol.*, 70, 412-27.

Liu, C., Wei, Y., Wang, J., Pi, L., Huang, J. and Wang, P. (2012). Carbonic anhydrases III and IV autoantibodies in rheumatoid arthritis, systemic lupus erythematosus, diabetes, hypertensive renal disease, and heart failure. *Clin. Dev. Immunol.*, 2012, 354594.

Lorthongpanich, C., Cheow, L. F., Balu, S., Quake, S. R., Knowles, B. B., Burkholder, W. F., et al. (2013). Single-cell DNA-methylation analysis reveals epigenetic chimerism in preimplantation embryos. *Science*, 341, 1110-2.

Luyckx, V. A., Bertram, J. F., Brenner, B. M., Fall, C., Hoy, W. E., Ozanne, S. E., et al. (2013). Effect of fetal and child health on kidney development and long-term risk of hypertension and kidney disease. *Lancet*, 382, 273-83.

Marchioni, R. M. and Lichtenstein, G. R. (2013). Tumor necrosis factor-alpha inhibitor therapy and fetal risk: a systematic literature review. *World. J. Gastroenterol.*, 19, 2591-602.

Maynard, S. E., Min, J. Y., Merchan, J., Lim, K. H., Li, J., Mondal, S., et al. (2003). Excess placental soluble fms-like tyrosine kinase 1 (sFlt1) may contribute to endothelial dysfunction, hypertension, and proteinuria in preeclampsia. *J. Clin. Invest.*, 111, 649-58.

Meroni, P. L., Borghi, M. O., Raschi, E. and Tedesco, F. (2011). Pathogenesis of antiphospholipid syndrome: understanding the antibodies. *Nat. Rev. Rheumatol.*, 7, 330-9.

Milicevic, N. M., Klaperski, K., Nohroudi, K., Milicevic, Z., Bieber, K., Baraniec, B., et al. (2011). TNF receptor-1 is required for the formation of splenic compartments during adult, but not embryonic life. *J. Immunol.*, 186, 1486-94.

Moodley, J., Bhoola, V., Duursma, J., Pudifin, D., Byrne, S. and Kenoyer, D. G. (1995). The association of antiphospholipid antibodies with severe early-onset pre-eclampsia. *S. Afr. Med. J.*, 85, 105-7.

Moroni, G. and Ponticelli, C. (2003). The risk of pregnancy in patients with lupus nephritis. *J. Nephrol.*, 16, 161-7.

Mouzat, K., Mercier, E., Polge, A., Evrard, A., Baron, S., Balducchi, J. P., et al. (2011). A common polymorphism in NR1H2 (LXRbeta) is associated with preeclampsia. *BMC Med. Genet.*, 12, 145.

Murphy, S. R., LaMarca, B. B., Parrish, M., Cockrell, K. and Granger, J. P. (2013). Control of soluble fms-like tyrosine-1 (sFlt-1) production response to placental ischemia/hypoxia: role of tumor necrosis factor-alpha. *Am. J. Physiol. Regul. Integr. Comp. Physiol.*, 304, R130-5.

Odaka, Y., Nakano, M., Tanaka, T., Kaburagi, T., Yoshino, H., Sato-Mito, N., et al. (2010). The influence of a high-fat dietary environment in the fetal period on postnatal metabolic and immune function. *Obesity (Silver Spring)*, 18, 1688-94.

Parker-Athill, E. C. and Tan, J. (2010). Maternal immune activation and autism spectrum disorder: interleukin-6 signaling as a key mechanistic pathway. *Neurosignals*, 18, 113-28.

Parrish, M. R., Murphy, S. R., Rutland, S., Wallace, K., Wenzel, K., Wallukat, G., et al. (2010). The effect of immune factors, tumor necrosis factor-alpha, and agonistic autoantibodies to the angiotensin II type I receptor on soluble fms-like tyrosine-1 and soluble endoglin production in response to hypertension during pregnancy. *Am. J. Hypertens.*, 23, 911-6.

Pegues, M., McCrory, M. A., Zarjou, A., Szalai, S. J. (2013). C-reactive protein exacerbates renal ischemia-reperfusion injury. *Am. J. Physiol. Renal. Physiol.*, 304, F1358-65.

Prins, J. R., Gomez-Lopez, N. and Robertson, S. A. (2012). Interleukin-6 in pregnancy and gestational disorders. *J. Reprod. Immunol.*, 95, 1-14.

Rampersad, R., Barton, A., Sadovsky, Y. and Nelson, D. M. (2008). The C5b-9 membrane attack complex of complement activation localizes to villous trophoblast injury in vivo and modulates human trophoblast function in vitro. *Placenta*, 29, 855-61.

Rand, J. H., Wu, X. X., Andree, H. A., Lockwood, C. J., Guller, S., Scher, J., et al. (1997). Pregnancy loss in the antiphospholipid-antibody syndrome--a possible thrombogenic mechanism. *N. Engl. J. Med.*, 337, 154-60.

Redman, C. W. and Sargent, I. L. (2005). Latest advances in understanding preeclampsia. *Science*, 308, 1592-4.

Richani, K., Romero, R., Soto, E., Espinoza, J., Nien, J. K., Chaiworapongsa, T., et al. (2005). Unexplained intrauterine fetal death is accompanied by activation of complement. *J. Perinat. Med.*, 33, 296-305.

Ricklin, D., Hajishengallis, G., Yang, K. and Lambris, J. D. (2010). Complement: a key system for immune surveillance and homeostasis. *Nat. Immunol.*, 11, 785-97.

Ridker, P. M. (2003). Clinical application of C-reactive protein for cardiovascular disease detection and prevention. *Circulation*, 107, 363-9.

Rose-John, S. (2012). IL-6 trans-signaling via the soluble IL-6 receptor: importance for the pro-inflammatory activities of IL-6. *Int. J. Biol. Sci.*, 8, 1237-47.

Rowe, J. H., Ertelt, J. M., Xin, L. and Way, S. S. (2012). Listeria monocytogenes cytoplasmic entry induces fetal wastage by disrupting maternal Foxp3+ regulatory T cell-sustained fetal tolerance. *PLoS Pathog.*, 8, e1002873.

Ruiz-Irastorza, G. and Khamashta, M. A. (2008). Lupus and pregnancy: ten questions and some answers. *Lupus*, 17, 416-20.

Saito, S. and Sakai, M. (2003). Th1/Th2 balance in preeclampsia. *J. Reprod. Immunol.*, 59, 161-73.

Salmon, J. E., Heuser, C., Triebwasser, M., Liszewski, M. K., Kavanagh, D., Roumenina, L., et al. (2011). Mutations in complement regulatory proteins predispose to preeclampsia: a genetic analysis of the PROMISSE cohort. *PLoS Med.*, 8, e1001013.

Sasaki, Y., Darmochwal-Kolarz, D., Suzuki, D., Sakai, M., Ito, M., Shima, T., et al. (2007). Proportion of peripheral blood and decidual CD4(+) CD25(bright) regulatory T cells in pre-eclampsia. *Clin. Exp. Immunol.*, 149, 139-45.

Sasaki, Y., Sakai, M., Miyazaki, S., Higuma, S., Shiozaki, A. and Saito, S. (2004). Decidual and peripheral blood CD4+CD25+ regulatory T cells in early pregnancy subjects and spontaneous abortion cases. *Mol. Hum. Reprod.*, 10, 347-53.

Scheller, J. and Rose-John, S. (2012). The interleukin 6 pathway and atherosclerosis. *Lancet*, 380, 338.

Shamonki, J. M., Salmon, J. E., Hyjek, E. and Baergen, R. N. (2007). Excessive complement activation is associated with placental injury in patients with antiphospholipid antibodies. *Am. J. Obstet. Gynecol.*, 196, 167.e1-5.

Sibai, B. M. (1992). Hypertension in pregnancy. *N. Engl. J. Med.*, 327, 733; author reply 733-4.

Sibai, B. M., Lindheimer, M., Hauth, J., Caritis, S., Vandorsten, P., Klebanoff, M., et al. (1998). Risk factors for preeclampsia, abruptio placentae, and adverse neonatal outcomes among women with chronic hypertension. National Institute of Child Health and Human Development Network of Maternal-Fetal Medicine Units. *N. Engl. J. Med.*, 339, 667-71.

Siddiqui, A. H., Irani, R. A., Blackwell, S. C., Ramin, S. M., Kellems, R. E. and Xia, Y. (2010). Angiotensin receptor agonistic autoantibody is highly prevalent in preeclampsia: correlation with disease severity. *Hypertension*, 55, 386-93.

Siddiqui, A. H., Irani, R. A., Zhang, Y., Dai, Y., Blackwell, S. C., Ramin, S. M., et al. (2011). Recombinant vascular endothelial growth factor 121 attenuates autoantibody-induced features of pre-eclampsia in pregnant mice. *Am. J. Hypertens.*, 24, 606-12.

Sjowall, C., Wettero, J., Bengtsson, T., Askendal, A., Almroth, G., Skogh, T., et al. (2007). Solid-phase classical complement activation by C-reactive protein (CRP) is inhibited by fluid-phase CRP-C1q interaction. *Biochem. Biophys. Res. Commun.*, 352, 251-8.

Smyth, A., Oliveira, G. H., Lahr, B. D., Bailey, K. R., Norby, S. M. and Garovic, V. D. (2010). A systematic review and meta-analysis of pregnancy outcomes in patients with systemic lupus erythematosus and lupus nephritis. *Clin. J. Am. Soc. Nephrol.*, 5, 2060-8.

Somerset, D. A., Zheng, Y., Kilby, M. D., Sansom, D. M. and Drayson, M. T. (2004). Normal human pregnancy is associated with an elevation in the immune suppressive CD25+ CD4+ regulatory T-cell subset. *Immunology*, 112, 38-43.

Souwer, E. T., Blaauw, J., Coffeng, S. M., Smit, A. J., Van Doormaal, J. J., Faas, M. M., et al. (2011). Decreased arterial elasticity in formerly early-onset preeclamptic women. *Acta. Obstet. Gynecol. Scand.*, 90, 797-801.

Sunderland, N. S., Thomson, S. E., Heffernan, S. J., Lim, S., Thompson, J., Ogle, R., et al. (2011). Tumor necrosis factor alpha induces a model of preeclampsia in pregnant baboons (Papio hamadryas). *Cytokine.*, 56, 192-9.

Taki, A., Abe, M., Komaki, M., Oku, K., Iseki, S., Mizutani, S., et al. (2012). Expression of angiogenesis-related factors and inflammatory cytokines in placenta and umbilical vessels in pregnancies with preeclampsia and chorioamnionitis/funisitis. *Congenit Anom. (Kyoto)*, 52, 97-103.

Taylor, P. V., Scott, J. S., Gerlis, L. M., Esscher, E. and Scott, O. (1986). Maternal antibodies against fetal cardiac antigens in congenital complete heart block. *N. Engl. J. Med.*, 315, 667-72.

Thurman, J. M., Kraus, D. M., Girardi, G., Hourcade, D., Kang, H. J., Royer, P. A., et al. (2005). A novel inhibitor of the alternative complement pathway prevents antiphospholipid antibody-induced pregnancy loss in mice. *Mol. Immunol.*, 42, 87-97.

Thway, T. M., Shlykov, S. G., Day, M. C., Sanborn, B. M., Gilstrap, L. C., 3rd, Xia, Y., et al. (2004). Antibodies from preeclamptic patients stimulate increased intracellular Ca2+ mobilization through angiotensin receptor activation. *Circulation*, 110, 1612-9.

Tincani, A., Cavazzana, I., Ziglioli, T., Lojacono, A., De Angelis, V. and Meroni, P. (2010). Complement activation and pregnancy failure. *Clin. Rev. Allergy Immunol.*, 39, 153-9.

Tjoa, M. L., van Vugt, J. M., Go, A.T., Blankenstein, M. A., Oudejans, C. B. and Van Wijk, I. J. (2003). Elevated C-reactive protein levels during first trimester of pregnancy are indicative of preeclampsia and intrauterine growth restriction. *J. Reprod. Immunol.*, 59, 29-37.

Torricelli, M., Bellisai, F., Novembri, R., Galeazzi, L. R., Iuliano, A., Voltolini, C., et al. (2011). High levels of maternal serum IL-17 and activin A in pregnant women affected by systemic lupus erythematosus. *Am. J. Reprod. Immunol.*, 66, 84-9.

Tower, C., Crocker, I., Chirico, D., Baker, P. and Bruce, I. (2011). SLE and pregnancy: the potential role for regulatory T cells. *Nat. Rev. Rheumatol.*, 7, 124-8.

Tron, K., Manolov, D. E., Röcker, C., Kächele, M., Torzewski, J. and Nienhaus, G. U. (2008). C-reactive protein specifically binds to Fcγ receptor type I on a macrophage-like cell line. *Eur. J. Immunol.*, 38, 1414-22.

Venkatesha, S., Toporsian, M., Lam, C., Hanai, J., Mammoto, T., Kim, Y. M., et al. (2006). Soluble endoglin contributes to the pathogenesis of preeclampsia. *Nat. Med.*, 12, 642-9.

Verthelyi, D., Petri, M., Ylamus, M. and Klinman, D. M. (2001). Disassociation of sex hormone levels and cytokine production in SLE patients. *Lupus*, 10, 352-8.

Von Ehrenstein, O. S., Neta, G. I., Andrews, W., Goldenberg, R., Goepfert, A. and Zhang, J. (2012). Child intellectual development in relation to cytokine levels in umbilical cord blood. *Am. J. Epidemiol.*, 175, 1191-9.

Wallukat, G., Homuth, V., Fischer, T., Lindschau, C., Horstkamp, B., Jupner, A., et al. (1999). Patients with preeclampsia develop agonistic autoantibodies against the angiotensin AT1 receptor. *J. Clin. Invest.*, 103, 945-52.

Wand, W., Irani, R. A., Zhang, Y., Ramin, S. M., Blackwell, S. C., Tao, L., et al. (2012). Autoantibody-mediated complement C3a receptor activation contributes to the pathogenesis of preeclampsia. *Hypertension*, 60, 712-21.

Wegmann, T. G., Lin, H., Guilbert, L. and Mosmann, T. R. (1993). Bidirectional cytokine interactions in the maternal-fetal relationship: is successful pregnancy a TH2 phenomenon? *Immunol. Today*, 14, 353-6.

Wei, L. H., Chou, C. H., Chen, M. W., Rose-John, S., Kuo, M. L., Chen, S. U., et al. (2013). The role of IL-6 trans-signaling in vascular leakage: implications for ovarian hyperstimulation syndrome in a murine model. *J. Clin. Endocrinol. Metab.*, 98, E472-84.

Weiss, T. W., Arnesen, H. and Seljeflot, I. (2013). Components of the interleukin-6 transsignalling system are associated with the metabolic syndrome, endothelial dysfunction and arterial stiffness. *Metabolism*, 62, 1008-13.

Xia, Y. and Kellems, R. E. (2009). Is preeclampsia an autoimmune disease? *Clin. Immunol.*, 133, 1-12.

Xia, Y., Ramin, S. M. and Kellems, R. E. (2007). Potential roles of angiotensin receptor-activating autoantibody in the pathophysiology of preeclampsia. *Hypertension*, 50, 269-75.

Xia, Y., Wen, H., Bobst, S., Day, M. C. and Kellems, R. E. (2003). Maternal autoantibodies from preeclamptic patients activate angiotensin receptors on human trophoblast cells. *J. Soc. Gynecol. Investig.*, 10, 82-93.

Xu, D. X., Chen, Y. H., Wang, H., Zhao, L., Wang, J. P. and Wei, W. (2006). Tumor necrosis factor alpha partially contributes to lipopolysaccharide-induced intra-uterine fetal growth restriction and skeletal development retardation in mice. *Toxicol. Lett.*, 163, 20-9.

Yamada, H., Atsumi, T., Kobashi, G., Ota, C., Kato, E. H., Tsuruga, N., et al. (2009). Antiphospholipid antibodies increase the risk of pregnancy-induced hypertension and adverse pregnancy outcomes. *J. Reprod. Immunol.*, 79, 188-95.

Yu, K. Y., Kwon, B., Ni, J., Zhai, Y., Ebner, R. and Kwon, B. S. (1999). A newly identified member of tumor necrosis factor receptor superfamily (TR6) suppresses LIGHT-mediated apoptosis. *J. Biol. Chem.*, 274, 13733-6.

Zhang, W., Wang, W., Yu, H., Zhang, Y., Dai, Y., Ning, C., et al. (2012). Interleukin 6 underlies angiotensin II-induced hypertension and chronic renal damage. *Hypertension*, 59, 136-44.

Zhou, C. C., Ahmad, S., Mi, T., Abbasi, S., Xia, L., Day, M. C., et al. (2008). Autoantibody from women with preeclampsia induces soluble Fms-like tyrosine kinase-1 production via angiotensin type 1 receptor and calcineurin/nuclear factor of activated T-cells signaling. *Hypertension*, 51, 1010-9.

Zhou, C. C., Ahmad, S., Mi, T., Xia, L., Abbasi, S., Hewett, P. W., et al. (2007). Angiotensin II induces soluble fms-Like tyrosine kinase-1 release via calcineurin signaling pathway in pregnancy. *Circ. Res.*, 100, 88-95.

Zhou, C. C., Irani, R. A., Dai, Y., Blackwell, S. C., Hicks, M. J., Ramin, S. M., et al. (2011). Autoantibody-mediated IL-6-dependent endothelin-1 elevation underlies pathogenesis in a mouse model of preeclampsia. *J. Immunol.*, 186, 6024-34.

Zhou, C. C., Irani, R. A., Zhang, Y., Blackwell, S. C., Mi, T., Wen, J., et al. (2010). Angiotensin receptor agonistic autoantibody-mediated tumor necrosis factor-alpha induction contributes to increased soluble endoglin production in preeclampsia. *Circulation*, 121, 436-44.

In: Stress and Developmental Programming …   ISBN: 978-1-63321-836-9
Editors: Lubo Zhang and Lawrence D. Longo   © 2014 Nova Science Publishers, Inc.

Chapter 10

Stress and the HPA Axis Response: The Ovine Model of Developmental Programming

Dean A. Myers[1] and Charles A. Ducsay[2,*]
[1]Dept. of Obstetrics and Gynecology,
University of Oklahoma Health Sciences Center,
Oklahoma City, OK, US
[2]Center for Perinatal Biology, Loma Linda University,
School of Medicine, Loma Linda, CA, US

Abstract

The sheep has served as a well-studied model of the fetal hypothalamo-pituitary-adrenal (HPA) response to stress. More recently, it has become evident that the potential programming effects of prenatal stress on HPA function are related not only to genetic factors but also to the type, duration and severity of the stressor. In order to fully understand the programming of the fetal HPA axis and other physiological systems, it is imperative to understand that the insult is not only derived from the mother (e.g., excess transplacental passage of cortisol or nutritional deficits) but from the fetus itself through excessive activation of the fetal HPA axis. The use of the ovine model to delineate the potential mechanisms of both maternal and fetal stressors on programming of the HPA axis will be discussed in detail.

Keywords: Adrenal, hypoxia, fetus, hypothalamus, cortisol, pituitary, programming, stress

---

* Corresponding Author: Charles A. Ducsay, PhD. Center for Perinatal Biology, Loma Linda University, School of Medicine. E-mail: cducsay@llu.edu.

Introduction

Glucocorticoids (cortisol, corticosterone) are produced in the adrenal cortex under regulation by adrenocorticotropic hormone (ACTH) from the anterior pituitary, and are a major component of the stress response. In turn, ACTH synthesis and release is regulated via two hypothalamic neuropeptide secretagogues, corticotropin-releasing hormone (CRH) and arginine vasopressin (AVP), expressed by neurons in the parvocellular division of hypothalamic paraventricular nucleus (PVN). Collectively, this endocrine system is known as the hypothalamo-pituitary-adrenal axis (HPA axis). Under basal, non-stress conditions, glucocorticoid levels in plasma are maintained within a narrow range and play an essential role in homeostasis, targeting a variety of critical physiological systems. Aptly named for their regulation of hepatic gluconeogenesis, glucocorticoids play critical roles in governing metabolism, as well as immune regulation, inflammation and cardiovascular function. At the level of the central nervous system, glucocorticoids modulate a variety of functions such as fear and anxiety, mood, memory and cognition. During acute stress, there is a rapid CRH/AVP dependent release of ACTH from the anterior pituitary resulting in increased production of glucocorticoids in the adrenal cortex leading to elevated plasma glucocorticoid concentrations. In a classic negative feedback mechanism, glucocorticoids limit their own production by suppressing the release of CRH and AVP and therefore, ACTH. Thus, during 'normal' low stress situations, the HPA axis plays a critical role in homeostasis and the capacity to respond to an acute stress, limiting the damage or physiological impact of the acute stress.

The adult HPA axis exhibits considerable plasticity in its ability to respond or adapt/maladapt to the physiological/psychological environment of an individual (McEwen and Morrison, 2013, Rodrigues et al., 2009). For instance, during chronic or repeated stress, there is both a perturbation of negative feedback mechanisms as well as centers regulating the PVN resulting in overproduction of glucocorticoids [reviewed in (Schulkin et al., 1998)]. Unlike the critical role of cortisol in maintaining homeostasis, however, excess stress-induced and/or basal glucocorticoid production is associated with a plethora of homeostatic disturbances including immune suppression, hyperglycemia, excess adipose deposition, bone loss and hypertension. Changes in CNS function are also observed, including increased depression, fear and anxiety, memory loss and changes in cognitive function (Schulkin et al., 1998). Indeed, the concept of 'allostasis' or allostatic load has been promoted to describe the effect of an increasing stress load or repeated stressors on the function of the HPA axis (Schulkin et al., 1998). However, hyper- or hypo- responsive HPA activity, both basal and stress-induced, is not uncommon in individuals despite living a relatively stress-free life. Over the past few decades, studies primarily performed in rodents found that early life events have profound impacts on the developing HPA axis, permanently modifying, or programming, the HPA axis for altered function in adulthood (Barbazanges et al., 1996, Vallee et al., 1997, Weinstock et al., 1992) despite these animals having seemingly normal stress loads. The concept of programming was not unique to the HPA axis however, as epidemiological studies (Barker, 2007, Hales and Barker, 1992, 2001) found that adverse early life events, those occurring in utero, could program humans for increased susceptibility to early death from a constellation of associated disorders including cardiovascular disease, stroke and metabolic disorders. Thus was born the field of programming.

Two different, but not necessarily mutually exclusive, concepts have been proposed to understand fetal or early developmental programming. The first of these important concepts, the so-called 'Barker Hypothesis', centers around the impact of maternal malnutrition on the developing fetus. The concept that an under- or malnourished fetus is at increased risk for heart disease and stroke in adulthood was highlighted by the epidemiologic studies of the late Dr. David Barker. The 'Barker Hypothesis' was then expanded upon both by further epidemiological studies as well as experimental animal studies as the 'Developmental Origins of Health and Disease (DoHAD)' hypothesis. A key component of the Barker hypothesis is that maternal nutritional events result in a 'thin' fetus at birth (low ponderal index), which in turn can impact later extra uterine life (Barker, 2007, Hales and Barker, 1992, 2001). Barker noted that the intrauterine insults that lead to the decreased ponderal index deleteriously impacted or permanently 'programmed' fetal physiological systems, leading to dysfunction of these systems and contributing to a variety of related adult diseases that included cardiovascular and metabolic systems. The fetal responses to the 'adverse intrauterine environment' created by maternal mal- or undernutrition are likely adaptive, and as such promote fetal survival during development in a restrictive nutritional environment. However, postnatally, with relatively abundant nutrient availability, these same responses become maladaptive, leading to impaired glucose metabolism and obesity as well as cardiovascular disease (Hales and Barker, 2001). Barker further suggested that the paradoxical responses seen in these malnourished fetuses, thinness at birth but increased adiposity and altered metabolism post-birth through adulthood, actually increases the likelihood of these individuals being born into potentially famine environments to be thrifty, i.e. the "thrifty phenotype". This would increase the probability of surviving to reproductive age and passing on one's genes, but alas rendering one susceptible to death at an earlier age. Reynolds (Reynolds, 2013) suggested that reduced birth weight in itself is not necessarily responsible for programming; rather, it serves as a surrogate or marker for development under adverse intrauterine conditions.

Glucocorticoids As Programming Agents: Endogenous Glucocorticoids

In addition to fetal programming via nutritional restriction championed in the Barker hypothesis, overexposure to glucocorticoids during fetal life (Edwards et al., 1993) has also been shown to play a key role in programming. Excess prenatal glucocorticoids, either exogenous or endogenous, clearly impact a variety of physiological and endocrine systems in a pattern similar to maternal nutritional restriction leading to programming of adult metabolic disorders such as insulin resistance/hyperglycemia, dyslipidemia, obesity and hypertension/heart disease. Importantly, in utero exposure to excess glucocorticoids also alters basal and stress induced hypothalamo-pituitary-adrenocortical (HPA) responses during adult life in a wide range of species (Mina and Reynolds, 2014, de Vries et al., 2007). The overlap between the programming phenotype noted in the Barker hypothesis/undernutrition paradigm and that invoked by glucocorticoid excess is not simply coincidence. More likely it reflects a singular mechanism, alteration of the HPA axis, shared by a variety of maternal insults that lead to fetal programming. Indeed, a reciprocal interaction between maternal stress and under-nutrition occurs; maternal stress during gestation decreases food intake resulting in perinatal undernutrition (Gardner et al., 1997) and maternal undernutrition triggers HPA stress responses in the mother (Gardner et al., 1997, Langley-Evans et al., 1996). Until late gestation, the primary source of fetal glucocorticoids is by transplacental transport of maternally derived glucocorticoids. The placenta does offer some protection to the fetus from maternal glucocorticoids via inactivation of cortisol/corticosterone by 11βHSD2 (an enzyme that metabolizes cortisol to cortisone and corticosterone to 11 deoxycorticosterone). However, there is still a significant transfer of maternal steroid that does occur. Cumulatively though, glucocorticoids play a role in the observed programming effects in both hypotheses (Cottrell et al., 2012).

It becomes quite evident that the fetus has the capacity for developmental plasticity that allows it to adapt to the immediate intrauterine environment, thus improving its chances for intrauterine survival as well as preparing it for an anticipated harsh extrauterine existence. As several groups have described, elevated levels of glucocorticoids during the perinatal period can have a significant impact on the HPA axis at multiple sites (Barbazanges et al., 1996, Cottrell and Seckl, 2009, Langley-Evans, 2009, Welberg et al., 2001). For instance, glucocorticoids increased expression of the key hypothalamic ACTH secretagogue (CRH), and decreased hippocampal glucocorticoid receptors (both the mineralocorticoid receptor; [MR] and glucocorticoid receptor [GR]) thus attenuating negative feedback (Barbazanges et al., 1996). Further, glucocorticoids have been shown to upregulate 11βHSD1, which converts cortisone/11 deoxycorticosterone to active glucocorticoids thus amplifying HPA effects at target tissues. Similar to metabolic and cardiovascular programming, programming of the HPA axis is a prediction of the environment in which the fetus is to be born into, allowing the offspring to be prepared for a more hostile existence with more efficient metabolism, accelerated age at puberty, and enhanced stress responses (Cottrell and Seckl, 2009).

Not surprisingly, stress related behaviors such as fear and anxiety are also programmed via maternal stressors/glucocorticoids, thus preparing the offspring to be more vigilant in a potentially hostile environment. Unfortunately, activation of the fear/anxiety pathways invokes an HPA response as well as cardiovascular activity and alterations in metabolism. Welberg and co-workers (Welberg et al., 2000, 2001) elegantly demonstrated that maternal stress or perinatal glucocorticoids program increases in GR expression in amygdala and bed nucleus of the stria terminalis (BNST); the amygdala and BNST are key CNS structures mediating fear and anxiety. In addition, Shepard and colleagues (Shepard and Myers, 2008, Shepard et al., 2006) showed that glucocorticoids in adult rats act directly at the central amygdaloid nucleus to increase fear/anxiety behavior as well as the HPA response to psychological stress. Thus, fetal programming creates a situation in which a dangerous positive feedback loop, while being beneficial in the short term, is not optimal for a long and happy life.

Glucocorticoids as Programming Agents: Synthetic Glucocorticoids

The capacity of maternally administered glucocorticoids to permanently alter the developing nervous system of the rat has been known for approximately 30 years. Synthetic glucocorticoids readily cross the placenta and are not substrates for inactivation by placental or tissue 11 βHSD2 (Welberg et al., 2000). Permanently altered function of the HPA axis and fear/anxiety related behaviors have been reported in rats and other species in response to exogenous glucocorticoid administration during gestation. In rats, daily administration of dexamethasone throughout gestation or during only the final week results in elevated basal plasma corticosterone levels in adult male offspring (Levitt et al., 1996, Welberg et al., 2001) associated with elevated blood pressure. Another study demonstrated that daily maternal dexamethasone administration on day 17-19 of gestation resulted in male offspring that exhibited enhanced corticosterone production in response to a pure behavioral stressor (Muneoka et al., 1997). Of relevance, dexamethasone treatment also programs the offspring to exhibit increased indices of fear/anxiety (Vallee et al., 1997, Welberg et al., 2001). Increased fear/anxiety is physiologically detrimental since activation of the central fear circuit increases cardiovascular function, alters pain perception and is a potent activator of the HPA axis. Therefore an increased perception of a situation as fearful would lead to an increased activation of the HPA axis over the lifespan of an individual.

Studies in humans and non-human primates have also implicated maternally administered glucocorticoids as impacting the offspring HPA axis and CNS in general. An obvious indication that synthetic glucocorticoids compromise brain development is the reduction in head circumference reported in infants exposed to antenatal glucocorticoid regimens, even after correction for overall growth retardation and gestational age at birth (Abbasi et al., 2000, Barbazanges et al., 1996, Romagnoli et al., 1999). Similarly, imaging of infants indicates significantly impaired brain growth with glucocorticoid treatment and an associated increase in behavioral disorders by three years of age (Bloom et al., 2001, Modi et al., 2001, Newnham, 2001). Effects of maternally administered synthetic glucocorticoids have been noted on offspring behavior in humans, suggesting an increased risk for neurological disorders such as autism, increased emotionality (anxiety or enhanced fearfulness) in children, and adult depression (Aylward, 2005, Barker et al., 1995, Burd et al., 1999). In children (ages 3 to 6,) exposed to three or more courses of antenatal corticosteroids, higher rates of hyperactivity, aggressiveness, destructive behavior, and distractibility have been observed (French et al., 2004). Another study (Trautman et al., 1995) indicated that antenatal dexamethasone affects behavioral development consistent with increased fear/anxiety as reflected by increased shyness and avoidance, with no effect on cognition. Stoelhorst et al., (Stoelhorst et al., 2003) observed that perinatal dexamethasone treatment was associated with higher scores in the somatic problems scale and higher syndrome scale scores, mainly for anxious/depressed and/or withdrawn behavior. Preterm infants were found to have higher indices of social disorders consistent with increased anxiety and linked with use of perinatal steroids. Antenatal dexamethasone administration to mothers carrying fetuses at risk for 21-hydroxylase deficiency resulted in delayed psychomotor development in the children (Lajic et al., 1998). Abnormal HPA axis reactivity to stress in childhood and elevated blood pressure in adolescence have also been noted in children exposed perinatally to synthetic glucocorticoids (Doyle et al., 2000, Glover et al., 2005, Karlsson et al., 2000). The effect on the infant HPA appears early after birth (Glover et al., 2005, Karlsson et al., 2000) with decreased cortisol response to immunization stress at four months of age (Glover et al., 2010). With direct relevance to humans, once daily administration of dexamethasone to pregnant rhesus monkeys at 132 days of gestation for four consecutive days resulted in offspring (age 10 months) that exhibited elevated basal and stress-stimulated cortisol levels (Uno et al., 1994).

Collectively, these studies demonstrate how relatively short-term fetal exposure to glucocorticoids can effectively program HPA function in humans and an important non-human primate model.

In addition to increased HPA axis function, rodent studies also clearly show that exogenous glucocorticoid administration during pregnancy perturbs peripheral physiological systems in which glucocorticoids play a major role in regulation. For instance, maternal administration of dexamethasone results in the development of hypertension and insulin resistance/glucose intolerance (type II diabetes-like) in the offspring by adulthood (Levitt et al., 1996, Nyirenda et al., 1998). Pharmacological blockade of maternal glucocorticoid production prevents hypertension in the offspring as adults subjected to maternal undernutrition during gestation (Langley-Evans, 1997). Preventing maternal corticosterone increases in response to stress during pregnancy also circumvents prenatal stress induced sequelae in the offspring (Barbazanges et al., 1996).

Studies in sheep examining the effect of synthetic glucocorticoids on the offspring HPA have also been reported, but unlike the rat, there have been relatively few studies where the effect of maternally (or fetally) delivered synthetic steroids on the offspring was examined post-birth, and into adulthood. Sloboda and co-workers described a series of studies examining the effect of single or multiple delivery of betamethasone to either the fetus or ewe on the offspring HPA axis at various ages post-birth (Sloboda et al., 2000). Neither maternal nor fetal prenatal betamethasone administration significantly altered the ACTH and cortisol responses to CRH and AVP administration. However, at 1 year of age, a previous single injection of betamethasone to the mother resulted in significantly elevated basal and stimulated cortisol concentrations, without affecting the ACTH response. In contrast, betamethasone administration to the fetus resulted in significantly attenuated ACTH responses to CRH and AVP at one year of age, without any significant changes in basal or stimulated cortisol levels. In a subsequent study, Sloboda et al., (Sloboda et al., 2002) reported that by two years of age, single maternal betamethasone injections had no effect on basal plasma ACTH or cortisol concentrations, while repeated maternal injections elevated the ACTH response to stress. By three years of age, basal ACTH was elevated by repeated maternal injections, while both basal and stimulated cortisol concentrations were suppressed. These authors also found that both basal and stimulated cortisol:ACTH and basal cortisol:CYP17 mRNA ratios were suppressed by repeated maternal betamethasone injections. Multiple fetal betamethasone exposures decreased both basal ACTH and cortisol concentrations in offspring at 2 but not 3 years of age. Using this same model, Sloboda (Sloboda et al., 2007) also noted effects of maternally delivered betamethasone on hippocampal MR mRNA in adult offspring exposed to either one or multiple doses. MR mRNA as well as 11βHSD1 were elevated in the hippocampus, consistent with increased negative feedback programming of the HPA axis. Based on their findings, HPA function in sheep appears to undergo developmental changes that are influenced by prenatal glucocorticoid exposure. Furthermore, the effects of glucocorticoid on postnatal HPA responses appears to vary dependent on fetal vs. maternal delivery.

One of the most striking studies on the programming effects of synthetic glucocorticoid treatment examined multigenerational effects of maternal glucocorticoid treatment in pregnant ewes (Long et al., 2013). In this study, pregnant F0 ewes were treated with multiple doses dexamethasone at 0.7 gestation. The F1 female offspring were then bred to produce F2 offspring and HPA axis function was examined in both groups post-pubertally. Both F1 and

F2 demonstrated reduced birth weight. More importantly as adults, there was enhanced basal cortisol in the F1 offspring and elevated basal ACTH and cortisol in the F2 generation. Further, with ACTH and CRH/AVP challenges, both groups of offspring demonstrated reduced hypothalamic and pituitary responses. This was the first study to demonstrate multigenerational effects of synthetic glucocorticoid administration in the sheep model.

Recently, Su et al., (Su et al., 2013) studied ovine offspring at one and one-half years of age that were exposed to maternally administered betamethasone at 80 days of gestation. Glucocorticoid treated females showed greater plasma cortisol and adrenocortical cells obtained from these female offspring exhibited greater ACTH-stimulated cortisol production. These authors also examined the role of leptin in the programming of the HPA axis. Antenatal betamethasone increased plasma leptin in both males and females at 1.5 years of age. Leptin exerted a greater inhibitory effect on basal and stimulated cortisol production in adrenocortical cells obtained from betamethasone treated males, with no differences in females at 1.5 years of age. Enhanced inhibitory effects of leptin on both basal and ACTH-stimulated StAR and ACTH-Receptor mRNA were also noted in adrenocortical cells prepared from betamethasone exposed males with no effect in these cells obtained from females (Su et al., 2013). This study suggests that synthetic glucocorticoids may not only have direct programming effects but may also secondarily influence the HPA axis through regulation of leptin. The role of leptin in fetal programming of the HPA axis will be discussed in greater detail later in this chapter.

Species Considerations in Programming of the HPA Axis

It is imperative to emphasize that the choice of the animal model will have a dramatic impact on the outcome of prenatal stress programming of the HPA axis, specifically the differences as to when the HPA axis matures during development. In the most widely studied model, the rodent, a large portion of development of the neuroendocrine axis occurs after birth (Dent et al., 2000, Galeeva et al., 2006). In marked contrast, in precocial animals such as sheep, primates and guinea pigs, the largest degree of brain development and a significant portion of neuroendocrine development and CNS maturation, in general occurs *in utero* (Challis et al., 2000, Dobbing and Sands, 1979, Matthews, 2002). With this in mind, any data interpretation must take into account not only when the stressor(s) was introduced but also the animal model studied. In both rodents and precocial species, windows of development have been identified in which the CNS (and other organs in general) is apparently protected from endogenous glucocorticoids by a 'stress hypo-responsive period' (SHRP) (Schmidt et al., 2003, 2005). In rodents, this period is in the first two weeks post-birth and represents a time when the neonate is relatively unable to mount a stress response to a variety of physiological stressors. The SHRP is primarily a central inability to activate the HPA axis and/or heightened glucocorticoid negative feedback sensitivity. Ultimately, during this period post birth in rodents, basal plasma corticosterone levels are low and there is little stress induced ACTH or corticosterone release. Conversely, in sheep, the SHRP appears to occur in utero and is driven by a suppression of adrenocortical expression of CYP11A1 and CYP17, the two rate-limiting enzymes for cortisol synthesis. This period is from ~90 through ~125 days of gestation (term is ~148 days). During this time, cortisol circulates at very low levels and is not increased by acute fetal stressors. The circulating cortisol during this window of development is largely derived therefore, from maternal transplacental transport. It is likely not coincidental that the major events in CNS development in the rodent coincide with the SHRP and similarly these events occur in fetal life in precocial species. In the sheep fetus, this is also a period of major growth of fetal organs, and considering that glucocorticoids are maturational and anti-mitotic, protecting these organs from fluctuating and even high levels of glucocorticoids will promote maximal organogenesis.

As reviewed by Symonds and Budge (Symonds and Budge, 2009), species consideration becomes a key issue in studies on HPA axis programming. In altricial species such as the rat in which neuroendocrine maturation occurs to a large extent postnatally, the appetite regulatory circuitry would be seemingly less susceptible to *in utero* programming actions of maternal dietary manipulations. In contrast, in the sheep (and human), the appetite regulatory neuroendocrine system largely differentiates and matures between mid and late gestation and as such, would render this system susceptible to maternally transmitted programming. The authors (Symonds and Budge, 2009) also highlighted another key difference between rodents and longer-gestation precocial species, which is that the placenta may play a role in fetal programming. In the rodent model, placental growth continues until term to meet the higher protein demands (Spray and Widdowson, 1950, Widdowson, 1950) whereas in sheep and humans, maximal placental growth happens earlier in pregnancy in preparation for the greater demands near term. Further, in the sheep, placental growth restriction results in decreased nutrient transport to the fetus as well as perturbed placental hemodynamics, and is therefore associated with fetal growth restriction at a time where numerous organ maturational events are occurring (McMillen et al., 2001). While maternal nutritional restriction has similar consequences in rodents on placental growth and subsequently fetal growth, the maturation of the offspring occurs largely post birth. This may reflect why so many offspring programming paradigms in rodents can be achieved by manipulations of the post-birth maternal-infant environment. It is also important to consider the number of fetuses per pregnancy, since multiple studies have shown that having more than one offspring can itself alter neuroendocrine function including that of the HPA axis (Begum et al., 2012, Edwards and McMillen, 2002, Gardner et al., 2004, Rumball et al., 2009). Unlike polytocus species like the rat and guinea pig, the sheep, like the human, is more likely to have singleton pregnancies (Begum et al., 2013).

A number of studies have attempted to examine the effects of prenatal stress in humans (See Weinstock, 2001 for review). In general, maternal psychological stress during pregnancy has been shown to give rise to alterations in brain development with attendant psychological disorders in children including depression, ADD and schizophrenia. Additional studies on the effects of glucocorticoid overexposure have demonstrated reduced reactivity of the HPA axis in infants (Tegethoff et al., 2009) while maternal stress has been shown to result in disruption of neurobehavioral function (Talge et al., 2007). However, the results are highly variable due to differences in experimental design and outcome measurements. Further, the data are correlative since obvious ethical reasons prevent studies of intentional manipulation of the maternal intrauterine environment. The non-human primate model offers some insight into the effects of maternal stressors on resultant programming of the HPA axis. In particular, studies by Pryce et al., (Pryce et al., 2011) have shed light on alterations of the maternal environment and subsequent effects on the HPA axis in offspring. However, the overall availability and high cost make this a model of limited and highly specific use.

In summary, the rodent offers an attractive model for studying programming of the HPA axis. Advantages include availability, ease of housing and handling, and relatively short time period to adulthood (a few months), not to mention the very large database of research that has been performed on these species. This model does however, have significant translational drawbacks due to the different developmental trajectories previously described. The sheep offer significant strengths over the rodent model including the maturation of the HPA axis in utero that occurs similarly in sheep and primates, including humans. Studies on the HPA axis in rodents during development are largely restricted to 'snapshots' of gene expression at selected developmental ages, with physiological studies on fetal rodents largely unattainable. In contrast, the ovine fetus is readily 'instrumented' at various gestational periods from mid through late gestation, including placement of vascular catheters for the measurement of circulating hormones and delivery of agents to manipulate the fetal HPA axis. This also allows a direct examination of programming mechanisms to the fetus, unlike rodents where the transmitting mechanism(s) from the dam to the fetus during programming remain largely enigmatic. Other manipulations of the ovine fetus, like adrenalectomy and selective hypothalamic ablations, allow a direct manipulation of the developing HPA axis not attainable in rodents. Stereotaxic manipulation of the hypothalamic PVN and other CNS structures can also be performed, probing the role of central structures in the regulation of the HPA axis during development. Further, with the availability of both the nearly complete ovine and completed bovine genome, molecular tools available to study sheep are no longer limiting. Nonetheless, there are some drawbacks of the sheep model, namely, the time needed from birth to adulthood (years vs. months), and housing issues – not every research institution has the housing available for using sheep as a research tool- and finally, local availability of timed pregnant sheep. Despite these drawbacks however, the sheep has and will continue to provide a valuable model for studying programming of the HPA axis.

Development of the Ovine HPA Axis and Critical Windows for Programming

Much of what is known regarding development and function of the *fetal* HPA axis has been gleaned from long gestation species such as the sheep (and to a much lesser extent, the non-human primate). Unlike rodents, which, although exhibiting a term gestation corticosterone surge, do not mature their HPA axis and gain the typical response to stresses until well after birth (after the SHRP), the ovine fetus gains the capacity to exert an adrenocortical response to various physiological stressors in utero. From approximately the time of adrenal formation at around day 40 gestation until approximately 80 to 90 days gestation, fetal adrenocortical cortisol formation in vivo is negligible. During this period, the majority of circulating fetal cortisol is derived from transplacental passage of maternal cortisol (Hennessy et al., 1982). A large portion of the cortisol is inactivated to cortisone via 11-beta hydroxysteroid dehydrogenase type 2 (11βHSD2). Thus, the fetus during this period is exposed to relatively low concentrations of cortisol, approx. 20% or less that of the maternal non-stressed levels. Surprisingly however, fetal adrenocortical cells (FACs) taken from fetuses during this window of gestation (60 days) have been described as exhibiting a high capacity to respond to ACTH. Fetal adrenocortical cells, by ~80-90 days of gestation express all the enzymes necessary for cortisol synthesis (CYP11A1, CYP17, HSD3B2, CYP21, CYP11B1), however, ACTH receptor expression is lower than at later stages of gestation. The inability of the fetus during this period of gestation to mount a cortisol response to stress is due to several factors including the immaturity of the developing CNS pathways that stimulate CRH and AVP release, and very low levels of expression of CRH and AVP in the PVN as these neurons are differentiating.

At approximately 80 to 90 days gestation, expression of key enzymes, primarily the rate limiting enzymes, CYP11A1 and CYP17, declines in the FACs to nearly undetectable levels and remains repressed until approximately 125-130 days gestation when their expression re-emerges. Expression of these enzymes then gradually increases, reaching a peak at term gestation. The progressive increase in expression coincides with the prepartum fetal plasma cortisol surge. The mechanism responsible for repressing the expression of the steroidogenic enzymes, however, remains enigmatic. At the level of the anterior pituitary, although immunoreactive ACTH (IR-ACTH) is observed as found in the fetal circulation by midgestation, its bioactivity is relatively low. This is due to an immaturity of proteolytic processing of the ACTH precursor, proopiomelanocortin (POMC) to the mature 39-residue peptide, ACTH. Therefore, in the fetal circulation (and anterior pituitary), the primary contribution to the IR-ACTH is from POMC itself and a major partially processed form of POMC (22 kDa proACTH). 22 kD proACTH is formed by limited processing of POMC by the subtilisin like enzyme SPC3 which cleaves POMC to biologically active peptides at specific di-basic residues. Thus, with the immaturity of hypothalamic neuropeptide regulation (CRH/AVP), anterior pituitary processing of POMC to ACTH in secretory vesicles is limited.

In an elegant study by Schwartz and colleagues, both POMC and 22kDa ACTH were shown to inhibit ACTH induced cortisol production by FACs (Schwartz et al., 1995). There is speculation from these authors that as the FACs mature toward term they may lose the capacity to respond to the precursors while gaining increased capacity to respond to ACTH via expression of the ACTH receptor (the melanocortin 2 receptor, MC2R). The MC2R is a member of the melanocortin receptor family that includes the alpha MSH receptor (MC1R) and gamma MSH receptors, MC3, 4 and 5R. At ~110-130 days gestation, the fetal adrenal expresses MC1R and MC5R as well as MC2R and expression of MC1R and MC5R declines as term gestation approaches. Rose and colleagues showed that the expression of the MC2R increases during the final weeks of gestation in the fetal adrenal cortex paralleling the late gestation cortisol surge (Su et al., 2005). Interestingly, the MC2R, the shortest of all G protein-coupled receptors, requires a 'chaperone' protein termed MRAP. The expression of this protein parallels that of the MC2R during late gestation and when transfected into immature (~110-120 days gestation) FACs lead to increased response to ACTH. Thus, although highly speculative, one hypothesis for the 'stress hyporesponsive' period in the ovine fetal adrenal cortex between ~90-125 days gestation may be a combination of the low degree of bioactivity of fetal IR-ACTH, the presence of high levels of inhibitory POMC and 22kDa proACTH (compared to ACTH) and specific melanocortin receptors via which they act and a paucity of expression of the critical co-receptor, MRAP.

The biological significance of the developmental period when the fetal adrenal cortex loses its capacity for cortisol synthesis remains unclear, but as discussed earlier, it is interesting that this phenomenon is observed in a wide range of species including rodents, which exhibit the SHRP period during the early post-birth period. It is noteworthy, however, that this period of development in rodents, in particular CNS development corresponds to the period of gestation in the ovine fetus that coincides with the shutting down of fetal adrenal cortisol biosynthetic capacity. Thus, this may be a critical developmental time in which the CNS and other organs such as liver, kidney, lung and pancreas are developmentally highly active with critical differentiation occurring (i.e. nephrogenesis in the kidney) and as such need protection from exposure to elevated levels of glucocorticoids. Indeed, from the classical studies of the late G.C. (Mont) Liggins in the ovine fetus (Kitterman et al., 1981, Liggins, 1976, Liggins et al., 1973, 1985), we know that fetal glucocorticoids are essential for maturation of the fetal lung, kidney, gut, liver, adipose and certain aspects of CNS function. This role of glucocorticoids is not surprisingly universal amongst mammals and likely pinpoints to these steroids as playing a major role in fetal programming of various systems, including the HPA axis itself.

It is also noteworthy that during this period of adrenocortical "insufficiency", PVN expression of CRH and AVP increases dramatically. We found that between 105 and ~125-130 days gestation, CRH in the PVN undergoes a major increase in expression (Myers et al., 1993). Although plasma ACTH remains constant throughout the period of the re-emergence in adrenal cortical steroidogenic enzyme expression, an increase in the bioactivity of fetal plasma IR-ACTH occurs during this period as do increases in the ratio of ACTH to POMC and 22 kDa proACTH. In studies with the late Dr. Tom McDonald, one of the pioneers of fetal stereotaxic neurosurgery, we determined that lesioning the fetal PVN at 120 days gestation prevents the re-emergence of adrenocortical steroidogenic enzyme expression (Myers et al., 1992a). In a subsequent study, we also noted that lesion of the fetal PVN also blocked processing of POMC to ACTH in the fetal anterior pituitary leading to fetal plasma ACTH levels that were below the limit of detection while maintaining fetal plasma POMC and 22 kDa proACTH (Bell et al., 2005). Interestingly, levels of anterior pituitary SPC3 did not change in response to PVN lesion, but the number of corticotropes (POMC expressing cells) expressing SPC3 was significantly reduced. To a large extent, POMC processing is not simply dependent upon the expression level of SPC3. It is more closely related to neuropeptide stimulated secretory vesicle formation during which the maturing secretory vesicle undergoes acidification and calcium influx; SPC3 is a calcium dependent enzyme with a pH optimum for ACTH production of ~2-3. Thus, POMC and 22 kDa proACTH are likely released from either non-SPC3 expressing corticotropes or via a constitutive secretory pathway independent of CRH and/or AVP stimulation.

After the re-emergence of fetal adrenocortical steroidogenic enzyme expression at ~125-130 days of gestation, and the initiation of the prepartum cortisol surge, PVN expression of CRH declines by ~140 days, and as reviewed by Matthews and Challis (Matthews and Challis, 1996), increases again at term gestation, likely in response to the stresses of labor. Although significantly lower at ~140, there is still substantial CRH and AVP expression in the PVN, and this likely reflects the emergence of glucocorticoid negative feedback during the final third of gestation. This permits a progressive exponential rise in fetal cortisol necessary for proper organ maturation. While there is a demonstrated glucocorticoid negative feedback, the presence of the cortisol surge indicates that the negative feedback mechanisms in the fetus are immature compared to adults. This is obviously needed to provide the maturational surge in cortisol. Using stereotaxic placement of dexamethasone adjacent to the fetal PVN, we noted that young fetuses exhibited a profound suppression of CRH expression while older fetuses near term were relatively resistant to dexamethasone suppression of CRH. This observation is consistent with a decrease in the negative feedback efficacy of cortisol that allows the prepartum cortisol surge (Myers et al., 1992b). Whether this is a decreased feedback at known CNS sites which glucocorticoids act upon to suppress PVN function such as hippocampus and BNST, or simply from hyper-stimulation of CNS sites stimulating the PVN (brainstem adrenergic, noradrenergic centers) overriding negative feedback, remains to be determined. We found in adult rats that glucocorticoids act at the level of the central amygdaloid nucleus to increase CRH in the PVN and the HPA response itself (Shepard et al., 2006); thus, it may be worth exploring this key site regulating the PVN as a possible feed-forward site for the HPA axis in the ovine fetus.

Fetal HPA Responses to Stress

It is imperative to emphasize that the potential programming effects of prenatal stress on HPA function are related not only to genetic factors but also the type, duration and severity of the stressor (Harris and Seckl, 2011). In order to fully understand the programming of the fetal HPA axis and other physiological systems, with particular emphasis on the programming of the human fetus, it is imperative to understand that not only the insult can be derived from the mother (e.g., excess transplacental passage of cortisol or nutritional deficits) but from the fetus itself via excessive activation of the fetal HPA axis. In rodents, as discussed above, the fetal HPA axis, while providing for a short-lived burst of corticosterone sufficient to mature organ systems, is largely unresponsive to stressors until well after birth in the later neonatal stages. However in sheep and primate fetuses, the HPA axis can mount a cortisol response above basal levels in response to acute stress during the final third of gestation. Physiological stressors that can activate the stress response in an adult (e.g., hypotension, hypoglycemia, hypoxia) are potent stimulators of a fetal HPA response. Of course, as described above, the amount of cortisol produced in response to an acute stress in the fetus depends on the both the stage of gestation and the duration of the stressor. In the ovine fetus, prior to approximately 120-125 days of gestation, there is little cortisol produced in response to acute stress. Indeed, even in the period prior to the steroidogenic 'shutdown' at ~90 days gestation, fetal stress does not produce an increase in fetal plasma cortisol even though the adrenal cortex expresses all the necessary enzymes and genes and is fully capable of releasing cortisol in response to exogenous ACTH. This largely reflects the immaturity of the HPA axis at the level of the PVN and its regulatory sites in the CNS. As shown by Rose and colleagues (Rose et al., 1981), the ovine fetus at approximately 120 days gestation is capable of eliciting an ACTH response to acute stress (hemorrhage or hypotension) but not cortisol, reflective of the maturing CNS and PVN aspects of the HPA axis relative to the adrenal cortex. However, by approximately day 130, the cortisol response to an acute stressor is notable, and by day 135 - 140 or later, the cortisol response is more adult like while the ACTH response declines, reflecting negative feedback invoked by the larger cortisol response.

Considering development of the capacity to mount an HPA axis response to stress during the final weeks of gestation, acute stress activation of the fetal HPA axis would play two potential roles in the fetus. In the event of an isolated acute stressor (i.e. the occasional positional umbilical cord occlusion leading to an acute hypoxic episode), the release of cortisol would play a similar role as it would in the adult stress response: maintenance of homeostasis. Thus, the fetal HPA axis plays a protective role during the final weeks of gestation (in addition to its organ maturational role from the increasing basal cortisol levels as term approaches). However, in the event of a persistent stressor (i.e. sustained hypoxia) during the final weeks of gestation, there is an acute increase in fetal plasma cortisol followed by a latent increase in basal cortisol as maturation of the adrenal cortex is hastened. In sheep, this sustained cortisol response would both impact the developing organs and fetus by invoking early maturation while limiting growth resulting in a smaller (potentially growth restricted) fetus with similar impacts (programming) of critical organ systems. Since cortisol also drives parturition in sheep, this might still be seen as 'beneficial' since the early delivery of the fetus would be coordinated with an earlier fetal maturation increasing the likelihood of survival of the lamb. In humans, where fetal cortisol is maturational only and plays a negligible role in parturition, the sustained fetal stressor would result in arrested organ development and fetal growth with increased maturation. Since the fetus would potentially remain in utero until normal term, the duration of exposure of the fetus to the stressor (and thus elevated fetal cortisol) would be longer with a more significant impact (programming) on target organs. In both scenarios (sheep and human), however, the role of the HPA axis would be similar with increased chances of survival at birth, but an increased susceptibility to succumbing to a variety of diseases as adults, as the result of an inappropriately programmed HPA axis.

Recapitulating the Barker Hypothesis in Experimental Animals: Maternal Undernutrition

It is evident that not only the type of alteration of maternal nutrition, but also more importantly, when the alteration takes place during development has a major impact on the programming outcome (Symonds and Budge, 2009). This is, as expected, related to organ growth and key windows of developmental plasticity for each organ system.

There are an abundance of studies in rodents exploring the fetal programming effects of maternal undernutrition or nutritional restriction [see (Breton, 2013, Wattez et al., 2013) for review]. In these various studies, the degree to which maternal nutrients were restricted varied considerably with regard to both duration and amount. Further, some studies approached undernutrition in terms of malnutrition, where protein intake was reduced relative to carbohydrate and fat. In general maternal under/mal-nutrition has been found to program the rodent offspring for susceptibility to a plethora of diseases related to those described by David Barker and colleagues, namely cardiovascular disease and metabolic disorders including insulin resistance, dyslipidemia, hypercholesterolemia and obesity. Further, maternal nutritional restriction programs the HPA axis of the offspring, likely contributing to the attainment of these diseases or at a minimum aiding in their progression. In rodents, maternal under/mal-nutrition is associated with fetal growth restriction and typically creates an IUGR model (Langley-Evans, 2009, Ross and Desai, 2005). How the IUGR phenotype of the rodent newborn relates to the epidemiological studies of Barker are unclear since his epidemiological findings on thinness at birth, or low ponderal index, were not IUGR infants (lowest 10th percentile of newborns) but rather simply 'thin' for their size.

The effect of maternal undernutrition has also been studied in sheep and baboons, both long gestation species, where a more detailed assessment of the effect of maternal undernutrition on both fetal-placental physiology as well as programming can be attained. Studies from the McMillen lab in Australia have clearly demonstrated that maternal undernutrition *during* gestation has profound effects on the fetal HPA in the sheep (Edwards and McMillen, 2002, Edwards et al., 2002). Interestingly, periconceptional nutrition before or immediately after conception also had an impact, albeit differential, on programming of the fetal HPA (Edwards and McMillen, 2002). Periconceptional undernutrition is quite relevant in relation to the human situation described by Barker where nutritional restriction or malnutrition likely occurred prior to conception and was hence maintained during gestation (and continued during lactation). Maternal nutrient restriction of 70% of control feed from day 60 before, until day 7 after conception, resulted in elevated fetal ACTH levels from 110 days gestation as well as an enhanced cortisol response to exogenous ACTH in twin pregnancies. It is important to remember that the brief undernutrition during the first 7 days post-conception is at a time when there are minimal nutrient demands by the developing conceptus. A subsequent study determined that the effect on the HPA axis did not appear to be mediated though changes in expression of POMC in the pituitary or change in adrenal MC2R, StAR or key steroidogenic enzymes (Edwards et al., 2002). However, it was suggested that the potential effects of undernutrition on POMC and adrenal enzymes could have been obscured by the ontogenic rise in fetal ACTH at term.

This laboratory also examined the effect of maternal undernutrition during gestation. In ovine fetuses exposed to maternal undernutrition during pregnancy (days 8 to 147 of gestation), there was no effect on fetal ACTH but a trend toward an increased prepartum rise in cortisol typically associated with maturation and larger adrenals observed in twin but not singleton fetuses. This is likely the result of the observed increased expression of mRNA for MC2R and StAR, without alterations in expression of steroidogenic enzymes like CYP11A1, CYP17 and 3β-HSD (Edwards et al., 2002). This appears to be a potential mechanism for the enhanced activation of the fetal HPA axis that occurs with alterations in the fetal nutrient environment. The finding that the effects were restricted to twin fetuses likely reflects the greater nutritional demand of twins compared to singleton fetuses. An effect on singletons might occur therefore if the ewe was undernourished prior to conception and the undernutrition maintained throughout gestation. In these studies, there was no effect of either periconceptional or gestational undernutrition on fetal weight in singletons. However in twin pregnancies, twin fetuses from the gestational undernutrition group were smaller.

An additional consequence of activation of the fetal HPA axis is preterm delivery. It is well established in the sheep that the fetal HPA axis plays a key role in the timing of delivery (Challis et al., 2000, Liggins et al., 1973). Studies by Bloomfield et al., (Bloomfield et al., 2003b, 2004) found that limiting maternal food intake during gestation resulted in an enhanced ACTH and cortisol increase with subsequent preterm delivery in approximately half of the pregnancies studied. However, the fetuses were not growth restricted. Maternal undernutrition was initiated 60 days before, and continued for 30 days after conception. As indicated by Bloomfield et al. (Bloomfield et al., 2003b), at 30 days gestation, the nutrient requirements of the developing fetus are very small so that maternal undernutrition itself was unlikely to play a role in programming. This was confirmed by the fact that the fetuses were not growth restricted. Instead, the enhanced delivery was attributed to precocious maturation of the fetal HPA axis (Bloomfield et al., 2003b, 2004).

Maternal undernutrition also has a significant programming effect on the POMC gene in the hypothalamus. Since maternal undernutrition alters the HPA axis and is associated with obesity, it seems likely that it also affects neuropeptides in the hypothalamus that regulate appetite and energy homeostasis. As described by Stevens et al., (Stevens et al., 2010, 2011), maternal undernutrition during the periconceptional period in the sheep results in dramatic epigenetic alterations in fetal hypothalamic genes and enhances brain POMC and glucocorticoid receptor (GR) gene expression. Specifically, they observed reduced methylation of the hypothalamic POMC promoter coupled with a reduction in DNA methyltransferase activity and changes in histone acetylation and methylation. The lack of OCT4 promoter methylation coupled with enhanced glucocorticoid receptor (GR) message expression suggested gene specific effects. These changes were proposed to be a key factor in the fetal programming of obesity in the offspring through altered regulation of POMC and NPY by GR with attendant alterations in appetite, glucose homeostasis and energy utilization (Stevens et al., 2011).

In addition to the standard models of maternal undernutrition of programming, twinning is an endogenous model of potential undernutrition during development. Analogous to maternal undernutrition, twins are also born small for gestational age both in sheep (De Matteo et al., 2008, Noia et al., 2002) and humans (Buckler and Green, 2004, The et al., 2010), and as adults, twins experience a higher incidence of metabolic disorders (Poulsen et al., 1997, 2009). A number of studies suggested that in twin pregnancies, the effect is different from maternal undernutrition. Unlike the accelerated maturation achieved in fetuses from nutrient restricted mothers, twin fetuses appear to have a delayed maturation of the HPA, with a reduction in circulating cortisol concentrations and blunted adrenal responsiveness (Edwards and McMillen, 2002, Gardner et al., 2004, Rumball et al., 2009). This reduced adrenal sensitivity may be an adaptive mechanism to compensate for the potential heightened intrauterine stress experienced in a twin pregnancy, with a concomitant reduction in cortisol biosynthesis, thereby reducing the chance of preterm delivery (McMillen et al., 2004).

More recently Begum et al., (Begum et al., 2012) provided the first evidence for actual epigenetic changes in the hypothalami of ovine twins compared to singleton controls. In this study the emphasis was on fetal hypothalamic pathways regulating metabolism. They demonstrated that in twins compared to singletons, there was a reduction in methylation of the hypothalamic POMC promoter that was correlated with altered histone methylation and acetylation as well as DNA methyltransferase activity. Glucocorticoid receptor (GR) methylation was also decreased. Similar changes were observed in singleton fetuses from ewes that were subjected to undernutrition for day 60 before until day 30 after mating in this as well as an earlier study (Stevens et al., 2010). In this case, when hypothalamic metabolic pathways were studied, maternal undernutrition and twinning had a similar programming effect. These data are in agreement with earlier studies in twins that demonstrated an increased likelihood of developing abdominal obesity and type 2 diabetes in later life (Poulsen et al., 1997, 2009). Taken together, both maternal under nutrition and twinning were correlated with epigenetic changes that could impact energy balance.

In the studies described above, maternal undernutrition clearly impacts development of the HPA axis in the *fetus*. The key question is do these changes translate to extrauterine life? Studies by Wallace et al., (Wallace et al., 2011) argue that maternal undernutrition/fetal growth restriction do not result in lasting programmed alterations in HPA function in the offspring. These studies utilized a model of fetal growth restriction designed to mimic the human condition of adolescent pregnancies (Wallace et al., 2010). Prepubertal ewe lambs received embryos and were fed to maintain body weight at conception resulting in modestly growth restricted lambs with normal placental weights (Luther et al., 2007a, 2007b). At 6 months of age, there were no differences in response to CRH/AVP challenge in the lambs from the undernutrition group compared to the control fed group. Although there were age and sex dependent effects on the HPA axis, the authors concluded that there was no long term programming effect that could play a role in the observed altered metabolic phenotype of the offspring.

There is an important caveat however, since although this is a prenatal nutrient restriction model, it is different from those previously described above. The animals in these studies were immature ewes while those in the majority of the other studies were mature animals. Like the issue with twins vs. singletons (Edwards and McMillen, 2002, Edwards et al., 2002), data interpretation is dependent upon the type of periconceptional model chosen.

In studies using a periconceptional model of maternal undernutrition with mature ewes, there is clearly a programming effect that lasts into adulthood with impaired glucose tolerance (Todd et al., 2009), and increased adiposity in males (Jaquiery et al., 2012). More recently, studies by Begum et al., (Begum et al., 2013) provide clear evidence that epigenetic changes programmed in fetal life (Stevens et al., 2010) persist 5 years into adulthood. Specifically, they found dramatic changes in offspring from undernutrition ewes at 5 years of age that affect GR expression in hypothalamic neurons responsible for regulation of energy balance. These exciting epigenetic changes included decreased GR promoter CpG methylation coupled with enhanced hypothalamic histone H3 K9 acetylation concomitant with decreases in H3 K27 trimethylation. These alterations are certainly compatible with, and even predictive of, the accompanying increase in GR mRNA and protein. In the male offspring, there was also decreased POMC, likely a result of the increased GR suppressing POMC expression, which correlated with the increased obesity observed in the male progeny from undernourished ewes at 5 years of age. Interestingly, there is also hypomethylation of the POMC promoter despite decreased expression of POMC in the offspring of undernourished ewes. While this may seem counterintuitive, the decreased CpG methylation of the POMC promoter could provide for increased availability of the GR or other repressors to their target DNA elements. Of note, in the fetus, undernutrition was associated with both hypomethylation of the POMC promoter and increased POMC expression in the arcuate nucleus of these fetal sheep. This emphasizes that epigenetic modifications may simply provide a more accessible promoter for both up and down regulation dependent upon other developmental age dependent regulatory factors (i.e. GR).

A global function for glucocorticoids via the GR may be proper establishment of the epigenetic pattern of the fetus. As shown by the exquisite studies by the Grange laboratory (Kress et al., 2001, Thomassin et al., 2001), during the late gestation maturation of fetal hepatic gluconeogenic capacity in rodents (commensurate with the rodent prenatal corticosterone surge), there is a gradual remodeling of the promoters for critical gluconeogenic enzymes such as PEPCK and tyrosine aminotransferase (TAT). The GR drives this remodeling via CpG demethylation in critical regions of the promoter allowing for shift from heterochromatin to euchromatin. This shift in chromatin structure is prerequisite for other transcription factors, regulated by insulin and glucagon, to regulate the expression of these genes post birth and thus provide for glucose homeostasis. It is interesting that the GR seems capable of interacting with its response element in the context of closed CpG methylated chromatin while other transcription factors (e.g., CREB, C/EBP) cannot. This may represent an intriguing means by which glucocorticoids can affect the epigenetics of numerous target genes, and emphasizes the impact that early or excessive glucocorticoid exposure can have on the developing fetus.

Another important question in regard to maternal undernutrition and programming of hypothalamic appetite centers revolves around energy intake/expenditure in the offspring. Studies by Sebert and colleagues (Sebert et al., 2009) determined the degree to which appetite may be reset in offspring from nutritionally restricted pregnancies, followed by an obesogenic environment postpartum from weaning to one year of age. This consisted of ad lib feed and a reduced area for movement i.e. reduced energy expenditure (Williams et al., 2007). While all animals exhibited elevated plasma insulin, non-esterified fatty acids and leptin, the nutrient restricted offspring raised in the obesogenic environment demonstrated an enhanced effect on insulin. They also exhibited reduced food intake as well as elevated hypothalamic mRNA for insulin and melanocortin-4 receptors (MC4-R), AMP-activated kinase, and acetyl CoA with no difference in NPY or AgRP (Sebert et al., 2009). As suggested by the authors, this is analogous to observations in obese humans with elevated plasma non-esterified fatty acids and leptin (Jequier, 2002, Karpe et al., 2011) and leptin resistance (Askari et al., 2005). Further, since insulin crosses the blood brain barrier and binds to the insulin receptor resulting in diminished gene expression of NPY in both the PVN and arcuate nucleus (Gnanapavan et al., 2002, Masaki et al., 2004), it could impact resetting of the hypothalamic appetite centers (Sebert et al., 2009).

Taken together, these studies clearly show major programming effects of maternal undernutrition on the development and function of the HPA axis. In addition to the potential programming effects of insulin described by (Sebert et al., 2009), the most likely causative factor is enhanced fetal exposure to cortisol (Bloomfield et al., 2003a). As described earlier, exposure to cortisol in the ovine fetus is affected not only by changes in maternal levels, but also placental 11βHSD2. A number of studies have demonstrated that maternal undernutrition results in reduced placental 11βHSD2 expression. However, this appears to be limited to midgestation when 11βHSD2 was significantly lower in the maternal nutrient restriction group but was undetectable in term placentas (Whorwood et al., 2001).

Maternal undernutrition has also been examined in baboons by the Nathanielsz laboratory (Choi et al., 2011, Li et al., 2013a, 2013b). In their model, dams were fed a balanced diet at a level 70% that of controls from 30 days gestation (term is ~184d days). At 3.5 years of age, offspring exhibited elevated glucose and altered glucose tolerance consistent with effects they previously noted on development of the pancreatic islets (Choi et al., 2011). They also observed hypothalamic effects on appetitive neuropeptides, with changes in the ratio of NPY to POMC, favoring that of the orexigenic NPY (Li et al., 2013b). Whether these changes persist post birth, and if appetite is altered in the offspring, remain to be determined. Effects of maternal nutritional restriction on the fetal HPA were also noted. Fetal cortisol and ACTH were elevated in late gestation, as was PVN expression of CRH (but not AVP). These findings indicate that elevated fetal cortisol may be involved as a mechanism contributing to both the fetal growth restriction noted in this non-human primate model as well as programming effects of maternal nutritional restriction on the various organs leading to potential lifelong disorders.

Maternal Overnutrition:
The Other Side of the Barker Hypothesis

It is well established that during the prenatal period, maternal undernutrition or nutrient restriction results in intrauterine growth restriction (IUGR) with the resultant low birth weight offspring. However, with the global epidemic of obesity, there is now increased interest in the role of maternal overnutriton or maternal obesity and their programming effects on the fetus. As reviewed (Catalano and Ehrenberg, 2006, Zhang et al., 2011), maternal obesity, both before and during pregnancy, are strongly linked to childhood obesity. Perhaps surprisingly, both maternal undernutrition and obesity are linked to the development of similar metabolic diseases in adulthood (Vieau, 2011). However the pathophysiology of these programming events appears to be different.

As with maternal undernutrition, a vast majority of the studies examining the effect of maternal obesity on programming of the offspring have been conducted in rodents (Desai and Ross, 2011). The typical model has been one of diet induced maternal obesity where the diet was a so-called "Western" or 'high fat" diet (HFD), high in saturated fats and simple carbohydrates relative to protein. Along with maternal overnutrition, the role of obesity vs. the HFD itself has been examined. As with maternal undernutrition, maternal obesity programs offspring for a similar pattern of disorders such as cardiovascular disease, metabolic disorders, obesity and programming of not only hypothalamic neuropeptide systems governing appetite but the HPA axis as well. It is difficult however, to ascertain whether maternal obesity programming effects occur in utero or during the early post-natal period.

In terms of programming of adipose/obesity, metabolism and related behaviors such as appetite, a considerable impact in rodents is likely to occur during the neonatal stage, since much of the differentiation of these systems occurs during this period in these species. In primates and sheep, adipose deposition begins in utero and as noted by the studies of Ford and Long (Ford and Long, 2011), maternal obesity in sheep results in increased adipose deposition in the fetus. Further, studies in ewes fed to become obese during pregnancy resulted in an absence of a leptin surge compared to lambs from control ewes who demonstrated a leptin surge on days 6-9 post birth (Long et al., 2011). Lambs from overnourished ewes clearly showed alterations in appetite with a significant increase in milk intake at 30 days post-partum (Muhlhausler et al., 2006). Importantly hypothalamic expression of the active form of the leptin receptor (ObRb) was inversely related to relative fat mass and the relationship between the anorexigenic peptide, CART, and adiposity was disrupted. Together these data indicate that maternal overnutrition during pregnancy dysregulates the central regulation of appetite sensitivity to adiposity, resulting in a predisposition to obesity in later life.

At least in part, leptin appears to exert its effect on energy balance by regulating the HPA axis. The hypothalamus is an important site of leptin action and has high levels of expression of the OB-Rb (Muhlhausler et al., 2004, Sahu, 2003, 2004). The OB-Rb receptor is predominantly found in hypothalamic neurons that express neuropeptide Y (NPY), agouti-related peptide (AgRP), cocaine- and amphetamine-regulated transcript (CART) and POMC (Elias et al., 1999, Mercer et al., 1997, Rondini et al., 2004). Leptin infusion was shown to regulate POMC and CART message and downregulate NPY and AGRP with an overall inhibition of appetite and fat accumulation. Therefore POMC/CART are anorectic while

NPY/AgRP are orexigenic (Sahu, 2003, Schwartz et al., 2000). Leptin target neurons are localized primarily in the arcuate nucleus (ARC), the paraventricular nucleus (PVN) and lateral hypothalamus (LH) (Sahu, 2004).

CART is abundant in hypothalamic nuclei controlling anterior pituitary function. In the PVN, CART mRNA is co-localized with vasopressin and CRF containing neurons and central CART infusion enhanced ACTH secretion in the rat *in vivo* while *in vitro* studies also demonstrated enhanced hypothalamic release of CRF by CART (Stanley et al., 2001). Therefore, leptin binding to the OB-Rb may act on CART neurons to regulate hypothalamic neuroendocrine functions. Further studies in *adult* sheep showed that intracerebroventricular infusion of leptin resulted in decreased expression of mRNA for NPY in the hypothalamic arcuate nucleus (Henry et al., 1999). This is consistent with isolation of OB-Rb in 60% of NPY containing cells in sheep hypothalamus (Iqbal et al., 2001). In the sheep hypothalamus, NPY can also regulate ACTH secretagogues CRF and AVP (Liu et al., 1994). Further, OB-R has been localized in the PVN, indicating that leptin can have direct effects on CRH/AVP neurons as well (Ahima et al., 2000).

Using in situ hybridization, Muhlhausler et al., demonstrated expression of OB-Rb, NPY, AgRP, CART and POMC in the hypothalamus of fetal sheep (Muhlhausler et al., 2004). All mRNAs were expressed in the arcuate nucleus with additional sites expression including the dorsomedial hypothalamus (DMH) for NPY, the paraventricular nucleus (PVN), ventromedial hypothalamus (VMH) and lateral hypothalamic area for CART, and the DMH, PVN and VMH for OB-Rb. Compared with the adult, relative intensity of staining of OB-Rb was higher in the ventromedial hypothalamus but overall, there was adult-like localization of expression for OB-Rb, as well as key hypothalamic regulatory peptides.

In addition to potential effects on appetite programming, Long et al., found that maternal obesity resulted in altered stress responses in ovine offspring in adulthood (Long et al., 2012). Offspring from obese ewes (fed 150% of NRC recommendations) from 60 days before mating until delivery were compared with offspring from ewes on a control diet (100% NRC). The 19-month-old lambs were treated with ACTH, followed by CRH/AVP a day later. This was followed 30 days later by isolation stress tests. Offspring from the obese ewes had significantly elevated basal cortisol and ACTH concentrations. Again, there should be caution on interpretation of the data since the control group had all singletons while the obese group had 3 sets of twins. Previous studies (Begum et al., 2012, Symonds and Budge, 2009) indicated that twins vs. singletons have a major impact on potential programming effects of maternal dietary manipulations during development. Unfortunately, in the sheep, the effect of maternal obesity on programming of the HPA axis has been largely understudied.

The effect of maternal obesity and/or Western diet on programming of the offspring has been studied in the macaque by Grove and colleagues (Sullivan et al., 2011). Indeed, these studies highlighted an interesting finding, namely emphasizing the negative impact of a Western, high fat, high caloric diet on the offspring. In the development of the macaque model, these researchers found that a portion of the pre-pregnant female macaques were resistant to diet induced obesity on the Western diet. Thus, they were able to examine the impact of chronic intake of a high fat, high caloric diet vs. maternal obesity on the fetal outcome, in the absence of gestational diabetes. Using this model, they reported that the maternal HFD resulted in fetuses that exhibited an early rise in hepatic gluconeogenic enzymes, elevated triglyceride content, oxidative stress and steatosis by term (Suter et al., 2012). The offspring of the HFD mothers also exhibited early-onset obesity predictive of a programming of long term metabolic disorders. Indications of programming were supported by epigenetic changes in genes in the liver and at one year of age, there was a decrease in hepatic sympathetic innervation.

Although the effects of maternal obesity/HFD in the macaque model on the HPA axis have not been described, the offspring did exhibit perturbations in the central serotonergic system as well as increased indices of anxiety (Sullivan et al., 2010). When considering that anxiety is a potent activator of the HPA axis, it seems likely that these offspring would be more prone to exhibit elevated activation of the HPA axis and exposure to cortisol. The HFD/maternal obesity was also noted to exert profound effects on the fetal hypothalamic melanocortin system as well as AgRP. There was also a noted increase in hypothalamic inflammatory markers in these fetuses as well.

While studies in rodents, and for that matter, translational studies in humans, have not identified a mechanism(s) via which maternal obesity and/or a maternal HFD could program the fetus, the macaque studies did note that a maternal HFD resulted in disturbed utero-placental hemodynamics with decreased umbilical blood. These findings implicate fetal hypoxia as one of the mechanisms by which maternal obesity/HFD may impact/program the developing fetus.

Hypoxia: A Common Programming Mechanism?

The vast majority of studies on programming of the HPA axis in the sheep have focused on nutrition. Similar to the nutrient restriction studies previously described, fetal hypoxia can also be viewed as a nutrient restriction model of programming since oxygen is a critical "nutrient" for normal fetal growth and development. Further fetal responses to hypoxia may dictate changes in responses of the HPA axis in post-natal life. Since both acute and chronic hypoxia represent a major threat to fetal survival, the HPA axis, primarily through modulation of cortisol, plays a key role in responding to this dangerous intrauterine environment. As with other stressors affecting programming of the HPA, the magnitude of these responses is dependent on both the duration and severity of the hypoxic stress, as well as the stage of development. Further, underlying adverse intrauterine conditions may alter the ability of the fetus to respond to a secondary hypoxic episode (Gardner et al., 2002). Potential programming effects of acute and chronic hypoxia are discussed below.

Acute Hypoxia

Acute hypoxia (6 h) at 135 dG increases CRH mRNA in the PVN (Matthews & Challis, 1995). Green et al., (Green et al., 2000b) found that POMC mRNA in the *pars distalis* of ovine fetuses increased 2.5 fold following repeated hypoxic insults. Further, 48 h of hypoxia at either 126-130 or 134-136 days of gestation resulted in increased anterior pituitary POMC mRNA and increased plasma IR-ACTH (Braems et al., 1996). IR-ACTH returned to baseline by 12-24 h post-initiation of hypoxia while cortisol increased at both ages in response to hypoxia. However, in the older fetuses, plasma cortisol remained elevated even after IR-ACTH had decreased to baseline. The latter finding is also in agreement with a study that showed that fetal hypoxia for 48 h resulted in increased 3βHSD and P450$_{C21}$ (CYP21) but not P450$_{C17}$ (CYP17) mRNA in the fetal adrenal gland (Braems et al., 1998). In a later study, the same lab also showed that 48 h hypoxia increased the bioactivity of fetal plasma ACTH coupled with increased adrenal steroidogenic enzymes and cortisol production. Since PVN lesions prevents the increase in plasma ACTH and cortisol in response to acute hypoxia (McDonald & Nathanielsz, 1991), it is likely that the hypoxic modulation of the anterior pituitary and adrenal cortex were via specific activation of CRH and/or AVP neurons in a classic stress response manner. Further, studies by Fraser et al., (Fraser et al., 2001) demonstrated that sustained hypoxia upregulated ACTH receptor mRNA. POMC processing to ACTH is clearly affected by fetal stress (Castro et al., 1993). As Braems suggested (Braems, 2003), the observed changes in response to hypoxemia in their studies were a logical and expected result, allowing the fetus to cope with the acute stress. Thus, hypoxia ranging from hours to days during the final weeks of gestation clearly has an activating effect on the ovine fetal HPA axis. The question is, in response to more chronic hypoxia, will the fetal HPA axis be programmed to generate a "logical" response?

Chronic/Long Term Hypoxia

In an effort to determine the effects of truly chronic, long term hypoxia on programming of the HPA axis, we developed an ovine model of long term hypoxia (LTH) in which pregnant ewes are maintained at altitude (3,820 m) for the last 100 days of gestation (Adachi et al., 2004, Myers et al., 2005a, Vargas et al., 2011). In marked contrast to activation of the HPA axis in response to acute or prolonged hypoxia when initiated during the final third of gestation, we found that the HPA axis of the fetus adapts divergently in response to development under conditions of LTH from day 40 of gestation. Unlike some maternal nutrient restriction models (Edwards et al., 2002, Gao et al., 2007, Luther et al., 2007a) or placental restriction models (McMillen et al., 2001, Morrison, 2008), the fetuses in our LTH model are not growth restricted nor do they deliver preterm, however, they do undergo dynamic adaptive reprogramming of the HPA axis, reflective of the ability to maintain normal basal cortisol production in spite of the hypoxic condition. This capacity to maintain normal basal plasma concentrations of cortisol the LTH fetus at levels similar to that observed in normoxic fetuses occurs despite elevated basal plasma ACTH concentrations (Adachi et al., 2004, Imamura et al., 2004, Monau et al., 2010, Myers et al., 2005a, 2005b). Intriguingly, the LTH fetus, despite maintaining normal basal cortisol levels, responds to a secondary stressor with enhanced cortisol output compared to normoxic control fetuses (Adachi et al., 2004, Imamura et al., 2004).

At the hypothalamic level, POMC processing to ACTH is clearly affected by fetal stress (Castro et al., 1993). As described previously, Green et al., (Green et al., 2000) established that repeated hypoxic insults enhanced POMC mRNA in ovine fetuses. In our LTH fetuses, we observed enhanced processing of proopiomelanocortin (POMC) to ACTH in the anterior pituitary of the long-term hypoxic (LTH) sheep fetus concomitant with an apparent increase in CRH activity (Myers et al., 2005a). In fetal sheep, processing of POMC to ACTH is not efficient, resulting in about a 10-fold greater amount of fetal plasma ACTH precursors (POMC and 22-kDa pro-ACTH) compared to ACTH. Further, we also showed that LTH appears to increase pituitary sensitivity to CRH (Ducsay et al., 2009). Together, these studies can explain the enhanced basal ACTH levels observed in the LTH fetuses. However, there is a contradiction since despite elevated ACTH, basal cortisol levels are not elevated in the LTH fetuses compared to normoxic controls, suggesting that programming of the adrenal gland is directed at offsetting the effects of LTH in the hypothalamus/pituitary. When adrenal steroidogenic enzymes were studied, we found that mRNA of both CYP17 and CYP11A1 was dramatically reduced in the LTH fetal adrenal cortex (Myers et al., 2005b). This is in contrast to the effects of short term hypoxia in which CYP17 and CYP11A1 were upregulated (Myers et al., 2005b).

Cumulatively, these seemingly contradictory adaptations in the hypothalamo-pituitary vs. adrenocortical components of the HPA axis result in maintenance of basal cortisol levels, yet greater cortisol production in response to a secondary stressor in the LTH fetus. While the increased function observed at the level of the hypothalamic-pituitary component in the LTH fetus is consistent with the known stimulatory actions of short-term hypoxia on fetal HPA function, the adaptive changes observed at the level of the adrenal cortex seem paradoxical. Thus, we hypothesize that LTH has invoked a mechanism(s) that prevents premature maturation of the adrenal cortex in the face of elevated basal ACTH1-39, yet allows increased cortisol production in response to a life-threatening secondary stressor. In response to LTH, these adaptations in the HPA axis likely aid in the survival of the compromised LTH fetus, while preventing preterm delivery in response to the hypoxic intrauterine environment.

At present, there are a number of candidate mechanisms that could be responsible for the dissociation between elevated basal ACTH and maintenance of normal cortisol levels that is overridden in response to a secondary stressor. One of these is nitric oxide that is elevated in the LTH adrenal and has inhibitory effects on cortisol production [For review, see (Ducsay and Myers, 2011)]. Another potential regulatory mechanism that may have profound programming effects on the HPA axis is leptin.

The regulation of fetal plasma leptin concentrations is poorly defined. Glucocorticoids are known to induce adipocyte differentiation. Forhead and co-workers (Forhead et al., 2002) found that cortisol and leptin both increase as term approaches in fetal sheep and adrenalectomy caused a reduction in leptin after 136 dG, consistent with a known adipogenic role for glucocorticoids in adipocyte differentiation. Therefore, these results are in agreement with data in adult adipocytes where glucocorticoids stimulate both leptin gene expression and leptin secretion (De Vos et al., 1998). It appears that there is a positive relationship between fetal HPA activation and leptin. In contrast, developmental studies in the sheep fetus actually demonstrated a decrease in leptin mRNA expression in adipose tissue from 75-110 dG to term (Devaskar et al., 2002).

We showed that in the LTH fetus, adipose expression of leptin in fetal perirenal adipose tissue is upregulated, resulting in elevated fetal plasma leptin levels compared to control fetuses (Ducsay et al., 2006), without affecting basal cortisol concentrations. Studies by McMillen and co-workers (McMillen et al., 2004) demonstrated an inhibitory effect of leptin on the fetal ovine HPA. Intravenous leptin infusions suppressed the prepartum rise in both ACTH and cortisol. Infusion after day 144 did not affect ACTH but there was still marked suppression of cortisol up to three days prior to delivery.

More recently, we detailed additional evidence that leptin in the fetal circulation can program the HPA axis. Infusion of a leptin antagonist in late gestation restored adrenal mRNA levels of both CYP17 and CYP11A1 in LTH fetuses (Ducsay et al., 2013). These data clearly define the role of leptin as another key programming agent on the fetal ovine HPA axis by having a direct effect on enzymes responsible for cortisol production. This is in addition to the more clearly defined role of leptin in programming hypothalamic appetite centers (Long et al., 2011, Muhlhausler et al., 2006). Together, the data from our LTH studies show that gestational, long term hypoxia can have dramatic effects on the function and gene expression of the HPA axis.

Psychological Stress

The effects of prenatal maternal psychological stress on developmental programming of the HPA axis vary widely depending on the species studied. However, the effects are most likely mediated through elevations in maternal glucocorticoids. Although studies with psychological stressors are not widely performed on the sheep model, Rakers et al., (Rakers et al., 2013) recently reported that maternal isolation in pregnant ewes had a significant effect on altering fetal responses to hypotension. In this study, ewes were subjected to isolation stress either early in gestation (days 30 to 100) or late (days 100 to 120) which resulted in 2 to 4 fold increases in maternal plasma cortisol concentrations. In the same study an additional group of ewes were treated with synthetic glucocorticoids to mimic the dose and stage of gestation used in the clinical setting. Although fetal ACTH was not reported in this study, fetal cortisol responses to hypotension were enhanced in both the early and late maternal stress groups as well as in the betamethasone treated group. Importantly, the response was greatest in the early maternal stress group. Since like the human, the ovine fetal HPA axis develops late in gestation, this again emphasizes different periods of vulnerability of the HPA axis.

Summary/Conclusion

The fetal HPA axis plays key roles not only in response to stress during the later stages of gestation, but also in ensuring an adequate production of cortisol for organ maturation at term gestation. It is not surprising then that this important regulatory pathway is exquisitely sensitive to alterations in the intrauterine environment. Changes in nutrient availability, whether by altered maternal nutritional intake or increased nutrient demands imposed by the presence of a twin, clearly have profound effects on the HPA axis not only during fetal life, but also carried into adulthood. In addition, other stressors during development including glucocorticoid overexposure itself as well as hypoxia also contribute to alteration of the HPA axis "set-point" resulting in alterations in central metabolic regulation.

While providing the late gestation fetus a mechanism for surviving intrauterine stressors via its known effects on homeostatic mechanisms, the fetal (and maternal) HPA axis may also play a more sinister role. Early, prolonged or repeated activation of the maturing fetal HPA axis and resulting exposure to excessive or mistimed (prior to the normal ontogenic surge at term) glucocorticoids may play a role in the epigenetic modifications that are involved in programming. Thus, the short term in utero homeostatic HPA actions during an acute stressor are likely 'beneficial' in allowing the fetus to persevere through an adverse situation. However, the epigenetic effects that result from the excess or miss timed glucocorticoids could program target tissues and organs for long term changes in function in preparation for perhaps an adverse extra-uterine environment. With the increasing life span of humans, these programming changes appear detrimental; yet on a grand scale, they may impart a beneficial metabolic effect on the younger individuals, yet result in a predisposition to disorders later in life. If overly excessive, the programming may even be detrimental at earlier ages after birth.

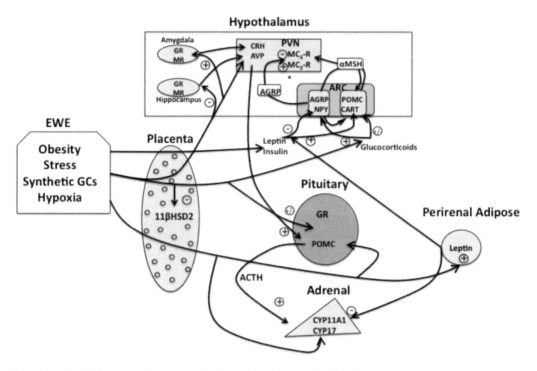

Figure 1. The HPA axis and programming in the fetal sheep highlighting key programming stimuli and potential targets. ARC = arcuate nucleus, CART = cocaine-amphetamine regulated transcript, GR= glucocorticoid receptor, MC3-R = melanocortin receptor 3, MC4-R = melanocortin receptor 4, NPY = neuropeptide Y, MR = mineralocorticoid receptor, POMC = proopiomelanocortin, PVN = paraventricular nucleus, [*this portion of the diagram adapted from (Stevens et al., 2011)].

Because of its similar developmental trajectory to the human HPA axis, the sheep has proven to be a valuable model. Figure 1 summarizes the vast array of programming stimuli and potential targets in the fetal sheep discussed in this chapter. Despite a great number of studies in this valuable model, there are still a number of gaps in our knowledge of the precise mechanisms involved in fetal programming. As studies progress in this and other animal models, is critical to always take into consideration the duration, intensity and the developmental window in which the stressor was introduced. With the help of the sheep along with other well-established models of programming, we will continue to elucidate the mechanisms involved in programming of adult health and disease ultimately arriving at effective preventative and or/treatment strategies.

Supported by NIH grants HDPO131226 and HDRO151951.

References

Abbasi, S., Hirsch, D., Davis, J., Tolosa, J., Stouffer, N., Debbs, R., et al. (2000). Effect of single versus multiple courses of antenatal corticosteroids on maternal and neonatal outcome. *Am. J. Obstet. Gynecol*, 182, 1243-9.

Adachi, K., Umezaki, H., Kaushal, K. M. & Ducsay, C. A. (2004). Long-term hypoxia alters ovine fetal endocrine and physiological responses to hypotension. *Am. J. Physiol. Regul. Integr. Comp. Physiol.*, 287, R209-17.

Ahima, R. S., Saper, C. B., Flier, J. S. & Elmquist, J. K. (2000). Leptin regulation of neuroendocrine systems. *Front Neuroendocrinol*, 21, 263-307.

Askari, H., Liu, J. & Dagogo-Jack, S. (2005). Energy adaptation to glucocorticoid-induced hyperleptinemia in human beings. *Metabolism*, 54, 876-80.

Aylward, G. P. (2005). Neurodevelopmental outcomes of infants born prematurely. *J. Dev. Behav. Pediatr*, 26, 427-40.

Barbazanges, A., Piazza, P. V., Le Moal, M. & Maccari, S. (1996). Maternal glucocorticoid secretion mediates long-term effects of prenatal stress. *J. Neurosci*, 16, 3943-9.

Barker, D. J. (2007). The origins of the developmental origins theory. *J. Intern. Med*, 261, 412-7.

Barker, D. J., Osmond, C., Rodin, I., Fall, C. H. & Winter, P. D. (1995). Low weight gain in infancy and suicide in adult life. *BMJ*, 311, 1203.

Begum, G., Davies, A., Stevens, A., Oliver, M., Jaquiery, A., Challis, J., et al. (2013). Maternal undernutrition programs tissue-specific epigenetic changes in the glucocorticoid receptor in adult offspring. *Endocrinology*, 154, 4560-9.

Begum, G., Stevens, A., Smith, E. B., Connor, K., Challis, J. R., Bloomfield, F., et al. (2012). Epigenetic changes in fetal hypothalamic energy regulating pathways are associated with maternal undernutrition and twinning. *FASEB J*, 26, 1694-703.

Bell, M. E., McDonald, T. J. & Myers, D. A. (2005). Proopiomelanocortin processing in the anterior pituitary of the ovine fetus after lesion of the hypothalamic paraventricular nucleus. *Endocrinology*, 146, 2665-73.

Bloom, S. L., Sheffield, J. S., McIntire, D. D. & Leveno, K. J. (2001). Antenatal dexamethasone and decreased birth weight. *Obstet. Gynecol*, 97, 485-90.

Bloomfield, F. H., Oliver, M. H., Giannoulias, C. D., Gluckman, P. D., Harding, J. E. & Challis, J. R. (2003a). Brief undernutrition in late-gestation sheep programs the hypothalamic-pituitary-adrenal axis in adult offspring. *Endocrinology*, 144, 2933-40.

Bloomfield, F. H., Oliver, M. H., Hawkins, P., Campbell, M., Phillips, D. J., Gluckman, P. D., et al. (2003b). A periconceptional nutritional origin for noninfectious preterm birth. *Science*, 300, 606.

Bloomfield, F. H., Oliver, M. H., Hawkins, P., Holloway, A. C., Campbell, M., Gluckman, P. D., et al. (2004). Periconceptional undernutrition in sheep accelerates maturation of the fetal hypothalamic-pituitary-adrenal axis in late gestation. *Endocrinology*, 145, 4278-85.

Braems, G. (2003). Fetal hypoxemia on a molecular level: adaptive changes in the hypothalamic-pituitary-adrenal (HPA) axis and the lungs. *Eur. J. Obstet. Gynecol. Reprod. Biol*, 110 Suppl 1, S63-9.

Braems, G. A., Han, V. K. & Challis, J. R. (1998). Gestational age-dependent changes in the levels of mRNAs encoding cortisol biosynthetic enzymes and IGF-II in the adrenal gland of fetal sheep during prolonged hypoxemia. *J Endocrinol.*, 159, 257-264.

Braems, G. A., Matthews, S. G. & Challis, J. R. (1996). Differential regulation of proopiomelanocortin messenger ribonucleic acid in the pars distalis and pars intermedia of the pituitary gland after prolonged hypoxemia in fetal sheep. *Endocrinology,* 137, 2731-2738.

Breton, C. (2013). The hypothalamus-adipose axis is a key target of developmental programming by maternal nutritional manipulation. *J. Endocrinol,* 216, R19-31.

Buckler, J. M. & Green, M. (2004). A comparison of the early growth of twins and singletons. *Ann. Hum. Biol,* 31, 311-32.

Burd, L., Severud, R., Kerbeshian, J. & Klug, M. G. (1999). Prenatal and perinatal risk factors for autism. *J. Perinat. Med,* 27, 441-50.

Castro, M. I., Valego, N. K., Zehnder, T. J. & Rose, J. C. (1993). Bioactive-to-immunoreactive ACTH activity changes with severity of stress in late-gestation ovine fetus. *Am J Physiol,* 265, E68-E73.

Catalano, P. M. & Ehrenberg, H. M. (2006). The short- and long-term implications of maternal obesity on the mother and her offspring. *BJOG,* 113, 1126-33.

Challis, J. R., Matthews, S. G., Gibb, W. & Lye, S. J. (2000). Endocrine and paracrine regulation of birth at term and preterm. *Endocr. Rev,* 21, 514-50.

Choi, J., Li, C., McDonald, T. J., Comuzzie, A., Mattern, V. & Nathanielsz, P. W. (2011). Emergence of insulin resistance in juvenile baboon offspring of mothers exposed to moderate maternal nutrient reduction. *Am. J. Physiol. Regul. Integr. Comp. Physiol,* 301, R757-62.

Cleasby, M. E., Kelly, P. A., Walker, B. R. & Seckl, J. R. (2003). Programming of rat muscle and fat metabolism by in utero overexposure to glucocorticoids. *Endocrinology,* 144, 999-1007.

Cottrell, E. C., Holmes, M. C., Livingstone, D. E., Kenyon, C. J. & Seckl, J. R. (2012). Reconciling the nutritional and glucocorticoid hypotheses of fetal programming. *FASEB J,* 26, 1866-74.

Cottrell, E. C. & Seckl, J. R. (2009). Prenatal stress, glucocorticoids and the programming of adult disease. *Front Behav. Neurosci,* 3, 19.

De Matteo, R., Stacy, V., Probyn, M., Desai, M., Ross, M. & Harding, R. (2008). The perinatal development of arterial pressure in sheep: effects of low birth weight due to twinning. *Reprod. Sci.,* 15, 66-74.

De Vos, P., Lefebvre, A. M., Shrivo, I., Fruchart, J. C. & Auwerx, J. (1998). Glucocorticoids induce the expression of the leptin gene through a non-classical mechanism of transcriptional activation. *Eur. J. Biochem,* 253, 619-26.

De Vries, A., Holmes, M. C., Heijnis, A., Seier, J. V., Heerden, J., Louw, J., et al. (2007). Prenatal dexamethasone exposure induces changes in nonhuman primate offspring cardiometabolic and hypothalamic-pituitary-adrenal axis function. *J. Clin. Invest,* 117, 1058-67.

Dent, G. W., Smith, M. A. & Levine, S. (2000). Rapid induction of corticotropin-releasing hormone gene transcription in the paraventricular nucleus of the developing rat. *Endocrinology,* 141, 1593-8.

Desai, M. & Ross, M. G. (2011). Fetal programming of adipose tissue: effects of intrauterine growth restriction and maternal obesity/high-fat diet. *Semin. Reprod. Med,* 29, 237-45.

Devaskar, S. U., Anthony, R. & Hay, W., Jr. (2002). Ontogeny and insulin regulation of fetal ovine white adipose tissue leptin expression. *Am. J. Physiol. Regul. Integr. Comp. Physiol*, 282, R431-8.

Dobbing, J. & Sands, J. (1979). Comparative aspects of the brain growth spurt. *Early Hum. Dev*, 3, 79-83.

Doyle, L. W., Ford, G. W., Davis, N. M. & Callanan, C. (2000). Antenatal corticosteroid therapy and blood pressure at 14 years of age in preterm children. *Clin. Sci. (Lond)*, 98, 137-42.

Ducsay, C. A., Furuta, K., Vargas, V. E., Kaushal, K. M., Singleton, K., Hyatt, K., et al. (2013). Leptin receptor antagonist treatment ameliorates the effects of long-term maternal hypoxia on adrenal expression of key steroidogenic genes in the ovine fetus. *Am. J. Physiol. Regul. Integr. Comp. Physiol*, 304, R435-42.

Ducsay, C. A., Hyatt, K., Mlynarczyk, M., Kaushal, K. M. & Myers, D. A. (2006). Long-term hypoxia increases leptin receptors and plasma leptin concentrations in the late-gestation ovine fetus. *Am. J. Physiol. Regul. Integr. Comp. Physiol*, 291, R1406-13.

Ducsay, C. A., Mlynarczyk, M., Kaushal, K. M., Hyatt, K., Hanson, K. & Myers, D. A. (2009). Long-term hypoxia enhances ACTH response to arginine vasopressin but not corticotropin-releasing hormone in the near-term ovine fetus. *Am. J. Physiol. Regul. Integr. Comp. Physiol*, 297, R892-9.

Ducsay, C. A. & Myers, D. A. (2011). eNOS activation and NO function: differential control of steroidogenesis by nitric oxide and its adaptation with hypoxia. *J. Endocrinol*, 210, 259-69.

Edwards, C. R., Benediktsson, R., Lindsay, R. S. & Seckl, J. R. (1993). Dysfunction of placental glucocorticoid barrier: link between fetal environment and adult hypertension? *Lancet*, 341, 355-7.

Edwards, L. J., Bryce, A. E., Coulter, C. L. & McMillen, I. C. (2002). Maternal undernutrition throughout pregnancy increases adrenocorticotrophin receptor and steroidogenic acute regulatory protein gene expression in the adrenal gland of twin fetal sheep during late gestation. *Mol. Cell Endocrinol*, 196, 1-10.

Edwards, L. J. & McMillen, I. C. (2002). Impact of maternal undernutrition during the periconceptional period, fetal number, and fetal sex on the development of the hypothalamo-pituitary adrenal axis in sheep during late gestation. *Biol. Reprod*, 66, 1562-9.

Elias, C. F., Aschkenasi, C., Lee, C., Kelly, J., Ahima, R. S., Bjorbaek, C., et al. (1999). Leptin differentially regulates NPY and POMC neurons projecting to the lateral hypothalamic area. *Neuron*, 23, 775-86.

Ford, S. P. & Long, N. M. (2011). Evidence for similar changes in offspring phenotype following either maternal undernutrition or overnutrition: potential impact on fetal epigenetic mechanisms. *Reprod. Fertil. Dev*, 24, 105-11.

Forhead, A. J., Thomas, L., Crabtree, J., Hoggard, N., Gardner, D. S., Giussani, D. A., et al. (2002). Plasma leptin concentration in fetal sheep during late gestation: ontogeny and effect of glucocorticoids. *Endocrinology*, 143, 1166-73.

Faser, M., Braems, G. A. & Challis, J. R. (2001). Developmental regulation of corticotrophin receptor gene expression in the adrenal gland of the ovine fetus and newborn lamb: effects of hypoxia during late pregnancy. *J Endocrinol*, 169, 1-10.

French, N. P., Hagan, R., Evans, S. F., Mullan, A. & Newnham, J. P. (2004). Repeated antenatal corticosteroids: effects on cerebral palsy and childhood behavior. *Am. J. Obstet. Gynecol*, 190, 588-95.

Galeeva, A., Ordyan, N., Pivina, S. & Pelto-Huikko, M. (2006). Expression of glucocorticoid receptors in the hippocampal region of the rat brain during postnatal development. *J. Chem. Neuroanat*, 31, 216-25.

Gao, F., Hou, X. & Liu, Y. (2007). Effect of hormonal status and metabolic changes of restricted ewes during late pregnancy on their fetal growth and development. *Sci. China C Life Sci*, 50, 766-72.

Gardner, D. S., Fowden, A. L. & Giussani, D. A. (2002). Adverse intrauterine conditions diminish the fetal defense against acute hypoxia by increasing nitric oxide activity. *Circulation,* 106, 2278-83.

Gardner, D. S., Jackson, A. A. & Langley-Evans, S. C. (1997). Maintenance of maternal diet-induced hypertension in the rat is dependent on glucocorticoids. *Hypertension*, 30, 1525-30.

Gardner, D. S., Jamall, E., Fletcher, A. J., Fowden, A. L. & Giussani, D. A. (2004). Adrenocortical responsiveness is blunted in twin relative to singleton ovine fetuses. *J. Physiol*, 557, 1021-32.

Glover, V., Miles, R., Matta, S., Modi, N. & Stevenson, J. (2005). Glucocorticoid exposure in preterm babies predicts saliva cortisol response to immunization at 4 months. *Pediatr. Res*, 58, 1233-7.

Glover, V., O'Connor, T. G. & O'Donnell, K. (2010). Prenatal stress and the programming of the HPA axis. *Neurosci. Biobehav. Rev*, 35, 17-22.

Gnanapavan, S., Kola, B., Bustin, S. A., Morris, D. G., McGee, P., Fairclough, P., et al. (2002). The tissue distribution of the mRNA of ghrelin and subtypes of its receptor, GHS-R, in humans. *J. Clin. Endocrinol. Metab*, 87, 2988.

Green, L. R., Kawagoe, Y., Fraser, M., Challis, J. R. & Richardson, B. S. (2000). Activation of the hypothalamic-pituitary-adrenal axis with repetitive umbilical cord occlusion in the preterm ovine fetus. *J Soc. Gynecol Investig.,* 7, 224-232.

Hales, C. N. & Barker, D. J. (1992). Type 2 (non-insulin-dependent) diabetes mellitus: the thrifty phenotype hypothesis. *Diabetologia*, 35, 595-601.

Hales, C. N. & Barker, D. J. (2001). The thrifty phenotype hypothesis. *Br. Med. Bull*, 60, 5-20.

Harris, A. & Seckl, J. (2011). Glucocorticoids, prenatal stress and the programming of disease. *Horm. Behav*, 59, 279-89.

Hennessy, D. P., Coghlan, J. P., Hardy, K. J., Scoggins, B. A. & Wintour, E. M. (1982). The origin of cortisol in the blood of fetal sheep. *J. Endocrinol*, 95, 71-9.

Henry, B. A., Goding, J. W., Alexander, W. S., Tilbrook, A. J., Canny, B. J., Dunshea, F., et al. (1999). Central administration of leptin to ovariectomized ewes inhibits food intake without affecting the secretion of hormones from the pituitary gland: evidence for a dissociation of effects on appetite and neuroendocrine function. *Endocrinology*, 140, 1175-82.

Imamura, T., Umezaki, H., Kaushal, K. M. & Ducsay, C. A. (2004). Long-term hypoxia alters endocrine and physiologic responses to umbilical cord occlusion in the ovine fetus. *J. Soc. Gynecol. Investig*, 11, 131-40.

Iqbal, J., Pompolo, S., Murakami, T., Grouzmann, E., Sakurai, T., Meister, B., et al. (2001). Immunohistochemical characterization of localization of long-form leptin receptor (OB-Rb) in neurochemically defined cells in the ovine hypothalamus. *Brain Res*, 920, 55-64.

Jaquiery, A. L., Oliver, M. H., Honeyfield-Ross, M., Harding, J. E. & Bloomfield, F. H. (2012). Periconceptional undernutrition in sheep affects adult phenotype only in males. *J. Nutr. Metab*, 2012, 123610.

Jequier, E. (2002). Leptin signaling, adiposity, and energy balance. *Ann. N. Y. Acad. Sci*, 967, 379-88.

Karlsson, R., Kallio, J., Toppari, J., Scheinin, M. & Kero, P. (2000). Antenatal and early postnatal dexamethasone treatment decreases cortisol secretion in preterm infants. *Horm. Res*, 53, 170-6.

Karpe, F., Dickmann, J. R. & Frayn, K. N. (2011). Fatty acids, obesity, and insulin resistance: time for a reevaluation. *Diabetes*, 60, 2441-9.

Kitterman, J. A., Liggins, G. C., Campos, G. A., Clements, J. A., Forster, C. S., Lee, C. H., et al. (1981). Prepartum maturation of the lung in fetal sheep: relation to cortisol. *J. Appl. Physiol. Respir. Environ. Exerc. Physiol*, 51, 384-90.

Kress, C., Thomassin, H. & Grange, T. (2001). Local DNA demethylation in vertebrates: how could it be performed and targeted? *FEBS Lett*, 494, 135-40.

Lajic, S., Wedell, A., Bui, T. H., Ritzen, E. M. & Holst, M. (1998). Long-term somatic follow-up of prenatally treated children with congenital adrenal hyperplasia. *J. Clin. Endocrinol. Metab*, 83, 3872-80.

Langley-Evans, S. C. (1997). Hypertension induced by foetal exposure to a maternal low-protein diet, in the rat, is prevented by pharmacological blockade of maternal glucocorticoid synthesis. *J. Hypertens*,15, 537-44.

Langley-Evans, S. C. (2009). Nutritional programming of disease: unravelling the mechanism. *J. Anat*, 215, 36-51.

Langley-Evans, S. C., Gardner, D. S. & Jackson, A. A. (1996). Maternal protein restriction influences the programming of the rat hypothalamic-pituitary-adrenal axis. *J. Nutr*, 126, 1578-85.

Levitt, N. S., Lindsay, R. S., Holmes, M. C. & Seckl, J. R. (1996). Dexamethasone in the last week of pregnancy attenuates hippocampal glucocorticoid receptor gene expression and elevates blood pressure in the adult offspring in the rat. *Neuroendocrinology*, 64, 412-8.

Li, C., McDonald, T. J., Wu, G., Nijland, M. J. & Nathanielsz, P. W. (2013a). Intrauterine growth restriction alters term fetal baboon hypothalamic appetitive peptide balance. *J. Endocrinol*, 217, 275-82.

Li, C., Ramahi, E., Nijland, M. J., Choi, J., Myers, D. A., Nathanielsz, P. W., et al. (2013b). Up-regulation of the fetal baboon hypothalamo-pituitary-adrenal axis in intrauterine growth restriction: coincidence with hypothalamic glucocorticoid receptor insensitivity and leptin receptor down-regulation. *Endocrinology*, 154, 2365-73.

Liggins, G. C. (1976). Adrenocortical-related maturational events in the fetus. *Am. J. Obstet. Gynecol*, 126, 931-41.

Liggins, G. C., Fairclough, R. J., Grieves, S. A., Kendall, J. Z. & Knox, B. S. (1973). The mechanism of initiation of parturition in the ewe. *Recent Prog. Horm. Res*, 29, 111-59.

Liggins, G. C., Schellenberg, J. C., Finberg, K., Kitterman, J. A. & Lee, C. H. (1985). The effects of ACTH1-24 or cortisol on pulmonary maturation in the adrenalectomized ovine fetus. *J. Dev. Physiol*, 7, 105-11.

Liu, J. P., Clarke, I. J., Funder, J. W. & Engler, D. (1994). Studies of the secretion of corticotropin-releasing factor and arginine vasopressin into the hypophysial-portal circulation of the conscious sheep. II. The central noradrenergic and neuropeptide Y pathways cause immediate and prolonged hypothalamic-pituitary-adrenal activation. Potential involvement in the pseudo-Cushing's syndrome of endogenous depression and anorexia nervosa. *J. Clin. Invest*, 93, 1439-50.

Long, N. M., Ford, S. P. & Nathanielsz, P. W. (2011). Maternal obesity eliminates the neonatal lamb plasma leptin peak. *J. Physiol*, 589, 1455-62.

Long, N. M., Ford, S. P. & Nathanielsz, P. W. (2013). Multigenerational effects of fetal dexamethasone exposure on the hypothalamic-pituitary-adrenal axis of first- and second-generation female offspring. *Am. J. Obstet. Gynecol*, 208, 217.e1-8.

Long, N. M., Nathanielsz, P. W. & Ford, S. P. (2012). The impact of maternal overnutrition and obesity on hypothalamic-pituitary-adrenal axis response of offspring to stress. *Domest. Anim. Endocrinol*, 42, 195-202.

Luther, J., Aitken, R., Milne, J., Matsuzaki, M., Reynolds, L., Redmer, D., et al. (2007a). Maternal and fetal growth, body composition, endocrinology, and metabolic status in undernourished adolescent sheep. *Biol. Reprod*, 77, 343-50.

Luther, J., Milne, J., Aitken, R., Matsuzaki, M., Reynolds, L., Redmer, D., et al. (2007b). Placental growth, angiogenic gene expression, and vascular development in undernourished adolescent sheep. *Biol. Reprod*, 77, 351-7.

Masaki, T., Chiba, S., Noguchi, H., Yasuda, T., Tobe, K., Suzuki, R., et al. (2004). Obesity in insulin receptor substrate-2-deficient mice: disrupted control of arcuate nucleus neuropeptides. *Obes. Res*, 12, 878-85.

Matthews, S. G. (2002). Early programming of the hypothalamo-pituitary-adrenal axis. *Trends Endocrinol. Metab*, 13, 373-80.

Matthews, S. G. & Challis, J. R. (1995). Regulation of CRH and AVP mRNA in the developing ovine hypothalamus: effects of stress and glucocorticoids. *Am.J Physiol*, 268, E1096-E1107.

Matthews, S. G. & Challis, J. R. (1996). Regulation of the hypothalamo-pituitary-adrenocortical axis in fetal sheep. *Trends Endocrinol. Metab*, 7, 239-46.

McDonald, T. J. & Nathanielsz, P. W. (1991). Bilateral destruction of the fetal paraventricular nuclei prolongs gestation in sheep. *Am.J Obstet. Gynecol*, 165, 764-770

McEwen, B. S. & Morrison, J. H. (2013). The brain on stress: vulnerability and plasticity of the prefrontal cortex over the life course. *Neuron*, 79, 16-29.

McMillen, I. C., Adams, M. B., Ross, J. T., Coulter, C. L., Simonetta, G., Owens, J. A., et al. (2001). Fetal growth restriction: adaptations and consequences. *Reproduction*, 122, 195-204.

McMillen, I. C., Schwartz, J., Coulter, C. L. & Edwards, L. J. (2004). Early embryonic environment, the fetal pituitary-adrenal axis and the timing of parturition. *Endocr. Res*, 30, 845-50.

Mercer, J. G., Moar, K. M., Rayner, D. V., Trayhurn, P. & Hoggard, N. (1997). Regulation of leptin receptor and NPY gene expression in hypothalamus of leptin-treated obese (ob/ob) and cold-exposed lean mice. *FEBS Lett*, 402, 185-8.

Mina, T. H. & Reynolds, R. M. (2014). Mechanisms Linking In Utero Stress to Altered Offspring Behaviour. *Curr. Top Behav. Neurosci*.

Modi, N., Lewis, H., Al-Naqeeb, N., Ajayi-Obe, M., Dore, C. J. & Rutherford, M. (2001). The effects of repeated antenatal glucocorticoid therapy on the developing brain. *Pediatr. Res*, 50, 581-5.

Monau, T. R., Vargas, V. E., Zhang, L., Myers, D. A. & Ducsay, C. A. (2010). Nitric oxide inhibits ACTH-induced cortisol production in near-term, long-term hypoxic ovine fetal adrenocortical cells. *Reprod. Sci*, 17, 955-62.

Morrison, J. L. (2008). Sheep models of intrauterine growth restriction: fetal adaptations and consequences. *Clin. Exp. Pharmacol. Physiol*, 35, 730-43.

Muhlhausler, B. S., Adam, C. L., Findlay, P. A., Duffield, J. A. & McMillen, I. C. (2006). Increased maternal nutrition alters development of the appetite-regulating network in the brain. *FASEB J*, 20, 1257-9.

Muhlhausler, B. S., McMillen, I. C., Rouzaud, G., Findlay, P. A., Marrocco, E. M., Rhind, S. M., et al. (2004). Appetite regulatory neuropeptides are expressed in the sheep hypothalamus before birth. *J. Neuroendocrinol*, 16, 502-7.

Muneoka, K., Mikuni, M., Ogawa, T., Kitera, K., Kamei, K., Takigawa, M., et al. (1997). Prenatal dexamethasone exposure alters brain monoamine metabolism and adrenocortical response in rat offspring. *Am. J. Physiol*, 273, R1669-75.

Myers, D. A., Bell, P. A., Hyatt, K., Mlynarczyk, M. & Ducsay, C. A. (2005a). Long-term hypoxia enhances proopiomelanocortin processing in the near-term ovine fetus. *Am. J. Physiol. Regul. Integr. Comp. Physiol*, 288, R1178-84.

Myers, D. A., Hyatt, K., Mlynarczyk, M., Bird, I. M. & Ducsay, C. A. (2005b). Long-term hypoxia represses the expression of key genes regulating cortisol biosynthesis in the near-term ovine fetus. *Am. J. Physiol. Regul. Integr. Comp. Physiol*, 289, R1707-14.

Myers, D. A., McDonald, T. J. & Nathanielsz, P. W. (1992a). Effect of bilateral lesions of the ovine fetal hypothalamic paraventricular nuclei at 118-122 days of gestation on subsequent adrenocortical steroidogenic enzyme gene expression. *Endocrinology*, 131, 305-10.

Myers, D. A., McDonald, T. J. & Nathanielsz, P. W. (1992b). Effect of placement of dexamethasone adjacent to the ovine fetal paraventricular nucleus on adrenocortical steroid hydroxylase messenger ribonucleic acid. *Endocrinology*, 131, 1329-35.

Myers, D. A., Myers, T. R., Grober, M. S. & Nathanielsz, P. W. (1993). Levels of corticotropin-releasing hormone messenger ribonucleic acid (mRNA) in the hypothalamic paraventricular nucleus and proopiomelanocortin mRNA in the anterior pituitary during late gestation in fetal sheep. *Endocrinology*, 132, 2109-16.

Newnham, J. P. (2001). Is prenatal glucocorticoid administration another origin of adult disease? *Clin. Exp. Pharmacol. Physiol*, 28, 957-61.

Noia, G., Romano, D., Terzano, G. M., De Santis, M., Di Domenico, M., Cavaliere, A., et al. (2002). Ovine fetal growth curves in twin pregnancy: ultrasonographic assessment. *Clin. Exp. Obstet. Gynecol*, 29, 251-6.

Nyirenda, M. J., Lindsay, R. S., Kenyon, C. J., Burchell, A. & Seckl, J. R. (1998). Glucocorticoid exposure in late gestation permanently programs rat hepatic phosphoenolpyruvate carboxykinase and glucocorticoid receptor expression and causes glucose intolerance in adult offspring. *J. Clin. Invest*, 101, 2174-81.

Poulsen, P., Grunnet, L. G., Pilgaard, K., Storgaard, H., Alibegovic, A., Sonne, M. P., et al. (2009). Increased risk of type 2 diabetes in elderly twins. *Diabetes*, 58, 1350-5.

Poulsen, P., Vaag, A. A., Kyvik, K. O., Moller Jensen, D. & Beck-Nielsen, H. (1997). Low birth weight is associated with NIDDM in discordant monozygotic and dizygotic twin pairs. *Diabetologia*, 40, 439-46.

Pryce, C. R., Aubert, Y., Maier, C., Pearce, P. C. & Fuchs, E. (2011). The developmental impact of prenatal stress, prenatal dexamethasone and postnatal social stress on physiology, behaviour and neuroanatomy of primate offspring: studies in rhesus macaque and common marmoset. *Psychopharmacology (Berl)*, 214, 33-53.

Rakers, F., Frauendorf, V., Rupprecht, S., Schiffner, R., Bischoff, S. J., Kiehntopf, M., et al. (2013). Effects of early- and late-gestational maternal stress and synthetic glucocorticoid on development of the fetal hypothalamus-pituitary-adrenal axis in sheep. *Stress*, 16, 122-9.

Reynolds, R. M. (2013). Glucocorticoid excess and the developmental origins of disease: two decades of testing the hypothesis--2012 Curt Richter Award Winner. *Psychoneuroendocrinology*, 38, 1-11.

Rodrigues, S. M., Ledoux, J. E. & Sapolsky, R. M. (2009). The influence of stress hormones on fear circuitry. *Annu. Rev. Neurosci*, 32, 289-313.

Romagnoli, C., Zecca, E., Vento, G., Maggio, L., Papacci, P. & Tortorolo, G. (1999). Effect on growth of two different dexamethasone courses for preterm infants at risk of chronic lung disease. A randomized trial. *Pharmacology*, 59, 266-74.

Rondini, T. A., Baddini, S. P., Sousa, L. F., Bittencourt, J. C. & Elias, C. F. (2004). Hypothalamic cocaine- and amphetamine-regulated transcript neurons project to areas expressing gonadotropin releasing hormone immunoreactivity and to the anteroventral periventricular nucleus in male and female rats. *Neuroscience*, 125, 735-48.

Rose, J. C., Meis, P. J. & Morris, M. (1981). Ontogeny of endocrine (ACTH, vasopressin, cortisol) responses to hypotension in lamb fetuses. *Am. J. Physiol*, 240, E656-61.

Ross, M.G. & Desai, M. (2005). Gestational programming: population survival effects of drought and famine during pregnancy. *Am. J. Physiol. Regul. Integr. Comp. Physiol*, 288, R25-33.

Rumball, C. W., Bloomfield, F. H., Oliver, M. H. & Harding, J. E. (2009). Different periods of periconceptional undernutrition have different effects on growth, metabolic and endocrine status in fetal sheep. *Pediatr. Res*, 66, 605-13.

Sahu, A. (2003). Leptin signaling in the hypothalamus: emphasis on energy homeostasis and leptin resistance. *Front Neuroendocrinol*, 24, 225-53.

Sahu, A. (2004). Minireview: A hypothalamic role in energy balance with special emphasis on leptin. *Endocrinology*, 145, 2613-20.

Schmidt, M. V., Enthoven, L., Van der Mark, M., Levine, S., De Kloet, E. R. & Oitzl, M. S. (2003). The postnatal development of the hypothalamic-pituitary-adrenal axis in the mouse. *Int. J. Dev. Neurosci*, 21, 125-32.

Schmidt, M. V., Levine, S., Oitzl, M. S., Van der Mark, M., Muller, M. B., Holsboer, F., et al. (2005). Glucocorticoid receptor blockade disinhibits pituitary-adrenal activity during the stress hyporesponsive period of the mouse. *Endocrinology*, 146, 1458-64.

Schulkin, J., Gold, P. W. & McEwen, B. S. (1998). Induction of corticotropin-releasing hormone gene expression by glucocorticoids: implication for understanding the states of fear and anxiety and allostatic load. *Psychoneuroendocrinology*, 23, 219-43.

Schwartz, J., Kleftogiannis, F., Jacobs, R., Thorburn, G. D., Crosby, S. R. & White, A. (1995). Biological activity of adrenocorticotropic hormone precursors on ovine adrenal cells. *Am. J. Physiol*, 268, E623-9.

Schwartz, M. W., Woods, S. C., Porte, D., Jr., Seeley, R. J. & Baskin, D. G. (2000). Central nervous system control of food intake. *Nature*, 404, 661-71.

Sebert, S. P., Hyatt, M. A., Chan, L. L., Patel, N., Bell, R. C., Keisler, D., et al. (2009). Maternal nutrient restriction between early and midgestation and its impact upon appetite regulation after juvenile obesity. *Endocrinology*, 150, 634-41.

Shepard, J. D. & Myers, D. A. (2008). Strain differences in anxiety-like behavior: association with corticotropin-releasing factor. *Behav. Brain Res*, 186, 239-45.

Shepard, J. D., Schulkin, J. & Myers, D. A. (2006). Chronically elevated corticosterone in the amygdala increases corticotropin releasing factor mRNA in the dorsolateral bed nucleus of stria terminalis following duress. *Behav. Brain Res*, 174, 193-6.

Sloboda, D. M., Moss, T. J., Gurrin, L. C., Newnham, J. P. & Challis, J. R. (2002). The effect of prenatal betamethasone administration on postnatal ovine hypothalamic-pituitary-adrenal function. *J. Endocrinol*, 172, 71-81.

Sloboda, D. M., Moss, T. J., Li, S., Doherty, D., Nitsos, I., Challis, J. R., et al. (2007). Prenatal betamethasone exposure results in pituitary-adrenal hyporesponsiveness in adult sheep. *Am. J. Physiol. Endocrinol. Metab*, 292, E61-70.

Sloboda, D. M., Newnham, J. P. & Challis, J. R. (2000). Effects of repeated maternal betamethasone administration on growth and hypothalamic-pituitary-adrenal function of the ovine fetus at term. *J. Endocrinol*, 165, 79-91.

Spray, C. M. & Widdowson, E. M. (1950). The effect of growth and development on the composition of mammals. *Br. J. Nutr*, 4, 332-53.

Stanley, S. A., Small, C. J., Murphy, K. G., Rayes, E., Abbott, C. R., Seal, L. J., et al. (2001). Actions of cocaine- and amphetamine-regulated transcript (CART) peptide on regulation of appetite and hypothalamo-pituitary axes in vitro and in vivo in male rats. *Brain Res*, 893, 186-94.

Stevens, A., Begum, G., Cook, A., Connor, K., Rumball, C., Oliver, M., et al. (2010). Epigenetic changes in the hypothalamic proopiomelanocortin and glucocorticoid receptor genes in the ovine fetus after periconceptional undernutrition. *Endocrinology*, 151, 3652-64.

Stevens, A., Begum, G. & White, A. (2011). Epigenetic changes in the hypothalamic pro-opiomelanocortin gene: a mechanism linking maternal undernutrition to obesity in the offspring? *Eur. J. Pharmacol*, 660, 194-201.

Stoelhorst, G. M., Martens, S. E., Rijken, M., van Zwieten, P. H., Zwinderman, A. H., Wit, J. M., et al. (2003). Behaviour at 2 years of age in very preterm infants (gestational age < 32 weeks). *Acta Paediatr*, 92, 595-601.

Su, Y., Carey, L. C., Rose, J. C. & Pulgar, V. M. (2013). Antenatal glucocorticoid exposure enhances the inhibition of adrenal steroidogenesis by leptin in a sex-specific fashion. *Am. J. Physiol. Endocrinol. Metab*, 304, E1404-11.

Su, Y., Carey, L. C., Valego, N. K. & Rose, J. C. (2005). Developmental changes in adrenocorticotrophin (ACTH)-induced expression of ACTH receptor and steroid acute regulatory protein mRNA in ovine fetal adrenal cells. *J. Soc. Gynecol. Investig*, 12, 416-20.

Sullivan, E. L., Grayson, B., Takahashi, D., Robertson, N., Maier, A., Bethea, C. L., et al. (2010). Chronic consumption of a high-fat diet during pregnancy causes perturbations in the serotonergic system and increased anxiety-like behavior in nonhuman primate offspring. *J. Neurosci*, 30, 3826-30.

Sullivan, E. L., Smith, M. S. & Grove, K. L. (2011). Perinatal exposure to high-fat diet programs energy balance, metabolism and behavior in adulthood. *Neuroendocrinology*, 93, 1-8.

Suter, M. A., Chen, A., Burdine, M. S., Choudhury, M., Harris, R. A., Lane, R. H., et al. (2012). A maternal high-fat diet modulates fetal SIRT1 histone and protein deacetylase activity in nonhuman primates. *FASEB J*, 26, 5106-14.

Symonds, M. E. & Budge, H. (2009). Nutritional models of the developmental programming of adult health and disease. *Proc. Nutr. Soc*, 68, 173-8.

Talge, N. M., Neal, C., Glover, V. & Early Stress, Translational Research and Prevention Science Network: Fetal and Neonatal Experience on Child and Adolescent Mental Health. (2007). Antenatal maternal stress and long-term effects on child neurodevelopment: how and why? *J. Child Psychol Psychiatry*, 48, 245-61.

Tegethoff, M., Pryce, C. & Meinlschmidt, G. (2009). Effects of intrauterine exposure to synthetic glucocorticoids on fetal, newborn, and infant hypothalamic-pituitary-adrenal axis function in humans: a systematic review. *Endocr. Rev*, 30, 753-89.

The, N. S., Adair, L. S. & Gordon-Larsen, P. (2010). A study of the birth weight-obesity relation using a longitudinal cohort and sibling and twin pairs. *Am. J. Epidemiol*, 172, 549-57.

Thomassin, H., Flavin, M., Espinas, M. L. & Grange, T. (2001). Glucocorticoid-induced DNA demethylation and gene memory during development. *EMBO J*, 20, 1974-83.

Todd, S. E., Oliver, M. H., Jaquiery, A. L., Bloomfield, F. H. & Harding, J. E. (2009). Periconceptional undernutrition of ewes impairs glucose tolerance in their adult offspring. *Pediatr. Res*, 65, 409-13.

Trautman, P. D., Meyer-Bahlburg, H. F., Postelnek, J. & New, M. I. (1995). Effects of early prenatal dexamethasone on the cognitive and behavioral development of young children: results of a pilot study. *Psychoneuroendocrinology*, 20, 439-49.

Uno, H., Eisele, S., Sakai, A., Shelton, S., Baker, E., Dejesus, O., et al. (1994). Neurotoxicity of glucocorticoids in the primate brain. *Horm. Behav*, 28, 336-48.

Vallee, M., Mayo, W., Dellu, F., Le Moal, M., Simon, H. & Maccari, S. (1997). Prenatal stress induces high anxiety and postnatal handling induces low anxiety in adult offspring: correlation with stress-induced corticosterone secretion. *J. Neurosci*, 17, 2626-36.

Vargas, V. E., Kaushal, K. M., Monau, T., Myers, D. A. & Ducsay, C. A. (2011). Long-term hypoxia enhances cortisol biosynthesis in near-term ovine fetal adrenal cortical cells. *Reprod. Sci*, 18, 277-85.

Vieau, D. (2011). Perinatal nutritional programming of health and metabolic adult disease. *World J. Diabetes*, 2, 133-6.

Wallace, J. M., Milne, J. S. & Aitken, R. P. (2010). Effect of weight and adiposity at conception and wide variations in gestational dietary intake on pregnancy outcome and early postnatal performance in young adolescent sheep. *Biol. Reprod*, 82, 320-30.

Wallace, J. M., Milne, J. S., Green, L. R. & Aitken, R. P. (2011). Postnatal hypothalamic-pituitary-adrenal function in sheep is influenced by age and sex, but not by prenatal growth restriction. *Reprod. Fertil. Dev*, 23, 275-84.

Wattez, J. S., Delahaye, F., Lukaszewski, M. A., Risold, P. Y., Eberle, D., Vieau, D., et al. (2013). Perinatal nutrition programs the hypothalamic melanocortin system in offspring. *Horm. Metab. Res*, 45, 980-90.

Weinstock, M. (2001). Alterations induced by gestational stress in brain morphology and behaviour of the offspring. *Prog. Neurobiol*, 65, 427-51.

Weinstock, M., Matlina, E., Maor, G. I., Rosen, H. & McEwen, B. S. (1992). Prenatal stress selectively alters the reactivity of the hypothalamic-pituitary adrenal system in the female rat. *Brain Res*, 595, 195-200.

Welberg, L. A., Seckl, J. R. & Holmes, M. C. (2000). Inhibition of 11beta-hydroxysteroid dehydrogenase, the foeto-placental barrier to maternal glucocorticoids, permanently programs amygdala GR mRNA expression and anxiety-like behaviour in the offspring. *Eur. J. Neurosci*, 12, 1047-54.

Welberg, L. A., Seckl, J. R. & Holmes, M. C. (2001). Prenatal glucocorticoid programming of brain corticosteroid receptors and corticotrophin-releasing hormone: possible implications for behaviour. *Neuroscience*, 104, 71-9.

Whorwood, C. B., Firth, K. M., Budge, H. & Symonds, M. E. (2001). Maternal undernutrition during early to midgestation programs tissue-specific alterations in the expression of the glucocorticoid receptor, 11beta-hydroxysteroid dehydrogenase isoforms, and type 1 angiotensin ii receptor in neonatal sheep. *Endocrinology*, 142, 2854-64.

Widdowson, E. M. (1950). Chemical composition of newly born mammals. *Nature*, 166, 626-8.

Williams, P. J., Kurlak, L. O., Perkins, A. C., Budge, H., Stephenson, T., Keisler, D., et al. (2007). Hypertension and impaired renal function accompany juvenile obesity: the effect of prenatal diet. *Kidney Int*, 72, 279-89.

Zhang, S., Rattanatray, L., Morrison, J. L., Nicholas, L. M., Lie, S. & McMillen, I. C. (2011). Maternal obesity and the early origins of childhood obesity: weighing up the benefits and costs of maternal weight loss in the periconceptional period for the offspring. *Exp. Diabetes Res*, 2011, 585749.

In: Stress and Developmental Programming …
Editors: Lubo Zhang and Lawrence D. Longo

ISBN: 978-1-63321-836-9
© 2014 Nova Science Publishers, Inc.

Chapter 11

Increased Central and Peripheral Glucocorticoid Synthesis Act As an Orchestrator of Developmental Programming

Elena Zambrano[1], Nuermaimaiti Tuersunjiang[2], Nathan M. Long [3], Chunming Guo [2], Kang Sun [2], Laura A. Cox[4], Stephen P. Ford[5], Peter W. Nathanielsz[2] and Cun Li[2]

[1]Instituto Nacional de la Nutricion, Mexico
[2]Center for Pregnancy and Newborn Research, The University of Texas Health Science Center San Antonio, San Antonio, TX, US
[3]Dept Animal and Veterinary Science, Clemson University, Clemson, SC, US
[4]Dept Genetic, Texas Biomedical Research Institute, San Antonio, TX, US
[5]Center for the Study of Fetal Programming, Dept Animal Science, University of Wyoming, Laramie, WY, US

Abstract

Physiological challenges experienced during development can alter lifetime function as a result of Developmental Programming. Gene environment interactions in developmental programming are receiving growing interest due to their effects as major determinants of lifetime health. This chapter considers commonalities and differences between precocial and altricial species in relation to the hypothalamo-pituitary-adrenal axis. It focuses on the roles of glucocorticoids both as immediate and long-term mechanisms in the responses to the challenges that give rise to programming. Profound changes occur in fetal and neonatal glucocorticoids in both altricial and precocial species that are involved in maturing organs in preparation for an independent post-natal life. At the other end of the life-course there is no clear agreement as to changes in the HPAA. Interestingly maternal age at conception may affect the rate of aging of the offspring HPAA. Evidence is presented of increased peripheral production of cortisol by 11-Betahydroxysteroid dehydrogenase 1 in both sheep and baboons in response to poor maternal nutrition. Finally we address recent data that indicate that glucocorticoids are involved in the programming of the post natal leptin peak that itself programs appetitive behavior. This collection of evidence suggests that their ubiquitous impact on multiple organ systems indicates that glucocorticoids are central orchestrators of many aspects of developmental programming.

Keywords: Baboon, developmental programming, glucocorticoids, hypothalamo-pituitary-adrenal axis, nutrition, sheep

Introduction

Comparative physiology of normal perinatal development of the hypothalamo-pituitary-adrenal axis in precocial and altricial species.

This chapter will focus on the role of normal and altered development of the hypothalamo-pituitary adrenal axis (HPAA) in developmental programming. The *Developmental Programming Hypothesis* states that *challenges during critical windows of differentiation alter the trajectory of fetal and neonatal development with persistent effects on offspring phenotype.* Considerable human epidemiologic evidence and data from controlled animal studies clearly show that altered phenotypes that result from a variety of different challenges during fetal and neonatal development predispose to a wide range of adult disease. In the past it was usual to refer to developmental programming as only affecting non-communicable disease (Barker, 1998, Nathanielsz, 1999) but growing evidence indicates that programming of the immune system can occur. Thus we should add predisposition to communicable disease as a programming outcome in response to challenges during development (Fall, 2013). Another growing area of interest is the potential of developmental programming to affect the rate of aging (Carr et al., 2014, Guzman et al., 2006, Morimoto et al., 2012). It has also been suggested that some challenges may increase the risk of cancer (Kaur et al., 2013) although those links are not as well established. These altered disease predispositions are the result of gene-environment interactions at plastic periods of development in the fetus and neonate and show that our understanding of phenotype has moved from being solely gene-centric to acknowledgement of the importance of the epigenome. Programming is now seen as a major factor in determining human health over the full life-course.

Evolution has produced a wide spectrum of pregnancy strategies including widely divergent trajectories of fetal and neonatal offspring developmental patterns that serve to adapt each mammalian species' for survival and reproduction in its specific environmental niche. *Polytocous altricial* species, such as most rodents, are born after short pregnancies and considerable maternal care is essential in the immediate post-natal period to ensure survival of immature young while they develop the systems necessary for independent survival, such as maintenance of body temperature and metabolic homeostasis, in the absence of provision of food by the mother. There are rodents that are exceptions such as the guinea-pig, which is born at a very mature stage and able to eat solid food from birth. *Monotocous precocial* species, such as humans, nonhuman primates and sheep have attained a more mature level of function in most organs by the time they are born. But even precocial species are not equally mature at birth. Humans are precocial in many respects but not compared with sheep for example with respect to organized locomotion or ability to control their body temperature. Altricial and precocial species have differing strengths and limitations as models to study the challenges, outcomes and mechanisms of developmental programming. From the comparative physiology point of view, study of the wide range of developmental trajectories provides important information on mechanisms by which different developing systems – adrenal steroid production for example, respond to a challenge during development and what regulatory factors are involved - neural influences, growth factors, gene changes and epigenetic marks and whether they persist into post-natal life and lead changes in phenotype.

The nutritional burden in pregnancy and lactation born by the mother also differs greatly between polytocous species – mostly altricial, and monotocous species mostly precocial species. Humans are monotocous species. Mothers generally bear only a single fetus though one in eighty natural pregnancies results in twins. Women are physiologically able to bear multiple pregnancies as assisted reproductive techniques clearly indicate. However offspring outcomes are less optimal when even twins are present. In polytocous species raising large litters places a greater relative maternal nutritional demand. It is perhaps most striking to equate the feto-placental biomass raised by a pregnant rat as equivalent to a pregnant woman bearing a 25-30 Kg baby relative to her own size. These differences in litter size mean that the maternal nutrient burden imposed by pregnancy and lactation differs greatly in these two groups of mammals resulting in different needs for macronutrients (e.g. specific essential amino acids) and micronutrients such as vitamins and other factors affecting key metabolic functions. As a result extrapolation of data between precocial, monotocous and polytocous altricial species requires careful evaluation. The methionine cycle, which is important in gene methylation, and vitamin C which is a powerful anti-oxidant are two examples of differences in micronutrient metabolism between rodents and primates with potential significant effects on programming mechanisms. To provide one example central to several issues discussed related to programming during development in this review, the rodent one carbon cycle, central to methylation of genes in processes fundamental to epigenetic effects, differs between primates and rodents. For example, folic acid reduction to active tetrahydrofolate by dihydrofolate reductase in human liver occurs at less than 2% of the rate in rat liver (Bailey and Ayling, 2009). These species biochemical differences present several interesting issues that will clearly produce differences in mechanisms and outcomes between rodents and primate in response to nutritional challenges such as maternal over-nutrition or low protein diets lacking methionine.

Thus, although the altricial and precocial species division is not all-embracing, it must be taken into account since many maturational changes that are postnatal in altricial rodents occur during fetal life in precocial species. In both precocial and altricial species the prenatal environment differs greatly from the post-natal environment. Before birth developing tissues are exposed to an arterial PO_2 of about 40 mm.Hg. After birth arterial PO_2 is 100 mm.Hg. These differences have many potential consequences for the outcomes to the same challenge delivered in fetal or neonatal life such as oxidative metabolism and production of oxidative stress which are now more and more seen as a potential mechanism for both normative and programmed development (Zambrano and Nathanielsz, 2013). Similarly before birth fetal glucose concentration is half that in post-natal life. Importantly also, the fetus is exposed to a very different endocrine milieu before birth compared to post natal life as it is exposed to hormones and metabolites produced by the mother and placenta which are not present in the neonatal environment. These differences likely determine very different responses to challenges in key windows of vulnerability that are fetal in precocial mammals and postnatal in altricial mammals.

Differences also occur at the cellular level in key metabolic systems. For example, the key gluconeogenic enzyme phosphoenolpyruvatecarboxykinase (PEPCK) exists in two different forms at different sub-cellular sites, one mitochondrial (PEPCKM) and the other cytosolic PEPCKC. mRNA or protein levels for PEPCK are commonly used as indices of the rate of gluconeogenesis – a central response to nutrient deficiency (Nijland et al., 2010).

PEPCKC comprises 90% of hepatic PEPCK in rat and mouse livers. As a result PEPCKM only represents 5-10% of the total PEPCK activity. In contrast, in human liver, 50% of the PEPCK activity is PEPCKM a balance seen in most mammalian species (Hanson and Garber, 1972).

However there are no studies on the impact of specific nutritional challenges during development on both of these isoforms in either altricial species or precocial species similar to humans who have both forms of the enzyme. In a stimulating discussion of the need to understand the comparative physiology of this important metabolic pathway in the liver, Hanson (Hanson and Reshef, 1997) writes of what he calls a *"tyranny of species. As more and more data become available about a given species the more that species becomes a standard for further study."* This *"tyranny" as he calls it, is demonstrated by the intense focus* over the past 25 years using the techniques of mouse genetics combined with metabolic analysis but there is also a need for studies in precocial species – sheep and nonhuman primates, for comparative evaluation and translation to the human situation. This caution is especially true in relation to developmental programming.

The best data available on the normative changes in the fetal HPAA in late gestation during the weeks leading up to parturition have been obtained in chronically catheterized, unanesthetized fetal sheep.

The pregnant sheep is unique in the ability to undertake long-term fetal studies throughout the second half of gestation. Because of the size of both mother and fetus and the tolerance of the myometrium to surgical incisions, it is possible to anesthetize the ewe, incise the uterus, open the amniotic cavity and place instrumentation such as electrocardiogram leads on the fetus and catheters in a wide variety of fetal vessels. By catheterizing the terminal aorta and the umbilical vein, the concentration gradient for hormones and metabolic substrates can be determined. Coupled with the placement of a flow probe around the common umbilical artery the total exchange across the placenta from mother to fetus can be calculated.

Following completion of the surgery, the fetal membranes and uterus can be closed. Catheters can be placed in maternal blood vessels and the mother allowed to recover from anesthesia. Maternal and fetal blood samples can then be taken at frequent intervals under sterile conditions over several weeks. Infusions and challenges to fetal systems such as intravenous glucose tolerance tests, endocrine challenges to the HPAA (e.g. CRH challenges) can be performed in both mother and fetus. This tolerance to surgery and investigation is not present in any other large precocial species and certainly not in small laboratory rodents.

The fetal sheep is thus a unique model for evaluation of fetal development without the complication of administration of anesthetics or other pharmacological agents needed or analgesia after it has recovered from the surgery. Importantly nonhuman primate species are not as tolerant of intrauterine surgery which although possible, is frequently followed by increased nocturnal myometrial contractions and premature delivery (Farber et al., 1997, Pepe et al., 2003).

Cortisol is the major circulating glucocorticoid in the five species shown in Figure 2. As can be seen fetal plasma cortisol increases in an exponential fashion in late gestation in all five species but the trajectory and importantly, the time at which the increase begins in relation to delivery varies considerably among species.

An exponential prenatal increase in fetal cortisol, occurring over the last 20 days or so (13%) of fetal life has been characterized in fetal sheep instrumented with fetal vascular catheters enabling daily fetal blood sampling from the same fetus throughout the second half of gestation (Magyar et al., 1980). This fetal cortisol rise is driven by increased fetal HPAA activity as shown by increased fetal pituitary ACTH and adrenal ACTH sensitivity (Challis et al., 2001) as well as experimental inhibition of the fetal ACTH and cortisol rise by stereotaxic ablation of fetal hypothalamic paraventricular nuclear production of CRH (McDonald and Nathanielsz, 1991).

Whether similar changes occur in primates including man has been questioned since the structure of the fetal primate adrenal and control of fetal steroidogenesis show significant differences from sheep and other precocial species as well as from altricial polytocous species.

The nonhuman primate and human fetal adrenal possess a fetal zone absent in ruminant and rodent species. *In vitro* studies show that mid-gestation cultured human adrenal fetal zone cells produce the C19 steroid dehydroepiandrosterone sulfate rather than the C21 steroid, cortisol, when stimulated by ACTH (Mesiano and Jaffe, 1997) an observation that explains the rise in plasma fetal DHEAS that has been shown in fetal monkey blood over the final 15% of gestation concomitant with increasing fetal adrenal weight (Serón-Ferré and Jaffe, 1981).

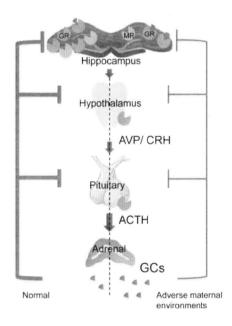

Figure 1. Hippocampal-hypothalamo-pituitary-adrenal axis. Reproduced with permission from (Xiong and Zhang, 2013). Green triangles represent cortisol. Side lines represent feedback.

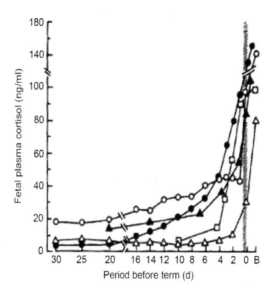

Figure 2. Mean fetal plasma cortisol concentration with respect to days (d) from delivery in sheep (closed circles), pig (open circles), human (solid triangles), guinea-pig (open squares), and horse (open triangles). Hatched vertical line represents birth. Reproduced with permission from (Fowden et al., 1998).

Hypothalamo-Pituitary-Adrenal Development in Nonhuman Primates

We and others have hypothesized that, since as discussed below, fetal cortisol plays a central role in preparation for independent external life and all fetal mammals must mature the same vital organ systems (lung, gut, kidney, thyroid) in order to survive independently in the extra-uterine world, fetal primate ACTH and cortisol would rise in the second half of gestation in a fashion similar to the increases observed in fetal sheep. To provide the necessary data to address this hypothesis, we evaluated fetal plasma ACTH and cortisol at four stages of fetal development, 0.5, 0.65, 0.9 and 0.95 gestation (G) in the baboon a well-established and characterized nonhuman primate model of pregnancy and fetal development (Albrecht and Pepe, 1990, Ducsay et al., 1991, Henson et al., 2004, Wilson et al., 1991). Pregnant baboons were group housed with normal socialization and physical activity. Since it is well established that cortisol crosses the placenta from mother to fetus in primates (Albrecht and Pepe, 1990), we measured maternal ACTH and cortisol to determine any significant maternal HPAA changes, particularly those that might change the maternal: fetal cortisol ratio. Adrenal ACTH sensitivity increases in late gestation fetal sheep (Poore et al., 1998) so we evaluated the cortisol:ACTH ratio as an index of fetal adrenal ACTH responsiveness.

ACTH and cortisol both rose significantly in the fetal baboon between 0.65 and 0.9 G. The rise in ACTH in the presence of a rise in cortisol indicates that ACTH is the driver of the system (Figure 3).

There were no parallel changes in maternal ACTH or cortisol or in the maternal:fetal ACTH or cortisol ratios that would explain the rise in fetal cortisol (data not shown). To our knowledge these are the first combined ACTH and cortisol data to show increased *in vivo* activity of the fetal HPAA in a primate species.

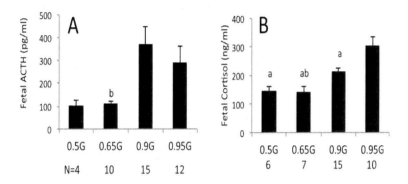

Figure 3. Fetal baboon A) ACTH and B) cortisol from 0.5 to 0.95 G. M ± SEM. [b] p < 0.05 0.65 vs. 0.9G; [a] different from 0.95 p < 0.05.

There is considerable controversy as to whether glucocorticoid production increases, is unchanged or decreases during the aging process. Despite an extensive search of the literature we were unable to find the necessary longitudinal data in the literature to provide a clear answer to this question. Most reported data came to conclusions based on comparisons between studies by different groups at different ages. We have measured cortisol concentrations in samples from aged baboons between 16 and 23 years of age (human equivalent 64 – 92 years) (Fig 4). Although the numbers are limited in our study the data do seem to support the view that cortisol levels decrease at older ages with the suggestion of a greater change in males than females. The conclusion that male values are lower than female and that circulating glucocorticoids decrease in aging is supported by data from rats presented below (Figure 7).

Responses of the Fetal Baboon HPAA to Moderately Reduced Nutrient Availability That Results in Intrauterine Growth Restriction

We have developed a model of moderate global nutrient reduction in the pregnant baboon. Experimental animals are group housed allowing normal physical and social interaction. In this model we maximize the power of the study by ensuring similar pre-study body weights and morphometric features (Schlabritz-Loutsevitch et al., 2004) in the females recruited to the study before randomly assigning them to one of two feeding groups: 1) *ad libitum* fed control or 2) 30% globally reduced nutrition in which the mothers are fed 70% of the global control diet from 30 days of pregnancy (term 185 days). Housing, feeding and environmental enrichment have been published in detail elsewhere. Diet fed was Purina Monkey Diet 5038 (Purina, St. Louis, MO). C-sections/necropsies were conducted at 0.9 of gestation (term ~ 185 days) (Nijland et al., 2010).

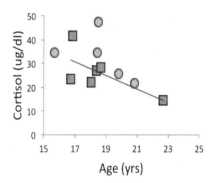

Figure 4. Baboon plasma cortisol in female (circles) and male (squares) over 15 years old (60 years human equivalent). Male and female values were not different. The decrease in male cortisol with age (solid line) was significant over the age range studied (r = 0.8; p < 0.04).

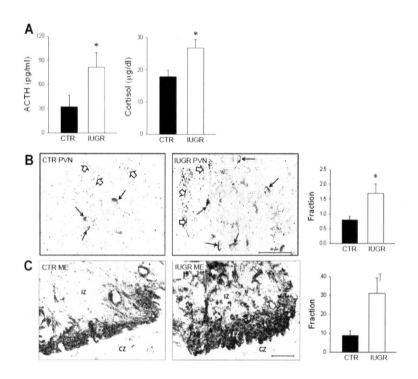

Figure 5. Data at 0.9 gestation from baboon fetuses of control mothers (CTR, n=7 - solid histograms) fed *ad libitum* and IUGR n=6, fetuses of moderately globally nutrient restricted mothers (eating 70% of control mothers (open histograms). **A)** Fetal ACTH and cortisol; **B)** Immunostaining for CRH peptide expression (black product) in neuronal perikarya (black arrows) and beaded neuronal fibers (open arrows) in the hypothalamic paraventricular nucleus of CTR and IUGR fetuses. **C)** CRH peptide expression (black product) in terminal axons of the median eminence external zone (EZ) IZ, internal zone of median eminence; EZ, external zone; CZ, capsule. * p<0.05 vs. CTR; Data mean ± SEM. (Modified from Li et al., 2013b).

Moderate reduction of fetal nutrient availability produced a similar degree of IUGR in males and females – approximately 11% (Li et al., 2013a). This moderate reduction in food intake has a surprisingly marked effect on offspring phenotype - impaired placental structure and function (Cox et al., 2013, Farley et al., 2009, Schlabritz-Loutsevitch et al., 2007) development of the brain frontal cortex (Antonow-Schlorke et al., 2011, Xie et al., 2013) as well as in the kidney (Cox et al., 2006) liver (Nijland et al., 2010) and appetitive centers of the fetal hypothalamus (Li et al., 2013a).

IUGR increased fetal plasma ACTH and cortisol at 0.9 G compared to CTR (Figure 5) as well as fetal hypothalamic paraventricular nucleus and median eminence CRH but not arginine vasopressin (AVP) peptide expression indicating that CRH and not AVP is the major releasing hormone regulating increased ACTH and cortisol secretion in primate IUGR. Phosphorylated and unphosphorylated glucocorticoid receptor were unchanged in the IUGR fetuses compared with controls despite the increased HPAA activity suggesting that decreased cortisol feed back contributes to the increased HPAA activity. Fetal adrenal weights expressed as either mg or % body weight were similar between CTR and IUGR (Li et al., 2013a, 2013b). These HPAA findings in this nonhuman primate model of programming also support a role for fetal glucocorticoids as orchestrators of programming of the HPAA as has been shown most extensively in sheep (Braun et al., 2013, Long et al., 2013).

Rodent Studies

One of the clearest demonstrations of the significant differences between perinatal glucocorticoid changes in precocial and altricial mammals such as common laboratory rodents was made forty years ago. Like so many classic studies its implications have been somewhat forgotten (Daniels et al., 1973, Hardy et al., 1972, Malinowska et al., 1972). In these studies corticosterone, the major glucocorticoid in rodents was shown to be low at delivery in contrast to precocial species such as sheep, baboons and including humans (Figures 2 and 3). Corticosterone then rose over the first 26 days of life in an exponential fashion similar to the late fetal rise in the sheep (Figure 6).

To the best of our knowledge data in Figure 7 are the first data on changes in rat corticosterone across the life course including aged rats. At postnatal day (PND) 220 and 450, female values are higher than male. In both males and females corticosterone is highest at 450 PND days – roughly half the life span of the Wistar rat strain we have studied. Thus we can state firmly that there is a fall in rat serum corticosterone in the second half of life. The controversy over whether there is a decrease in later life in this species is probably due to the absence of adequate longitudinal data from the same laboratory with the same strain managed in the same way.

Figure 8 shows the changes that occur in the maternal and neonatal rat consequent on feeding mothers either a control diet with 20% protein or an isocaloric diet with 10% protein. Maternal corticosterone is elevated at the end of pregnancy while neonatal corticosterone on PND 2 is decreased. The potential explanation for this postnatal decrease is continuing suppressive effects on the offspring HPAA that result from increased passage of corticosterone across the placenta from the mother resulting from the elevated maternal corticosterone that then inhibits the offspring HPAA. In the setting of maternal obesity, maternal and offspring corticosterone are also elevated. (Nathanielsz et al., 2013).

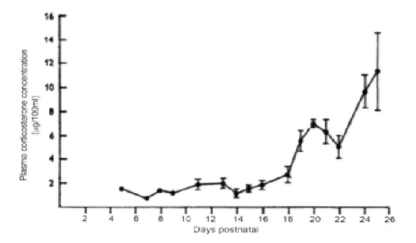

Figure 6. Plasma corticosterone concentrations in the first 26 days of postnatal life in the rat. (Modified from Malinowska et al., 1972).

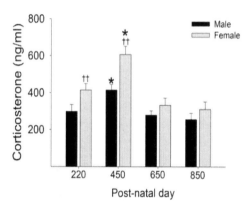

Figure 7. Rat serum corticosterone over the life course - M ± SEM, p<0.05 †† male vs. female at the same age; * 450 vs. the other ages in the same sex. "n" 5 – 11 all from different litters.

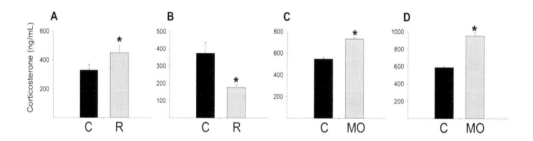

Figure 8. Serum corticosterone in *ad lib* fed rats fed a control (C) diet of 20% protein or a restricted diet (R) of low 10 % protein in pregnancy; *A)* maternal blood corticosterone at 19 days gestation; *B)* offspring neonatal values on neonatal day 2 – male and female offspring combined. *C and D:* Serum corticosterone in the maternal obesity (MO) fed a high fat diet. C) MO mothers at breeding (120 days old). D) offspring neonatal values on neonatal day 2 – male and female combined. M ± SEM; * p<0.05 vs. C.

Effect of Maternal Age on Basal Offspring Corticosterone Levels at Aging of Offspring

Figure 9 shows that offspring corticosterone levels in old age (PND 850) are highest in the offspring of young mothers. There was a suggestion of an increase in the oldest mothers. These interesting findings highlight the ability of maternal age in pregnancy to program rates of aging of physiological systems. They also show an interesting inverse correlation between corticosterone and DHEA.

In one study treatment of rats with DHEA reduced serum triglycerides while corticosterone treatment raised levels. DHEA raised IGF-1 compared to controls while corticosterone lowered IGF.

Thus the lower DHEA and increased corticosterone in offspring of aged mothers indicates that maternal age has a major effect on developmental programming of metabolism and endocrine function (McIntosh et al., 1999).

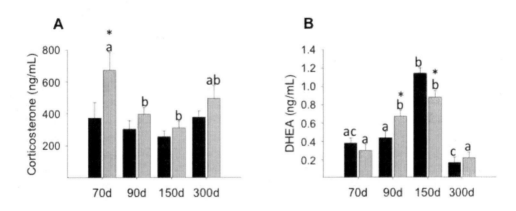

Figure 9. Male (black bars) and females (grey bars) A) Corticosterone and B) DHEA at postnatal day 850 in rat offspring of mothers bred at different ages. M $\pm$ SEM; * p<0.05 male vs. female; n = 5 to 12 per group. p<0.05 in male or female offspring not sharing at least one letter at different maternal ages.

Peripheral Production and Activity of Glucocorticoids

Cortisol is produced in peripheral tissues – especially fat and liver - by reduction of inactive cortisone to active cortisol by 11-BHSD-1 (Figure 10). Transgenic overespression of 11ß-HSD1 in mouse adipose tissue induces a phenotype resembling salt-sensitive or angiotensin II–mediated hypertension (Masuzaki H et al., 2001). In contrast, transgenic overexpression of 11ß-HSD1 and subsequent increased local corticosterone production in mouse liver induces fatty liver, dyslipidemia, hypertension, and insulin resistance in the absence of obesity (Paterson et al., 2004). Glucocorticoids stimulate differentiation and proliferation of human adipocytes via their specific glucocorticoid receptor.

We have conducted studies on peripheral cortisol production in IUGR fetal baboon peri-renal fat and liver (Figure 11) (Guo et al., 2013). Increased active cortisol generation by 11β-

HSD1 in peripheral tissues is a method of increasing cortisol production in the body without ACTH stimulation. NADPH provision is essential for 11β-HSD1 reductase activity, which depends on hexose-6-phosphate-dehydrogenase (H6PD). CCAAT enhancer binding proteins (C/EBPs) mediate basal and GC-induced 11β-HSD1 expression. Thus circulating cortisol may not represent the whole picture of cellular cortisol exposure. IUGR baboon maternal and fetal plasma cortisol is increased but additionally there is increased local cortisol production in adipose tissue and liver in IUGR fetuses (Figure 11).

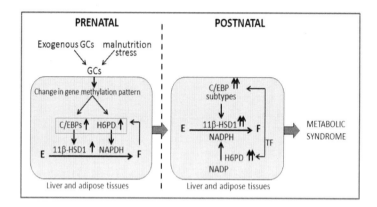

Figure 10. Cartoon of hypothesized 11β-HSD-1 interactions pre and post-natally.

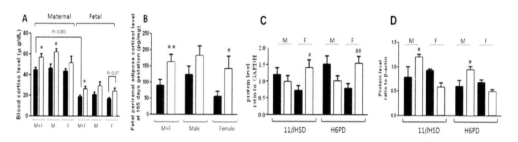

Figure 11. Peripheral cortisol production in IUGR baboon fetuses at 0.9G. Control mothers were fed *ad lib* (solid bars) and IUGR in which baboon mothers eat 70% of global intake of controls (open bars) for *A)* maternal and fetal plasma cortisol; *B)* fetal peri-renal adipose tissue cortisol concentrations; *C)* 11β-HSD-1 and hexose-6-phosphate-dehydrogenase protein in male and female fetal peri-renal fat and *D)* in fetal liver. * p< 0.05, # p<0.03, ## p < 0.01. n=6 for all groups.

We observed interesting fetal sex dependent changes. IUGR increased in 11β-HSD1, H6PD, C/EBPα, β, δ and GR mRNA or protein in female but not male peri-renal adipose tissue, and in male but not female liver at 0.9G. 11β-HSD1 expression correlated positively with C/EBPα, β and δ expression in adipose and liver tissues of both sexes. These findings suggest local glucocorticoid regeneration represents a sexually dimorphic response in a tissue specific manner in IUGR fetuses. In addition, these results are consistent with human clinical investigations of the children of the Dutch Hunger Winter which report increased BMI in women but not men at 50 years of age (Ravelli A et al. 1999).

Fetal Glucocorticoids as Orchestrators of Normal Late Fetal Organ Maturation

As mentioned above, in precocial species fetal adrenal glucocorticoids play a central role in orchestrating maturation of multiple organ systems in preparation for independent post-natal function vital to neonatal survival. There are compelling data for this important function in the fetal lung (Kitterman et al., 1981), thyroid (Thomas et al., 1978), kidney (Franko et al., 2007), heart (Giraud et al., 2006), gut (Moog, 1979), pancreas (Breant et al., 2006) and liver (Franko et al., 2007). One common pathway in the final phases of development of fetal organs is the switch from proliferation to differentiation and maturation. Cortisol plays a central role in this switch.

It is important to first determine the normal trajectory of development and then consider modifications by various challenges faced by the developing organism. In a series of elegant *in vivo* and *in vitro* studies in sheep, Thornburg and colleagues have addressed the complex interactive roles of fetal cortisol and the fetal thyroid in regulating the conflicting processes of proliferation and differentiation in fetal cardiac development. Early in gestation the fetal myocardium consists almost entirely of mononuclear cardiomyocytes that proliferate to produce a heart well endowed with contractile cells and hence contractile ability. Towards the end of gestation, mononuclear cardiomyocytes undergo terminal differentiation into bipolar cardiomyocytesin preparation for postnatal life. To investigate the role of glucocorticoids in regulating fetal heart development these investigators infused cortisol directly into the fetal coronary artery at 0.8 gestation using doses that did not alter fetal blood pressure. There was no effect on cardiomyocyte size or maturational state but cardiomyocyte entry into the cell cycle was stimulated. They concluded that subpressor cortisol doses produce cardiomyocyte proliferation and not hypertrophic growth (Giraud et al., 2006). At first sight these findings suggest that cortisol stimulates proliferation rather than differentiation and that the concept that cortisol is a major factor in regulating terminal organ differentiation does not apply to the heart. However, further studies by these and other investigators showed a central role for an interaction between the fetal thyroid axis and glucocorticoids. Before birth the fetal sheep thyroid axis is functioning at a high level. Indeed fetal plasma thyroxine (T4) levels are in the hyperthyroid range (Thomas et al., 1978).

However, fetal conversion of T4 to the more biologically active tri-iodothyronine (T3) is minimal and most deiodinating activity produces the inactive reverse −T3. Thus the fetus is protected against the physiological effects of a high level of T3 stimulation, which would impair growth (Thomas et al., 1978). There are three major deiodinases types D1, D2 and D3. D1 and D2 convert T4 to T3. In contrast deiodinase D3 inactivates T3 producing rT3 from T4 (Bianco and Kim, 2006). Cortisol Infusion to fetal sheep from 125 to 130 days gestation increased hepatic, renal, and perirenal adipose tissue D1 and reduced renal and placental D3. T3 Infusion increased hepatic D1 and decreased renal D3. Thus in fetal sheep the rise in cortisol at term appears to induce altered deiodinase activity generating T3 for important neonatal functions such as thermoregulation. T3 itself may exert further effects on T4 to T3 deiodination (Forhead et al., 2006).

While the low doses of cortisol delivered locally were not pressor, cortisol levels present at the end of gestation do elevate fetal blood pressure (Unno et al., 1999). It is important to consider effects at various levels of cortisol to which the cardiomyocyte and other cells in the body are exposed at different times in development. T3 *in vitro* inhibits mitosis in cardiomyocytes taken from fetal sheep two thirds of the way through gestation (Chattergoon et al., 2012b) and T3 in late gestation drives maturation of cardiomyocytes (Chattergoon et al., 2012a). Thus the effect of cortisol in driving differentiation and inhibiting proliferation may be secondary to its function in generating T3 from T4 as well as stage of gestation dependent.

These studies on the interaction of the developing thyroid and cortisol were conducted in the sheep, one of the most commonly investigated precocial species. As mentioned above, attention must be paid to differences between precocial and altricial species. Evidence for a role of glucocorticoids in fetal cardiac development also has been obtained in the rat. In this altricial species, cardiomyocytes proliferate after birth and only reach a terminally differentiated state around the time of the rat's neonatal corticosterone rise shown in Figure 6 (Clubb and Bishop, 1984).

The power of mouse models and now in some rat models is their ability to design and conduct studies following knock-out (decreased expression) or knock-in (augmentation of expression) of specific genes. In one recent study in mice the effects of glucocorticoids acting though the glucocorticoid receptor were studied in glucocorticoid receptor knock-out mice (Rog-Zielinska et al., 2013). Generalized edema indicating impaired cardiac function associated with short, disorganized myofibrils and cardiomyocytes was observed at embryonic day 17.5 (e17.5) in glucocorticoid receptor knock-out mice. The fetal cardiomyocytes did not align correctly.

The inability to activate the glucocorticoid receptor resulted in decreased expression of key genes that regulate myocardial contraction. The authors concluded that fetal heart structural, functional and biochemical maturation requires normal cardiomyocyte glucocorticoid signaling.

Interestingly not all features of myocyte development were glucocorticoid receptor dependent. For example atrial naturetic peptide expression was not affected in glucocorticoid receptor knock-out mice. Corticosterone is present in the fetal mouse heart from e15.5 doubling in concentration by e 16.5. GR are expressed in the fetal heart from e10.5. In wild type mice 11β-HSD-1 mRNA increases and 11β-HSD-2 mRNA decreases between e14.5 and e17.5 supporting the view that local production of corticosterone increases in late gestation and is important in cardiac maturation. The glucocorticoid but not mineralocorticoid receptor increases over this critical developmental period as well.

Glucocorticoids as Orchestrators of Developmental Programming Outcomes Following the Challenge of Maternal Nutrient Reduction

A central question in relation to developmental programming is whether there are some factors and metabolic pathways such as increased or decreased micronutrients e.g., vitamins or key amino acids such as the branched chain amino acids – valine, leucine and isoleucine that play a common role in response to different challenges. Our own studies and those of others lead us to support the view that glucocorticoids are common orchestrators of responses to many challenges to the developing organism. Glucocorticoids have fundamental roles in mobilizing metabolic responses that enable survival and thus it is not too surprising that they should be recruited in the body's response to very different challenges if those challenges put survival at risk. Clearly there are other potential mechanisms that may be recruited in several challenges, one being increased oxidative stress (OS). Glucocorticoids are likely involved with responses that modify reactive oxygen species (ROS) production since considerable data exist supporting glucocorticoid effects on production of ROS (McIntosh and Sapolsky, 1996, McIntosh et al., 1998)

Data have been presented above for increased activity of the maternal HPAA resulting from decreased nutrient availability in both a precocial species – the baboon, and an altricial species the rat. Initial interest in developmental programming resulted in large part from publication of human epidemiological studies on the challenge of maternal nutrient reduction that occurred during the Dutch Hunger Winter (Barker, 1998, Nathanielsz, 1999). As a result, the initial studies on mechanisms in rodents were almost exclusively focused on the challenges, mechanism and outcomes of feeding mothers with low protein diets (Armitage et al., 2004, Fernandez-Twinn et al., 2003, Langley-Evans, 2013, Langley-Evans et al., 1996, Ozaki et al., 2001, Shepherd et al., 1997). Maternal nutrient reduction was also the major challenge in the early sheep models (Ozaki, et al., 2000, Vonnahme et al., 2003). In a classic set of rodent studies Langley-Evans and co-workers showed the key role of glucocorticoids of maternal origin on the adverse cardiovascular outcomes in offspring (Langley-Evans and McMullen, 2010, Langley-Evans et al., 1996). In these studies he showed that offspring hypertension resulted from feeding rats a low protein diet and that consequence could be prevented by maternal adrenalectomy. He then demonstrated that low protein diets fed to adrenalectomized mothers given replacement corticoids that returned maternal steroid levels to those reached in mothers on the low protein diet resulted in programming of hypertension in offspring.

Studies on Effects of Maternal Obesity on the HPAA in Pregnant Sheep and their Offspring

In our studies of developmental programming by obesity in sheep pregnancy, control non-pregnant Founder (F0) ewes are fed the normal National Research Council (NRC) recommended requirements before breeding and throughout pregnancy.

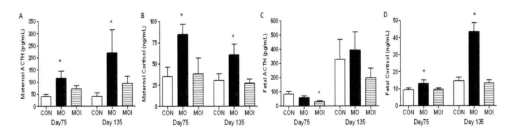

Figure 12. Maternal A) ACTH and B) cortisol, and fetal C) ACTH and D) cortisol at 75 and 135 days gestation (Term 150 days). Control (CON - open) maternal obesity (MO - solid), maternal obesity intervention – see tex - (MOI lines) n=6 M ± SEM * p<0.05 vs. CON.

Obese mothers receive 150% of NRC requirements from 60 days prior to conception. Obese ewes achieve 21% body fat prior to conception compared to 11% body fat in controls. A third group of ewes undergo an intervention (maternal obesity intervention – MOI) in which the obesity protocol is maintained up to 28 days of pregnancy after which mothers are put back on the control regimen. Maternal obesity increases both circulating maternal ACTH and cortisol compared to control fed, non-obese mothers at 75 and 135 days gestation (Term 150 days) (Figure 12).

The MOI Intervention restores the ACTH and cortisol. Interestingly in the fetus, cortisol is only marginally raised at 75 days with no rise in ACTH (Tuersunjiang et al., 2013). This is in keeping with observations that the main activity of the fetal sheep HPAA does not begin until around 120 days gestation (Magyar et al., 1980). Thus at 75 days gestation the maternal:fetal gradient for cortisol is high and most fetal cortisol is likely of maternal origin. At 135 days of gestation cortisol is higher in fetuses of obese than control mothers although the ACTH values are similar in both groups. These findings suggest that peripheral, non-ACTH dependent cortisol generation is occurring in a manner similar to that discussed above in the IUGR baboon fetuses.

The Postnatal Leptin Peak in the Neonatal Lamb: An Example of Glucocorticoid Programming?

In altricial neonatal rodents there is a peak in plasma leptin that occurs over the first two weeks of life and plays a central role in regulating development of the hypothalamic appetite control centers. In offspring of obese mice this peak is augmented and extended over a longer period of time than in controls (Kirk et al., 2009). This alteration in the neonatal leptin profile is both an example of programming in itself and leads to programming of increased appetite and predisposition to obesity in the offspring. It is important to determine whether the timing and effects of maternal obesity on this leptin peak differs in precocial species from the patterns observed in rodents.

There has been much debate as to whether there is a leptin peak in precocial mammals that performs the same programming function in precocial species such as man, nonhuman primates and sheep as in altricial mammals. Using the obesity model described above we determined the effect of maternal obesity on neonatal leptin values (Long et al., 2011). We observed a leptin peak between days 6 and 9 of postnatal life in F1 lambs of F0 control ewes. This peak is a few days earlier in neonatal life than occurs in mice. The peak was totally abolished in lambs of obese ewes. Cortisol is among the factors that control fetal and adult leptin production (Soret et al., 1999). Cortisol was increased on the first day of life in lambs born to obese ewes and correlated with an increase in leptin (Figure 13). These data indicate that cortisol may play a role in disrupting the normal leptin peak in lambs of obese ewes. Offspring of these obese mothers have increased appetite, weight gain and obesity in response to *ad libitum* feeding at nineteen months of age.

Recently we demonstrated that when F1 ewes born to obese F0 mothers are maintained on a normal diet post weaning and through their own pregnancies, their F2 offspring show a very similar flattening of the leptin peak to that seen in the F1 offspring of obese mothers (Figure 13).

Interestingly the F2 granddaughters of the F0 obese mothers show a very similar profile of neonatal cortisol to the F1 offspring of F0 obese mothers. These findings are to our knowledge, the first demonstration of a transgenerational passage of programming of the leptin peak in any species.

The existence of transgenerational passage does not necessarily indicate epigenetic change. An alternative possibility is that F0 maternal obesity could increase cortisol in the F1 fetus thereby resetting its HPAA which then leads to obesity in the F1 lamb. As a result F1 female lambs become obese producing a generationally recurring mechanism. A similar cycle probably occurs in the transgenerational passage of predisposition to gestational diabetes in women who are the offspring of mothers with gestational diabetes. In this instance with hyperglycemia is the active factor in the F0 and F1 mothers responsible for the transgenerational passage of the predisposition. Further studies are needed to show that the effects are due to epigenetic change.

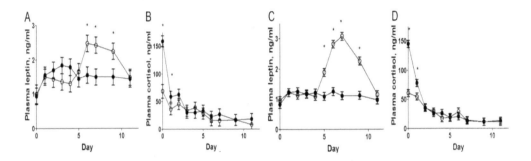

Figure 13. Neonatal plasma leptin A) F1 and C) F2 and cortisol B) F1 and D) F2 lambs. Offspring of obese F0 (full circles) and control F0 ewes (open circles). Mean ±SEM. * p < 0.05 obese vs. control; n= 5-7.

Studies Involving Administration of Synthetic Glucocorticoids to Pregnant Sheep

The potential for developmental programming by fetal exposure to glucocorticoid concentrations in excess of those appropriate for the current stage of maturation exists when women threatening premature labor before 34 weeks of pregnancy are given very high doses of synthetic glucocorticoids (sGC) to accelerate fetal lung maturation thereby increasing survival and decreasing morbidity if the baby delivers early (Howie and Liggins, 1973, Kitterman et al., 1981, Liggins and Howie, 1972). However, although life-saving, 70 percent of pregnancies in which the mother threatens premature labor and receives sGC continue to term and thus, although only revealed by hindsight, 70% of the fetuses are unnecessarily exposed to the inappropriately high level of glucocorticoid. The clinical regimen administers either betamethasone or dexamethasone 12 mg per day for two days. These two sGC's have an activity of about 17 times that of hydrocortisone. Thus 12mg betamethasone or dexamethasone is equivalent to about 40 times the normal daily secretion of glucocorticoid (5mg) – a very large dose. There has never been a clinical trial of a lower dose to test efficacy.

It is now clear that these high doses of glucocorticoid can have potential short and long term effects on the fetus and offspring. Immediate effects include suppression of the fetal HPAA and elevation of fetal blood pressure (Koenen et al., 2002). Long term effects include altered offspring carbohydrate metabolism and programmed effects on HPAA activity due to a resetting of feedback (Braun et al., 2013). These programmed effects are currently being extensively investigated in many laboratories around the world.

The effects of sGC in programming feedback are exerted at many HPA levels and are highly complex as shown by other investigators and ourselves mostly in sheep studies (Braun et al., 2013, Long et al., 2013). Newnham and colleagues treated pregnant ewes with sGC early in the second half of gestation and increased late-gestation ACTH and cortisol in their fetuses (Sloboda et al., 2000). In our recent study pregnant F0 ewes received dexamethasone (4 i.m. doses of 2 mg 12 hourly) or saline (control, C) (Long et al., 2013). This dose is one third the clinical dose. F1 female offspring were bred to produce F2 female offspring. Post-pubertal HPAA function was tested in F1 and F2 ewes. Dexamethasone administration to the F0 mothers increased baseline but reduced stimulated HPAA responses in F1 and F2 female offspring. Thus programming of the fetal HPAA by fetal exposure to high levels of glucocorticoids can be passed transgenerationally (Long et al., 2013).

Conclusion

The perinatal period is a time of major changes in the HPAA. Great plasticity exists in both the response of the developing HPAA to various challenges such as maternal under- or over-nutrition, maternal stress as well as the effects of excess glucocorticoids on multiple developing systems – heart, endocrine system, metabolism and brain. These widespread effects indicate that glucocorticoids are fundamental orchestrators of mechanisms and outcomes that are at the heart of developmental programming.

Acknowledgments

NIH HD P01 21350. R01HD070096. INBRE P20-RR-016474.

References

Albrecht, E.D. & Pepe, G.J. (1990). Placental steroid hormone biosynthesis in primate pregnancy. *Endocr. Rev.*, 11, 124-50.

Antonow-Schlorke, I., Schwab, M., Cox, L.A., Li, C., Stuchlik, K., Witte, O.W., et al. (2011). Vulnerability of the fetal primate brain to moderate reduction in maternal global nutrient availability. *Proc. Natl. Acad. Sci. USA*, 108, 3011-6.

Armitage, J.A., Khan, I.Y., Taylor, P.D., Nathanielsz, P.W. & Poston, L. (2004). Developmental programming of the metabolic syndrome by maternal nutritional imbalance: how strong is the evidence from experimental models in mammals? *J. Physiol.*, 561, 355-77.

Bailey, S.W. & Ayling, J.E. (2009). The extremely slow and variable activity of dihydrofolate reductase in human liver and its implications for high folic acid intake. *Proc. Natl. Acad. Sci. USA*, 106, 15424-9.

Barker, D.J.P. (1998). Mothers, babies and diseases in later life. 2nd edn. Edinburgh: Churchill Livingstone.

Bianco, A.C. & Kim, B.W. (2006). Deiodinases: implications of the local control of thyroid hormone action. *J. Clin. Invest.*, 116, 2571-9.

Braun, T., Challis, J.R., Newnham, J.P. & Sloboda, D.M. (2013). Early-life glucocorticoid exposure: the hypothalamic-pituitary-adrenal axis, placental function, and long-term disease risk. *Endocr. Rev.*, 34, 885-916.

Breant, B., Gesina, E. & Blondeau, B. (2006). Nutrition, glucocorticoids and pancreas development. *Horm. Res.*, 65 Suppl 3, 98-104.

Carr, S.K., Chen, J.H., Cooper, W.N., Constância, M., Yeo, G.S. & Ozanne, S.E. (2014). Maternal diet amplifies the hepatic aging trajectory of Cidea in male mice and leads to the development of fatty liver. *FASEB J.*, 28, 2191-2201.

Challis, J.R., Sloboda, D., Matthews, S.G., Holloway, A., Alfaidy, N., Patel, F.A., et al. (2001). The fetal placental hypothalamic-pituitary-adrenal (HPA) axis, parturition and post natal health. *Mol. Cell Endocrinol.*, 185, 135-44.

Chattergoon, N.N., Giraud, G.D., Louey, S., Stork, P., Fowden, A.L. & Thornburg, K.L. (2012a). Thyroid hormone drives fetal cardiomyocyte maturation. *FASEB J.*, 26, 397-408.

Chattergoon, N.N., Louey, S., Stork, P., Giraud, G.D. & Thornburg, K.L. (2012b). Mid-gestation ovine cardiomyocytes are vulnerable to mitotic suppression by thyroid hormone. *Reprod. Sci.*, 19, 642-9.

Clubb, F.J., Jr. & Bishop, S.P. (1984). Formation of binucleated myocardial cells in the neonatal rat. An index for growth hypertrophy. *Lab. Invest.*, 50, 571-7.

Cox, L.A., Li, C., Glenn, J.P., Lange, K., Spradling, K.D., Nathanielsz, P.W., et al. (2013). Expression of the placental transcriptome in maternal nutrient reduction in baboons is dependent on fetal sex. *J. Nutr.*, 143, 1698-708.

Cox, L.A., Nijland, M.J., Gilbert, J.S., Schlabritz-Loutsevitch, N.E., Hubbard, G.B., McDonald, T.J., et al. (2006). Effect of 30 per cent maternal nutrient restriction from 0.16 to 0.5 gestation on fetal baboon kidney gene expression. *J. Physiol.*, 572, 67-85.

Daniels, V.G., Hardy, R.N. & Malinowska, K.W. (1973). The effect of adrenalectomy or pharmacological inhibition of adrenocortical function on macromolecule uptake by the new-born rat intestine. *J. Physiol.*, 229, 697-707.

Ducsay, C.A., Hess, D.L., McClellan, M.C. & Novy, M.J. (1991). Endocrine and morphological maturation of the fetal and neonatal adrenal cortex in baboons. *J. Clin. Endocrinol. Metab.*, 73, 385-95.

Fall, C.H. (2013). Fetal malnutrition and long-term outcomes. *Nestle Nutr. Inst. Workshop Ser.*, 74, 11-25.

Farber, D.M., Giussani, D.A., Jenkins, S.L., Mecenas, C.A., Winter, J.A., Wentworth, R.A, et al. (1997). Timing of the switch from myometrial contractures to contractions in late-gestation pregnant rhesus monkeys as recorded by myometrial electromyogram during spontaneous term and androstenedione-induced labor. *Biol. Reprod.*, 56, 557-62.

Farley, D., Tejero, M.E., Comuzzie, A.G., Higgins, P.B., Cox, L., Werner, S.L., et al. (2009). Feto-placental adaptations to maternal obesity in the baboon. *Placenta*, 30, 752-60.

Fernandez-Twinn, D.S., Ozanne, S.E., Ekizoglou, S., Doherty, C., James, L., Gusterson, B., et al. (2003). The maternal endocrine environment in the low-protein model of intrauterine growth restriction. *Br. J. Nutr.,* 90, 815-22.

Forhead, A.J., Curtis, K., Kaptein, E., Visser, T.J. & Fowden, A.L. (2006). Developmental control of iodothyronine deiodinases by cortisol in the ovine fetus and placenta near term, *Endocrinology,* 147, 5988-94.

Fowden, A.L., Li, J. & Forhead, A.J. (1998). Glucocorticoids and the preparation for life after birth: are there long-term consequences of the life insurance? *Proc. Nutr. Soc.,* 57, 113-22.

Franko, K.L., Giussani, D.A., Forhead, A.J. & Fowden, A.L. (2007). Effects of dexamethasone on the glucogenic capacity of fetal, pregnant, and non-pregnant adult sheep. *J. Endocrinol.,* 192, 67-73.

Giraud, G.D., Louey, S., Jonker, S., Schultz, J. & Thornburg, K.L. (2006). Cortisol stimulates cell cycle activity in the cardiomyocyte of the sheep fetus. *Endocrinology,* 147, 3643-9.

Guo, C., Li, C., Myatt, L., Nathanielsz, P.W. & Sun, K. (2013). Sexually dimorphic effects of maternal nutrient reduction on expression of genes regulating cortisol metabolism in fetal baboon adipose and liver tissue, *Diabetes,* 62, 1175-85.

Guzman, C., Cabrera, R., Cardenas, M., Larrea, F., Nathanielsz, P.W. & Zambrano, E. (2006). Protein restriction during fetal and neonatal development in the rat alters reproductive function and accelerates reproductive ageing in female progeny. *J. Physiol.,* 572, 97-108.

Hanson, R.W. & Garber, A.J. (1972). Phosphoenolpyruvate carboxykinase. I. Its role in gluconeogenesis. *Am. J. Clin. Nutr.,* 25, 1010-21.

Hanson, R.W. & Reshef, L. (1997). Regulation of phosphoenolpyruvate carboxykinase (GTP) gene expression. *Annu. Rev. Biochem.,* 66, 581-611.

Hardy, R.N., Malinowska, K.W. & Nathanielsz, P.W. (1972). Plasma adrenocortical steroids immediately after birth in the rat, rabbit and guinea-pig. *J. Endocrinol.,* 55, xxxiv.

Henson, M.C., Swan, K.F., Edwards, D.E., Hoyle, G.W., Purcell, J. & Castracane, V.D. (2004). Leptin receptor expression in fetal lung increases in late gestation in the baboon: a model for human pregnancy. *Reproduction,* 127, 87-94.

Howie, R.N. & Liggins, G.C. (1973). Prevention of respiratory distress syndrome in premature infants by antepartum glucocorticoid treatment. *Resp. Distress Synd.,* 369-80.

Kaur, P., Shorey, L.E., Ho, E., Dashwood, R.H. & Williams, D.E., (2013). The epigenome as a potential mediator of cancer and disease prevention in prenatal development. *Nutr. Rev.,* 71, 441-57.

Kirk, S.L., Samuelsson, A.M., Argenton, M., Dhonye, H., Kalamatianos, T., Poston, L., et al. (2009). Maternal obesity induced by diet in rats permanently influences central processes regulating food intake in offspring. *PloS One,* 4, e5870.

Kitterman, J.A., Liggins, G.C., Campos, G.A., Clements, J.A., Forster, C.S., Lee, C.H., et al. (1981). Prepartum maturation of the lung in fetal sheep: relation to cortisol. *J. Appl. Physiol. Respir. Environ. Physiol.,* 51, 384-90.

Koenen, S.V., Mecenas, C.A., Smith, G.S., Jenkins, S. & Nathanielsz, P.W. (2002). Effects of maternal betamethasone administration on fetal and maternal blood pressure and heart rate in the baboon at 0.7 of gestation. *Am. J. Obstet. Gynecol.,* 186, 812-7.

Langley-Evans, S.C. (2013). Fetal programming of CVD and renal disease: animal models and mechanistic considerations. *Proc. Nutr. Soc.,* 72, 317-25.

Langley-Evans, S.C., Gardner, D.S. & Jackson, A.A. (1996). Maternal protein restriction influences the programming of the rat hypothalamic-pituitary-adrenal axis. *J. Nutr.,* 126, 1578-85.

Langley-Evans, S.C. & McMullen, S. (2010). Developmental origins of adult disease. *Med. Princ. Pract.,* 19, 87-98.

Li, C., McDonald, T.J., Wu, G., Nijland, M.J. & Nathanielsz, P.W. (2013a). Intrauterine growth restriction alters term fetal baboon hypothalamic appetitive peptide balance. *J. Endocrinol.,* 217, 275-82.

Li, C., Ramahi, E., Nijland, M.J., Choi, J., Myers, D.A., Nathanielsz, P.W., et al. (2013b). Up-regulation of the fetal baboon hypothalamo-pituitary-adrenal axis in intrauterine growth restriction: coincidence with hypothalamic glucocorticoid receptor insensitivity and leptin receptor down-regulation. *Endocrinology,* 154, 2365-73.

Liggins, G.C. & Howie, R.N. (1972). A controlled trial of antepartum glucocorticoid treatment for prevention of the respiratory distress syndrome in premature infants. *Pediatrics,* 50, 515-25.

Long, N. M., L. A. George, A. B. Uthlaut, D. T. Smith, M. J. Nijland, P. W. Nathanielsz & S. P. Ford. (2010) Maternal obesity and increased nutrient intake before and during gestation in the ewe results in altered growth, adiposity, and glucose tolerance in adult offspring. *Journal of Animal Science* 88, 3546-53.

Long, N.M., Ford, S.P. & Nathanielsz, P.W. (2011). Maternal obesity eliminates the neonatal lamb plasma leptin peak. *J. Physiol.,* 589, 1455-62.

Long, N.M., Ford, S.P. & Nathanielsz, P.W. (2013). Multigenerational effects of fetal dexamethasone exposure on the hypothalamic-pituitary-adrenal axis of first- and second-generation female offspring. *Am. J. Obstet. Gynecol.,* 208, 217.e1-8.

Magyar, D.M., Fridshal, D., Elsner, C.W., Glatz, T., Eliot, J., Klein, A.H., et al. (1980). Time-trend analysis of plasma cortisol concentrations in the fetal sheep in relation to parturition. *Endocrinology,* 107, 155-9.

Malinowska, K.W., Hardy, R.N. & Nathanielsz, P.W. (1972). Plasma adrenocorticosteroid concentrations immediately after birth in the rat, rabbit and guinea-pig. *Experientia,* 28, 1366-7.

Masuzaki, H., Hiroshi Yamamoto, H., Kenyon, J. et al. (2003). Transgenic amplification of glucocorticoid action. in adipose tissue causes high blood pressure in mice. J. Clin. Invest., 112:83–90.

McDonald, T.J. & Nathanielsz, P.W. (1991). Bilateral destruction of the fetal paraventricular nuclei prolongs gestation in sheep. *Am. J. Obstet. Gynecol.,* 165, 764-70.

McIntosh, L.J. & Sapolsky, R.M. (1996). Glucocorticoids increase the accumulation of reactive oxygen species and enhance adriamycin-induced toxicity in neuronal culture. *Exp. Neurol.,* 141, 201-6.

McIntosh, L.J., Hong, K.E. & Sapolsky, R.M. (1998). Glucocorticoids may alter antioxidant enzyme capacity in the brain: baseline studies. *Brain Res.,* 791, 209-14.

McIntosh, M., Bao, H. & Lee, C. (1999). Opposing actions of dehydroepiandrosterone and corticosterone in rats. *Proc. Soc. Exp. Biol. Med.,* 221, 198-206.

Mesiano, S. & Jaffe, R.B. (1997). Developmental and functional biology of the primate fetal adrenal cortex. *Endocr. Rev.,* 18, 378-403.

Moog, F. (1979). The differentiation and redifferentiation of the intestinal epithelium and its brush border membrane. *Ciba Found Symp.,* (70), 31-50.

Morimoto, S., Calzada, L., Sosa, T.C., Reyes-Castro, L.A., Rodriguez-González, G.L., Morales, A., et al. (2012). Emergence of ageing-related changes in insulin secretion by pancreatic islets of male rat offspring of mothers fed a low-protein diet. *Br. J. Nutr.*, 107, 1562-5.

Nathanielsz, P.W. (1999). Life in the womb: The origin of health and disease. Ithaca, NY: Promethean Press.

Nathanielsz, P.W., Ford, S.P., Long, N.M., Vega, C.C., Reyes-Castro, L.A. & Zambrano, E. (2013). Interventions to prevent adverse fetal programming due to maternal obesity during pregnancy. *Nutr. Rev.*, 71 Suppl 1, S78-87.

Nijland, M.J., Mitsuya, K., Li, C., Ford, S., McDonald, T.J., Nathanielsz, P.W. et al. (2010). Epigenetic modification of fetal baboon hepatic phosphoenolpyruvate carboxykinase following exposure to moderately reduced nutrient availability. *J. Physiol.*, 588, 1349-59.

Ozaki, T., Hawkins, P., Nishina, H., Steyn, C., Poston, L. & Hanson, M.A. (2000). Effects of undernutrition in early pregnancy on systemic small artery function in late-gestation fetal sheep. *Am. J. Obstet. Gynecol.*, 183, 1301-7.

Ozaki, T., Nishina, H., Hanson, M.A. & Poston, L. (2001). Dietary restriction in pregnant rats causes gender-related hypertension and vascular dysfunction in offspring. *J. Physiol.*, 530, 141-52.

Paterson, J.M., Morton, N.M., Fievet, C., Kenyon, C.J., Holmes, M.C., Staels, B., et al. (2004). Metabolic syndrome without obesity: Hepatic overexpression of 11beta-hydroxysteroid dehydrogenase type 1 in transgenic mice. *Proc. Natl. Acad. Sci. USA*, 101, 7088-93.

Pepe, G.J., Ballard, P.L. & Albrecht, E.D. (2003). Fetal lung maturation in estrogen-deprived baboons. *J. Clin. Endocrinol. Metab.*, 88, 471-7.

Poore, K.R., Young, I.R., Canny, B.J. & Thorburn, G.D. (1998). Studies on the role of ACTH in the regulation of adrenal responsiveness and the timing of parturition in the ovine fetus. *J. Endocrinol.*, 158, 161-71.

Ravelli AC, van Der Meulen JH, Osmond C, Barker DJ, Bleker OP. (1999) Obesity at the age of 50 y in men and women exposed to famine prenatally. *Am J Clin Nutr* 70:811–816

Rog-Zielinska, E.A., Thomson, A., Kenyon, C.J., Brownstein, D.G., Moran, C.M., Szumska, D., et al. (2013). Glucocorticoid receptor is required for foetal heart maturation. *Hum. Mol. Genet.*, 22, 3269-82.

Schlabritz-Loutsevitch, N., Ballesteros, B., Dudley, C., Jenkins, S., Hubbard, G., Burton, G.J., et al. (2007). Moderate maternal nutrient restriction, but not glucocorticoid administration, leads to placental morphological changes in the baboon (Papio sp.). *Placenta*, 28, 783-93.

Schlabritz-Loutsevitch, N.E., Howell, K., Rice, K., Glover, E.J., Nevill, C.H., Jenkins, S.L., et al. (2004). Development of a system for individual feeding of baboons maintained in an outdoor group social environment. *J. Med. Primatol.*, 33, 117-26.

Serón-Ferré, M. & Jaffe, R.B. (1981). The fetal adrenal gland. *Annu. Rev. Physiol.*, 43, 141-62.

Shepherd, P.R., Crowther, N.J., Desai, M., Hales, C.N. & Ozanne, S.E. (1997). Altered adipocyte properties in the offspring of protein malnourished rats. *Br. J. Nutr.*, 78, 121-9.

Sloboda, D.M., Newnham, J.P. & Challis, J.R. (2000). Effects of repeated maternal betamethasone administration on growth and hypothalamic-pituitary-adrenal function of the ovine fetus at term. *J. Endocrinol.*, 165, 79-91.

Soret, B., Lee, H.J., Finley, E., Lee, S.C. & Vernon, R.G. (1999). Regulation of differentiation of sheep subcutaneous and abdominal preadipocytes in culture. *J. Endocrinol.,* 161, 517-24.

Thomas, A.L., Krane, E.J. & Nathanielsz, P.W. (1978). Changes in the fetal thyroid axis after induction of premature parturition by low dose continuous intravascular cortisol infusion to the fetal sheep at 130 days of gestation. *Endocrinology,* 103, 17-23.

Tuersunjiang, N., Odhiambo, J. F., Long, N. M., Shasa, D. R., Nathanielsz, P. W., & Ford, S. P. (2013). Diet reduction to requirements in obese/overfed ewes from early gestation prevents glucose/insulin dysregulation and returns fetal adiposity and organ development to control levels. *American Journal of Physiology-Endocrinology and Metabolism,* *305*(7), E868-E878.

Unno, N., Wong, C.H., Jenkins, S.L., Wentworth, R.A., Ding, X.Y., Li, C., et al. (1999). Blood pressure and heart rate in the ovine fetus: ontogenic changes and effects of fetal adrenalectomy. *Am. J. Physiol.,* 276, H248-56.

Vonnahme, K.A., Hess, B.W., Hansen, T.R., McCormick, R.J., Rule, D.C., Moss, G.E., et al. (2003). Maternal undernutrition from early- to mid-gestation leads to growth retardation, cardiac ventricular hypertrophy, and increased liver weight in the fetal sheep. *Biol. Reprod.,* 69, 133-40.

Wilson, L., Jr., Parsons, M.T. & Flouret, G. (1991). Forward shift in the initiation of the nocturnal estradiol surge in the pregnant baboon: is this the genesis of labor? *Am. J. Obstet. Gynecol.,* 165, 1487-98.

Xie, L., Antonow-Schlorke, I., Schwab, M., McDonald, T.J., Nathanielsz, P.W. & Li, C. (2013). The frontal cortex IGF system is down regulated in the term, intrauterine growth restricted fetal baboon. *Growth Horm. IGF Res.,* 23, 187-92.

Xiong, F. & Zhang, L., (2013). Role of the hypothalamic-pituitary-adrenal axis in developmental programming of health and disease. *Front Neuroendocrinol.,* 34, 27-46.

Zambrano, E. & Nathanielsz, P.W. (2013). Mechanisms by which maternal obesity programs offspring for obesity: evidence from animal studies. *Nutr. Rev.,* 71 Suppl 1, S42-54.

In: Stress and Developmental Programming ...
Editors: Lubo Zhang and Lawrence D. Longo

ISBN: 978-1-63321-836-9
© 2014 Nova Science Publishers, Inc.

Chapter 12

Early Life Stress and Predisposition to Cardiovascular Disease

D. A. Giussani[1], and M. A. Hanson[2]*

[1]Department of Physiology, Development and Neuroscience,
University of Cambridge, Cambridge, UK
[2]Human Development and Health, Institute of Developmental Sciences,
Faculty of Medicine, University of Southampton, and National Institute of Health
Research Nutrition Biomedical Research Centre, University Hospital Southampton, UK

Abstract

Cardiovascular disease (CVD) is a major health concern globally, as it is the greatest cause of death, produces substantial long-term morbidity and brings enormous humanitarian and economic cost. No longer thought to result from a combination of genetic predisposition and an unhealthy adult lifestyle, CVD prevalence is rising rapidly in developing societies. Recent research has revealed how CVD risk can be set in early life, particularly as a result of an unbalanced maternal diet, materno-fetal exposure to excess glucocorticoids or reduced oxygenation, risks that are amplified across the lifecourse in terms of reduced compensatory responses to later challenges. Developmental challenges, transduced by the mother and the placenta, can be viewed as stressors of the developing offspring's physiological phenotype, even though they may operate within the normal range of the developmental environment. Such stressors induce integrated responses which modulate the offspring's cardiovascular phenotype to maximise potential later fitness but can increase CVD risk, especially with unhealthy lifestyle and ageing. More severe challenges disrupt development. We discuss the processes underlying the adaptive responses, with particular emphasis on the interaction between blood flow and tissue and organ growth, and the role of reactive oxygen species in mediating these effects. At the molecular level, epigenetic processes by which environmental stressors can affect gene expression and alter offspring phenotype without changing the fixed genetic sequence, are thought to underlie the adaptive processes.

---

* Corresponding Author: Dino A. Giussani, Department of Physiology, Development and Neuroscience, University of Cambridge, E-ail: dag26@cam.ac.uk

These new insights hold promise for the early detection of individuals and groups at greater risk of later CVD and for devising and monitoring early life interventions to reduce this risk.

Keywords: Cardiovascular disease, epigenetic, glucocorticoids, maternal diet, hypoxia, reactive oxygen species, stress

Introduction

Cardiovascular disease is the greatest killer in the world today, imposing a staggering burden on every nation's health and wealth (World Health Organization, 2012). Worldwide, 1 in 3 people die of heart disease per year. Furthermore, the economic costs are tremendous in terms of treatment, family income and workforce productivity, amounting to over £30 billion in the United Kingdom (European Heart Network, 2012) and well over $US 100 billion in the United States per year (Heidenreich et al., 2011). Therefore, to ameliorate the increasing clinical, social and economic burden of treating cardiovascular disease once established, there is an urgent need to understand the science behind its earliest origin to give possible insight into preventative therapy.

Traditionally, it was widely believed that individual variations in genetic makeup interact with adult lifestyle risk factors, such as smoking, obesity and lack of exercise to determine the risk of cardiovascular disease (Agarwal et al., 2005). Only comparatively recently, has it also become widely established that gene-environment interactions during early life may be just as, if not more important in predisposing to later cardiovascular dysfunction (Barker, 1994, Gluckman et al., 2008). Different types of environmental stressors during early life may induce pathological changes in important organs and systems, such as in the heart and the circulation that persist until, or are amplified, in later life, expressing themselves as dysfunction in adulthood. Alternatively, early life environmental stressors may alter adaptive responses to later challenges such as an unhealthy lifestyle, making physiological changes maladaptive, and this can progress to overt cardiovascular disease. It is also clear that exposure to stress during different critical time windows of development, including the pre-conceptional, peri-conceptional, embryonic, fetal and neonatal periods can increase the risk of later cardiovascular dysfunction, that the magnitude and duration of the developmental stress can modify the time of onset and severity of later cardiovascular disease, that developmental stress can affect later cardiovascular function in men and women differentially, and that phenotypes with an increased risk of cardiovascular disease can be intergenerational, being passed on from parent to offspring. Therefore, there is no question regarding the importance and far-reaching implications that the early environment has in shaping our cardiovascular health and that of our children and their offspring. Likewise, it is now becoming obvious that the opportunity for correction of a change in the developmental trajectory moulding our cardiovascular health diminishes drastically from early life to adulthood. Hence, the concept of developmental origins of disease creates an exciting opportunity to halt the development of heart disease at its very origin, through preventative medicine in the womb and even prior to conception, or by instituting interventions post-natally following a pregnancy which conveyed high risk to the offspring in order to diminish and control the progression of disease. The mechanisms underlying developmental origins of cardiovascular dysfunction following development complicated by stress are beginning to emerge, making potential clinical therapy with rational interventional strategies a realistic possibility in the near future.

Stress in Early Life and Risk of Cardiovascular Disease in Later Life: Evidence from Human and Animal Studies

The concept of developmental origins of cardiovascular disease is supported by overwhelming evidence derived from human studies now dating back nearly four decades and encompassing six continents; evidence that strongly links development under sub-optimal environmental conditions with alterations in fetal and/or postnatal growth and increased rates of coronary heart disease and the metabolic syndrome in adulthood (Barker et al., 1989, Fall et al., 1998, Forsdahl, 1977, Forsén et al., 1999, Gennser et al., 1988, Huang et al., 2012, Leon et al., 1998, Levitt and Lambert, 2002, Li et al., 2010, Rich-Edwards et al., 1976, Roseboom et al., 1999, Silva et al., 2012). Early evidence that linked phenotypic changes mediated by developmental plasticity with chronic cardiovascular disease in humans in the UK and the US stemmed from the association between coronary heart disease, type 2 diabetes, or hypertension in adult life and low birth weight (Barker et al., 1989, Rich-Edwards et al., 1976). Similar evidence has since been obtained in Sweden (Leon et al., 1998), Finland (Forsén et al., 1999), India (Fall et al., 1998), Australia (Huang et al., 2012), Africa (Levitt and Lambert, 2002), China (Li et al., 2010) and Latin America (Silva et al., 2012). Epidemiological and clinical studies have also related different types of suboptimal early environmental conditions not only with alterations in growth but also with physiological dysfunction in later life. For instance, there have been studies of human development affected by maternal psychological stress or by exposure to stress hormones during pregnancy or of human populations or cohorts undergoing substantial nutritional challenges (Dalziel et al., 2005, Eskenazi et al., 2007, Roseboom et al., 1999, 2011). Roseboom and colleagues (Roseboom et al., 1999) reported findings from a large cohort of middle-aged men and women, born as term singletons around the time of the Dutch famine between 1944 and 1945. These data not only revealed an association between maternal under-nutrition and adult-onset cardiovascular disease in the offspring, but the results showed that the prevalence of coronary heart disease was best related to exposure to famine in early gestation while impaired glucose tolerance was related to exposure to famine in late gestation (Roseboom et al., 2011). Furthermore, impaired maternal diet during pregnancy could predispose men but not women to later hypertension (van Abeelen et al., 2011) and offspring of prenatally undernourished fathers but not mothers during the Dutch famine were heavier and more obese than offspring of parents who had not been undernourished prenatally (Veenendaal et al., 2013). Therefore, the Dutch famine cohort provide an example of data derived from human studies linking nutritional stress during early life with later cardiovascular dysfunction in the offspring, with time of onset, sexually dimorphic as well as intergenerational effects.

Complementing the human data, a large number of investigations in experimental animal models provide robust evidence linking different types of stress in early life with increased risk of cardiovascular disease in adulthood. These data from animal models emphasise similar considerations to the human data: they reveal effects of timing, magnitude and duration of the stress, varying outcomes in male and female offspring and transmission of phenotypic traits between generations. Several groups have reported that fetal exposure to under- or over-nutrition, or to inappropriate concentrations of glucocorticoids can all predispose the offspring to alterations in cardiac structure and function, to endothelial dysfunction in peripheral resistance circulations and to hypertension in adult life (for reviews, see Braun et al., 2013, Cripps et al., 2007, Desai et al., 2013, Galjaard et al., 2013, Gluckman et al., 2005, McMillen and Robinson, 2005, Seckl and Meany, 2004). For example, Seckl and colleagues (Seckl, 2001) and Langley-Evans and colleagues (Langley-Evans, 1997) have used maternal treatment with carbenoxolone to inhibit placental inactivation of maternal glucocorticoids, allowing passage to the fetal circulation in rats. Invariably, such experiments have produced IUGR, hypertension and cardiovascular dysfunction in adult offspring. Pregnancies affected by maternal stress lead to preterm onset of labour (Hoffman and Hatch, 1996). Both exposure to maternal stress and prematurity have been linked with increased susceptibility of cardiovascular disease in later life (Roggero et al., 2013). We and others have also shown that exposure to synthetic steroids in early life promotes endothelial dysfunction and cardiac remodelling with associated dysfunction in later life (Adler et al., 2010, Bal et al., 2008, Herrera et al., 2010, Niu et al., 2013). These effects are of additional clinical importance because pregnancies threatened with preterm labour and/or premature infants are routinely treated with synthetic glucocorticoids to accelerate fetal lung maturation and prevent the development of chronic lung disease (Crowley, 2006, Halliday et al., 2010, Liggins and Howie, 1972).

In addition to alterations in maternal nutrition and maternal stress hormones, fetal hypoxia is one of, if not the most common consequence of complicated pregnancy (Hutter et al., 2010). Further, over 140 million people live at altitudes higher than 2500 m where the lower oxygen availability has been shown to reduce fetal growth and birth weight (Giussani et al., 2001, Moore et al., 2011), thereby comprising the largest single human group at risk for fetal growth restriction and/or early origins of cardiovascular disease. A cluster of research groups have employed the chick embryo as a model to isolate the effects of chronic hypoxia on fetal growth and the developing cardiovascular system independent of effects on the maternal and placental physiology. In the chick, chronic hypoxia promotes fetal growth restriction, cardiac and aortic hypertrophic growth, altered cardiac function, and sympathetic hyper-innervation of peripheral resistance arteries by the end of the incubation period (Giussani et al., 2007, Lindgren and Altimiras, 2009, 2011, Rouwet et al., 2002, Ruijtenbeek et al., 2003a, Salinas et al., 2010, Sharma et al., 2006, Tintu et al., 2007, 2009, Villamor et al., 2004). The growth restriction and cardiac and aortic wall remodelling that develops in sea level chick embryos incubated at high altitude no longer occurs in sea level embryos incubated at high altitude with oxygen supplementation (Giussani et al., 2007, Salinas et al., 2010), underlying the direct but not necessarily linked effects of isolated chronic hypoxia on fetal growth and cardiovascular development. Growth restriction, aortic wall thickening, cardiac and vascular dysfunction have also been reported in the chronically hypoxic fetus of mammalian species, such as in sheep, rodents and guinea pigs (Alonso et al., 1989, Browne et al., 1997a, 1997b, Camm et al., 2010, Gilbert, 1998, Gilbert et al., 2003, Hemmings et al., 2005, Herrera et al., 2012a, Jacobs et al., 1988, Kamitomo et al., 1992, 1994, 2002, Kim et al., 2005, Onishi et al., 2004, Thompson, 2003, Thompson et al., 1999, 2000, 2011, Williams et al., 2005a, 2005b). Fetal aortic wall thickening is particularly relevant in the clinical setting, as increased large artery stiffness predicts cardiovascular risk in humans (McEniery and Wilkinson, 2005), being a key component in the development of hypertension, atherosclerosis and coronary heart disease (Arnett et al., 1994). Four separate human clinical studies (Akira and Yoshiyuki, 2006, Cosmi et al., 2009, Koklu et al., 2006, Skilton et al., 2005) have now reported that babies born from pregnancies complicated by placental insufficiency show aortic thickening with increased vascular stiffness and reduced distensibility. Additional reported abnormalities in cardiovascular morphology and function of the human IUGR fetus include an increase in relative heart weight and ventricular wall hypertrophy, a decrease in ventricle and myocyte volume, and compromised biventricular ejection force and diastolic filling (Mayhew et al., 1999, Miyague et al., 1997, Rizzo et al., 1995, Veille et al., 1993). A more recent clinical study reported that 3 to 6 year old children born IUGR had more globular hearts, reduced longitudinal motion, and impaired relaxation with an increase in radial function. They also had increased blood pressure and carotid intima-media thickness (Crispi et al., 2012). Several studies in rats have also reported cardiac dysfunction and an increased susceptibility to an episode of ischaemia and reperfusion (I/R) injury in hearts isolated from adult offspring of hypoxic pregnancy (Hauton, 2012, Hauton and Ousley, 2009, Li et al., 2003, 2004, Patterson and Zhang, 2010, Patterson et al., 2010, 2012, Rueda-Clausen et al., 2009, 2011, 2012, Xu et al., 2006, Xue and Zhang, 2009, Xue et al., 2011). Davidge and colleagues reported that adult offspring of hypoxic pregnancy have several cardiac structural and functional changes including *in vivo* evidence of elevated left ventricular end diastolic pressure (LVEDP) (Rueda-Clausen et al., 2009). Giussani and colleagues (Giussani et al., 2012) reported reciprocal changes in β_1-adrenergic and muscarinic receptor responsiveness in hearts from rat adult offspring of hypoxic pregnancy. Both effects are of further clinical relevance, as elevated LVEDP is associated with increased mortality (Salem et al., 2006), and sustained increases in myocardial contractility due to heightened sympathetic excitation and diminished parasympathetic reactivity have been strongly associated with cardiovascular disease, being an unsustainable condition and leading to eventual heart failure in humans (Bristow, 2002, Danson et al., 2009). A number of studies by various groups in different species have also now reported that developmental hypoxia can predispose to endothelial dysfunction in later life. Ruijtenbeek et al. (Ruijtenbeek et al., 2003b) first reported that isolated femoral arteries of adult chickens following hypoxic incubation were more sensitive to electrical stimulation and pharmacological stimulation of peri-arterial sympathetic nerves, while showing reduced NO-dependent vasorelaxation. The developmental induction of NO-dependent endothelial dysfunction in peripheral resistance circulations has now been confirmed in adult offspring of mammalian species by the groups of Davidge and Giussani (Giussani et al., 2012, Williams et al., 2005b). Interestingly, two reports have shown a significant inverse relationship between low birth weight and endothelial dysfunction in children in the first decade of life and in early adulthood (Leeson et al., 1997, 2001).

Exposure to synthetic glucocorticoids in early life in animal models could be used as an example to highlight differential effects of timing of the stress during development in predisposing to later cardiovascular disease. A remarkable finding was that treatment of pregnant sheep with dexamethasone for only two days, at the end of the first month of pregnancy but not at the end of the second month of pregnancy, produced hypertension in lambs at 19 months of age (Dodic et al., 1998). Langley Evans and colleagues reported that in rats the hypertensive effect in the offspring at weaning of a maternal low-protein diet was unaffected if the period of undernutrition occurred during the first, middle or last third of pregnancy. However, the blood pressure increases elicited by these discrete periods of maternal under-nutrition were all lower than those induced by feeding a low-protein diet to the dams throughout pregnancy (Langley-Evans et al., 1996). Furthermore, when feeding pregnant dams diets containing a range of protein levels at the same stage of gestation, an inverse relationship between maternal protein intake and the degree of hypertension in the offspring was reported (Langley and Jackson, 1994). Combined, these studies provide experimental evidence to complement the human data reflecting how changes in the duration and the magnitude of the stress period during development can alter the cardiovascular phenotype of the adult offspring.

There is a growing body of evidence indicating sex differences in the developmental programming of cardiovascular dysfunction by stressful conditions in early life, with the weight of the evidence supporting protection or altered strategies in female offspring. Most of the experimental evidence complementing data derived from human studies comes from models of maternal alterations in nutrition, or of maternal stress or of exposure of the pregnancy to excessive glucocorticoid concentrations (see Aiken and Ozanne, 2013, Gilbert and Nijland, 2008). However, a few studies have also reported sexually dimorphic effects of prenatal hypoxia on cardiovascular dysfunction in the adult offspring, with effects being diminished in female relative to male offspring (Morton et al., 2010, Rueda-Clausen et al., 2009, Xue and Zhang, 2009).

Emerging evidence in rodents and in sheep also indicates that the environment during development can induce non-genomically phentotypic changes across generations. Studies in animal models have focussed on the intergenerational transmission by maternal behaviour, by altered nutrition or by excess glucocorticoid exposure (Aiken and Ozanne, 2014, Crudo et al., 2012, Drake et al., 2005, Francis et al., 1999, Harrison and Langley-Evans, 2009, Iqbal et al., 2012, Long et al., 2012, Torrens et al., 2008, Zambrano et al., 2005). For instance, Torrens et al. (Torrens et al., 2008) and Harrison & Langley-Evans (Harrison and Langley-Evans, 2009) reported on the intergenerational transmission of impaired nephrogenesis, peripheral vascular endothelial dysfunction and hypertension in rats following maternal protein restriction during pregnancy. There have also been reports of heritable impaired glucose tolerance in offspring across several generations in rodent models of maternal exposure during pregnancy to a high-fat diet, to undernutrition or to excess glucocorticoids (Drake et al., 2005, Dunn and Bale, 2009, Jimenez-Chillaron et al., 2009).

Stress in Early Life and Risk of Cardiovascular Disease in Later Life: Underlying Mechanisms and Potential Interventions

Altered regional blood flow to the fetus One of the earliest mechanisms proposed to increase risk of disease in later life relates to permanent changes in the structure and thereby function of important organs. For example, if the period of stress occurs in late gestation, when defence mechanisms in the fetus have had a chance to mature, there are physiological adaptive responses which may improve viability in the short term but they may claim costs in later life. For instance, the late gestation fetal circulatory defence to hypoxic stress involves dilatation of essential vascular beds and constriction of peripheral circulations (Cohn et al.,

1974, Giussani et al., 1993). Therefore, the fetal cardiac output is redistributed away from less essential vascular beds to maintain oxygen and nutrient delivery to the brain - the so-called brain sparing effect (Giussani and Davidge, 2013, Rudolph et al., 1981). The physiology underlying this response is well delineated. The fetal peripheral vasoconstriction is triggered exclusively by a carotid body chemoreflex (Giussani et al., 1993) and maintained by the release of hormones, such as catecholamines, into the fetal circulation (Jones and Robinson, 1975). More recently, we have discovered that the neuroendocrine peripheral constrictor response is further fine-tuned by a vascular oxidant tone. This is created by the interaction between vascular $\cdot O_2^-$ and NO during hypoxia, whereby a fall in the ratio favours dilatation and an increase enhances constriction (Herrera et al., 2012b, Kane et al., 2012, Morrison et al., 2003, Thakor et al., 2010a, 2010b). In response to chronic hypoxic stress in the fetus, the maintained redistribution of blood flow away from peripheral circulations may become problematic, triggering a number of biological trade-offs in the fetus and increasing the risk of morbidity in later life. The most described adverse side effect is asymmetric intrauterine growth restriction (IUGR), yielding offspring whose brain growth is spared, but having bodies which are thin for their length with a low ponderal index (Barker, 1994). Such infants show a greater impact of hypoxia on body growth relative to brain growth, usually represented in neonatology by an increase in the ratio of the bi-parietal diameter to the body length (Barker, 1994). In response to fetal hypoxic stress, improved shunting of blood flow through the *ductus venosus* into the inferior vena cava further improves preferential blood flow to the brain at the expense of oxygen and nutrient delivery to the liver, impairing its growth (Ebbing et al., 2009, Godfrey et al., 2012). Persistent redistribution of blood flow away from peripheral beds may also explain the reduced growth of the fetal kidneys and of the pancreas, and the impaired endowment of nephrons and of beta cells in the Islets of Langerhans, respectively, in infants born from chronically stressed pregnancies (Barker and Hanson, 2004, Duque-Guimarães and Ozanne, 2013, Fowden and Hill, 2001, Latini et al., 2004, Mackenzie and Brenner, 1995). In turn, a reduced nephron number at birth will limit glomerular filtration and promote excess extracellular sodium retention throughout the life course, providing a mechanistic link between stress in early life, asymmetric IUGR and risk of risk of hypertension in later life (Mackenzie and Brenner, 1995). Similarly, a reduced number of pancreatic beta cells and impaired insulin secretion at birth has been associated with compensatory increases in insulin sensitivity in target tissues, such as in skeletal muscle and fat, in the young offspring of compromised pregnancy (Duque-Guimarães and Ozanne, 2013, Fowden and Hill, 2001). Increased glucose uptake promotes fat deposition, particularly if the postnatal nutrient availability is better than predicted *in utero*. In turn, adipogenesis via the increased secretion of adipokines favours insulin resistance, glucose intolerance and type II diabetes, again, providing a mechanistic link between stress in early life, the thin-for-length infant phenotype and an increased risk of developing the metabolic syndrome in later life (Duque-Guimarães and Ozanne, 2013, Fowden and Hill, 2001, Phillips et al., 1994). In addition, sustained increases in fetal peripheral vascular resistance will increase fetal arterial blood pressure if cardiac output is maintained. A sustained increase in fetal cardiac afterload will overwhelm the Frank-Starling mechanism, triggering compensatory changes in the morphology and function of the fetal heart. In turn, remodelling of the walls of the fetal aorta may occur in response to the greater pressure generated by the fetal heart (Akira and Yoshiyuki, 2006, Cosmi et al., 2009, Gilbert, 1998, Herrera et al., 2012a, Koklu et al., 2006, Skilton et al., 2005). This may, once more, provide a mechanistic link between stress in early life, asymmetric IUGR and cardiac and aortic wall hypertrophy; first order indices of an increased cardiovascular risk in later life.

Oxidative stress The idea that common pathways might mediate responses to suboptimal environments during early life has regained support recently as the phenotypic outcomes of various environmental stressors during development are so similar. Converging lines of evidence suggest that oxidative stress in early life might be one such common link (Davidge et al., 2008, Giussani et al., 2012, Nuyt, 2008, Patterson et al., 2012, Simmons, 2012, Thompson and Al-Hasan, 2012). Various groups have reported that common adverse intrauterine conditions, including under-nutrition, over-nutrition, excess glucocorticoid exposure, infection and hypoxia all lead to increased markers of oxidative stress in the fetal cardiovascular system (Davidge et al., 2008, Giussani et al., 2012, Nuyt, 2008, Patterson et al., 2012, Simmons, 2012, Thompson and Al-Hasan, 2012). Similarly, there are several reports of increased placental and fetal oxidative stress in pregnancies complicated by IUGR and/or pre-eclampsia (Biri et al., 2007, Burton et al., 2009, Karabulut et al., 2005, Negi et al., 2012). Giussani et al. (Giussani et al., 2012) tested the hypothesis that oxidative stress in the fetal cardiovascular system links chronic fetal hypoxia with cardiovascular dysfunction in later life, by an interventional study using antioxidants. They reported that chronic fetal hypoxia promoted fetal aortic wall thickening and molecular markers of oxidative stress in the fetal heart and vasculature by the end of gestation. By adulthood, these effects resolved but chronic fetal hypoxia set a dysfunctional phenotype in both the heart and the peripheral circulation. Maternal treatment with vitamin C during pregnancy prevented the adverse effects in fetal offspring and reversed the enhanced myocardial contractility due to sympathetic dominance and the NO-dependent endothelial dysfunction in peripheral resistance vessels in adult offspring (Giussani et al., 2012). Thompson and colleagues have also reported that treatment with *N*-acetyl cysteine of pregnant guinea pigs inhibited the adverse effects on the fetal liver of chronic prenatal hypoxia (Thompson and Al-Hasan, 2012). To better mimic the clinical situation and treat IUGR offspring of hypoxic pregnancy following diagnosis, the Davidge and Dyck laboratories used the natural polyphenolic antioxidant resveratrol. Their studies demonstrated that early postnatal administration of resveratrol in the diet of weanling rats born IUGR from hypoxic pregnancy and fed an obesogenic diet also prevented features of cardiovascular dysfunction and of the metabolic syndrome in later life (Dolinsky et al., 2011, Rueda-Clausen et al., 2012). In a series of studies, we have now also reported that treatment of neonatal rat pups with glucocorticoids, modelling steroid therapy for the treatment of chronic lung disease in premature infants, also induces oxidative stress and alterations in structure and function of the cardiovascular system of the offspring (Adler et al., 2010, Herrera et al., 2010, Niu et al., 2013). Excess glucocorticoid exposure promotes oxidative stress with consequent decreases in NO bioavailability via several pathways (Iuchi et al., 2003, Wallwork et al., 2003, Zhang et al., 2004). Consequently, combined neonatal glucocorticoid with either antioxidant vitamins or with statins restored NO bioavailability, improved postnatal survival, protected the developing brain and prevented overt cardiac dysfunction at adulthood (Adler et al., 2010, Herrera et al., 2010, Niu et al., 2013, Tijsseling et al., 2013). Such data have raised the question of whether it is finally time to review current perinatal clinical practice and fine-tune it to maintain beneficial effects on the developing lung but to diminish adverse side-effects of synthetic steroid therapy on the developing brain and heart in perinatal medicine (Bonanno and Wapner, 2012, Nijland, 2003, Wapner and Jobe, 2011). Combined neonatal glucocorticoid and antioxidant therapy may provide one such effective strategy and be a safer clinical intervention in the treatment of the premature infant. The groups of Torrens, Hanson and Clough have further reported that in mice and in rats either maternal intake of a low protein diet or of fat during pregnancy could perturb redox status, impair endothelial NO-mediated vasorelaxation in peripheral circulations and induce hypertension in the adult offspring (Rodford et al., 2008, Torrens et al., 2012). Furthermore, statin administration to the dams during pregnancy or to the offspring after weaning could protect against the adult onset cardiovascular dysfunction triggered by either suboptimal environment during early life (Elahi et al., 2013, Torrens et al., 2009). Combined, therefore, there is mounting evidence to support oxidative stress being a mechanistic link between various stressors in early life with increased risk of cardiovascular disease in later life.

Epigenetics Recent advances in the field of epigenetics are beginning to explore the mechanistic link between stress in early life with cardiovascular disease in later life, and have also refuelled the once popular heretical idea that ancestral environment could affect the physiology of future generations. During development, epigenetic processes can alter gene expression without a change in DNA sequence through several processes including DNA methylation and/or histone modification and/or changes to small non coding RNAs. In a study series in rats, Zhang and colleagues linked the reduced expression of the cardio-protective gene protein kinase C epsilon (PKCε) with increased cardiac susceptibility to ischaemic/reperfusion (I/R) injury in adult offspring (Li et al., 2003, 2004, Patterson and Zhang, 2010, Patterson et al., 2010, 2012, Xue and Zhang, 2009, Xue et al., 2011). Not only was the expression of PKCε reduced in hearts of offspring of hypoxic pregnancy, but treatment of hearts from adult offspring of normoxic pregnancy with a PKCε translocation inhibitor mimicked the defects in hearts of offspring from hypoxic pregnancy (Li et al., 2003, 2004, Patterson and Zhang, 2010, Patterson et al., 2010, 2012, Xue and Zhang, 2009, Xue et al., 2011). The mechanism via which hypoxic pregnancy caused heightened offspring cardiac susceptibility to I/R injury was shown to be epigenetic, as they also reported both an increase in the promoter methylation and the reduced expression of the PKCε gene in fetal pup hearts of hypoxic pregnancy, and the prevention of both effects by treatment with a DNA methylation inhibitor (Li et al., 2003, 2004, Patterson and Zhang, 2010, Patterson et al., 2010, 2012, Xue and Zhang, 2009, Xue et al., 2011). Patterson et al. (Patterson et al., 2012) confirmed a role for prenatal hypoxia-derived oxidative stress in programming cardiac dysfunction in adulthood and expanded this idea by linking it to epigenetic mechanisms, reporting that maternal treatment in rats with the antioxidant *N*-acetyl-cysteine inhibited the hypoxia-induced increase in methylation of the SP1-binding sites, reversed the decreased SP1 binding to the PKCε promoter, restored PKCε mRNA and protein abundance and abrogated the hypoxia-induced increase in susceptibility of the heart to I/R injury in adult offspring. Recently, they have further shown that noradrenaline causes the epigenetic repression of the PKCε gene in rodent hearts by activating Nox1-dependent ROS generation (Xiong et al., 2012). Developmental hypoxia may therefore increase the risk of a sympathetically dominant cardiac phenotype by catecholamine-induced ROS, which in turn causes the epigenetic repression of cardiac PKCε, thereby enhancing cardiac susceptibility to I/R injury in adult offspring.

Accordingly, treatment with the selective PKCε activator peptide ψ-εRACK of fetal hearts isolated from hypoxic pregnancy markedly improved their recovery from an I/R challenge (Patterson et al., 2010).

Epigenetic pathways may also represent the molecular substrate for the influence of the early environment in the regulation of vascular function (Fish et al., 2010, Krause et al., 2013, Yan et al., 2010). For example, epigenetic mechanisms have been reported to play a key role in the control of vasodilatation by altering the expression of key genes involved in endothelial-dependent relaxation, such as *NOS3* and *ARG2* (Yan et al., 2010). Using human umbilical vein endothelial cells (HUVEC), Marsden and colleagues have reported that hypoxia causes a rapid decrease in the transcription of the eNOS/*NOS3* gene, accompanied by decreased acetylation and lysine 4 (histone H3) methylation of eNOS proximal promoter histones (Fish et al., 2010). Recently, Casanello and colleagues have also reported the epigenetically regulated expression of eNOS and arginase-2 in HUVEC derived from IUGR pregnancies. They also reported that the altered eNOS expression in IUGR-derived endothelial cells could be reversed by transient silencing of the DNA methylation machinery (Krause et al., 2013).

Therefore, accumulating evidence of the epigenetic regulation of key genes, important in the control of cardiac and vascular function, is beginning to provide another mechanistic link between stress in early life and increased cardiovascular risk in later life, identifying other possible avenues of potential clinical therapy.

It is clear that the three examples described above of underlying mechanisms linking stress in early life with risk of cardiovascular disease in later life do not constitute an exhaustive list; accelerated cellular ageing and more rapid telomere shortening comprising another possibility (Martin-Gronert and Ozanne, 2012). It is also clear that a number of these mechanisms are likely to be inter-linked. For instance, environmental stressors in early life may promote oxidative stress. Higher levels of ROS are not only associated with telomere shortening but with epigenetic repression of key genes involved in cardiovascular function, such as *NOS3* (Fish et al., 2010, Krause et al., 2013, Martin-Gronert and Ozanne, 2012). Reduced expression of eNOS and consequent impaired NO bioavailability may tip the vascular oxidant tone towards sustained constriction in peripheral vascular beds, thereby altering regional blood flow. Sustained redistribution of the fetal cardiac output favours the thin-for-length baby phenotype with increased cardiac afterload, altered autonomic control of the cardiovascular system, decreased nephron number and reduced pancreatic β-cell endowment, all of which increase cardiovascular risk in later life.

Stress in Early Life and Risk of Cardiovascular Disease in Later Life: Bench to Hospital Bedside and Health Policy

The challenge posed by cardiovascular disease is on a global scale and necessitates a lifecourse strategy as part of NCD prevention (WHO Global Action Plan for the Prevention and Control of Non-communicable Diseases 2013-20). It is now widely recognised that interventions to reduce risk need to commence in early life. This requires action to promote health literacy and healthy lifestyle in young people if they are to become healthy adults. In addition this may reduce the transmission of risk to subsequent generations. Whilst cardiovascular disease constitutes a major medical problem, the solution will involve broader social interventions and, whilst culturally specific, need to engage the widest range of the population possible.

A large body of research, in animal models, human cohorts and clinical settings, has identified processes by which the developmental environment induces changes in the developing phenotype of the offspring. Environmental challenges may disrupt development altogether if severe. Of more relevance to the lifecourse aetiology of CVD, however, are the range of stressors which alter CV development within the normal range. The responses to a variety of stressors, e.g. unbalanced materno-fetal nutrition or oxygenation may operate via similar effect pathways, e.g. involving oxidative stress, glucocorticoids, the sympathetic nervous system etc., to induce stereotypical adaptive responses. These may induce pathological changes in important organs and systems that persist until, or are amplified, in later life. Alternatively, they may affect the ability of an individual to respond to later stresses to the CV system, especially those associated with aspects of lifestyle such as diet, physical activity and psychological stress. The degree of response to such stressors sets the trajectory of the individual's increasing risk of CVD over time.

The developmental processes influenced by environment operate at several levels. By affecting organ and tissue perfusion, they influence growth and subsequent functional capacity. At the tissue level, many of these processes involve changes in the balance of pro- and anti-oxidant systems which are also intimately involved in growth and a range of signalling and response pathways. At the molecular level, the processes may involve epigenetic processes which can affect the developing phenotype through altering gene expression without fixed genetic changes. There is accumulating data that such effects can be passed across generations to influence the inheritance of CVD risk.

Increasing knowledge of the mechanistic pathways underlying the developmental origins of later CV risk is leading to the discovery of biomarkers which may be measured in early life to give a prediction of later risk. In addition, the knowledge of underlying processes, for example those involving oxidative stress, is likely to lead to novel preventative strategies. There is encouraging evidence in this respect from the use of anti-oxidant therapy in animal models.

Acknowledgments

DG is Professor of Cardiovascular Physiology & Medicine at the Department of Physiology Development & Neuroscience at the University of Cambridge, Professorial Fellow and Director of Studies in Medicine at Gonville & Caius College, a Lister Institute Fellow and a Royal Society Wolfson Research Merit Award Holder. He is supported by the British Heart Foundation, The Biotechnology and Biological Sciences Research Council and the Isaac Newton Trust. MAH is British Heart Foundation Professor of Cardiovascular Science, Director of the Academic Unit of Human Development and Health and the Institute of Developmental Sciences at the University of Southampton UK.

Statement of Interest: None.

References

Adler, A., Camm, E.J., Hansell, J.A., Richter, H.G. & Giussani, D.A. (2010). Investigation of the use of antioxidants to diminish the adverse effects of postnatal glucocorticoid treatment on mortality and cardiac development. *Neonatology*, 98, 73-83.

Agarwal, A., Williams, G.H. & Fisher, N.D. (2005). Genetics of human hypertension. *Trends Endocrinol. Metab.*, 16, 127-33.

Aiken, C.E. & Ozanne, S.E. (2013). Sex differences in developmental programming models. *Reproduction*, 145, R1-13.

Aiken, C.E. & Ozanne, S.E. (2014). Transgenerational developmental programming. *Hum Reprod. Update*, 20, 63-75.

Akira, M. & Yoshiyuki, S. (2006). Placental circulation, fetal growth, and stiffness of the abdominal aorta in newborn infants. *J. Pediatr.*, 148, 49-53.

Alonso, J.G., Okai, T., Longo, L.D. & Gilbert, R.D. (1989). Cardiac function during long-term hypoxemia in fetal sheep. *Am J Physiol*, 257, H581-9.

Arnett, D.K., Evans, G.W. & Riley, W.A. (1994). Arterial stiffness: a new cardiovascular risk factor? *Am J Epidemiol*, 140, 669-82.

Bal, M.P., de Vries, W.B., van Oosterhout, M.F., Baan, J., van der Wall, E.E., van Bel, F., et al. (2008). Long-term cardiovascular effects of neonatal dexamethasone treatment: hemodynamic follow-up by left ventricular pressure-volume loops in rats. *J. Appl. Physiol.*, 104, 446-50.

Barker, D.J. & Hanson, M.A. (2004). Altered regional blood flow in the fetus: the origins of cardiovascular disease? *Acta Paediatr.*, 93, 1559-60.

Barker, D.J.P. (1994). Mothers, babies and disease in later life. London: BMJ Publishing Group.

Barker, D.J.P., Osmond, C., Winter, P.D., Margetts, B. & Simmonds, S.J. (1989). Weight in infancy and death from ischaemic heart disease. *Lancet*, 2, 577–80.

Biri, A., Bozkurt, N., Turp, A., Kavutcu, M., Himmetoglu, O. & Durak, I. (2007). Role of oxidative stress in intrauterine growth restriction. *Gynecol. Obstet. Invest*, 64, 187-92.

Bonanno, C. & Wapner, R.J. (2012). Antenatal corticosteroids in the management of preterm birth: are we back where we started? *Obstet. Gynecol. Clin. North Am.*, 39, 47-63.

Braun, T., Challis, J.R., Newnham, J.P. & Sloboda, D.M. (2013). Early-life glucocorticoid exposure: The hypothalamic-pituitary-adrenal axis, placental function and long-term disease risk. *Endocr. Rev.*, 34, 885-916.

Bristow, M.R. (2002). Beta-adrenergic receptor blockade in chronic heart failure. *Circulation*, 101, 558-69.

Browne, V.A., Stiffel, V.M., Pearce, W.J., Longo, L.D. & Gilbert, R.D. (1997a). Activator calcium and myocardial contractility in fetal sheep exposed to long-term high-altitude hypoxia. *Am. J. Physiol.*, 272, H1196-204.

Browne, V.A., Stiffel, V.M., Pearce, W.J., Longo, L.D. & Gilbert, R.D. (1997b). Cardiac beta-adrenergic receptor function in fetal sheep exposed to long-term high-altitude hypoxemia. *Am. J. Physiol.*, 273, R2022-31.

Burton, G.J., Yung, H.W., Cindrova-Davies, T. & Charnock-Jones, D.S. (2009). Placental endoplasmic reticulum stress and oxidative stress in the pathophysiology of unexplained intrauterine growth restriction and early onset preeclampsia. *Placenta*, 30 Suppl A, S43-8.

Camm, E.J., Hansell, J.A., Kane, A.D., Herrera, E.A., Lewis, C., Wong, S., et al. (2010). Partial contributions of developmental hypoxia and undernutrition to prenatal alterations in somatic growth and cardiovascular structure and function. *Am. J. Obstet. Gynecol.*, 203, 495.e24-34.

Cohn, H.E., Sacks, E.J., Heymann, M.A. & Rudolph, A.M. (1974). Cardiovascular responses to hypoxemia and acidemia in fetal lambs. *Am. J. Obstet. Gynecol.*, 120, 817-24.

Cosmi, E., Visentin, S., Fanelli, T., Mautone, A.J. & Zanardo, V. (2009). Aortic intima media thickness in fetuses and children with intrauterine growth restriction. *Obstet. Gynecol.*, 114, 1109-14.

Cripps, R.L., Archer, Z.A., Mercer, J.G. & Ozanne, S.E. (2007). Early life programming of energy balance. *Biochem. Soc. Trans*, 35, 1203-4.

Crispi, F., Figueras, F., Cruz-Lemini, M., Bartrons, J., Bijnens, B. & Gratacos, E. (2012). Cardiovascular programming in children born small for gestational age and relationship with prenatal signs of severity. *Am. J. Obstet. Gynecol.*, 207, 121.e1-9.

Crowley P. (2000). Prophylactic corticosteroids for preterm birth. *Cochrane Database Syst. Rev.*, (2), CD000065. Review. Update in: *Cochrane Database Syst. Rev.*, 2006;(3):CD000065.

Crudo, A., Petropoulos, S., Moisiadis, V.G., Iqbal, M., Kostaki, A., Machnes, Z., et al. (2012). Prenatal synthetic glucocorticoid treatment changes DNA methylation states in male organ systems: multigenerational effects. *Endocrinology*, 153, 3269-83.

Dalziel, S.R., Walker, N.K., Parag, V., Mantell, C., Rea, H.H., Rodgers, A., et al. (2005). Cardiovascular risk factors after exposure to antenatal betamethasone: 30-year follow-up of a randomised controlled trial. *Lancet*, 365, 1856-62.

Danson, E.J., Li, D., Wang, L., Dawson, T.A. & Paterson, D.J. (2009). Targeting cardiac sympatho-vagal imbalance using gene transfer of nitric oxide synthase. *J. Mol. Cel. Cardiol.*, 46, 482-9.

Davidge, S.T., Morton, J.S. & Rueda-Clausen, C.F. (2008). Oxygen and perinatal origins of adulthood diseases: is oxidative stress the unifying element? *Hypertension*, 52, 808-10.

Desai, M., Beall, M. & Ross, M.G. (2013). Developmental origins of obesity: programmed adipogenesis. *Curr. Diab. Rep.*, 13, 27-33.

Dodic, M., May, C.N., Wintour, E.M. & Coghlan, J.P. (1998). An early prenatal exposure to excess glucocorticoid leads to hypertensive offspring in sheep. *Clin. Sci. (Lond)*, 94, 149-55.

Dolinsky, V.W., Rueda-Clausen, C.F., Morton, J.S., Davidge, S.T. & Dyck, J.R. (2011). Continued postnatal administration of resveratrol prevents diet-induced metabolic syndrome in offspring born growth restricted. *Diabetes*, 60, 2274-84.

Drake, A.J., Walker, B.R. & Seckl, J.R. (2005). Intergenerational consequences of fetal programming by in utero exposure to glucocorticoids in rats. *Am. J. Physiol. Regul. Integr. Comp. Physiol.*, 288, R34-8.

Dunn, G.A. & Bale, T.L. (2009). Maternal high-fat diet promotes body length increases and insulin insensitivity in second-generation mice. *Endocrinology*, 150, 4999-5009.

Duque-Guimarães, D.E. & Ozanne, S.E. (2013). Nutritional programming of insulin resistance: causes and consequences. *Trends Endocrinol. Metab.*, 24, 525-35.

Ebbing, C., Rasmussen, S., Godfrey, K.M., Hanson, M.A. & Kiserud, T. (2009). Redistribution pattern of fetal liver circulation in intrauterine growth restriction. *Acta Obstet Gynecol Scand*, 88, 1118-23.

Elahi, M.M., Cagampang, F.R., Ohri, S.K. & Hanson, M.A. (2013). Long-term statin administration to dams on high-fat diet protects not only them but also their offspring from cardiovascular risk. *Ann. Nutr. Metab.*, 62, 250-6.

Eskenazi, B., Marks, A.R., Catalano, R., Bruckner, T. & Toniolo, P.G. (2007). Low birth weight in New York City and upstate New York following the events of September 11th. *Hum. Reprod.*, 22, 3013-20.

European Cardiovascular Disease Statistics (2012). European Heart Network and European Society of Cardiology, September 2012. ISBN 978-2-9537898-1-2.

Fall, C.H., Stein, C.E., Kumaran, K., Cox, V., Osmond, C., Barker, D.J., et al. (1998). Size at birth, maternal weight, and Type 2 diabetes in South India. *Diabet Med.*, 15, 220–7.

Fish, J.E., Yan, M.S., Matouk, C.C., St Bernard, R., Ho, J.J., Gavryushova, A., et al. (2010). Hypoxic repression of endothelial nitric-oxide synthase transcription is coupled with eviction of promoter histones. *J. Biol. Chem.*, 285, 810-26.

Forsdahl, A. (1977). Are poor living conditions in childhood and adolescence an important risk factor for arteriosclerotic heart disease? *Br. J. Prev. Soc. Med.*, 31, 91-5.

Forsén, T., Eriksson, J.G., Tuomilehto, J., Osmond, C. & Barker, D.J. (1999). Growth in utero and during childhood among women who develop coronary heart disease: longitudinal study. *BMJ*, 319, 1403-7.

Fowden, A.L. & Hill, D.J. (2001). Intra-uterine programming of the endocrine pancreas. *Br Med Bull*, 60, 123-42.

Francis, D., Diorio, J., Liu, D. & Meaney, M.J. (1999). Nongenomic transmission across generations of maternal behavior and stress responses in the rat. *Science,* 286, 1155-8.

Galjaard, S., Devlieger, R. & Van Assche, F.A. (2013). Fetal growth and developmental programming. *J. Perinat. Med.*, 41, 101-5.

Gennser, G., Rymark, P. & Isberg, P.E. (1988). Low birth weight and risk of high blood pressure in adulthood. *BMJ*, 296, 1498-500.

Gilbert, J.S. & Nijland, M.J. (2008). Sex differences in the developmental origins of hypertension and cardiorenal disease. *Am. J. Physiol. Regul. Integr. Comp. Physiol.*, 295, R1941-52.

Gilbert, R.D. (1998). Fetal myocardial responses to long-term hypoxemia. *Comp Biochem Physiol. A Mol. Integr. Physiol.*, 119, 669-74.

Gilbert, R.D., Pearce, W.J. & Longo, L.D. (2003). Fetal cardiac and cerebrovascular acclimatization responses to high altitude, long-term hypoxia. *High Alt Med. Biol.*, 4, 203-13.

Giussani, D.A., Camm, E.J., Niu, Y., Richter, H.G., Blanco, C.E., Gottschalk, R., et al. (2012). Developmental programming of cardiovascular dysfunction by prenatal hypoxia and oxidative stress. *PLoS One*, 7, e31017.

Giussani, D.A. & Davidge, S.T. (2013). Developmental programming of cardiovascular disease by prenatal hypoxia. *J. Dev. Orig. Health Dis.*, 4, 328–37.

Giussani, D.A., Phillips, P.S., Anstee, S. & Barker, D.J. (2001). Effects of altitude versus economic status on birth weight and body shape at birth. *Pediatr. Res.*, 49, 490-4.

Giussani, D.A., Salinas, C.E., Villena, M. & Blanco, C.E. (2007) The role of oxygen in prenatal growth: studies in the chick embryo. *J. Physiol.*, 585, 911-7.

Giussani, D.A., Spencer, J.A., Moore, P.J., Bennet, L. & Hanson, M.A. (1993). Afferent and efferent components of the cardiovascular reflex responses to acute hypoxia in term fetal sheep. *J. Physiol.*, 461, 431-49.

Gluckman, P.D., Cutfield, W., Hofman, P. & Hanson, M.A. (2005). The fetal, neonatal, and infant environments-the long-term consequences for disease risk. *Early Hum. Dev.*, 81, 51-9.

Gluckman, P.D., Hanson, M.A., Cooper, C. & Thornburg, K.L. (2008). Effect of in utero and early-life conditions on adult health and disease. *N. Engl. J. Med.*, 359, 61-73.

Godfrey, K.M., Haugen, G., Kiserud, T., Inskip, H.M., Cooper, C., Harvey, N.C., et al. (2012). Fetal liver blood flow distribution: role in human developmental strategy to prioritize fat deposition versus brain development. *PLoS One*, 7, e41759.

Halliday, H.L., Ehrenkranz, R.A. & Doyle, L.W. (2010). Early (< 8 days) postnatal corticosteroids for preventing chronic lung disease in preterm infants. *Cochrane Database Syst. Rev.*, (1), CD001146.

Harrison, M. & Langley-Evans, S.C. (2009). Intergenerational programming of impaired nephrogenesis and hypertension in rats following maternal protein restriction during pregnancy. *Br. J. Nutr.*, 101, 1020-30.

Hauton, D. (2012). Hypoxia in early pregnancy induces cardiac dysfunction in adult offspring of Rattus norvegicus, a non-hypoxia-adapted species. *Comp. Biochem. Physiol. A Mol. Integr. Physiol.*, 163, 278-85.

Hauton, D. & Ousley, V. (2009). Prenatal hypoxia induces increased cardiac contractility on a background of decreased capillary density. *BMC Cardiovasc Disord,*, 9, 1.

Heidenreich, P.A., Trogdon, J.G., Khavjou, O.A., Butler, J., Dracup, K., Ezekowitz, M.D., et al. (2011). Forecasting the future of cardiovascular disease in the United States: a policy statement from the American Heart Association. *Circulation*, 123, 933-44.

Hemmings, D.G., Williams, S.J. & Davidge, S.T. (2005). Increased myogenic tone in 7-month-old adult male but not female offspring from rat dams exposed to hypoxia during pregnancy. *Am. J. Physiol. Heart Circ Physiol.*, 289, H674-82.

Herrera, E.A., Camm, E.J., Cross, C.M., Mullender, J.L., Wooding, F.B. & Giussani, D.A. (2012a). Morphological and functional alterations in the aorta of the chronically hypoxic fetal rat. *J. Vasc. Res.*, 49, 50-8.

Herrera, E.A., Kane, A.D., Hansell, J.A., Thakor, A.S., Allison, B.J., Niu, Y., et al. (2012b). A role for xanthine oxidase in the control of fetal cardiovascular function in late gestation sheep. *J. Physiol.*, 590, 1825-37.

Herrera, E.A., Verkerk, M.M., Derks, J.B. & Giussani, D.A. (2010). Antioxidant treatment alters peripheral vascular dysfunction induced by postnatal glucocorticoid therapy in rats. *PLoS One*, 5, e9250.

Hoffman, S. & Hatch, M.C. (1996). Stress, social support and pregnancy outcome: a reassessment based on recent research. *Paediatr. Perinat. Epidemiol.*, 10, 380–405.

Huang, R.C., Mori, T.A. & Beilin, L.J. (2012). Early life programming of cardiometabolic disease in the Western Australian pregnancy cohort (Raine) study. *Clin. Exp. Pharmacol. Physiol.*, 39, 973-8.

Hutter, D., Kingdom, J. & Jaeggi, E. (2010). Causes and mechanisms of intrauterine hypoxia and its impact on the fetal cardiovascular system: a review. *Int. J. Pediatr.*, 2010, 401323.

Iqbal, M., Moisiadis, V.G., Kostaki, A. & Matthews, S.G. (2012). Transgenerational effects of prenatal synthetic glucocorticoids on hypothalamic-pituitary-adrenal function. *Endocrinology,* 153, 3295-307.

Iuchi, T., Akaike, M., Mitsui, T., Ohshima, Y., Shintani, Y., Azuma, H., et al. (2003). Glucocorticoid excess induces superoxide production in vascular endothelial cells and elicits vascular endothelial dysfunction. *Circ. Res.,* 92, 81-7.

Jacobs, R., Robinson, J.S., Owens, J.A., Falconer, J. & Webster, M.E. (1988). The effect of prolonged hypobaric hypoxia on growth of fetal sheep. *J. Dev. Physiol.,* 10, 97-112.

Jimenez-Chillaron, J.C., Isganaitis, E., Charalambous, M., Gesta, S., Pentinat-Pelegrin, T., Faucette, R.R., et al. (2009). Intergenerational transmission of glucose intolerance and obesity by in utero undernutrition in mice. *Diabetes,* 58, 460-8.

Jones, C.T. & Robinson, R.O. (1975). Plasma catecholamines in foetal and adult sheep. *J. Physiol.,* 248, 15-33.

Kamitomo, M., Longo, L.D. & Gilbert, R.D. (1992). Right and left ventricular function in fetal sheep exposed to long-term high-altitude hypoxemia. *Am. J. Physiol.,* 262, H399-405.

Kamitomo, M., Longo, L.D. & Gilbert, R.D. (1994). Cardiac function in fetal sheep during two weeks of hypoxemia. *Am. J. Physiol.,* 266, R1778-85.

Kamitomo, M., Onishi, J., Gutierrez, I., Stiffel, V.M. & Gilbert, R.D. (2002). Effects of long-term hypoxia and development on cardiac contractile proteins in fetal and adult sheep. *J. Soc. Gynecol. Investig.,* 9, 335-41.

Kane, A.D., Herrera, E.A., Hansell, J.A. & Giussani, D.A. (2012). Statin treatment depresses the fetal defence to acute hypoxia via increasing nitric oxide bioavailability. *J. Physiol.,* 590, 323-34.

Karabulut, A.B., Kafkasli, A., Burak, F. & Gozukara, E.M. (2005). Maternal and fetal plasma adenosine deaminase, xanthine oxidase and malondialdehyde levels in pre-eclampsia. *Cell Biochem. Funct.,* 23, 279-83.

Kim, Y.H., Veille, J.C., Cho, M.K., Kang, M.S., Kim, C.H., Song, T.B., et al. (2005). Chronic hypoxia alters vasoconstrictive responses of femoral artery in the fetal sheep. *J. Korean Med. Sci.,* 20, 13-9.

Koklu, E., Kurtoglu, S., Akcakus, M., Koklu, S., Buyukkayhan, D., Gumus, H., et al. (2006). Increased aortic intima-media thickness is related to lipid profile in newborns with intrauterine growth restriction. *Horm. Res.,* 65, 269-75.

Krause, B.J., Costello, P.M., Muñoz-Urrutia, E., Lillycrop, K.A., Hanson, M.A. & Casanello, P. (2013). Role of DNA methyltransferase 1 on the altered eNOS expression in human umbilical endothelium from intrauterine growth restricted fetuses. *Epigenetics,* 8, 944-52.

Langley, S.C. & Jackson, A.A. (1994). Increased systolic blood pressure in adult rats induced by fetal exposure to maternal low protein diets. *Clin. Sci. (Lond),* 86, 217-22.

Langley-Evans, S.C. (1997). Intrauterine programming of hypertension by glucocorticoids. *Life Sci.,* 60, 1213-21.

Langley-Evans, S.C., Welham, S.J., Sherman, R.C. & Jackson, A.A. (1996). Weanling rats exposed to maternal low-protein diets during discrete periods of gestation exhibit differing severity of hypertension. *Clin. Sci. (Lond),* 91, 607-15.

Latini, G., De Mitri, B., Del Vecchio, A., Chitano, G., De Felice, C. & Zetterström, R. (2004). Foetal growth of kidneys, liver and spleen in intrauterine growth restriction: "programming" causing "metabolic syndrome" in adult age. *Acta Paediatr.,* 93, 1635-9.

Leeson, C.P., Kattenhorn, M., Morley, R., Lucas, A. & Deanfield, J.E. (2001). Impact of low birth weight and cardiovascular risk factors on endothelial function in early adult life. *Circulation,* 103, 1264-8.

Leeson, C.P., Whincup, P.H., Cook, D.G., Donald, A.E., Papacosta, O., Lucas, A., et al. (1997). Flow-mediated dilation in 9- to 11-year-old children: the influence of intrauterine and childhood factors. *Circulation,* 96, 2233-8.

Leon, D.A., Lithell, H.O., Vagero, D., Koupilova, I., Mohsen, R., Berglund, L., et al. (1998). Reduced fetal growth rate and increased risk of death from ischaemic heart disease: cohort study of 15000 Swedish men and women born 1915–29. *BMJ,* 317, 241–5.

Levitt, N.S. & Lambert, E.V. (2002). The foetal origins of the metabolic syndrome - a South African perspective. *Cardiovasc. J. S Afr.,* 13, 179-80.

Li, G., Bae, S. & Zhang, L. (2004). Effect of prenatal hypoxia on heat stress-mediated cardioprotection in adult rat heart. *Am. J. Physiol. Heart Circ. Physiol.,* 286, H1712-9.

Li, G., Xiao, Y., Estrella, J.L., Ducsay, C.A., Gilbert, R.D. & Zhang, L. (2003). Effect of fetal hypoxia on heart susceptibility to ischemia and reperfusion injury in the adult rat. *J. Soc. Gynecol. Investig.,* 10, 265-74.

Li, Y., He, Y., Qi, L., Jaddoe, V.W., Feskens, E.J., Yang, X., et al. (2010). Exposure to the Chinese famine in early life and the risk of hyperglycemia and type 2 diabetes in adulthood. *Diabetes,* 59, 2400-6.

Liggins, G.C. & Howie, R.N. (1972). A controlled trial of antepartum glucocorticoid treatment for prevention of the respiratory distress syndrome in premature infants. *Pediatrics,* 50, 515-25.

Lindgren, I. & Altimiras, J. (2009). Chronic prenatal hypoxia sensitizes beta-adrenoceptors in the embryonic heart but causes postnatal desensitization. *Am. J. Physiol. Regul. Integr. Comp. Physiol.,* 297, R258-64.

Lindgren, I. & Altimiras, J. (2011). Sensitivity of organ growth to chronically low oxygen levels during incubation in Red Junglefowl and domesticated chicken breeds. *Poult. Sci.,* 90, 126-35.

Long, N.M., Shasa, D.R., Ford, S.P. & Nathanielsz, P.W. (2012). Growth and insulin dynamics in two generations of female offspring of mothers receiving a single course of synthetic glucocorticoids. *Am. J. Obstet. Gynecol.,* 207, 203.e1-8.

Mackenzie, H.S. & Brenner, B.M. (1995). Fewer nephrons at birth: a missing link in the etiology of essential hypertension? *Am. J. Kidney Dis.,* 26, 91-8.

Martin-Gronert, M.S. & Ozanne, S.E. (2012). Mechanisms underlying the developmental origins of disease. *Rev. Endocr. Metab. Disord.,* 13, 85-92.

Mayhew, T.M., Gregson, C. & Fagan, D.G. (1999). Ventricular myocardium in control and growth-retarded human fetuses: growth in different tissue compartments and variation with fetal weight, gestational age, and ventricle size. *Hum. Pathol.,* 30, 655-60.

McEniery, C.M. & Wilkinson, I.B. (2005). Large artery stiffness and inflammation. *J. Hum. Hypertens,* 19, 507-9.

McMillen, I.C. & Robinson, J.S. (2005). Developmental origins of the metabolic syndrome: prediction, plasticity, and programming. *Physiol. Rev.,* 85, 571-633.

Miyague, N.I., Ghidini, A., Fromberg, R. & Miyague, L.L. (1997). Alterations in ventricular filling in small-for-gestational-age fetuses. *Fetal Diagn. Ther.,* 12, 332-5.

Moore, L.G., Charles, S.M. & Julian, C.G. (2011). Humans at high altitude: hypoxia and fetal growth. *Respir. Physiol. Neurobiol.,* 178, 181-90.

Morrison, S., Gardner, D.S., Fletcher, A.J., Bloomfield, M.R. & Giussani, D.A. (2003). Enhanced nitric oxide activity offsets peripheral vasoconstriction during acute hypoxaemia via chemoreflex and adrenomedullary actions in the sheep fetus. *J. Physiol.,* 547, 283-91.

Morton, J.S., Rueda-Clausen, C.F. & Davidge, S.T. (2010). Mechanisms of endothelium-dependent vasodilation in male and female, young and aged offspring born growth restricted. *Am. J. Physiol. Regul. Integr. Comp. Physiol.,* 298, R930-8.

Negi, R., Pande, D., Kumar, A., Khanna, R.S. & Khanna, H.D. (2012). In vivo oxidative DNA damage and lipid peroxidation as a biomarker of oxidative stress in preterm low-birthweight infants. *J. Trop. Pediatr.,* 58, 326-8.

Nijland, M.J. (2003). Fetal exposure to corticosteroids: how low can we go? *J. Physiol.,* 549, 1.

Niu, Y., Herrera, E.A., Evans, R.D. & Giussani, D.A. (2013). Antioxidant treatment improves neonatal survival and prevents impaired cardiac function at adulthood following neonatal glucocorticoid therapy. *J. Physiol.,* 591, 5083-93.

Nuyt, A.M. (2008). Mechanisms underlying developmental programming of elevated blood pressure and vascular dysfunction: evidence from human studies and experimental animal models. *Clin. Sci. (Lond),* 114, 1-17.

Onishi, J., Browne, V.A., Kono, S., Stiffel, V.M. & Gilbert, R.D. (2004). Effects of long-term high-altitude hypoxia and troponin I phosphorylation on cardiac myofilament calcium responses in fetal and nonpregnant sheep. *J. Soc. Gynecol. Investig.,* 11, 1-8.

Patterson, A.J., Chen, M., Xue, Q., Xiao, D. & Zhang, L. (2010). Chronic prenatal hypoxia induces epigenetic programming of PKC{epsilon} gene repression in rat hearts. *Circ. Res.,* 107, 365-73.

Patterson, A.J., Xiao, D., Xiong, F., Dixon, B. & Zhang, L. (2012). Hypoxia-derived oxidative stress mediates epigenetic repression of PKCε gene in foetal rat hearts. *Cardiovasc. Res.,* 93, 302-10.

Patterson, A.J. & Zhang, L. (2010). Hypoxia and fetal heart development. *Curr. Mol. Med.,* 10, 653-66.

Phillips, D.I., Barker, D.J., Hales, C.N., Hirst, S. & Osmond, C. (1994). Thinness at birth and insulin resistance in adult life. *Diabetologia,* 37, 150-4.

Rich-Edwards, J.W., Stampfer, M.J., Manson, J.E., Rosner, B., Hankinson, S.E., Colditz, G.A., et al. (1997). Birth weight and risk of cardiovascular disease in a cohort of women followed up since 1976. *BMJ,* 315, 396–400.

Rizzo, G., Capponi, A., Rinaldo, D., Arduini, D. & Romanini, C. (1995). Ventricular ejection force in growth-retarded fetuses. *Ultrasound. Obstet. Gynecol.,* 5, 247-55.

Rodford, J.L., Torrens, C., Siow, R.C., Mann, G.E., Hanson, M.A. & Clough, G.F. (2008). Endothelial dysfunction and reduced antioxidant protection in an animal model of the developmental origins of cardiovascular disease. *J. Physiol.,* 586, 4709-20.

Roggero, P., Giannì, M.L., Garbarino, F. & Mosca, F. (2013). Consequences of prematurity on adult morbidities. *Eur. J. Intern. Med.,* 24, 624-6.

Roseboom, T.J., Painter, R.C., van Abeelen, A.F., Veenendaal, M.V. & de Rooij, S.R. (2011). Hungry in the womb: what are the consequences? Lessons from the Dutch famine. *Maturitas,* 70, 141-5.

Roseboom, T.J., van der Meulen, J.H., Ravelli, A.C., van Montfrans, G.A., Osmond, C., Barker, D.J., et al. (1999). Blood pressure in adults after prenatal exposure to famine. *J. Hypertens.*, 17, 325-30.

Rouwet, E.V., Tintu, A.N., Schellings, M.W., van Bilsen, M., Lutgens, E., Hofstra, L., et al. (2002). Hypoxia induces aortic hypertrophic growth, left ventricular dysfunction, and sympathetic hyperinnervation of peripheral arteries in the chick embryo. *Circulation,* 105, 2791-6.

Rudolph, A.M., Itskovitz, J., Iwamoto, H., Reuss, M.L. & Heymann, M.A. (1981). Fetal cardiovascular responses to stress. *Semin. Perinatol.*, 5, 109-21.

Rueda-Clausen, C.F., Morton, J.S. & Davidge, S.T. (2009). Effects of hypoxia-induced intrauterine growth restriction on cardiopulmonary structure and function during adulthood. *Cardiovasc. Res.*, 81, 713-22.

Rueda-Clausen, C.F., Morton, J.S., Dolinsky, V.W., Dyck, J.R. & Davidge, S.T. (2012). Synergistic effects of prenatal hypoxia and postnatal high-fat diet in the development of cardiovascular pathology in young rats. *Am. J. Physiol. Regul. Integr. Comp. Physiol.*, 303, R418-26.

Rueda-Clausen, C.F., Morton, J.S., Lopaschuk, G.D. & Davidge, S.T. (2011). Long-term effects of intrauterine growth restriction on cardiac metabolism and susceptibility to ischaemia/reperfusion. *Cardiovasc. Res.*, 90, 285-94.

Ruijtenbeek, K., Kessels, L.C., De Mey, J.G. & Blanco, C.E. (2003a). Chronic moderate hypoxia and protein malnutrition both induce growth retardation, but have distinct effects on arterial endothelium-dependent reactivity in the chicken embryo. *Pediatr. Res.*, 53, 573-9.

Ruijtenbeek, K., Kessels, C.G., Janssen, B.J., Bitsch, N.J., Fazzi, G.E., Janssen, G.M., et al. (2003b). Chronic moderate hypoxia during in ovo development alters arterial reactivity in chickens. *Pflugers Arch.*, 447, 158-67.

Salem, R., Denault, A.Y., Couture, P., Bélisle, S., Fortier, A., Guertin, M.C., et al. (2006). Left ventricular end-diastolic pressure is a predictor of mortality in cardiac surgery independently of left ventricular ejection fraction. *Br. J. Anaesth.*, 97, 292-7.

Salinas, C.E., Blanco, C.E., Villena, M., Camm, E.J., Tuckett, J.D., Weerakkody, R.A., et al. (2010). Cardiac and vascular disease prior to hatching in chick embryos incubated at high altitude. *J. DOHaD*, 1, 60-6.

Seckl, J.R. (2001). Glucocorticoid programming of the fetus; adult phenotypes and molecular mechanisms. *Mol. Cell Endocrinol.*, 185, 61-71.

Seckl, J.R. & Meaney, M.J. (2004). Glucocorticoid programming. *Ann. NY Acad. Sci.*, 1032, 63-84.

Sharma, S.K., Lucitti, J.L., Nordman, C., Tinney, J.P., Tobita, K. & Keller, B.B. (2006). Impact of hypoxia on early chick embryo growth and cardiovascular function. *Pediatr. Res.*, 59, 116-20.

Silva, A.A., Santos, C.J., Amigo, H., Barbieri, M.A., Bustos, P., Bettiol, H., et al. (2012). Birth weight, current body mass index, and insulin sensitivity and secretion in young adults in two Latin American populations. *Nutr. Metab. Cardiovasc. Dis.*, 22, 533-9.

Simmons, R.A. (2012). Developmental origins of diabetes: The role of oxidative stress. *Best Pract. Res. Clin. Endocrinol. Metab.*, 26, 701-8.

Skilton, M.R., Evans, N., Griffiths, K.A., Harmer, J.A. & Celermajer, D.S. (2005). Aortic wall thickness in newborns with intrauterine growth restriction. *Lancet,* 365, 1484-6.

Thakor, A.S., Herrera, E.A., Serón-Ferré, M. & Giussani, D.A. (2010a). Melatonin and vitamin C increase umbilical blood flow via nitric oxide-dependent mechanisms. *J. Pineal. Res.,* 49, 399-406.

Thakor, A.S., Richter, H.G., Kane, A.D., Dunster, C., Kelly, F.J., Poston, L., et al. (2010b). Redox modulation of the fetal cardiovascular defence to hypoxaemia. *J. Physiol.,* 588, 4235-47.

Thompson, J.A., Richardson, B.S., Gagnon, R. & Regnault, T.R. (2011). Chronic intrauterine hypoxia interferes with aortic development in the late gestation ovine fetus. *J. Physiol.,* 589, 3319-32.

Thompson, L.P. (2003). Effects of chronic hypoxia on afetal coronary responses. *High Alt Med. Biol.,* 4, 215-24.

Thompson, L.P., Aguan, K., Pinkas, G. & Weiner, C.P. (2000). Chronic hypoxia increases the NO contribution of acetylcholine vasodilation of the fetal guinea pig heart. *Am. J. Physiol. Regul. Integr. Comp. Physiol.,* 279, R1813-20.

Thompson, L.P. & Al-Hasan, Y. (2012). Impact of oxidative stress in fetal programming. *J. Pregnancy,* 2012, 582748.

Thompson, L.P. & Weiner, C.P. (1999). Effects of acute and chronic hypoxia on nitric oxide-mediated relaxation of fetal guinea pig arteries. *Am. J. Obstet. Gynecol.,* 181, 105-11.

Tijsseling, D., Camm, E.J., Richter, H.G., Herrera, E.A., Kane, A.D., Niu, Y., et al. (2013). Statins prevent adverse effects of postnatal glucocorticoid therapy on the developing brain in rats. *Pediatr. Res.,* 74, 639-45.

Tintu, A., Rouwet, E., Verlohren, S., Brinkmann, J., Ahmad, S., Crispi, F., et al. (2009). Hypoxia induces dilated cardiomyopathy in the chick embryo: mechanism, intervention, and long-term consequences. *PLoS One,* 4, e5155.

Tintu, A.N., Noble, F.A. & Rouwet, E.V. (2007). Hypoxia disturbs fetal hemodynamics and growth. *Endothelium,* 14, 353-60.

Torrens, C., Ethirajan, P., Bruce, K.D., Cagampang, F.R., Siow, R.C., Hanson, M.A., et al. (2012). Interaction between maternal and offspring diet to impair vascular function and oxidative balance in high fat fed male mice. *PLoS One,* 7, e50671.

Torrens, C., Kelsall, C.J., Hopkins, L.A., Anthony, F.W., Curzen, N.P. & Hanson, M.A. (2009). Atorvastatin restores endothelial function in offspring of protein-restricted rats in a cholesterol-independent manner. *Hypertension,* 53, 661-7.

Torrens, C., Poston, L. & Hanson, M.A. (2008). Transmission of raised blood pressure and endothelial dysfunction to the F2 generation induced by maternal protein restriction in the F0, in the absence of dietary challenge in the F1 generation. *Br. J. Nutr.,* 100, 760-6.

van Abeelen, A.F., de Rooij, S.R., Osmond, C., Painter, R.C., Veenendaal, M.V., Bossuyt, P.M., et al. (2011). The sex-specific effects of famine on the association between placental size and later hypertension. *Placenta,* 32, 694-8.

Veenendaal, M.V., Painter, R.C., de Rooij, S.R., Bossuyt, P.M., van der Post, J.A., Gluckman, P.D., et al. (2013). Transgenerational effects of prenatal exposure to the 1944-45 Dutch famine. *BJOG,* 120, 548-53.

Veille, J.C., Hanson, R., Sivakoff, M., Hoen, H. & Ben-Ami, M. (1993). Fetal cardiac size in normal, intrauterine growth retarded, and diabetic pregnancies. *Am. J. Perinatol.,* 10, 275-9.

Villamor, E., Kessels, C.G., Ruijtenbeek, K., van Suylen, R.J., Belik, J., de Mey, J.G., et al. (2004). Chronic in ovo hypoxia decreases pulmonary arterial contractile reactivity and induces biventricular cardiac enlargement in the chicken embryo. *Am. J. Physiol. Regul. Integr. Comp. Physiol.*, 287, R642-51.

Wallwork, C.J., Parks, D.A. & Schmid-Schönbein, G.W. (2003). Xanthine oxidase activity in the dexamethasone-induced hypertensive rat. *Microvasc. Res.*, 66, 30-7.

Wapner, R. & Jobe, A.H. (2011). Controversy: antenatal steroids. *Clin. Perinatol.*, 38, 529-45.

Williams, S.J., Campbell, M.E., McMillen, I.C. & Davidge, S.T. (2005a). Differential effects of maternal hypoxia or nutrient restriction on carotid and femoral vascular function in neonatal rats. *Am. J. Physiol. Regul. Integr. Comp. Physiol.*, 288, R360-7.

Williams, S.J., Hemmings, D.G., Mitchell, J.M., McMillen, I.C. & Davidge, S.T. (2005b). Effects of maternal hypoxia or nutrient restriction during pregnancy on endothelial function in adult male rat offspring. *J. Physiol.*, 565, 125-35.

World Health Organization. (2012). World Health Statistics 2012. ISBN 978 92 4 156444 1.

Xiong, F., Xiao, D. & Zhang, L. (2012). Norepinephrine causes epigenetic repression of PKCε gene in rodent hearts by activating Nox1-dependent reactive oxygen species production. *FASEB J.*, 26, 2753-63.

Xu, Y., Williams, S.J., O'Brien, D. & Davidge, S.T. (2006). Hypoxia or nutrient restriction during pregnancy in rats leads to progressive cardiac remodeling and impairs postischemic recovery in adult male offspring. *FASEB J.*, 20, 1251-3.

Xue, Q., Dasgupta, C., Chen, M. & Zhang, L. (2011). Foetal hypoxia increases cardiac AT(2)R expression and subsequent vulnerability to adult ischaemic injury. *Cardiovasc. Res.*, 89, 300-8.

Xue, Q. & Zhang, L. (2009). Prenatal hypoxia causes a sex-dependent increase in heart susceptibility to ischemia and reperfusion injury in adult male offspring: role of protein kinase C epsilon. *J. Pharmacol. Exp. Ther.*, 330, 624-32.

Yan, M.S., Matouk, C.C. & Marsden, P.A. (2010). Epigenetics of the vascular endothelium. *J. Appl. Physiol.*, 109, 916-26.

Zambrano, E., Martínez-Samayoa, P.M., Bautista, C.J., Deás, M., Guillén, L., Rodríguez-González, G.L., et al. (2005). Sex differences in transgenerational alterations of growth and metabolism in progeny (F2) of female offspring (F1) of rats fed a low protein diet during pregnancy and lactation. *J. Physiol.*, 566, 225-36.

Zhang, Y., Croft, K.D., Mori, T.A., Schyvens, C.G., McKenzie, K.U. & Whitworth, J.A. (2004). The antioxidant tempol prevents and partially reverses dexamethasone-induced hypertension in the rat. *Am. J. Hypertens,* 17, 260-5.

In: Stress and Developmental Programming …   ISBN: 978-1-63321-836-9
Editors: Lubo Zhang and Lawrence D. Longo   © 2014 Nova Science Publishers, Inc.

Chapter 13

Stress and Preterm Birth

Inge Christiaens[1], David M. Olson[2] and Gerlinde A. Metz[3]*
[1]Academic Clinical Fellow, Obstetrics and Gynaecology
Newcastle University, Newcastle upon Tyne, United Kingdom
[2]Professor, Departments of Obstetrics and Gynecology,
Pediatrics and Physiology, University of Alberta, Edmonton, Canada
[3]Professor, Department of Neuroscience
AHFMR Senior Scholar, Canadian Centre for Behavioural Neuroscience
University of Lethbridge, Lethbridge, Canada

Abstract

Each year 15 million babies are born preterm and the global rate of preterm birth (PTB) of >10% is steadily rising. PTB programs life-long complications, including long term motor, cognitive, growth and health problems. A major obstacle in determining the causes of this global problem is that PTB is multifactorial with several different etiologies. These various etiologies ultimately converge on identifiable pathways that are critically influenced by stress. In this review we focus on lifetime and transgenerational aspects of stress related to PTB and discuss possible mechanisms that translate stress and associated allostatic load into the physiological changes that transform the uterus of pregnancy to the uterus of delivery preterm. The concept of allostatic load induced by a severe stressor provides a compelling rationale for the contribution of stress to spontaneous PTB. Although it is challenging to demonstrate a clear causal relationship in humans, PTB was recognized as a consequence of severe maternal distress preconceptionally. For example, adverse childhood experiences increase the risk for PTB.

Being born preterm is the most powerful predictor for a woman to be at higher risk for a PTB of her own. Recent findings in rodents indicate that prenatal stress may generate an epigenetic signature that may be passed on to the offspring, thus enhancing stress sensitivity and interfering with pregnancy maintenance in the next and future generations. Based on this work in animal models, prenatal stress may predispose women, their daughters and granddaughters to greater PTB risk. Epigenetic mechanisms

---
* Email: dmolson@ualberta.ca

may help explain gene x environment interactions that link childhood abuse and expression of genetic risk factors.

We propose that PTB represents a multifactorial condition, which according to the "Two-Hit Hypothesis" can be triggered or worsened by an episode of prenatal stress or a traumatic life event. New cost-effective technologies, including stress assessments and interventions, need to be developed to firstly identify women at high risk of PTB and then treat them in order to delay preterm delivery, prolong pregnancy and thereby improve newborn health outcomes.

Keywords: Allostasis, cortisol, preterm birth, stress, transgenerational programming

Introduction

The publication of the report, *Born Too Soon,* in 2012 by the World Health Association, the March of Dimes and other international sponsors focused worldwide attention on the problem of preterm birth (PTB, birth before 37 completed weeks of pregnancy) (World Health Organization, 2012). Not only were the statistics alarming, that each year 15 million babies are born preterm, 1.1 million of these will die, and the global PTB rate of >10% is rising, but equally concerning was the revelation that there is no jurisdiction anywhere that is exempt from the problem. In a very real sense, PTB is a global health problem.

One of the major factors contributing to this global problem is that PTB is multifactorial with several different etiologies. While these various etiologies ultimately converge on identifiable pathways that transform the uterus of pregnancy to the uterus of delivery, teams of investigators are seeking the initiating causes in order to identify the modifiable risk factors in the hope that suitable prognostics and interventions will ultimately be available to identify those at risk, reduce the incidence of PTB and prolong pregnancy in order to improve newborn health outcomes. The highest rates of PTB, those at 15% or higher, typically occur in low and middle-income countries in sub-Sahara Africa, southern Asia and extend to Indonesia and the Philippines where health status, poverty, poor or uneven nutrition or limited access to care are frequently considered major causes. But this axiom is not consistent as the United States, a high-income country, has one of the highest rates at around 12%. Such information highlights the diversity of the problem and one wonders if indeed there are any common causal threads that cross income, social status, access, ethnic, or cultural lines. Increasingly, stress is being examined as one possible common denominator in the etiology of PTB. In this review we will focus on lifetime and transgenerational aspects of stress related to PTB and identify possible mechanisms that translate allostatic load into the physiological changes that transform the uterus of pregnancy to the uterus of delivery preterm. We will not attempt to cover all the stress and PTB literature nor address acute stress and PTB, rather we will present representative examples from our work and that of others that address the above.

Stress

Stress is a word that is heard everywhere and every day. Yet, it is a very ambiguous term as it means something different to everyone. It is often used in a negative sense, but is stress always bad for you? In general terms, stress can be defined as any challenge – psychological or physical – that threatens or that is perceived to threaten homeostasis (Berhman and Butler, 2006). It encompasses both environmental demands and cognitive and emotional responses, such as stress perception, to those demands. Over the years, scientists have developed various biological and psychological concepts to define stress and the stress response.

Homeostasis. Walter Cannon (1871-1945) developed the concept of homeostasis, based on the *milieu intérieur* (Claude Bernard), and he used the following concept in defining homeostasis: physiological reactions are coordinated to maintain a steady state or equilibrium in the body (Cannon, 1928, 1929). This is required to sustain life. Homeostasis includes the regulation of body temperature, pH, blood glucose and oxygen tension. Cannon stressed the importance of the autonomic nervous system as a homeostatic control mechanism. Hans Selye (1907-1982) was an endocrinologist and a pioneer in the field of biological stress. He introduced the well-known 'General Adaptation Syndrome' (GAS) model in 1936, based on endocrine experiments in mice. The general adaptation syndrome describes the physiological adaptive reactions in the body in response to a stressor (Selye, 1998, Selye and Fortier, 1950):

1. Alarm reaction – 'Fight or flight' response: initial reaction stage in the body with activation of the autonomous nervous system and hormonal systems to prepare for 'action.'
2. Stage of resistance: adaptation stage in which the body actively copes with the stressor and attempts to return to a homeostatic state.
3. Stage of exhaustion: when stress persists beyond the capability of the body to cope, the body becomes exhausted resulting in (permanent) damage to internal organs and increased susceptibility to disease.

According to Selye, GAS is largely dependent on the function of the autonomic nervous system. In his model, a stressor – whether an injury, damaging agent or psychological event – always influences certain tissues directly, followed by systemic damage and defence due to nervous and hormonal mediation. In his search to identify the hormonal mediators of GAS, Selye was the first to describe the role of the hypothalamic-pituitary-adrenocortical axis (HPA axis) in response to a stressor.

The HPA axis. Any type of physical or mental stress in a human can elicit a rapid and greatly enhanced secretion of the main stress hormone, the glucocorticoid (GC) cortisol (or corticosterone in rodents). The physiologic stress response involves the autonomic nervous system, in particular the sympathetic adrenal medullary (SAM) axis and the HPA axis (Guyton and Hall, 2006, Stratakis and Chrousos, 1995). Both systems originate in the brain. The hypothalamus, located in the middle of the base of the brain, is the 'control center' of the neuroendocrine system in the body and plays a vital role in maintaining homeostasis. The paraventricular nucleus of the hypothalamus contains neuroendocrine neurons that synthesize and secrete corticotropin-releasing hormone (CRH) (Vale et al., 1981). CRH release from the hypothalamus is under nervous control and influenced by the sleep/wake cycle, by cortisol levels in the blood, and by stress. After secretion, CRH is transported through the portal blood vessel system of the pituitary stalk to the anterior pituitary gland, where it binds to the corticotropin releasing hormone receptor (CRHR1) on the corticotrope cells. This stimulates the anterior pituitary to secrete adrenocorticotropic hormone (ACTH) stored in corticotrope cells. ACTH is then released into the blood stream and transported to the adrenal cortex of the adrenal glands. ACTH stimulates the synthesis of glucocorticoids, mainly cortisol, from cholesterol via activation of adenylyl cyclase and formation of cAMP in the zona fasciculata of the adrenal cortex (Smith et al., 1982).

Cortisol, or hydrocortisone, is a steroid hormone that acts on the glucocorticoid receptor (GR) and the mineralocorticoid receptor (MR), but it has a higher affinity for the GR (De Kloet et al., 1998). The GR is present in almost every cell in the body (Lu et al., 2006). When bound to the GR, cortisol has important effects on carbohydrate metabolism, protein metabolism, fat metabolism, and on stress and inflammatory responses (Guyton and Hall, 2006). Cortisol stimulates gluconeogenesis and glycogenesis in the liver while reducing the utilization of glucose by the cells, resulting in an increased blood glucose level in the body. Cortisol has catabolic effects, such as proteolysis and lipolysis, in tissues. The resulting mobilization of amino acids and fatty acids, together with higher blood glucose levels, can be considered as adaptive processes to provide energy substrates for the body, in particular the heart and the brain, to cope with demands. Cortisol also exhibits anti-inflammatory effects. It suppresses leukocyte proliferation and migration, and it inhibits the synthesis of pro-inflammatory cytokines resulting in a suppressed inflammatory response (Elenkov et al., 1999, Wadhwa et al., 2001). Circulating cortisol also inhibits the secretion of ACTH. It exerts its negative feedback effect both at the level of the anterior pituitary gland and the hypothalamus.

The autonomic nervous system via the SAM axis also plays a vital role in the stress response. The catecholamines, epinephrine (adrenaline) and, in much lesser extent, norepinephrine (noradrenaline), are produced by the adrenal medulla through sympathetic stimulation and indirectly through cortisol. Epinephrine is especially important in acute or emergency situations when the sympathetic nervous system is activated – the fight or flight response. Circulating (nor)epinephrine causes vasoconstriction in essentially all blood vessels and stimulates the heart. In addition, epinephrine has a metabolic effect by increasing both plasma glucose and plasma fatty acid concentrations due to enhanced utilization of fat during stress.

Cognitive appraisal and coping. Whereas Cannon and Selye mainly measured the physiological responses to external stressors, it was later thought that external stressors are mediated by the perception of the individual. Therefore Lazarus and Cohen defined a biobehavioural model of the stress response (Lazarus and Cohen, 1977). They stated that when 'environmental demands, such as chronic stressors, exceed the adaptive capacity of an organism, the result can be psychological and biological changes that may place persons at risk of disease.' Adding to the complexity of their model, they argued that cognitive appraisal plays a central role (Folkman et al., 1986a, 1986b). Each individual evaluates whether a particular encounter with the environment is relevant to his or her well-being and whether it will be perceived as stressful. In addition, individual coping skills – cognitive and behavioural efforts to manage the internal and external demands – and modifiers of the stress response, such as social support, are important elements in the stress response. For instance, someone with an extensive and adequate support network may well appraise stressors more optimistically or use adaptive coping styles to solve a problem since friends and family are available for support. In contrast, people in an abusive environment may have a more negative outlook on the world and this affects their cognitive appraisal of stressors. Adequate social support, adaptive coping skills, resilience and optimism are all moderators of stress and can be seen as 'protective,' resulting in decreasing perceived stress and better health outcomes. Conversely, maladaptive coping styles and risky behaviour and lifestyle, such as smoking and alcohol use, may initially seem to reduce perceived stress for many people, however they can actually increase the stress response and lead to negative health outcomes (Dai et al., 2007, Steptoe and Ussher, 2006).

Allostasis and allostatic load. In the late 1980's, an alternative term to homeostasis was introduced into the stress literature: allostasis. Originally proposed by Sterling and Eyer, allostasis is the adaptive process for actively maintaining stability through change (Sterling and Ever, 1988). Allostasis is derived from the Greek 'allo', meaning 'variable', while 'stasis' means 'stand.' Therefore, allostasis means 'stable by being variable,' and it is a fundamental process supporting homeostasis through which the body can adjust to stressors. Allostasis – extensively described by McEwen – is achieved through the production of mediators of the stress response such as adrenal hormones, inflammatory cytokines and neurotransmitters that help us adapt to new situations and challenges (McEwen, 1998a, 1998b, McEwen and Seeman, 1999, McEwen and Wingfield, 2003). The brain plays a central role in allostasis, by controlling various mechanisms simultaneously. In acute situations, allostasis is beneficial for the body, as it is essential for the body to respond and adapt to stressors. As a result, an effective physiological solution to the threat is achieved. However, when allostasis is prolonged – in chronic or repetitive stress – the autonomic nervous system and HPA axis are repetitively activated and the neuroendocrine and inflammatory adaptive processes now become damaging to the body. For this, McEwen coined the term 'allostatic load,' defined as the cumulative results of allostasis. In other words, it comprises the 'wear and tear' of allostasis over a lifetime on the body and the brain. In chronic stress, the allostatic load increases as the body attempts to cope with stressors. Thus, the main hormonal mediators, cortisol and epinephrine, that normally maintain homeostasis, now have a negative effect on the body, resulting in the acceleration of disease processes such as cardiovascular disease. In addition, allostatic load over a long period of time might cause the allostatic systems to become exhausted leading to dysregulation of the HPA axis and compensatory responses by other systems. Chronic stress can therefore result in an increase in inflammatory cells and cytokines and increased susceptibility to infection and inflammation (Djuric et al., 2008, Elenkov et al., 1999, McEwen, 1998a).

Preterm Birth

Preterm infants are at greater risk for mortality, developmental delay, adverse health conditions, morbidity, lower quality of life and lost potential than infants born at term (Mikkola et al., 2005). PTB programs life-long complications, including long term motor, cognitive, visual, hearing, behavioural, social-emotional, health, and growth problems (Mikkola et al., 2005), presumably contributing to an individual's allostatic load. Having a previous preterm delivery or being born preterm are amongst the most powerful predictors known at present for a woman to have a PTB in her current pregnancy (Ekwo et al., 1992,

Goldenberg et al., 2008) – an effect often related to genetics (likely epigenetics), but possibly also to a high allostatic load.

Stress and Preterm Birth

Long-term health complications, such as increased risk of PTB, may result from adverse perinatal programming by stress and low birth weight (Challis and Smith, 2001, Hobel, 2004, Rich-Edwards and Grizzard, 2005, Wainstock et al., 2013, Zhu et al., 2010). Preterm birth, a leading cause of neonatal morbidity and mortality, is associated with an intrauterine pro-inflammatory state triggered by unknown causes in about 50% of cases. It has been difficult to demonstrate a clear causal relationship in humans (Kramer et al., 2013), although it was noted that PTB risk may be influenced from cumulative effects of lifetime stress (Rich-Edwards and Grizzard, 2005). PTB was recognized as a consequence of severe maternal distress during pregnancy (Hobel, 2004, Zhu et al., 2010) or due to preconceptional factors (Emanuel et al., 1999).

Gestational stress may affect levels of hormones and neuropeptides, including prolactin, progesterone, and oxytocin, which are involved in maintenance of pregnancy and timing of delivery (Arck, 2001, Miller and Riegle, 1985) In animal studies, adverse experience was suggested to compromise the continuation of gestation (Arck, 2001). Cumulative effects of stress over a lifetime seem to be of particular importance to PTB (Rich-Edwards and Grizzard, 2005). Arguably, prenatal stress in the offspring, by permanently altering the cytokine milieu, may predispose to pregnancy complications in later life (Coussons-Read et al., 2012). Such programming of physiological and inflammatory responses in early life may transmit through subsequent generations (Crews et al., 2012). Inter-generational programming of hypothalamic-pituitary-adrenal (HPA) axis activity during pre- and early postnatal development can become a key regulator of adult disease (Kaati et al., 2002, Zucchi et al., 2013) and behaviour (Franklin et al., 2011, Ward et al., 2013, Weiss et al., 2011). Thus, it is reasonable to assume that maternal stress during pregnancy may program physiological responses, PTB risk and birth outcomes across multiple generations. Indeed, PTB risk was noted to propagate through generations (Porter et al., 1997).

Prenatal Stress and Offspring Development

The gestational state is a period of particular vulnerability to stress for both the mother and her offspring. The effects of maternal stress before or during pregnancy have been shown to have considerable adverse effects upon the offspring and examples of this follow.

Exposure of a fetus to GCs during maternal stress is regulated by the placental enzyme 11-β hydroxysteroid dehydrogenase type 2 (11β-HSD2). Circulating levels of physiological GC are much higher in the maternal than in the fetal blood. This gradient is ensured by the 11β-HSD2 which catalyzes the rapid inactivation of GCs to their inert 11-keto forms, thus forming a natural barrier to maternal GCs (Charil et al., 2010, Yang et al., 1990). Nevertheless, the feto-placental 11β-HSD2 gene is down-regulated by maternal stress (Sarkar et al., 2001) and excess GC levels caused by severe maternal stress may pass the placenta to reach the fetus (Newnham, 2001, Seckl, 2008). Thus, excessive maternal GCs or 11β-HSD2 inhibition are able to modulate the developing fetal HPA axis and its regulation in later life, altering brain development and HPA axis functions throughout the lifetime (Harris and Seckl, 2011).

In the long-term, HPA axis programming by prenatal stress causes a reduction in its negative feedback mechanism to elevate stress sensitivity and generate loss of resilience to adverse challenges. It was suggested that greater stress sensitivity leads to greater vulnerability to neuropsychiatric conditions, including depression, bipolar affective disorder and schizophrenia (Fine et al., 2014, Kleinhaus et al., 2013, Zucchi et al., 2013), as well as metabolic and cardiovascular disease (Boersma et al., 2014, Buchwald et al., 2012, van Dijk et al., 2012, Zucchi et al., 2014).

Stress sensitivity contributes to vulnerability to stress-associated endocrine and immunological manifestations through both excessive catecholamine and GC secretion and through GC receptor (GR) resistance (Cohen et al., 2012). The latter in particular increases production of pro-inflammatory cytokines (Cohen et al., 2012), which in turn attenuate 11β-HSD2 enzymatic activity in human placenta (Challis and Smith, 2001, Kossintseva et al., 2006). These and related mechanisms critically determine maternal health and alter offspring brain physiology with life-long consequences (Harris and Seckl, 2011, Schwab, 2009), generating a state of particular vulnerability to PTB.

Immune stress to pregnant Long-Evans rat dams in the form of interleukin (IL)-1β administration from gestational days (GD) 17-21 leads to impaired cognitive performance (less time spent investigating a novel object) in male and female offspring and to affective behaviour in female offspring (Paris et al., 2011). It also reduces utilization of progesterone in the hippocampus of female offspring as defined by conversion to dihydroprogesterone and allopregnanolone (see section on Neuroendocrine mechanisms). Allopregnanolone plays an important role in the development of the central nervous system by promoting neuronal growth early in fetal life and later protecting neural development, promoting cognitive function, attenuating anxiety, and attenuating the oxytocin release apparatus (Chin et al., 2011, Herbison, 2001). Very similar results in terms of impaired offspring cognitive function were obtained when this group substituted restraint stress or chronic unpredictable stressors to pregnant dams for immune stress (Paris and Frye, 2011a, 2011b).

Prenatal Stress and Transgenerational Programming

The perinatal period is a time of high vulnerability to environmental influences. As discussed above, maternal stress can influence offspring development and stress responses with consequences potentially lasting to adulthood. This raises the possibility that prenatal stress, or the long-term endocrine, metabolic, immunological or behavioural consequences associated with it, may produce a phenotype that is not confined to the first generation but may propagate to subsequent generations. Transgenerational changes have been reported for many environmental stimuli, with one of the most potent being stress (Crews et al., 2012, Drake et al., 2005, Dygalo et al., 1999).

To date, the most-investigated mechanisms of phenotypic programming by perinatal adversity include altered gestational endocrine milieu, maternal behaviour and transgenerational epigenetic programming (Champagne and Meaney, 2007, Harris and Seckl, 2011, Migicovsky and Kovalchuk, 2011, Zucchi et al., 2012). Recent studies focusing on transmission through the male germ line in rodents have suggested that altered stress responses and associated emotional traits are caused by ancestral exposure to environmental toxins (Crews et al., 2012) and stressful experiences (Dias and Ressler, 2014, Gapp et al., 2014, Morgan and Bale, 2011). In the maternal lineage, prenatal exposure to endocrine disruptors (Nilsson et al., 2008, Skinner et al., 2013) or to maternal undernutrition in humans (Veenendaal et al., 2013) has been associated with increased metabolic and endocrine disease risk in the offspring.

The function of transgenerational epigenetic programming may assist in preparing the offspring's progeny to certain postnatal conditions through inherited, acquired epigenetic modifications (Migicovsky and Kovalchuk, 2011, Skinner et al., 2010). However, in the long term perinatal stress may also lead to maladaptive re-programming that promotes pathological processes leading to disease (Babenko et al., 2012, Relton and Davey Smith, 2010). Transgenerational programming occurs when an epigenetic change is incorporated into the germ line escaping the reprogramming process and manifests itself in the absence of the causative agent in the female F3 generation (Crews et al., 2012). It is the F3 generation that allows the unequivocal determination of transgenerational phenotypes and will assist in identifying epigenetic prognostic markers and preventive strategies.

Stress-Associated PTB Studies

Maternal stress during pregnancy is increasingly recognized as a variable of interest in the etiology of spontaneous PTB, however its contribution to the risk of PTB remains controversial (see Wadhwa et al., 2011 and Chen et al., 2011 for a more comprehensive review of the issues associated with assessing correlations between stress and PTB in women). Studies examining the effect of maternal stress during pregnancy on PTB have shown varied results, partly due to the fact that they have only explored separate stressors and their relationship with PTB. Often, cognitive appraisal of stressors or individual responses were not considered in the studies. Moreover, there is a lack of the use of a comprehensive measure of chronic stress. The concept of allostatic load provides a compelling rationale for the contribution of chronic stress to spontaneous PTB. Therefore, examining the exposure to stressors over a mother's life course might give a better perspective on the role of maternal stress in the etiology of spontaneous PTB.

Natural Disasters, Terrorist Attacks and Chemical Disasters

Harville, Xiong and Buekens (2010) published an excellent systematic review of the relationship between several types of natural or man-caused disasters on adverse pregnancy outcomes that we will summarize (Harville et al., 2010). The United Nations defines disaster as "a serious disruption of the functioning of a community or a society involving widespread human, material, economic, or environmental losses and impacts, which exceeds the ability of the affected community or society to cope using its own resources" (http://www.eird.org/wikien/index/php/Glossary). The authors also defined *disaster* as 'a discrete precipitating event, such as a hurricane, earthquake, terrorist attack, or chemical spill because such events share some similar qualities, but differ as well.' The former revolves around the degree of exposure to the disaster and the consequent issues of variable access to food and health care, whereas the latter is that each disaster and its 'environmental exposure' is unique (Baum and Fleming, 1993, Bongers et al., 2008, Callaghan et al., 2007, Kusuda et al., 1995, Norris and Uhl, 1993, Sapir, 1993).

World Trade Centre, September 11, 2001. Fetuses of women exposed to the environmental effects of 9/11 had an increased risk of intrauterine growth retardation at birth (Berkowitz et al., 2003). Infants born to women residing near the World Trade Centre were born slightly earlier than those outside a two-mile radius (Lederman et al., 2004). Interestingly, risk among women with symptoms of post-traumatic stress disorder (PTSD) or depression was reduced (Engel et al., 2005). Generally, knowing of the disaster had no adverse effects except for a slight shortening of gestation length reported in Dutch women post-9/11 who learned about the disaster through the media (0.7 days, p=0.07) (Smits et al., 2006).

Terrorist attacks. A reduction in birthweight was found for women exposed to terrorist attacks in Colombia in 1998-2003 and during a three-month bombing of Belgrade in Serbia in 1999, but there was no difference in birth length or gestational age at birth (Camacho, 2008, Maric et al., 2010). After the U. S. Embassy bombing in Nairobi in 1998, several women reported, anecdotally, of spontaneous abortions and premature labor (Njenga and Nyamai, 2005).

Environmental and chemical disasters. There was no PTB in association with the Love Canal disaster (identified in 1978) in a population-based cohort (Goldman et al., 1985). The Chernobyl nuclear disaster had no PTB associations directly, but Levi found that anxiety due to Chernobyl, but not the environmental threat itself, was associated with earlier births in a sample of Swedish women (Levi et al., 1989).

Earthquakes. Perhaps because of its severity, the 2008 Chinese earthquake that caused 70,000 deaths was associated with many birth complications, including higher rates of low birth weight, PTB, birth defects, and lower Apgar scores in a large study of survivors (Tan et al., 2009). The 1999 Chi-Chi earthquake in Taiwan, which displaced at least 100,000 people (Chen et al., 2003), was not associated with changes in birth length, in a hospital-based cohort (Chang et al., 2002). Women exposed to the 1994 Northridge earthquake in California gave birth earlier than expected, and the effect was strongest for those exposed in the first trimester (38.06 weeks observed versus 39.29 weeks expected) (Glynn et al., 2001). An increase in PTB was seen in a hospital after two of five Israeli earthquakes, although there was no difference in Apgar scores (Weissman et al., 1989).

Hurricanes and floods. Hurricane Katrina was associated with a fall in very PTB but no change in low birth weight or overall PTB (Hamilton et al., 2009), while a smaller study reported a higher rate of low birth weight and an insignificant increase in PTB after Katrina (Xiong et al., 2008). In flood studies, an increased incidence of PTB and low birth weight was seen among a village in southern Poland in 1997 (Neuberg et al., 1998) and the flooding of the Red River in North Dakota in 1997 (Tong et al., 2011), although there was no increase in small for gestational age in the North Dakota sample.

Storms. An ice storm hit Quebec in 1998, causing widespread power outages to 3 million people for up to 5 weeks (King and Laplante, 2005). Gestational lengths were shorter when women were pregnant during the storm in the first or second trimesters; pre-conceptual or third trimester exposure was not related to PTB (Dancause et al., 2011). In the 1994 storm-related sinking of the Swedish ferry Estonia, 501 people died. A subsequent 15% increase in very low birth weight births was reported in the Swedish population (Catalano and Hartig, 2001).

Overall conclusion of natural disasters. The authors (Harville et al., 2010) conclude that the empirical literature on pregnant and postpartum women during disaster is limited. Many of the published reports and recommendations are anecdotal or based on the experience and impressions of relief workers (Campbell, 2005) and clinicians (Carballo et al., 2005, Ewing et al., 2008, Pascali-Bonaro, 2002) rather than systematic studies. They fail to examine whole populations and instead largely gather data from women who presented for clinical care or were the most affected. In conclusion, the literature related to disaster-associated adverse pregnancy outcomes, including PTB, is limited and disaster, in and of itself, does not seem to shorten gestation or cause PTB in any consistent fashion.

Chronic Stress

In spite of the overall outcome of disaster-related events, there are indeed epidemiological studies that have shown that pregnant women who experience high levels of psychosocial stress before or during pregnancy are at significant risk for PTB regardless of their ethnicity and socioeconomic status (Copper et al., 1996, Dole et al., 2003, International HapMap Consortium, 2005, Neggers et al., 2006, Steer, 2005, Wadhwa et al., 2001). This especially includes women who experienced major and traumatic life events early in pregnancy. Examples given above plus others include Hurricane Katrina (Buekens et al., 2006), the Quebec Ice Storm (Dancause et al., 2011) and the World Trade Center disaster (Lederman et al., 2004) Hedegaard et al., found that major life events during pregnancy were only associated with PTB when they were perceived to be stressful (Hedegaard et al., 1996). Indeed, women who have increased perceptions of stress also have a higher risk of PTB (Austin and Leader, 2000, Orr et al., 2002, Rini et al., 1999). In addition, physically demanding work, prolonged standing, shift and night work, and a high cumulative work fatigue score have been associated with PTB (Luke et al., 1995, Mozurkewich et al., 2000). Perceived racial discrimination can increase the risk of PTB. In Canada, Heaman et al., indicated that spontaneous PTB among Aboriginal women was related to a high level of perceived stress (Heaman et al., 2005). Research suggests that physical and emotional abuse or domestic violence prior to or during pregnancy is associated with PTB (Coker et al., 2004, Covington et al., 2001, Fernandez and Krueger, 1999, Neggers et al., 2004). Distressed states such as depression and anxiety play a role in the onset of PTB (Dayan et al., 2002, Orr et al., 2002). In addition, depression and anxiety can increase a woman's stress levels. Conversely, high levels of stress can result in the development of depression and anxiety (Stratakis and Chrousos, 1995). As previously mentioned, low socio-economical status is believed to be an important risk factor for PTB (Berkowitz and Papiernik, 1993, Kramer et al., 2000, 2001). Socio-economic disadvantage is associated with unhealthy or risky behaviours, including smoking, alcohol abuse and poor eating habits, perception of increased stress levels, and psychological reactions that influence gestation negatively (Kramer et al., 2001). Indeed, behavioural risk factors, like cigarette smoking, alcohol and drug use, sexually transmitted infections, poor food intake and obesity are all associated with PTB. (Andres and Day, 2000,

Hayatbakhsh et al., 2012, Hendler et al., 2005, Mann et al., 2010, O'Leary et al., 2009, Quesada et al., 2012, Shah and Bracken, 2000).

Christiaens et al., (Christiaens, 2012, Christiaens et al., 2012) assessed chronic, lifelong stressors and related these to spontaneous PTB by designing the 'Well-being and Pregnancy Questionnaire.' This is a compilation involving perceived stress (based on the Perceived Stress Scale), common stressors, interpersonal support evaluation list (ISEL, short form), live events check list (CAPS 1), coping (Brief COPE), adverse childhood experiences (ACE), abuse assessment screen (AAS), depression and suicidality (Mini International Neuropsychiatric Interview). Using this questionnaire, both individual and contextual variables that influence the stress response were examined for all subjects. Several checklists designed for this study and validated research instruments were used to measure concepts related to stress and personal resources. Where possible, validated tools that are available in the public domain were used.

Participating subjects were contacted by telephone between three months and one year postpartum where possible for follow-up and administration of the 'Well-being and Pregnancy Questionnaire.' To maximise the number of respondents, at least three attempts to contact each participant at different times during days and evenings were made. The questionnaire was administered during the telephone interview, and answers were entered into a secure online database. There were 223 completed telephone questionnaires in the study comprising 148 controls and 75 cases.

Univariate analysis of the socio-demographic and medical variables demonstrated that maternal age, smoking, alcohol use, educational status, and a history of miscarriage were significantly associated with PTB. Physical and emotional abuse as an adult, assessed with the AAS on its own, was not associated with PTB in this study. However, the combined abuse score of childhood and adult abuse was significantly associated with PTB (crude odds ratio (OR) 1.40; 95% CI 1.13-1.74). A significant relationship was found between the computed total stress score and spontaneous PTB after univariate logistic regression, showing a crude OR for the risk of PTB of 1.46, and after dichotomization, a high stress score had an even greater crude OR of 1.86 (95% CI 1.06-3.328). The score for depressive symptoms during pregnancy was significantly associated with PTB (crude OR 1.53; 95% CI 1.01-2.33). A history of major lifetime depression had a fairly high crude OR of 1.70, however this was not significant (95% CI 0.90-3.24).

Of all the separate questionnaire instruments, only the Adverse Childhood Experiences score was significantly associated with spontaneous PTB. Its crude odds ratio when dichotomized into high ($\geq$2 ACEs) versus low ACE, based on median split, was 2.45 (95% CI 1.37-4.38) , which was confirmed with multivariate analysis. When looking more specifically at the relationship between ACE score and spontaneous PTB, it was observed that the proportion of women with PTB gradually increased with a greater number of adverse childhood experiences. Inversely, the percentage of women with a term birth decreased as the number of ACEs increased. When exploring the effect of lifetime abuse – combining childhood and adult abuse scores – it was determined that with each additional increment of 1 on the abuse score scale, the risk of spontaneous PTB increased by 34% (adjusted OR 1.30; 95% CI 1.02-1.65).

It is very likely that ACEs interact with the various sociodemographic and medical risk factors for PTB thereby increasing risk for PTB; unfortunately the sample size in Christiaens' et al. study was not adequately powered to test for these possible interactions. Adult abuse on its own was not associated with spontaneous PTB, but when combined with the ACE scores of childhood abuse and neglect and the AAS adult abuse score, a significant relationship between lifetime abuse and PTB was revealed. These data demonstrate that, in this small patient population, that measures of childhood and adult abuse taken together are useful predictors of risk.

Genes and Environment

Cortisol acts on two receptors, the glucocorticoid receptor (GR or NR3C1) and the mineralocorticoid receptor (MR or NR3C2). There is evidence of genetic associations between single nucleotide polymorphisms (SNPs) in genes involved in the HPA axis and adverse mental health outcomes. Several published reports have demonstrated the association between polymorphisms in CRHR1 and depression and suicidality (Boscarino et al., 2012, Bradley et al., 2008, Ishitobi et al., 2012, Liu et al., 2006). In addition, various polymorphisms in the GR gene have been associated with depression and HPA axis regulation (Kumsta et al., 2009, van West et al., 2009). A recent Dutch study found two functional haplotypes in the NR3C2 gene to be associated with perceived chronic stress and increased levels of salivary and plasma cortisol, plasma ACTH and heart rate (van Leeuwen et al., 2011). FK506 binding protein 5 (FKBP5) is part of a receptor complex regulating the sensitivity of the GR (Gillespie et al., 2009). Several SNPs of the FKBP5 gene were found to interact with child abuse and adult post-traumatic stress disorder (Binder et al., 2008, Boscarino et al., 2012, Xie et al., 2010), and were found to increase the risk of depression (Velders et al., 2011).

The serotonin (5HT) pathway is, together with the dopamine pathway, part of the meso-corticolimbic system in the brain and involved in the regulation of stress sensitive mood states. Reuptake and availability of 5HT is controlled by the serotonin transporter (5HTT or SLC6A4) and the importance of this transporter in the regulation of 5HT has long been recognized (Lesch, 2007). A gene-environment interaction study linking childhood abuse, SLC6A4 risk allele and depression found that individuals homozygous for the effect allele and who were abused during childhood had a three-fold increase in their risk of developing major depression (Caspi et al., 2003). The enzymes monoamine oxidase A (MAO-A) and catechol-oxymethyltransferase (COMT) control the metabolism of serotonin, dopamine and norepinephrine in the brain. Polymorphisms in the genes encoding for these enzymes have been linked to depression and anxiety (Boscarino et al., 2012, Hettema et al., 2008, Leuchter et al., 2009, Zhang et al., 2010). Christiaens et al., (Christiaens, 2012, Christiaens et al., 2013) studied whether candidate SNPs associated with altered stress response or mental health complications would also be associated with spontaneous PTB.

Seven key genes involved in the stress response and mood regulation were selected for examination using a haplotype approach that provided broad coverage of functional and non-functional SNPs. They code for the corticotropin releasing hormone receptor (CRHR1), the glucocorticoid receptor (NR3C1), the mineralocorticoid receptor (NR3C2), FK506 binding protein 5 (FKBP5), the serotonin transporter (SLC6A4) and the enzymes MAOA and COMT. Tag SNPs for all genes were identified using the TagSNP function on the SNPinfo web server (Xu and Taylor, 2009). All identified tag SNPs were then compared to a database. SNPs that were found to be associated with PTB in this database at $p<0.05$ were selected for the candidate gene study. As a result, 9 tag SNPs in three different genes – NR3C1, NR3C2 and CRHR1 – were studied.

DNA from salivary samples was analyzed from 190 cases and 369 controls. Using a multivariate model that included maternal age, smoking, alcohol use, education, and history of spontaneous abortion as covariates, two SNPs found in the MR, rs1784063 and rs2883929, remained significantly associated with spontaneous PTB after adjustment. In both cases, the effect allele was found to be protective of the risk of spontaneous PTB. For each additional effect allele, the risk of PTB was reduced by an odds of 2.00 and 2.04 for rs1784063 and rs2883929, respectively.

While the GR is present in almost every cell in the body (Lu et al., 2006), the MR occurs mainly in brain areas of the limbic system and the hippocampus (van Leeuwen et al., 2011). The affinity of cortisol for the MR is much higher than for GR, and binding of cortisol to MR is maintained at basal levels while the GR is only activated in response to a stressor. It is thought that the MR mainly regulates basal activity and the stimulation of the HPA axis, while the GR regulates its termination (Joels et al., 2008). Functional polymorphisms in the human NR3C2 gene have been identified (DeRijk et al., 2011, Muhtz et al., 2011, van Leeuwen et al., 2011). These were found to be associated with increased levels of cortisol and psychosocial stress. These candidate gene studies demonstrated that the polymorphisms rs17484063 and rs2883929, both located in the NR3C2 gene coding for the mineralocorticoid receptor are significantly associated with spontaneous PTB in a protective manner. This association is independent of the known PTB risk factors maternal age, smoking status, alcohol use, educational status and history of miscarriage. For each additional effect allele, the risk of PTB was reduced by an odds of 2.00 for rs17484063 and 2.04 for rs2883929. In other words, in women who are heterozygous for the rs17484063 or the rs2883929 effect allele, the risk of spontaneous PTB is halved. If a woman is homozygous for either risk allele, the risk of delivering preterm is further cut in half.

The relationship between genetics and risk for PTB is only 20-40%, and since PTB is a multifactorial disease, the likelihood that the environment can affect gene expression must be examined. Such gene x environment interactions are not uncommon in other complex diseases. For instance, Bogdan et al., observed a significant gene x childhood neglect interaction when studying the effect of a different NR3C2 genotype on amygdala reactivity (Bogdan et al., 2012). And a gene x environment interaction was found when linking childhood abuse, SLC6A4 risk allele and depression (Caspi et al., 2003). Individuals who were homozygous for the effect allele and who were abused during childhood had a three-fold increase in their risk of developing major depression.

Christiaens et al. (Christiaens, 2012, Christiaens et al., 2012, 2013) therefore decided to test whether the presence of protective SNPs for MR in women who also had a low number of ACEs (<2) offered a greater level of protection against PTB risk than either the SNP or low ACEs alone. Indeed, they found that when only women with low ACE scores also had the rs17484063 SNP, they demonstrated an adjusted OR of 0.37 (95% CI 0.16-0.87) for the risk of PTB. Similarly, the analyses of rs2883929 showed comparable results; the adjusted OR of rs2883929 for spontaneous PTB in women with a low ACE score was OR 0.37 (95% CI 0.17-0.81). Combining the genetic effect (SNP) with the environmental effect (low stress) demonstrates more protection against risk for PTB than either alone or added together, although due to the small sample size, this was not a true gene-environment interaction. For women who experienced 0 or 1 adverse childhood events, a preliminary analysis revealed that each additional risk allele of either rs17484063 or rs2883929 was associated with a 2.7-fold decrease in the risk of spontaneous PTB.

The role of gene-environment interactions in the etiology of PTB is relatively unexplored. Only a few reports examining the role of gene-environment interactions on PTB have been published, and the results have been inconsistent. Some studies found evidence that the presence of an environmental factor, bacterial vaginosis, modifies the genetic association with PTB (Gomez et al., 2010, Macones et al., 2004). There is evidence in the literature that gene x environment interactions also play a role in the development of adverse mental health outcomes, such as post-traumatic stress disorder and depression (Keers and Uher, 2012, Kolassa et al., 2010). Several studies showed an interaction of childhood adverse experience with polymorphisms in predicting depression, post-traumatic stress disorder and alcohol dependence (Bradley et al., 2008, Caspi et al., 2003, 2010, Schellekens et al., 2012).

Animal Studies

A recent study by our laboratories exposed pregnant female Long-Evans rats to transient stress (Yao et al., 2014). Their gestating F1 daughters were either exposed to transient stress again or remained as non-stress controls. Their gestating F2 grand-daughters were again exposed to transient stress or remained as non-stress controls, thus generating two lineages: one of repeated, multigenerational stress and one of in which stress was limited to F0 parental exposure. With each generation, stress in both lineages gradually reduced gestational length, maternal weight gain and maternal behavioural activity, and increased the risk of gestational diabetes. Thus both trans- and multigenerational stress exposure equally modulated gestational length, pregnancy outcomes and offspring health.

Concerning offspring health, delayed offspring development was recognizable as early as postnatal day 7, with the greatest effect in the F3 offspring whose F0 parental generation experienced stress only (Yao et al., 2014). Thus, although context-dependent programming occurs, programming of the germ-line became evident in the F3 generation. In the F3 generation, gestational stress that was imposed on the great-maternal generation seems to have been passed on, via the gametes, to impede development. The F3 generation showed more impairments than any of the other generations in a sensorimotor task that required animals to respond to placement on an inclined ramp with the head facing down (Yao et al., 2014). A failure to quickly turn around and ascend the plane in 7-day old offspring may be indicative of delayed proprioceptive, musculoskeletal, and vestibular development. The striking phenotypic impairments in the F3 generation suggest a genuine transgenerational epigenetic inheritance whereby the epigenetic modifications have been passed via the gametes that have escaped reprogramming (Migicovsky and Kovalchuk, 2011, Zucchi et al., 2012).

The phenotypic findings in behaviour and physiology were supported by molecular changes involving epigenetic regulation of gene expression in the brain and uterus. Our study indicated that the multigenerational stress altered microRNA (miRNA) expression patterns in brain and uterus of F2 mothers, including the miR-200 family (Yao et al., 2014). In particular, stress led to upregulation of miR-200b and downregulation of miR-429. In the uterus, both miR-200b and miR-429 were suggested to modulate gestational length through interaction with their gene targets *Stat5b*, *Zeb1* and *Zeb2* (Renthal et al., 2010). The data indicated that when upregulated, miR-200b may suppress *Stat5b*, *Zeb1* and *Zeb2* mRNA levels in the lineage that exposed each generation of pregnant dams to prenatal stress (i.e., the F2 offspring from stressed F0 and F1 generations). Furthermore, stress also increased miR-181a expression in the placenta (Yao et al., 2014) miR-181a has been associated with PTB in humans and may serve as a marker of shortened gestation (Mayor-Lynn et al., 2011). These findings suggest that the mechanisms involved in the timing of parturition and associated behavioural and physiological signatures may be programmed through the maternal lineage. The identification of epigenetic signatures of PTB in clinically accessible tissues, such as placenta, offers the potential for predictive and preventive studies related to poor pregnancy outcomes.

Transgenerational studies. A healthy pregnancy starts long before conception. Cumulative effects of stress throughout the lifetime and even in ancestors seem to be particularly important for PTB risk (Rich-Edwards and Grizzard, 2005). Such cumulative effects may include increased sensitivity to stress due to programming by stress in the ancestors. Interestingly, elevated PTB risk was noted to propagate through generations (Porter et al., 1997), suggesting that factors determining PTB risk may be passed on to the offspring through the maternal lineage. Our data suggest that indeed that exposure of a mother, grandmother or great-grandmother to gestational stress may increase the risk of PTB. While high levels of psychological stress have been positively correlated with PTB in humans (Hedegaard et al., 1993, Hobel, 2004), the causal link may involve the endocrine regulation and cytokine milieu for maintenance of pregnancy and timing of delivery (Arck, 2001, Coussons-Read et al., 2012, Miller and Riegle, 1985). Protective mechanisms, such as a down-regulation of the HPA axis activity during pregnancy, add a level of endocrine complexity to the study of stress influences on pregnancy outcomes (Glynn et al., 2001). The timing and severity of the stressor are critical in that stress in early pregnancy has greater effects on gestation length than stress experienced in the last trimester (Glynn et al., 2001).

Mechanisms of prenatal stress to modulate gestational length likely include the modulation of pro-inflammatory pathways leading to PTB (Arck, 2001). Furthermore, stress may alter relevant neuropeptide and hormone levels, including prolactin, progesterone, and oxytocin, which are involved in pregnancy maintenance and the timing of parturition (Miller and Riegle, 1985). Moreover, fetal HPA axis stimulation may induce prostaglandin production by fetal membranes and decidua and result in uterine activation (Christiaens et al., 2008). Stress may also stimulate cytokines, which regulate the activity of placental 11-beta-hydroxysteroid dehydrogenase (type 2) (Kossintseva et al., 2006) to elevate PTB risk. Based on these endocrine regulations by early experience it was proposed that PTB risk may have roots in childhood (Rich-Edwards and Grizzard, 2005).

Possible mechanisms of transgenerational transmission of PTB risk may be linked to a stress-associated epigenotype involving microRNAs (miRNAs) that are replicated in subsequent generations. The rapid response of epigenetic components to maternal stress may represent the intersection of genetic and environmental factors determining PTB risk. Thus, the characterization of epigenetic regulators of genes or single nucleotide polymorphisms and their environmental regulation may provide exciting new predictive signatures and therapeutic interventions for PTB and associated health outcomes.

Mediators

Evidence suggests that adverse childhood experiences can lead to hyperreactivity of the HPA and SAM axis in response to stress in adulthood (Heim et al., 2000). This effect is even stronger in women with symptoms of depression. It is believed that ACEs can induce persistent changes in the systems involved in the stress response leading to negative health outcomes such as depression (Heim et al., 2001). This is in complete agreement with the concept of allostatic load as described earlier in this chapter. It is biologically very plausible that lifetime experience, including some disaster experiences, chronic stress, and adverse childhood experiences, can increase the risk of PTB via the inflammatory, neuroendocrine and epigenetic pathways.

Uterine-Placental Endocrine-Immune Mechanisms

Parturition at term or preterm requires a transformation of the uterus of pregnancy to the uterus of delivery as evidenced by changes in the expression and levels of uterine transformation proteins (UTFs). Typically, the prostaglandin F ($PGF_{2\alpha}$) receptor (PTGFR), oxytocin receptor, inducible cyclooxygenase-2 and gap junction protein, connexin-43, are UTFs used as proxies to monitor changes in dozens of 'transforming' proteins. The process of transformation requires three integrated components, positive feedback, synergy and amplification. Positive feedback involves the actions of key mediators, such as IL-1β, $PGF_{2\alpha}$ and CRH whereby they each stimulate expression of several cytokines, chemokines, CRH, PGs, receptors including PTGFR, and, in the case of IL-1β, its own receptor and accessory protein (Erickson et al., 2001, Ishiguro et al., 2014, You et al., 2014). In the fetal membranes and placenta, maternal cortisol can drive both CRH and PG synthesis (Challis et al., 1999, Erickson et al., 2001, Jones et al., 1989, Karalis et al., 1996, Li et al., 2014, Smith, 1998). Hence elevated levels of maternal cortisol could potentially initiate positive feedback in the uterine tissues.

Synergy is where the action of two or more mediators is more than additive of their actions alone in stimulating the events in positive feedback. An excellent example of this is when $PGF_{2\alpha}$ and IL-1β together stimulate the mRNA expression of IL-6 in human uterine smooth muscle cells several hundred-fold, which is multiples of their independent actions (Leimert et al., 2014). Amplification involves the recruitment of peripheral leukocytes to the uterine tissues whereby the release of their mediators amplifies the action of transformation. Amplification is achieved when mediators such as CRH, $PGF_{2\alpha}$ or IL-1β stimulate the release of chemoattractants from uterine tissues. Recent evidence demonstrates that CRH releases a myometrial chemoattractant (You et al., 2014).

A further consequence of upregulating uterine transformation might be that cytokines produced on the maternal side of the placenta inhibit the enzymatic action of 11BHSD2 (Kossintseva et al., 2006). This would allow more maternal cortisol to cross the placenta where the above positive feedback actions could occur on the fetal side of the placenta and in fetal membranes, leading to increases in fetal PGs, cytokines and CRH.

Neuroendocrine Mechanisms

During pregnancy either progesterone produced by the corpus luteum or by the placenta in species with long gestations can be converted via 5a-reductase, found in both the placenta and in the maternal and fetal brain cortex, into allopregnanolone, a neurosteroid that is found in both the maternal and fetal circulation. Allopregnanolone does not interact with the traditional nuclear progesterone receptors (PR) A or B, but rather with the GABA$_A$ membrane receptor, whereby it promotes chloride ion flux. It has a significant role in influencing the fetal central nervous system in late pregnancy in part by promoting neuronal growth, neuroprotection or normal cognition and behaviour, and by contributing to the sleep-like behavioural traits typical of the fetus (Hirst et al., 2009). One of the most important roles for allopregnanolone is to suppress the release of neurohypophyseal oxytocin, a uterine contractile agonist (Brunton et al., 2014).

A number of stressors in pregnancy, such as restraint stress (Frye and Walf, 2004), reduce brain allopregnanolone levels, whereas others such as hypoxic ischemia, increase allopregnanolone production (Kelleher et al., 2011). Being born preterm separates the fetus from its placental source of progesterone and puts it at considerable risk, especially to hypoxic stress. This vulnerability may be even greater in the IUGR fetus, which is likely to already have compromised growth trajectories.

Epigenetic Mechanisms

As discussed in the sections above, environmental conditions, lifestyle and stress may be linked to altered inflammatory status, health and disease, and even elevated PTB risk. A central mechanism how such dynamic gene-environment interactions are made possible is by epigenetic regulation that mediates rapid adaptation of gene expression patterns to diverse environments and experiences. Epigenetics is the study of heritable changes in gene activity without altering the DNA sequence (Migicovsky and Kovalchuk, 2011). The major epigenetic events include DNA cytosine methylation, histone modifications and post-transcriptional control through microRNA (miRNA) expression. The vital importance of epigenetic regulation in regulating gene expression is illustrated during development and maturation (Iyengar et al., 2014, Kolb et al., 2012). While each cell in a given organism shares the same genome, epigenetic regulation of gene expression allows cells, tissues, and organs to differ because certain sets of genes are "turned on" or expressed, while other sets are "turned off" or inhibited.

Considering the striking inter-generational programming of ancestral stress on PTB risk and other health complications, it is important to consider the potentially central role of inheritance of epigenetic marks. Epigenetic mechanisms may mediate a gradually altering physiological response to recurrent stress across various generations of individuals. The formation of an epigenetic memory to a single or recurrent adverse event within a family history may assist in adjusting physiological and/or behavioural patterns to a stressful environment. Epigenetic memory refers to transgenerationally stable, yet dynamic re-programming of the germline epigenome that transfers information across generations (Migicovsky and Kovalchuk, 2011, Skinner, 2008). Such heritable epigenetic changes facilitate rapid adaptation to adverse environmental conditions, but may also result in a mismatch of physiological profiles to later-life challenges, thus enhancing disease risk. Importantly, tissue-specific miRNA signatures can be found in blood plasma (Laterza et al., 2009), emphasizing the possibility to determine epigenetic signatures of prognostic significance for disease. Many common health conditions share a suspected etiology that includes both the influence of adverse perinatal origins as well as a transcriptomic component, suggesting that epigenetic regulation of gene expression may represent a central unifying feature in individual complex disease etiology (Petronis, 2010).

Transgenerational programming of PTB risk may be linked to a stress-associated epigenotype involving miRNAs that are transferred to subsequent generations. miRNAs are reasonable candidates for such a role since they are differentially regulated by progesterone during myometrial quiescence and initiation of parturition (Renthal et al., 2010, Williams et al., 2012). Including the downregulated miR-200b, the miR-200 family may exert peripheral effects to control uterine quiescence and contractility during pregnancy and labour (Renthal et al., 2010). Interestingly, members of the miR-200 family are expressed in term labour in mice and humans and upregulated in mouse models of preterm labour (Renthal et al., 2010). Members of the miR-200 family may specifically interact with the endocrine cascade involved in pregnancy maintenance and termination, including progesterone and oxytocin (Renthal et al., 2010).

Target genes of the miR-200 family include three particular genes, *Stat5b*, *Zeb1* and *Zeb2*, involved in pregnancy maintenance. In our study by Yao et al., (Yao et al., 2014), all three were downregulated by multigenerational stress in the uterus of dams of the F1 generation. The downregulation of *Zeb2* expression was still present in the F2 generation (Yao et al., 2014), and thus may be linked to the observed reduction in gestational length among F1 and F2 dams (Yao et al., 2014). A decrease in *Stat5b* expression was also linked to reduced progesterone activity and the initiation of labor, particularly PTB (Williams et al., 2012). Furthermore, ZEB1 serves as a transcription factor to inhibit the miR-200 family, thus enhancing *Stat5b* expression) (Williams et al., 2012). As the myometrium transitions to term or preterm labor, reduced progesterone activity decreases ZEB1 and ZEB2 levels via a feed-forward mechanism (Renthal et al., 2010, Williams et al., 2012), thus regulating the timing of parturition. The upregulation of uterine miR-200b may be causative for the suppression of *Stat5b* and ZEB1 and ZEB2. Differential expression of these components across generations coincides with shortened gestational length and indicates a causal or at least predictive signature of PTB.

Perhaps the most common, and the most widely studied, epigenetic modification is DNA methylation. DNA methylation occurs primarily at CpG sites of the DNA strand. Cytosines in CpG dinucleotides can be methylated, i.e., one or more methyl groups are appended to form 5-methylcytosine by enzymes called DNA methyltransferases. In mammals, methylating the cytosine within a gene can turn the gene off and suppress the expression of this gene. By contrast, hypomethylation of a CpG site is commonly associated with over-expression of the respective gene. Notably, in the human genome ~70-80% of cytosines in CpG dinucleotides are methylated (Ziller et al., 2013). Most cell types, except germ cells and pre-implantation embryos, maintain relatively stable DNA methylation patterns and only a fraction of CpG sites will alter methylation status as part of a coordinated regulatory program (Ziller et al., 2013). Consequently, DNA methylation patterns are highly tissue-specific. Importantly, a large body of evidence suggests that stress is a potent influence to alter DNA methylation patterns.

In rat mothers exposed to gestational stress, the buffering action of placental HSD11B2 may be reduced by downregulation of this enzyme (Mairesse et al., 2007, Sarkar et al., 2001). For example, restraint stress during gestational days 11–20 in rats was shown to decrease placental 11ß–HSD2 enzymatic activity and also decrease mRNA levels of this gene (Mairesse et al., 2007). Furthermore, a study by Jensen Peña and colleagues (2012) provided insights into underlying epigenetic regulation associated with altered HSD11B2 function. Here, prenatal stress increased placental mRNA levels of the DNA methyltransferase, DNMT3a, and increased DNA methylation at specific CpG sites within the HSD11B2 gene promoter, thus reducing gene expression activity at this site. Based on a comparative analysis of placenta and fetal brain, the authors also proposed that placental DNA methylation status has clinical predictive value for brain (Jensen Pena et al., 2012).

Altered DNA methylation has also been suggested to be partially responsible for the significant developmental consequences of prenatal stress in offspring brain and behaviour. For example, prenatal stress in rats alters the expression of DNA methyltransferases (Dnmt) 1 and 3a in the amygdala and hippocampus, and increases DNA methylation of exon IV of the gene for brain-derived neurotrophic factor (BDNF), a vital neurotrophic factor for brain development and axonal guidance (Boersma et al., 2014). These findings may in part explain altered affective behaviours, such as anxiety, in prenatally stressed rats, but also developmental delays associated with the exposure to elevated glucocorticoid levels *in utero*. These findings are in line with a recent study of pregnant women exposed to extreme maternal psychosocial stress in the Democratic Republic of Congo (Mulligan et al., 2012). In this study, exposure to severe stress in the mother was positively associated with low newborn birth weight and elevated newborn methylation in the promoter of the glucocorticoid receptor NR3C1, thus reducing the expression of glucocorticoid receptors and potentially impairing the ability of negative feedback regulation of the newborn's stress response (Mulligan et al., 2012). The authors suggest that increased methylation of the NR3C1 gene and the subsequently reduced GR density in the brain, such as the hippocampus, of affected newborns may ultimately reduce the range of stress adaptation responses, thus increasing their risk for adult-onset diseases (Mulligan et al., 2012). These findings support the increasingly prominent notion that many complex adult onset diseases, including the risk of preterm birth, share a multifactorial etiology.

Integration

Two-hit hypothesis. To explain the etiology of many diseases that involve a complex pathogenesis, the "multiple-hit" hypothesis has been proposed. This model has been originally developed by Nordling (1953) and Knudsen (1971) to explain the pathogenesis of cancer (Knudson, 1971, Nordling, 1953). The model proposes that genetic and environmental factors disrupt early cell and/or organ development and generate a long-term vulnerability to a "second hit" that then leads to the onset of disease symptoms. This model is now widely accepted when neither genetic nor environmental factors can be clearly identified to cause a disease. In the case of PTB, genetic factors or adverse environmental stimuli in the womb, such as maternal stress, may set the stage for endocrine and inflammatory dysregulation without any significant symptoms. A second event in adolescence or early adulthood, however, may then trigger or worsen the pathological condition and transform a previously "silent" condition into an overt health problem. In the case of PTB, such a "second hit" may be a major life event or an episode of stress.

Conclusion and Future Work

Evidence is accumulating that links stress, especially chronic and transgenerational stress, with PTB. The human data are less convincing than the animal data, but that derives mostly from the difficulty of systematically studying the problem in natural experiments that rely upon lifetime experience or natural disaster to introduce the insult that results in an adverse pregnancy outcome. The animal models are improving and through them investigators will be able to ascertain mechanisms and pathway points of convergence that will both identify markers to study in humans and potential therapeutic targets. An immediately achievable goal, even with the human data already available, should be to develop tools based upon lifetime experiences for assessing populations of vulnerable women for PTB risk as early as possible in pregnancy. This would enable closer surveillance of their pregnancies. Simple, low-cost tools capable of identifying women at the greatest risk would provide tremendous advances in improving women's pregnancy and newborn health and possibly ameliorate adverse transgenerational health outcomes.

Acknowledgments

The authors thank Kelycia Leimert, Barbara Verstraeten and Nanlin Yin for excellent editorial assistance. Studies in the authors' laboratories were funded by Alberta Innovates-Health Solutions, the Canadian Institutes of Health Research and the Global Alliance for the Prevention of Prematurity and Stillbirth, an initiative of Seattle Children's.

References

Andres, R.L. & Day, M.C. (2000). Perinatal complications associated with maternal tobacco use. *Semin. Neonatol.*, 5, 231-41.

Arck, P.C. (2001). Stress and pregnancy loss: role of immune mediators, hormones and neurotransmitters. *Am. J. Reprod. Immunol.*, 46, 117-23.

Austin, M.P. & Leader, L. (2000). Maternal stress and obstetric and infant outcomes: epidemiological findings and neuroendocrine mechanisms. *Aust. N. Z. J. Obstet. Gynaecol.*, 40, 331-7.

Babenko, O., Kovalchuk, I. & Metz, G.A. (2012). Epigenetic programming of neurodegenerative diseases by an adverse environment. *Brain Res.*, 1444, 96-111.

Baum, A. & Fleming, I. (1993). Implications of psychological research on stress and technological accidents. *Am. Psychol.*, 48, 665-72.

Berhman, R. & Butler, A. (2006). *Preterm Birth: Causes, Consequences, and Prevention*, Washington, D.C.: The National Academies Press.

Berkowitz, G.S. & Papiernik, E. (1993). Epidemiology of preterm birth. *Epidemiol. Rev.*, 15, 414-43.

Berkowitz, G.S., Wolff, M.S., Janevic, T.M., Holzman, I.R., Yehuda, R. & Landrigan, P.J. (2003). The World Trade Center disaster and intrauterine growth restriction. *JAMA*, 290, 595-6.

Binder, E.B., Bradley, R.G., Liu, W., Epstein, M.P., Deveau, T.C., Mercer, K.B., et al., (2008). Association of FKBP5 polymorphisms and childhood abuse with risk of posttraumatic stress disorder symptoms in adults. *JAMA*, 299, 1291-305.

Boersma, G.J., Moghadam, A.A., Cordner, Z.A. & Tamashiro, K.L. (2014). Prenatal stress and stress coping style interact to predict metabolic risk in male rats. *Endocrinology*, 155, 1302-12.

Bogdan, R., Williamson, D.E. & Hariri, A.R. (2012). Mineralocorticoid receptor Iso/Val (rs5522) genotype moderates the association between previous childhood emotional neglect and amygdala reactivity. *Am. J. Psychiatry*, 169, 515-22.

Bongers, S., Janssen, N.A., Reiss, B., Grievink, L., Lebret, E. & Kromhout, H. (2008). Challenges of exposure assessment for health studies in the aftermath of chemical incidents and disasters. *J. Expo. Sci. Environ. Epidemiol.*, 18, 341-59.

Boscarino, J.A., Erlich, P.M., Hoffman, S.N. & Zhang, X. (2012). Higher FKBP5, COMT, CHRNA5, and CRHR1 allele burdens are associated with PTSD and interact with trauma exposure: implications for neuropsychiatric research and treatment. *Neuropsychiatr. Dis. Treat*, 8, 131-9.

Bradley, R.G., Binder, E.B., Epstein, M.P., Tang, Y., Nair, H.P., Liu, W., et al., (2008). Influence of child abuse on adult depression: moderation by the corticotropin-releasing hormone receptor gene. *Arch. Gen. Psychiatry*, 65, 190-200.

Brunton, P.J., Russell, J.A. & Hirst, J.J. (2014). Allopregnanolone in the brain: protecting pregnancy and birth outcomes. *Prog. Neurobiol.*, 113, 106-36.

Buchwald, U., Teupser, D., Kuehnel, F., Grohmann, J., Schmieder, N., Beindorff, N., et al., (2012). Prenatal stress programs lipid metabolism enhancing cardiovascular risk in the female F1, F2, and F3 generation in the primate model common marmoset (Callithrix jacchus). *J. Med. Primatol.*, 41, 231-40.

Buekens, P., Xiong, X. & Harville, E. (2006). Hurricanes and pregnancy. *Birth,* 33, 91-3.

Callaghan, W.M., Rasmussen, S.A., Jamieson, D.J., Ventura, S.J., Farr, S.L., Sutton, P.D., et al., (2007). Health concerns of women and infants in times of natural disasters: lessons learned from Hurricane Katrina. *Matern Child Health J.*, 11, 307-11.

Camacho, A. (2008). Stress and birth weight: Evidence from terrorist attacks. *Am. Economic Rev*, 98, 511-5.

Campbell, M.M. (2005). Tsunami and the silent tide: the invisible challenge of women's health. *J. Fam. Plann Reprod. Health Care*, 31, 95, 97.

Cannon, W.B. (1928). The mechanism of emotinal disturbance of bodily functions. *N. Engl. J. Med.*, 198, 877-84.

Cannon, W.B. (1929). Organization for physiological homeostasis. *Physiol. Rev.*, 9, 399-431.

Carballo, M., Hernandez, M., Schneider, K. & Welle, E. (2005). Impact of the Tsunami on reproductive health. *J. R. Soc. Med.*, 98, 400-3.

Caspi, A., Hariri, A.R., Holmes, A., Uher, R. & Moffitt, T.E. (2010). Genetic sensitivity to the environment: the case of the serotonin transporter gene and its implications for studying complex diseases and traits. *Am. J. Psychiatry*, 167, 509-27.

Caspi, A., Sugden, K., Moffitt, T.E., Taylor, A., Craig, I.W., Harrington, H., et al., (2003). Influence of life stress on depression: moderation by a polymorphism in the 5-HTT gene. *Science*, 301, 386-9.

Catalano, R. & Hartig, T. (2001). Communal bereavement and the incidence of very low birthweight in Sweden. *J. Health Soc. Behav.*, 42, 333-41.

Challis, J.R., Patel, F.A. & Pomini, F. (1999). Prostaglandin dehydrogenase and the initiation of labor. *J. Perinat Med.*, 27, 26-34.

Challis, J.R. & Smith, S.K. (2001). Fetal endocrine signals and preterm labor. *Biol. Neonate*, 79, 163-7.

Champagne, F.A. & Meaney, M.J. (2007). Transgenerational effects of social environment on variations in maternal care and behavioral response to novelty. *Behav. Neurosci.*, 121, 1353-63.

Chang, H.L., Chang, T.C., Lin, T.Y. & Kuo, S.S. (2002). Psychiatric morbidity and pregnancy outcome in a disaster area of Taiwan 921 earthquake. *Psychiatry Clin. Neurosci.*, 56, 139-44.

Charil, A., Laplante, D.P., Vaillancourt, C. & King, S. (2010). Prenatal stress and brain development. *Brain Res. Rev.*, 65, 56-79.

Chen, K.T., Chen, W.J., Malilay, J. & Twu, S.J. (2003). The public health response to the Chi-Chi earthquake in Taiwan, 1999. *Public Health Rep*, 118, 493-9.

Chen, M.J., Grobman, W.A., Gollan, J.K. & Borders, A.E. (2011). The use of psychosocial stress scales in preterm birth research. *Am. J. Obstet. Gynecol.*, 205, 402-34.

Chin, V.S., Van Skike, C.E., Berry, R.B., Kirk, R.E., Diaz-Granados, J. & Matthews, D.B. (2011). Effect of acute ethanol and acute allopregnanolone on spatial memory in adolescent and adult rats. *Alcohol*, 45, 473-83.

Christiaens, I. (2012). *Chronic maternal stress and genetic variants in the etiology of spontaneous preterm birth.* Doctor of Philosophy, University of Alberta.

Christiaens, I., Hegadoren, K. & Olson, D.M. (2012). Adverse childhood experiences are associated with spontaneous preterm birth: a case-control study. *Reprod. Sci.*, 19, 183A.

Christiaens, I., Pennell, C.E., Fang, X., Ang, Q.W. & Olson D.M. (2013). Two novel genetic variants in the mineralocorticoid receptor gene associate with spontaneous preterm birth. *Reprod. Sci.*, 20, 111A.

Christiaens, I., Zaragoza, D.B., Guilbert, L., Robertson, S.A., Mitchell, B.F. & Olson, D.M. (2008). Inflammatory processes in preterm and term parturition. *J. Reprod. Immunol.*, 79, 50-7.

Cohen, S., Janicki-Deverts, D., Doyle, W.J., Miller, G.E., Frank, E., Rabin, B.S., et al., (2012). Chronic stress, glucocorticoid receptor resistance, inflammation, and disease risk. *Proc. Natl. Acad. Sci. USA*, 109, 5995-9.

Coker, A.L., Sanderson, M. & Dong, B. (2004). Partner violence during pregnancy and risk of adverse pregnancy outcomes. *Paediatr Perinat Epidemiol*, 18, 260-9.

Copper, R.L., Goldenberg, R.L., Das, A., Elder, N., Swain, M., Norman, G., et al., (1996). The preterm prediction study: maternal stress is associated with spontaneous preterm birth at less than thirty-five weeks' gestation. National Institute of Child Health and Human Development Maternal-Fetal Medicine Units Network. *Am. J. Obstet. Gynecol.*, 175, 1286-92.

Coussons-Read, M.E., Lobel, M., Carey, J.C., Kreither, M.O., D'Anna, K., Argys, L., et al.,
(2012). The occurrence of preterm delivery is linked to pregnancy-specific distress and
elevated inflammatory markers across gestation. *Brain Behav. Immun.*, 26, 650-9.

Covington, D.L., Hage, M., Hall, T. & Mathis, M. (2001). Preterm delivery and the severity
of violence during pregnancy. *J. Reprod. Med.*, 46, 1031-9.

Crews, D., Gillette, R., Scarpino, S.V., Manikkam, M., Savenkova, M.I. & Skinner, M.K.
(2012). Epigenetic transgenerational inheritance of altered stress responses. *Proc. Natl.
Acad. Sci. USA*, 109, 9143-8.

Dai, X., Thavundayil, J., Santella, S. & Gianoulakis, C. (2007). Response of the HPA-axis to
alcohol and stress as a function of alcohol dependence and family history of alcoholism.
Psychoneuroendocrinology, 32, 293-305.

Dancause, K.N., Laplante, D.P., Oremus, C., Fraser, S., Brunet, A. & King, S. (2011).
Disaster-related prenatal maternal stress influences birth outcomes: project Ice Storm.
Early Hum. Dev, 87, 813-20.

Dayan, J., Creveuil, C., Herlicoviez, M., Herbel, C., Baranger, E., Savoye, C. et al., (2002).
Role of anxiety and depression in the onset of spontaneous preterm labor. *Am. J.
Epidemiol.*, 155, 293-301.

De Kloet, E.R., Vreugdenhil, E., Oitzl, M.S. & Joels, M. (1998). Brain corticosteroid receptor
balance in health and disease. *Endocr. Rev.*, 19, 269-301.

DeRijk, R.H., De Kloet, E.R., Zitman, F.G. & Van Leeuwen, N. (2011). Mineralocorticoid
receptor gene variants as determinants of HPA axis regulation and behavior. *Endocr.
Dev.*, 20, 137-48.

Dias, B.G. & Ressler, K.J. (2014). Parental olfactory experience influences behavior and
neural structure in subsequent generations. *Nat. Neurosci.*, 17, 89-96.

Djuric, Z., Bird, C.E., Furumoto-Dawson, A., Rauscher, G.H., Ruffin, M.T., 4th, Stowe, R.P.,
et al., (2008). Biomarkers of Psychological Stress in Health Disparities Research. *Open
Biomark J*, 1, 7-19.

Dole, N., Savitz, D.A., Hertz-Picciotto, I., Siega-Riz, A.M., McMahon, M.J. & Buekens, P.
(2003). Maternal stress and preterm birth. *Am. J. Epidemiol.*, 157, 14-24.

Drake, A.J., Walker, B.R. & Seckl, J.R. (2005). Intergenerational consequences of fetal
programming by in utero exposure to glucocorticoids in rats. *Am. J. Physiol. Regul.
Integr. Comp. Physiol*, 288, R34-8.

Dygalo, N.N., Sakharov, D.G., Kalinina, T.S. & Shishkina, G.T. (1999). [The behavioral
effects of a single adverse exposure in a number of rat generations: the role of maternal
glucocorticoids]. *Zh Vyssh Nerv Deiat Im I P Pavlova*, 49, 489-94.

Ekwo, E.E., Gosselink, C.A. & Moawad, A. (1992). Unfavorable outcome in penultimate
pregnancy and premature rupture of membranes in successive pregnancy. *Obstet.
Gynecol.*, 80, 166-72.

Elenkov, I.J., Webster, E.L., Torpy, D.J. & Chrousos, G.P. (1999). Stress, corticotropin-
releasing hormone, glucocorticoids, and the immune/inflammatory response: acute and
chronic effects. *Ann. N Y Acad. Sci.*, 876, 1-11; discussion 11-3.

Emanuel, I., Leisenring, W., Williams, M.A., Kimpo, C., Estee, S., O'Brien, W., et al.,
(1999). The Washington State Intergenerational Study of Birth Outcomes: methodology
and some comparisons of maternal birthweight and infant birthweight and gestation in
four ethnic groups. *Paediatr Perinat Epidemiol.*, 13, 352-69.

Engel, S.M., Berkowitz, G.S., Wolff, M.S. & Yehuda, R. (2005). Psychological trauma associated with the World Trade Center attacks and its effect on pregnancy outcome. *Paediatr Perinat Epidemiol.*, 19, 334-41.

Erickson, K., Thorsen, P., Chrousos, G., Grigoriadis, D.E., Khongsaly, O., McGregor, J. et al., (2001). Preterm birth: associated neuroendocrine, medical, and behavioral risk factors. *J. Clin. Endocrinol. Metab.*, 86, 2544-52.

Ewing, B., Buchholtz, S. & Rotanz, R. (2008). Assisting pregnant women to prepare for disaster. *MCN Am. J. Matern Child Nurs*, 33, 98-103.

Fernandez, F.M. & Krueger, P.M. (1999). Domestic violence: effect on pregnancy outcome. *J. Am. Osteopath Assoc.*, 99, 254-6.

Fine, R., Zhang, J. & Stevens, H.E. (2014). Prenatal stress and inhibitory neuron systems: implications for neuropsychiatric disorders. *Mol. Psychiatry*.

Folkman, S., Lazarus, R.S., Dunkel-Schetter, C., DeLongis, A. & Gruen, R.J. (1986a). Dynamics of a stressful encounter: cognitive appraisal, coping, and encounter outcomes. *J. Pers. Soc. Psychol.*, 50, 992-1003.

Folkman, S., Lazarus, R.S., Gruen, R.J. & DeLongis, A. (1986b). Appraisal, coping, health status, and psychological symptoms. *J. Pers. Soc. Psychol.*, 50, 571-9.

Franklin, T.B., Linder, N., Russig, H., Thony, B. & Mansuy, I.M. (2011). Influence of early stress on social abilities and serotonergic functions across generations in mice. *PLoS One*, 6, e21842.

Frye, C.A. & Walf, A.A. (2004). Hippocampal 3alpha, 5alpha-THP may alter depressive behavior of pregnant and lactating rats. *Pharmacol. Biochem. Behav.*, 78, 531-40.

Gapp, K., Jawaid, A., Sarkies, P., Bohacek, J., Pelczar, P., Prados, J., et al., (2014). Implication of sperm RNAs in transgenerational inheritance of the effects of early trauma in mice. *Nat. Neurosci.*, 17, 667-9.

Gillespie, C.F., Phifer, J., Bradley, B. & Ressler, K.J. (2009). Risk and resilience: genetic and environmental influences on development of the stress response. *Depress Anxiety*, 26, 984-92.

Glynn, L.M., Wadhwa, P.D., Dunkel-Schetter, C., Chicz-Demet, A. & Sandman, C.A. (2001). When stress happens matters: effects of earthquake timing on stress responsivity in pregnancy. *Am. J. Obstet. Gynecol.*, 184, 637-42.

Goldenberg, R.L., Culhane, J.F., Iams, J.D. & Romero, R. (2008). Epidemiology and causes of preterm birth. *Lancet*, 371, 75-84.

Goldman, L.R., Paigen, B., Magnant, M.M. & Highlant, J.H. (1985). Low birth-weight, prematurity and birth-defects in children living near the hazardous-waste site, Love Canal. *Hazardous Waste & Hazardous Materials*, 2, 209-23.

Gomez, L.M., Sammel, M.D., Appleby, D.H., Elovitz, M.A., Baldwin, D.A., Jeffcoat, M.K., et al., (2010). Evidence of a gene-environment interaction that predisposes to spontaneous preterm birth: a role for asymptomatic bacterial vaginosis and DNA variants in genes that control the inflammatory response. *Am. J. Obstet. Gynecol.*, 202, 386.e1-6.

Guyton, A.C. & Hall, J.E. (2006). *Textbook of medical physiology*. Philadelphia, Pennsylvania: Elsevier Inc.

Hamilton, B.E., Sutton, P.D., Mathews, T.J., Martin, J.A. & Ventura, S.J. (2009). The effect of Hurricane Katrina: births in the U.S. Gulf Coast region, before and after the storm. *Natl Vital Stat Rep*, 58, 1-28, 32.

Harris, A. & Seckl, J. (2011). Glucocorticoids, prenatal stress and the programming of disease. *Horm Behav*, 59, 279-89.

Harville, E., Xiong, X. & Buekens, P. (2010). Disasters and perinatal health: a systematic review. *Obstet. Gynecol. Surv.*, 65, 713-28.

Hayatbakhsh, M.R., Flenady, V.J., Gibbons, K.S., Kingsbury, A.M., Hurrion, E., Mamun, A.A., et al., (2012). Birth outcomes associated with cannabis use before and during pregnancy. *Pediatr Res.*, 71, 215-9.

Heaman, M.I., Gupton A.L. & Moffatt, M.E. (2005). Prevalence and predictors of inadequate prenatal care: a comparison of aboriginal and non-aboriginal women in Manitoba. *J. Obstet. Gynaecol. Can.*, 27, 237-46.

Hedegaard, M., Henriksen, T.B., Sabroe, S. & Secher, N.J. (1993). Psychological distress in pregnancy and preterm delivery. *BMJ*, 307, 234-9.

Hedegaard, M., Henriksen, T.B., Secher, N.J., Hatch, M.C. & Sabroe, S. (1996). Do stressful life events affect duration of gestation and risk of preterm delivery? *Epidemiology*, 7, 339-45.

Heim, C., Newport, D.J., Bonsall, R., Miller, A.H. & Nemeroff, C.B. (2001). Altered pituitary-adrenal axis responses to provocative challenge tests in adult survivors of childhood abuse. *Am. J. Psychiatry*, 158, 575-81.

Heim, C., Newport, D.J., Heit, S., Graham, Y.P., Wilcox, M., Bonsall, R., et al., (2000). Pituitary-adrenal and autonomic responses to stress in women after sexual and physical abuse in childhood. *JAMA*, 284, 592-7.

Hendler, I., Goldenberg, R.L., Mercer, B.M., Iams, J.D., Meis, P.J., Moawad, A.H., et al., (2005). The Preterm Prediction Study: association between maternal body mass index and spontaneous and indicated preterm birth. *Am. J. Obstet. Gynecol.*, 192, 882-6.

Herbison, A.E. (2001). Physiological roles for the neurosteroid allopregnanolone in the modulation of brain function during pregnancy and parturition. *Prog. Brain Res.*, 133, 39-47.

Hettema, J.M., An, S.S., Bukszar, J., Van den Oord, E.J., Neale, M.C., Kendler, K.S., et al., (2008). Catechol-O-methyltransferase contributes to genetic susceptibility shared among anxiety spectrum phenotypes. *Biol. Psychiatry*, 64, 302-10.

Hirst, J.J., Walker, D.W., Yawno, T. & Palliser, H.K. (2009). Stress in pregnancy: a role for neuroactive steroids in protecting the fetal and neonatal brain. *Dev. Neurosci.*, 31, 363-77.

Hobel, C.J. (2004). Stress and preterm birth. *Clin. Obstet. Gynecol.*, 47, 856-80; discussion 881-2.

International HapMap Consortium. (2005). A haplotype map of the human genome. *Nature*, 437, 1299-320.

Ishiguro, T., Bronson, H., Takeda, J., Fang, X. & Olson, D.M. (2014). Interleukin-1 (IL-1) Receptor 1 and (IL-1) Receptor Accessory Protein increase at delivery in rat uterus. *Reprod. Sci.*, 21 (3 Suppl), 238A.

Ishitobi, Y., Nakayama, S., Yamaguchi, K., Kanehisa, M., Higuma, H., Maruyama, Y., et al., (2012). Association of CRHR1 and CRHR2 with major depressive disorder and panic disorder in a Japanese population. *Am. J. Med. Genets B Neuropsychiatr Genet*, 159B, 429-36.

Iyengar, B.R., Choudhary, A., Sarangdhar, M.A., Venkatesh, K.V., Gadgil, C.J. & Pillai, B. (2014). Non-coding RNA interact to regulate neuronal development and function. *Front Cell Neurosci.*, 8, 47.

Jensen Peña, C., Monk, C. & Champagne, F.A. (2012). Epigenetic effects of prenatal stress on 11beta-hydroxysteroid dehydrogenase-2 in the placenta and fetal brain. *PLoS One*, 7, e39791.

Joels, M., Karst, H., DeRijk, R. & de Kloet, E.R. (2008). The coming out of the brain mineralocorticoid receptor. *Trends Neurosci.*, 31, 1-7.

Jones, S.A., Brooks, A.N. & Challis, J.R. (1989). Steroids modulate corticotropin-releasing hormone production in human fetal membranes and placenta. *J. Clin. Endocrinol. Metab.*, 68, 825-30.

Kaati, G., Bygren, L.O. & Edvinsson, S. (2002). Cardiovascular and diabetes mortality determined by nutrition during parents' and grandparents' slow growth period. *Eur. J. Hum. Genet.*, 10, 682-8.

Karalis, K., Goodwin, G. & Majzoub, J.A. (1996). Cortisol blockade of progesterone: a possible molecular mechanism involved in the initiation of human labor. *Nat Med*, 2, 556-60.

Keers, R. & Uher, R. (2012). Gene-environment interaction in major depression and antidepressant treatment response. *Curr. Psychiatry Rep*, 14, 129-37.

Kelleher, M.A., Palliser, H.K., Walker, D.W. & Hirst, J.J. (2011). Sex-dependent effect of a low neurosteroid environment and intrauterine growth restriction on foetal guinea pig brain development. *J. Endocrinol.*, 208, 301-9.

King, S. & Laplante, D.P. (2005). The effects of prenatal maternal stress on children's cognitive development: Project Ice Storm. *Stress*, 8, 35-45.

Kleinhaus, K., Harlap, S., Perrin, M., Manor, O., Margalit-Calderon, R., Opler, M., et al., (2013). Prenatal stress and affective disorders in a population birth cohort. *Bipolar Disord*, 15, 92-9.

Knudson, A.G., Jr. (1971). Mutation and cancer: statistical study of retinoblastoma. *Proc. Natl. Acad. Sci. USA*, 68, 820-3.

Kolassa, I.T., Kolassa, S., Ertl, V., Papassotiropoulos, A. & De Quervain, D.J. (2010). The risk of posttraumatic stress disorder after trauma depends on traumatic load and the catechol-o-methyltransferase Val(158)Met polymorphism. *Biol. Psychiatry*, 67, 304-8.

Kolb, B., Mychasiuk, R., Muhammad, A., Li, Y., Frost, D.O. & Gibb, R. (2012). Experience and the developing prefrontal cortex. *Proc. Natl. Acad. Sci. USA*, 109 Suppl 2, 17186-93.

Kossintseva, I., Wong, S., Johnstone, E., Guilbert, L., Olson, D.M. & Mitchell, B.F. (2006). Proinflammatory cytokines inhibit human placental 11beta-hydroxysteroid dehydrogenase type 2 activity through Ca2+ and cAMP pathways. *Am. J. Physiol. Endocrinol. Metab.*, 290, E282-8.

Kramer, M.S., Goulet, L., Lydon, J., Seguin, L., McNamara, H., Dassa, C., et al., (2001). Socio-economic disparities in preterm birth: causal pathways and mechanisms. *Paediatr Perinat Epidemiol.*, 15 Suppl 2, 104-23.

Kramer, M.S., Lydon, J., Goulet, L., Kahn, S., Dahhou, M., Platt, R.W., et al., (2013). Maternal stress/distress, hormonal pathways and spontaneous preterm birth. *Paediatr Perinat Epidemiol.*, 27, 237-46.

Kramer, M.S., Seguin, L., Lydon, J. & Goulet, L. (2000). Socio-economic disparities in pregnancy outcome: why do the poor fare so poorly? *Paediatr Perinat Epidemiol.*, 14, 194-210.

Kumsta, R., Moser, D., Streit, F., Koper, J.W., Meyer, J. & Wust, S. (2009). Characterization of a glucocorticoid receptor gene (GR, NR3C1) promoter polymorphism reveals functionality and extends a haplotype with putative clinical relevance. *Am. J. Med. Genet. B Neuropsychiatr Genet*, 150B, 476-82.

Kusuda, S., Fujimura, M. & Takeuchi, T. (1995). Perinatal medical support in the area surrounding the Hanshin-Awaji earthquake. *Acta Paediatr Jpn*, 37, 731-4.

Laterza, O.F., Lim, L., Garrett-Engele, P.W., Vlasakova, K., Muniappa, N., Tanaka, W.K., et al., (2009). Plasma microRNAs as sensitive and specific biomarkers of tissue injury. *Clin. Chem.*, 55, 1977-83.

Lazarus, R.S. & Cohen, J.B. (1977). Environmental Stress. In: *Human behavior and the environment: Current theory and research*. Altman, I. & Wohlwill, J.F. (eds). New York: Plenum.

Lederman, S.A., Rauh, V., Weiss, L., Stein, J.L., Hoepner, L.A., Becker, M., et al., (2004). The effects of the World Trade Center event on birth outcomes among term deliveries at three lower Manhattan hospitals. *Environ. Health Perspect*, 112, 1772-8.

Leimert, K.B., Fang, X., Chemtob., S. & Olson, D.M. (2014). Synergistic effects of Prostaglandin F2α and Interleukin-1β on uterine activation proteins Cyclooxygenase-2 and IL-6 mRNA abundance in human myometrial smooth muscle cells suggest amplification is a key mechanism for labour. *Reprod. Sci.*, 21 (3 Suppl), 244A.

Lesch, K.P. (2007). Linking emotion to the social brain. The role of the serotonin transporter in human social behaviour. *EMBO Rep.*, 8 Spec No, S24-9.

Leuchter, A.F., McCracken, J.T., Hunter, A.M., Cook, I.A. & Alpert, J.E. (2009). Monoamine oxidase a and catechol-o-methyltransferase functional polymorphisms and the placebo response in major depressive disorder. *J. Clin. Psychopharmacol.*, 29, 372-7.

Levi, R., Lundberg, U., Hanson, U. & Frankenhacuser, M. (1989). Anxiety during pregnancy after the Chernobyl accident as related to obstetric outcome. *J. Psychosom. Obstet. Gynecol.*, 10, 221-30.

Li, X.Q., Zhu, P., Myatt, L. & Sun, K. (2014). Roles of glucocorticoids in human parturition: A controversial fact? *Placenta*, 35, 291-6.

Liu, Z., Zhu, F., Wang, G., Xiao, Z., Wang, H., Tang, J., et al., (2006). Association of corticotropin-releasing hormone receptor 1 gene SNP and haplotype with major depression. *Neurosci. Lett.*, 404, 358-62.

Lu, N.Z., Wardell, S.E., Burnstein, K.L., Defranco, D., Fuller, P.J., Giguere, V., et al., (2006). International Union of Pharmacology. LXV. The pharmacology and classification of the nuclear receptor superfamily: glucocorticoid, mineralocorticoid, progesterone, and androgen receptors. *Pharmacol. Rev.*, 58, 782-97.

Luke, B., Mamelle, N., Keith, L., Munoz, F., Minogue, J., Papiernik, E. et al., (1995). The association between occupational factors and preterm birth: a United States nurses' study. Research Committee of the Association of Women's Health, Obstetric, and Neonatal Nurses. *Am. J. Obstet. Gynecol.*, 173, 849-62.

Macones, G.A., Parry, S., Elkousy, M., Clothier, B., Ural, S.H. & Strauss, J.F., 3rd. (2004). A polymorphism in the promoter region of TNF and bacterial vaginosis: preliminary evidence of gene-environment interaction in the etiology of spontaneous preterm birth. *Am. J. Obstet. Gynecol.*, 190, 1504-8; discussion 3A.

Mairesse, J., Lesage, J., Breton, C., Breant, B., Hahn, T., Darnaudery, M., et al., (2007). Maternal stress alters endocrine function of the feto-placental unit in rats. *Am. J. Physiol. Endocrinol. Metab.*, 292, E1526-33.

Mann, J.R., McDermott, S. & Gill, T. (2010). Sexually transmitted infection is associated with increased risk of preterm birth in South Carolina women insured by Medicaid. *J. Matern Fetal Neonatal Med.*, 23, 563-8.

Maric, N.P., Dunjic, B., Stojiljkovic, D.J., Britvic, D. & Jasovic-Gasic, M. (2010). Prenatal stress during the 1999 bombing associated with lower birth weight-a study of 3,815 births from Belgrade. *Arch. Womens Ment Health*, 13, 83-9.

Mayor-Lynn, K., Toloubeydokhti, T., Cruz, A.C. & Chegini, N. (2011). Expression profile of microRNAs and mRNAs in human placentas from pregnancies complicated by preeclampsia and preterm labor. *Reprod. Sci.*, 18, 46-56.

McEwen, B.S. (1998a). Protective and damaging effects of stress mediators. *N. Engl. J. Med.*, 338, 171-9.

McEwen, B.S. (1998b). Stress, adaptation, and disease. Allostasis and allostatic load. *Ann. N Y Acad. Sci.*, 840, 33-44.

McEwen, B.S. & Seeman, T. (1999). Protective and damaging effects of mediators of stress. Elaborating and testing the concepts of allostasis and allostatic load. *Ann. N Y Acad. Sci.*, 896, 30-47.

McEwen, B.S. & Wingfield, J.C. (2003). The concept of allostasis in biology and biomedicine. *Horm Behav*, 43, 2-15.

Migicovsky, Z. & Kovalchuk, I. (2011). Epigenetic memory in mammals. *Front Genet*, 2, 28.

Mikkola, K., Ritari, N., Tommiska, V., Salokorpi, T., Lehtonen, L., Tammela, O., et al., (2005). Neurodevelopmental outcome at 5 years of age of a national cohort of extremely low birth weight infants who were born in 1996-1997. *Pediatrics*, 116, 1391-400.

Miller, A.E. & Riegle, G.D. (1985). Progesterone and luteinizing hormone secretion following stress-induced interruption of constant estrus in aged rats. *J. Gerontol.*, 40, 129-32.

Morgan, C.P. & Bale, T.L. (2011). Early prenatal stress epigenetically programs dysmasculinization in second-generation offspring via the paternal lineage. *J. Neurosci.*, 31, 11748-55.

Mozurkewich, E.L., Luke, B., Avni, M. & Wolf, F.M. (2000). Working conditions and adverse pregnancy outcome: a meta-analysis. *Obstet. Gynecol.*, 95, 623-35.

Muhtz, C., Zyriax, B.C., Bondy, B., Windler, E. & Otte, C. (2011). Association of a common mineralocorticoid receptor gene polymorphism with salivary cortisol in healthy adults. *Psychoneuroendocrinology*, 36, 298-301.

Mulligan, C.J., D'Errico, N.C., Stees, J. & Hughes, D.A. (2012). Methylation changes at NR3C1 in newborns associate with maternal prenatal stress exposure and newborn birth weight. *Epigenetics*, 7, 853-7.

Neggers, Y., Goldenberg, R., Cliver, S. & Hauth, J. (2004). Effects of domestic violence on preterm birth and low birth weight. *Acta Obstet. Gynecol. Scand.*, 83, 455-60.

Neggers, Y., Goldenberg, R., Cliver, S. & Hauth, J. (2006). The relationship between psychosocial profile, health practices, and pregnancy outcomes. *Acta Obstet. Gynecol. Scand*, 85, 277-85.

Neuberg, M., Pawlosek, W., Lopuszanski, M. & Neuberg, J. (1998). [The analysis of the course of pregnancy, delivery and postpartum among women touched by flood disaster in Kotlin Klodzki in July 1997]. *Ginekol. Pol.*, 69, 866-70.

Newnham, J.P. (2001). Is prenatal glucocorticoid administration another origin of adult disease? *Clin. Exp. Pharmacol. Physiol.*, 28, 957-61.

Nilsson, E.E., Anway, M.D., Stanfield, J. & Skinner, M.K. (2008). Transgenerational epigenetic effects of the endocrine disruptor vinclozolin on pregnancies and female adult onset disease. *Reproduction*, 135, 713-21.

Njenga, F. & Nyamai, C. (2005). The experience of the Nairobi US Embassy bombing. In: *Disasters and mental health.* Lopez-Ibor, J.J., Christodoulou, G., Maj, M., Sartorius, N. & Okasha, A. (Eds). New York, NY: John Wiley & Sons Ltd.

Nordling, C.O. (1953). A new theory on cancer-inducing mechanism. *Br. J. Cancer*, 7, 68-72.

Norris, F.H. & Uhl, G.A. (1993). Chronic stress as a mediator of acute stress: The case of Hurricane Hugo. *J. Appl. Soc. Psychol.*, 23, 1263-84.

O'Leary, C.M., Nassar, N., Kurinczuk, J.J. & Bower, C. (2009). The effect of maternal alcohol consumption on fetal growth and preterm birth. *BJOG*, 116, 390-400.

Orr, S.T., James, S.A. & Blackmore Prince, C. (2002). Maternal prenatal depressive symptoms and spontaneous preterm births among African-American women in Baltimore, Maryland. *Am. J. Epidemiol.*, 156, 797-802.

Paris, J.J., Brunton, P.J., Russell, J.A. & Frye, C.A. (2011). Immune stress in late pregnant rats decreases length of gestation and fecundity, and alters later cognitive and affective behaviour of surviving pre-adolescent offspring. *Stress*, 14, 652-64.

Paris, J.J. & Frye, C.A. (2011a). Gestational exposure to variable stressors produces decrements in cognitive and neural development of juvenile male and female rats. *Curr. Top. Med. Chem.*, 11, 1706-13.

Paris, J.J. & Frye, C.A. (2011b). Juvenile offspring of rats exposed to restraint stress in late gestation have impaired cognitive performance and dysregulated progestogen formation. *Stress*, 14, 23-32.

Pascali-Bonaro, D. (2002). Pregnant and widowed on September 11: the birth community reaches out. *Birth*, 29, 62-4.

Petronis, A. (2010). Epigenetics as a unifying principle in the aetiology of complex traits and diseases. *Nature*, 465, 721-7.

Porter, T.F., Fraser, A.M., Hunter, C.Y., Ward, R.H. & Varner, M.W. (1997). The risk of preterm birth across generations. *Obstet. Gynecol.*, 90, 63-7.

Quesada, O., Gotman, N., Howell, H.B., Funai, E.F., Rounsaville, B.J. & Yonkers, K.A. (2012). Prenatal hazardous substance use and adverse birth outcomes. *J. Matern Fetal. Neonatal Med.*, 25, 1222-7.

Relton, C.L. & Davey Smith, G. (2010). Epigenetic epidemiology of common complex disease: prospects for prediction, prevention, and treatment. *PLoS Med.*, 7, e1000356.

Renthal, N.E., Chen, C.C., Williams, K.C., Gerard, R.D., Prange-Kiel, J. & Mendelson, C.R. (2010). miR-200 family and targets, ZEB1 and ZEB2, modulate uterine quiescence and contractility during pregnancy and labor. *Proc. Natl. Acad. Sci. USA*, 107, 20828-33.

Rich-Edwards, J.W. & Grizzard, T.A. (2005). Psychosocial stress and neuroendocrine mechanisms in preterm delivery. *Am. J. Obstet. Gynecol.*, 192, S30-5.

Rini, C.K., Dunkel-Schetter, C., Wadhwa, P.D. & Sandman, C.A. (1999). Psychological adaptation and birth outcomes: the role of personal resources, stress, and sociocultural context in pregnancy. *Health Psychol.*, 18, 333-45.

Sapir, D.G. (1993). Natural and man-made disasters: the vulnerability of women-headed households and children without families. *World Health Stat. Q*, 46, 227-33.

Sarkar, S., Tsai, S.W., Nguyen, T.T., Plevyak, M., Padbury, J.F. & Rubin, L.P. (2001). Inhibition of placental 11beta-hydroxysteroid dehydrogenase type 2 by catecholamines via alpha-adrenergic signaling. *Am. J. Physiol. Regul. Integr. Comp. Physiol.*, 281, R1966-74.

Schellekens, A.F., Franke, B., Ellenbroek, B., Cools, A., de Jong, C.A., Buitelaar, J.K., et al., (2012). COMT Val158Met modulates the effect of childhood adverse experiences on the risk of alcohol dependence. *Addict. Biol.*, 18, 344-56.

Schwab, M. (2009). [Intrauterine programming of disorders of brain function in later life]. *Gynakol Geburtshilfliche Rundsch*, 49, 13-28.

Seckl, J.R. (2008). Glucocorticoids, developmental 'programming' and the risk of affective dysfunction. *Prog. Brain Res.*, 167, 17-34.

Selye, H. (1998). A syndrome produced by diverse nocuous agents. 1936. *J. Neuropsychiatry Clin Neurosci*, 10, 230-1.

Selye, H. & Fortier, C. (1950). Adaptive reaction to stress. *Psychosom. Med.*, 12, 149-57.

Shah, N.R. & Bracken, M.B. (2000). A systematic review and meta-analysis of prospective studies on the association between maternal cigarette smoking and preterm delivery. *Am. J. Obstet. Gynecol.*, 182, 465-72.

Skinner, M.K. (2008). What is an epigenetic transgenerational phenotype? F3 or F2. *Reprod. Toxicol*, 25, 2-6.

Skinner, M.K., Manikkam, M. & Guerrero-Bosagna, C. (2010). Epigenetic transgenerational actions of environmental factors in disease etiology. *Trends Endocrinol. Metab.*, 21, 214-22.

Skinner, M.K., Manikkam, M., Tracey, R., Guerrero-Bosagna, C., Haque, M. & Nilsson, E.E. (2013). Ancestral dichlorodiphenyltrichloroethane (DDT) exposure promotes epigenetic transgenerational inheritance of obesity. *BMC Med.*, 11, 228.

Smith, E.M., Meyer, W.J. & Blalock, J.E. (1982). Virus-induced corticosterone in hypophysectomized mice: a possible lymphoid adrenal axis. *Science*, 218, 1311-2.

Smith, R. (1998). Alterations in the hypothalamic pituitary adrenal axis during pregnancy and the placental clock that determines the length of parturition. *J. Reprod. Immunol.*, 39, 215-20.

Smits, L., Krabbendam, L., De Bie, R., Essed, G. & Van Os, J. (2006). Lower birth weight of Dutch neonates who were in utero at the time of the 9/11 attacks. *J. Psychosom Res.*, 61, 715-7.

Steer, P. (2005). The epidemiology of preterm labour. *BJOG*, 112 Suppl 1, 1-3.

Steptoe, A. & Ussher, M. (2006). Smoking, cortisol and nicotine. *Int. J. Psychophysiol.*, 59, 228-35.

Sterling, P. & Ever, J. (1988). Allostasis: a new paradigm to explain arousal pathology. In: *Handbook of Life Stress, Cognition and Health.* Fisher, S. & Reason, J. (Eds). New York: John Wiley & Sons.

Stratakis, C.A. & Chrousos, G.P. (1995). Neuroendocrinology and pathophysiology of the stress system. *Ann. N Y Acad. Sci.*, 771, 1-18.

Tan, C.E., Li, H.J., Zhang, X.G., Zhang, H., Han, P.Y., An, Q., et al., (2009). The impact of the Wenchuan earthquake on birth outcomes. *PLoS One*, 4, e8200.

Tong, V.T., Zotti, M.E. & Hsia, J. (2011). Impact of the Red River catastrophic flood on women giving birth in North Dakota, 1994-2000. *Matern Child Health J.*, 15, 281-8.

Vale, W., Spiess, J., Rivier, C. & Rivier, J. (1981). Characterization of a 41-residue ovine hypothalamic peptide that stimulates secretion of corticotropin and beta-endorphin. *Science*, 213, 1394-7.

Van Dijk, A.E., Van Eijsden, M., Stronks, K., Gemke, R.J. & Vrijkotte, T.G. (2012). The association between prenatal psychosocial stress and blood pressure in the child at age 5-7 years. *PLoS One*, 7, e43548.

Van Leeuwen, N., Bellingrath, S., De Kloet, E.R., Zitman, F.G., Derijk, R.H., Kudielka, B.M. & Wust, S. (2011). Human mineralocorticoid receptor (MR) gene haplotypes modulate MR expression and transactivation: implication for the stress response. *Psychoneuroendocrinology*, 36, 699-709.

Van West, D., Del-Favero, J., Deboutte, D., Van Broeckhoven, C. & Claes, S. (2009). Arginine vasopressin receptor gene-based single-nucleotide polymorphism analysis in attention deficit hyperactivity disorder. *Psychiatr Genet*, 19, 102-3.

Veenendaal, M.V., Painter, R.C., De Rooij, S.R., Bossuyt, P.M., Van der Post, J.A., et al., (2013). Transgenerational effects of prenatal exposure to the 1944-45 Dutch famine. *BJOG*, 120, 548-53.

Velders, F.P., Kuningas, M., Kumari, M., Dekker, M.J., Uiterlinden, A.G., Kirschbaum, C., et al., (2011). Genetics of cortisol secretion and depressive symptoms: a candidate gene and genome wide association approach. *Psychoneuroendocrinology*, 36, 1053-61.

Wadhwa, P.D., Culhane, J.F., Rauh, V. & Barve, S.S. (2001). Stress and preterm birth: neuroendocrine, immune/inflammatory, and vascular mechanisms. *Matern Child Health J*, 5, 119-25.

Wadhwa, P.D., Entringer, S., Buss, C. & Lu, M.C. (2011). The contribution of maternal stress to preterm birth: issues and considerations. *Clin. Perinatol.*, 38, 351-84.

Wainstock, T., Anteby, E., Glasser, S., Shoham-Vardi, I. & Lerner-Geva, L. (2013). The association between prenatal maternal objective stress, perceived stress, preterm birth and low birthweight. *J. Matern Fetal Neonatal. Med.*, 26, 973-7.

Ward, I.D., Zucchi, F.C., Robbins, J.C., Falkenberg, E.A., Olson, D.M., Benzies, K., et al., (2013). Transgenerational programming of maternal behaviour by prenatal stress. *BMC Pregnancy Childbirth*, 13 Suppl 1, S9.

Weiss, I.C., Franklin, T.B., Vizi, S. & Mansuy, I.M. (2011). Inheritable effect of unpredictable maternal separation on behavioral responses in mice. *Front Behav. Neurosci.*, 5, 3.

Weissman, A., Siegler, E., Neiger, R., Jakobi, P. & Zimmer, E.Z. (1989). The influence of increased seismic activity on pregnancy outcome. *Eur J Obstet. Gynecol. Reprod Biol*, 31, 233-6.

Williams, K.C., Renthal, N.E., Condon, J.C., Gerard, R.D. & Mendelson, C.R. (2012). MicroRNA-200a serves a key role in the decline of progesterone receptor function leading to term and preterm labor. *Proc. Natl. Acad. Sci. USA*, 109, 7529-34.

World Health Organization, E.A. (2012). *Born too soon: the global action report on preterm birth* [Online]. Available: http://www.who.int/maternal_child_adolescent/documents/born_too_soon/en/ 2014.

Xie, P., Kranzler, H.R., Poling, J., Stein, M.B., Anton, R.F., Farrer, L.A. et al., (2010). Interaction of FKBP5 with childhood adversity on risk for post-traumatic stress disorder. *Neuropsychopharmacology*, 35, 1684-92.

Xiong, X., Harville, E.W., Mattison, D.R., Elkind-Hirsch, K., Pridjian, G. & Buekens, P. (2008). Exposure to Hurricane Katrina, post-traumatic stress disorder and birth outcomes. *Am. J. Med Sci*, 336, 111-5.

Xu, Z. & Taylor, J.A. (2009). SNPinfo: integrating GWAS and candidate gene information into functional SNP selection for genetic association studies. *Nucleic Acids Res*, 37, W600-5.

Yang, K., Jones, S.A. & Challis, J.R. (1990). Changes in glucocorticoid receptor number in the hypothalamus and pituitary of the sheep fetus with gestational age and after adrenocorticotropin treatment. *Endocrinology*, 126, 11-7.

Yao, Y., Robinson, A.M., Zucchi, F.C., Robbins, J.C., Babenko, O., Kovalchuk, I., et al., (2014). Ancestral exposure to stress epigenetically programs preterm birth risk and adverse maternal and newborn outcomes (submitted). *BMC Medicine*.

You, X., Liu, J., Xu, C., Liu, W., Zhu, X., Li, Y., et al., (2014). Corticotropin-releasing hormone (CRH) promotes inflammation in human pregnant myometrium: the evidence of CRH initiating parturition? *J. Clin. Endocrinol. Metab.*, 99, E199-208.

Zhang, J., Chen, Y., Zhang, K., Yang, H., Sun, Y., Fang, Y., et al., (2010). A cis-phase interaction study of genetic variants within the MAOA gene in major depressive disorder. *Biol Psychiatry*, 68, 795-800.

Zhu, P., Tao, F., Hao, J., Sun, Y. & Jiang, X. (2010). Prenatal life events stress: implications for preterm birth and infant birthweight. *Am. J. Obstet. Gynecol.*, 203, 34 e1-8.

Ziller, M.J., Gu, H., Muller, F., Donaghey, J., Tsai, L.T., Kohlbacher, O., et al., (2013). Charting a dynamic DNA methylation landscape of the human genome. *Nature*, 500, 477-81.

Zucchi, F.C., Yao, Y., Ilnytskyy, Y., Robbins, J.C., Soltanpour, N., Kovalchuk, I., et al., (2014). Lifetime stress cumulatively programs brain transcriptome and impedes stroke recovery: benefit of sensory stimulation. *PLoS One*, 9, e92130.

Zucchi, F.C., Yao, Y. & Metz, G.A. (2012). The secret language of destiny: stress imprinting and transgenerational origins of disease. *Front Genet*, 3, 96.

Zucchi, F.C., Yao, Y., Ward, I.D., Ilnytskyy, Y., Olson, D.M., Benzies, K., et al., (2013). Maternal stress induces epigenetic signatures of psychiatric and neurological diseases in the offspring. *PLoS One*, 8, e56967.

In: Stress and Developmental Programming …
Editors: Lubo Zhang and Lawrence D. Longo

ISBN: 978-1-63321-836-9
© 2014 Nova Science Publishers, Inc.

Chapter 14

Sex Dimorphism in Developmental Programming of Health and Disease

Kunju Sathishkumar[1] and Chandra Yallampalli[2]*

[1]Department of Obstetrics & Gynecology,
The University of Texas Medical Branch, Galveston, Texas, US
[2]Department of Obstetrics and Gynecology,
Baylor College of Medicine, Houston, Texas, US

Abstract

Events that occur in the early fetal environment have been linked to long-term health consequences in the adult. Human and animal studies have shown that unbalanced maternal nutrition is associated with the development of cardiovascular and metabolic disease in adulthood. In the maternal low protein model, protein deprivation throughout pregnancy in rats leads to elevated blood pressure in adult offspring. This model has been extensively used to study the mechanisms that may link maternal nutrition with impaired fetal growth and later cardiovascular disease. The onset and severity of hypertension is more pronounced in males than females similar to the gender differences in the occurrence of cardiovascular diseases in humans at various stages of life. This chapter discusses how recent findings using this model throw light on sex-specific peripheral vascular mechanisms that contribute for the development of hypertension in the offspring and discuss underlying mechanisms that mediate these adaptive responses. Studies from this model demonstrate that there are sex-specific disturbances in endothelial cell associated relaxations; EDHF-related in males and nitric oxide-related in females. Vasoconstriction to angiotensin II is exaggerated, with greater potency and efficacy in males. Alteration in steroid levels, estradiol and testosterone appears to have an underlying regulatory role in the development of hypertension in this model.

* Corresponding author: Chandra Yallampalli, DVM, PhD Professor and Director, Basic Sciences Perinatology Research Laboratories, Department of Obstetrics and Gynecology, Baylor College of Medicine, 1102 Bates Street, Suite # 450, Houston, Texas 77030, Phone: 832-824 4188, Fax: 832-825 7946, Email: cyallamp@bcm.edu

1. Introduction

Cardiovascular (CV) diseases are the leading cause of mortality and morbidity in the United States and worldwide. Among CV diseases, hypertension ranks first, affecting more than 73 million people—nearly 1 in 3 adults—in the United States (AHA statistics). Hypertension directly increases a patient's risk of coronary heart disease, which may lead to stroke or heart attack. Despite increased efforts to prevent, treat, and control hypertension and its sequelae, the prevalence of hypertension has not decreased. The pathogenesis of high blood pressure (BP) remains unclear, and consequently, treatment is currently based on using drugs with an emphasis on reducing the elevated BP rather than treating its causative factors.

Genetic animal models, such as spontaneously hypertensive rats (SHRs) or Dahl salt-sensitive rats, have contributed greatly to our understanding of hypertension pathophysiology. However, these genetically altered strains have abnormal vascular function prior to the development of elevated BP, thus making it difficult to precisely determine the underlying mechanisms (Mitchell et al., 2007). Also studies from these models do not truly reflect the hypertension setting in the general population partly because BP is modulated by nongenetic factors, such as exercise, endocrine hormones and diet. Recent studies show that hypertension has developmental origins, i.e., in utero exposure of the fetus to unforeseen conditions, such as under nutrition, hypoxia, or stress, resulting in the development of hypertension during adult life (Alexander, 2003, Bassan et al., 2000, Bertram et al., 2001, Edwards and McMillen, 2001, Gilbert et al., 2005, Hemmings et al., 2005, Hiraoka et al., 1991, Langley-Evans et al., 1999, Longo and Pearce, 2005, Merlet-Benichou et al., 1994, Ortiz et al., 2003, Vehaskari et al., 2001, Wintour et al., 2003, Woodall et al., 1996, Woods et al., 2001, Zhang et al., 2000). The association of etiology of CV disease with disturbances in early life was first proposed by Anders Forsdahl in 1973. Forsdahl's studies initiated the theory that poor social conditions during childhood and adolescence exerted a major influence on CV risk in adulthood (Forsdahl, 2002). David Barker expanded the concept to include the prenatal period during which variations in maternal conditions would influence CV risk later in life (Barker et al., 1989). Although both noted a strong positive correlation between coronary heart disease and infant mortality, Barker was the first to report an inverse relationship between weight at birth and BP (Barker and Osmond, 1988). Based on his observations, Barker proposed that fetal programming of adult disease occurs in response to an insult during intrauterine life, which leads to adaptations by the fetus to allow fetal survival, but also results in permanent structural and physiological changes with long-term consequences, such as an increased risk of CV disease in later life (Barker, 1994). Since the first reports by Barker and Forsdahl, numerous epidemiological studies have the link between the size at birth and BP later in life. To date, these findings have been confirmed by numerous experimental studies and provided insights into some of the mechanisms (Bertram et al., 2001, Brawley et al., 2003, Franco et al., 2002a, Gallo et al., 2013, Gangula et al., 2005, Gao et al., 2012a, 2012b, Intapad et al., 2013, Lamireau et al., 2002, Langley-Evans and Jackson, 1995, Lim and Sobey, 2011, Mizuno et al., 2013, Nanduri and Prabhakar, 2013, Ojeda et al., 2007a, 2013, Sahajpal and Ashton, 2003, Sathishkumar et al., 2012c, Sherman and Langley-Evans, 1998, Torrens et al., 2003). These experimental studies are providing insight into the mechanisms linking impaired fetal growth and the increased risk of CVD and hypertension in adulthood.

Maternal nutrition has been identified as one of the factors that influence fetal growth and the risk of adult disease. In rats, feeding of a diet with low protein during pregnancy retards fetal growth and induces hypertension in the adult offspring (Almeida and Mandarim-de-Lacerda, 2005, Augustyniak et al., 2010, Bertram et al., 2001, Brawley et al., 2003, Brennan et al., 2006, de Lima et al., 2013, Gangula et al., 2005, Mesquita et al., 2010, Pladys et al., 2005, Sathishkumar et al., 2008b, 2012a, 2012c, Scabora et al., 2013, Torrens et al., 2003, 2009, Woods et al., 2001, 2005, 2010). Other diverse techniques utilized in experimental models to induce a fetal insult during pregnancy include placental insufficiency, maternal exposure to stress, hypoxia, nicotine, alcohol, or fetal manipulation by genetic, surgical or pharmacological treatment (Alexander, 2003, Edwards et al., 2001, Gonzalez-Rodriguez et al., 2013, Gray et al., 2010, Langley-Evans, 1997, Lee et al., 2013, Nathanielsz, 2006, Ojeda et al., 2012, Ross et al., 2005, Singh et al., 2007, Tong and Zhang, 2012, van Dijk et al., 2012, Vehaskari and Woods, 2005, Woods et al., 2001, Xiao et al., 2013, Zhang, 2005). These experimental models have been applied to various species, including rat, mice and sheep, and report an important role for fetal life in the origin of a wide variety of diseases including the metabolic syndrome, obesity, diabetes, insulin resistance, CV disease and hypertension (Alexander, 2003, Bassan et al., 2000, Bertram et al., 2001, Edwards and McMillen, 2001, Gilbert et al., 2005, Hemmings et al., 2005, Hiraoka et al., 1991, Langley-Evans et al., 1999, Longo and Pearce, 2005, Merlet-Benichou et al., 1994, Ortiz et al., 2003, Vehaskari et al., 2001, Wintour et al., 2003, Woodall et al., 1996, Woods et al., 2001, Zhang et al., 2000). Rat models of low protein feeding have been extensively used to study the mechanisms that may link maternal nutrition with impaired fetal growth and later cardiovascular disease. It has been argued that such low protein (LP) diet model is relevant to humans in developing countries in which there are increased incidents of 'programmed' diseases particularly CV and metabolic syndrome (Reddy, 2002) and in poor socio-economic groups with carbohydrate-protein unbalance in developed countries. It is well-recognized that there are gender differences in the occurrence of CV diseases in humans at various stages of life (Reckelhoff, 2001) and that clinical responsiveness to antihypertensive therapies differ with gender (Ueno and Sato, 2012). The purpose of this review is specifically to discuss how recent findings using this LP model throw light on sex-specific peripheral vascular mechanisms that contribute for the development of hypertension in the offspring. This is highly relevant to the understanding of sex-specific mechanisms of programming of diseases in humans, as peripheral vascular dysfunction is associated with, and often precedes the development of hypertension, atherosclerosis, and type II diabetes (Hink et al., 2001, Jude et al., 2001, Petrie et al., 1996, Ross, 1993, 1999, Vanhala et al., 1997).

2. Sex Differences in BP Regulation

The incidence of CVD and hypertension is lower in premenopausal women compared with age-matched men and postmenopausal women (Reckelhoff, 2001). However, after menopause, the risk of hypertension increases with age (Reckelhoff, 2001, Rosamond et al., 2007) suggesting that the fully functional ovaries are protective. Sex differences in phenotypic outcome are more prevalent in LP model with increased severity of the protein restriction suggested the sex hormones may play a critical role in setting the programming response of adult BP (Sathishkumar et al., 2012c). Moderate maternal protein restriction (8-9% vs 18-22% protein in the diet in controls) during gestation results in marked elevations in BP in male, but not female offspring (Woods et al., 2001, 2005); whereas greater maternal protein restriction (4-6% protein) during gestation increases BP in offspring of both sexes (Sathishkumar et al., 2012a, 2012c, Woods et al., 2004). Therefore, the fetal response to fetal insult can be sex specific, leading to sex differences in adult phenotypic outcome. Sex differences in response to fetal programming are dependent not only on the severity of insult (Woods et al., 2005), but vary in response to different dietary insults (Khan et al., 2003), uterine hypoperfusion (Alexander, 2003), and variations in postnatal growth (Bieswal et al., 2006, Choi et al., 2007, Sathishkumar et al., 2011). Although females appeared to be more resistant to the programming in response to some of the nutritional insults (Woods et al., 2005), they are responsive to insults of excess fat in the diet (Khan et al., 2003), or glucocorticoid exposure (Matthews et al., 2004, McCormick et al., 1995).

3. Mechanisms Controlling Peripheral Vascular Reactivity

Many animal models of fetal programming report that impaired vascular function occurs in response to fetal insult (Gopalakrishnan et al., 2004, Lamireau et al., 2002, Molnar et al., 2003, Payne et al., 2003). Vascular dysfunction plays a critical role in the development of CV disease (Panza et al., 1990) and is implicated in the pathophysiology of hypertension (Christensen and Mulvany, 2001). Impaired vascular function is observed in clinical studies including healthy children with low birth weight (Beevers et al., 2001, Martin et al., 2000), suggesting that vascular consequences of fetal programming may precede the development of adult CV disease. The vascular dysfunction observed in the LP offspring may be attributed to an imbalance in the contraction and or relaxation responses to various vasoactive factors in the resistance vessels.

3.1. Vasodilator Responses

Endothelium is known to play a key role in the control of vasomotor tone and organ perfusion and significantly contributes to the regulation of arterial BP. Endothelium-dependent relaxation was found to be impaired in hypertensive human subjects (Ghiadoni et al., 1998, Panza et al., 1990, 1995, Taddei et al., 1993) and in vascular preparations from hypertensive rats (Luscher and Vanhoutte, 1986, Watt and Thurston, 1989). As a consequence of fetal programming, vascular defects such as endothelial dysfunction may be present at birth, thereby increasing the risk of cardiovascular disease in adulthood. In a number of human studies, low birth weight has been related to endothelial dysfunction in infants (Martin et al., 2000), children (Leeson et al., 1997), and young adults (Leeson et al., 2001).

Endothelium dependent mesenteric vasorelaxation to acetylcholine (ACh) was reduced in both LP male and female offspring compared to their controls (Brawley et al., 2003, Gray et al., 2013, Holemans et al., 1999, Rodford et al., 2008). Similarly, relaxation to bradykinin was also reduced in LP males (Brawley et al., 2003). Modest protein restriction was found either to decrease (Rodford et al., 2008) or not affect (Torrens et al., 2009) endothelium-dependent relaxation in LP females. Prostacyclin (PGI$_2$), nitric oxide (NO) and endothelium-derived hyperpolarizing factor (EDHF) contribute to endothelium-dependent relaxation mechanisms (Chinnathambi et al., 2013, Giles et al., 2012) in several vascular beds. However, in resistance arteries, both NO and EDHF appear to have a major, whereas PGI2 has minimal role in regulating endothelium-dependent vasodilation (Chinnathambi et al., 2013, Cooke and Davidge, 2003). The blunting of ACh and bradykinin-induced relaxation responses in LP offspring may be attributed to a reduction in endothelial NO or EDHF biosynthesis or may reflect a change in relaxation sensitivity of vascular smooth muscle to NO or EDHF.

In LP females, there were no differences in relaxation responses to sodium nitroprusside (SNP), an exogenous NO donor (Sathishkumar et al., 2008b). These observations suggest that the majority of the vascular dysfunctions in female LP offspring may be related to the endothelium and not the smooth muscle.

The L-NAME/ODQ-resistant component of ACh induced vasodilation which is attributed to EDHF, is similar in both LP and control females (Sathishkumar et al., 2008b) suggesting the involvement of NO from endothelium. Both basal and ACh-induced nitrate/nitrite (NO$_x$) generation, a surrogate marker for NO production, was significantly reduced in arteries from females in the LP compared with control animals (Sathishkumar et al., 2008b). Furthermore the decreased levels of NO appeared to be related to the decreased expression/activity of eNOS (Franco et al., 2002a), and/or to rapid degradation of NO by superoxide (Franco et al., 2002a, 2002b).

In LP males, the EDHF mediated vasodilation appeared to be reduced (Gray et al., 2013, Torrens et al., 2006) with evidence for altered gap junction functions (Gray et al., 2013). Additionally the NO-mediated endothelium dependent relaxation was reduced in LP males but this was attributed to the reduced sensitivity of vascular smooth muscle cells to NO in mesenteric arteries (Brawley et al., 2003), carotid arteries (Cambonie et al., 2007) and cortical brain microvessels (Lamireau et al., 2002). In one of these studies, significant attenuation of cGMP levels and soluble guanylate cyclase (sGC) expression together with increased expression/activity of phosphodiesterases (that degrade cGMP) were reported (Brawley et al., 2003, Lamireau et al., 2002). cGMP levels and immunoreactive soluble GC (α subunit) were approximately 3- to 4-fold lower in cortical brain microvessels of the LP compared to control group (Lamireau et al., 2002).

In addition, relaxation to cGMP analogue (8-bromo cGMP) and selective cGMP-dependent kinase stimulant (8-bromo PET cGMP) did not differ between diet groups (Lamireau et al., 2002). The mRNA levels of endothelial NO synthase in mesenteric arteries were either unchanged (Torrens et al., 2009) or increased (Rodford et al., 2008) in the LP males. These studies suggest that hypertension in adult LP male offspring is indeed associated with an altered NO-dependent vasorelaxation, which cannot be attributed to decreased NO production but rather to changes in the NO cGMP pathway in the vascular smooth muscle cells (Lamireau et al., 2002). Therefore, it appears that LP diet programs vascular dysfunction in a sex-specific manner: endothelial dysfunction involving decreased endothelial NO production in females and reduced EDHF-mediated relaxation and reduced NO sensitivity to smooth muscle cells in males.

3.2. Vasoconstrictor Responses

The primary mechanism of angiotensin II (ANG II) induced vasoconstriction involves ANG II type-1 receptor (AT_1R) on the vascular smooth muscle cells, perhaps independent of endothelial cells (de Gasparo et al., 2000). In both male and female offspring from LP group the ANG II induced contractile responses in mesenteric arteries are significantly greater than controls; these effects may primarily occur in vascular smooth muscle cells (Sathishkumar et al., 2012a). Further, the sensitivity and maximal contractile responses were greater in male than female LP offspring (Sathishkumar et al., 2012a). AT_1R exists in two forms in rats, $AT_{1a}R$ and $AT_{1b}R$. The exaggerated ANG II responses were associated with increases in mesenteric vascular $AT_{1a}R$ expression (Sathishkumar et al., 2012a). The magnitude of $AT_{1a}R$ expression was greater in the LP males than females consistent with vascular smooth muscle contractile responses observed (Sathishkumar et al., 2012a). Exaggerated vasomotor responses to ANG II in other vascular beds such as aorta, femoral, and carotid arteries were also reported (Ozaki et al., 2001, Yzydorczyk et al., 2006). However, the vasomotor responses to other potent vasoconstrictors, such as alpha-adrenoceptor agonist phenylephrine, thromboxane mimetic (U46619), or serotonin and 80 mM KPSS (potassium in physiological salt solution), were not enhanced in either male or female LP offspring (Brawley et al., 2003, Lamireau et al., 2002, Rodford et al., 2008, Yzydorczyk et al., 2006). Thus, it is likely that the effects of fetal programming on vasoconstrictors are agonist specific. In addition, these findings suggest that prenatal protein-restriction-mediated programming occurs at the agonist-specific level rather than at common intracellular signaling pathways. Furthermore, enhanced sensitivity to ANG II and hypertension in both LP male and female offspring was reversed by (angiotensin-converting enzyme (ACE) inhibitor captopril and ANG II receptor blocker losartan (Ceravolo et al., 2007, Langley-Evans and Jackson, 1995, Sathishkumar et al., 2012a, Sherman and Langley-Evans, 1998). Additionally, enhanced responsiveness to ANG II suggests a causative role for the RAS in the vascular dysfunction programmed by maternal protein restriction. Therefore, an enhanced contractile sensitivity to some vasoconstrictors may also contribute to impaired vascular function, leading to an increase in total peripheral resistance and the development of hypertension in response to maternal protein restriction.

4. Mechanisms of Programming of Vascular Dysfunction: Involvement of Sex Steroid Hormones

It is well established that the onset and severity of numerous adult onset diseases differ between men and women. For example, men have higher 24-hour mean BP, by approximately 6 to 10 mm Hg, compared to age-matched premenopausal women (Reckelhoff, 2001). Also the incidence of cardiovascular disease and hypertension is lower in premenopausal women compared with age-matched men (Schulman et al., 2006). After menopause, the risk for development and the rate of progression of hypertension in women become comparable to those seen in age-matched men (Schulman et al., 2006). These observations indicate that female sex hormones may protect against the development of hypertension premenopausally and that their absence after menopause may create a stage for the development of hypertension. Alternatively, the fact that the male sex is a risk for the development of hypertension suggests that male sex hormones may adversely regulate BP. Indeed, absence of testosterone in experimental models abolishes hypertension (Ojeda et al., 2007b). These observations suggest that both male and female sex hormones contribute to the development and progression of hypertension. However, few studies to date have examined the contribution of sex hormones in fetal programming of adult hypertension.

Sex hormones may have a significant influence on the development of hypertension in adult LP offspring with reference to its onset and severity. In the LP offspring it appears that the onset of hypertension is earlier and more severe in males than in females (Sathishkumar et al., 2012a). Prenatal LP diet may cause alteration in the offspring sex steroid hormone levels to induce endocrine disruption. It is possible that the changes in BP in both male and female offspring may be related to changes in sex steroid hormone levels. Testosterone is reported to play a role in the increased BP in male LP offspring (Sathishkumar et al., 2008a). Testosterone levels were significantly higher in intact male LP offspring of severe protein restricted dams compared to control offspring (Sathishkumar et al., 2008a) and this hypertension was abolished upon castration, and restored with testosterone treatment (Sathishkumar et al., 2008a). This is in contrast to that reported by Woods et al., (Woods et al., 2010), using a model of modest protein restriction. A severe protein restriction may trigger mechanisms to induce increased testosterone levels with subsequent increases in BP similar to that observed in other models. Castration of male IUGR (placental hypoperfusion model), spontaneously hypertensive rats (SHRs) or Dahl salt-sensitive rats at a young age (3–5 weeks) abolished hypertension (Ojeda et al., 2007b, Reckelhoff, 2001). Testosterone replacement to these castrated males returned to hypertensive state (Reckelhoff, 2001). Furthermore, chronic blockade of androgen receptors with an antagonist, flutamide, attenuated the hypertension in male SHRs and BP levels were lower than those found in female SHRs (Reckelhoff et al., 1999). Therefore, it appears that increased testosterone levels may play a role in the development of hypertension in males.

Many studies have shown that estrogens may play a protective role against the development of hypertension in female growth restricted offspring (Ojeda et al., 2007a). This is supported by the fact that postmenopausal women are at an increased risk for hypertension. It was also found that estradiol levels at 16 weeks of age were significantly lower in LP compared to control females (Sathishkumar et al., 2012c). Upon ovariectomy of these female LP offspring hypertension was exacerbated with an earlier onset and more severe hypertension comparable to that observed in their male littermates (Sathishkumar et al., 2012c). Thus, estrogens indeed appear to protect and limit the severity of hypertension in LP model and contribute for sex differences in the development of hypertension. The normotensive adult females that are born to pregnant rats with modest nutritional restriction have normal estradiol levels and upon ovariectomy they become hypertensive (Guzman et al., 2006, Ojeda et al., 2007a), suggesting that an optimal estradiol levels in the intact animals could have conferred cardiovascular protective effect. Estradiol replacement to ovariectomized LP female offspring only partially buffered the elevated BP (Sathishkumar et al., 2012c). Also, estradiol replacement to intact LP offspring given at a dose to restore plasma levels to that observed in ovary intact control offspring (Sokol et al., 1999) does not return BP back to that seen in ovary intact control offspring (Sathishkumar et al., 2012c). Thus it appears estradiol replacement only reverses the ovariectomy-induced increase in BP but not that induced by maternal protein restriction. This is in contrast to the findings observed in other models of hypertension (Ojeda et al., 2007a). In one model of genetically programmed hypertension, the mRen2.Lewis rat, it was shown that ovariectomy augments the BP of female animals and estrogen supplementation protects against this process (Chappell et al., 2006). Ovariectomy also exacerbated hypertension in the Dahl salt-sensitive rat model, which was reversed by estradiol supplementation (Hinojosa-Laborde et al., 2004). The reasons for the apparent discrepancies among these studies are not entirely clear. Both the SHR and the Dahl salt-sensitive rat are models of genetic hypertension, and thus may involve different mechanisms than fetal programming models. Presumably, protein restriction during prenatal period could have severely impacted developing systems such as the cardiovascular system such that it becomes less responsive to estradiol. In this regard it is important to note that the expression of ERα (but not ERβ), which is known to convey both vasodilatory (Bolego et al., 2005, Pinna et al., 2008) and long-term anti-inflammatory actions, is reduced in the vasculature of LP female offspring. The reduced ERα is consistent with the attenuated vasodilatory effect of 17β-estradiol in LP female offspring (Torrens et al., 2003). Alternatively, the LP adult female offspring are found to have higher circulating testosterone levels with a greater testosterone-to-estradiol ratio (3.5- to 4-fold) compared to controls. Chronic blockade of the AR with flutamide attenuated the hypertension in LP females (Gangula et al., 2005). Therefore, it appears that testosterone may also play a direct role in regulating BP in LP females.

Whether alteration in sex steroid hormones testosterone and estradiol impact BP by direct or indirect mechanisms is not known. Most likely sex steroids may regulate the development and progression of LP-induced hypertension in offspring via interaction with regulatory pathways, such as renin angiotensin system (RAS). Treatment with ACE inhibitor captopril and ANG II receptor blocker losartan abolished hypertension in both LP male and female offspring (Ceravolo et al., 2007, Langley-Evans and Jackson, 1995, Sathishkumar et al., 2012a, Sherman and Langley-Evans, 1998), indicating that the RAS is involved in the regulation of hypertension. Flutamide treatment reversed the enhanced contractile response to ANG II in LP females with no significant effect in controls (Sathishkumar et al., 2012b). Vascular reactivity to phenylephrine was unaffected in LP offspring with flutamide treatment (Sathishkumar et al., 2012b), suggesting that flutamide's reversal effect is specific to ANG II. Flutamide also reversed the increased arterial AT_1R/AT_2R ratio in LP females (Sathishkumar et al., 2012b). These results suggest that prenatally protein-restricted rats exhibit an enhanced responsiveness to ANG II that is testosterone dependent and indicate that the RAS may serve as an underlying mechanism in mediating hypertension programmed in response to maternal protein restriction. Taken together, it seems that altered steroid levels act as a stimulant of the RAS, which increases BP, while estrogen acts as an inhibitor, lowering BP in females.

Conclusion

Human studies and experimental animal models report that hypertension is programmed in response to an insult during fetal life. Fetal programming of hypertension includes a wide range of alterations in endocrine hormones and regulatory systems as well as modification in organs such as the vasculature involved in the long-term control of BP regulation (Figure 1 and 2).

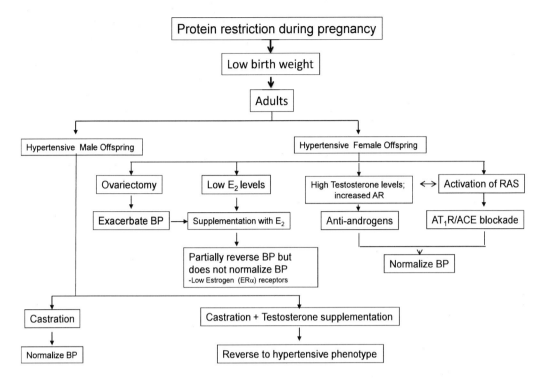

Figure 1. Sex hormones in regulation of hypertension programmed by prenatal protein restriction.

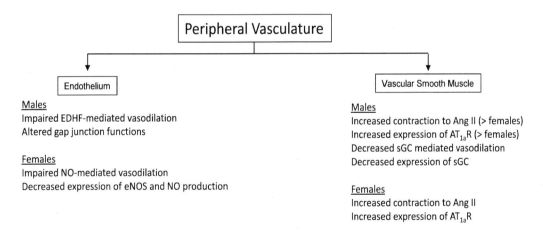

Figure 2. Sex-specific alterations in peripheral vascular reactivity in adult offspring from prenatal protein restricted mothers.

The onset and severity of hypertension is more pronounced in LP males than females similar to the gender differences in the occurrence of cardiovascular diseases in humans at various stages of life. There are sex-specific disturbances in endothelial cell associated relaxations; EDHF-related in males and nitric oxide-related in females. In addition, there is impairment of GC signaling pathway in the vascular smooth cells of LP males. Vasoconstriction to angiotensin II is exaggerated, with greater potency and efficacy in males. Alteration in steroid levels, estradiol and testosterone appears to have an underlying regulatory role in the development of hypertension in this model. The sex-specific vascular signaling mechanisms observed in this model might explain the observed gender differences in clinical responsiveness to antihypertensive therapies have been reported (Ueno and Sato, 2012). Better understanding of the complex and intrinsic sex-specific mechanisms involved in the fetal programming of hypertension will aid in the design of sex-specific approaches to treat or prevent these adverse adaptive phenotypic outcomes to fetal insult, and may lead to a decreased CV risk in individuals with a low birth weight.

References

Alexander, B.T. (2003). Placental insufficiency leads to development of hypertension in growth-restricted offspring. *Hypertension*, 41, 457-62.

Almeida, J.R. & Mandarim-de-Lacerda, C.A. (2005). Maternal gestational protein-calorie restriction decreases the number of glomeruli and causes glomerular hypertrophy in adult hypertensive rats. *Am. J. Obstet. Gynecol.*, 192, 945-51.

Augustyniak, R.A., Singh, K., Zeldes, D., Singh, M. & Rossi, N.F. (2010). Maternal protein restriction leads to hyperresponsiveness to stress and salt-sensitive hypertension in male offspring. *Am. J. Physiol. Regul. Integr. Comp. Physiol.*, 298, R1375-82.

Barker, D (1994). *Mother, Babies, and Disease in Later Life*. London: BMJ Publishing Group.

Barker, D.J. & Osmond, C. (1988). Low birth weight and hypertension. *BMJ*, 297, 134-5.

Barker, D.J., Winter, P.D., Osmond, C., Margetts, B. & Simmonds, S.J. (1989). Weight in infancy and death from ischaemic heart disease. *Lancet*, 2, 577-80.

Bassan, H., Trejo, L.L., Kariv, N., Bassan, M., Berger, E., Fattal, A., et al., (2000). Experimental intrauterine growth retardation alters renal development. *Pediatr Nephrol*, 15, 192-5.

Beevers, G., Lip, G.Y. & O'Brien, E. (2001). ABC of hypertension: The pathophysiology of hypertension. *BMJ*, 322, 912-6.

Bertram, C., Trowern, A.R., Copin, N., Jackson, A.A. & Whorwood, C.B. (2001). The maternal diet during pregnancy programs altered expression of the glucocorticoid receptor and type 2 11beta-hydroxysteroid dehydrogenase: potential molecular mechanisms underlying the programming of hypertension in utero. *Endocrinology*, 142, 2841-53.

Bieswal, F., Ahn, M.T., Reusens, B., Holvoet, P., Raes, M., Rees, W.D., et al., (2006). The importance of catch-up growth after early malnutrition for the programming of obesity in male rat. *Obesity (Silver Spring)*, 14, 1330-43.

Bolego, C., Cignarella, A., Sanvito, P., Pelosi, V., Pellegatta, F., Puglisi, L., et al., (2005) The acute estrogenic dilation of rat aorta is mediated solely by selective estrogen receptor-alpha agonists and is abolished by estrogen deprivation. *J. Pharmacol. Exp. Ther.*, 313, 1203-8.

Brawley, L., Itoh, S., Torrens, C., Barker, A., Bertram, C., Poston, L., et al., (2003) Dietary protein restriction in pregnancy induces hypertension and vascular defects in rat male offspring. *Pediatr Res*, 54, 83-90.

Brennan, K.A., Olson, D.M. & Symonds, M.E. (2006). Maternal nutrient restriction alters renal development and blood pressure regulation of the offspring. *Proc. Nutr. Soc.*, 65, 116-24.

Cambonie, G., Comte, B., Yzydorczyk, C., Ntimbane, T., Germain, N., Le, N.L., et al., (2007). Antenatal antioxidant prevents adult hypertension, vascular dysfunction, and microvascular rarefaction associated with in utero exposure to a low-protein diet. *Am. J. Physiol. Regul. Integr. Comp. Physiol.*, 292, R1236-45.

Ceravolo, G.S., Franco, M.C., Carneiro-Ramos, M.S., Barreto-Chaves, M.L., Tostes, R.C., Nigro, D., et al., (2007). Enalapril and losartan restored blood pressure and vascular reactivity in intrauterine undernourished rats. *Life Sci.*, 80, 782-7.

Chappell, M.C., Yamaleyeva, L.M. & Westwood, B.M. (2006). Estrogen and salt sensitivity in the female mRen(2). Lewis rat. *Am. J. Physiol. Regul. Integr. Comp. Physiol.*, 291, R1557-63.

Chinnathambi, V., Balakrishnan, M., Ramadoss, J., Yallampalli, C. & Sathishkumar, K. (2013). Testosterone Alters Maternal Vascular Adaptations: Role of the Endothelial NO System. *Hypertension*, 61, 647-54.

Choi, G.Y., Tosh, D.N., Garg, A., Mansano, R., Ross, M.G. & Desai, M. (2007). Gender-specific programmed hepatic lipid dysregulation in intrauterine growth-restricted offspring. *Am. J. Obstet. Gynecol.*, 196, 477e1-7.

Christensen, K.L. & Mulvany, M.J. (2001). Location of resistance arteries. *J. Vasc. Res.*, 38, 1-12.

Cooke, C.L. & Davidge, S.T. (2003). Pregnancy-induced alterations of vascular function in mouse mesenteric and uterine arteries. *Biol. Reprod.*, 68, 1072-7.

de Gasparo, M., Catt, K.J., Inagami, T., Wright, J.W. & Unger, T. (2000). International union of pharmacology. XXIII. The angiotensin II receptors. *Pharmacol. Rev.*, 52, 415-72.

de Lima, M.C., Scabora, J.E., Lopes, A., Mesquita, F.F., Torres, D., Boer, P.A., et al., (2013). Early changes of hypothalamic angiotensin II receptors expression in gestational protein-restricted offspring: effect on water intake, blood pressure and renal sodium handling. *J. Renin. Angiotensin Aldosterone Syst.*, 14, 271-82.

Edwards, L.J., Coulter, C.L., Symonds, M.E. & McMillen, I.C. (2001). Prenatal undernutrition, glucocorticoids and the programming of adult hypertension. *Clin. Exp. Pharmacol. Physiol.*, 28, 938-41.

Edwards, L.J. & McMillen, I.C. (2001). Maternal undernutrition increases arterial blood pressure in the sheep fetus during late gestation. *J. Physiol.*, 533, 561-70.

Forsdahl, A. (2002). Observations throwing light on the high mortality in the country of Finnmark. Is the high mortality today a late effect of very poor living conditions in childhood and adolescence? *Int. J. Epidemiol.*, 31, 302-8.

Franco, M.C., Arruda, R.M., Dantas, A.P., Kawamoto, E.M., Fortes, Z.B., Scavone, C., et al., (2002a). Intrauterine undernutrition: expression and activity of the endothelial nitric oxide synthase in male and female adult offspring. *Cardiovasc. Res.*, 56, 145-53.

Franco, M.C., Dantas, A.P., Akamine, E.H., Kawamoto, E.M., Fortes, Z.B., Scavone, C., et al., (2002b). Enhanced oxidative stress as a potential mechanism underlying the programming of hypertension in utero. *J. Cardiovasc. Pharmacol.*, 40, 501-9.

Gallo, L.A., Tran, M., Cullen-McEwen, L.A., Denton, K.M., Jefferies, A.J., Moritz, K.M., et al., (2013). Transgenerational programming of fetal nephron deficits and sex-specific adult hypertension in rats. *Reprod Fertil Dev.*, doi: 10.1071/RD13133.

Gangula, P.R., Reed, L. & Yallampalli, C. (2005). Antihypertensive effects of flutamide in rats that are exposed to a low-protein diet in utero. *Am. J. Obstet. Gynecol.*, 192, 952-60.

Gao, H., Yallampalli, U. & Yallampalli, C. (2012a). Gestational protein restriction reduces expression of Hsd17b2 in rat placental labyrinth. *Biol. Reprod.*, 97, 68.

Gao, H., Yallampalli, U. & Yallampalli, C. (2012b). Maternal protein restriction reduces expression of angiotensin I-converting enzyme 2 in rat placental labyrinth zone in late pregnancy. *Biol. Reprod.*, 86, 31.

Ghiadoni, L., Taddei, S., Virdis, A., Sudano, I., Di Legge, V., Meola, M., et al., (1998). Endothelial function and common carotid artery wall thickening in patients with essential hypertension. *Hypertension*, 32, 25-32.

Gilbert, J.S., Lang, A.L., Grant, A.R. & Nijland, M.J. (2005). Maternal nutrient restriction in sheep: hypertension and decreased nephron number in offspring at 9 months of age. *J. Physiol.*, 565, 137-47.

Giles, T.D., Sander, G.E., Nossaman, B.D. & Kadowitz, P.J. (2012). Impaired vasodilation in the pathogenesis of hypertension: focus on nitric oxide, endothelial-derived hyperpolarizing factors, and prostaglandins. *J. Clin. Hypertens (Greenwich)*, 14, 198-205.

Gonzalez-Rodriguez, P., Jr., Tong, W., Xue, Q., Li, Y., Hu, S. & Zhang, L. (2013). Fetal hypoxia results in programming of aberrant angiotensin ii receptor expression patterns and kidney development. *Int. J. Med. Sci.*, 10, 532-8.

Gopalakrishnan, G.S., Gardner, D.S., Rhind, S.M., Rae, M.T., Kyle, C.E., Brooks, A.N., et al., (2004). Programming of adult cardiovascular function after early maternal undernutrition in sheep. *Am. J. Physiol. Regul. Integr. Comp. Physiol.*, 287, R12-20.

Gray, C., Li, M., Reynolds, C.M. & Vickers, M.H. (2013). Pre-weaning growth hormone treatment reverses hypertension and endothelial dysfunction in adult male offspring of mothers undernourished during pregnancy. *PLoS One*, 8, e53505.

Gray, S.P., Denton, K.M., Cullen-McEwen, L., Bertram, J.F. & Moritz, K.M. (2010). Prenatal exposure to alcohol reduces nephron number and raises blood pressure in progeny. *J. Am. Soc. Nephrol.*, 21, 1891-902.

Guzman, C., Cabrera, R., Cardenas, M., Larrea, F., Nathanielsz, P.W. & Zambrano, E. (2006). Protein restriction during fetal and neonatal development in the rat alters reproductive function and accelerates reproductive ageing in female progeny. *J. Physiol.*, 572, 97-108.

Hemmings, D.G., Williams, S.J. & Davidge, S.T. (2005). Increased myogenic tone in 7-month-old adult male but not female offspring from rat dams exposed to hypoxia during pregnancy. *Am. J. Physiol. Heart Circ. Physiol.*, 289, H674-82.

Hink, U., Li, H., Mollnau, H., Oelze, M., Matheis, E., Hartmann, M., et al., (2001) Mechanisms underlying endothelial dysfunction in diabetes mellitus. *Circ. Res.*, 88, E14-22.

Hinojosa-Laborde, C., Craig, T., Zheng, W., Ji, H., Haywood, J.R. & Sandberg, K. (2004). Ovariectomy augments hypertension in aging female Dahl salt-sensitive rats. *Hypertension*, 44, 405-9.

Hiraoka, T., Kudo, T. & Kishimoto, Y. (1991). Catecholamines in experimentally growth-retarded rat fetus. *Asia Oceania J. Obstet. Gynaecol.*, 17, 341-8.

Holemans, K., Gerber, R., Meurrens, K., De Clerck, F., Poston, L. & Van Assche, F.A. (1999). Maternal food restriction in the second half of pregnancy affects vascular function but not blood pressure of rat female offspring. *Br. J. Nutr.*, 81, 73-9.

Intapad, S., Tull, F.L., Brown, A.D., Dasinger, J.H., Ojeda, N.B., Fahling, J.M., et al., (2013). Renal denervation abolishes the age-dependent increase in blood pressure in female intrauterine growth-restricted rats at 12 months of age. *Hypertension*, 61, 828-34.

Jude, E.B., Oyibo, S.O., Chalmers, N. & Boulton, A.J. (2001). Peripheral arterial disease in diabetic and nondiabetic patients: a comparison of severity and outcome. *Diabetes Care*, 24, 1433-7.

Khan, I.Y., Taylor, P.D., Dekou, V., Seed, P.T., Lakasing, L., Graham, D., et al., (2003). Gender-linked hypertension in offspring of lard-fed pregnant rats. *Hypertension*, 41, 168-75.

Lamireau, D., Nuyt, A.M., Hou, X., Bernier, S., Beauchamp, M., Gobeil, F., Jr., et al., (2002). Altered vascular function in fetal programming of hypertension. *Stroke*, 33, 2992-8.

Langley-Evans, S.C. (1997). Intrauterine programming of hypertension by glucocorticoids. *Life Sci.*, 60, 1213-21.

Langley-Evans, S.C. & Jackson, A.A. (1995). Captopril normalises systolic blood pressure in rats with hypertension induced by fetal exposure to maternal low protein diets. *Comp. Biochem. Physiol. A. Physiol.*, 110, 223-8.

Langley-Evans, S.C., Welham, S.J. & Jackson, A.A. (1999). Fetal exposure to a maternal low protein diet impairs nephrogenesis and promotes hypertension in the rat. *Life Sci.*, 64, 965-74.

Lee, J.H., Zhang, J., Flores, L., Rose, J.C., Massmann, G.A. & Figueroa, J.P. (2013). Antenatal betamethasone has a sex-dependent effect on the in vivo response to endothelin in adult sheep. *Am. J. Physiol. Regul. Integr. Comp. Physiol.*, 304, R581-7.

Leeson, C.P., Kattenhorn, M., Morley, R., Lucas, A. & Deanfield, J.E. (2001). Impact of low birth weight and cardiovascular risk factors on endothelial function in early adult life. *Circulation*, 103, 1264-8.

Leeson, C.P., Whincup, P.H., Cook, D.G., Donald, A.E., Papacosta, O., Lucas, A., et al., (1997). Flow-mediated dilation in 9- to 11-year-old children: the influence of intrauterine and childhood factors. *Circulation*, 96, 2233-8.

Lim, R. & Sobey, C.G. (2011). Maternal nicotine exposure and fetal programming of vascular oxidative stress in adult offspring. *Br. J. Pharmacol.*, 164, 1397-9.

Longo, L.D. & Pearce, W.J. (2005). Fetal cerebrovascular acclimatization responses to high-altitude, long-term hypoxia: a model for prenatal programming of adult disease? *Am. J. Physiol. Regul. Integr. Comp. Physiol.*, 288, R16-24.

Luscher, T.F. & Vanhoutte, P.M. (1986). Endothelium-dependent contractions to acetylcholine in the aorta of the spontaneously hypertensive rat. *Hypertension*, 8, 344-8.

Martin, H., Hu, J., Gennser, G. & Norman, M. (2000). Impaired endothelial function and increased carotid stiffness in 9-year-old children with low birthweight. *Circulation*, 102, 2739-44.

Matthews, S.G., Owen, D., Kalabis, G., Banjanin, S., Setiawan, E.B., Dunn, E.A., et al., (2004). Fetal glucocorticoid exposure and hypothalamo-pituitary-adrenal (HPA) function after birth. *Endocr Res*, 30, 827-36.

McCormick, C.M., Smythe, J.W., Sharma, S. & Meaney, M.J. (1995). Sex-specific effects of prenatal stress on hypothalamic-pituitary-adrenal responses to stress and brain glucocorticoid receptor density in adult rats. *Brain Res Dev. Brain Res.*, 84, 55-61.

Merlet-Benichou, C., Gilbert, T., Muffat-Joly, M., Lelievre-Pegorier, M. & Leroy, B. (1994). Intrauterine growth retardation leads to a permanent nephron deficit in the rat. *Pediatr Nephrol.*, 8, 175-80.

Mesquita, F.F., Gontijo, J.A. & Boer, P.A. (2010). Expression of renin-angiotensin system signalling compounds in maternal protein-restricted rats: effect on renal sodium excretion and blood pressure. *Nephrol. Dial Transplant*, 25, 380-8.

Mitchell, B.M., Wallerath, T. & Förstermann, U. (2007). Animal models of hypertension. *Methods Mol. Med.*, 139, 105-11.

Mizuno, M., Siddique, K., Baum, M. & Smith, S.A. (2013). Prenatal programming of hypertension induces sympathetic overactivity in response to physical stress. *Hypertension*, 61, 180-6.

Molnar, J., Howe, D.C., Nijland, M.J. & Nathanielsz, P.W. (2003). Prenatal dexamethasone leads to both endothelial dysfunction and vasodilatory compensation in sheep. *J. Physiol.*, 547, 61-6.

Nanduri, J. & Prabhakar, N.R. (2013). Developmental programming of O(2) sensing by neonatal intermittent hypoxia via epigenetic mechanisms. *Respir Physiol. Neurobiol.*, 185, 105-9.

Nathanielsz, P.W. (2006). Animal models that elucidate basic principles of the developmental origins of adult diseases. *ILAR J.*, 47, 73-82.

Ojeda, N.B., Grigore, D., Robertson, E.B. & Alexander, B.T. (2007a). Estrogen protects against increased blood pressure in postpubertal female growth restricted offspring. *Hypertension*, 50, 679-85.

Ojeda, N.B., Grigore, D., Yanes, L.L., Iliescu, R., Robertson, E.B., Zhang, H., et al., (2007b). Testosterone contributes to marked elevations in mean arterial pressure in adult male intrauterine growth restricted offspring. *Am. J. Physiol. Regul. Integr. Comp. Physiol.*, 292, R758-63.

Ojeda, N.B., Hennington, B.S., Williamson, D.T., Hill, M.L., Betson, N.E., Sartori-Valinotti, J.C., et al., (2012). Oxidative stress contributes to sex differences in blood pressure in adult growth-restricted offspring. *Hypertension*, 60, 114-22.

Ojeda, N.B., Royals, T.P. & Alexander, B.T. (2013). Sex differences in the enhanced responsiveness to acute angiotensin II in growth-restricted rats: role of fasudil, a Rho kinase inhibitor. *Am. J. Physiol. Renal. Physiol.*, 304, F900-7.

Ortiz, L.A., Quan, A., Zarzar, F., Weinberg, A. & Baum, M. (2003). Prenatal dexamethasone programs hypertension and renal injury in the rat. *Hypertension*, 41, 328-34.

Ozaki, T., Nishina, H., Hanson, M.A. & Poston, L. (2001). Dietary restriction in pregnant rats causes gender-related hypertension and vascular dysfunction in offspring. *J. Physiol.*, 530, 141-52.

Panza, J.A., Garcia, C.E., Kilcoyne, C.M., Quyyumi, A.A. & Cannon, R.O., III. (1995). Impaired endothelium-dependent vasodilation in patients with essential hypertension. Evidence that nitric oxide abnormality is not localized to a single signal transduction pathway. *Circulation*, 91, 1732-8.

Panza, J.A., Quyyumi, A.A., Brush, J.E., Jr. & Epstein, S.E. (1990). Abnormal endothelium-dependent vascular relaxation in patients with essential hypertension. *N. Engl. J. Med.*, 323, 22-7.

Payne, J.A., Alexander, B.T. & Khalil, R.A. (2003). Reduced endothelial vascular relaxation in growth-restricted offspring of pregnant rats with reduced uterine perfusion. *Hypertension*, 42, 768-74.

Petrie, J.R., Ueda, S., Webb, D.J., Elliott, H.L. & Connell, J.M. (1996). Endothelial nitric oxide production and insulin sensitivity. A physiological link with implications for pathogenesis of cardiovascular disease. *Circulation*, 93, 1331-3.

Pinna, C., Cignarella, A., Sanvito, P., Pelosi, V. & Bolego, C. (2008). Prolonged ovarian hormone deprivation impairs the protective vascular actions of estrogen receptor alpha agonists. *Hypertension*, 51, 1210-7.

Pladys, P., Sennlaub, F., Brault, S., Checchin, D., Lahaie, I., Lê, N.L., et al., (2005). Microvascular rarefaction and decreased angiogenesis in rats with fetal programming of hypertension associated with exposure to a low-protein diet in utero. *Am. J. Physiol. Regul. Integr. Comp. Physiol.*, 289, R1580-8.

Reckelhoff, J.F. (2001). Gender differences in the regulation of blood pressure. *Hypertension*, 37, 1199-208.

Reckelhoff, J.F., Zhang, H., Srivastava, K. & Granger, J.P. (1999). Gender differences in hypertension in spontaneously hypertensive rats: role of androgens and androgen receptor. *Hypertension*, 34, 920-3.

Reddy, K.S. (2002). Cardiovascular diseases in the developing countries: dimensions, determinants, dynamics and directions for public health action. *Public Health Nutr.*, 5, 231-7.

Rodford, J.L., Torrens, C., Siow, R.C., Mann, G.E., Hanson, M.A. & Clough, G.F. (2008). Endothelial dysfunction and reduced antioxidant protection in an animal model of the developmental origins of cardiovascular disease. *J. Physiol.*, 586, 4709-20.

Rosamond, W., Flegal, K., Friday, G., Furie, K., Go, A., Greenlund, K., et al., (2007). Heart disease and stroke statistics--2007 update: a report from the American Heart Association Statistics Committee and Stroke Statistics Subcommittee. *Circulation*, 115, e69-171.

Ross, M.G., Desai, M., Guerra, C. & Wang, S. (2005). Programmed syndrome of hypernatremic hypertension in ovine twin lambs. *Am. J. Obstet. Gynecol.*, 192, 1196-204.

Ross, R. (1993). Atherosclerosis: current understanding of mechanisms and future strategies in therapy. *Transplant Proc*, 25, 2041-3.

Ross, R. (1999). Atherosclerosis is an inflammatory disease. *Am. Heart J.*, 138, S419-20.

Sahajpal, V. & Ashton, N. (2003). Renal function and angiotensin AT1 receptor expression in young rats following intrauterine exposure to a maternal low-protein diet. *Clin. Sci. (Lond)*, 104, 607-14.

Sathishkumar, K., Balakrishnan, M., Chinnathambi, V., Gao, H. & Yallampalli, C. (2012a). Temporal alterations in vascular angiotensin receptors and vasomotor responses in offspring of protein-restricted rat dams. *Am. J. Obstet. Gynecol.*, 206, 507-10.

Sathishkumar, K., Chinnathambi, V., Balakrishnan, M. & Yallampalli, C. (2012b). Enhanced mesenteric arterial responsiveness to angiotensin II in prenatally protein restricted adult offspring is reversed by flutamide. *Reprod. Sci.*, 19, S-028.

Sathishkumar, K., Elkins, R. & Yallampalli, C. (2008a). Testosterone teases but estrogen eases blood pressure in the offspring of rats fed with low protein diet during pregnancy. *Biol. Reprod.*, 78, 199-200.

Sathishkumar, K., Elkins, R., Yallampalli, U., Balakrishnan, M. & Yallampalli, C. (2011). Fetal programming of adult hypertension in female rat offspring exposed to androgens in utero. *Early Hum. Dev.*, 87, 407-14.

Sathishkumar, K., Elkins, R., Yallampalli, U. & Yallampalli, C. (2008b). Protein Restriction during Pregnancy Induces Hypertension and Impairs Endothelium-Dependent Vascular Function in Adult Female Offspring. *J. Vasc. Res.*, 46, 229-39.

Sathishkumar, K., Elkins, R., Yallampalli, U. & Yallampalli, C. (2012c). Protein restriction during pregnancy induces hypertension in adult female rat offspring - influence of oestradiol. *Br. J. Nutr.*, 107, 665-73.

Scabora, J.E., de Lima, M.C., Lopes, A., de Lima, I.P., Mesquita, F.F., Bráz Torres, D., et al., (2013). Impact of taurine supplementation on blood pressure in gestational protein-restricted offspring: Effect on the medial solitary tract nucleus cell numbers, angiotensin receptors, and renal sodium handling. *J. Renin Angiotensin Aldosterone Syst*, [Epub ahead of print].

Schulman, I.H., Aranda, P., Raij, L., Veronesi, M., Aranda, F.J. & Martin, R. (2006). Surgical menopause increases salt sensitivity of blood pressure. *Hypertension*, 47, 1168-74.

Sherman, R.C. & Langley-Evans, S.C. (1998). Early administration of angiotensin-converting enzyme inhibitor captopril, prevents the development of hypertension programmed by intrauterine exposure to a maternal low-protein diet in the rat. *Clin. Sci. (Lond)*, 94, 373-81.

Singh, R.R., Cullen-McEwen, L.A., Kett, M.M., Boon, W.M., Dowling, J., Bertram, J.F., et al., (2007). Prenatal corticosterone exposure results in altered AT1/AT2, nephron deficit and hypertension in the rat offspring. *J. Physiol.*, 579, 503-13.

Sokol, R.Z., Okuda, H., Stanczyk, F.Z., Wolfe, G.W., Delaney, J.C. & Chapin, R.E. (1999). Normative reproductive indices for male and female adult Sprague-Dawley rats. *Contraception*, 59, 203-7.

Taddei, S., Virdis, A., Mattei, P. & Salvetti, A. (1993). Vasodilation to acetylcholine in primary and secondary forms of human hypertension. *Hypertension*, 21, 929-33.

Tong, W. & Zhang, L. (2012). Fetal hypoxia and programming of matrix metalloproteinases. *Drug Discov. Today*, 17, 124-34.

Torrens, C., Brawley, L., Anthony, F.W., Dance, C.S., Dunn, R., Jackson, A.A., et al., (2006). Folate supplementation during pregnancy improves offspring cardiovascular dysfunction induced by protein restriction. *Hypertension*, 47, 982-7.

Torrens, C., Brawley, L., Barker, A.C., Itoh, S., Poston, L. & Hanson, M.A. (2003). Maternal protein restriction in the rat impairs resistance artery but not conduit artery function in pregnant offspring. *J. Physiol.*, 547, 77-84.

Torrens, C., Kelsall, C.J., Hopkins, L.A., Anthony, F.W., Curzen, N.P. & Hanson, M.A. (2009). Atorvastatin restores endothelial function in offspring of protein-restricted rats in a cholesterol-independent manner1. *Hypertension*, 53, 661-7.

Ueno, K. & Sato, H. (2012). Sex-related differences in pharmacokinetics and pharmacodynamics of anti-hypertensive drugs. *Hypertens Res*, 35, 245-50.

van Dijk, A.E., van Eijsden, M., Stronks, K., Gemke, R.J. & Vrijkotte, T.G. (2012). The association between prenatal psychosocial stress and blood pressure in the child at age 5-7 years. *PLoS One*, 7, e43548.

Vanhala, M.J., Kumpusalo, E.A., Pitkajarvi, T.K., Notkola, I.L. & Takala, J.K. (1997). Hyperinsulinemia and clustering of cardiovascular risk factors in middle-aged hypertensive Finnish men and women. *J. Hypertens*, 15, 475-81.

Vehaskari, V.M., Aviles, D.H. & Manning, J. (2001). Prenatal programming of adult hypertension in the rat. *Kidney Int*, 59, 238-45.

Vehaskari, V.M. & Woods, L.L. (2005). Prenatal programming of hypertension: lessons from experimental models. *J. Am. Soc. Nephrol,*, 16, 2545-56.

Watt, P.A. & Thurston, H. (1989). Endothelium-dependent relaxation in resistance vessels from the spontaneously hypertensive rats. *J Hypertens*, 7, 661-6.

Wintour, E.M., Moritz, K.M., Johnson, K., Ricardo, S., Samuel, C.S. & Dodic, M. (2003). Reduced nephron number in adult sheep, hypertensive as a result of prenatal glucocorticoid treatment. *J. Physiol.*, 549, 929-35.

Woodall, S.M., Johnston, B.M., Breier, B.H. & Gluckman, P.D. (1996). Chronic maternal undernutrition in the rat leads to delayed postnatal growth and elevated blood pressure of offspring. *Pediatr. Res.*, 40, 438-43.

Woods, L.L., Ingelfinger, J.R., Nyengaard, J.R. & Rasch, R. (2001). Maternal protein restriction suppresses the newborn renin-angiotensin system and programs adult hypertension in rats. *Pediatr. Res.*, 49, 460-7.

Woods, L.L., Ingelfinger, J.R. & Rasch, R. (2005). Modest maternal protein restriction fails to program adult hypertension in female rats. *Am. J. Physiol. Regul. Integr. Comp. Physiol.*, 289, R1131-6.

Woods, L.L., Morgan, T.K. & Resko, J.A. (2010). Castration fails to prevent prenatally programmed hypertension in male rats. *Am. J. Physiol. Regul. Integr. Comp. Physiol.*, 298, R1111-6.

Woods, L.L., Weeks, D.A. & Rasch, R. (2004). Programming of adult blood pressure by maternal protein restriction: role of nephrogenesis. *Kidney Int.*, 65, 1339-48.

Xiao, D., Huang, X., Yang, S. & Zhang, L. (2013). Estrogen normalizes perinatal nicotine-induced hypertensive responses in adult female rat offspring. *Hypertension*, 61, 1246-54.

Yzydorczyk, C., Gobeil, F., Jr., Cambonie, G., Lahaie, I., Le, N.L., Samarani, S., et al., (2006). Exaggerated vasomotor response to ANG II in rats with fetal programming of hypertension associated with exposure to a low-protein diet during gestation. *Am. J. Physiol. Regul. Integr. Comp. Physiol.*, 291, R1060-8.

Zhang, D.Y., Lumbers, E.R., Simonetta, G., Wu, J.J., Owens, J.A., Robinson, J.S., et al., (2000). Effects of placental insufficiency on the ovine fetal renin-angiotensin system. *Exp Physiol*, 85, 79-84.

Zhang, L. (2005). Prenatal hypoxia and cardiac programming. *J Soc Gynecol Investig*, 12, 2-13.

In: Stress and Developmental Programming …
Editors: Lubo Zhang and Lawrence D. Longo

ISBN: 978-1-63321-836-9
© 2014 Nova Science Publishers, Inc.

Chapter 15

Epigenetic Mechanisms in Developmental Programming of Health and Disease

Fuxia Xiong, Lawrence D. Longo and Lubo Zhang [*]

Center for Perinatal Biology, Loma Linda University School of Medicine,
Loma Linda, CA, US

Abstract

For the fetus *in utero*, programming encompasses the role of plasticity in response to early life environments, with its profound influence on health and risk of disease in adult life. Although the adaptation response of the fetus to intrauterine environmental and nutritional signals ensures its survival, the mismatch between early environmental conditions and conditions that the individual will confront later in life, may result in adverse long-term effects. The fundamental mechanisms underlying regulation of this process remains unclear. Observations in humans and experimental data in animals suggest that epigenetic regulations of gene expression patterns play a significant role in the developmental origins of adult health and disease (DOHaD). This chapter summarizes recent studies elucidating the role of epigenetic mechanisms, including DNA methylation, histone modification, and microRNA, in the developmental programming of adult physiological functions and diseases. An increased understanding of the epigenetic mechanisms in fetal programming would help identify epigenetic biomarkers for individuals at high risk of adult disease with fetal origins.

Keywords: DNA methylation, epigenetics, fetal programming, histone modification

---

[*] Corresponding Author: Lubo Zhang, PhD, Center for Perinatal Biology Loma Linda University School of Medicine, lzhang@llu.edu.

1. Introduction

The global prevalence of obesity and impaired metabolic health has become a worldwide health issue, as well as a considerable financial burden on health care systems. In addition to genetic factors and adult lifestyle, the relationship between our early life environment (during prenatal and postnatal periods) and higher risk of diseases has been the focus of numerous studies. One general mechanism by which prenatal and postnatal exposures may be linked to phenotypic changes later in life is the alteration of epigenetic marks, which have a central role in determining the functional output of the information that is stored in the genome.

Epigenetics is defined as all heritable changes in gene expression not associated with concomitant alterations in the DNA sequence. Within the body of an organism, all cells have identical genomes which produce and store extremely stable genetic information. However, each cell type has its lineage-specific expression profile associated with time and tissue specificity. The information for this transcriptional program of gene expression is epigenetically controlled by mechanisms that include DNA methylation/demethylation, post-translational modifications of histone, and non-coding RNAs. Epigenetic events are highly responsive to endogenous and environmental signals therefore, epigenetic instructions play pivotal roles in the regulation of gene expression. Accumulating evidence from both human and animal studies indicates that epigenetic modifications serve as a memory of early life events, which can induce long-term changes in gene expression profiles with potential result of diseases in later life.

2. Epigenetic Mechanisms and the Machineries

2.1. DNA Methylation and Demethylation

Human DNA methylation is the most widely investigated epigenetic modification. Compared to other epigenetic marks, which more or less can be removed before or within several cell divisions, DNA methylation has been regarded as a stable epigenetic mark that can be maintained and inherited after many cell divisions. However, evidence from recent studies indicates the role of active DNA demethylation in gene transcription regulation, suggesting that DNA methylation is not as stable as it has been previously thought. DNA demethylation, the reverse process of methylation, has played important roles in cleaning the genomic slate during embryogenesis, thus achieving rapid reactivation of previously silenced genes.

2.1.1. DNA Methylation

DNA methylation is the process in which methyl groups are transferred from S-adenosyl methionine to DNA sequences containing cytosine dinucleotides (CpG), thereby regulating local and genome-wide gene transcription. The entire process is catalyzed by DNA methyltransferases (DNMTs) (Klose and Bird, 2006). Five members of the DNMTs have been reported in mammals, including DNMT1, DNMT2, DNMT3A, DNMT3B and DNMT3L. Only DNMT1, DNMT3A and DNMT3B possess methyltransferase activity, however (Portela and Esteller, 2010). According to their different roles in DNA methylation, the catalytic members of the DNMT family are generally grouped into *de novo* DNMTs (basically DNMT3A and DNMT3B) and maintenance DNMT (DNMT1). Although DNMT3L appears to be catalytically inactive, it is closely related to DNMT3A and DNMT3B in structure and is critical for DNA methylation. The *de novo* DNMTs are highly expressed in embryonic stem cells (ESCs) and are down-regulated in differentiated cells. Basically, DNMT3A and DNMT3B are believed to be responsible for establishing the pattern of methylation during development (Esteller, 2007), and DNMT3L is required for this process (Bourc'his et al., 2001). The presence of DNMT3L enhances the activity of DNMT3A and DNMT3B, interacting and co-localizing with them in the nucleus (Chen et al., 2005, Holz-Schietinger and Reich, 2010). DNMT1, which is the most abundant DNMT in the cell, is transcribed chiefly during the S phase of the cell cycle, and often is needed to methylate hemimethylated sites that are generated during semi-conservative DNA replication (Klose and Bird, 2006).

DNA methylation occurs almost exclusively on the cytosine nucleotide in the symmetrical dinucleotide CpG sequence (Jones and Takai, 2001). Rather than being found randomly through the genome, they tend to cluster in regions called CpG islands (Crews and McLachlan, 2006). CpG islands are defined as short interspersed DNA sequences that deviate significantly from the average genomic pattern by a G+C content of at least 50%. CpG islands are highly enriched at or near the gene promoter region. In mammalian genomes, about 60% of gene promoters are associated with CpG islands. In normal cells, most CpG islands are unmethylated, although some of them (~6%) become methylated in a tissue-specific manner during early development or in differentiated tissues (Straussman et al., 2009). In contrast, 80% of CpGs located outside of CpG islands are methylated (Trasler, 2006). Additionally, non-CG methylation has been found in humans at CHG and CHH sites (where H is the nucleic acid A, C or T). Methylation in non-CG contexts shows enrichment in gene bodies while depletion in protein binding sites, and enhancers in gene expression regulation. In ESCs, different methylation mechanisms may be used, since nearly 25% of all methylation identified in ESCs is in non-CG methylation (Lister et al., 2009). Moreover, the non-CG methylation level is decreased during differentiation while restored in induced pluripotent stem cells. This indicates that it plays a key role in the maintenance of pluripotent status (Laurent et al., 2010, Lister et al., 2009), although the mechanisms of non-CpG methylation are still unclear. The new term CpG "island shores" has recently been brought forward, which refers to regions of lower CpG density that lie in close proximity (~2 kb) to CpG islands. It has been reported that tissue-specific DNA methylation usually takes place at CpG island shores, not CpG islands (Doi et al., 2009, Irizarry et al., 2009), and methylation of CpG island shores is also closely associated with transcriptional suppression. About 70% of the differentially methylated regions in reprogramming are associated with CpG island shores, which are sufficient to distinguish between specific tissues (Doi et al., 2009, Ji et al., 2010).

The major function of DNA methylation of CpG islands is to transcriptionally silence the associated gene. In addition, transcriptional repression generally correlates with the degree of methylation within CpG islands at the promoter and the extent of interference with the binding of transcription factors (Freitag and Selker, 2005, Weber et al., 2007). DNA methylation can inhibit gene expression by several mechanisms (Figure 1). It may directly interfere with the binding of transcription factors to the gene regulating sequences.

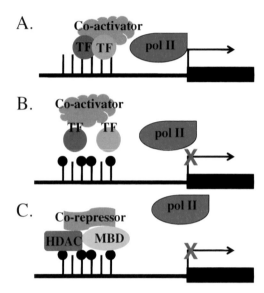

Figure 1. Effects of DNA methylation on regulation of gene expression. A: Low level of DNA methylation at gene promoters is related with active gene expression through increased binding of transcription factors. B: Increased DNA methylation levels at gene promoters lead to inactive gene expression via directly interfering the binding of transcription factors to the gene regulating sequences. C: DNA methylation represses gene expression via methyl-CpG binding proteins (MBDs), which may recruit histone-modifying enzymes (e.g. HDACs) and transcriptional co-repressors, resulting in transcriptional suppression. Black filled circle: methylated CpG dinucleotides.

In some cases, DNA methylation does not directly inhibit transcription factor binding, however transcriptional repression occurs nevertheless. In these cases, methyl-CpG binding proteins (MBDs) can bind to methylated CpG residues independent of the DNA sequence. MBDs can intimately link DNA methylation to patterns of histone post-translational modifications. Initially, methylated DNA promotes the recruitment of MBDs at specific sites in the genome, which will in turn recruit histone-modifying enzymes and chromatin-remodeling complexes to the methylated sites (Esteller, 2007, Lopez-Serra and Esteller, 2008). This helps to orchestrate DNA replication and repair, thus reinforcing and stabilizing transcriptional suppression. Although usually associated with transcriptional suppression, recent studies suggest that DNA methylation may also be involved in the transcriptional activation of some genes. In mouse hypothalamus tissue, MeCP2 dysfunction was shown to induce changes in the expression levels of thousands of genes. The majority of genes (approximately 85%) appeared to be activated instead of suppressed by MeCP2 (Chahrour et al., 2008). MeCP2 was associated with the transcriptional activator CREB1 of an activated target, but not a repressed target at the promoter (Cohen et al., 2008). These mechanisms remain to be determined, however.

2.1.2. DNA Demethylation

Although DNA methylation is viewed as a stable epigenetic modification, evidence from recent studies suggests that loss of DNA methylation, or DNA demethylation, has been observed in specific contexts, including both early development and somatic cells. DNA demethylation can occur through both passive and active mechanisms (Figure 2).

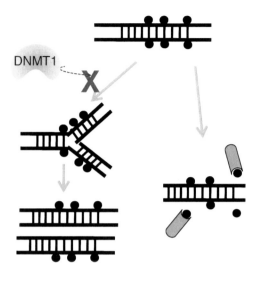

Passive demethylation   Active demethylation

Figure 2. Passive demethylation and active demethylation. Passive DNA demethylation occurs as a consequence of replication process in the absence of the maintenance DNA methyltransferase 1 (DNMT1). Contrary to passive demethylation, active demethylation is the enzymatic process that results in the removal of the methyl group from 5-methylcytosine. Black filled circle, methylated CpG dinucleotides.

Passive DNA demethylation refers to the loss of the methyl group from 5meC when the maintenance DNMT1 is absent or inhibited during DNA replication. In contrast, active DNA demethylation is the enzymatic process that results in the removal of the methyl group from 5meC by breaking a carbon-carbon bond.

Mechanisms of DNA methylation has been extensively studied and well understood. In contrast, the molecular mechanisms of DNA demethylation, particularly active DNA demethylation are only beginning to be addressed. Based on various studies, several mechanisms have been proposed, including: direct enzymatic removal of the methyl group of 5meC, base excision repair (BER) through direct excise of 5meC, nucleotide excision repair (NER), deamination of 5meC to T followed by BER, and oxidative demethylation (Bhutani et al., 2011). In plants, BER is known to be used to achieve DNA demethylation, whereas evidence supporting a similar mechanism in mammals is less compelling. Some proteins, including MBD4 and a human T DNA glycosylase (TDG), have been proven to have glycosylase activity against 5meC *in vivo* in mammals. However, their excision activity against 5meC is comparatively low and decisive genetic and biochemical evidence supporting their roles in active DNA methylation remain to be elucidated. *In vitro*, activity-induced deaminase (AID) has been shown to be capable of delaminating 5meC to T, and is implicated in the DNA demethylation process. A recent large-scale bisulphite sequencing study indicates a slightly increased level of methylation in primordial germ cells (PGCs) derived from AID-knockout mouse embryo, suggesting the contribution of AID in PGC demethylation. Oxidative demethylation has recently garnered extensive attention as another possible mechanism by which DNA demethylation can be achieved. Recently, 5hmC was detected at moderately low levels (~10% of 5mC and ~0.4% of all cytosine) in mammalian genomes, leading to the hypothesis that 5hmC may be an intermediate in the removal of 5mC (Branco et al., 2012, Wu et al., 2011). The presence of 5hmC depends on the pre-existence of 5mC *in vivo*, suggesting that 5mC may be the only source of genomic 5hmC. The demonstration that members of the Ten-eleven translocation (Tet) family of proteins can convert 5mC to 5-hydroxymethylcytosine (5hmC) provides further evidence of the role of Tets in active demethylation. The Tet family proteins consist of three members, namely Tet1, Tet2 and Tet3, and show broad expression patterns in different tissues (Mohr et al., 2011). In the mouse, all three Tets have the catalytic capacity to convert 5mC to 5hmC both *in vitro* and *in vivo*. Tet1 is abundantly expressed in ESCs and is required for the maintenance of embryonic status. The Tet1 mRNA level declines during ESC differentiation, accompanied by a decrease of the 5hmC levels (Tahiliani et al., 2009). Although Tet2 expression is also observed in ESCs, the silencing of Tet2 fails to show obvious phenotypic changes in ESC biology. Tet3 expression is highest in oocytes and zygotes, and zygotes with Tet3 depletion fail to demethylate the male pronucleus. Knockout of Tet1, but not Tet2 or Tet3, results in impaired ES cell self-renewal and maintenance (Ito et al., 2010), and leads to embryonic lethality. The existence of three mammalian Tet enzymes raises the possibility that each has a distinct panel of genomic targets, such that their tissue specific expression may generate unique physiological effects.

Several potential mechanisms have been proposed involving effects of deaminase and glycocylase activity in the further removal of 5hmC. Another active pathway involved is further oxidation of 5hmC that will lead first to 5fmC and then 5caC (He et al., 2011, Ito et al., 2011). Indeed, all three Tets possess the capacity to catalyze these additional oxidation steps, and both 5fmC and 5caC are present in the ESCs although at very low levels. It is likely that there are multiple pathways for the removal of 5mC from the genome and that Tet enzymes are involved in several of them. One interesting possibility is that dependent on whether demethylation is genome-wide or loci-specific, different tissues might use different demethylation pathways. Current evidence indicates that genome-wide demethylation occurs at specific times during early development, while gene-specific demethylation serves as a response to certain signals in somatic cells. During development, by extensive genome-wide DNA demethylation, the previous paternal-specific methylation marks are removed in the zygote shortly after fertilization (Kishigami et al., 2006, Mayer et al., 2000, Wossidlo et al., 2010). Although passive demethylation may be involved, it is likely that active demethylation plays a major role mediating this process, as loss of methylation is detected before the completion of the first cell division. In addition, inhibition of DNA replication failed to prevent the demethylation of the paternal genome (Kishigami et al., 2006, Mayer et al., 2000, Wossidlo et al., 2010). As the zygote undergoes continuous cell division and forms the blastocyst, passive DNA demethylation of the maternal genome occurs in a replication-dependent manner (Howlett and Reik, 1991). Global *de novo* methylation commences at the time of implantation on both maternal and paternal DNA (Li, 2002, Mayer et al., 2000). Both methylation and demethylation are resisted by imprinted genes, which are epigenetically modified at a different critical period of gametogenesis (Reik et al., 2001). On specific genomic loci in somatic cells, active DNA demethylation has also been observed in response to certain signals. For example, in unstimulated neurons, the brain-derived neurotrophic factor (BDNF) is maintained in a repressed state through methylation of promoter and binding of MeCP2. When the neurons are depolarized with KCl, demethylation of the promoter occurs and MeCP2 is released, resulting in upregulation of BDNF (Martinowich et al., 2003).

Another example is the trefoil factor 1 gene which undergoes a switch from repression to expression under stimulation of estrogen, accompanied by cyclical rounds of active methylation and demethylation at its promoter (Metivier et al., 2008). Activation of T lymphocytes results in active demethylation on the promoter-enhancer region of the interleukin-2 gene (Bruniquel and Schwartz, 2003). These data indicate that in addition to long-term gene expression regulation, methylation and demethylation also functions in the dynamic regulation of gene expression as a rapid response to specific stimuli.

2.2. Histone Modifications

In eukaryotic nuclei, a complex of DNA and histones efficiently packages heritable genetic information in the form of chromatin. Histone and non-histone proteins promote the proper three-dimensional folding of DNA and the dynamic regulation of whole genome functions within the nucleus (Kouzarides, 2007). Nucleosomes, the smallest functional unit of chromatin, are made of 147 bp of DNA wrapped around an octamer of core pairs of histone proteins, namely H2A, H2B, H3, and H4. Linker histone, H1, is located on the outer surface of the nucleosome and fixes DNA to the nucleosome. Histones are key players in epigenetic regulation, and their modifications work together with DNA methylation to ensure specific gene transcriptional regulation, DNA repair, DNA replication, alternative splicing, and chromosome condensation. It is already known that all histones are subject to post-transcriptional modifications, including acetylation, methylation, phosphorylation, and ubiquitination, which are mainly positioned within the N-terminal tails of core histones. Each of these modifications serves as an epigenetic mark and is directed by a series of enzymes with complex activity profiles. These enzymes can add or remove histone modifications that collectively modulate gene expression.

2.2.1. Histone Acetylation

Histone acetylation occurs at lysine (K) residues, specifically on their side-chain amino group, which effectively neutralizes their positive charge. Histone acetyltransferases (HATs) catalyze the direct transfer of an acetyl group from acetyl-CoA to the ε-NH$^+$ group of the lysine residues. Histone acetylation is a reversible process, and the histone deacetylases (HDACs) catalyze the acetylation reversal. HDACs consist of 11 isoforms and are classically divided into two types: HDACs 1, 2, 3 and 8 are Class I HDACs, while Class II encompasses HDAC isoform 4, 5, 6, 7, 9, 10, and 11. A new type, Class III, was discovered in 2004 which belongs to the SIR2 family of HDACs. Most of the HATs and HDACs are not highly specific and can modify more than one residue. Intriguingly, a large number of transcriptional co-activators have been described to possess intrinsic HAT activity, whereas many transcriptional co-repressor complexes contain subunits possessing HDAC activity (Wang et al., 2008). Thus, most HDACs in the human genome function to reset chromatin by removing acetylation at active genes. In contrast, HATs are mainly linked to transcriptional activation (Wang et al., 2009).

2.2.2. Histone Methylation

Another histone-mediated epigenetic tag is a methyl group. Similar to acetylation, histone methylation happens on ε-NH$^+$ groups of lysine residues, and is catalyzed by lysine methyltransferases (KMTs). Unlike acetylation, methylation of lysines preserves their positive charge. In addition, lysines can be methylated up to three times and therefore, exist in mono-, di- or trimethylated states, showing complex effects on gene regulation. The various valences of methylation on several different lysine residues can mediate either transcriptional repression or activation. Histone H3 lysine 4 trimethylation H3K4 (H3K4me3) is always enriched at active genes, while methylation of histone H3 at lysine 9 (H3K9me) and 27 (H3K27me) are important modifications for gene repression (Karlic et al., 2010). In addition to lysine residues, arginine residues within histones can also form mono- or dimethylated states, which are catalyzed by protein arginine methyltransferases (PRMTs). Playing a central role in orchestration of the histone code, arginine methylation of histone tails can promote or prevent the docking of key transcriptional regulating molecules. Several histone methyltransferases are able to direct DNA methylation by recruiting DNMTs to specific genomic targets (Tachibana et al., 2008, Zhao et al., 2009). This helps to set the silenced state established by the repressive histone marks. In addition, histone methyltransferases and demethylases can regulate DNA methylation levels, thereby affecting the stability of DNMT proteins (Esteve et al., 2009, Wang et al., 2009).

2.2.3. Histone Phosphorylation and Ubiquitination

All of the four histone tails have receptor sites for phosphorylation which can occur on serine, threonine, and tyrosine residues of histones. Phosphorylation of histone can be catalyzed by a number of protein kinases, and dephosphorylation of histone is catalyzed by phosphatases. Phosphorylation of histone constitutes an important part of the combinatory function of post transcriptional modifications, and participates in regulation of various cellular processes (Rossetto et al., 2012). For example, phosphorylation of H2A(X) plays a major role in response to DNA damage. A large number of phosphorylated histone residues have been associated with gene expression, especially genes related to regulation of proliferation. Phosphorylation of H3 has been reported as a response to activation of mitogenic signaling pathways (Mahadevan et al., 1991). H3S10, H3S28 and H2BS32 phosphorylation are associated with transcription of epidermal growth factor-responsive genes, as well as expression of proto-oncogenes such as c-fos, c-jun and c-myc (Chadee et al., 1999, Lau et al., 2011). As an essential part of the "histone code", histone phosphorylation has also been clearly associated with other posttranscriptional modifications such as histone methylation and acetylation. For instance, phosphorylation of H3S10, T11 and S28 are associated with H3 acetylation, which plays a role in transcription activation. Although histone phosphorylation is usually associated with gene activation, the mechanisms remain to be elucidated.

In the eukaryotic genome, ubiquitination of histone H2A, H2B, H3 and H1 has been observed. Ubiquitin is a protein with 76 amino acids, named for its ubiquitous distribution in all cell types and high degree of conservation across species. The conjugation of ubiquitin to other cellular proteins regulates a broad range of eukaryotic cell functions. Usually, but not always, ubiquitin is attached to proteins as a signal for degradation by the proteosome. Similar to other proteins, histones are ubiquitinated through attachment of an ubiquitin to the lysine ε-NH$^+$ group (Nickel and Davie, 1989). Histone can be mono-ubiquitinated and poly-ubiquitinated as well. To date, the role of histone ubiquitination in gene transcription regulation remains poorly understood.

In summary, histone-modifying enzymes catalyze histone modifications in response to local profiles of regulating signals. They also coordinate actions of higher-order chromatin modifiers and additional cellular signaling pathways. This in turn helps to coordinate associated metabolic and environmental cues to collectively modulate gene expression (Hogan and Varga-Weisz, 2007, Kouzarides, 2007, Ruthenburg et al., 2007, Taniura et al., 2007). Modified histones serve as components of larger multi-protein transcriptional complexes involved in coordinated chromosomal interactions, and play significant roles in organization of nuclear territories to execute integrated genome-wide gene regulation profile (Akhtar and Gasser, 2007, Ooi and Wood, 2007, Rosenfeld, 2006, Ruthenburg et al., 2007, Schneider and Grosschedl, 2007).

2.3. MicroRNAs

In humans, only 1-2% of the genome encodes protein, while noncoding RNAs (ncRNAs) that don't produce protein, represent the majority of human transcripts and play important post-transcriptional regulatory roles in gene expression. MicroRNAs (miRNAs), one type of ncRNA, are 18-25 nucleotides in length, and can lead to suppression of their target genes. In mammals, about 50% of all genes are currently found to be regulated by miRNAs. To date, mirBase, the primary miRNA information database has annotated over 2000 human, 1300 mouse and 700 rat mature miRNAs. A large number of mammalian specific miRNA have been described in the regulation of various biological processes, including development, differentiation, apoptosis, and cell proliferation (Ambros and Lee, 2004, Bartel et al., 2004, He and Hannon, 2004, Pasquinelli et al., 2005, Plasterk, 2006).

miRNAs arise from either intergenic or intragenic regions of a host protein coding or non-coding gene (Mattick and Makunin, 2005). In the nucleus, miRNAs chiefly are transcribed from those genomic regions by RNA polymerase II as primary miRNAs (pri-miRNAs). These are long segments and typically contain 1-6 precursors of mature miRNAs. Then the hairpin structure of the pri-miRNAs are trimmed to pre-miRNAs by a microprocessor complex containing RNase type III (Drosha) and the dsRNA binding protein DiGeorge syndrome critical region gene 8 (DGCR8). This latter contains a stem-loop structure and is approximately 70 to 100 nucleotides in length (Kim et al., 2009). With a nuclear transport receptor complex, exportin-5-RanGTP, pre-miRNAs are transported to the cytoplasm and further processed by a dsRNase type III, Dicer to a ~22-nt double-stranded miRNA duplex, which is incorporated into a RNA-induced silencer complex (RISC)-loading complex (RLC) in an ATP-dependent manner (Yoda et al., 2010). The sense strand is then deleted from the RLC by a helicase, whereas the antisense strand remains in the complex to form a mature RNA-induced silencer complex (mature RISC) and serves as a template for capturing target mRNAs (Figure 3). Both the transcription of pri-miRNA and post-transcriptional process leading to mature miRNA are finely regulated. Alterations of the processing molecules can result in a global change of mature miRNA levels.

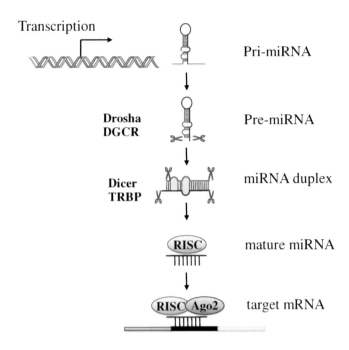

Figure 3. Biogenesis and effect of microRNA (miRNA). microRNAs originate in the nucleus as RNA polymerase II primary transcripts (pri-miRNAs), which is trimmed into ~70-nucleotide hairpins (pre-miRNA) by Drosha and DGCR8 complex and translocated into cytoplasm. Next, pre-miRNA is cleaved by Dicer-TRBP complex to yield mature ~22 nucleotide miRNA duplexes, one strand of which is loaded into the RISC and functions as mature miRNA. This complex with Ago2 directs the miRNA to the target mRNA and leads to translational repression or mRNA degradation. RISC: RNA-induced silencing complex; DGCR8: double-stranded RNA binding protein Pasha; TRBP: TAR RNA binding protein. Ago2: argonaute 2.

The RISC is a complex containing multiple factors which work together to regulate the target mRNA expression. Depending on the extent of the complementary sequence between miRNA and target mRNAs, RISC plays different roles in regulating gene expression (Behm-Ansmant et al., 2006). For highly complementary target mRNAs, the mature RISC complex cleaves and leads to degradation of the target mRNAs. For partially complementary targets, the RISC complex may decap and deadenylate target mRNAs, thereby decreasing the stability of target mRNAs. Actually, the majority of animal miRNAs are only partially complementary to their targets, and several recent reports have indicated that miRNAs can also induce significant degradation of target mRNAs despite imperfect mRNA-miRNA base-pairing (Bagga et al., 2005, Lim et al., 2005).

2.4. Mitochondrial DNA

Within the cells, two cellular organelles that contain DNA are the nucleus and mitochondria. Although mitochondrial DNA (mtDNA) represents less than 1% of total cellular DNA, its products are essential for oxidative phosphorylation and other normal cellular function. Each mitochondria has its own genome of approximately 16 kb in length, encoding for two rRNAs, 22 tRNAs, and 13 proteins in the electron transport chain. It also contains a short non-coding region with control elements, named displacement loop (D-Loop).

Similar to the genomic DNA that is surrounded by epigenetic regulators, mtDNA can also be regulated by epigenetic mechanisms, including DNA methylation and miRNA (Barrey et al., 2011). The mtDNA contains only 435 CpG sites and 4747 cytosine residues at non-CpG sites. Both cytosine at CpG sites and cytosine at non-CpG sites can be methylated (Mushkambarov et al., 1976, Shmookler Reis and Goldstein, 1983, Shock et al., 2011). DNMTs have been discovered in mitochondria (Nass, 1973, Shock et al., 2011). Although the general consensus is that mitochondria possess no histone, a recent study suggests the existence of several histone family members in the mitochondria (Choi et al., 2011). Due to a lack of histone complexes, DNA methylation may play a particularly important role in mtDNA stability and mitochondrial function. Unusual CpG and non-CpG methylation patterns were observed in the D-Loop control region of mtDNA (Bellizzi et al., 2013, Sun et al., 2013). Both methylated and hydroxymethylated cytosines were identified on all samples analyzed, particularly on non-CpG sites in the promoter region of the heavy strand. In mouse ESCs, inactivation of DNMTs resulted in a significant reduction of CpG methylation but not non-CpG methylation, indicating different factors are involved in the regulation of non-CpG methylation (Bellizzi et al., 2013). Investigation of mitochondrial DNA methylation has led to several disease-related studies including neuroepigenetics, aging, and cancer (Chestnut et al., 2011, Iacobazzi et al., 2013, Manev et al., 2012, Sun et al., 2011). Decreased methylation on the D-Loop control region is closely associated with the regulation of the NADH dehydrogenase2 expression during development of colorectal cancer (Feng et al., 2012). Similarly, methylation of the NADH dehydrogenase 6 promoter was inversely correlated with expression of the gene in patients with nonalcoholic fatty liver disease (Pirola et al., 2013). However, further functional studies are needed to elucidate the role of mtDNA methylation in controlling gene expression.

3. Interplay between Different Epigenetic Modifications

Although DNA methylation/demethylation, histone modification, and miRNAs play different roles in regulation of protein-coding genes, they coordinate their activities to create a complex interconnection to maintain gene expression at both transcriptional and post-transcriptional levels.

3.1. Links Between DNA Methylation and Histone Modifications

The gene expression profile is closely related with chromatin structure, which is chiefly influenced by modifications to DNA or chromatin-associated proteins, especially histones. Both DNA methylation and histone modifications are involved in establishing patterns of gene repression during development. Moreover, there appears to be a relationship between the two systems that work dependently to modulate gene expression (Figure 4). DNA methylation may serve as a template for some histone modifications, and histone methylation, in turn, may direct DNA methylation modification.

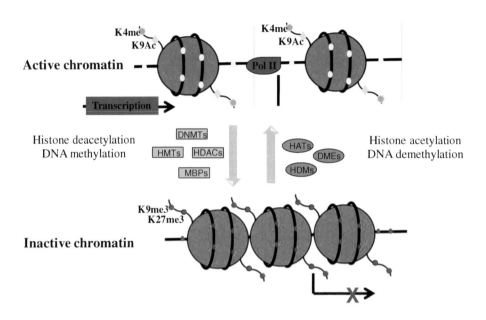

Figure 4. DNA methylation and histone modification cooperatively regulate gene expression. Transcriptionally active DNA has been packaged into active chromatin structure with widely spaced nucleosomes. This is associated with unmethylated CpGs (white filled ovals) and specific modifications on N-termini of histone, including acetylated histone 3 lysine 9 (H3-K9) and trimethylated H3-K4. The resultant DNA is transcriptionally accessible to histone acetyl transferases (HATs), histone demethylases (HDMs) and DNA demethylases (DMEs) which are important in gene transcription. Chromatin may be transformed into inactive conformation with compacted nucleosomes and transcriptional silencing of DNA, which is characterized by methylated CpGs on the DNA (red filled ovals) and specific histone modifications such as trimethylation of H3-K9 and H3-K27. This inactive conformation of chromatin is established and maintained by proteins, including methyl-CpG binding proteins (MBPs), histone deacetylases (HDACs), histone methyltransferases (HMTs) and DNA methyltransferases (DNMTs).

It is well known that MBDs bind to methylated DNA, and proteins with MBD are capable of recruiting other chromatin modifiers. These may reposition nucleosomes or induce changes in post-translational histone modification states leading to chromatin compaction (Nan et al., 1998). For instance, MeCP2 can bind tightly to chromosomes and mediate transcriptional repression through recruitment of a chromatin-modifying complex containing the transcriptional repressor mSin3A and HDACs. This suggests that DNA methylation-related chromatin remodeling is critical for gene regulation.

Other evidence indicates that although DNA and histone methylation are catalyzed by different sets of enzymes, they are connected through interactions between the enzymes. In the mammalian genome, CpGs islands are protected from methylation reprogramming during early development. Although the precise mechanisms are not clear, studies suggest that common *cis*-acting sequences and active demethylation may direct this process (Brandeis et al., 1994, Frank et al., 1991). Other studies suggest that histone modification may also play a role in the establishment of the basic DNA methylation profile (Ooi et al., 2007). According to this model, the H3K4 methylation pattern might be formed throughout the genome before occurrence of *de novo* demethylation. This process is mediated by RNA polymerase II, which is mostly bound to CpG islands in the early embryo. Thus, only CpG islands are marked with H3K4me, while the rest of the genome still contains unmethylated H3K4. *De novo* demethylation is directed by DNA methyltransferase DNMT3A and 3B with the assistance of DNMT3L. The methylated histone H3 inhibits the interaction between DNMT3L and the nucleosome, however. Thus, methylation of histone H3 prevents DNA sequences within the CpG islands from *de novo* methylation.

3.2. Epigenetic Regulation of miRNA Expression

It is estimated about half of miRNA genes are associated with CpG islands, indicating DNA methylation may play an important role in miRNA regulation. Indeed, hypermethylation of CpG islands is a common feature of aberrant miRNA expression profiles. Administration of 5-Aza-2'-deoxycytidine (5-Aza), a DNMT inhibitor, highly induces the expression of miR-127, which is embedded in a CpG island promoter (Saito et al., 2006). In contrast, miR-9-1, which is found to be hypermethylated and down-regulated in breast cancer, can be induced with reduction of methylation and concomitant reactivation of expression by 5-Aza treatment (Lehmann et al., 2008). The miR-34 family miRNAs can be inactivated by the methylation of a CpG island at the transcription stat site (TSS) of its host gene (Lodygin et al., 2008). Similarly, methylation of a CpG island near the predicted TSS of miR-200c/miR-141 gene is significantly correlated with their expression levels (Neves et al., 2010).

DNA methylation as well as histone modifications regulate microRNA expression. In a genome-wide study of miRNA expression profiles, the abundantly expressed miRNA clusters, miR-200b and miR-17, are associated with an enrichment of H3k4me3 at their upstream CpG islands, while the silencing of miRNAs, such as miR34b/c, miR-124-1 and miR-9-3, are related with a lack of H3K4me3 and H3K79me2 (Suzuki et al., 2011). An extensive and rapid alteration of miRNA level is shown in response to the potent HDAC inhibitor hydroxamic acid treatment in breast cancer cell lines. The dietary component butyrates, which possess anti-HDAC activity, show effect on regulating expression of multiple miRNAs, including miR-17, miR-20a/b, miR-93 and miR-106a/b. Since miRNA levels are highly regulated not only by the transcription of pri-mRNA but also the molecules involved in the post-transcriptional process, it is conceivable that epigenetic regulation of those processing proteins may contribute to the alteration of miRNA profile.

3.3. Regulation of Epigenetic Pathways by miRNA

miRNAs are involved in the establishment and maintenance of DNA methylation (Rajewsky, 2006). Epi-miRNAs, a specific group of miRNAs, can regulate the expression of epigenetic machinery related genes, including DNMTs, HATs/HDACs, histone phosphorylases, and histone methyltransferases/demethylases. The miR-29 family members have been reported to down-regulate directly DNMT3A and 3B by reactivating methylation silenced tumor suppressor genes. This can restore normal patterns of DNA methylation in non-small cell lung cancer cells (Fabbri et al., 2007). Whereas overexpression of miR-148 results in decreased DNMT3B expression, short-hairpin RNA-mediated miR-148 repression leads to an increase in DNMT3B expression. Moreover, it has been demonstrated that the miR-148 represses DNMT3B expression by targeting at the coding sequences, as mutation of the putative miR-148 target site in Dnmt3B abolishes the suppression by miR-148 (Duursma et al., 2008). Expression of HDACs is also modulated by a subset of miRNAs. In prostate cancer cells, the miR-449a was found to regulate cell growth and viability, in part, by directly repressing the expression of HDAC1 (Noonan et al., 2009). HDAC4 is one of the important targets of miR-140 that induces expression of *p53* and *p21* in colon cancer cells through suppression of HDAC4 (Song et al., 2009).

A growing body of evidence indicates that miRNAs may also influence chromatin structure by directly affecting effectors of epigenetic machinery, such as the post-transcriptional regulatory polycomb repressive complex (PRC) genes. The polycomb group proteins are transcriptional repressors that regulate lineage choices occurring during development and differentiation. They silence a large number of genes including those that encode crucial developmental regulators in organisms ranging from plants to humans. Two main families of complexes, called PRC1 and PRC2, are targeted to repressed regions. EZH2 is a histone methyltransferase belonging to the PRC2 family. In adult neurogenesis, miR-137 mediated repression of EZH2 results in a global decrease in H3K27me3 level (Szulwach et al., 2010). In addition, other miRNAs including miR-101, miR-26a, and miR214, target the EZH2 gene and modulate its expression to alter the effect of PRC.

3.4. Epigenetics in Genomic Imprinting

Genomic imprinting is an epigenetic process guiding the allele-specific marking of parental alleles in mammals. Genes regulated by imprinting are expressed only from a single allele obtained maternally or paternally during development and in the adult. Imprinted genes are physically diploid (both copies are present) but functionally haploid (only one copy can be expressed). Therefore, imprinted genes are marked by activating and repressing histone marks, respectively (John and Lefebvre, 2011). Generally, imprinted genes are positioned within about 1Mb clusters throughout the genome, which contain genes exclusively expressed from maternally or paternally inherited chromosomes. These are controlled by the imprinting control region (ICR) or imprinting center (IC). To date, approximate 144 mouse genes and a small number of human genes have been identified as been imprinted (Weksberg, 2010). More than 80% of these are grouped into 16 clusters that contain more than two genes (Edwards and Ferguson-Smith, 2007). The parental-specific mark must be stable, heritable, and erasable so that the correct allele-specific expression can be maintained throughout development. DNA methylation during gametogenesis has been regarded as the only epigenetic modification to achieve genomic imprinting, although histone modifications may also be involved in this process. Differentially methylated regions (DMRs) are allele-specific methylated regions of the two parental chromosomes. There are two types of DMRs, the gametic DMRs, which are directly inherited from the mature gametes at fertilization, and the somatic DMRs, which are only obtained in embryos following implantation. Compelling evidence suggests that genomic imprinting plays a role in the development of some of their distinguishing characteristics, particularly in placentation and behaviors (Constancia et al.,

2004, Edwards and Ferguson-Smith, 2007, John and Lefebvre, 2011, Kaneko-Ishino and Ishino, 2010).

3.4.1. Gametic Imprints

Due to specific expression patterns, imprinting genes are one of the important targets for epigenetic regulation. Imprinting gene expression commences within the male and female germlines during gametogenesis (Surani, 1998). These genes usually contain CpG-rich regions that acquired an epigenetic mark, such as DNA-methylation, on only one of the two DMRs. At some DMRs, differential DNA methylation is also observed between sperm and oocytes, and is referred to as primary or gametic imprints. In some cases, the germline DMR functions as an imprinting control region, which regulates the mono-allelic expression (Reik and Walter, 2001b). To date, the majority of the germline DMRs are methylated in the maternal germline of the growing oocyte. Only four characterized DMRs (*H19*, *Dlk1-Gtl2*, *Rasgrf1* and *Zdbf2*) acquire DNA-methylation in the male germline (Arnaud, 2010, Reik and Walter, 2001a).

Gametic imprints are dependent on the DNMT3A and the accessory protein DNMT3L (Arima et al., 2006, Hata et al., 2002, Kaneda et al., 2004, Kato et al., 2007), which recognizes the CpGs spacing (Jia et al., 2007, Jurkowska et al., 2008, Suetake et al., 2004), and is believed to play a role in stimulating the *de novo* activity of DNMT3A (Chedin et al., 2002, Suetake et al., 2004). In addition to the cooperation of DNMT3A and 3L in establishing DNA methylation in the germline, mounting evidence has shown that other trans-acting factors play a critical role in this process. For instance, a *Kdm1b* gene encoding a histone H3 lysine 4 demethylase, and is necessary to methylate the gametic DMRs from *Mest, Grb10, Zac1, etc.* (Ciccone et al., 2009). The Lsh, a member of the SNF2 family of chromatin remodeling proteins, is another factor that plays an essential role in methylation of imprinted genes. Although Lsh is not required for maintenance of imprinting markers in general, it is crucial for imprinting at specific genome sites, such as the imprinted *Cdkn1c* gene (Dennis et al., 2001, Fan et al., 2005). Evidence indicates that DNMT1 is necessary and sufficient for the imprint maintenance up to the blastocyst stage (Hirasawa et al., 2008). Both active and passive DNA demethylation steps occurred in the zygotic genome after fertilization until implantation (Reik and Walter, 2001b). Basically, the paternal pronucleus is actively demethylated before the first cleavage after fertilization (Mayer et al., 2000, Oswald et al., 2000). Then genome DNA methylation levels decrease. This process is possibly accompanied by a failure of DNMT1 to maintain DNA methylation patterns (Rougier et al., 1998). Two factors, the *Zfp57* and *Stella,* are required for the maintenance of gametic imprints. *Zfp57* encodes a putative KRAB zinc finger protein and is involved in the maintenance of DNA methylation after fertilization at some IC (For instance, the *Dlk1, Peg1, Peg3* and *Nnat* domains). *Stella* (also known as *Pgc7* or *Dppa3*) has similar functions as *Zfp57* to maintain imprints at a subset of loci. These include the maternally imprinted *Peg1, Peg3* and *Peg10* domains and the paternally imprinted *H19-Igf2* (H19DMR) and *Rasgrf1* domains (Nakamura et al., 2007).

3.4.2. Somatic Imprints

Somatic imprints are established during postimplantation development. These lack differential DNA methylation in the germlines, and are only detected in postimplantation tissues and adult somatic cells. Therefore, somatic imprints are called somatic, secondary, or post-fertilization DMRs. Unlike gametic imprinted genes, somatic DMRs can be maintained autonomously by DNMT1. They may continue to maintain imprinted expression in the adult once the somatic imprints are established. Several somatic imprinted genes have been identified including *Cdkn1c, Igf2r, Gtl2, Nesp, Igf2* and *H19. Cdkn1c* is positioned within a complex imprinted domain on human chromosome 11p15. The *Cdkn1c* locus is unmethylated in sperm, ESCs, and the early embryo (E6.5), but has obtained paternal methylation by E8.5 after the maternal allele-specific expression is well established (Bhogal et al., 2004, Wood et al., 2010). *H19* gene in somatic cells has two distinct regions subjected to differential DNA methylation. One region is located 2 kb upstream of the transcription start site. Methylation of this region occurs only in sperm but will be maintained in the blastocyst and mid-gestation embryos to regulate mono-allelic expression of *H19, Igf2* and *Ins2* (Leighton et al., 1995). The other region located in the promoter of the *H19* gene is unmethylated in either sperm or blastocysts, but obtains DNA methylation in the mid-gestation embryo (Bartolomei et al., 1993, Ferguson-Smith et al., 1993).

In mammals, expression of *Igf2* is generally obtained from the paternal allele while the maternal allele of *Igf2* is silenced. There are three regions of differential DNA methylation identified in the vicinity of *Igf2*, called DMR0, DMR1 and DMR2 (Feil et al., 1994, Moore et al., 1997, Sasaki et al., 1993). DMR0 only shows maternal hypermethylation in the placenta. DMR1 and DMR2 show some evidence of DNA methylation in sperm, whereas this methylation is lost after fertilization and re-established by E9 and E15, respectively (Brandeis et al., 1993, Lopes et al., 2003). *Igf2r* domain has two DMRs, with DMR1 spanning the *Igf2r* promoter and DMR2 located in intron 2 of *Igf2r*. Maternal allele methylation on DMR2 was obtained during oogenesis and persisted in all somatic tissues (Hu et al., 1998, Pauler et al., 2005). In contrast, the methylation of DMR1 is acquired on the paternal allele only after fertilization, coincident with paternal allele silencing of *Igf2r* in postimplantation embryos (Hu et al., 1999, Stoger et al., 1993). *Igf2r* domain has two additional protein-coding imprinted genes called *Slc22a2* and *Slc22a3*, which are imprinted in the placenta and also rely on the gametic DMR2 (Zwart et al., 2001).

4. Epigenetic Programming of Health and Disease

From the perspective of evolution, environmental alterations can induce integrated adjustments in the phenotype of an organism, and this process of adaption is generally underpinned by epigenetic mechanisms. The antenatal and postnatal periods are critical times for establishment of epigenetic marks that have potential long-term consequences in phynotypical diversity and disease susceptibility. Studies on monozygotic twins provide important evidence for the role of epigenetic modifications in phenotype establishment (Poulsen et al., 2007). These show that in most cases twins are epigenetically concordant at birth, and the epigenetic differences accumulate with age. Remarkably, the twins who live together for the smallest amount of time are shown to have the greatest epigenetic differences (Fraga et al., 2005). In addition, the overall patterns of DNA methylation and histone acetylation are remarkably different in elder twins, although they were epigenetically indistinguishable at a younger age. In great probability, the dynamic changes on epigenetic marks of an individual's genome caused by environmental events over their lifetimes are the reason for the phenotype discordance on monozygotic twins. Studies in assisted reproduction technology (ART) further demonstrate that the *in vitro* environment affects global DNA methylation (Katari et al., 2009). Gametes or early embryos from couples undergoing treatment for infertility may therefore display epigenetic modifications. Indeed, an association was observed between *in vitro* conception and changes in DNA methylation, potentially affecting the long-term pattern of gene expression involved in chronic metabolic disorders.

4.1. Epigenetic Programming of Metabolic Disorders

Obesity, "western diet", and reduced physical activity in adult life, have been related to the prevalence of metabolic disorders including insulin resistance, metabolic syndrome, and type 2 diabetes (T2D). Nonetheless, many individuals exposed to these factors do not develop these disorders, indicating individual susceptibility. Genetic reasons may partially explain the inherited susceptibility difference; however, they cannot explain the worldwide prevalence of these metabolic disorders. As an example, multiple diabetes susceptibility loci have been identified in a recent genome-wide array study carried out in a diabetic cohort. Nonetheless, the robust detection of such related genetic variants can explain only a small part (10 to 15%) of the inherited disease susceptibility. Mounting evidence suggests a major role for early environment-driven epigenetic programming in the susceptibility to and development of metabolic disorders (Maier and Olek, 2002, Wren and Garner, 2005).

As is well known, famine during one's early-life has been associated with various adverse phenotypes expressed later in life, depending upon the gestational timing of the insult and the sex of the individual exposed. Changes in epigenetic markers induced during early exposure to harsh conditions have been proposed to underlie these associations. For example, the methylation patterns of genes implicated in growth and metabolic disease were compared between individuals who were exposed prenatally to a war-time famine and their unexposed same-sex siblings or individuals exposed late in gestation. The results showed that the methylation of *IGF* was lower (Dominguez-Salas et al., 2012), whereas methylation of the non-imprinted *IL10* promoters, *LEP, ABCA1,* imprinted loci of signaling G-protein alpha subunit gene GNAS-antisense 1 (*GNASAS1*), and maternally expressed protein *MEG3* genes were higher. The altered epigenetic marks induced by exposure at specific time windows during pregnancy might be the reason for the phenotypic discordance and association with increased risk of disease.

Over the past several decades, accumulating evidence has shown that the primary mechanism regulating energy metabolism *in vivo* is cross-talk between energy-sensing, endocrine (i.e., via insulin and leptin receptors), and proinflammatory pathways. This fits with the establishment of such mechanisms in the central (i.e., via hypothalamus) and peripheral tissues (i.e., via pancreas, muscle, adipose tissue and liver etc.). Both maternal under- or over-nutrition can stimulate similar programming mechanisms that regulate mitochondrial bioactivity, cellular stress, and inflammation, which further will determine cell destiny and tissue development. Nutrient availability of the developing fetus, over-exposure to stress hormones, and application of adverse substances during pregnancy, all have been indicated in setting the cellular control of energy oxidation and storage in the development of metabolic disorders.

4.2. Epigenetic Programming of Cardiovascular Disease

Based on epidemiologic studies of birth and death records in the United Kingdom, Barker and colleagues examined the role of early life environmental influences that impair growth and development as risk factors in the development of cardiovascular diseases (CVD). Since that time, numerous retrospective and prospective clinical reports have elucidated on the correlation between newborn body weight at birth and the development of CVD during adulthood. Most recently, studies have demonstrated strong correlations between maternal metabolic dysfunction and the intrauterine environment with the progression of adult CVD (Palinski and Napoli, 2008). As an example, intrauterine exposure to maternal hypercholesterolemia has been reported to promote fatty streak formation in the vasculature of adult humans. Compared with fetuses from normocholesterolemic mothers, the lesion size in aortas of fetuses from hypercholesterolemic mothers is enhanced and lesion progression remained accelerated after birth (Napoli et al., 1997, 1999). The pathogenic mechanisms of these relationships remain to be elucidated, however.

Animal models designed to evaluate the epigenetic mechanisms of intrauterine programming provide more concrete data in the context of carefully controlled dietary interventions. In these experimental animal models, mounting studies have shown the dramatic influence of prenatal nutritional or other environmental alterations on the pattern of DNA methylation of specific genes, resulting in permanent phenotypic changes, such as body weight and blood pressure. For examples, Van Straten and colleagues investigated the epigenetic effects of intrauterine protein restriction on specific genes that may contribute to CVD risk (van Straten et al., 2010). Pregnant mice were fed low-protein diets to induce programming events in offspring, and the epigenetic adaptations associated with fetal lipid metabolism were investigated. The results showed that due to antenatal protein restriction the DNA methylation patterns in 204 genes in the fetal liver were changed, including liver X receptor α (*Lxra*), a nuclear receptor that targets downstream genetic regulators of lipid and fatty acid metabolism. Transcription of *Lxra* is dependent on DNA methylation level, and as would be anticipated, hypermethylation of the *Lxra* promoter leads to the reduction of LXRα expression, together with reduced expression of *Abcg5/Abcg8/Abca1* genes that encode the established lipid regulators (van Straten et al., 2010). Studies carried out in a maternal apolipoprotein E-deficient (apoE-/-) mouse model provide epigenetic evidence in the programming of this arthrosclerosis-susceptibility by maternal hypercholesterolemia. Neointima formation of adult heterozygous apoE(+/-) offspring from hypercholesterolemic apoE(-/-) mothers was significantly increased, compared with genetically identical apoE(+/-) offspring from normocholesterolemic wild-type mothers. A mechanistic study in vascular endothelial and smooth muscle cells indicated that modifications in histone methylation were associated with increased atherosclerosis-susceptibility and hypercholesterolemia on neointima formation (Alkemade et al., 2010).

An important risk factor for cardiovascular and cerebrovascular disease is hypertension. Of importance, epigenetic modification of the renin-angiotensin system (RAS) is associated with the fetal programming of hypertension. Previous studies have implicated the important role of RAS in the progress of hypertension. In early life, this can be prevented by the application of angiotensin-converting enzyme (ACE) inhibitors or angiotensin receptor antagonists (Manning and Vehaskari, 2005). In pregnant rats, antenatal maternal low protein diet has been shown to upregulate expression level of the angiotensin II receptor type 1b

(AT1b) in the adrenal gland by the first week of life, accompanied by significant undermethylation of Agtr1b proximal promoter (Bogdarina et al., 2007). Epigenetic and gene expression changes in the brain RAS have also been observed in mouse fetus exposed to maternal low protein diet. Goyal and colleagues found that both mRNA and protein levels of ACE-1 and angiotensin II receptor type 2 (AT2R) were significantly reduced in the fetal brain from the MLPD dams. Hypomethylation of the CpG islands in the promoter regions of *ACE-1* gene, and upregulation of the miRNAs, mmu-mir-27a and 27b, are considered to be responsible for the alteration of ACE-1 transcription (Goyal et al., 2010). Their findings suggest that the effect of these epigenetic changes may play an important role in the manifestation of brain dysfunction and other disorders later in life. These studies uncover a link between the maternal insults to epigenetic modification of genes and the resultant alteration of gene expression in adults that ultimately leads to the development of hypertension.

The kidney is central to the development of hypertension, due to its important role in the handling of renal sodium and intravascular fluid volume homeostasis. In low birth weight subjects, a number of human and animal studies have shown reduced nephron numbers, and a lower number of nephrons is an important predictor for hypertension. Development of the kidney is a complex process involving tightly controlled expression of several genes and constant remodeling. Environmental factors have their greatest impact if they are encountered during the period of active nephrogenesis, which in human begins from around 8 weeks of gestation and continues until 36 weeks. Although approximately two thirds of the nephrons develop during the last trimester of gestation, earlier insults may have a major impact on subsequent nephrogenesis. In rats, maternal dietary composition can program embryonic kidney gene expression early in the course of gestation, which later impacts nephron number (Zandi-Nejad et al., 2006). More importantly, the relative amount of specific amino acids (e.g., methionine or glycine) appears to be more important than the extent of total restriction of maternal nutrition. These effects are proposed to be largely mediated by changes in DNA methylation that modulate gene expression and thus regulate kidney development and remodeling.

Fetal hypoxia, prenatal exposure to tobacco smoking or hypersympathetic activity of the pregnant mother all have been shown to induce alterations in DNA methylation and increase the risk of disease later in the offspring. Methylation of specific transcription factor binding sites (Egr-1 and Sp1) at the PKCε promoter have been shown to be increased in the heart tissue of subjects exposed to fetal stress, resulting in decreased expression of PKCε and loss of protection to the heart during ischemia-reperfusion injury (Lawrence et al., 2011, Patterson et al., 2010, Xiong et al., 2012). In a cohort study including 348 children, altered DNA methylation patterns were found to be associated with *in utero* exposure to maternal smoking. Exposed children had significantly lower methylation of the DNA repetitive elements of the long interspersed element 1 *(LINE-1)* and *AluYb8*, two classes of repetitive sequences that are normally hypermethylated. The smoking-exposed children had significantly lower levels of *AluYb8* methylation when compared with controls, whereas smoking-related effects on *LINE-1* methylation were observed only in children who lacked a detoxifying enzyme, glutathione *S*-transferase P (GSTP1). Moreover, they identified differential methylation of CpG loci in eight genes through the screen, and found that these associations were varied due to the specific alleles of other detoxifying genes (Breton et al., 2009). As in the case of maternal malnutrition, fetal exposure to smoking or hypoxia may produce short-term metabolic changes that compromise long-term survival. This compromise may produce epigenetic adaptations that exacerbate metabolic dysregulation and lead to increased CVD risk in the individual.

4.3. Epigenetic Programming of Neurological Health and Disease

4.3.1. Epigenetic Mechanisms and Neural Development

Epigenetic mechanisms orchestrate nervous system development and neuron plasticity. Each epigenetic mechanism contributes to the establishment and maintenance of neural cell identity. A broad range of evidence has shown that epigenetic factors, including DNA methyltransferases, MBDs, histone- and chromatin modifying enzymes, and ncRNA biogenesis factors are essential for neurogenesis and gliogenesis.

During embryonic neural stem cell differentiation, numerous genes related to this process were methylated on their promoter. DNA methylation is responsible for silencing these genes which are associated with pluripotency and alternative lineage program, thereby preventing premature neural stem cell maturation and promoting commitment to a specific neural lineage. DNMT is expressed throughout brain development. Even in the adult brain, this enzyme also functions in specific regions mediating ongoing neurogenesis. In a similar manner, histone modifications and chromatin remodeling are involved in establishing neural cell identity, as the histone-modifying enzymes are involved in regulating the evolving neural network programs. Moreover, histone modifications and chromatin remodeling play important roles in neurodevelopment, including neural stem cell maintenance and fate restriction, as well as neuronal and glia subtype specification, differentiation, neural network plasticity, and brain aging. As may be evident, the dysfunction of these processes leads to various neurological diseases. In addition, a large amount of microRNA exists in mammalian brain play with specialized roles in neurodevelopment and adult homeostasis/plasticity. For instance, it has been reported that miR-184 promotes neural stem cell proliferation and inhibits neuronal differentiation. MiR-125b, miR-128, miR-132, miR134 and miR-138, are also associated with neuronal maturation and neural network integration (Qureshi and Mehler, 2013). miRNA also targets genes encoding synaptic proteins, and plays important roles in activity-dependent synaptic plasticity and memory formation. Similar to other epigenetic mechanisms, dysregulation of miRNA leads to various brain disorders.

4.3.2. Epigenetic Programming of Neurological Disorders

Many epigenetic modifications have been associated with neurological disease in adults. As is well known, maternal cigarette smoking may increase the risk of neonatal neurological morbidity. Although the underlying mechanisms remain unclear, the nicotine-induced down-regulation of AT2R in the developing brain may be involved. This AT2R downregulation is mediated by epigenetic mechanisms (Li et al., 2013). Methylation of a single CpG locus near the TATA-box at AT2R promoter resulted in decreased binding affinity of TATA-binding protein (TBP), and finally leads to the AT2R gene repression in the developing brain (Li et al., 2013). BDNF plays a vital role in brain development and its expression is regulated by alternations in DNA methylation (Dennis and Levitt, 2005). The BDNF-4 promoter, BDNF-6 promoter and 5'-untranslated region were modulated by stress hormones, antidepressant treatment, and by DNA methyltransferase inhibitors (Aid et al., 2007, Dwivedi et al., 2006).

Human studies have discovered that cigarette smoking is associated with reduced blood level of BDNF protein (Kim et al., 2007), however, the extent to which maternal smoking is related to BDNF methylation in adolescent offspring remains unknown. Toledo-Rodriguez and colleagues conducted an epidemiologic study in adolescents whose mothers smoked during pregnancy and revealed that nicotine exposure during the prenatal period increases the methylation level of the BDNF-6 promoter, and this may lead to changes in the plasticity and development of the brain (Toledo-Rodriguez et al., 2010).

In addition to environment stressors, a continuous supply of methyl group donors in food is pivotal to regulate nervous system development and function via epigenetic mechanisms. Maternal diet deficient of methyl donors showed elevated anxiety and increased learning ability in aged female offspring. However, the DNA methylation patterns of the genes coding GR, 11β-HSD2, neuronatin and reelin in hippocampus of the offspring rats, were not altered significantly when compared to offspring from mothers on a control diet (Konycheva et al., 2011). A large number of candidate genes were related to the neurobehavior, but only a small group of genes were investigated in this study. Therefore, it is possible that other DNA regions or other uninvestigated epigenetic mechanisms were involved. In rats, this notion was confirmed by a large scale study in offspring exposed to maternal stress during gestational days 12 to 16. The study identified over 700 genes in the frontal cortex and hippocampus that were differentially expressed following prenatal stress. The levels of DNA methylation associated with behavioral changes in offspring rats were increased, and these epigenetic changes demonstrate both sex-dependent and region-specific profiles, with little overlap between sexes and brain area. Frontal cortex changes were largely related to neurotransmitter function, whereas changes in the hippocampus were more prominent in females and concentrated around growth factors.

5. Links Between Epigenetic and Fetal Programming of Health And Disease

5.1. Nutrition and Epigenetic Programming

Appropriate prenatal nutrients have pivotal effects in optimal fetal growth and development. Similarly, postnatal nutritional exposures are critical for the ongoing developmental maturation of many organ systems for optimal physiological functions. Birth weight is an important marker for appropriate fetal development. The relationship between birth weight and adult adiposity is a 'U'-shaped curve with both low (<2.5 kg) and high birth weight (>4 kg) predisposing to the onset of later diseases. Antenatal maternal undernutrition leading to low birth weight may predispose for disorders of energy balance throughout life. High birth weight due to maternal obesity or diabetes may also increase risk of obesity and metabolic syndrome in later life.

Certain developmental stages are identified as critical time windows for nutritional programming. These include the periconceptional period, the embryonic stages, mid and late gestation, early postnatal life, the post-weaning period, and puberty. Environmental challenges during one or more of these development windows can lead to a "resetting" of cardiovascular metabolic, neural and other structures and regulating mechanisms that determine life as an adult. Maternal nutrition during fetal and early postnatal periods have been proposed to be of major importance. As mentioned above, in mammals there are two critical developmental periods of genome-wide epigenetic reprogramming in vivo: gametogenesis and early preimplantation development. The environmental changes triggered at these stages of development can lead to the self-propagation of epigenetic marks associated with changes in gene expression and an adult-onset phenotype. Nutritional deprivation or availability of one-carbon moieties is especially critical in this phase to establish a normal methylation pattern, as alterations in DNA methylation have been linked to nutritional programming of the phenotype. In humans, exposure to famine during the periconceptional period was associated with hypomethylation of the maternally imprinted *Igf2* DMR in offspring. In contrast, exposure to famine late in gestation was not associated with *Igf2* DMR methylation.

Studies in various animal models provide solid evidence that perinatal food manipulation causes epigenetic alterations by modifying methylation of gene promoter regions, chromatin histone modification, and/or miRNA expression in the offspring, thus permanently imprinting the offspring genome and sensitizing the offspring to disease in adulthood. Protein restriction in the diet of pregnant rats can induce hypomethylation of the glucocorticoid receptor and PPARa promoters in the livers of juvenile and adult offspring, accompanied by increased levels of associated mRNA expression (Lillycrop et al., 2008). Studies have shown that the methylation level of hepatic GR gene promoter exon 1_{10} is 33 % lower and GR expression 84 % higher in the protein restricted offspring liver at postnatal day 34. In accordance to this result, the DNA methyltransferase-1 (Dnmt1) expression was 17 % lower, while Dnmt3A/B and MBD2 expression was not altered in the offspring (Lillycrop et al., 2007). Histone modifications also are involved in regulating GR and PPARa expression with an increase in acetylation of histones H3, H4 and methylation of histone H3 at lysine K453 (Heijmans et al., 2008, Tobi et al., 2009). In contrast to the effect of the maternal protein restricted diet, adult female offspring of dams exposed to 70% reduction in maternal total nutrient intake showed hypermethylation of GR and PPARa promoters and decreased expression of GR and PPARa in the liver. Similarly, alterations in paternal diet have been associated with altered DNA methylation in the offspring. Feeding the father a low protein diet prior to mating resulted in modest changes in DNA methylation (10-20%) in the offspring, including a substantial increase in methylation at an intergenic CpG island 50 kb upstream of the PPARa gene (Carone et al., 2010).

5.2. Epigenetic Programming of HPA Axis

The HPA axis plays a pivotal role in the regulation of energy balance and metabolic function. Nutritionally epigenetic mechanisms may persistently affect transcription of key genes involved in energy balance, thus programming a long-term dysfunctional HPA axis. In mammals, the HPA axis is functional *in utero* and becomes more responsive during late gestation before birth. Many studies indicate that the HPA axis is highly susceptible to programming during development and plays a key role in the determination of health and disease. Whatever the original injury to the fetus, it increases the exposure of the embryo to high concentrations of glucocorticoids, either derived from the maternal circulation or produced following direct stimulation to the fetal HPA axis. Glucocorticoid-induced plasticity of the neural circuitry regulating the HPA axis may constitute a means through which exposure to stress plays a role in a spectrum of HPA abnormalities, including aberrant HPA circadian rhythms, abnormalities in the HPA response to stress, and basal HPA dysregulation (Figure 5).

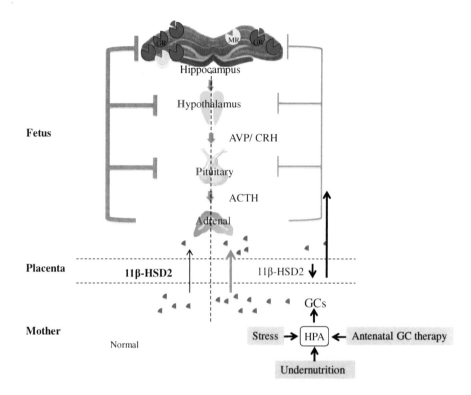

Figure 5. The hypothalamic-pituitary-adrenal axis (HPA) components and developmental programming of the fetal HPA axis by overexposure to glucocorticoids. The arginine vasopressin (AVP) and corticotrophin-releasing hormone (CRH) produced from PVN of the hypothalamus stimulate the synthesis and secretion of adrenocorticotropic hormone (ACTH) in the anterior pituitary. The ACTHs then promote the production and release of glucocorticoids (GCs) from the adrenal cortex. The HPA activity is controlled by feedback regulation of GCs at the pituitary, PVN and limbic system level through effects of glucocorticoid receptor (GR) and mineralocorticoid receptor (MR). Maternal stress results in elevated levels of maternal glucocorticoid and decreased effect of 11-Beta hydroxysteroid dehydrogenase type 2 (11β-HSD2) in the placenta. Synthetic GCs directly pass through the placenta and reach the fetal circulation. The resultant overexposure of the developing fetus to GCs leads to attenuated feedback regulation of HPA activity through decreased expression of GR.

Increased HPA activity resulting from adverse early life events has been shown to result in permanent changes in systems that regulate metabolic processes. Exposure of glucocorticoid-responsive organs (such as the brain, liver or pancreas) to excess glucocorticoids during the critical period of development may result in permanent physiological alterations. This process is partially mediated by epigenetic mechanisms. In rodents, the hypothalamic proopiomelanocortin (*POMC*) gene promoter region is a key target of epigenetic changes following perinatal nutritional manipulation (Plagemann et al., 2009). The *POMC* promoter was found to be less methylated in weanling rat offspring from low protein dams, whereas it showed hypermethylation in weanling small litter offspring that underwent catch-up growth (Breton, 2013). In the latter case, these mechanisms might impair hormone effects on *POMC* expression and account for hypothalamic leptin/insulin resistance.

Epigenetic regulation of glucocorticoid receptor (GR) expression plays a pivotal role in the programming of response to stress. Female mice possess different nurturing behaviours with some mothers showing high pup licking and grooming (LG) and arch-back nursing compared to others. Offspring from high-LG dams show reduced fearfulness and more modest HPA response to stress. It has been demonstrated that the NGFI-A binding site at the promoter of the GR exon 1_7 contains two CpG dinucleotides which are potential targets for epigenetic modification. The 5' CpG dinucleotide is commonly methylated in the offspring of low LG mothers, whereas it is rarely methylated in the offspring of high-LG mothers. The hypomethylation of CpG dinucleotides in high-LG offspring is associated with increased NGFI-A binding, increased hippocampal GR expression and enhanced HPA feedback regulation (Weaver et al., 2004b). These changes in methylation at the NGFI-A binding site, together with some other alterations may be reversed by cross-fostering, indicating there is a direct association between maternal care level and alterations of DNA methylation of the GR exon1_7 promoter. These studies demonstrate the direct effects of postnatal manipulation on the programming of HPA function through epigenetic modification of the GR promoter. In the human hippocampus, the GR exon 1-F promoter is generally not methylated at the NGFI-A binding site as it is in the rat homologue exon 1_7, yet prenatal exposure to maternal depression and/or anxiety result in a significant increase in GR promoter methylation and increased stress response in the adult.

5.3. Epigenetic Programming of Endocrine Organs and Type 2 Diabetes

T2D is composed of a complex disorder with multi-factorial etiology, but is very much an insulin-centric disease. This is manifest by elevated fasting plasma glucose, reduced insulin sensitivity and beta-cell dysfunction. Insulin is one of the major regulators of blood glucose, and insulin secretion deficit or reduced response of the body to insulin can result in impaired glucose utilization and diabetes. Both nutritional and hormonal disturbances during fetal development have been shown to cause long-term consequences for pancreatic structure and function, altering the process of beta-cell development and resulting in an irreversible decrease in beta-cell mass that affects insulin function in later life. Altered epigenetic modifications of pivotal genes that control beta-cell development undoubtedly play a key role in this regard.

Pdx-1 is a critical transcription factor for beta-cell development, and its expression is decreased in fetal growth restriction (FGR) subjects, promoting the development of diabetes in adulthood. Study of the epigenetic events at the Pdx-1 promoter indicates that FGR induces a self-propagating epigenetic cycle at the promoter, resulting in transcriptional repression of Pdx-1 (Park et al., 2008). During the fetal period, the mSin3A/HDAC complex is recruited to the Pdx-1 promoter, leading to deacetylation of histones and a loss of transcription factors binding to the promoter, which suppress expression of Pdx-1. In the postnatal period, as histone deacetylation progresses, levels of trimethylated H3K4 decrease while dimethylated H3K9 accumulates. This promotes the recruitment of DNMT3A and initiates *de novo* DNA methylation at the promoter and maintains Pdx-1 in a silent state in the pancreas of adults born with FGR and influences risk of T2D (Pinney and Simmons, 2010). Moreover, decreased beta-cell mass affect not only insulin secretion but also the expression of pancreatic growth factors, including IGF1, IGF2, vascular endothelial growth factor, fibroblast growth factor, which play important roles in both fetal development and physiologic process in postnatal life.

As noted, insulin resistance is a characteristic feature of T2D, and plays a major role in the pathogenesis of the disease. Glut4, the primary glucose transporter in muscle and fat cells, is an important regulator of peripheral glucose transport and insulin resistance. Reduced expression of Glut4 is observed in both human and rat offspring with FGR (Ozanne et al., 2005, Thamotharan et al., 2005). Glut4 promoter is capable of binding to different DNMTs at different ages: DNMT1 bound postnatally, whereas DNMT3A and DNMT3B bound in adults. Although DNA methylation levels at the Glut4 promoter are not altered, greater binding of DNMTs to the Glut4 promoter is observed in individuals with FGR, resulting in higher levels of MeCP2 that suppresses gene expression. Covalent modifications of the histone code also are observed in FGR individuals that have reduced level of Glut4. HDAC1 mediated deacetylation of H3K14 and enhanced binding of HDAC4 enzymes were observed in FGR individuals, which may set the stage for H3K9 dimethylation and increase recruitment of heterochromatin protein 1. These contribute to inactivation of postnatal and adult Glut4 gene transcription in individuals with FGR (Raychaudhuri et al., 2008).

6. Environmental Epigenetic Modifications and Disease Susceptibility

In traditional research, study of disease susceptibility often has been focused on the environmental influence on genetic factors such as individual genotype variation, which is mostly a result of environmental exposure and germline mutations in the gene coding and promoter regions. However, it becomes clear that environmental exposure encountered early in life influences the health and risk of disease in adulthood. A general mechanism by which this early environmental exposure could be linked to adult phenotypic changes is the alteration of epigenetic marks which are critical to regulate the output of genomic information. Therefore, understanding of disease susceptibility will require consideration of both genetic and epigenetic information that indicates integrating environmental interactions with the genome. It is well known that prenatal and early postnatal environmental factors, including maternal nutritional supplements (Waterland et al., 2006a), maternal diet, (Waterland et al., 2006b), low-dose radiation (Koturbash et al., 2006), maternal behavior (Weaver et al., 2004a), and xenobiotic chemicals (Ho et al., 2006), can result in altered reprogramming of epigenetic marks and lead to subsequent changes of disease susceptibility in the developing individual.

Some genomic targets, including gene promoter regions, transposable elements (transposon), and regulatory elements of imprinted genes, are likely to be susceptible to gene-expression changes caused by environmental perturbations. These targets usually contain regions that are CpG rich sequences with differentially methylation status, and some regions also are subject to histone modifications for gene expression regulation. Transposable elements are repetitive elements that distribute throughout mammalian genomes, and comprise about 45% of the human genome. Although most of these are silenced by CpG methylation, the epigenetic state of a subset of transposable elements is metastable and may potentially affect the expression of adjacent genes. Metastable epialleles are alleles that can be epigenetically modified in a variable and reversible manner, and are expressed variably in genetically identical individuals (Dolinoy et al., 2007). Importantly, epigenetic marks at metastable epialleles can be altered by gestational exposure to nutritional agents and other environmental factors (Dolinoy et al., 2006, Waterland et al., 2006a). One good example of such epigenetically based phenotype viability is the A^{vy} allele of the mouse Agouti gene. The Agouti gene encodes a paracrine signaling molecule involved in the production of a yellow pigment in mice melanocytes. Transcription of the A allele normally occurs only in the skin, where transit expression in fair follicles during a specific stage of hair growth results in a yellow subapical band on each black hair, causing the brown coat color of wild type mice. The A^{vy} allele is the result of the insertion of a transposon upstream of the transcriptional start site of the Agouti gene. Insertion of this transposon promotes constitutive expression of Agouti gene, leading to yellow fur, obesity, diabetes and tumorigenesis. CpG methylation in the A^{vy} correlates inversely with expression of agouti gene. The degree of methylation varies dramatically among individual A^{vy}/a mouse, causing a wide distribution of coat color from yellow (unmethylated) to brown (methylated) (Duhl et al., 1994). Moreover, supplementation of pregnant mice with betaine, choline, folic acid and vitamin B12 can shift coat color from yellow to brown and provide protection against obesity in the offspring. This effect has been shown to result from an increase in DNA methylation of the CpG sites in the transposon (Waterland and Jirtle, 2003, Wolff et al., 1998). These findings further indicate the epigenetic changes induced by environmental factors during early development on disease susceptibility in adulthood.

7. Intergenerational Inheritance of Epigenetic Patterns

Intergenerational inheritance involves the transmission of a phenotype to subsequent generations through the germ line. An intergenerational transmission of epigenetic effects requires that the inherited biological trait must be caused by the epigenetic modifications in the germ line. An increasing body of evidence, most of which is from animal studies, has indicated intergenerational effects of fetal programming. For example, continued poor maternal nutrition in multiple generations produces amplified effects on low birth weight of offspring. It takes three generations for fetal growth and development to return to normal, despite a return of the dams to normal nutrition (Stewart et al., 1975). Evidence from rodent studies indicates that maternal exposure to nutritional or hormonal interventions results in epigenetic changes that persist for at least two generations in the offspring. Maternal low protein diet induces altered metabolic phenotype and methylation patterns of PPARa and GR promoter in the F1 generation, and this altered methylation is transmitted to the F2 generation (Burdge et al., 2007).

The disease phenotype and epigenetic alterations in subsequent generations of the one with embryonic exposure may be owned to the influenced development of the reproductive tract in the F1 embryo or F2 generation germ line, which are also directly exposed to adverse environmental factors with the F0 generation (the exposed mother). In addition, epigenetic alterations produced during programming may, in part, mediate such intergenerational inheritance. Maternal treatment of an endocrine disruptor during the period of testis development results in male fertility defects in the offspring through F1 to F4 generation, and these effects on reproduction correlate with altered DNA methylation patterns in the testis (Anway et al., 2005). Exposure of embryos to the HDAC inhibitor valproic acid results in an increase in H4ac and H3K4me on the promoters of Hoxb1 and Hoxb9, and these changes were heritable in the subsequent generations (Gamble et al., 2010).

The DNA methylation pattern normally is reset through demethylation and methylation reprogramming some time after fertilization. Therefore, only epigenetic marks that either induce stable chromosomal alterations or involve epigenetic modification which is maintained through germ cell maturation can be transgenerationally inherited. In addition, some phenotypic and epigenetic effects may be inherited by subsequent generations through behavioral, but not germline transmission. Studies in mice have demonstrated that adult female offspring of dams with high-LG show an increase in pup licking and grooming and arch-back nursing behaviors, as well as more modest HPA response to stress. These nurturing behaviors in the female offspring are acquired from the mother through behavior transmission but not germline transmission, since similar behaviors were observed in low-LG offspring cross-fostered to high-LG mother. As indicated above, these effects are mediated by epigenetic modifications to the brain specific $GR1_7$ promoter (Weaver et al., 2004a).

8. Reversibility of Epigenetic Changes and Potential Therapeutic Interventions for Developmental Programming Disease

Although epigenetic modifications are usually thought of as being stable once established, evidence from recent studies indicates that manipulations of these modifications interfere with the phenotype or behavior outcomes. One example is that infusion of the HDAC inhibitor trichostatin A (TSA) or the essential amino acid L-methionine into the brain ventricles of adult offspring from dams showing different level of maternal care reverses the epigenetic modifications in the hippocampus, the alteration of GR expression, and the HPA response to stress (Weaver et al., 2004a, 2005, 2006). Such evidence indicates that the inherent plasticity of the epigenome potentially allows for reversal in adulthood, which provides an important finding in terms of possible therapeutic strategies.

As can be appreciated, the etiology of non-communicable disease is complicated, because genetic factors, developmental influences and adult lifestyle each can contribute to the disease risk. Thus, identifying the at-risk individuals becomes an important point of timely and customized interventions for potential disease prevention strategies. Low birth weight has commonly been used as an indicator of abnormal fetal growth and is associated with later metabolic dysfunction. However, disease risk exists throughout the normal birth weight range and an appropriate weight-for-age at birth does not exclude prior adverse intrauterine exposures. Also, either catch-up growth in SGA or catch-down growth in LGA infants predisposes the risk for diabetes in later life. Given that the epigenetic control of key genes is central to organ development and the onset of disease, the application of developmental epigenetics has enormous potential as a target for therapeutic interventions. In a recent study, the DNA methylation level of umbilical cord tissue at a specific site in the *RXRA* promoter was associated with lower maternal carbohydrate intake in early pregnancy and higher childhood body fat (Godfrey et al. 2011). RXRA is a transcription factor involved in fat metabolism and insulin sensitivity, and the finding of epigenetic alteration to its promoter may assist in identifying individuals vulnerable to obesity and metabolic disease, and /or other conditions later in life.

Recent laboratory studies have explored the reversibility of induced phenotypic effects by *in utero* factors. Several compounds have been shown to regulate DNMT or HDAC activity, and are capable of reversing programmed phenotypic effects. For example, the plant-derived isoflavone genistein can reactivate methylation-silenced genes. Maternal dietary genistein supplementation of mice during gestation increased methylation of six CpG sites in the transposon upstream of the Agouti gene and led to fur color shift of A^{vy} mouse offspring to pseudoagouti (Dolinoy et al., 2006). Supplementation of the methyl donor folate to low protein diet dams prevents the elevation of blood pressure, impairment of vasodilatation and decrease of nitric oxide synthase mRNA levels in the offspring. Folate supplementation during pregnancy improves offspring cardiovascular dysfunction induced by maternal protein restriction (Torrens et al., 2006). Exogenous leptin administration from day 3 to 13 in the neonatal offspring of undernourished rats rescues the phenotypic changes, gene expression and associated methylation changes in PPARa promoter. This suggests that developmental metabolic programming is potentially reversible by an intervention late in the phase of developmental plasticity (Vickers et al., 2005).

Presently, due to the worldwide prevalence of obesity, rates of both maternal and childhood obesity as well as diabetes are higher than in previous years. As a result, perinatal over-nutrition becomes an apparent adverse environmental factor and is associated with long-term disease. There remains much uncertainty regarding the relative importance of developmental factors in contributing to the development of disease. Obviously, much more research is needed in the contemporary cohorts to better define early life growth patterns. An optimal nutritional management for the mother and infant is important to reduce long-term risk of metabolic diseases. Epigenetic marks may become useful to evaluate the nutritional exposure profile of infants, and epigenetic measures may provide instruction for desirable changes to the developmental trajectory.

Conclusion and Perspectives

Accumulating evidence from human epidemiologic and laboratory animal studies clearly suggests that one's environment during early development sets the stage for subsequent health and disease in adulthood. A growing body of evidence indicates that at the molecular level, developmental programming is reflected by transcriptional changes in the growth and metabolic pathways. These changes are achieved, at least partly, through alteration of epigenetic modifications of the genes involved in these pathways (Figure 6). Various complications during development, including nutritional signals, hormonal interference, and exposure to adverse substances, are capable of altering the epigenetic marks surrounding the DNA. Epigenetic mechanisms include methylation/demethylation of DNA, modification of histone and miRNA at post-transcriptional level, and other biochemical changes.

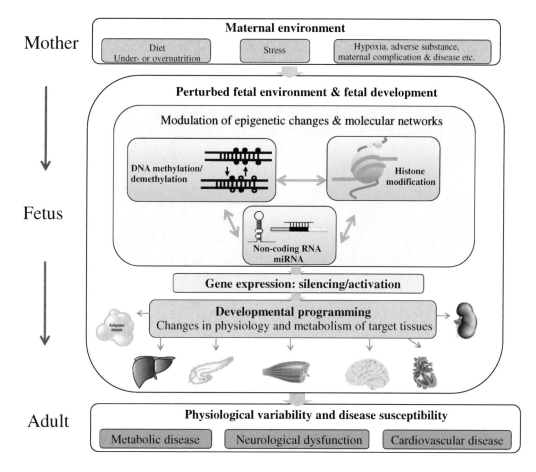

Figure 6. Schematic diagram showing the role of epigenetic mechanisms in developmental programming of adult disease. A tightly controlled gene expression profile plays a pivotal role in the optimal development and growth of a fetus. Exposure of the mother to adverse factors during pregnancy (e.g., imbalanced diet and maternal stress) results in perturbed maternal-fetal environment, leading to modulated epigenetic changes that alter the gene expression profile. Changes in physiology and metabolism of the developing tissues promote the survival of the individual, however, may permanently affect the structure and/or function of associated tissues and result in increased disease susceptibility in adult.

Although each epigenetic pattern has its own characteristics, they function as an orchestrated and complicated network, to ensure integrated and fine-tuning of gene regulation. Moreover, altered epigenetic marks resulting from prenatal insults can be inherited trans-generationally and affect more than one generation. Fortunately, the concept of developmental programming of adult health and disease has been demonstrated by numerous studies and has attracted extensive attention. In addition to avoiding possible prenatal insults, further understanding of the underlying molecular mechanisms of fetal programming will promote timely intervention and valid therapy approaches to minimize the existing consequences induced by prenatal programming. Such approaches have not only great implications for each individual pregnant mother, but awareness of, and striving for preventative and therapeutic approaches has enormous national and global relevance.

References

Aid, T., Kazantseva, A., Piirsoo, M., Palm, K. & Timmusk, T. (2007). Mouse and rat BDNF gene structure and expression revisited. *J. Neurosci. Res.*, 85, 525-35.

Akhtar, A. & Gasser, S.M. (2007). The nuclear envelope and transcriptional control. *Nat. Rev. Genet.*, 8, 507-17.

Alkemade, F.E., van Vliet, P., Henneman, P., van Dijk, K.W., Hierck, B.P., van Munsteren, J.C., et al. (2010). Prenatal exposure to apoE deficiency and postnatal hypercholesterolemia are associated with altered cell-specific lysine methyltransferase and histone methylation patterns in the vasculature. *Am. J. Pathol.*, 176, 542-8.

Ambros, V. & Lee, R.C. (2004). Identification of microRNAs and other tiny noncoding RNAs by cDNA cloning. *Methods Mol. Biol.*, 265, 131-58.

Anway, M.D., Cupp, A.S., Uzumcu, M. & Skinner, M.K. (2005). Epigenetic transgenerational actions of endocrine disruptors and male fertility. *Science*, 308, 1466-9.

Arima, T., Hata, K., Tanaka, S., Kusumi, M., Li, E., Kato, K., et al. (2006). Loss of the maternal imprint in Dnmt3Lmat-/- mice leads to a differentiation defect in the extraembryonic tissue. *Dev. Biol.*, 297, 361-73.

Arnaud, P. (2010). Genomic imprinting in germ cells: imprints are under control. *Reproduction*, 140, 411-23.

Bagga, S., Bracht, J., Hunter, S., Massirer, K., Holtz, J., Eachus, R., et al. (2005). Regulation by let-7 and lin-4 miRNAs results in target mRNA degradation. *Cell*, 122, 553-63.

Barrey, E., Saint-Auret, G., Bonnamy, B., Damas, D., Boyer, O. & Gidrol, X. (2011). Pre-microRNA and mature microRNA in human mitochondria. *PLoS One*, 6, e20220.

Bartel, F., Schulz, J., Blumke, K., Kappler, M., Bache, M., Schmidt, H., et al. (2004). [HDMX amplification and high levels of HDMX-S splice variant are correlated with a poor prognosis in soft tissue sarcomas]. *Verh. Dtsch. Ges. Pathol.*, 88, 199-206.

Bartolomei, M.S., Webber, A.L., Brunkow, M.E. & Tilghman, S.M. (1993). Epigenetic mechanisms underlying the imprinting of the mouse H19 gene. *Genes Dev.*, 7, 1663-73.

Behm-Ansmant, I., Rehwinkel, J. & Izaurralde, E. (2006). MicroRNAs silence gene expression by repressing protein expression and/or by promoting mRNA decay. *Cold Spring Harb. Symp. Quant. Biol.*, 71, 523-30.

Bellizzi, D., D'Aquila, P., Scafone, T., Giordano, M., Riso, V., Riccio, A., et al. (2013). The control region of mitochondrial DNA shows an unusual CpG and non-CpG methylation pattern. *DNA Res.*, 20, 537-47.

Bhogal, B., Arnaudo, A., Dymkowski, A., Best, A. & Davis, T.L. (2004). Methylation at mouse Cdkn1c is acquired during postimplantation development and functions to maintain imprinted expression. *Genomics*, 84, 961-70.

Bhutani, N., Burns, D.M. & Blau, H.M. (2011). DNA demethylation dynamics. *Cell,* 146, 866-72.

Bogdarina, I., Welham, S., King, P.J., Burns, S.P. & Clark, A.J. (2007). Epigenetic modification of the renin-angiotensin system in the fetal programming of hypertension. *Circ. Res.*, 100, 520-6.

Bourc'his, D., Xu, G.L., Lin, C.S., Bollman, B. & Bestor, T.H. (2001). Dnmt3L and the establishment of maternal genomic imprints. *Science*, 294, 2536-9.

Branco, M.R., Ficz, G. & Reik, W. (2012). Uncovering the role of 5-hydroxymethylcytosine in the epigenome. *Nat. Rev. Genet.*, 13, 7-13.

Brandeis, M., Frank, D., Keshet, I., Siegfried, Z., Mendelsohn, M., Nemes, A., et al. (1994). Sp1 elements protect a CpG island from de novo methylation. *Nature*, 371, 435-8.

Brandeis, M., Kafri, T., Ariel, M., Chaillet, J.R., McCarrey, J., Razin, A., et al. (1993). The ontogeny of allele-specific methylation associated with imprinted genes in the mouse. *EMBO J.*, 12, 3669-77.

Breton, C. (2013). The hypothalamus-adipose axis is a key target of developmental programming by maternal nutritional manipulation. *J. Endocrinol.*, 216, R19-31.

Breton, C.V., Byun, H.M., Wenten, M., Pan, F., Yang, A. & Gilliland, F.D. (2009). Prenatal tobacco smoke exposure affects global and gene-specific DNA methylation. *Am. J. Respir. Crit. Care Med.*, 180, 462-7.

Bruniquel, D. & Schwartz, R.H. (2003). Selective, stable demethylation of the interleukin-2 gene enhances transcription by an active process. *Nat. Immunol.*, 4, 235-40.

Burdge, G.C., Slater-Jefferies, J., Torrens, C., Phillips, E.S., Hanson, M.A. & Lillycrop, K.A. (2007). Dietary protein restriction of pregnant rats in the F0 generation induces altered methylation of hepatic gene promoters in the adult male offspring in the F1 and F2 generations. *Br. J. Nutr.*, 97, 435-9.

Carone, B.R., Fauquier, L., Habib, N., Shea, J.M., Hart, C.E., Li, R., et al. (2010). Paternally induced transgenerational environmental reprogramming of metabolic gene expression in mammals. *Cell*, 143, 1084-96.

Chadee, D.N., Hendzel, M.J., Tylipski, C.P., Allis, C.D., Bazett-Jones, D.P., Wright, J.A., et al. (1999). Increased Ser-10 phosphorylation of histone H3 in mitogen-stimulated and oncogene-transformed mouse fibroblasts. *J. Biol. Chem.*, 274, 24914-20.

Chahrour, M., Jung, S.Y., Shaw, C., Zhou, X., Wong, S.T., Qin, J., et al. (2008). MeCP2, a key contributor to neurological disease, activates and represses transcription. *Science*, 320, 1224-9.

Chedin, F., Lieber, M.R. & Hsieh, C.L. (2002). The DNA methyltransferase-like protein DNMT3L stimulates de novo methylation by Dnmt3a. *Proc. Natl. Acad. Sci. U S A*, 99, 16916-21.

Chen, Z.X., Mann, J.R., Hsieh, C.L., Riggs, A.D. & Chedin, F. (2005). Physical and functional interactions between the human DNMT3L protein and members of the de novo methyltransferase family. *J. Cell Biochem.*, 95, 902-17.

Chestnut, B.A., Chang, Q., Price, A., Lesuisse, C., Wong, M. & Martin, L.J. (2011). Epigenetic regulation of motor neuron cell death through DNA methylation. *J. Neurosci.*, 31, 16619-36.

Choi, Y.S., Hoon Jeong, J., Min, H.K., Jung, H.J., Hwang, D., Lee, S.W. et al. (2011). Shotgun proteomic analysis of mitochondrial D-loop DNA binding proteins: identification of mitochondrial histones. *Mol. Biosyst.*, 7, 1523-36.

Ciccone, D.N., Su, H., Hevi, S., Gay, F., Lei, H., Bajko, J., et al. (2009). KDM1B is a histone H3K4 demethylase required to establish maternal genomic imprints. *Nature*, 461, 415-8.

Cohen, S., Zhou, Z. & Greenberg, M.E. (2008). Medicine. Activating a repressor. *Science*, 320, 1172-3.

Constancia, M., Kelsey, G. & Reik, W. (2004). Resourceful imprinting. *Nature*, 432, 53-7.

Crews, D. & McLachlan, J.A. (2006). Epigenetics, evolution, endocrine disruption, health, and disease. *Endocrinology*, 147, S4-10.

Dennis, K., Fan, T., Geiman, T., Yan, Q. & Muegge, K. (2001). Lsh, a member of the SNF2 family, is required for genome-wide methylation. *Genes. Dev.*, 15, 2940-4.

Dennis, K.E. & Levitt, P. (2005). Regional expression of brain derived neurotrophic factor (BDNF) is correlated with dynamic patterns of promoter methylation in the developing mouse forebrain. *Brain Res. Mol. Brain Res.*, 140, 1-9.

Doi, A., Park, I.H., Wen, B., Murakami, P., Aryee, M.J., Irizarry, R., et al. (2009). Differential methylation of tissue- and cancer-specific CpG island shores distinguishes human induced pluripotent stem cells, embryonic stem cells and fibroblasts. *Nat. Genet.*, 41, 1350-3.

Dolinoy, D.C., Das, R., Weidman, J.R. & Jirtle, R.L. (2007). Metastable epialleles, imprinting, and the fetal origins of adult diseases. *Pediatr. Res.*, 61, 30R-37R.

Dolinoy, D.C., Weidman, J.R., Waterland, R.A. & Jirtle, R.L. (2006). Maternal genistein alters coat color and protects Avy mouse offspring from obesity by modifying the fetal epigenome. *Environ. Health Perspect.*, 114, 567-72.

Dominguez-Salas, P., Cox, S.E., Prentice, A.M., Hennig, B.J. & Moore, S.E. (2012). Maternal nutritional status, C(1) metabolism and offspring DNA methylation: a review of current evidence in human subjects. *Proc. Nutr. Soc.*, 71, 154-65.

Duhl, D.M., Vrieling, H., Miller, K.A., Wolff, G.L. & Barsh, G.S. (1994). Neomorphic agouti mutations in obese yellow mice. *Nat. Genet.*, 8, 59-65.

Duursma, A.M., Kedde, M., Schrier, M., Le Sage, C. & Agami, R. (2008). miR-148 targets human DNMT3b protein coding region. *RNA*, 14, 872-7.

Dwivedi, Y., Rizavi, H.S. & Pandey, G.N. (2006). Antidepressants reverse corticosterone-mediated decrease in brain-derived neurotrophic factor expression: differential regulation of specific exons by antidepressants and corticosterone. *Neuroscience*, 139, 1017-29.

Edwards, C.A. & Ferguson-Smith, A.C. (2007). Mechanisms regulating imprinted genes in clusters. *Curr. Opin. Cell Biol.*, 19, 281-9.

Esteller, M. (2007). Epigenetic gene silencing in cancer: the DNA hypermethylome. *Hum. Mol. Genet.*, 16 Spec No 1, R50-9.

Esteve, P.O., Chin, H.G., Benner, J., Feehery, G.R., Samaranayake, M., Horwitz, G.A., et al. (2009). Regulation of DNMT1 stability through SET7-mediated lysine methylation in mammalian cells. *Proc. Natl. Acad. Sci. U S A*, 106, 5076-81.

Fabbri, M., Garzon, R., Cimmino, A., Liu, Z., Zanesi, N., Callegari, E., et al. (2007). MicroRNA-29 family reverts aberrant methylation in lung cancer by targeting DNA methyltransferases 3A and 3B. *Proc. Natl. Acad. Sci. U S A*, 104, 15805-10.

Fan, T., Hagan, J.P., Kozlov, S.V., Stewart, C.L. & Muegge, K. (2005). Lsh controls silencing of the imprinted Cdkn1c gene. *Development*, 132, 635-44.

Feil, R., Walter, J., Allen, N.D. & Reik, W. (1994). Developmental control of allelic methylation in the imprinted mouse Igf2 and H19 genes. *Development*, 120, 2933-43.

Feng, S., Xiong, L., Ji, Z., Cheng, W. & Yang, H. (2012). Correlation between increased ND2 expression and demethylated displacement loop of mtDNA in colorectal cancer. *Mol. Med. Rep.*, 6, 125-30.

Ferguson-Smith, A.C., Sasaki, H., Cattanach, B.M. & Surani, M.A. (1993). Parental-origin-specific epigenetic modification of the mouse H19 gene. *Nature*, 362, 751-5.

Fraga, M.F., Ballestar, E., Paz, M.F., Ropero, S., Setien, F., Ballestar, M.L., et al. (2005). Epigenetic differences arise during the lifetime of monozygotic twins. *Proc. Natl. Acad. Sci. U S A*, 102, 10604-9.

Frank, D., Keshet, I., Shani, M., Levine, A., Razin, A. & Cedar, H. (1991). Demethylation of CpG islands in embryonic cells. *Nature*, 351, 239-41.

Freitag, M. & Selker, E.U. (2005). Controlling DNA methylation: many roads to one modification. *Curr. Opin. Genet. Dev.*, 15, 191-9.

Gamble, M.J., Frizzell, K.M., Yang, C., Krishnakumar, R. & Kraus, W.L. (2010). The histone variant macroH2A1 marks repressed autosomal chromatin, but protects a subset of its target genes from silencing. *Genes Dev.*, 24, 21-32.

Goyal, R., Goyal, D., Leitzke, A., Gheorghe, C.P. & Longo, L.D. (2010). Brain renin-angiotensin system: fetal epigenetic programming by maternal protein restriction during pregnancy. *Reprod. Sci.*, 17, 227-38.

Hata, K., Okano, M., Lei, H. & Li, E. (2002). Dnmt3L cooperates with the Dnmt3 family of de novo DNA methyltransferases to establish maternal imprints in mice. *Development*, 129, 1983-93.

He, L. & Hannon, G.J. (2004). MicroRNAs: small RNAs with a big role in gene regulation. *Nat. Rev. Genet.*, 5, 522-31.

He, Y.F., Li, B.Z., Li, Z., Liu, P., Wang, Y., Tang, Q., et al. (2011). Tet-mediated formation of 5-carboxylcytosine and its excision by TDG in mammalian DNA. *Science*, 333, 1303-7.

Heijmans, B.T., Tobi, E.W., Stein, A.D., Putter, H., Blauw, G.J., Susser, E.S., et al. (2008). Persistent epigenetic differences associated with prenatal exposure to famine in humans. *Proc. Natl. Acad. Sci. U S A*, 105, 17046-9.

Hirasawa, R., Chiba, H., Kaneda, M., Tajima, S., Li, E., Jaenisch, R., et al. (2008). Maternal and zygotic Dnmt1 are necessary and sufficient for the maintenance of DNA methylation imprints during preimplantation development. *Genes Dev.*, 22, 1607-16.

Ho, S.M., Tang, W.Y., Belmonte de Frausto, J. & Prins, G.S. (2006). Developmental exposure to estradiol and bisphenol A increases susceptibility to prostate carcinogenesis and epigenetically regulates phosphodiesterase type 4 variant 4. *Cancer Res.*, 66, 5624-32.

Hogan, C. & Varga-Weisz, P. (2007). The regulation of ATP-dependent nucleosome remodelling factors. *Mutat. Res.*, 618, 41-51.

Holz-Schietinger, C. & Reich, N.O. (2010). The inherent processivity of the human de novo methyltransferase 3A (DNMT3A) is enhanced by DNMT3L. *J. Biol. Chem.*, 285, 29091-100.

Howlett, S.K. & Reik, W. (1991). Methylation levels of maternal and paternal genomes during preimplantation development. *Development*, 113, 119-27.

Hu, J.F., Balaguru, K.A., Ivaturi, R.D., Oruganti, H., Li, T., Nguyen, B.T., et al. (1999). Lack of reciprocal genomic imprinting of sense and antisense RNA of mouse insulin-like growth factor II receptor in the central nervous system. *Biochem. Biophys. Res. Commun.*, 257, 604-8.

Hu, J.F., Oruganti, H., Vu, T.H. & Hoffman, A.R. (1998). Tissue-specific imprinting of the mouse insulin-like growth factor II receptor gene correlates with differential allele-specific DNA methylation. *Mol. Endocrinol.*, 12, 220-32.

Iacobazzi, V., Castegna, A., Infantino, V. & Andria, G. (2013). Mitochondrial DNA methylation as a next-generation biomarker and diagnostic tool. *Mol. Genet. Metab.*, 110, 25-34.

Irizarry, R.A., Ladd-Acosta, C., Wen, B., Wu, Z., Montano, C., Onyango, P., et al. (2009). The human colon cancer methylome shows similar hypo- and hypermethylation at conserved tissue-specific CpG island shores. *Nat. Genet.*, 41, 178-86.

Ito, S., D'Alessio, A.C., Taranova, O.V., Hong, K., Sowers, L.C. & Zhang, Y. (2010). Role of Tet proteins in 5mC to 5hmC conversion, ES-cell self-renewal and inner cell mass specification. *Nature*, 466, 1129-33.

Ito, S., Shen, L., Dai, Q., Wu, S.C., Collins, L.B., Swenberg, J.A., et al. (2011). Tet proteins can convert 5-methylcytosine to 5-formylcytosine and 5-carboxylcytosine. *Science*, 333, 1300-3.

Ji, H., Ehrlich, L.I., Seita, J., Murakami, P., Doi, A., Lindau, P., et al. (2010). Comprehensive methylome map of lineage commitment from haematopoietic progenitors. *Nature*, 467, 338-42.

Jia, D., Jurkowska, R.Z., Zhang, X., Jeltsch, A. & Cheng, X. (2007). Structure of Dnmt3a bound to Dnmt3L suggests a model for de novo DNA methylation. *Nature*, 449, 248-51.

John, R.M. & Lefebvre, L. (2011). Developmental regulation of somatic imprints. *Differentiation*, 81, 270-80.

Jones, P.A. & Takai, D. (2001). The role of DNA methylation in mammalian epigenetics. *Science*, 293, 1068-70.

Jurkowska, R.Z., Anspach, N., Urbanke, C., Jia, D., Reinhardt, R., Nellen, W., et al. 2008. Formation of nucleoprotein filaments by mammalian DNA methyltransferase Dnmt3a in complex with regulator Dnmt3L. *Nucleic Acids Res.*, 36, 6656-63.

Kaneda, M., Sado, T., Hata, K., Okano, M., Tsujimoto, N., Li, E., et al. (2004). Role of de novo DNA methyltransferases in initiation of genomic imprinting and X-chromosome inactivation. *Cold Spring Harb. Symp. Quant. Biol.*, 69, 125-9.

Kaneko-Ishino, T. & Ishino, F. (2010). Retrotransposon silencing by DNA methylation contributed to the evolution of placentation and genomic imprinting in mammals. *Dev. Growth Differ.*, 52, 533-43.

Karlic, R., Chung, H.R., Lasserre, J., Vlahovicek, K. & Vingron, M. (2010). Histone modification levels are predictive for gene expression. *Proc. Natl. Acad. Sci. U S A*, 107, 2926-31.

Katari, S., Turan, N., Bibikova, M., Erinle, O., Chalian, R., Foster, M., et al. (2009). DNA methylation and gene expression differences in children conceived in vitro or in vivo. *Hum. Mol. Genet*, 18, 3769-78.

Kato, Y., Kaneda, M., Hata, K., Kumaki, K., Hisano, M., Kohara, Y., et al. (2007). Role of the Dnmt3 family in de novo methylation of imprinted and repetitive sequences during male germ cell development in the mouse. *Hum. Mol. Genet*, 16, 2272-80.

Kim, T.S., Kim, D.J., Lee, H. & Kim, Y.K. (2007). Increased plasma brain-derived neurotrophic factor levels in chronic smokers following unaided smoking cessation. *Neurosci. Lett.*, 423, 53-7.

Kim, V.N., Han, J. & Siomi, M.C. (2009). Biogenesis of small RNAs in animals. *Nat. Rev. Mol. Cell Biol.*, 10, 126-39.

Kishigami, S., Van Thuan, N., Hikichi, T., Ohta, H., Wakayama, S., Mizutani, E., et al. (2006). Epigenetic abnormalities of the mouse paternal zygotic genome associated with microinsemination of round spermatids. *Dev. Biol.*, 289, 195-205.

Klose, R.J. & Bird, A.P. (2006). Genomic DNA methylation: the mark and its mediators. *Trends Biochem. Sci.*, 31, 89-97.

Konycheva, G., Dziadek, M.A., Ferguson, L.R., Krageloh, C.U., Coolen, M.W., Davison, M., et al. (2011). Dietary methyl donor deficiency during pregnancy in rats shapes learning and anxiety in offspring. *Nutr. Res.*, 31, 790-804.

Koturbash, I., Baker, M., Loree, J., Kutanzi, K., Hudson, D., Pogribny, I., et al. (2006). Epigenetic dysregulation underlies radiation-induced transgenerational genome instability in vivo. *Int. J. Radiat. Oncol. Biol. Phys.*, 66, 327-30.

Kouzarides, T. (2007). SnapShot: Histone-modifying enzymes. *Cell*, 131, 822.

Lau, A.T., Lee, S.Y., Xu, Y.M., Zheng, D., Cho, Y.Y., Zhu, F., et al. (2011). Phosphorylation of histone H2B serine 32 is linked to cell transformation. *J. Biol. Chem.*, 286, 26628-37.

Laurent, L., Wong, E., Li, G., Huynh, T., Tsirigos, A., Ong, C.T., et al. (2010). Dynamic changes in the human methylome during differentiation. *Genome Res.*, 20, 320-31.

Lawrence, J., Chen, M., Xiong, F., Xiao, D., Zhang, H., Buchholz, J.N., et al. (2011). Foetal nicotine exposure causes PKCepsilon gene repression by promoter methylation in rat hearts. *Cardiovasc. Res.*, 89, 89-97.

Lehmann, U., Hasemeier, B., Christgen, M., Muller, M., Romermann, D., Langer, F., et al. (2008). Epigenetic inactivation of microRNA gene hsa-mir-9-1 in human breast cancer. *J. Pathol.*, 214, 17-24.

Leighton, P.A., Saam, J.R., Ingram, R.S., Stewart, C.L. & Tilghman, S.M. (1995). An enhancer deletion affects both H19 and Igf2 expression. *Genes Dev.*, 9, 2079-89.

Li, E. (2002). Chromatin modification and epigenetic reprogramming in mammalian development. *Nat. Rev. Genet.*, 3, 662-73.

Li, Y., Xiao, D., Yang, S. & Zhang, L. (2013). Promoter methylation represses AT2R gene and increases brain hypoxic-ischemic injury in neonatal rats. *Neurobiol. Dis.*, 60, 32-8.

Lillycrop, K.A., Phillips, E.S., Torrens, C., Hanson, M.A., Jackson, A.A. & Burdge, G.C. (2008). Feeding pregnant rats a protein-restricted diet persistently alters the methylation of specific cytosines in the hepatic PPAR alpha promoter of the offspring. *Br. J. Nutr.*, 100, 278-82.

Lillycrop, K.A., Slater-Jefferies, J.L., Hanson, M.A., Godfrey, K.M., Jackson, A.A. & Burdge, G.C. (2007). Induction of altered epigenetic regulation of the hepatic glucocorticoid receptor in the offspring of rats fed a protein-restricted diet during pregnancy suggests that reduced DNA methyltransferase-1 expression is involved in impaired DNA methylation and changes in histone modifications. *Br. J. Nutr.*, 97, 1064-73.

Lim, L.P., Lau, N.C., Garrett-Engele, P., Grimson, A., Schelter, J.M., Castle, J., et al. (2005). Microarray analysis shows that some microRNAs downregulate large numbers of target mRNAs. *Nature*, 433, 769-73.

Lister, R., Pelizzola, M., Dowen, R.H., Hawkins, R.D., Hon, G., Tonti-Filippini, J., et al. (2009). Human DNA methylomes at base resolution show widespread epigenomic differences. *Nature*, 462, 315-22.

Lodygin, D., Tarasov, V., Epanchintsev, A., Berking, C., Knyazeva, T., Korner, H., et al. (2008). Inactivation of miR-34a by aberrant CpG methylation in multiple types of cancer. *Cell Cycle*, 7, 2591-600.

Lopes, S., Lewis, A., Hajkova, P., Dean, W., Oswalk, J., Forne, T., et al. (2003). Epigenetic modifications in an imprinting cluster are controlled by a hierarchy of DMRs suggesting long-range chromatin interactions. *Hum. Mol. Genet.*, 12, 295-305.

Lopez-Serra, L. & Esteller, M. (2008). Proteins that bind methylated DNA and human cancer: reading the wrong words. *Br. J. Cancer*, 98, 1881-5.

Mahadevan, L.C., Willis, A.C. & Barratt, M.J. (1991). Rapid histone H3 phosphorylation in response to growth factors, phorbol esters, okadaic acid, and protein synthesis inhibitors. *Cell*, 65, 775-83.

Maier, S. & Olek, A. (2002). Diabetes: a candidate disease for efficient DNA methylation profiling. *J. Nutr.*, 132, 2440S-2443S.

Manev, H., Dzitoyeva, S. & Chen, H. (2012). Mitochondrial DNA: A Blind Spot in Neuroepigenetics. *Biomol. Concepts*, 3, 107-115.

Manning, J. & Vehaskari, V.M. (2005). Postnatal modulation of prenatally programmed hypertension by dietary Na and ACE inhibition. *Am. J. Physiol. Regul. Integr. Comp. Physiol.*, 288, R80-4.

Martinowich, K., Hattori, D., Wu, H., Fouse, S., He, F., Hu, Y., et al. (2003). DNA methylation-related chromatin remodeling in activity-dependent BDNF gene regulation. *Science*, 302, 890-3.

Mattick, J.S. & Makunin, I.V. (2005). Small regulatory RNAs in mammals. *Hum. Mol. Genet.*, 14 Spec No 1, R121-32.

Mayer, W., Niveleau, A., Walter, J., Fundele, R. & Haaf, T. (2000). Demethylation of the zygotic paternal genome. *Nature*, 403, 501-2.

Metivier, R., Gallais, R., Tiffoche, C., Le Peron, C., Jurkowska, R.Z., Carmouche, R.P., et al. (2008). Cyclical DNA methylation of a transcriptionally active promoter. *Nature*, 452, 45-50.

Mohr, F., Dohner, K., Buske, C. & Rawat, V.P. (2011). TET genes: new players in DNA demethylation and important determinants for stemness. *Exp. Hematol.*, 39, 272-81.

Moore, T., Constancia, M., Zubair, M., Bailleul, B., Feil, R., Sasaki, H., et al. (1997). Multiple imprinted sense and antisense transcripts, differential methylation and tandem repeats in a putative imprinting control region upstream of mouse Igf2. *Proc. Natl. Acad. Sci. U S A*, 94, 12509-14.

Mushkambarov, N.N., Votrin, II & Debov, S.S. (1976). [Methylation of preformed DNA in rat liver cell nuclei and mitochondria]. *Dokl. Akad. Nauk SSSR*, 229, 1255-7.

Nakamura, T., Arai, Y., Umehara, H., Masuhara, M., Kimura, T., Taniguchi, H., et al. (2007). PGC7/Stella protects against DNA demethylation in early embryogenesis. *Nat. Cell Biol.*, 9, 64-71.

Nan, X., Ng, H.H., Johnson, C.A., Laherty, C.D., Turner, B.M., Eisenman, R.N., et al. (1998). Transcriptional repression by the methyl-CpG-binding protein MeCP2 involves a histone deacetylase complex. *Nature*, 393, 386-9.

Napoli, C., D'Armiento, F.P., Mancini, F.P., Postiglione, A., Witztum, J.L., Palumbo, G., et al. (1997). Fatty streak formation occurs in human fetal aortas and is greatly enhanced by maternal hypercholesterolemia. Intimal accumulation of low density lipoprotein and its oxidation precede monocyte recruitment into early atherosclerotic lesions. *J. Clin. Invest.*, 100, 2680-90.

Napoli, C., Glass, C.K., Witztum, J.L., Deutsch, R., D'Armiento, F.P. & Palinski, W. (1999). Influence of maternal hypercholesterolaemia during pregnancy on progression of early atherosclerotic lesions in childhood: Fate of Early Lesions in Children (FELIC) study. *Lancet*, 354, 1234-41.

Nass, M.M. (1973). Differential methylation of mitochondrial and nuclear DNA in cultured mouse, hamster and virus-transformed hamster cells. In vivo and in vitro methylation. *J. Mol. Biol.*, 80, 155-75.

Neves, R., Scheel, C., Weinhold, S., Honisch, E., Iwaniuk, K.M., Trompeter, H.I., et al. (2010). Role of DNA methylation in miR-200c/141 cluster silencing in invasive breast cancer cells. *BMC Res. Notes*, 3, 219.

Nickel, B.E. & Davie, J.R. (1989). Structure of polyubiquitinated histone H2A. *Biochemistry*, 28, 964-8.

Noonan, E.J., Place, R.F., Pookot, D., Basak, S., Whitson, J.M., Hirata, H., et al. (2009). miR-449a targets HDAC-1 and induces growth arrest in prostate cancer. *Oncogene*, 28, 1714-24.

Ooi, L. & Wood, I.C. (2007). Chromatin crosstalk in development and disease: lessons from REST. *Nat. Rev. Genet.*, 8, 544-54.

Ooi, S.K., Qiu, C., Bernstein, E., Li, K., Jia, D., Yang, Z., et al. (2007). DNMT3L connects unmethylated lysine 4 of histone H3 to de novo methylation of DNA. *Nature*, 448, 714-7.

Oswald, J., Engemann, S., Lane, N., Mayer, W., Olek, A., Fundele, R., et al. (2000). Active demethylation of the paternal genome in the mouse zygote. *Curr. Biol.*, 10, 475-8.

Ozanne, S.E., Jensen, C.B., Tingey, K.J., Storgaard, H., Madsbad, S. & Vaag, A.A. (2005). Low birthweight is associated with specific changes in muscle insulin-signalling protein expression. *Diabetologia*, 48, 547-52.

Palinski, W. & Napoli, C. (2008). Impaired fetal growth, cardiovascular disease, and the need to move on. *Circulation*, 117, 341-3.

Park, J.H., Stoffers, D.A., Nicholls, R.D. & Simmons, R.A. (2008). Development of type 2 diabetes following intrauterine growth retardation in rats is associated with progressive epigenetic silencing of Pdx1. *J. Clin. Invest.*, 118, 2316-24.

Pasquinelli, A.E., Hunter, S. & Bracht, J. (2005). MicroRNAs: a developing story. *Curr. Opin. Genet. Dev.*, 15, 200-5.

Patterson, A.J., Chen, M., Xue, Q., Xiao, D. & Zhang, L. (2010). Chronic prenatal hypoxia induces epigenetic programming of PKC{epsilon} gene repression in rat hearts. *Circ. Res.*, 107, 365-73.

Pauler, F.M., Stricker, S.H., Warczok, K.E. & Barlow, D.P. (2005). Long-range DNase I hypersensitivity mapping reveals the imprinted Igf2r and Air promoters share cis-regulatory elements. *Genome Res.*, 15, 1379-87.

Pinney, S.E. & Simmons, R.A. (2010). Epigenetic mechanisms in the development of type 2 diabetes. *Trends Endocrinol. Metab.*, 21, 223-9.

Pirola, C.J., Gianotti, T.F., Burgueno, A.L., Rey-Funes, M., Loidl, C.F., Mallardi, P., et al. (2013). Epigenetic modification of liver mitochondrial DNA is associated with histological severity of nonalcoholic fatty liver disease. *Gut*, 62, 1356-63.

Plagemann, A., Harder, T., Brunn, M., Harder, A., Roepke, K., Wittrock-Staar, M., et al. (2009). Hypothalamic proopiomelanocortin promoter methylation becomes altered by early overfeeding: an epigenetic model of obesity and the metabolic syndrome. *J. Physiol.*, 587, 4963-76.

Plasterk, R.H. (2006). Micro RNAs in animal development. *Cell*, 124, 877-81.

Portela, A. & Esteller, M. (2010). Epigenetic modifications and human disease. *Nat. Biotechnol.*, 28, 1057-68.

Poulsen, P., Esteller, M., Vaag, A. & Fraga, M.F. (2007). The epigenetic basis of twin discordance in age-related diseases. *Pediatr. Res.*, 61, 38R-42R.

Qureshi, I.A. & Mehler, M.F. (2013). Understanding neurological disease mechanisms in the era of epigenetics. *JAMA Neurol.*, 70, 703-10.

Rajewsky, N. (2006). microRNA target predictions in animals. *Nat Genet*, 38 Suppl, S8-13.

Raychaudhuri, N., Raychaudhuri, S., Thamotharan, M. & Devaskar, S.U. (2008). Histone code modifications repress glucose transporter 4 expression in the intrauterine growth-restricted offspring. *J. Biol. Chem.*, 283, 13611-26.

Reik, W., Dean, W. & Walter, J. (2001). Epigenetic reprogramming in mammalian development. *Science*, 293, 1089-93.

Reik, W. & Walter, J. (2001a). Evolution of imprinting mechanisms: the battle of the sexes begins in the zygote. *Nat. Genet.*, 27, 255-6.

Reik, W. & Walter, J. (2001b). Genomic imprinting: parental influence on the genome. *Nat. Rev. Genet.*, 2, 21-32.

Rosenfeld, S. (2006). Stochastic oscillations in genetic regulatory networks: application to microarray experiments. *EURASIP J. Bioinform Syst. Biol.*, 59526.

Rossetto, D., Avvakumov, N. & Cote, J. (2012). Histone phosphorylation: a chromatin modification involved in diverse nuclear events. *Epigenetics*, 7, 1098-108.

Rougier, N., Bourc'his, D., Gomes, D.M., Niveleau, A., Plachot, M., Paldi, A., et al. (1998). Chromosome methylation patterns during mammalian preimplantation development. *Genes Dev.*, 12, 2108-13.

Ruthenburg, A.J., Li, H., Patel, D.J. & Allis, C.D. (2007). Multivalent engagement of chromatin modifications by linked binding modules. *Nat. Rev. Mol. Cell Biol.*, 8, 983-94.

Saito, Y., Liang, G., Egger, G., Friedman, J.M., Chuang, J.C., Coetzee, G.A., et al. (2006). Specific activation of microRNA-127 with downregulation of the proto-oncogene BCL6 by chromatin-modifying drugs in human cancer cells. *Cancer Cell*, 9, 435-43.

Sasaki, H., Allen, N.D. & Surani, M.A. (1993). DNA methylation and genomic imprinting in mammals. *EXS*, 64, 469-86.

Schneider, R. & Grosschedl, R. (2007). Dynamics and interplay of nuclear architecture, genome organization, and gene expression. *Genes Dev.*, 21, 3027-43.

Shmookler Reis, R.J. & Goldstein, S. (1983). Mitochondrial DNA in mortal and immortal human cells. Genome number, integrity, and methylation. *J. Biol. Chem.*, 258, 9078-85.

Shock, L.S., Thakkar, P.V., Peterson, E.J., Moran, R.G. & Taylor, S.M. (2011). DNA methyltransferase 1, cytosine methylation, and cytosine hydroxymethylation in mammalian mitochondria. *Proc. Natl. Acad. Sci. U S A*, 108, 3630-5.

Song, B., Wang, Y., Xi, Y., Kudo, K., Bruheim, S., Botchkina, G.I., et al. (2009). Mechanism of chemoresistance mediated by miR-140 in human osteosarcoma and colon cancer cells. *Oncogene*, 28, 4065-74.

Stewart, R.J., Preece, R.F. & Sheppard, H.G. (1975). Twelve generations of marginal protein deficiency. *Br. J. Nutr.*, 33, 233-53.

Stoger, R., Kubicka, P., Liu, C.G., Kafri, T., Razin, A., Cedar, H., et al. (1993). Maternal-specific methylation of the imprinted mouse Igf2r locus identifies the expressed locus as carrying the imprinting signal. *Cell*, 73, 61-71.

Straussman, R., Nejman, D., Roberts, D., Steinfeld, I., Blum, B., Benvenisty, N., et al. (2009). Developmental programming of CpG island methylation profiles in the human genome. *Nat. Struct. Mol. Biol.*, 16, 564-71.

Suetake, I., Shinozaki, F., Miyagawa, J., Takeshima, H. & Tajima, S. (2004). DNMT3L stimulates the DNA methylation activity of Dnmt3a and Dnmt3b through a direct interaction. *J. Biol. Chem*, 279, 27816-23.

Sun, C., Reimers, L.L. & Burk, R.D. (2011). Methylation of HPV16 genome CpG sites is associated with cervix precancer and cancer. *Gynecol. Oncol.*, 121, 59-63.

Sun, Z., Terragni, J., Borgaro, J.G., Liu, Y., Yu, L., Guan, S., et al. (2013). High-resolution enzymatic mapping of genomic 5-hydroxymethylcytosine in mouse embryonic stem cells. *Cell Rep.*, 3, 567-76.

Surani, M.A. (1998). Imprinting and the initiation of gene silencing in the germ line. *Cell*, 93, 309-12.

Suzuki, H., Takatsuka, S., Akashi, H., Yamamoto, E., Nojima, M., Maruyama, R., et al. (2011). Genome-wide profiling of chromatin signatures reveals epigenetic regulation of MicroRNA genes in colorectal cancer. *Cancer Res.*, 71, 5646-58.

Szulwach, K.E., Li, X., Smrt, R.D., Li, Y., Luo, Y., Lin, L., et al. (2010). Cross talk between microRNA and epigenetic regulation in adult neurogenesis. *J. Cell Biol.*, 189, 127-41.

Tachibana, M., Matsumura, Y., Fukuda, M., Kimura, H. & Shinkai, Y. (2008). G9a/GLP complexes independently mediate H3K9 and DNA methylation to silence transcription. *EMBO J.*, 27, 2681-90.

Tahiliani, M., Koh, K.P., Shen, Y., Pastor, W.A., Bandukwala, H., Brudno, Y., et al. (2009). Conversion of 5-methylcytosine to 5-hydroxymethylcytosine in mammalian DNA by MLL partner TET1. *Science*, 324, 930-5.

Taniura, H., Sng, J.C. & Yoneda, Y. (2007). Histone modifications in the brain. *Neurochem. Int.*, 51, 85-91.

Thamotharan, M., Shin, B.C., Suddirikku, D.T., Thamotharan, S., Garg, M. & Devaskar, S.U. (2005). GLUT4 expression and subcellular localization in the intrauterine growth-restricted adult rat female offspring. *Am. J. Physiol. Endocrinol. Metab.*, 288, E935-47.

Tobi, E.W., Lumey, L.H., Talens, R.P., Kremer, D., Putter, H., Stein, A.D., et al. (2009). DNA methylation differences after exposure to prenatal famine are common and timing- and sex-specific. *Hum. Mol. Genet.*, 18, 4046-53.

Toledo-Rodriguez, M., Lotfipour, S., Leonard, G., Perron, M., Richer, L., Veillette, S., et al. (2010). Maternal smoking during pregnancy is associated with epigenetic modifications of the brain-derived neurotrophic factor-6 exon in adolescent offspring. *Am. J. Med. Genet. B Neuropsychiatr. Genet.*, 153B, 1350-4.

Torrens, C., Brawley, L., Anthony, F.W., Dance, C.S., Dunn, R., Jackson, A.A., et al. (2006). Folate supplementation during pregnancy improves offspring cardiovascular dysfunction induced by protein restriction. *Hypertension*, 47, 982-7.

Trasler, J.M. (2006). Gamete imprinting: setting epigenetic patterns for the next generation. *Reprod. Fertil. Dev.*, 18, 63-9.

Van Straten, E.M., Bloks, V.W., Huijkman, N.C., Baller, J.F., Van Meer, H., Lutjohann, D., et al. (2010). The liver X-receptor gene promoter is hypermethylated in a mouse model of prenatal protein restriction. *Am. J. Physiol. Regul. Integr. Comp. Physiol.*, 298, R275-82.

Vickers, M.H., Gluckman, P.D., Coveny, A.H., Hofman, P.L., Cutfield, W.S., Gertler, A., et al. (2005). Neonatal leptin treatment reverses developmental programming. *Endocrinology*, 146, 4211-6.

Wang, Z., Zang, C., Cui, K., Schones, D.E., Barski, A., Peng, W., et al. (2009). Genome-wide mapping of HATs and HDACs reveals distinct functions in active and inactive genes. *Cell*, 138, 1019-31.

Wang, Z., Zang, C., Rosenfeld, J.A., Schones, D.E., Barski, A., Cuddapah, S., et al. (2008). Combinatorial patterns of histone acetylations and methylations in the human genome. *Nat. Genet.*, 40, 897-903.

Waterland, R.A., Dolinoy, D.C., Lin, J.R., Smith, C.A., Shi, X. & Tahiliani, K.G. (2006a). Maternal methyl supplements increase offspring DNA methylation at Axin Fused. *Genesis*, 44, 401-6.

Waterland, R.A. & Jirtle, R.L. (2003). Transposable elements: targets for early nutritional effects on epigenetic gene regulation. *Mol. Cell Biol.*, 23, 5293-300.

Waterland, R.A., Lin, J.R., Smith, C.A. & Jirtle, R.L. (2006b). Post-weaning diet affects genomic imprinting at the insulin-like growth factor 2 (Igf2) locus. *Hum. Mol. Genet.*, 15, 705-16.

Weaver, I.C., Cervoni, N., Champagne, F.A., D'Alessio, A.C., Sharma, S., Seckl, J.R., et al. (2004a). Epigenetic programming by maternal behavior. *Nat. Neurosci.*, 7, 847-54.

Weaver, I.C., Champagne, F.A., Brown, S.E., Dymov, S., Sharma, S., Meaney, M.J. et al. (2005). Reversal of maternal programming of stress responses in adult offspring through methyl supplementation: altering epigenetic marking later in life. *J. Neurosci.*, 25, 11045-54.

Weaver, I.C., Diorio, J., Seckl, J.R., Szyf, M. & Meaney, M.J. (2004b). Early environmental regulation of hippocampal glucocorticoid receptor gene expression: characterization of intracellular mediators and potential genomic target sites. *Ann. N Y Acad. Sci.*, 1024, 182-212.

Weaver, I.C., Meaney, M.J. & Szyf, M. (2006). Maternal care effects on the hippocampal transcriptome and anxiety-mediated behaviors in the offspring that are reversible in adulthood. *Proc. Natl. Acad. Sci. U S A*, 103, 3480-5.

Weber, M., Hellmann, I., Stadler, M.B., Ramos, L., Paabo, S., Rebhan, M., et al. (2007). Distribution, silencing potential and evolutionary impact of promoter DNA methylation in the human genome. *Nat. Genet.*, 39, 457-66.

Weksberg, R. (2010). Imprinted genes and human disease. *Am. J. Med. Genet. C Semin. Med. Genet.*, 154C, 317-20.

Wolff, G.L., Kodell, R.L., Moore, S.R. & Cooney, C.A. (1998). Maternal epigenetics and methyl supplements affect agouti gene expression in Avy/a mice. *FASEB J.*, 12, 949-57.

Wood, M.D., Hiura, H., Tunster, S., Arima, T., Shin, J.Y., Higgins, M., et al. (2010). Autonomous silencing of the imprinted Cdkn1c gene in stem cells. *Epigenetics*, 5.

Wossidlo, M., Arand, J., Sebastiano, V., Lepikhov, K., Boiani, M., Reinhardt, R., et al. (2010). Dynamic link of DNA demethylation, DNA strand breaks and repair in mouse zygotes. *EMBO J.*, 29, 1877-88.

Wren, J.D. & Garner, H.R. (2005). Data-mining analysis suggests an epigenetic pathogenesis for type 2 diabetes. *J. Biomed. Biotechnol.*, 2005, 104-12.

Wu, H., D'Alessio, A.C., Ito, S., Wang, Z., Cui, K., Zhao, K., et al. (2011). Genome-wide analysis of 5-hydroxymethylcytosine distribution reveals its dual function in transcriptional regulation in mouse embryonic stem cells. *Genes Dev*, 25, 679-84.

Xiong, F., Xiao, D. & Zhang, L. (2012). Norepinephrine causes epigenetic repression of PKCepsilon gene in rodent hearts by activating Nox1-dependent reactive oxygen species production. *FASEB J.*, 26, 2753-63.

Yoda, M., Kawamata, T., Paroo, Z., Ye, X., Iwasaki, S., Liu, Q., et al. (2010). ATP-dependent human RISC assembly pathways. *Nat. Struct. Mol. Biol.*, 17, 17-23.

Zandi-Nejad, K., Luyckx, V.A. & Brenner, B.M. (2006). Adult hypertension and kidney disease: the role of fetal programming. *Hypertension*, 47, 502-8.

Zhao, Q., Rank, G., Tan, Y.T., Li, H., Moritz, R.L., Simpson, R.J., et al. (2009). PRMT5-mediated methylation of histone H4R3 recruits DNMT3A, coupling histone and DNA methylation in gene silencing. *Nat. Struct. Mol. Biol.*, 16, 304-11.

Zwart, R., Sleutels, F., Wutz, A., Schinkel, A.H. & Barlow, D.P. (2001). Bidirectional action of the Igf2r imprint control element on upstream and downstream imprinted genes. *Genes Dev.*, 15, 2361-6.

In: Stress and Developmental Programming …   ISBN: 978-1-63321-836-9
Editors: Lubo Zhang and Lawrence D. Longo   © 2014 Nova Science Publishers, Inc.

Chapter 16

Stress, the Immune System and Cancer

*Vonetta M. Williams and Penelope Duerksen-Hughes**
Department of Basic Sciences, Loma Linda University School of Medicine,
Loma Linda, CA, US

Abstract

Over the past 30 years, research has shown that the brain and the immune system are intimately connected *via* both the Hypothalamic Pituitary Axis (HPA) and the Sympathetic Nervous System (SNS). In addition, increasing evidence implicates psychological stress as a contributing factor to cancer development. Stress *via* both the HPA and the Autonomic Nervous system exerts various effects on the body, and in particular on immune function, with downstream effects that may include immune suppression and the formation of a favorable tumor microenvironment. In addition, chronic stress may produce a state of chronic inflammation (the seventh hallmark of cancer), thereby contributing to tumorigenesis. Tumorigenesis is a complex process involving myriad changes, and converging evidence indicates that psychological stress, through its effects on immunity and inflammation, plays a critical role in this process.

Keywords: HPA axis, SNS, Inflammation, Stress hormones, Immune surveillance and Tumor microenvironment

Introduction

It has long been hypothesized that psychological factors such as stress may contribute to cancer development. As far back as 200 AD, the ancient Greek physician Galen noticed that women with a "melancholic" demeanor were more susceptible to breast cancer than were "sanguine" women (Reiche et al., 2004). Research over the past 30 years has demonstrated

* Corresponding author. Mailing address: Department of Basic Sciences, Loma Linda University School of Medicine, 11021 Campus Street, 101 Alumni Hall, Loma Linda, CA 92354. Phone: (909) 558-4480. Fax: (909) 558-0177. E-mail: pdhughes@llu.edu.

that the brain and immune system are intimately connected through a system of pathways that include the Hypothalmic-Pituitary-Adrenal (HPA) axis and the autonomic nervous system (ANS) (Webster et al., 2002). The putative link between psychosocial stress, its effects on the immune system and its ability to produce a state of chronic inflammation that may lead to cancer is a field of research that has attracted much attention in recent times. While the connection between these factors has not yet been well established, this chapter seeks to explore the links that have been made to date.

Many factors are already known to contribute to cancer risk. These include, but are not limited to, exposure to tobacco smoke, dietary factors, infectious agents, radiation, lack of physical activity, obesity, environmental pollutants and genetic defects. Recently, studies have postulated that psychological stress itself may be an independent risk factor for cancer. Psychological stresses are first sensed and processed in the cerebral cortex of the forebrain. These stress processes initiate a cascade of information-processing pathways within the central nervous system (CNS) and periphery which trigger fight or flight responses *via* the autonomic nervous system (ANS) or defeat/withdrawal *via* the hypothalamic-pituitary-adrenal (HPA) axis. As noted above, experimental data increasingly supports a role for psychological stress in the development and spread of cancer. For example, recent studies have shown that in mice transplanted with human tumors, stress increased the tumors' ability to proliferate and metastasize (Antoni et al., 2006). In humans, epidemiological studies have shown that there is two-fold increase in the risk for breast cancer after a stressful life event such as a divorce or death of a spouse (Lillberg et al., 2003), and, cancer risk has been shown to increase after chronic depression that lasts for at least 6 years (Penninx et al., 1998).

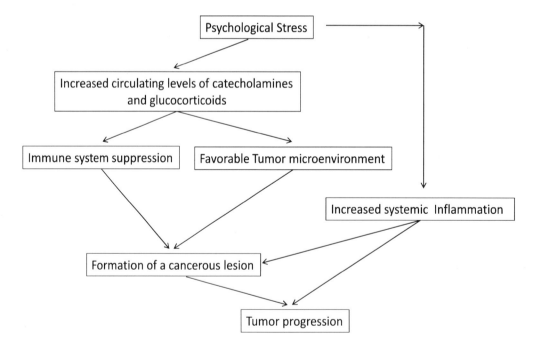

Figure 1. Working model for the relationships between psychological stress, the immune system, inflammation and cancer. These relationships are currently the subjects of active investigation.

Psychological stress refers to both the emotional and physiological reactions to a stressful life event or series of events. It is hypothesized that the effects of stress on tumor cells are mediated by the stress hormones and their receptors in the various interlinked stress-related pathways. Within the central nervous system, chronic stress exerts its effects particularly on the parvocellular neurosecretory neurons of the paraventricular nucleus and suprachiasmatic nucleus located in the hypothalamus. This leads to activation of the hypothalamic pituitary adrenal (HPA) axis as well as the sympathetic nervous system (SNS)-adrenal medullary axis.

Mediators of Stress

The Hypothalamic-Pituitary Adrenal (HPA) Axis

The anterior lobe of the pituitary is derived from the primitive foregut and functions primarily as an endocrine gland. It secretes six peptide hormones: thyroid stimulating hormone (TSH), follicle-stimulating hormone (FSH), luteinizing hormone (LH), growth hormone, prolactin, and, of most interest to this discussion, adrenocorticotrophic hormone (ACTH). The connection between the hypothalamus and the pituitary is both neural and endocrine in nature. The hypothalamus is linked directly to the anterior lobe *via* the hypothalamic-hypophysial blood vessels, which are responsible for the majority of the blood supply to the anterior pituitary. Arterial blood is delivered to the hypothalamus *via* the superior hypophysial arteries and is distributed *via* a capillary network to the entire hypothalamus. This capillary network then converges to form the hypophysial portal vessel, which then supplies the anterior pituitary with venous blood from the hypothalamus. This arrangement is significant because it allows the delivery of the hypothalamic hormones directly to the anterior pituitary at high concentrations.

Each of the six major hormones produced by the anterior pituitary lobe is secreted by a distinct cell type, with the exception of FSH and LH, which are both secreted by the same cell type. ACTH, our hormone of interest, is secreted by corticotrophs which make up approximately 15% of the cell mass of the anterior lobe. The hormone is stored in membrane-bound secretory granules prior to release. When the corticotroph cells are stimulated by Corticotrophin Releasing Hormone (CRH) to release ACTH, these secretory granules are exocytosed. CRH is released from the paraventricular nucleus of the hypothalamus during times of stress. ACTH then enters systemic circulation *via* capillary blood, and reaches the adrenal gland where it exerts its effects.

ACTH is a member of a family of hormones that are derived from pro-opiomelanocortin (POMC). The ACTH family of hormones includes ACTH, γ- and β- lipotrophin, β-endorphin and melanocyte-stimulating hormone (MSH). Of these, ACTH is the only member with known extensive physiologic actions on the body. ACTH acts on the adrenal glands *via* binding to cell surface ACTH receptors located on adrenocortical cells. The ACTH receptor is a G-protein coupled receptor, which upon binding to ACTH, undergoes a conformational change and stimulates adenylyl cyclase. This, in turn, increases intracellular cAMP levels and activates protein kinase A. This initiates both the long-term and short-term effects of the hormone. The short-term effect is the stimulation of cholesterol delivery to the mitochondria, where the P450 enzyme cholesterol desmolase catalyzes the first, rate-limiting step in the synthesis of all adrenocortical hormones. The long-term effect is the stimulation of lipoprotein uptake by cortical cells, which increases the bioavailability of cholesterol in these cells.

The two adrenal glands are located above each kidney in the retroperitonium. However, each adrenal gland can be considered to consist of two distinct glands itself, due to the different origins of each part: 1) The adrenal medulla, which is of neuroectodermal origin and comprises approximately 20% of the entire gland, is located in the innermost zone of each gland, and 2) the adrenal cortex, which is of mesodermal origin, and comprises the remaining 80% of the gland, is located in the outer zone of the gland. The hormones that both sections secrete are essential to the maintenance of life. Therefore, it is not surprising that, when normalized for weight, these glands receive the greatest blood flow of any organ in the body. The adrenal medulla secretes the two catecholamines, epinephrine and nor-epinephrine. The adrenal cortex consists of three distinct layers, the zona reticularis, zona fasciculata and the zona glomerulosa (listed from innermost to outermost). These layers secrete androgens, glucocorticoids and mineralocorticoids respectively. For the purposes of this chapter, we will focus primarily on the glucocorticoids.

Glucocorticoids are essential for life because they are essential for gluconeogenesis, for vascular responsiveness to catecholamines, for suppression of inflammatory and immune responses and for modulation of CNS functioning. The predominant glucocorticoid produced in the human body is cortisol, which is produced mainly in the zona fasciculata, with lesser amounts produced by the zona reticularis (which primarily produces androgens). However, cortisol is not the only hormone in the steroidogenesis synthetic pathway with glucocorticoid activity, as corticosterone, the precursor hormone to aldosterone, also has glucocorticoid activity. Thus, cortisol is not necessary to sustain life once corticosterone is present. However, in comparison to cortisol, corticosterone only has moderate glucocorticoid activity and lacks any anti-inflammatory effects. The effects of glucocorticoids are mediated through the glucocorticoid receptor, a ligand induced transcription factor that is a member of the nuclear receptor superfamily.

Cortisol secretion occurs in a pulsatile, diurnal pattern. On average during each 24 hr period, there are 10 secretory bursts. The highest rate occurs around 8 a.m., and the lowest during the evening time, during sleep, from about midnight to 4 a.m. The morning burst in secretion accounts for almost 50% of the daily cortisol secretion. ACTH secretion exhibits the same diurnal pattern. The central pacemaker located in the suprachiasmatic nucleus controls glucocorticoid secretion *via* the HPA axis and the SNS. The released glucocorticoids, in turn, exert feedback control of CRH release from the SCN and HPA axis. This rhythm is disrupted if there is a loss of feedback control on CRH, such as can be experienced during times of extreme stress.

Regulation of the HPA Axis

The HPA axis is regulated both from within the CNS and from the periphery. Secreted glucocorticoids exert a negative feedback response on the HPA axis at the both the hypothalamic and pituitary levels (see Figure 2).

Additionally, the HPA axis may be regulated by other mediators from the SNS, by cytokines and by other neuropeptides. CRH negatively regulates itself and ACTH.

Overstimulation of the HPA axis, as can occur during chronic stress, can lead an overall suppression of the immune response. This is because glucorticoids are capable of modulating the transcription of cytokines. They suppress the transcription of pro-inflammatory cytokines such as IL-1, IL-2, IL-6, IL-8, IL-11, IL-12, TNF-α, IFN-γ and GM-CSF, while up-regulating the expression of the anti-inflammatory IL-4 and IL-10. Therefore, during chronic stress when GC levels are elevated, the immune response is depressed (Webster et al., 2002).

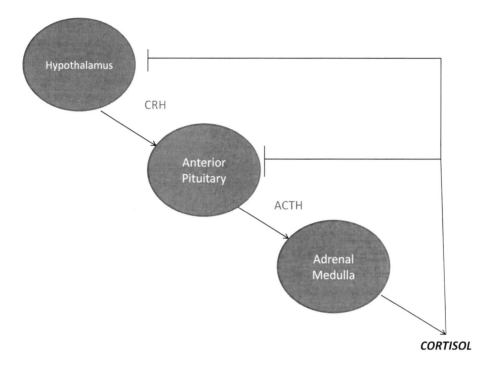

Figure 2. The HPA axis functions as the interface between stimuli from the external environment and the internal response to noxious stimuli. Following a stressful stimulus, the hypothalamus releases CRH and arginine vasopressin. These mediators are synthesisized in the paraventricular nucleus, then released into the hypothalamo-hypophyseal portal blood. This allows their transport to the anterior pituitary gland where they induce the release of ACTH. This released ACTH then acts on the zona fasculata cells of the adrenal cortex to initiate the release of glucocorticoids, such as cortisol. CRH-corticotrophin releasing hormone, ACTH-adrenocorticotrophic hormone.

The Effect of Glucocorticoids on Inflammation and Immunity

There are several mechanisms by which glucocorticoids affect the inflammatory response to trauma and irritants in the body. When glucocorticoids bind to the glucocorticoid receptor located in the cytoplasm, this binding activates the receptor. The receptor-ligand complex then translocates itself to the cell nucleus, where it can bind to the glucocorticoid response element (GRE) in the promoter region of target genes and regulate gene expression. In this manner, glucocorticoids induce the synthesis of lipocortin, which is an inhibitor of the phopholipase A_2 enzyme. By inhibiting phospholipase A_2, cortisol prevents the liberation of arachidonic acid from membrane phospholipids and thus inhibits the production of the prostaglandins and leukotrienes that mediate the inflammatory response.

The activated glucocorticoid receptor activates the inhibitor of NF-κB, IκB, while inhibiting expression of genes that are targets of activator protein-1 (AP-1) (Herr et al., 2003, Jonat et al., 1990). Glucocorticoids are thus able to prevent the transcription of pro-inflammatory genes such as IL-1β, IL-4, IL-5, IL-8, certain chemokines, cytokines, GM-CSF and TNF-α. For example, cortisol inhibits the production of interleukin 2 (IL-2), which in turn inhibits T cell proliferation and the activation of NK and B cells. Cortisol also inhibits the release of histamine and serotonin from mast cells and platelets.

Immune Regulatory Actions of Cortocotrophin Releasing Hormone (CRH)

Cortocotrophin releasing hormone (CRH), which ultimately stimulates the release of cortisol (see Figure 2), can also directly affect the immune response. CRH induces the secretion of POMC derived peptides such as ACTH and β-endorphin in human peripheral blood and mouse splenic leukocytes (Mahbub et al., 2011). In addition, it stimulates the secretion of the immune stimulatory cytokines IL-1 and IL-2 as well as IL-2 receptor expression and lymphocyte proliferation in peripheral blood leukocytes. In peripheral blood monocytes, the action of CRH is mediated through receptors found on the surfaces of the target cells (De Souza, 1995). CRH also stimulates B cell proliferation, NK cell activity and IL-6 production (Leu and Singh, 1992). CRH receptors are found on several types of immune cells, providing a possible explanation for these effects.

The Sympathetic Nervous System

Chronic stress also leads to stimulation of the sympathetic nervous system (SNS). The SNS, together with the parasympathetic nervous system (PNS), comprise the autonomic nervous system. The SNS is activated during times of stress, as it is responsible for the body's 'fight or flight" response. Pre- and post-ganglionic neurons are responsible for the transmission of signals through the sympathetic system. In response to a stimulus, the pre-ganglionic neurons release acetylcholine at the synapse between pre-and post-ganglionic neurons and activate nicotinic acetylcholine receptors on the post ganglionic neurons. Postganglionic neurons then release norepinephrine, which activates adrenergic receptors on peripheral target tissues. In the adrenal medulla, preganglionic neurons synapse with chromaffin cells instead of with post-ganglionic neurons to release norepinephrine and epinephrine directly into the blood. There are two main types of adrenoreceptors: α and β. These are further divided into α1, α2, β1 and β2 receptors, where each subtype has a different mechanism of action (with the exception of β1 and β2, which have the same mechanism of action but differ in their effects due to their predominance in different tissues).

α1 receptors are located in the vascular smooth muscle of skin, skeletal muscle, splanchnic smooth muscle, the sphincters of the bladder and gastrointestinal tract and even in the radial muscle of the eye. Activation of this receptor subtype leads to contraction. When norepinephrine binds to the α1 receptor in the cell membrane, this causes a conformational change in the coupled G_q protein, which induces the release of GDP and its replacement with GTP. The $α_q$-GTP complex then migrates to the cell membrane to activate phospholipase C, which catalyzes the release of diacylglycerol (DAG) and IP_3 from phosphatidylinositol 4,5-

disposphate. IP$_3$ causes the liberation of Ca^{2+}, which together with DAG, activates protein kinase C to mediate downstream effects.

α2 receptors are less abundant than α1, and are considered inhibitory in nature. They are located on presynaptic adrenergic and cholinergic nerve terminals and in the gastrointestinal tract. Those present on sympathetic postganglionic nerve terminals, when bound by norepinephrine, inhibit the further release of norepinephrine from those terminals, thus acting in a negative feedback loop to conserve norepinephrine. These receptors are not present on the adrenal medulla, so the adrenal medulla can become catecholamine depleted during prolonged periods of stress. In the gastrointestinal tract, the release of acetylcholine is inhibited when α2 receptors are activated by norepinephrine. Norepinephrine binds to the α2 receptor, which is coupled to adenylyl cyclase *via* the inhibitory G$_I$ protein. The G$_I$ protein releases GDP to bind GTP, which causes the α$_i$ subunit to dissociate and migrate in order to bind to and inhibit adenylyl cyclase. This then decreases cAMP and mediates downstream effects.

As mentioned earlier, both β1 and β2 receptors function *via* the same mechanism; namely, coupling *via* the G$_S$ protein to adenylyl cyclase. Activation of the β receptor by binding of an agonist such as norepinephrine leads to release of the α$_s$ subunit of the G$_S$ protein, which stimulates adenylyl cyclase and increases cAMP. β1 receptors predominate in the heart, particularly in the pacemaker regions of the SA node and atrioventricular node. They act to increase heart rate, conduction velocity and contractility. β2 are found in vascular smooth muscle, the GI tract, bladder and bronchioles. Activation of these leads to relaxation or dilation.

HPA and SNS Activation during Chronic Stress

During chronic stress, activation of the SNS leads to increased release of norepinephrine from the sympathetic nerve terminals and an increased release of both norepinephrine and epinephrine from the adrenal medulla. The HPA axis is also activated under these conditions, which causes an increased release of CRH from the paraventricular nucleus (PVN), thereby inducing increased secretion of adrenocorticotrophic hormone (ACTH) from the anterior pituitary. ACTH stimulates secretion of glucocorticoids from the adrenal cortex. Glucocorticoids control the HPA axis activity *via* negative feedback on the glucocorticoid receptors in the hippocampus (see Figure 2). During these periods of prolonged stress, the stress hormones are elevated due to inadequate suppression and central circadian rhythm disruption caused by dysfunction of the suprachiasmatic nucleus (SCN).

Stress can also disrupt the normal circadian rhythm of glucocorticoid secretion, and studies have linked this disruption to the promotion of tumor initiation and progression (Sephton and Spiegel, 2003). For example, individuals who work the night shift, a schedule known to disrupt endocrine rhythms, are at increased risk for colorectal and breast tumors (Schernhammer et al., 2003). In murine studies, disruption of circadian rhythms by manipulation of the light-dark cycles and by destruction of the SCN leads to a dramatic acceleration of tumor progression and mortality (Filipski et al., 2002).

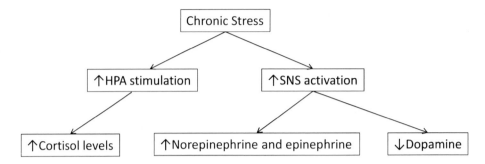

Figure 3. During chronic stress, the HPA and SNS axes are activated, increasing the levels of both glucocorticoids and catecholamines.

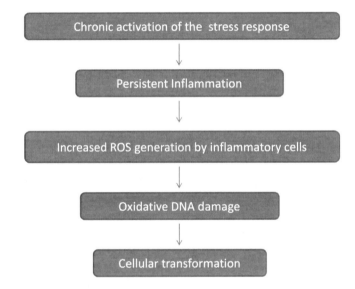

Figure 4. Chronic stress leads to persistent inflammation due to dysregulated glucocorticoid signaling, resulting in the generation of ROS by inflammatory cells. Increased levels of ROS then cause oxidative DNA damage. Accumulated DNA mutations may then eventually lead to cellular transformation.

Stress Hormones and Cancer

Glucocorticoids

Glucocorticoids regulate a wide variety of cellular processes, through either glucocorticoid receptor-mediated activation or repression of target genes. While it has been known for some time that glucocorticoid hormones induce apoptosis in lymphocytes, recent studies have demonstrated they promote survival of non-hematological cells such as mammary gland, liver, lung, glioma, and subcutaneous adipocytes (Bailly-Maitre, et al., 2002, Moran et al., 2000, Weller et al., 1997, Zhang et al., 2001). In addition, glucocorticoids can activate oncogenic viruses and inhibit anti-tumor and anti-viral cellular immune responses (Antoni et al., 2006). Glucocorticoids can function in synergy with stress hormones to promote cancer progression (Antoni et al., 2006), and studies have shown that glucocorticoids such as dexamethasone can promote cell survival and chemoresistance in ovarian cancer cells (Chen et al., 2010). The activated glucocorticoid receptor can function as a transcription factor through binding to glucocorticoid response elements on the regulatory sequence of target genes, or through crosstalk or interference with other transcription factors such as activator protein (AP-1), signal transducers and activators of transcription 5 (STAT 5) and NFκB to promote the growth and survival of cancer cells.

NF-κB can act as an endogenous promoter of tumorigenesis through its involvement in innate immunity and inflammatory pathways. NF-KB activates the expression of inflammatory cytokines, iNOS and angiogenic factors. It has also been shown to promote metastatic spread, as inactivation of IKK-α in the downstream pathway was found to reduce metastatic spread (Bollrath and Greten, 2009). STAT3 is constitutively activated in both tumor and immune cells. It is involved in oncogenesis and the initiation of apoptosis (Bollrath and Greten, 2009). STAT3 activation has been shown to inhibit the maturation of dentric cells, thereby increasing the ability of tumor cells to evade the immune system (Liu et al., 2013). Studies in human cervical and lung carcinomas have shown that glucocorticoid treatment results in an increase in the expression of the anti-apoptotic genes FLICE-inhibitory protein (FLIP) and the members of the B-cell lymphoma 2 (BCL-2) and inhibitor of apoptosis (IAP) family, while the pro-apoptotic elements of the death receptor and mitochondrial apoptotic signaling pathway were down-regulated (Herr et al., 2003).

Work on mouse models has shown that the effects of psychological stress on cancer cells are mediated primarily by norepinephrine and epinephrine and the β-adrenergic receptors present on cancer cells. Tumor growth and metastasis require adequate vascularization through the process of angiogenesis. Metaproterenol, a β agonist, increases lung tumor metastasis in a dose dependent manner (Melamed et al., 2005). Also, epinephrine injections promote breast metastases (Sloan et al., 2010). Interestingly, when animals were pretreated with β blockers, the SNS effects on lung metastases were inhibited. Norepinephrine up-regulates vascular endothelial factor (VEGF), the angiogenesis promoting factor, in ovarian tumors through β adrenergic receptor activation (Lutgendorf et al., 2003), and the effect was abolished by treatment with a β blocker. In *in vitro* experiments, norepinephrine increased colon cancer cell migration, and this effect was inhibited by β blockers (Masur et al., 2001). Furthermore, both norepinephrine and epinephrine increased nasopharengeal cell invasive capacity by increasing matrix metalloproteinase 2 (MMP2) and 9 (MMP9) expression (Yang et al., 2006).

G-Protein Coupled Receptors

Adrenoreceptors are all G-protein coupled receptors (GPCRs), with the G-protein-coupling specificity of each receptor determining the nature of the downstream effects. G-protein coupled receptors represent the largest family of receptors, with more than 800 members (Dorsam and Gutkind, 2007). They are involved in the control of essential functions such as neurotransmission, hormone and enzyme release from endocrine and exocrine glands, immune responses and blood pressure regulation. GPCRs are also the targets of both stress hormones and key inflammatory mediators, and therefore represent a possible connection between prolonged stress, chronic inflammation and cancer.

GPCRs are expressed in proliferating cells and contribute to the processes of embryogenesis, tissue repair, inflammation, angiogenesis and cancer (Gutkind, 1998). Potent mitogens such as thrombin, gastrin-releasing peptide (GRP), endothelin and prostaglandins stimulate cell proliferation by acting on their cognate GPCRs (Rozengurt et al., 2002). In

1980, the discovery of the MAS oncogene, a GPCR, linked GPCRs to cellular transformation (Young et al., 1986). Further research demonstrated that wild type GPCRs can be tumorigenic when exposed to an excess of their circulating agonists, while mutations in certain residues in GPCRs can cause them to induce cell transformation even in the absence of their agonist/ligand (Dorsam and Gutkind, 2007).

The prostaglandin inflammatory mediators, products of the cyclooxygenase 1 and 2 (COX1/2) enzymes, carry out proinflammatory functions when bound to their cognate GPCRs. Treatment with non-steriodal anti-inflammatory drugs (NSAIDs) that block the function of prostaglandins has been shown to decrease the risk of cancer, implying a role for COX overexpression and chronic inflammation in cancer (Brown and DuBois, 2005). Consistent with this observation, COX2 inhibition reduces the size and number of adenomas (pre-cancerous lesions) in patients with mutations in the adenomatous polyposis coli (APC) tumor suppressor gene; these patients are predisposed to colon cancer (Gupta and Dubois, 2001).

Norepinephrine and Epinephrine

The actions of norepinephrine (NE) and epinephrine (E) are mediated via the $\alpha1$, $\alpha2$ and β adrenergic receptor families. They act via β receptors to upregulate VEGF expression in several human tumors, which leads to an increase in tumor angiogenesis and growth (Dvorak, 2005). In experimental mouse models, chronic stress-mediated elevation of NE and E levels increases the tumor burden produced by HeyA8 and SKOV3 ip1 cells. Additionally, this chronic stress leads to elevated expression of angiogenic cytokines such as VEGF, MMP2, MMP9 and the pro-inflammatory cytokines IL6 and IL8 (Thaker et al., 2006), which also stimulate the growth of tumors.

E and NE, along with their receptors, play an important role in cancer development. Cancer cells need to acquire the ability to avoid anoikis, a form of programmed cell death, in order to metastasize to secondary sites (Shanmugathasan and Jothy, 2000). Catecholamines, including NE, were found to provide protection from anoikis in ovarian cancer cells though focal adhesion kinase (FAK) activation (Sood et al., 2010). β-adrenergic signaling can activate intracellular pro-proliferative and pro-migratory pathways such as the cAMP/protein kinase A and mitogen activated protein kinase (MAPK)/extracellular signal regulated kinase (ERK1/2) pathways (Cole and Sood, 2012), and activation of the cAMP-PKA pathway is thought to be the predominant pathway by which the β-adrenergic receptor mediates its effects on tumor cells (Cole and Sood, 2012). β-adrenergic activation, through norepinephrine administration, increases prostate metastases in mice, while the β-blocker propranolol inhibited this effect (Palm et al., 2006).

The catecholamines NE and E also play an important role in tumor immunity due to the presence of β adrenergic receptors on T lymphocytes, B lymphocytes, NK cells, monocytes/macrophages, and dendritic cells (Nance and Sanders, 2007). In fact, T and B lymphocytes almost exclusively express the $\beta2$ adrenergic receptor (Sanders, 2012). The increased levels of NE and E that occur during chronic stress lead to immune system suppression, thereby providing a favorable environment for tumor cells to grow and metastasize. Studies have shown that epinephrine, in particular, may play a significant role in cancer development. Epinephrine has been shown to reduce the sensitivity of tumor cells to cell death. The mechanism for this involves the phosphorylation and inactivation of the pro-apoptotic Bcl-2-associated death promoter (BAD) protein (Sastry et al., 2007). BAD phosphorylation was increased after chronic stress, providing another possible link between psychological stress and tumorigenesis (Sastry et al., 2007).

Other Mediators

While norepinephrine, epinephrine and cortisol are considered to be the major mediators of stress, other hormonal mediators such as substance P, dopamine, and prolactin are also affected by stress.

Substance P

Substance P functions in both the central and peripheral nervous systems, and is a peptide member of the neurokinin family. Kinins are important mediators of cardiovascular homeostasis, inflammation and the perception of pain. In the inflammatory pathway, Substance P is known to stimulate the expression of the proinflammatory cytokine IL-6 in astrocytoma cells (Entschladen et al., 2002), and can influence the migration of neutrophils across the endothelium in the inflamed lung. With regards to its role in tumor progression and growth, Substance P has been shown to promote the migration of colon and breast cancer cells and to act as a chemoattractant for squamous cell lung cancer (Drell et al., 2003, Entschladen et al., 2005).

Dopamine

Unlike other catecholamines, Dopamine (DA) possesses significant anti-tumor activities. Endogenous DA is secreted from several peripheral organs, and inhibits tumor growth and angiogenesis (Chakroborty et al., 2004, 2009). This was demonstrated in mice whose tumors were treated with exogenous DA, resulting in inhibited tumor growth and angiogenesis (Sarkar et al., 2008). DA acts via D2 receptors present on endothelial cells to inhibit VEGF-provoked phosphorylation of the VEGF R2 receptor, thus blocking the endothelial functions of VEGF (Sarkar et al., 2004). In addition to its anti-tumor effects on angiogenesis and growth, DA also mediates some of its anti-tumor effects *via* modulation of immune function. Multiple subtypes of DA receptors are present on the thymus and on circulating immune effector cells such as lymphocytes, monocytes, neutrophils, and dendritic cells, and DA can act through these receptors to inhibit tumor growth *via* stimulation of peritoneal macrophages, NK cells and cytotoxic T cells (Basu and Dasgupta, 2000). Recent work has demonstrated that Tregs, which play a vital role in immune homeostasis, contain substantial amounts of DA. When released, this DA acts on D1 receptors to suppress IL-10 and TGFβ synthesis (Cosentino et al., 2007).

Prolactin

Prolactin (PRL) is a pituitary derived polypeptide hormone whose function is to stimulate mammary gland development and lactation. PRL is secreted in response to stressful stimuli. In the 1970s, it was discovered that PRL can facilitate the initiation and promotion of mammary tumors in rodents (Damiano et al., 2013). More recently, it has been shown that a high circulating level of PRL in humans is correlated with an increased risk of breast cancer (Tworoger et al., 2007). Pharmacological agents that increase PRL are also associated with increased breast cancer risk (Wang et al., 2002).

PRL also plays a role in immune modulation, and is secreted from immune cells in addition to the anterior pituitary gland. PRL increases the synthesis of IFNγ and IL-2 by Th1 lymphocytes and activates Th2 lymphocytes (De Bellis et al., 2005).

Carcinogenesis

Tumorigenesis is a multi-step process that results in the transformation of normal cells into cancer cells. It requires a progression of changes at the cellular, genetic and epigenetic levels that leads to the ultimate re-programming of the cell such that it can undergo uncontrolled cell division and form a malignant mass. Hanahan and Weinberg, in their landmark review "Hallmarks of Cancer", listed six essential alterations that must occur in a cell's physiology to characterize malignant growth. These are: 1) Self-sufficiency in growth signals, 2) insensitivity to anti-growth signals, 3) evasion of apoptosis, 4) limitless replicative potential, 5) sustained angiogenesis and 6) tissue evasion and metastasis (Hanahan and Weinberg, 2000). In light of recent studies that have begun to elucidate links between inflammatory pathways and cancer development, Mantovani et al., in their 2009 review in Carcinogenesis, listed "Cancer Related Inflammation" as the seventh hallmark of cancer (Colotta et al., 2009). Recently, Hanahan and Weinberg updated their previous list to include the two "emerging" additional hallmarks: re-programming of energy metabolism and evading immune destruction (Hanahan and Weinberg, 2011). Subsequent to the development of the primary tumor, some tumors acquire the ability to metastasize. This requires a series of inter-related adaptations including proliferation and angiogenesis, invasion, embolism/circulation, transport, arrest in organs, adherence to the cell wall and extravasation (Fidler, 2003).

Inflammation

Inflammation is considered to serve as a protective mechanism, carried out by the innate immune system to remove injurious stimuli and initiate healing. It functions as part of the response of vascularized tissue to harmful stimuli, and is characterized by the controlled passage of cells from the blood into the traumatized tissue. Acute inflammation is the initial response to harmful stimuli, and is characterized by the classical signs of rubor (redness), dolor (pain), calor (heat), tumor (swelling) and function lasea (loss of function). In contrast, prolonged or chronic inflammation is characterized by persistent destruction and repair, and is associated with blood vessel proliferation, fibrosis and granuloma formation (Robbins et al., 2010).

During the process of acute inflammation, microbial invasion is initially detected by membrane bound Toll-like receptors (TLRs) and intracellular (NOD) pattern recognition receptors on and within inflammatory cells that are already present in all tissues, such as resident macrophages, dendritic cells, histiocytes, Kupffer cells and mastocytes. These receptors recognize molecules called PAMPs (pathogen-associated molecular patterns) that are shared by pathogens but are not present on host cells. Upon recognition of these PAMPS, the host inflammatory cells release the proinflammatory cytokines interleukin 1 (IL-1) and tumor necrosis factor α (TNF-α), and induce complement activation *via* the alternative pathway. Production of these cytokines initiates leukocyte extravasation. P-selectin expression on endothelial cells is induced by the plasma-derived mediators histamine and E-selection, and expression of the adhesion molecules ICAM-1 and VCAM-1 on endothelial cells is induced by cytokines. These adhesion molecules cause the binding of neutrophil integrins to these selectin adhesion molecules on the vascular endothelium, which slows their flow and allows for transmigration *via* diapedesis from blood vessels and into tissues. The leukocytes then make their way to the site of injury *via* chemotaxis. Chemokines such as IL-8 and monocytic chemotactic protein (MCP) act as chemoattractants, encouraging leukocytes to move along a chemotactic gradient to the site of injury.

Inflammation in Cancer

Activation of the inflammatory signaling pathway is associated with a variety of disease states including cardiovascular disease, neurodegenerative disorders, diabetes and cancer. Disrupted HPA signaling, such as can occur as a result of chronic stress, can result in an altered release of glucocorticoid hormones that have the potential to lead to sustained inflammation (Seruga et al., 2008). Chronic inflammation has long been established as a factor in the pathogenesis of cancer (Aggarwal et al., 2006, Bartsch and Nair, 2006, Coussens and Werb, 2002, Lu et al., 2006), and current estimates indicate that as many as 25% of all cancers are associated with this condition (Balkwill and Mantovani, 2012). Chronic inflammation has been implicated in the development of several epithelial cancers such as those of the stomach, colon and bladder (Carlson et al., 1998), while NSAIDS are known to reduce the risk of developing colon and breast cancer (DuBois and Smalley, 1996, Zhao et al., 2009). Hepatocellular cancer (HCC), the most common type of liver cancer, is a frequent result of years of chronic liver inflammation induced by Hepatitis B or C viral infection (Brechot et al., 2010, Di Bisceglie, 1997). Inflammation also plays a role in the development of Hodgkin's lymphoma. In this case, the observed inflammation is due to infection with Epstein Barr virus, a lymphotrophic herpes virus which induces the release of inflammatory cytokines and chemokines involved in carcinogenesis (Khan, 2006). Inflammatory mediators such as chemokines and cytokines are present in the tumor microenvironment from the earliest stages of tumor development. In fact, it is thought that greater than 15% of all deaths from cancer can be attributed to an underlying infection or inflammation (Moore et al., 2010). The longer the inflammation persists, the higher the risk of cancer.

Inflammation is the body's primary immune response to infection with pathogens, and is characterized by neutrophilic and mononuclear immune cell infiltration, tissue destruction and fibrosis. Typically, an inflammatory response will continue until the pathogens are eliminated, so that continuous infection frequently leads to chronic inflammation. In 1863, Virchow first hypothesized that malignant neoplasms can occur at sites of chronic inflammation. He reasoned that tissue injury, inflammation and increased cell proliferation were caused by various irritants (Balkwill and Mantovani, 2001, Coussens and Werb, 2002). We now know that chronic inflammation does indeed play a multifaceted role in carcinogenesis, and clinical studies point towards it as a driving force in the development of cancer. It can be viewed as a cancer "promoter" since it induces cell proliferation, recruits inflammatory cells, increases ROS leading to oxidative DNA damage, and reduces DNA repair (Coussens and Werb, 2002). Inflammation also promotes apoptosis resistance, proliferation, invasion, metastasis and the secretion of pro-angiogenic and immunosuppressive factors, all of which contribute to carcinogenesis (Peebles et al., 2007).

Inflammation and ROS

The chronic inflammatory response can lead to cell damage and cellular hyperplasia due to overproduction of reactive oxygen and nitrogen species (ROS and RNS). The main sources of ROS in cells are the mitochondria, cytochrome P450 and the peroxisome (Jezek and Hlavata, 2005). Under normal physiological conditions, there is a constant endogenous production of ROS and RNS, both of which play important roles as signaling molecules involved in metabolism, cell cycle and transduction pathways (Kröncke, 2003, Nathan, 2003). In order to maintain the beneficial effects of ROS, the cell must balance the production of ROS with its removal. During chronic inflammation, this balance is altered. In addition to ROS, NO and its derivatives (RNS) are produced in copious quantities in inflamed tissue (Bartsch and Nair, 2006). Furthermore, the mechanisms for removing ROS and RNS are down-regulated. These resulting increased levels of ROS and RNS can then cause direct and indirect damage to the cell (Tamir and Tannenbaum, 1996). For these reasons, the reactive oxygen species produced by inflammatory cells may act as endogenous carcinogens. For example, neutrophils have been shown to inhibit base excision repair in an alveolar epithelial cell line due to the effect of myeloperoxidase (Gungor et al., 2007).

Chronic inflammation causes the overproduction of ROS and RNS by increasing prostaglandin levels, which in turn induce the expression of pro-inflammatory cytokines such as IL-1, IL-6, TNF-α and IFN-γ (Baron and Sandler, 2000, Prescott and Fitzpatrick, 2000). These pro-inflammatory cytokines are then responsible for increasing the production of these free radicals through protein kinase-mediated signaling pathways; these effects are seen in both phagocytic and non-phagocytic cells (Dinarello, 2000). The ROS and RNS produced in this way can then interact with multiple types of macromolecules (Roede and Jones, 2010), including the DNA in mitotic cells to induce permanent genetic mutations such as point mutations, gene deletions and gene rearrangements. Cells normally respond to increases in ROS and RNS by activating their antioxidant systems, which reduce the levels of ROS and RNS and begin to repair the damage by activating genes responsible for DNA repair. However, in cases of chronic stress, which are characterized by a state of chronic inflammation (Lu et al., 2013), this DNA damage accumulates and is not repaired. Compounding the problem, this inflammation also reduces the levels of antioxidant enzyme defense in cells (DiSilvestro, 1988). For example, several studies have shown a decrease in the three main antioxidant enzymes SOD, CAT and Gpx in cervical cancer (Looi et al., 2008, Manju et al., 2002, Srivastava et al., 2009). This reduction in the antioxidant defense further exacerbates ROS induced DNA damage. Thus, chronic inflammation induces oxidative stress, a characteristic of inflammatory diseases, with its associated deleterious effects in cells.

Free radicals react with all components of the cell to form stable adducts. At present, there are more than 100 known oxidized DNA products. ROS-induced DNA damage includes single- and/or double-stranded DNA breaks, DNA base modifications, DNA intrastrand adducts and DNA-protein crosslinks (Valko et al., 2005). DNA damage can cause either arrest or induction of transcription, induction of signal transduction pathways, replication errors and genomic instability, all processes associated with the development of cancer

(Marnett, 2000, Valko et al., 2006). NO and superoxide (O_2^-) react to form peroxynitrite (ONOO⁻), a highly reactive species that induces nitrosative and oxidative DNA damage. Peroxynitrite mediates the formation of 8-oxo-7,8-dihydro-2'-deoxyguanosine (Inoue and Kawanishi, 1995) and 8-nitroguanine (Akaike et al., 2003, Yermilov et al., 1995), two of the most common base modifications (Kawanishi et al., 2001), and thus potential biomarkers of inflammation-related carcinogenesis (Valko et al., 2006, 2007). 8-nitroguanine is a mutagenic substance that preferentially causes G-T transversions (Sawa et al., 2003, Suzuki et al., 2005, Yermilov et al., 1995). These G-T transversions have been observed *in vivo* both in the *ras* gene and in the p53 tumor suppressor gene (Takahashi et al., 1989), indicating that DNA damage mediated by RNS and ROS may contribute to carcinogenesis *via* both the activation of protooncogenes and the inactivation of tumor suppressor genes. Oxidative damage to mitochondria can also contribute to carcinogenesis. For example, numerous mutations and altered expression of mitochondrial genes have been identified in various human cancers (Horton et al., 1996, Tamura et al., 1999), and fragments of mtDNA have been found inserted into genomic DNA, suggesting an additional mechanism for oncogene activation (Aggarwal et al., 2006). Because mtDNA codes for enzymes important in respiration, damage to this DNA can cause mitochondrial respiratory chain dysfunction, thus increasing the production of hydroxyl radicals that can cause oxidative damage to DNA (Beckman and Ames, 1997, Berlett and Stadtman, 1997). Proteins are susceptible to oxidation by free radicals, more so than any other cell component. For example, the oxidation of SH groups on cysteine reduces the activity of various enzymes as well as the synthesis of GSH, a major intracellular free radical scavenger that functions as part of the anti-oxidant defense system (Subrahmanyam et al., 1987). Lipid oxidation produces aldehydes and lipid peroxides. At low, nontoxic concentrations, these molecules act as signaling transducers of ROS-mediated reactions, allowing them to modulate several cell functions, including gene expression and cell proliferation (Uchida, 2003). At high concentrations, however, they react with proteins, DNA and phospholipids to generate a variety of intra- and intermolecular toxic covalent adducts that lead to the propagation and amplification of oxidative stress (Blair, 2001). The most abundant ROS- lipid derived product found under conditions of oxidative stress is 4-hydroxynonenal (HNE), which promotes oxidative alterations of DNA and induces apoptosis (Cheng et al., 1999, Nair et al., 1999, Ruef et al., 1998). HNE is directly involved in cell cycle regulation, and also causes mutations in p53 gene expression (Hu et al., 2002). In addition, HNE forms etheno adducts with DNA and up-regulates COX-2 expression. COX-2, an enzyme responsible for prostaglandin formation, is known to be up-regulated in HPV-related cancers, such as those found in the head and neck (Lin et al., 2002). This increased COX-2 expression in turn induces enhanced ROS production (Kumagai et al., 2000). Therefore, the copious amounts of ROS and RNS that are released as a consequence of inflammation can initiate a set of reactions that amplify, leading to even higher levels of these mediators, thus causing severe damage to cellular DNA.

The Immune System: An Overview

In order to understand any role the immune system may play in cancer, it is first necessary to understand some basic points about the functioning of the immune system. The immune system is a complex system made up of several different cell types that interact with lymphoid tissue that is dispersed throughout the body. The immune system is capable of defending the body from attack by foreign infectious agents and, in some cases, abnormal cells such as tumor cells. It carries out these functions through the identification of specific molecular entities, referred to as antigens, made by these agents. Innate immune cells consist of granulocytes, dendritic cells, macrophages, natural killer cells and mast cells. These cells express pattern recognition receptors called TLRs (Toll-Like receptors) that recognize conserved molecular patterns such as lipopolysaccharide (LPS) and lipoteichoic acid (LTA), which are found on microbes but not host cells. The activation of TLRs upon infection leads to a cascade of events involving the activation of NF-κB signaling, increased antigen presentation and enhanced recruitment and activation of leukocytes. Upon identification, the immune system uses various defense strategies to neutralize or destroy these foreign agents and infected or abnormal cells. The two main strategies used are referred to as the humoral immune response, which is based upon circulating molecules such as antibodies, and the cellular immune response, which is based upon the actions of specific cells. Thus, the immune system exists to defend the organism by mounting both humoral and cell-mediated responses against microorganisms, virus-infected cells and tumor cells.

In the humoral response, antibodies, molecules capable of specifically recognizing and binding antigens, are generated. In this defense strategy, a virus particle, bacterium or infected cell displaying antigens on its surface becomes coated with antibodies. Once coated with antibodies, the foreign agent or infected/abnormal cell is recognized and destroyed by a phagocytic cell such as a macrophage or cytotoxic natural killer (NK) cell. It is important to note that antibody coating is essential to this process.

In the cellular immune response, specialized cytotoxic T lymphocyte cells (CTLs) are the major actors. These cells are capable of recognizing and directly attacking other cells that display foreign antigens on their surface without the need for them to be first coated with antibodies. This is possible because CTLs have developed their own antigen recognizing machinery, called the T-cell receptor (TCR), which targets cells with particular antigens. CTLs require prior exposure, or "education", to an antigen in order to mount a vigorous, secondary attack upon re-exposure, and is therefore considered an adaptive immune response (discussed in more detail later). In contrast, some other components of the cellular immune response are endowed with an inherent ability to recognize certain infectious agents or abnormal cells without prior exposure, and are thus components of the innate immune response. Innate immune cells consist of granulocytes, dendritic cells, macrophages, natural killer cells and mast cells. These cells express pattern recognition receptors called TLRs (Toll-Like receptors), which recognize conserved molecular patterns such as lipopolysaccharide (LPS) and lipoteichoic acid (LTA) that are found on microbes but not on host cells. The activation of TLRs upon infection leads to a cascade of events involving the activation of NF-KB signaling, increased antigen presentation and enhanced recruitment and activation of leukocytes.

The Complement Pathway

The complement system involves the action of more than 30 serum proteins, a number that represents almost 15% of all serum proteins. Most complement components are synthesized in the liver. Complement proteins interact in a cascade to recognize and target foreign cells, and may be either beneficial or harmful to the host, depending on the cell type targeted. The complement cascade plays an important role in both inflammation and humoral immunity. Three pathways lead to complement activation and the generation of variants of the protease C3 convertase, which in turn leads to formation of the membrane attack complex (MAC). The classical pathway is triggered by activation of the C1 complex; the alternate pathway is continuously activated at low levels, but is further activated by molecules such as lipopolysaccharide (LPS) and teichoic acid; and the lectin pathway is triggered by mannose binding lectin (MBL) and ficolins rather than by C1q. Regardless of which pathway is triggered, C3 convertase produces C3b, which enhances opsonization by phagocytes, while formation of the MAC complex leads to cell lysis.

The Immune System and Cancer

As early as the nineteenth century, William Coley observed that cancer patients who developed severe postoperative infections at their tumor site sometimes experienced spontaneous and lasting tumor regression (Coley, 1991). Findings such as these led to the discovery and naming of the inflammatory cytokine Tumor Necrosis Factor, or TNF. A more recent application of this principle is the administration of the BCG vaccine to treat certain bladder cancers (Kawai et al., 2013).

On the other hand, there is also significant evidence to suggest that immune inflammatory cells can be linked to the generation of cancer (Elinav et al., 2013). Inflammatory cells are recruited to the microenvironment of a developing tumor, and clinical data indicates that innate immune cells play a role in promoting neoplastic progression (Elinav et al., 2013).

The immune system is designed to detect and eliminate foreign pathogens from the body while leaving host tissue unharmed. How then does the immune system protect us from cancer cells when they are essentially host tissue? The immune system can prevent the development of cancer *via* three distinct pathways. One, it can prevent virus-induced tumors such as those caused by HPV through the clearance or suppression of such infections. Two, it causes the resolution of inflammation that could otherwise lead to the production of an inflammatory environment that is conducive to tumorigenesis. Three, the immune system can eliminate tumor cells due to their expression of tumor specific antigens (Swann and Smyth, 2007). This last process is referred to as tumor immune surveillance and will be discussed in depth later in this chapter.

Cells of the Immune System and Their Role in Cancer

T cells

T lymphocytes consist of a variety of functional distinct subpopulations of cells involved in both cell mediated (cytotoxic T lymphocytes-CTLs) and humoral (helper T lymphocytes-T_H) immune responses. Specialized receptors, referred to as T cell receptors (TCRs), are present on the surfaces of these T lymphocytes and recognize only protein antigens or epitopes that are bound to MHC molecules; this attribute is why T cells are considered to be "MHC restricted." T cell development begins in the bone marrow, while maturation and differentiation occurs in the thymus. The thymic cortex contains immature T cells (thymocytes) while the medulla contains mature T cells. In the thymic cortex, thymocytes undergo gene rearrangements to express antigen specific T cell receptor (TCRs) to become immunocompetent. Thymus induced cluster of differentiation (CD) markers such as CD2, CD3, CD4, CD8 and CD28 are expressed on cortical T cells. On moving to the medulla, some T cells lose either their CD4 or CD8 markers and become $CD8^+$ or $CD4^+$ cells. $CD8^+$ and $CD4^+$ T cells are effector T cells that are capable of initiating an immune response.

Upon activation, $CD4^+$ cells/T helper cells synthesize and release cytokines (growth and other factors). There are three subtypes of T helper cells: T_H1, T_H2 and T17 cells. T_H2 cells release IL4, IL5, IL6 and IL10, while T_H1 cells release IL2 and IFNγ. As a result of these actions, T_H cells can activate either the humoral immune response (T_H2) or the cell-mediated response (T_H1), and are therefore involved in both "arms" of the immune response. Upon activation with antigenic stimulation *via* an Antigen Presenting Cell, $CD8^+$/cytotoxic T cells are induced to proliferate by IL2 (released by T_H1), thus forming CTL clones that can induce cell death through two separate mechanisms. In the first, perforin is used to punch holes in the target cell's plasma membrane; then, granzymes are injected into these pores. The granzymes then cleave and activate pro-apoptotic caspases so as to trigger intrinsic apoptosis. In the second mechanism, CTLs present Fas L (the Fas death receptor ligand) to the Fas death receptor displayed on the target cells. This activates the receptor and triggers the extrinsic apoptotic pathway. Research shows that T cell function is often impaired in cancer (Finke et al., 1999). For example, there is an increased ratio of T_H2 and its related cytokine mediators to T_H1 cells and mediators in several types of cancer (Tan and Coussens, 2007). This results in a diminished pro-inflammatory response, which inhibits the clearance of tumor cells.

Research in the 1990s enabled the identification of a new class of $CD4^+$ T cells called Tregs. These cells are distinguished from T_H cells by their expression of CD25 and the transcription factor FOXP3. Tregs are capable of blocking the action of those CTLs whose TCRs recognize the same antigenic epitopes, and can inhibit the formation of T_H1 cells so as to suppress the immune response. They have also been shown to release TGFβ and IL10, which are used to inhibit or kill T lymphocytes, thus suppressing the immune response to tumors and inducing self tolerance (Wang and Wang, 2007). Tregs are elevated in certain cancers such as lung, pancreas, breast, liver and skin (Cools et al., 2007). It is possible that these Tregs may impair anti-tumor responses. Elevated Tregs appear to be associated with increased mortality rates and reduced rates of disease-free survival (Sonabend et al., 2008).

B Cells

The development of both B and T cells begins in the bone marrow. In contrast to the situation with T cells, however, the maturation and differentiation of B cells also occurs within the bone marrow. B cells are responsible for soluble antibody production once they differentiate into plasma cells, a process that is the foundation of the humoral immune response. B cells are also involved in the activation of the cell mediated immune response in their role as APCs.

B cells produce five classes of immunoglobulins (Ig), or antibodies: IgG, IgA, IgM, IgE and IgD. Each class is made up of a 4 polypeptide chains, with 2 heavy (H) and 2 light (L) chain polypeptides joined by disulphide bonds. A portion of the H chain amino acid sequence (on the constant region) allows for the classification into five isotypes designated gamma (γ), alpha (α), mu (μ), epsilon (ε) and delta (δ), which correspond to the immunoglobulins IgG,

IgA, IgM, IgE and IgD respectively. Upon recognition of an antigen presented by a B cell to a T_H cell, the CD 40 receptor present on the B cell must interact with the CD 40 ligand on the T_H cell in order to activate the B cell. The T_H2 cell then releases cytokines that allow for the transformation of B cells into plasma cells, and their subsequent proliferation to produce antibodies specific to the antigen presented. B memory cells are also produced upon activation to produce long-lived immunocompetent cells that remain in circulation to provide a faster, enhanced response to future challenge by the same antigen.

While the role of different populations of T cells in both anticancer immunity responses and tumor promotion has been well-studied the role of B cells in cancer has not been as intensively studied (Fremd et al., 2013). However, recent studies demonstrate increasing evidence for the role of B cells in regulatory response of T cells to tumors (Shimomura et al., 2008, Yanaba et al., 2008). Interestingly, other recent studies seem to suggest that B cells may also exert tumor promoting properties (Ammirante et al., 2010, Olkhanud et al., 2011). These findings further illustrate the complexity of the role that the immune system plays in cancer.

Natural Killer Cells (NK)

NK cells are peripheral blood lymphocytes that lack the surface markers of both T and B lymphocytes. Unlike CTLs, NK cells are not MHC-restricted and exhibit a non-specific cytotoxicity against tumor and virus infected cells. NK cells utilize perforins and granzymes in a similar manner to CTLs to induce apoptosis. They also kill cells that have antibody bound to their surface antigens by a mechanism known as antibody-dependent cell mediated cytotoxicity (ADCC), in which the NK cells release cytokines such as IFNγ that, in turn, recruit other immune cells such as macrophages. NK cells play a potentially significant role in tumor immunology, since their inherent ability to recognize tumor cells makes it likely that they are among the first group of cells to interact with tumor cells during the early stages of cancer.

Dendritic Cells (DCs)

Dendritic cells are considered "professional" APCs, and as such, express MHC Class II on their surfaces for specialized antigen presentation. Dendritic cells present in skin are referred to as Langerhans cells, and are an essential part of the adaptive immune response. Antigen presentation to certain T_H cells induces the activation of B cells, which in turn leads to a population of plasma cells that secrete antibody specific to the antigen presented by the dendritic cell. It is possible that tumor cells with distinct (not present on normal cells) antigenic proteins can also provoke a similar antibody response from the adaptive immune system. The response of dentritic cells to cancer seems to be dependent on the level of maturation of the DCs. Immature DCs have the ability to facilitate immune tolerance towards cancer cells. Studies have demonstrated that in a well-established tumor, cancer cells can prevent the maturation of DCs resulting in dysfunctional antigen presentation and abnormal DC motility (Ma et al., 2013, Vicari et al., 2002). Conversely, it appears that mature DCs strongly promote anticancer immunity when they secrete the correct combinations of cytokines (Ma et al., 2013).

Macrophages

Macrophages differentiate from peripheral blood monocytes and are activated by IFNγ. They function as both an APC (through their expression of MHC II) and as a cytotoxic effector cell during ADCC (described in the NK section). Macrophages produce and release IL1 to activate T_H cells. They also release TNFα, which contributes to self-activation of macrophages. TNFα, together with IFNγ, facilitates bactericidal activities. Macrophages also secrete prostaglandins (PGE_2), which dampen some immune responses. Activation of the innate immune response results in the activation of a mix of macrophages, with either an M1 or M2 phenotype, that produce different cytokine profiles (Seruga et al., 2008). M1 macrophages produce pro-inflammatory cytokines, such as TNF-α, that stimulate cell-mediated immunity, while the M2 macrophages stimulate the humoral response and induce tissue remodeling and angiogenesis (Allavena et al., 2008). Macrophages with an M1 phenotype possess antitumor activity.

Other Immune System Molecules and Their Roles in Cancer

Toll-Like Receptors

Toll-like receptors (TLRs) play a key role in innate immunity through the recognition of conserved molecules present in microbes such as lipopolysaccharides (LPS) and double-stranded RNA. TLRs are receptor proteins expressed on APCs such as macrophages and dendritic cells, and allow for the recognition of microbes; this recognition then leads to activation of the immune response. These conserved molecules are collectively referred to as pathogen-associated molecular patterns (PAMPs). Recently, it has been shown that in addition to exogenous PAMPs, certain TLRs also recognize endogenous damage-associated molecular patterns (DAMPs) such as the heat shock proteins that are released from dying or stressed cells (Chen and Nunez, 2010). TLR activation leads to activation of NF-κB and the production of cytokines, which in turn modulate the magnitude of the inflammatory response (Iwasaki and Medzhitov, 2004). It has been suggested that TLRs may also play a pivotal role in anticancer immunity (Hennessy et al., 2010, Standiford and Keshamouni, 2012). Under steady state conditions, TLR signaling maintains tissue architecture. However, under the dysregulated inflammation that occurs during tumorigenesis, the TLR response may promote neoangiogenesis and tumor growth by mechanisms that remain to be elucidated (Rakoff-Nahoum and Medzhitov, 2009).

TLR signaling regulates cell death through the activation of the P13K-Akt signaling pathway, which promotes cell survival (Rakoff-Nahoum and Medzhitov, 2009). It has also been associated with increased expression of the anti-apoptotic proteins inhibitor of apoptosis 1 (IAP1) and Bcl-2 related protein A1 (BCL2A1) (Salaun et al., 2007). TLRs are involved in several aspects of tissue homeostasis such as repair and regeneration. Also, TLR ligands have been shown to augment the growth of adoptively transferred tumors (Huang et al., 2007, Pidgeon et al., 1999), and stimulation of TLR in a variety of tumor cell lines leads to increased survival and proliferation *in vitro* (Rakoff-Nahoum and Medzhitov, 2009). Studies demonstrate that when the inflammatory response to *H. pylori* infection is reduced through expression of a non-functional TLR1 genotype, the risk of *H. pylori*-induced gastric diseases such as gastric cancer is decreased, suggesting that the inflammation induced by TLR1 expression contributes to carcinogenesis (Yang et al., 2013). In general, TLR2 stimulation induces a T_H2, Treg or T_H17 predominant immune response (Beutler et al., 2006), and the TLR2-MyD88/NFκB pathway has been shown to enhance the self-renewal capabilities of ovarian cancer stem cells and to promote tumor repair and recurrence after chemotherapy (Chefetz et al., 2013).

Cytokines

The term cytokine refers to a broad category of small soluble polypeptides or glycoproteins that are involved in various signaling pathways. They exert pleiotrophic and sometime redundant effects to promote growth, differentiation and activation of normal cells (Borish and Steinke, 2003). Their actions can be either pro-inflammatory or anti-inflammatory, depending on the microenvironment.

This class of molecules includes chemokines, interferons, interleukins, lymphokines and tumor necrosis factor. They are produced and secreted primarily by immune cells such as macrophages, B lymphocytes, T lymphocytes and mast cells. They are also produced by non-immune cells such as endothelial cells and fibroblasts (Borish and Steinke, 2003). Cytokines play an important role in immune system modulation, as they regulate the growth and maturation of various immune cell populations. They also interact with each other to inhibit or enhance the actions of other cytokines. Cortisol produced by the adrenal glands acts as a potent anti-inflammatory agent. However, when the HPA axis is disturbed, such as during chronic stress, it can cause an altered release of glucocorticoid hormones and disruption of the glucocorticoid receptor functioning. These events may lead to a state of sustained inflammation. Studies have demonstrated that levels of the pro-inflammatory cytokines IL-6 and TNF-α are elevated in cases of chronic stress (Kiecolt-Glaser et al., 2003).

TNF-α can inhibit DNA repair enzymes through a process involving elevation of NO; this has the potential to promote DNA damage (Jaiswal et al., 2000). The cytokine also promotes angiogenesis through mediators such as VEGF, VEGFR2, fibroblast growth factor 2 (FGF2), NO and E-selectin (Yoshida et al., 1997). Also, it stimulates matrix metalloproteinases (MMPs) to promote tissue remodeling and tumor metastasis through expression of the chemokine CXCR4 and its receptor CLCL12, as well as through up-regulation of migration inhibitory factor (MIF), IL-8 and ICAM-1 (Kulbe et al., 2005).

Immune Surveillance

The process by which the immune system is able to identify and sometimes eliminate tumors is known as cancer immune surveillance. However, tumors may still arise in immune competent hosts even after the three phases of immune editing. In phase one, which is referred to as the elimination phase, the immune system detects the presence of developing tumor cells and destroys them (Vesely et al., 2011). In phase two, the equilibrium phase, tumor cells that survive the elimination phase are prevented from proliferating by the immune system. In the final "escape phase", these cells acquire the ability to avoid immune recognition and tumor outgrowth occurs (Vesely et al., 2011).

Tumor cells employ a variety of techniques to avoid detection by the immune system, thus rendering immune surveillance techniques impotent. One mechanism employed is the suppression of tumor specific antigens (TSAs) on their surface. This technique avoids detection by cytotoxic T cells. In cases where expression of the TSA is important to neoplastic proliferation and thus cannot be suppressed, tumor cells repress the expression of MHCI antigen presentation molecules.

Tumor Microenvironment

Studies have shown that tumor cells have the ability to create an immune environment where immune function is impaired and thus is conducive to tumor growth. The tumor microenvironment contains an abundant mix of cytokines and inflammatory mediators that can influence the growth, immunity and vascularization of developing tumors (Balkwill, 2004, Mantovani, 2005). Tumor cells utilize several mechanisms to modulate this microenvironment and the cells within it. Normally, cytotoxic T cells can kill unwanted cells (such as tumor cells) through the interaction of their Fas ligand with the Fas death receptor on the target cell, thus activating the extrinsic apoptotic pathway. Cancer cells counteract this *via* a two-fold attack. First, the cancer cells develop resistance to Fas-L induced killing through mechanisms that have not yet been fully elucidated. Next, cancer cells can also acquire the ability to produce and release soluble forms of the Fas L; these molecules do not affect the cancer cells (which have become resistant to Fas L-induced cell death) but do kill surrounding lymphocytes. In addition to these mechanisms, some tumor cells secrete the immunosuppressive proteins IL-10 and TGF-β (Weinberg, 2007).

Changes in the levels of neuroendocrine transmitters during chronic stress can lead to changes in the microenvironment surrounding tumor cells. Modulation of the immune function is one of the most important changes, as it can lead to suppression of both cellular and humoral immunity. Immune cells possess glucocorticoid receptors that can activate cells to release cytokines when glucocorticoid levels rise (Cidlowski et al., 1996). The released cytokines can then modulate the activity of the hypothalamus (Turnbull and Rivier, 1995). The glucocorticoid receptors present on these immune cells can also interfere with the function of NF-κB, which normally regulates immune cells. Incorrect regulation of NFκB has been linked to tumor formation and inflammatory diseases (Scheinman et al., 1995). Adrenergic receptors on immune cells can bind both norepinephrine and epinephrine to activate the cAMP response element-binding (CREB) protein, which induces the transcription of genes encoding cytokines (Kohm and Sanders, 2001). Induced changes in gene expression can then shift the immune response from being predominantly T_H1 to T_H2 driven, which impairs immune defense against tumors (Ramer-Quinn et al., 1997). In addition, an increased level of mitogenic factors is observed in the tumor microenvironment. These elevated levels of cytokines and stress-related transmitters can promote growth and metastasis of tumor cells. Additionally, the disruption in circadian rhythm that occurs during stress can affect cell division and lead to immune suppression (Sephton and Spiegel, 2003).

Immune cells such as inflammatory macrophages, natural killer (NK) cells and cytotoxic T-cells are found within the tumor microenvironment, as are Tumor Associated Macrophages (TAMs), mast cells and T cells. TAMs, in particular, are an important part of the infiltrate. Recent studies have demonstrated that co-culturing tumor cells with macrophages increases their invasive capacity through NF-KB and TNF-α dependent mechanisms (Hagemann et al., 2004, 2005). Within the tumor microenvironment, TAMs and Tregs are major sources of the anti-inflammatory cytokines such as IL-4, IL-10, IL-13 and TGF-β. The presence of these cytokines leads to the suppression of anticancer immunity mediated by NK cells and cytotoxic T cells at the tumor site (Seruga et al., 2008).

The tumor microenvironment also contains myeloid-derived suppressor cells (MDSC), which are a mixed population of myeloid derived progenitor cells such as macrophages, granulocytes and dendritic cells which can exert potent immunosuppressive properties (Gabrilovich and Nagaraj, 2009). In cancer, these cells respond to factors such as IL-6, GM-CSF and IL-1β that are secreted by tumor cells and migrate from the bone marrow to accumulate in neoplastic tissues (Ostrand-Rosenberg and Sinha, 2009). Here, their differentiation is inhibited so that they secrete immunosuppressive mediators. This results in the inhibition of T-cell and NK responses in the tumor microenvironment (Liu et al., 2007).

Conclusion

From the time of the ancient Greeks to the present, mankind has pondered the question of whether a link exists between psychological states such as stress and cancer. Epidemiological studies have revealed correlations between chronic stress and cancer incidence, with the strongest correlation linked to the most severe stressors. Recent meta-analyses have even linked stressors such as depression and social isolation with poorer survival in patients who have already been diagnosed with cancer.

As mentioned earlier, tumorigenesis is a complex process, requiring the acquisition of several modifications for complete cell transformation. Following transformation, the tumor cell must be able to grow and acquire a "food source" in order to thrive. There is converging evidence, some of which has been presented here, that chronic stress through its influence on the immune system and inflammatory cells plays a critical role in carcinogenesis.

Chronic stress leads to dysregulated HPA axis regulation, which leads to dysregulated glucocorticoid release and aberrant glucocorticoid signaling. These lead to a state of widespread inflammation while suppressing the immune response to the tumor. Inflammation, through increased ROS production, facilitates the cellular changes that promote tumor formation, while the favorable tumor environment produced as a result of aberrant HPA axis activation and dysregulated glucocorticoid signaling allow for growth and progression of the tumor. For instance, norepinephrine and epinephrine levels increase during chronic stress while dopamine levels decrease. This is significant because NE and E are known to stimulate angiogenesis while DA inhibits tumor angiogenesis and stimulates tumor immunity.

These connections between stress, the immune system and cancer therefore highlight the importance of understanding and appreciating each of these three aspects as we search for better ways to prevent, diagnose, intercept and cure cancer. They also encourage a broader perspective in exploring such options, suggesting that interventions from numerous directions, including those that impact psychological stress, should be considered.

References

Aggarwal, B.B., Shishodia, S., Sandur, S.K., Pandey, M.K. & Sethi, G. (2006). Inflammation and cancer: how hot is the link? *Biochem. Pharmacol.*, 72, 1605-21.

Akaike, T., Okamoto, S., Sawa, T., Yoshitake, J., Tamura, F., Ichimori, K., et al., (2003). 8-Nitroguanosine formation in viral pneumonia and its implication for pathogenesis. *Proc. Natl. Acad. Sci. USA*, 100, 685-90.

Allavena, P., Sica, A., Solinas, G., Porta, C. & Mantovani, A. (2008). The inflammatory micro-environment in tumor progression: The role of tumor-associated macrophages. *Crit. Rev. Oncol. Hemat.*, 66, 1-9.

Ammirante, M., Luo, J.L., Grivennikov, S., Nedospasov, S. & Karin, M. (2010). B-cell-derived lymphotoxin promotes castration-resistant prostate cancer. *Nature*, 464, 302-5.

Antoni, M.H., Lutgendorf, S.K., Cole, S.W., Dhabhar, F.S., Sephton, S.E., McDonald, P.G., et al., (2006). The influence of bio-behavioural factors on tumour biology: pathways and mechanisms. *Nat. Rev. Cancer*, 6, 240-8.

Bailly-Maitre, B., de Sousa, G., Zucchini, N., Gugenheim, J., Boulukos, K.E. & Rahmani, R. (2002). Spontaneous apoptosis in primary cultures of human and rat hepatocytes: molecular mechanisms and regulation by dexamethasone. *Cell Death Differ.*, 9, 945-55.

Balkwill, F. (2004). Cancer and the chemokine network. *Nat. Rev. Cancer*, 4, 540-50.

Balkwill, F. & Mantovani, A. (2001). Inflammation and cancer: back to Virchow? *Lancet*, 357, 539-45.

Balkwill, F.R. & Mantovani, A. (2012). Cancer-related inflammation: common themes and therapeutic opportunities. *Semin. Cancer Biol.*, 22, 33-40.

Baron, J.A. & Sandler, R.S. (2000). Nonsteroidal anti-inflammatory drugs and cancer prevention. *Annu. Rev. Med.* 51, 511-23.

Bartsch, H. & Nair, J. (2006). Chronic inflammation and oxidative stress in the genesis and perpetuation of cancer: role of lipid peroxidation, DNA damage, and repair. *Langenbecks Arch. Surg*, 391, 499-510.

Basu, S. & Dasgupta, P.S. (2000). Dopamine, a neurotransmitter, influences the immune system. *J. Neuroimmunol.*, 102, 113-24.

Beckman, K.B. & Ames, B.N. (1997). Oxidative decay of DNA. *J. Biol. Chem.*, 272, 19633-6.

Berlett, B.S. & Stadtman, E.R. (1997). Protein oxidation in aging, disease, and oxidative stress. *J. Biol. Chem.*, 272, 20313-6.

Beutler, B., Jiang, Z., Georgel, P., Crozat, K., Croker, B., Rutschmann, S., et al., (2006). Genetic analysis of host resistance: Toll-like receptor signaling and immunity at large. *Annu. Rev. Immunol.*, 24, 353-89.

Blair, I.A. (2001). Lipid hydroperoxide-mediated DNA damage. *Exp. Gerontol.*, 36, 1473-81.

Bollrath, J. & Greten, F.R. (2009). IKK/NF-kappaB and STAT3 pathways: central signalling hubs in inflammation-mediated tumour promotion and metastasis. *EMBO Rep.*, 10, 1314-9.

Bonmort, M., Dalod, M., Mignot, G., Ullrich, E., Chaput, N. & Zitvogel, L. (2008). Killer dendritic cells: IKDC and the others. *Curr Opin Immunol*, 20, 558-65.

Borish, L.C. & Steinke, J.W. (2003). 2. Cytokines and chemokines. *J. Allergy Clin. Immunol.*, 111(2 Suppl), S460-75.

Brechot, C., Kremsdorf, D., Soussan, P., Pineau, P., Dejean, A., Paterlini-Brechot, P., et al., (2010). Hepatitis B virus (HBV)-related hepatocellular carcinoma (HCC): Molecular mechanisms and novel paradigms. *Pathol. Biol. (Paris)*, 58, 278-87.

Brown, J.R. & DuBois, R.N. (2005). COX-2: a molecular target for colorectal cancer prevention. *J. Clin. Oncol.*, 23, 2840-55.

Carlson, J.A., Ambros, J., Malfetano, J., Ross, J., Grabowski, R., Lamb, P., et al., (1998). Vulvar lichen sclerosus and squamous cell carcinoma: A cohort, case control, and investigational study with historical perspective; implications for chronic inflammation and sclerosis in the development of neoplasia. *Hum. Pathol.*, 29, 932-48.

Chakroborty, D., Sarkar, C., Basu, B., Dasgupta, P.S. & Basu, S. (2009). Catecholamines regulate tumor angiogenesis. *Cancer Res.*, 69, 3727-30.

Chakroborty, D., Sarkar, C., Mitra, R.B., Banerjee, S., Dasgupta, P.S. & Basu, S. (2004). Depleted dopamine in gastric cancer tissues: dopamine treatment retards growth of gastric cancer by inhibiting angiogenesis. *Clin. Cancer Res.*, 10, 4349-56.

Chefetz, I., Alvero, A.B., Holmberg, J.C., Lebowitz, N., Craveiro, V., Yang-Hartwich, Y., et al., (2013). TLR2 enhances ovarian cancer stem cell self-renewal and promotes tumor repair and recurrence. *Cell Cycle*, 12, 511-21.

Chen, G.Y. & Nunez, G. (2010). Sterile inflammation: sensing and reacting to damage. *Nat. Rev. Immunol.*, 10, 826-37.

Chen, Y.X., Wang, Y., Fu, C.C., Diao, F., Song, L.N., Li, Z.B., et al., (2010). Dexamethasone enhances cell resistance to chemotherapy by increasing adhesion to extracellular matrix in human ovarian cancer cells. *Endocr. Relat. Cancer*, 17, 39-50.

Cheng, J.Z., Singhal, S.S., Saini, M., Singhal, J., Piper, J.T., Van Kuijk, F.J., et al., (1999). Effects of mGST A4 transfection on 4-hydroxynonenal-mediated apoptosis and differentiation of K562 human erythroleukemia cells. *Arch. Biochem. Biophys.*, 372, 29-36.

Cidlowski, J.A., King, K.L., Evans-Storms, R.B., Montague, J.W., Bortner, C.D. & Hughes, F.M., Jr. (1996). The biochemistry and molecular biology of glucocorticoid-induced apoptosis in the immune system. *Recent Prog. Horm. Res.*, 51, 457-90; discussion 490-1.

Cole, S.W. & Sood, A.K. (2012). Molecular pathways: beta-adrenergic signaling in cancer. *Clin. Cancer Res.*, 18, 1201-6.

Coley, W.B. (1991). The treatment of malignant tumors by repeated inoculations of erysipelas. With a report of ten original cases. 1893. *Clin. Orthop Relat. Res.*, (262), 3-11.

Colotta, F., Allavena, P., Sica, A., Garlanda, C. & Mantovani, A. (2009). Cancer-related inflammation, the seventh hallmark of cancer: links to genetic instability. *Carcinogenesis*, 30, 1073-81.

Cools, N., Ponsaerts, P., Van Tendeloo, V.F. & Berneman, Z.N. (2007). Regulatory T cells and human disease. *Clin. Dev. Immunol.*, 2007, 89195.

Cosentino, M., Fietta, A.M., Ferrari, M., Rasini, E., Bombelli, R., Carcano, E., et al., (2007). Human CD4+CD25+ regulatory T cells selectively express tyrosine hydroxylase and contain endogenous catecholamines subserving an autocrine/paracrine inhibitory functional loop. *Blood*, 109, 632-42.

Coussens, L.M. & Werb, Z. (2002). Inflammation and cancer. *Nature*, 420, 860-7.

Damiano, J.S., Rendahl, K.G., Karim, C., Embry, M.G., Ghoddusi, M., Holash, J., et al., (2013). Neutralization of prolactin receptor function by monoclonal antibody LFA102, a novel potential therapeutic for the treatment of breast cancer. *Mol. Cancer Ther.*, 12, 295-305.

De Bellis, A., Bizzarro, A., Pivonello, R., Lombardi, G. & Bellastella, A. (2005). Prolactin and autoimmunity. *Pituitary*, 8, 25-30.

De Souza, E.B. (1995). Corticotropin-releasing factor receptors: physiology, pharmacology, biochemistry and role in central nervous system and immune disorders. *Psychoneuroendocrinology*, 20, 789-819.

Di Bisceglie, A.M. (1997). Hepatitis C and hepatocellular carcinoma. *Hepatology*, 26 (3 Suppl 1), 34S-38S.

DiSilvestro, R.A. (1988). Influence of copper intake and inflammation on rat serum superoxide dismutase activity levels. *J. Nutr.*, 118, 474-9.

Dinarello, C.A. (2000). Proinflammatory cytokines. *Chest*, 118, 503-8.

Dorsam, R.T. & Gutkind, J.S. (2007). G-protein-coupled receptors and cancer. *Nat. Rev. Cancer*, 7, 79-94.

Drell, T.L., 4th, Joseph, J., Lang, K., Niggemann, B., Zaenker, K.S. & Entschladen, F. (2003). Effects of neurotransmitters on the chemokinesis and chemotaxis of MDA-MB-468 human breast carcinoma cells. *Breast Cancer Res. Treat.*, 80, 63-70.

DuBois, R.N. & Smalley, W.E. (1996). Cyclooxygenase, NSAIDs, and colorectal cancer. *J. Gastroenterol.*, 31, 898-906.

Dvorak, H.F. (2005). Angiogenesis: update 2005. *J. Thromb Haemost*, 3, 1835-42.

Elinav, E., Nowarski, R., Thaiss, C.A., Hu, B., Jin, C.C. & Flavell, R.A. (2013). Inflammation-induced cancer: crosstalk between tumours, immune cells and microorganisms. *Nat. Rev. Cancer*, 13, 759-71.

Entschladen, F., Drell, T.L., 4th, Lang, K., Joseph, J. & Zaenker, K.S. (2005). Neurotransmitters and chemokines regulate tumor cell migration: potential for a new pharmacological approach to inhibit invasion and metastasis development. *Curr. Pharm. Des.*, 11, 403-11.

Entschladen, F., Lang, K., Drell, T.L., Joseph, J. & Zaenker, K.S. (2002). Neurotransmitters are regulators for the migration of tumor cells and leukocytes. *Cancer Immunol. Immunother*, 51, 467-82.

Fidler, I.J. (2003). The pathogenesis of cancer metastasis: the 'seed and soil' hypothesis revisited. *Nat. Rev. Cancer*, 3, 453-8.

Filipski, E., King, V.M., Li, X.M., Granda, T.G., Mormont, M.C., Liu, X.H., et al., (2002). Host circadian clock as a control point in tumor progression. *J. Natl. Cancer Inst.*, 94, 690-7.

Finke, J., Ferrone, S., Frey, A., Mufson, A. & Ochoa, A. (1999). Where have all the T cells gone? Mechanisms of immune evasion by tumors. *Immunol. Today*, 20, 158-60.

Fremd, C., Schuetz, F., Sohn, C., Beckhove, P. & Domschke, C. (2013). B cell-regulated immune responses in tumor models and cancer patients. *Oncoimmunology*, 2, e25443.

Gabrilovich, D.I. & Nagaraj, S. (2009). Myeloid-derived suppressor cells as regulators of the immune system. *Nat. Rev. Immunol.*, 9, 162-74.

Güngör, N., Godschalk, R.W., Pachen, D.M., Van Schooten, F.J. & Knaapen, A.M. (2007). Activated neutrophils inhibit nucleotide excision repair in human pulmonary epithelial cells: role of myeloperoxidase. *FASEB J.*, 21, 2359-67.

Gupta, R.A. & Dubois, R.N. (2001). Colorectal cancer prevention and treatment by inhibition of cyclooxygenase-2. *Nat. Rev. Cancer*, 1, 11-21.

Gutkind, J.S. (1998). Cell growth control by G protein-coupled receptors: from signal transduction to signal integration. *Oncogene*, 17 (11 Reviews), 1331-42.

Hagemann, T., Robinson, S.C., Schulz, M., Trumper, L., Balkwill, F.R. & Binder, C. (2004). Enhanced invasiveness of breast cancer cell lines upon co-cultivation with macrophages is due to TNF-alpha dependent up-regulation of matrix metalloproteases. *Carcinogenesis*, 25, 1543-9.

Hagemann, T., Wilson, J., Kulbe, H., Li, N.F., Leinster, D.A., Charles, K., et al., (2005). Macrophages induce invasiveness of epithelial cancer cells via NF-kappa B and JNK. *J. Immunol.*, 175, 1197-205.

Hanahan, D. & Weinberg, R.A. (2000). The hallmarks of cancer. *Cell*, 100, 57-70.

Hanahan, D. & Weinberg, R.A. (2011). Hallmarks of cancer: the next generation. *Cell*, 144, 646-74.

Hennessy, E.J., Parker, A.E. & O'Neill, L.A. (2010). Targeting Toll-like receptors: emerging therapeutics? *Nat. Rev. Drug Discov*, 9, 293-307.

Herr, I., Ucur, E., Herzer, K., Okouoyo, S., Ridder, R., Krammer, P.H., et al., (2003). Glucocorticoid cotreatment induces apoptosis resistance toward cancer therapy in carcinomas. *Cancer Res.*, 63, 3112-20.

Horton, T.M., Petros, J.A., Heddi, A., Shoffner, J., Kaufman, A.E., Graham, S.D., Jr., et al., (1996). Novel mitochondrial DNA deletion found in a renal cell carcinoma. *Genes Chromosomes Cancer*, 15, 95-101.

Hu, W., Feng, Z., Eveleigh, J., Iyer, G., Pan, J., Amin, S., et al., (2002). The major lipid peroxidation product, trans-4-hydroxy-2-nonenal, preferentially forms DNA adducts at codon 249 of human p53 gene, a unique mutational hotspot in hepatocellular carcinoma. *Carcinogenesis*, 23, 1781-9.

Huang, B., Zhao, J., Shen, S., Li, H., He, K.L., Shen, G.X., et al., (2007). Listeria monocytogenes promotes tumor growth via tumor cell toll-like receptor 2 signaling. *Cancer Res.*, 67, 4346-52.

Inoue, S. & Kawanishi, S. (1995). Oxidative DNA damage induced by simultaneous generation of nitric oxide and superoxide. *FEBS Lett.*, 371, 86-8.

Iwasaki, A. & Medzhitov, R. (2004). Toll-like receptor control of the adaptive immune responses. *Nat. Immunol.*, 5, 987-95.

Jaiswal, M., LaRusso, N.F., Burgart, L.J. & Gores, G.J. (2000). Inflammatory cytokines induce DNA damage and inhibit DNA repair in cholangiocarcinoma cells by a nitric oxide-dependent mechanism. *Cancer Res.*, 60, 184-90.

Jezek, P. & Hlavata, L. (2005). Mitochondria in homeostasis of reactive oxygen species in cell, tissues, and organism. *Int. J. Biochem. Cell Biol.*, 37, 2478-503.

Jonat, C., Rahmsdorf, H.J., Park, K.K., Cato, A.C., Gebel, S., Ponta, H., et al., (1990). Antitumor promotion and antiinflammation: down-modulation of AP-1 (Fos/Jun) activity by glucocorticoid hormone. *Cell*, 62, 1189-204.

Kawai, K., Miyazaki, J., Joraku, A., Nishiyama, H. & Akaza, H. (2013). Bacillus Calmette-Guerin (BCG) immunotherapy for bladder cancer: current understanding and perspectives on engineered BCG vaccine. *Cancer Sci.*, 104, 22-7.

Kawanishi, S., Hiraku, Y. & Oikawa, S. (2001). Mechanism of guanine-specific DNA damage by oxidative stress and its role in carcinogenesis and aging. *Mutat Res.*, 488, 65-76.

Khan, G. (2006). Epstein-Barr virus, cytokines, and inflammation: a cocktail for the pathogenesis of Hodgkin's lymphoma? *Exp. Hematol.*, 34, 399-406.

Kiecolt-Glaser, J.K., Preacher, K.J., MacCallum, R.C., Atkinson, C., Malarkey, W.B. & Glaser, R. (2003). Chronic stress and age-related increases in the proinflammatory cytokine IL-6. *Proc. Natl. Acad. Sci. USA*, 100, 9090-5.

Kohm, A.P. & Sanders, V.M. (2001). Norepinephrine and beta 2-adrenergic receptor stimulation regulate CD4+ T and B lymphocyte function in vitro and in vivo. *Pharmacol. Rev.*, 53, 487-525.

Kröncke, K.D. (2003). Nitrosative stress and transcription. *Biol. Chem.*, 384, 1365-77.

Kulbe, H., Hagemann, T., Szlosarek, P.W., Balkwill, F.R. & Wilson, J.L. (2005). The inflammatory cytokine tumor necrosis factor-alpha regulates chemokine receptor expression on ovarian cancer cells. *Cancer Res.*, 65, 10355-62.

Kumagai, T., Kawamoto, Y., Nakamura, Y., Hatayama, I., Satoh, K., Osawa, T., et al., (2000). 4-Hydroxy-2-nonenal, the end product of lipid peroxidation, is a specific inducer of cyclooxygenase-2 gene expression. *Biochem. Biophys. Res. Commun.*, 273, 437-41.

Leu, S.J. & Singh, V.K. (1992). Stimulation of interleukin-6 production by corticotropin-releasing factor. *Cell Immunol.*, 143, 220-7.

Lillberg, K., Verkasalo, P.K., Kaprio, J., Teppo, L., Helenius, H. & Koskenvuo, M. (2003). Stressful life events and risk of breast cancer in 10,808 women: a cohort study. *Am. J. Epidemiol.*, 157, 415-23.

Lin, D.T., Subbaramaiah, K., Shah, J.P., Dannenberg, A.J. & Boyle, J.O. (2002). Cyclooxygenase-2: a novel molecular target for the prevention and treatment of head and neck cancer. *Head Neck*, 24, 792-9.

Liu, C., Yu, S., Kappes, J., Wang, J., Grizzle, W.E., Zinn, K.R., et al., (2007). Expansion of spleen myeloid suppressor cells represses NK cell cytotoxicity in tumor-bearing host. *Blood*, 109, 4336-42.

Liu, W.H., Liu, J.J., Wu, J., Zhang, L.L., Liu, F., Yin, L., et al., (2013). Novel mechanism of inhibition of dendritic cells maturation by mesenchymal stem cells via interleukin-10 and the JAK1/STAT3 signaling pathway. *PLoS One*, 8, e55487.

Looi, M.L., Mohd Dali, A.Z., Md Ali, S.A., Wan Ngah, W.Z. & Mohd Yusof, Y.A. (2008). Oxidative damage and antioxidant status in patients with cervical intraepithelial neoplasia and carcinoma of the cervix. *Eur. J. Cancer Prev.*, 17, 555-60.

Lu, X.T., Liu, Y.F., Zhao, L., Li, W.J., Yang, R.X., Yan, F.F., et al., (2013). Chronic psychological stress induces vascular inflammation in rabbits. *Stress*, 16, 87-98.

Lu, H., Ouyang, W. & Huang, C. (2006). Inflammation, a key event in cancer development. *Mol. Cancer Res.*, 4, 221-33.

Lutgendorf, S.K., Cole, S., Costanzo, E., Bradley, S., Coffin, J., Jabbari, S., et al., (2003). Stress-related mediators stimulate vascular endothelial growth factor secretion by two ovarian cancer cell lines. *Clin. Cancer Res.*, 9, 4514-21.

Ma, Y., Shurin, G.V., Peiyuan, Z. & Shurin, M.R. (2013). Dendritic cells in the cancer microenvironment. *J. Cancer*, 4, 36-44.

Mahbub, E.S., Haque, N., Salma, U. & Ahmed, A. (2011). Immune modulation in response to stress and relaxation. *Pak. J. Biol. Sci.*, 14, 363-74.

Manju, V., Kalaivani Sailaja, J. & Nalini, N. (2002). Circulating lipid peroxidation and antioxidant status in cervical cancer patients: a case-control study. *Clin. Biochem.*, 35, 621-5.

Mantovani, A. (2005). Cancer: inflammation by remote control. *Nature*, 435, 752-3.

Marnett, L.J. (2000). Oxyradicals and DNA damage. *Carcinogenesis*, 21, 361-70.

Masur, K., Niggemann, B., Zanker, K.S. & Entschladen, F. (2001). Norepinephrine-induced migration of SW 480 colon carcinoma cells is inhibited by β-blockers. *Cancer Res.*, 61, 2866-9.

Melamed, R., Rosenne, E., Shakhar, K., Schwartz, Y., Abudarham, N. & Ben-Eliyahu, S. (2005). Marginating pulmonary-NK activity and resistance to experimental tumor metastasis: suppression by surgery and the prophylactic use of a β-adrenergic antagonist and a prostaglandin synthesis inhibitor. *Brain Behav. Immun.*, 19, 114-26.

Moore, M.M., Chua, W., Charles, K.A. & Clarke, S.J. (2010). Inflammation and cancer: causes and consequences. *Clin. Pharmacol. Ther.*, 87, 504-8.

Moran, T.J., Gray, S., Mikosz, C.A. & Conzen, S.D. (2000). The glucocorticoid receptor mediates a survival signal in human mammary epithelial cells. *Cancer Res.*, 60, 867-72.

Nair, J., Barbin, A., Velic, I. & Bartsch, H. (1999). Etheno DNA-base adducts from endogenous reactive species. *Mutat Res.*, 424, 59-69.

Nance, D.M. & Sanders, V.M. (2007). Autonomic innervation and regulation of the immune system (1987-2007). *Brain Behav. Immun.*, 21, 736-45.

Nathan, C. (2003). Specificity of a third kind: reactive oxygen and nitrogen intermediates in cell signaling. *J. Clin. Invest.*, 111, 769-78.

Olkhanud, P.B., Damdinsuren, B., Bodogai, M., Gress, R.E., Sen, R., Wejksza, K., et al., (2011). Tumor-evoked regulatory B cells promote breast cancer metastasis by converting resting CD4(+) T cells to T-regulatory cells. *Cancer Res.*, 71, 3505-15.

Ostrand-Rosenberg, S. & Sinha, P. (2009). Myeloid-derived suppressor cells: linking inflammation and cancer. *J. Immunol.*, 182, 4499-506.

Palm, D., Lang, K., Niggemann, B., Drell, T.L., 4th, Masur, K., Zaenker, K.S., et al., (2006). The norepinephrine-driven metastasis development of PC-3 human prostate cancer cells in BALB/c nude mice is inhibited by β-blockers. *Int. J. Cancer*, 118, 2744-9.

Peebles, K.A., Lee, J.M., Mao, J.T., Hazra, S., Reckamp, K.L., Krysan, K., et al., (2007). Inflammation and lung carcinogenesis: applying findings in prevention and treatment. *Expert Rev. Anticancer Ther*, 7, 1405-21.

Penninx, B.W., Guralnik, J.M., Pahor, M., Ferrucci, L., Cerhan, J.R., Wallace, R.B., et al., (1998). Chronically depressed mood and cancer risk in older persons. *J. Natl. Cancer Inst.*, 90, 1888-93.

Pidgeon, G.P., Harmey, J.H., Kay, E., Da Costa, M., Redmond, H.P. & Bouchier-Hayes, D.J. (1999). The role of endotoxin/lipopolysaccharide in surgically induced tumour growth in a murine model of metastatic disease. *Br. J. Cancer*, 81, 1311-7.

Prescott, S.M. & Fitzpatrick, F.A. (2000). Cyclooxygenase-2 and carcinogenesis. *Biochim Biophys Acta*, 1470, M69-78.

Rakoff-Nahoum, S. & Medzhitov, R. (2009). Toll-like receptors and cancer. *Nat. Rev. Cancer*, 9, 57-63.

Ramer-Quinn, D.S., Baker, R.A. & Sanders, V.M. (1997). Activated T helper 1 and T helper 2 cells differentially express the beta-2-adrenergic receptor: a mechanism for selective modulation of T helper 1 cell cytokine production. *J. Immunol.*, 159, 4857-67.

Reiche, E.M., Nunes, S.O. & Morimoto, H.K. (2004). Stress, depression, the immune system, and cancer. *Lancet Oncol.*, 5, 617-25.

Robbins, S.L., Kumar, V. & Cotran, R.S. (2010). Robbins and Cotran pathologic basis of disease. 8th edn. Philadelphia, PA: Saunders/Elsevier, xiv, p. 1450.

Roede, J.R. & Jones, D.P. (2010). Reactive species and mitochondrial dysfunction: Mechanistic significance of 4-hydroxynonenal. *Environ. Mol. Mutagen*, 51, 380-90.

Rozengurt, E., Guha, S. & Sinnett-Smith, J. (2002). Gastrointestinal peptide signalling in health and disease. *Eur. J. Surg. Suppl.*, (587), 23-38.

Ruef, J., Rao, G.N., Li, F., Bode, C., Patterson, C., Bhatnagar, A., et al., (1998). Induction of rat aortic smooth muscle cell growth by the lipid peroxidation product 4-hydroxy-2-nonenal. *Circulation*, 97, 1071-8.

Salaun, B., Romero, P. & Lebecque, S. (2007). Toll-like receptors' two-edged sword: when immunity meets apoptosis. *Eur. J. Immunol.*, 37, 3311-8.

Sanders, V.M. (2012). The beta2-adrenergic receptor on T and B lymphocytes: Do we understand it yet? *Brain Behav. Immun.*, 26, 195-200.

Sarkar, C., Chakroborty, D., Chowdhury, U.R., Dasgupta, P.S. & Basu, S. (2008). Dopamine increases the efficacy of anticancer drugs in breast and colon cancer preclinical models. *Clin. Cancer Res.*, 14, 2502-10.

Sarkar, C., Chakroborty, D., Mitra, R.B., Banerjee, S., Dasgupta, P.S. & Basu, S. (2004). Dopamine in vivo inhibits VEGF-induced phosphorylation of VEGFR-2, MAPK, and focal adhesion kinase in endothelial cells. *Am. J. Physiol. Heart Circ. Physiol.*, 287, H1554-60.

Sastry, K.S., Karpova, Y., Prokopovich, S., Smith, A.J., Essau, B., Gersappe, A., et al., (2007). Epinephrine protects cancer cells from apoptosis via activation of cAMP-dependent protein kinase and BAD phosphorylation. *J. Biol. Chem.*, 282, 14094-100.

Sawa, T., Akaike, T., Ichimori, K., Akuta, T., Kaneko, K., Nakayama, H., et al., (2003). Superoxide generation mediated by 8-nitroguanosine, a highly redox-active nucleic acid derivative. *Biochem. Biophys. Res. Commun.*, 311, 300-6.

Scheinman, R.I., Gualberto, A., Jewell, C.M., Cidlowski, J.A. & Baldwin, A.S., Jr. (1995). Characterization of mechanisms involved in transrepression of NF-kappa B by activated glucocorticoid receptors. *Mol. Cell Biol.*, 15, 943-53.

Schernhammer, E.S., Laden, F., Speizer, F.E., Willett, W.C., Hunter, D.J., Kawachi, I., et al., (2003). Night-shift work and risk of colorectal cancer in the nurses' health study. *J. Natl. Cancer Inst.*, 95, 825-8.

Sephton, S. & Spiegel, D. (2003). Circadian disruption in cancer: a neuroendocrine-immune pathway from stress to disease? *Brain Behav. Immun.*, 17, 321-8.

Seruga, B., Zhang, H., Bernstein, L.J. & Tannock, I.F. (2008). Cytokines and their relationship to the symptoms and outcome of cancer. *Nat. Rev. Cancer*, 8, 887-99.

Shanmugathasan, M. & Jothy, S. (2000). Apoptosis, anoikis and their relevance to the pathobiology of colon cancer. *Pathol Int.*, 50, 273-9.

Shimomura, Y., Mizoguchi, E., Sugimoto, K., Kibe, R., Benno, Y., Mizoguchi, A., et al., (2008). Regulatory role of B-1 B cells in chronic colitis. *Int. Immunol.*, 20, 729-37.

Sloan, E.K., Priceman, S.J., Cox, B.F., Yu, S., Pimentel, M.A., Tangkanangnukul, V., et al., (2010). The sympathetic nervous system induces a metastatic switch in primary breast cancer. *Cancer Res.*, 70, 7042-52.

Sonabend, A.M., Rolle, C.E. & Lesniak, M.S. (2008). The role of regulatory T cells in malignant glioma. *Anticancer Res.*, 28, 1143-50.

Sood, A.K., Armaiz-Pena, G.N., Halder, J., Nick, A.M., Stone, R.L., Hu, W., et al., (2010). Adrenergic modulation of focal adhesion kinase protects human ovarian cancer cells from anoikis. *J. Clin. Invest.*, 120, 1515-23.

Srivastava, S., Natu, S.M., Gupta, A., Pal, K.A., Singh, U., Agarwal, G.G., et al., (2009). Lipid peroxidation and antioxidants in different stages of cervical cancer: Prognostic significance. *Indian J. Cancer*, 46, 297-302.

Standiford, T.J. & Keshamouni, V.G. (2012). Breaking the tolerance for tumor: Targeting negative regulators of TLR signaling. *Oncoimmunology*, 1, 340-5.

Subrahmanyam, V.V., McGirr, L.G. & O'Brien, P.J. (1987). Glutathione oxidation during peroxidase catalysed drug metabolism. *Chem. Biol. Interact*, 61, 45-59.

Suzuki, N., Yasui, M., Geacintov, N.E., Shafirovich, V. & Shibutani, S. (2005). Miscoding events during DNA synthesis past the nitration-damaged base 8-nitroguanine. *Biochemistry*, 44, 9238-45.

Swann, J.B. & Smyth, M.J. (2007). Immune surveillance of tumors. *J. Clin. Invest.* 117, 1137-46.

Takahashi, T., Nau, M.M., Chiba, I., Birrer, M.J., Rosenberg, R.K., Vinocour, M., et al., (1989). p53: a frequent target for genetic abnormalities in lung cancer. *Science*, 246, 491-4.

Tamir, S. & Tannenbaum, S.R. (1996). The role of nitric oxide (NO·) in the carcinogenic process. *Biochim. Biophys. Acta*, 1288, F31-6.

Tamura, G., Nishizuka, S., Maesawa, C., Suzuki, Y., Iwaya, T., Sakata, K., et al., (1999). Mutations in mitochondrial control region DNA in gastric tumours of Japanese patients. *Eur. J. Cancer*, 35, 316-9.

Tan, T.T. & Coussens, L.M. (2007). Humoral immunity, inflammation and cancer. *Curr. Opin. Immunol.*, 19, 209-16.

Thaker, P.H., Han, L.Y., Kamat, A.A., Arevalo, J.M., Takahashi, R., Lu, C., et al., (2006). Chronic stress promotes tumor growth and angiogenesis in a mouse model of ovarian carcinoma. *Nat. Med.*, 12, 939-44.

Turnbull, A.V. & Rivier, C. (1995). Regulation of the HPA axis by cytokines. *Brain Behav. Immun.*, 9, 253-75.

Tworoger, S.S., Eliassen, A.H., Sluss, P. & Hankinson, S.E. (2007). A prospective study of plasma prolactin concentrations and risk of premenopausal and postmenopausal breast cancer. *J. Clin. Oncol.*, 25, 1482-8.

Uchida, K. (2003). 4-Hydroxy-2-nonenal: a product and mediator of oxidative stress. *Prog Lipid Res*, 42, 318-43.

Valko, M., Leibfritz, D., Moncol, J., Cronin, M.T., Mazur, M. & Telser, J. (2007). Free radicals and antioxidants in normal physiological functions and human disease. *Int. J. Biochem. Cell Biol.*, 39, 44-84.

Valko, M., Morris, H. & Cronin, M.T. (2005). Metals, toxicity and oxidative stress. *Curr. Med. Chem.*, 12, 1161-208.

Valko, M., Rhodes, C.J., Moncol, J., Izakovic, M. & Mazur, M. (2006). Free radicals, metals and antioxidants in oxidative stress-induced cancer. *Chem. Biol. Interact*, 160, 1-40.

Vesely, M.D., Kershaw, M.H., Schreiber, R.D. & Smyth, M.J. (2011). Natural innate and adaptive immunity to cancer. *Annu. Rev. Immunol.*, 29, 235-71.

Vicari, A.P., Caux, C., Trinchieri, G. (2002). Tumour escape from immune surveillance through dendritic cell inactivation. *Semin. Cancer Biol.*, 12, 33-42.

Wang, P.S., Walker, A.M., Tsuang, M.T., Orav, E.J., Glynn, R.J., Levin, R., et al., (2002). Dopamine antagonists and the development of breast cancer. *Arch. Gen. Psychiatry*, 59, 1147-54.

Wang, H.Y. & Wang, R.F. (2007). Regulatory T cells and cancer. *Curr. Opin. Immunol*, 19, 217-23.

Webster, J.I., Tonelli, L. & Sternberg, E.M. (2002). Neuroendocrine regulation of immunity. *Annu. Rev. Immunol.*, 20, 125-63.

Weinberg, R.A. (2007). *The biology of cancer*. New York: Garland Science.

Weller, M., Schmidt, C., Roth, W. & Dichgans, J. (1997). Chemotherapy of human malignant glioma: prevention of efficacy by dexamethasone? *Neurology*, 48, 1704-9.

Yanaba, K., Bouaziz, J.D., Haas, K.M., Poe, J.C., Fujimoto, M. & Tedder, T.F. (2008). A regulatory B cell subset with a unique CD1dhiCD5+ phenotype controls T cell-dependent inflammatory responses. *Immunity*, 28, 639-50.

Yang, C.A., Scheibenbogen, C., Bauer, S., Kleinle, C., Wex, T., Bornschein, J., et al., (2013). A frequent toll-Like receptor 1 gene polymorphism affects NK- and T-cell IFN-γ production and is associated with Helicobacter pylori-induced gastric disease. *Helicobacter* 18, 13-21.

Yang, E.V., Sood, A.K., Chen, M., Li, Y., Eubank, T.D., Marsh, C.B., et al., (2006). Norepinephrine up-regulates the expression of vascular endothelial growth factor, matrix metalloproteinase (MMP)-2, and MMP-9 in nasopharyngeal carcinoma tumor cells. *Cancer Res.*, 66, 10357-64.

Yermilov, V., Rubio, J., Becchi, M., Friesen, M.D., Pignatelli, B. & Ohshima, H. (1995). Formation of 8-nitroguanine by the reaction of guanine with peroxynitrite in vitro. *Carcinogenesis*, 16, 2045-50.

Yoshida, S., Ono, M., Shono, T., Izumi, H., Ishibashi, T., Suzuki, H., et al., (1997). Involvement of interleukin-8, vascular endothelial growth factor, and basic fibroblast growth factor in tumor necrosis factor alpha-dependent angiogenesis. *Mol. Cell Biol.*, 17, 4015-23.

Young, D., Waitches, G., Birchmeier, C., Fasano, O. & Wigler, M. (1986). Isolation and characterization of a new cellular oncogene encoding a protein with multiple potential transmembrane domains. *Cell*, 45, 711-9.

Zhang, H.H., Kumar, S., Barnett, A.H. & Eggo, M.C. (2001). Dexamethasone inhibits tumor necrosis factor-alpha-induced apoptosis and interleukin-1 beta release in human subcutaneous adipocytes and preadipocytes. *J. Clin. Endocrinol. Metab.*, 86, 2817-25.

Zhao, Y.S., Zhu, S., Li, X.W., Wang, F., Hu, F.L., Li, D.D., et al., (2009). Association between NSAIDs use and breast cancer risk: a systematic review and meta-analysis. *Breast Cancer Res. Treat*, 117, 141-50.

In: Stress and Developmental Programming …
Editors: Lubo Zhang and Lawrence D. Longo

ISBN: 978-1-63321-836-9
© 2014 Nova Science Publishers, Inc.

Chapter 17

Developmental Programming of Telomere Biology: Role of Stress and Stress Biology

Sonja Entringer[1,5*] *and Pathik Wadhwa*[1,2,3,4]

[1]Departments of Pediatrics, [2]Psychiatry & Human Behavior, [3]Obstetrics & Gynecology,
[4]Epidemiology, University of California, Irvine, US
[5]Department of Medical Psychology, Charité Universitätsmedizin Berlin, Germany

Abstract

A substantial body of epidemiological, clinical, physiological, cellular and molecular evidence converges to suggest that suboptimal conditions in intrauterine and early postnatal life play a critical role in subsequent health and susceptibility for a range of complex, common disorders that confer a major, global burden of disease (i.e., the concept of fetal or developmental programming of health and disease). The elucidation of biological mechanisms underlying these observed effects is an area of active interest and intense investigation. It is important to determine whether there are some common underlying pathways that may account for the effects of disparate prenatal and early postnatal conditions on various health and disease risk phenotypes. In this chapter we advance the hypothesis that telomere biology may represent a novel, common mechanism underlying the observed effects of a disparate set of suboptimal intrauterine exposures on health and disease risk. Moreover, we propose that context- and time-inappropriate exposures to various forms of physiological stress (maternal-placental-fetal endocrine, immune, inflammatory, and oxidative stress) during the intrauterine period of development may alter or program the telomere biology system in a manner that accelerates cellular dysfunction, aging, and disease susceptibility over the lifespan.

Keywords: Fetal/developmental programming, prenatal, stress, telomere biology, epigenetic

* Corresponding author: Sonja Entringer, PhD, Department of Pediatrics, University of California, Irvine, 333 The City Blvd. W, Suite 1200, Orange, CA 92868, Phone: 714-940-1924, E-mail: sentring@uci.edu.

Introduction

A substantial body of epidemiological, clinical, experimental, cellular and molecular evidence converges to suggest that conditions in the intrauterine and early postnatal period of life play a critical role in influencing subsequent health and susceptibility for many common, complex, non-communicable disorders that confer a major burden of disease in society (i.e., the concept of fetal or developmental programming of health (Gluckman and Hanson, 2004)). The elucidation of biological mechanisms underlying these effects is an area of active interest and investigation. We propose here that telomere biology may represent a novel common underlying mechanism. Based, in part, on findings related to the relatively high heritability of telomere length but the relatively small contribution of genetic variation (from candidate gene as well as GWAS approaches) to explaining variation in telomere length (e.g., Codd et al., 2010, Levy et al., 2010, Prescott et al., 2011), we argue for a major potential role of maternal systemic and intrauterine effects in the initial setting of telomere length and telomerase expression capacity. Based on the consideration that extrinsic and intrinsic conditions representing energetic resources and challenges (threats) to survival and reproduction epitomize the key processes underlying selection and developmental plasticity, we propose that intrauterine and early postnatal stress warrants particular consideration as a candidate mechanism implicated in the programming of the telomere biology system. Stress-related maternal-placental-fetal endocrine, immune and oxidative processes represent an attractive candidate mechanism because (a) they are exquisitely sensitive to a diverse array of potentially adverse physiological (metabolic), social, environmental and clinical exposures (summarized in Entringer et al., 2010), (b) they serve as the key signaling molecules between the fetal and maternal compartments during intrauterine development (Wadhwa, 2005), and (c) they may exert stable, long-term effects via epigenetic and other processes on key components of the developing telomere biology system that influence the initial setting of telomere length and the tissue- and stage-of-development-specific regulation of telomerase expression.

The Role of Stress and Stress Biology in Developmental Programming of Health and Disease Risk

We have previously argued that the maternal-placental fetal stress system (endocrine, immune, and oxidative stress-related processes) may play a major role in mediating the effects of many disparate intrauterine insults exert on different physiological systems in the developing offspring (Wadhwa, 2005) for the following reasons: 1) One of the key functions of the stress response is redistribution of energetic resources across different systems. It is this function that may be particularly relevant in the context of development, when, in accordance with the principles underlying life history theory, decisions about energy allocation are made in response to current or previous environmental conditions. Through an evolutionary lens, it appears that the most salient environmental variations underlying natural selection relate to energy substrate (nutrition) and challenges that impact integrity and survival until reproductive age (stress). It is for this reason that prenatal stress would be expected to influence many, if not all, developmental outcomes. 2) Another reason for considering a role for prenatal stress in future health and disease outcomes has to do with the large socioeconomic status and racial or ethnic disparities that characterize the population distribution of complex common disorders. Stress has been hypothesized as a mediator of this association, and if this is the case it stands to reason that exposure to excessive prenatal stress may contribute to the well-documented socioeconomic and sociodemographic disparities in developmental, birth, and child health outcomes. 3) Responses to endocrine, immune, and oxidative stress are among the most reliable, objective indicators of human fetal exposure to in utero stress. Several animal and human studies, including work from our research program, suggest that a broad array of intrauterine perturbations, including clinical, nutritional, behavioral, and psychosocial stressors cause perturbations in maternal-placental-fetal (MPF) endocrine, immune and oxidative stress related processes. Moreover, there are no direct neural or vascular connections between the mother and her developing fetus. All communication between the maternal and fetal compartments is mediated by the placenta, an organ of fetal origin, and endocrine and immune stress responses serve as key communication signals between the maternal and the fetal compartments. In line with this thinking, epidemiological, clinical, cellular, and molecular evidence converge to suggest that stress-related endocrine and immune processes, particularly proinflammatory cytokines and the glucocorticoid axis, may serve as a key physiological pathways mediating the effects of intrauterine perturbations on the fetus. Taken together, MPF endocrine, immune and oxidative stress related processes act as a sensor, transducer as well as effector of stress. They are responsive to many classes of intrauterine perturbations (sensor); they act as a conduit of cues about the stress-related milieu between the maternal and fetal compartments (transducer); and they act directly on multiple targets of fetal programming in the brain and peripheral systems (effector) (Entringer et al., 2010, 2012a). Unlike exposure to toxins and teratogens, it is important to appreciate the fact that maternal-placental-fetal hormones and cytokines play an essential role in orchestrating key events underlying cellular growth, replication and differentiation in the brain and peripheral tissues (Entringer et al., 2012a). Thus, perturbations in the level and/or time of exposure of these biologic effectors are likely to produce alterations of normal structure and function.

Long-Term Effects of Prenatal Stress Exposure on Human Adult Physiology and Health

The majority of human epidemiological studies of the fetal programming hypothesis have operationalized unfavorable intrauterine environments using indicators such as low birth weight. However, the long-term effects on child or adult disease-related phenotypes of interest may not necessarily be mediated by adverse birth outcomes. Only a very small number of studies have investigated this issue in humans. As a first step to addressing this question, we conducted a retrospective case-control study in a sample of healthy young adults born to mothers with healthy pregnancies and normal birth outcomes. One half of the study population of young adults was born to mothers who had experienced a major stressful life event during the index pregnancy (prenatal stress group; PS), whereas the other half was a sociodemographically-matched population with no history of maternal exposure to prenatal stress (comparison group; CG).

We selected a study population of younger as opposed to older adults in order to focus on pre-disease markers of physiological dysregulation of metabolic, endocrine and immune systems as early predictors of disease susceptibility. The potential effects of other established obstetric, newborn and childhood risk factors on adult health were controlled using a stringent set of exclusionary criteria. Our results indicated that the young adults exposed during intrauterine life to maternal psychosocial stress consistently exhibited significant dysregulation in key physiological parameters, thereby placing them at increased risk for developing complex common disorders. Specifically, individuals in the PS group exhibited higher BMI and percent body fat, primary insulin resistance, and a lipid profile consistent with the metabolic syndrome (Entringer et al., 2008b); altered immune function with a TH2 shift in the TH1/TH2 balance (consistent with increased risk of asthma and autoimmune disorders (Entringer et al., 2008a); altered endocrine function, with increased ACTH and reduced cortisol levels during pharmacological and psychological stimulation paradigms; accelerated cellular aging (as indexed by shortened leukocyte telomere length that extrapolated to approximately a 3.5 year increase in the rate of cell aging (Entringer et al., 2011)); and impaired prefrontal cortex (PFC)-related cognitive performance (impairments in working memory performance after hydrocortisone administration) (Entringer et al., 2009).

Consistent with the finding on cognitive function are results from one of our other recent prospective, longitudinal studies on the long-term effects of prenatal stress (anxiety) on child brain morphology. After excluding cases with low birth weight and adjusting for total gray matter volume, age, gestational age at birth, handedness and postpartum stress, maternal pregnancy-specific anxiety in mid-gestation was associated with gray matter volume reductions in several child brain regions, including the prefrontal cortex (Buss et al., 2010). Furthermore, higher maternal cortisol concentrations in early gestation were associated with a larger right amygdala volume and more affective problems in girls. The association between maternal cortisol concentrations during early gestation and affective problems was mediated, in part, by amygdala volume (Buss et al., 2012).

Taken together, our findings suggest that *in utero* exposure to prenatal psychosocial stress may confer increased long-term risk of a range of negative physiological and cognitive health outcomes in humans; these effects are independent from those of other established obstetric and childhood risk factors; and these long-term effects are not necessarily mediated by unfavorable birth outcomes such as low birth weight. It is possible that there are separate outcome-specific mechanisms, or there may be a common underlying mechanism mediating the effects of a diverse range of intrauterine perturbations on a range of health and disease risk outcomes. With respect to the latter possibility we and others have advanced the hypothesis that telomere biology may represent an important mechanism underlying the observed effects of disparate conditions in fetal life on subsequent health and disease risk–related phenotypes (Barnes and Ozanne, 2011, Entringer et al., 2011, 2012b).

The Importance of Telomere Biology for Disease Risk and Life Span

Telomere biology refers to the structure and function of telomeres as well as the production and function of telomerase. Telomeres are non-coding double-stranded repeats of guanine-rich tandem DNA sequences [$5'$-(TTAGGG)$_n$-$3'$] that cap the ends of linear chromosomes and are bound by the multiprotein complex shelterin (Blackburn and Gall, 1978, Moyzis et al., 1988). Shelterin mediates the formation of nucleotide loops that protect the end of the chromosome from being recognized by the DNA damage repair system as DNA breaks. Telomerase is the reverse transcriptase enzyme that adds telomeric DNA to existing telomeres (Blackburn et al., 1989). Because DNA polymerase is unable to fully replicate the 3' end of the DNA strand (the 'end-replication problem') telomeres lose approximately 30-150 bp with each cell division.

As somatic cells divide, telomeres eventually reach a critical short length, resulting in a decreased ability to recruit shelterin proteins, thus leading to cellular senescence or apoptosis (see Figure 1) (Stewart and Weinberg, 2006). Loss of telomere function causes chromosomal fusion, activation of DNA damage checkpoint responses, genome instability, and impaired stem cell function. After cells become senescent, they exhibit various genetic and morphological changes that result in loss of tissue function. Consistent with these observations, shortened telomeres or reduced telomerase production, or both, have been linked to several diseases including, but not limited to, cardiovascular disease, hypertension, atherosclerosis, heart failure, type 2 diabetes (Aviv et al., 2006, Benetos et al., 2001, Brouilette et al., 2003, Gardner et al., 2005, Jeanclos et al., 2000, Nawrot et al., 2004, Samani et al., 2001, Sampson et al., 2006, Valdes et al., 2005, Zhu et al., 2011), and shortened life span and early mortality (Bakaysa et al., 2007, Cawthon et al., 2003, Honig et al., 2006, Kimura et al., 2008, Martin-Ruiz et al., 2006).

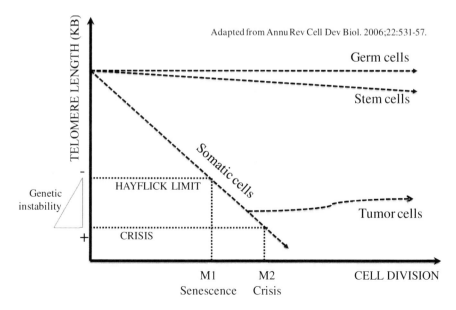

Figure 1. Telomeres and cellular senescence.

Stress and Telomere Biology

The link between exposure to excess stress and adverse health outcomes is well established (Cohen et al., 2007, McEwen, 1998). In recent years, accumulating evidence supports the crucial role of telomere biology as a potential mechanism linking stress exposure and disease risk. Epel and colleagues were the first to propose this hypothesis and to publish a study demonstrating a link between chronic psychosocial stress and telomere biology (Epel et al., 2004). This relationship between stress and/or socioeconomic disadvantage has since been replicated several times (Cherkas et al., 2006, Damjanovic et al., 2007, Steptoe et al., 2011). Exposure to severe psychological trauma or other psychopathological conditions (PTSD, depression) has also been linked to telomere length (Hartmann et al., 2011, Humphreys et al., 2012, Simon et al., 2006, Wolkowitz et al., 2011). In addition to stress, other behavioral processes have been associated with telomere length, such as obesity, smoking, diet (dietary intake and nutrition biomarkers), sleep quality and physical activity (reviewed in Lin et al., 2012). Finally, some studies suggest that lifestyle interventions may increase telomerase activity and thereby slow down cellular aging (Daubenmier et al., 2012, Jacobs et al., 2011).

Biological Pathways Linking Stress and Telomere Biology

There are 3 major, inter-related biological pathways linking stress and health behaviors with telomere biology: stress hormones, inflammation and oxidative stress.

Stress hormones: In vivo, elevated levels of cortisol and catecholamines, larger cortisol responses to acute stress and dysregulation of the diurnal cortisol rhythm have all been linked in several studies to telomere length (Epel et al., 2006, Parks et al., 2009, Tomiyama et al., 2012). Moreover, telomerase activity in PBMCs varies dynamically in response to acute psychological stress. Epel et al. have shown that exposure to a brief laboratory psychological stressor increased telomerase activity within one hour, and that this increase was associated with greater cortisol increases in response to the stressor (Epel et al., 2010). In vitro treatment of stimulated human T-cells with cortisol causes a decrease in cell proliferation, decreased telomerase activity and lower telomerase reverse transcriptase (TERT) mRNA levels after cell activation (Choi et al., 2008). In chicken, embryonic exposure to cortisol produced higher levels of reactive oxygen metabolites and an over-representation of short telomeres (Haussmann et al., 2012).

Oxidative stress: It is well established that stress, depression and many unhealthy behaviors (smoking, alcohol, high fat diet) increase oxidative stress (summarized in Epel, 2009, Lin et al., 2012). Oxidative stress is known to decrease TERT (telomerase protein) activity and preferentially damage telomeric as opposed to other genomic DNA regions. Conversely, antioxidants decelerate TL shortening in cultured cells and increases telomerase activity. It has been reported that an oxidative stress imbalance (ratio of oxidative stress to antioxidants) *in vivo* is associated with shorter TL length (Epel et al., 2004), and others have found similar associations using various markers of oxidative stress (Adaikalakoteswari et al., 2005, 2007, Demissie et al., 2006).

Inflammation: The link between stress, obesity and unhealthy behavioral lifestyle with high levels of proinflammatory cytokines is well established (Epel, 2009). Several studies have demonstrated that markers of inflammation such as IL-6 and CRP are linked to TL shortening (Carrero et al., 2008, Fitzpatrick et al., 2007), and telomerase activity via NFkB-mediated pathways (Bu et al., 2010).

Fetal Programming of Telomere Biology

The initial, or newborn, setting of telomere length (TL) represents a critically important characteristic of an individual's telomere biology system (Aviv, 2012). It constitutes one of two major determinants of TL at any subsequent age (the other determinant is TL attrition over time) (Armanios and Blackburn, 2012, Hewitt et al., 2012). A reduction in the newborn TL could confer greater susceptibility in later life for pathophysiological outcomes, highlighting the importance of understanding factors that determine an individual's newborn TL (Aviv, 2012, Entringer et al., 2012b, Heidinger et al., 2012). TL in early life was, in fact, recently shown to be a strong prospective predictor of realized lifespan in zebra finches (Heidinger et al., 2012). Moreover, the rate of age-dependent TL shortening in humans appears to be similar across different somatic tissues (leukocyte, skeletal muscle, skin and fat), suggesting the observed TL differences between tissues are established in early life and highlighting the importance of a better understanding of the determinants of inter-individual variation in the initial setting of TL at birth (Daniali et al., 2013).

The determinants of newborn TL are poorly understood. Despite the relatively high heritability estimates, genetic variation (from candidate gene as well as GWAS approaches) accounts for only a small proportion of the variance in TL throughout the lifespan (e.g., Aviv, 2012, Prescott et al., 2011). This highlights the particular importance of a better understanding of intrauterine environmental factors that may contribute to newborn TL.

It appears that the initial setting and regulation of telomere homeostasis, including chromosomal telomere length and both the telomeric and extra-telomeric activities of telomerase, may be plastic and receptive to the influence of intrauterine or other early postnatal life conditions (see below). Also, telomere homeostasis in various cell types including the germ line, stem cells, and proliferating as well as post-mitotic tissue, may serve as a fundamental integrator and regulator of processes underlying cell genomic integrity, function, aging, and senescence over the life span. This may have major implications for health and disease susceptibility for complex common disorders. We have advance the hypothesis that context- and time-inappropriate exposures to physiological stresses during the embryonic, fetal, and early postnatal periods of development may alter or program the telomere biology system in a manner that accelerates cellular dysfunction, aging, and disease susceptibility over the lifespan (Entringer et al., 2012b).

Developmental Ontogeny of the Telomere System

Telomerase Activity. Telomerase activity in germ cells ensures the maintenance of the telomere length and transmission of full-length chromosomes to progeny (Hiyama et al., 1995, Kim et al., 1994, Schaetzlein et al., 2004). Soon after fertilization, in the blastocyst and during early embryonic stages, telomerase is abundant, but it decreases with increasing gestational age and cellular differentiation (Ulaner et al., 1998, Wright et al., 1996). In children and adults, telomerase is inactive in most tissues except for rapidly proliferating tissues such as stem cells and active lymphocytes (Forsyth et al., 2002). However, many stem or stem-like cells in adult humans exhibit some telomerase activity when stimulated to divide. This lower amount of activity is apparently sufficient to slow, but not prevent, telomere shortening (Forsyth et al., 2002).

Telomere length. Consistent with the high levels of telomerase activity in germ cells, these cells also have significantly longer telomeres than somatic cells (de Lange et al., 1990), possibly because of telomere elongation during germ cell maturation (Achi et al., 2000). Furthermore, there is evidence from a study in two different species (mice and cattle) that telomeres are elongated during embryonic development, and that this process is telomerase-dependent, and possibly required to ensure sufficient telomere reserves for species integrity (summarized in Schaetzlein et al., 2004). A study that examined tissue samples from aborted fetuses and from normal newborns found that telomere length was comparable in most fetal tissues, and did not decline during gestation (Youngren et al., 1998). Thus, telomere length seems to be initially extended and then maintained at a constant level across tissues throughout gestation. In human newborns telomere length is highly correlated across white blood cells, umbilical artery cells, and foreskin tissues, but there is high variability across individuals (Okuda et al., 2002). Furthermore, among the different hematopoietic cells in cord blood (hematopoietic progenitor cells, T cells, and granulocytes), correlations in telomere length across the different cell types are very high (Kimura et al., 2010). After birth, infants show a rapid decrease in telomere length (Frenck et al., 1998, Zeichner et al., 1999) that corresponds with rapid growth rates and high production of turnover of immune cells in the process of developing acquired immunity (Eisenberg, 2011). We are only aware of one prospective study that quantified telomere shortening during the first few years of life. In this study, leukocyte telomere length from birth until 3 years age was repeatedly assessed in nine children (Zeichner et al., 1999). Their results suggest that telomere shortening is accelerated during the first years of life (about 270 base pairs per year) compared to early adulthood (about 60 bp per year at 20 years of age) and old age (Eisenberg, 2011) (about 26 bp per year) (Eisenberg, 2011). Furthermore, there is considerable variation in the rate of telomere shortening among young children (Zeichner et al., 1999).

Prenatal Adverse Exposure and Subsequent TL in the Offspring

Recent studies in animals and humans suggest that adverse or suboptimal conditions in intrauterine life are associated with shorter offspring TL (Entringer et al., 2011, Haussmann et al., 2012, Jennings et al., 1999, Raqib et al., 2007, Tarry-Adkins et al., 2008, 2009), thereby supporting the notion that TL may, in part, be programmed in utero. There is relatively little empirical literature to date that has addressed the link between exposure to prenatal stress and telomere biology. A few experimental studies in animals provide evidence of a causal link between exposure to adverse intrauterine conditions and shortened offspring telomeres in cells across different tissues (Haussmann et al., 2012, Jennings et al., 1999, Tarry-Adkins et al., 2008, 2009). For instance, a very recent study by Haussmann and colleagues in chickens reported that prenatal administration of cortisol in the yolk resulted in a higher proportion of blood cells with short telomeres and increased abundance of reactive oxygen metabolites as well as increased duration of the acute stress response compared to untreated controls (Haussmann et al., 2012). Several human studies have examined the associations between adverse prenatal conditions and various aspects of offspring telomere biology. Most of these studies assessed the association between obstetric risk conditions during pregnancy and TL or telomerase activity in placental tissue or cord blood at birth, and only three addressed the longer-term effects on telomere length in children or young adults. The adverse conditions assessed during pregnancy in relation to offspring TL and telomerase activity included fetal growth restriction, and obstetric risk conditions such as diabetes and preeclampsia (Akkad et al., 2006, Biron-Shental et al., 2010, 2011, Cross et al., 2009, 2011, Davy et al., 2009, Izutsu et al., 1998, Okuda et al., 2002, Raqib et al., 2007, Sukenik-Halevy et al., 2009).

Prenatal Stress Exposure and Subsequent TL in the Offspring

With our collaborators, we recently published the first human study of the effects of maternal psychosocial stress exposure during pregnancy on offspring TL. We found a significant association between exposure to maternal prenatal psychosocial stress (experience of negative life events during pregnancy) and reduced leukocyte TL in young adult offspring (Entringer et al., 2011). The effect was more pronounced in female offspring and was unchanged after adjusting for potential confounding factors (subject characteristics, birth weight percentile, and early life and concurrent stress). The TL of individuals in the prenatally stressed group was, on average, 178 base pairs (bp) shorter than that of individuals in the comparison group and 295 bp shorter in female subjects. The most recent and comprehensive review of studies of age-related attrition in TL suggests that in adults TL attrition averages approximately 60 bp/year at 20 years of age, and the attrition rate appears to decrease to approximately 20 bp/year by age 80 (Eisenberg, 2011). Given that the participants in our study were approximately 25 years old, translating telomere shortening of this observed difference of 178 bp (295 bp for the women-only group) to years of aging indicates that the lymphocytes of individuals in the prenatally stressed group had aged the equivalent of approximately 3.5 additional years (5 additional years in the women-only group) relative to those in the comparison group. We then set out to determine how early in life this effect of stress on TL is apparent by quantifying the association of maternal psychosocial stress during pregnancy with newborn TL. In a prospective study of N=27 mother-newborn dyads maternal pregnancy-specific stress was assessed in early gestation and cord blood was subsequently collected and analyzed for TL measurement. After accounting for the effects of potential determinants of newborn TL (gestational age at birth, weight, sex and exposure to antepartum obstetric complications), there was a significant, independent, linear effect of pregnancy-specific stress on newborn TL that accounted for 25% of the variance in adjusted cord blood TL (see Figure 2) (Entringer et al., 2013).

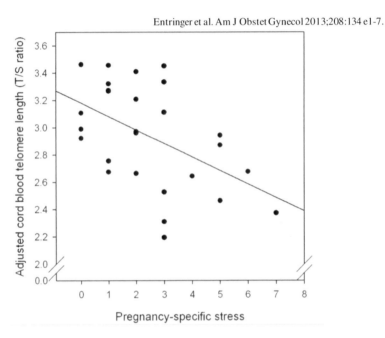

Figure 2. Scatterplot of association between maternal pregnancy-specific stress and newborn (cord blood) telomere length. T/S ratio is adjusted for covariates (newborn gestational age at birth, weight, sex, and exposure to antepartum obstetric complications). T/S, telomere repeat copy number to single gene copy number.

Taken together, these finding provides the first evidence in humans that maternal psychological stress during pregnancy may exert a "programming" effect on the developing telomere biology system, and that this effect is already apparent at birth.

Childhood Adversity and Subsequent TL in the Offspring

A considerable body of evidence in humans and animals has demonstrated that exposure to adverse conditions in childhood (e.g., neglect, abuse, trauma) is associated with increased risk for an array of psychological and physical disorders in later life, and that these effects are mediated, in part, by alterations in stress-sensitive biological systems (Loman and Gunnar, 2010, Miller et al., 2011). It has only been within the past few years that evidence has emerged suggesting that exposure to adverse conditions in childhood is significantly associated with shorter telomeres in children or adults. The first study in this area found that history of childhood maltreatment was associated with shorter adult leukocyte telomere length (Tyrka et al., 2010). Other early life factors that have been associated with telomere length later in life are time spent in institutionalized care among Romanian orphanages (Drury et al., 2012), the presence of childhood abuse and other adversities (Kiecolt-Glaser et al., 2011), number of reported childhood adverse life events (Kananen et al., 2010), and adverse circumstances reported in childhood (Surtees et al., 2011). A recent longitudinal study found an association between exposure to violence and higher TL attrition rate in children from 5 to 10 years (Shalev et al., 2013). Moreover, history of childhood adversity was found to moderate the effect of psychopathology on adult telomere length. Among adults with either posttraumatic stress disorder (PTSD) or anxiety disorder, only those individuals with a history of exposure to childhood trauma had shorter telomere length than the respective matched comparison groups (O'Donovan et al., 2011).

Mechanisms of Programming of TL Biology by Prenatal Stress

Although a link between developmental processes in early life and changes in telomere biology has been established as reviewed above, not much is known about potential mechanisms of how these effects are mediated. Epigenetic modifications have been discussed in the context of fetal programming as a process of how developmental exposures can affect the fetal gene expression and subsequent disease risk (e.g., Hanson et al., 2011). The telomere system seems to be under tight epigenetic control, and in particular methylation changes in subtelomeric loci and epigenetic modulation of the core promoter region of the telomerase reverse transcriptase gene (TERT) that regulates telomerase activity seem to be involved in regulation of telomere maintenance and telomere length (Buxton et al. 2014, Daniel et al. 2012). There is evidence that chromatin modifications are important regulators of mammalian telomeres, subtelomeric regions are enriched in epigenetic marks that are characteristic of heterochromatin, and the abrogation of master epigenetic regulators, such as histone methyltransferases and DNA methyltransferases, correlate with loss of telomere length control (reviewed in Blasco, 2007). Specifically, the regulation of TL is dependent on the level of methylation of the histones H3 and H4 associated with subtelomeric regions. The methylation of these histones decreases access to telomere sequences and thus reduces telomerase activity (Blasco, 2007). Hence, proteins that play a role in regulation of these methylations, such as DNA methyltransferase, have an impact on telomere length. DNA methyltransferase is a key candidate mechanism by which early life conditions (e.g., nutrition (Burdge and Lillycrop, 2011), stress (Weaver et al., 2004)) produce stable, long term epigenetic alterations. In addition, several studies have suggested that epigenetic modulation of the core promoter region of the telomerase reverse transcriptase gene (TERT) that regulates telomerase activity are involved in regulation of the telomere maintenance (see Daniel et al., 2012). Studying how these epigenetic mechanisms can potentially be modified by early stress-biology related factors in animal and human models is a priority of our future studies.

Conclusion

Based on the conceptual framework and empirical findings presented here we suggest it is important to consider the potential role of intrauterine stress and stress biology in arriving at a better understanding of the developmental programming of the telomere biology system and aging-related diseases. Questions remain regarding the molecular mechanism(s) underlying this effect and potential interactions with other biological processes. However, in so far as the newborn setting of TL is an important determinant of subsequent telomere biology-related processes and health outcomes, the findings summarized in this chapter add evidence to the growing awareness that age-related complex, common disorders may have their foundations very early in life, and second, they point to potentially modifiable factors for possible clinical intervention with implications for primary prevention.

References

Achi, M. V., Ravindranath, N. & Dym, M. (2000). Telomere length in male germ cells is inversely correlated with telomerase activity. *Biol Reprod, 63*, 591-8.

Adaikalakoteswari, A., Balasubramanyam, M. & Mohan, V. (2005). Telomere shortening occurs in Asian Indian Type 2 diabetic patients. *Diabet Med, 22*, 1151-6.

Adaikalakoteswari, A., Balasubramanyam, M., Ravikumar, R., Deepa, R. & Mohan, V. (2007). Association of telomere shortening with impaired glucose tolerance and diabetic macroangiopathy. *Atherosclerosis, 195*, 83-9.

Akkad, A., Hastings, R., Konje, J. C., Bell, S. C., Thurston, H. & Williams, B. (2006). Telomere length in small-for-gestational-age babies. *BJOG, 113*, 318-23.

Armanios, M. & Blackburn, E. H. (2012). The telomere syndromes. *Nat Rev Genet, 13*, 693-704.

Aviv, A. (2012). Genetics of leukocyte telomere length and its role in atherosclerosis. *Mutat Res, 730*, 68-74.

Aviv, A., Valdes, A., Gardner, J. P., Swaminathan, R., Kimura, M. & Spector, T. D. (2006). Menopause modifies the association of leukocyte telomere length with insulin resistance and inflammation. *J Clin Endocrinol Metab, 91*, 635-40.

Bakaysa, S. L., Mucci, L. A., Slagboom, P. E., Boomsma, D. I., McClearn, G. E., Johansson, B., et al. (2007). Telomere length predicts survival independent of genetic influences. *Aging Cell, 6*, 769-74.

Barnes, S. K. & Ozanne, S. E. (2011). Pathways linking the early environment to long-term health and lifespan. *Prog Biophys Mol Biol, 106*, 323-36.

Benetos, A., Okuda, K., Lajemi, M., Kimura, M., Thomas, F., Skurnick, J., et al. (2001). Telomere length as an indicator of biological aging: The gender effect and relation with pulse pressure and pulse wave velocity. *Hypertension, 37*, 381-5.

Biron-Shental, T., Kidron, D., Sukenik-Halevy, R., Goldberg-Bittman, L., Sharony, R., Fejgin, M. D., et al. (2011). TERC telomerase subunit gene copy number in placentas from pregnancies complicated with intrauterine growth restriction. *Early Hum Dev*, *87*, 73-5.

Biron-Shental, T., Sukenik Halevy, R., Goldberg-Bittman, L., Kidron, D., Fejgin, M. D. & Amiel, A. (2010). Telomeres are shorter in placental trophoblasts of pregnancies complicated with intrauterine growth restriction (IUGR). *Early Hum Dev*, *86*, 451-6.

Blackburn, E. H. & Gall, J. G. (1978). A tandemly repeated sequence at the termini of the extrachromosomal ribosomal RNA genes in Tetrahymena. *J Mol Biol*, *120*, 33-53.

Blackburn, E. H., Greider, C. W., Henderson, E., Lee, M. S., Shampay, J. & Shippen-Lentz, D. (1989). Recognition and elongation of telomeres by telomerase. *Genome*, *31*, 553-60.

Blasco, M. A. (2007). The epigenetic regulation of mammalian telomeres. *Nat Rev Genet*, *8*, 299-309.

Brouilette, S., Singh, R. K., Thompson, J. R., Goodall, A. H. & Samani, N. J. (2003). White cell telomere length and risk of premature myocardial infarction. *Arterioscler Thromb Vasc Biol*, *23*, 842-6.

Bu, D. X., Johansson, M. E., Ren, J., Xu, D. W., Johnson, F. B., Edfeldt, K. & Yan, Z. Q. (2010). Nuclear factor {kappa}B-mediated transactivation of telomerase prevents intimal smooth muscle cell from replicative senescence during vascular repair. *Arterioscler Thromb Vasc Biol*, *30*, 2604-10.

Burdge, G. C. & Lillycrop, K. A. (2011). Nutrition, epigenetics, and developmental plasticity: implications for understanding human disease. *Annu Rev Nutr*, *30*, 315-39.

Buss, C., Davis, E. P., Muftuler, L. T., Head, K. & Sandman, C. A. (2010). High pregnancy anxiety during mid-gestation is associated with decreased gray matter density in 6-9-year-old children. *Psychoneuroendocrinology*, *35*, 141-53.

Buss, C., Davis, E. P., Shahbaba, B., Pruessner, J. C., Head, K. & Sandman, C. A. (2012). Maternal cortisol over the course of pregnancy and subsequent child amygdala and hippocampus volumes and affective problems. *Proc Natl Acad Sci U S A*, *109*, E1312-9.

Buxton JL, Suderman M, Pappas JJ, Borghol N, McArdle W, Blakemore AI, Hertzman C, Power C, Szyf M, Pembrey M. Human leukocyte telomere length is associated with DNA methylation levels in multiple subtelomeric and imprinted loci. Scientific reports. 2014;4:4954.

Carrero, J. J., Stenvinkel, P., Fellstrom, B., Qureshi, A. R., Lamb, K., Heimburger, O., et al. (2008). Telomere attrition is associated with inflammation, low fetuin-A levels and high mortality in prevalent haemodialysis patients. *J Intern Med*, *263*, 302-12.

Cawthon, R., Smith, K., O'Brien, E., Sivatchenko, A. & Kerber, R. (2003). Association between telomere length in blood and mortality in people aged 60 years or older. *Lancet*, *361*, 393-5.

Cherkas, L. F., Aviv, A., Valdes, A. M., Hunkin, J. L., Gardner, J. P., Surdulescu, G. L., et al. (2006). The effects of social status on biological aging as measured by white-blood-cell telomere length. *Aging Cell*, *5*, 361-5.

Choi, J., Fauce, S. R. & Effros, R. B. (2008). Reduced telomerase activity in human T lymphocytes exposed to cortisol. *Brain Behav Immun*, *22*, 600-5.

Codd, V., Mangino, M., van der Harst, P., Braund, P. S., Kaiser, M., Beveridge, A. J., et al. (2010). Common variants near TERC are associated with mean telomere length. *Nat Genet*, *42*, 197-9.

Cohen, S., Janicki-Deverts, D. & Miller, G. E. (2007). Psychological stress and disease. *JAMA*, *298*, 1685-7.

Cross, J. A., Brennan, C., Gray, T., Temple, R. C., Dozio, N., Hughes, J. C., et al. (2009). Absence of telomere shortening and oxidative DNA damage in the young adult offspring of women with pre-gestational type 1 diabetes. *Diabetologia*, *52*, 226-34.

Cross, J. A., Temple, R. C., Hughes, J. C., Dozio, N. C., Brennan, C., Stanley, K., et al. (2011). Cord blood telomere length, telomerase activity and inflammatory markers in pregnancies in women with diabetes or gestational diabetes. *Diabet Med*, *27*, 1264-70.

Damjanovic, A. K., Yang, Y., Glaser, R., Kiecolt-Glaser, J. K., Nguyen, H., Laskowski, B., et al. (2007). Accelerated telomere erosion is associated with a declining immune function of caregivers of Alzheimer's disease patients. *J Immunol*, *179*, 4249-54.

Daniali, L., Benetos, A., Susser, E., Kark, J. D., Labat, C., Kimura, M., et al. (2013). Telomeres shorten at equivalent rates in somatic tissues of adults. *Nat Commun*, *4*, 1597.

Daniel, M., Peek, G. W. & Tollefsbol, T. O. (2012). Regulation of the human catalytic subunit of telomerase (hTERT). *Gene*, *498*, 135-46.

Daubenmier, J., Lin, J., Blackburn, E., Hecht, F. M., Kristeller, J., Maninger, N., et al. (2012). Changes in stress, eating, and metabolic factors are related to changes in telomerase activity in a randomized mindfulness intervention pilot study. *Psychoneuroendocrinology*, *37*, 917-28.

Davy, P., Nagata, M., Bullard, P., Fogelson, N. S. & Allsopp, R. (2009). Fetal growth restriction is associated with accelerated telomere shortening and increased expression of cell senescence markers in the placenta. *Placenta*, *30*, 539-42.

De Lange, T., Shiue, L., Myers, R. M., Cox, D. R., Naylor, S. L., Killery, A. M., et al. (1990). Structure and variability of human chromosome ends. *Mol Cell Biol*, *10*, 518-27.

Demissie, S., Levy, D., Benjamin, E. J., Cupples, L. A., Gardner, J. P., Herbert, A., et al. (2006). Insulin resistance, oxidative stress, hypertension, and leukocyte telomere length in men from the Framingham Heart Study. *Aging Cell*, *5*, 325-30.

Drury, S. S., Theall, K., Gleason, M. M., Smyke, A. T., De Vivo, I., Wong, J. Y., et al. (2012). Telomere length and early severe social deprivation: linking early adversity and cellular aging. *Mol Psychiatry*, *17*, 719-27.

Eisenberg, D. T. (2011). An evolutionary review of human telomere biology: The thrifty telomere hypothesis and notes on potential adaptive paternal effects. *Am J Hum Biol*, *23*, 149-67.

Entringer, S., Buss, C., Kumsta, R., Hellhammer, D. H., Wadhwa, P. D. & Wust, S. (2009). Prenatal psychosocial stress exposure is associated with subsequent working memory performance in young women. *Behav Neurosci*, *123*, 886-93.

Entringer, S., Buss, C., Swanson, J. M., Cooper, D. M., Wing, D. A., Waffarn, F., et al. (2012a). Fetal programming of body composition, obesity, and metabolic function: the role of intrauterine stress and stress biology. *J Nutr Metab*, *2012*, 632548.

Entringer, S., Buss, C. & Wadhwa, P. D. (2010). Prenatal stress and developmental programming of human health and disease risk: concepts and integration of empirical findings. *Curr Opin Endocrinol Diabetes Obes*, *17*, 507-16.

Entringer, S., Buss, C. & Wadhwa, P. D. (2012b). Prenatal stress, telomere biology, and fetal programming of health and disease risk. *Sci Signal*, *5*, pt12.

Entringer, S., Epel, E. S., Kumsta, R., Lin, J., Hellhammer, D. H., Blackburn, E. H., et al. (2011). Stress exposure in intrauterine life is associated with shorter telomere length in young adulthood. *Proc Natl Acad Sci U S A*, *108*, E513-8.

Entringer, S., Epel, E. S., Lin, J., Buss, C., Shahbaba, B., Blackburn, E. H., et al. (2013). Maternal psychosocial stress during pregnancy is associated with newborn leukocyte telomere length. *Am J Obstet Gynecol*, *208*, 134 e1-7.

Entringer, S., Kumsta, R., Nelson, E. L., Hellhammer, D. H., Wadhwa, P. D. & Wust, S. (2008a). Influence of prenatal psychosocial stress on cytokine production in adult women. *Dev Psychobiol*, *50*, 579-587.

Entringer, S., Wust, S., Kumsta, R., Layes, I. M., Nelson, E. L., Hellhammer, D. H. et al. (2008b). Prenatal psychosocial stress exposure is associated with insulin resistance in young adults. *Am J Obstet Gynecol*, *199*, 498. e1-7.

Epel, E. S. (2009). Psychological and metabolic stress: a recipe for accelerated cellular aging? *Hormones (Athens)*, *8*, 7-22.

Epel, E. S., Blackburn, E. H., Lin, J., Dhabhar, F. S., Adler, N. E., Morrow, J. D., et al. (2004). Accelerated telomere shortening in response to life stress. *Proc Natl Acad Sci U S A*, *101*, 17312-5.

Epel, E. S., Lin, J., Dhabhar, F. S., Wolkowitz, O. M., Puterman, E., Karan, L., et al. (2010). Dynamics of telomerase activity in response to acute psychological stress. *Brain Behav Immun*, *24*, 531-9.

Epel, E. S., Lin, J., Wilhelm, F. H., Wolkowitz, O. M., Cawthon, R., Adler, N. E., et al. (2006). Cell aging in relation to stress arousal and cardiovascular disease risk factors. *Psychoneuroendocrinology*, *31*, 277-87.

Fitzpatrick, A. L., Kronmal, R. A., Gardner, J. P., Psaty, B. M., Jenny, N. S., Tracy, R. P., et al. (2007). Leukocyte telomere length and cardiovascular disease in the cardiovascular health study. *Am J Epidemiol*, *165*, 14-21.

Forsyth, N. R., Wright, W. E. & Shay, J. W. (2002). Telomerase and differentiation in multicellular organisms: turn it off, turn it on, and turn it off again. *Differentiation*, *69*, 188-97.

Frenck, R. W., Jr., Blackburn, E. H. & Shannon, K. M. (1998). The rate of telomere sequence loss in human leukocytes varies with age. *Proc Natl Acad Sci U S A*, *95*, 5607-10.

Gardner, J. P., Li, S., Srinivasan, S. R., Chen, W., Kimura, M., Lu, X., et al. (2005). Rise in insulin resistance is associated with escalated telomere attrition. *Circulation*, *111*, 2171-7.

Gluckman, P. D. & Hanson, M. A. (2004). Living with the past: evolution, development, and patterns of disease. *Science*, *305*, 1733-6.

Hanson, M., Godfrey, K. M., Lillycrop, K. A., Burdge, G. C. & Gluckman, P. D. (2011). Developmental plasticity and developmental origins of non-communicable disease: theoretical considerations and epigenetic mechanisms. *Prog Biophys Mol Biol*, *106*, 272-80.

Hartmann, N., Boehner, M., Groenen, F. & Kalb, R. (2011). Telomere length of patients with major depression is shortened but independent from therapy and severity of the disease. *Depress Anxiety*, *27*, 1111-6.

Haussmann, M. F., Longenecker, A. S., Marchetto, N. M., Juliano, S. A. & Bowden, R. M. (2012). Embryonic exposure to corticosterone modifies the juvenile stress response, oxidative stress and telomere length. *Proc Biol Sci*, *279*, 1447-56.

Heidinger, B. J., Blount, J. D., Boner, W., Griffiths, K., Metcalfe, N. B. & Monaghan, P. (2012). Telomere length in early life predicts lifespan. *Proc Natl Acad Sci U S A, 109,* 1743-8.

Hewitt, G., Jurk, D., Marques, F. D., Correia-Melo, C., Hardy, T., Gackowska, A., et al. (2012). Telomeres are favoured targets of a persistent DNA damage response in ageing and stress-induced senescence. *Nat Commun, 3,* 708.

Hiyama, K., Hirai, Y., Kyoizumi, S., Akiyama, M., Hiyama, E., Piatyszek, M. A., et al. (1995). Activation of telomerase in human lymphocytes and hematopoietic progenitor cells. *J Immunol, 155,* 3711-5.

Honig, L. S., Schupf, N., Lee, J. H., Tang, M. X. & Mayeux, R. (2006). Shorter telomeres are associated with mortality in those with APOE epsilon4 and dementia. *Ann Neurol, 60,* 181-7.

Humphreys, J., Epel, E. S., Cooper, B. A., Lin, J., Blackburn, E. H. & Lee, K. A. (2012). Telomere shortening in formerly abused and never abused women. *Biol Res Nurs, 14,* 115-23.

Izutsu, T., Kudo, T., Sato, T., Nishiya, I., Ohyashiki, K., Mori, M. et al. (1998). Telomerase activity in human chorionic villi and placenta determined by TRAP and in situ TRAP assay. *Placenta, 19,* 613-8.

Jacobs, T. L., Epel, E. S., Lin, J., Blackburn, E. H., Wolkowitz, O. M., Bridwell, D. A., et al. (2011). Intensive meditation training, immune cell telomerase activity, and psychological mediators. *Psychoneuroendocrinology, 36,* 664-81.

Jeanclos, E., Schork, N. J., Kyvik, K. O., Kimura, M., Skurnick, J. H. & Aviv, A. (2000). Telomere length inversely correlates with pulse pressure and is highly familial. *Hypertension, 36,* 195-200.

Jennings, B. J., Ozanne, S. E., Dorling, M. W. & Hales, C. N. (1999). Early growth determines longevity in male rats and may be related to telomere shortening in the kidney. *FEBS Lett, 448,* 4-8.

Kananen, L., Surakka, I., Pirkola, S., Suvisaari, J., Lonnqvist, J., Peltonen, L., et al. (2010). Childhood adversities are associated with shorter telomere length at adult age both in individuals with an anxiety disorder and controls. *PLoS One, 5,* e10826.

Kiecolt-Glaser, J. K., Gouin, J. P., Weng, N. P., Malarkey, W. B., Beversdorf, D. Q. & Glaser, R. (2011). Childhood adversity heightens the impact of later-life caregiving stress on telomere length and inflammation. *Psychosom Med, 73,* 16-22.

Kim, N. W., Piatyszek, M. A., Prowse, K. R., Harley, C. B., West, M. D., Ho, P. L., et al. (1994). Specific association of human telomerase activity with immortal cells and cancer. *Science, 266,* 2011-5.

Kimura, M., Gazitt, Y., Cao, X., Zhao, X., Lansdorp, P. M. & Aviv, A. (2010). Synchrony of telomere length among hematopoietic cells. *Exp Hematol, 38,* 854-9.

Kimura, M., Hjelmborg, J. V., Gardner, J. P., Bathum, L., Brimacombe, M., Lu, X., et al. (2008). Telomere length and mortality: a study of leukocytes in elderly Danish twins. *Am J Epidemiol, 167,* 799-806.

Levy, D., Neuhausen, S. L., Hunt, S. C., Kimura, M., Hwang, S. J., Chen, W., et al. (2010). Genome-wide association identifies OBFC1 as a locus involved in human leukocyte telomere biology. *Proc Natl Acad Sci U S A, 107,* 9293-8.

Lin, J., Epel, E. & Blackburn, E. (2012). Telomeres and lifestyle factors: roles in cellular aging. *Mutat Res, 730,* 85-9.

Loman, M. M. & Gunnar, M. R. (2010). Early experience and the development of stress reactivity and regulation in children. *Neurosci Biobehav Rev, 34*, 867-76.

Martin-Ruiz, C., Dickinson, H. O., Keys, B., Rowan, E., Kenny, R. A. & Von Zglinicki, T. (2006). Telomere length predicts poststroke mortality, dementia, and cognitive decline. *Ann Neurol, 60*, 174-80.

McEwen, B. S. (1998). Protective and damaging effects of stress mediators. *N Engl J Med, 338*, 171-9.

Miller, G. E., Chen, E. & Parker, K. J. (2011). Psychological stress in childhood and susceptibility to the chronic diseases of aging: moving toward a model of behavioral and biological mechanisms. *Psychol Bull, 137*, 959-97.

Moyzis, R. K., Buckingham, J. M., Cram, L. S., Dani, M., Deaven, L. L., Jones, M. D., et al. (1988). A highly conserved repetitive DNA sequence, (TTAGGG)n, present at the telomeres of human chromosomes. *Proc Natl Acad Sci U S A, 85*, 6622-6.

Nawrot, T. S., Staessen, J. A., Gardner, J. P. & Aviv, A. (2004). Telomere length and possible link to X chromosome. *Lancet, 363*, 507-10.

O'Donovan, A., Epel, E., Lin, J., Wolkowitz, O., Cohen, B., Maguen, S., et al. (2011). Childhood trauma associated with short leukocyte telomere length in posttraumatic stress disorder. *Biol Psychiatry, 70*, 465-71.

Okuda, K., Bardeguez, A., Gardner, J. P., Rodriguez, P., Ganesh, V., Kimura, M., et al. (2002). Telomere length in the newborn. *Pediatr Res, 52*, 377-81.

Parks, C. G., Miller, D. B., McCanlies, E. C., Cawthon, R. M., Andrew, M. E., Deroo, L. A., et al. (2009). Telomere length, current perceived stress, and urinary stress hormones in women. *Cancer Epidemiol Biomarkers Prev, 18*, 551-60.

Prescott, J., Kraft, P., Chasman, D. I., Savage, S. A., Mirabello, L., Berndt, S. I., et al. (2011). Genome-wide association study of relative telomere length. *PLoS One, 6*, e19635.

Raqib, R., Alam, D. S., Sarker, P., Ahmad, S. M., Ara, G., Yunus, M., et al. (2007). Low birth weight is associated with altered immune function in rural Bangladeshi children: a birth cohort study. *Am J Clin Nutr, 85*, 845-52.

Samani, N. J., Boultby, R., Butler, R., Thompson, J. R. & Goodall, A. H. (2001). Telomere shortening in atherosclerosis. *Lancet, 358*, 472-3.

Sampson, M. J., Winterbone, M. S., Hughes, J. C., Dozio, N. & Hughes, D. A. (2006). Monocyte telomere shortening and oxidative DNA damage in type 2 diabetes. *Diabetes Care, 29*, 283-9.

Schaetzlein, S., Lucas-Hahn, A., Lemme, E., Kues, W. A., Dorsch, M., Manns, M. P., et al. (2004). Telomere length is reset during early mammalian embryogenesis. *Proc Natl Acad Sci U S A, 101*, 8034-8.

Shalev, I., Moffitt, T. E., Sugden, K., Williams, B., Houts, R. M., Danese, A., et al. (2013). Exposure to violence during childhood is associated with telomere erosion from 5 to 10 years of age: a longitudinal study. *Mol Psychiatry, 18*, 576-81.

Simon, N. M., Smoller, J. W., McNamara, K. L., Maser, R. S., Zalta, A. K., Pollack, M. H., et al. (2006). Telomere shortening and mood disorders: preliminary support for a chronic stress model of accelerated aging. *Biol Psychiatry, 60*, 432-5.

Steptoe, A., Hamer, M., Butcher, L., Lin, J., Brydon, L., Kivimaki, M., et al. (2011). Educational attainment but not measures of current socioeconomic circumstances are associated with leukocyte telomere length in healthy older men and women. *Brain Behav Immun, 25*, 1292-8.

Stewart, S. A. & Weinberg, R. A. (2006). Telomeres: cancer to human aging. *Annu Rev Cell Dev Biol*, 22, 531-57.

Sukenik-Halevy, R., Fejgin, M., Kidron, D., Goldberg-Bittman, L., Sharony, R., Biron-Shental, T., et al. (2009). Telomere aggregate formation in placenta specimens of pregnancies complicated with pre-eclampsia. *Cancer Genet Cytogenet*, 195, 27-30.

Surtees, P. G., Wainwright, N. W., Pooley, K. A., Luben, R. N., Khaw, K. T., Easton, D. F., et al. (2011). Life stress, emotional health, and mean telomere length in the European Prospective Investigation into Cancer (EPIC)-Norfolk population study. *J Gerontol A Biol Sci Med Sci*, 66, 1152-62.

Tarry-Adkins, J. L., Chen, J. H., Smith, N. S., Jones, R. H., Cherif, H. & Ozanne, S. E. (2009). Poor maternal nutrition followed by accelerated postnatal growth leads to telomere shortening and increased markers of cell senescence in rat islets. *FASEB J*, 23, 1521-8.

Tarry-Adkins, J. L., Martin-Gronert, M. S., Chen, J. H., Cripps, R. L. & Ozanne, S. E. (2008). Maternal diet influences DNA damage, aortic telomere length, oxidative stress, and antioxidant defense capacity in rats. *FASEB J*, 22, 2037-44.

Tomiyama, A. J., O'Donovan, A., Lin, J., Puterman, E., Lazaro, A., Chan, J., et al. (2012). Does cellular aging relate to patterns of allostasis? An examination of basal and stress reactive HPA axis activity and telomere length. *Physiol Behav*, 106, 40-5.

Tyrka, A. R., Price, L. H., Kao, H. T., Porton, B., Marsella, S. A. & Carpenter, L. L. (2010). Childhood maltreatment and telomere shortening: preliminary support for an effect of early stress on cellular aging. *Biol Psychiatry*, 67, 531-4.

Ulaner, G. A., Hu, J. F., Vu, T. H., Giudice, L. C. & Hoffman, A. R. (1998). Telomerase activity in human development is regulated by human telomerase reverse transcriptase (hTERT) transcription and by alternate splicing of hTERT transcripts. *Cancer Res*, 58, 4168-72.

Valdes, A. M., Andrew, T., Gardner, J. P., Kimura, M., Oelsner, E., Cherkas, L. F., et al. (2005). Obesity, cigarette smoking, and telomere length in women. *Lancet*, 366, 662-4.

Wadhwa, P. D. (2005). Psychoneuroendocrine processes in human pregnancy influence fetal development and health. *Psychoneuroendocrinology*, 30, 724-43.

Weaver, I. C., Cervoni, N., Champagne, F. A., D'Alessio, A. C., Sharma, S., Seckl, J. R., et al. (2004). Epigenetic programming by maternal behavior. *Nat Neurosci*, 7, 847-54.

Wolkowitz, O. M., Mellon, S. H., Epel, E. S., Lin, J., Dhabhar, F. S., Su, Y., et al. (2011). Leukocyte telomere length in major depression: correlations with chronicity, inflammation and oxidative stress--preliminary findings. *PLoS One*, 6, e17837.

Wright, W. E., Piatyszek, M. A., Rainey, W. E., Byrd, W. & Shay, J. W. (1996). Telomerase activity in human germline and embryonic tissues and cells. *Dev Genet*, 18, 173-9.

Youngren, K., Jeanclos, E., Aviv, H., Kimura, M., Stock, J., Hanna, M., et al. (1998). Synchrony in telomere length of the human fetus. *Hum Genet*, 102, 640-3.

Zeichner, S. L., Palumbo, P., Feng, Y., Xiao, X., Gee, D., Sleasman, J., et al. (1999). Rapid telomere shortening in children. *Blood*, 93, 2824-30.

Zhu, H., Belcher, M. & van der Harst, P. (2011). Healthy aging and disease: role for telomere biology? *Clin Sci (Lond)*, 120, 427-40.

In: Stress and Developmental Programming …
Editors: Lubo Zhang and Lawrence D. Longo

ISBN: 978-1-63321-836-9
© 2014 Nova Science Publishers, Inc.

Chapter 18

Cranial Compression Ischemic Encephalopathy: Fetal Neurological Injury Related to the Mechanical Forces of Labor and Delivery

Barry S. Schifrin[1]*, Pierre Deymier[2] and Wayne R. Cohen[3]
[1]Formerly, Obstetrics & Gynecology, University of Southern California School of Medicine, Los Angeles, California, US
[2]Materials Science and Engineering, University of Arizona, Tucson, Arizona, US
[3]Obstetrics and Gynecology, University of Arizona College of Medicine Tucson, Arizona, US

Abstract

Intrapartum events including asphyxia in term fetuses account for significant amounts of subsequent neurological handicap, including cerebral palsy (CP). The prevention of such handicap is a major justification for fetal surveillance during labor as well as for the increasing cesarean delivery rate. Despite the pervasive application of electronic fetal heart rate (FHR) monitoring for the detection of fetal asphyxia and the rising cesarean rate, there has been no diminution of the rates of CP, neonatal seizures or neonatal encephalopathy, despite a reduction in the frequency of stillbirth attributable to asphyxia

Fetal neurological injury during labor may result from mechanical forces associated with excessive uterine activity, prolonged labor, marked molding, malposition and difficult delivery, although such events currently are not commonly considered as an explanation for adverse neurological outcomes. In this review we trace the development of the understanding of the forces of labor as a mechanism of fetal head trauma and subsequent fetal neurological injury. In so doing, we illustrate the limitations of classical interpretations of fetal heart rate patterns and neuroradiological imaging used for the detection and timing of injury. Reliance upon these approaches has impeded our

---

* Corresponding author: Barry S. Schifrin, MD, bpm, inc., 9018 Balboa Blvd. #595, Northridge, CA. USA, Phone:
+ 1 818 907-1877, Fax: +1 818 907 1477, Email: bschifrinmd@aol.com.

understanding of deleterious mechanical effects on fetal cerebral perfusion during labor. We propose the concept of cranial compression ischemic encephalopathy (CCIE) and present a strategy for the recognition and management of related, correctable obstetrical factors that predispose the fetus to hypoxic-ischemic injury.

Keywords: Asphyxia, cerebral palsy, cranial compression, encephalopathy, fetal neurological injury, hypoxia, neonatal seizure

Introduction

Despite widely varying estimates of the relationship of perinatal asphyxial to subsequent fetal neurological injury, general consensus exists that intrapartum events at term account for a significant percentage of cases of cerebral palsy (CP) (Blair and Stanley, 1988, Hagberg et al., 2001). Prevention of neurological injury is a major justification for intrapartum fetal surveillance and the reliance on cesarean delivery (Himmelmann et al., 2011). Recent decades have seen a changing panorama in perinatal outcome statistics. While here have been dramatic reductions in intrapartum stillbirths and complications attributable to intrapartum asphyxia, there has been no diminution in the frequency of CP, neonatal seizures or neonatal encephalopathy in term infants (Foley et al., 2005, Perlman, 2006, Walsh et al., 2008). Indeed, the majority of babies with encephalopathy of perinatal origin are neither severely acidotic nor severely compromised at birth; their ischemic brain injuries may not even be identified during the neonatal period (Yeh et al., 2012). Furthermore, in addition to classical ischemic lesions detectable on neuroradiological examination, hemorrhagic lesions and ischemic stroke are now common neuroradiological diagnoses (Laugesaar et al., 2007, Takenouchi et al., 2012). The presence of non-classical ischemic lesions and the declining prevalence of asphyxia strongly suggest that mechanisms other than severe asphyxia have substantial influence on neurologic outcomes (Ferriero, 2004, McLean and Ferriero, 2004).

The idea that fetal neurological injury can result from mechanical forces of labor is centuries old (Amiel-Tison, 1988). In current practice, however, such forces are generally not considered an underlying mechanism for many of the adverse neurological outcomes in the perinatal period (Murray et al., 2009). This review traces the development of and roadblocks to understanding this relationship and illustrates the benefits and limitations of contemporary surveillance and diagnostic techniques in preventing the potentially correctable obstetrical factors that predispose the fetus to this type of injury.

The earliest reference to the interaction between the fetal head and the maternal pelvis was that of the Dutch obstetrician Hendrik van Deventer (1651-1724) who called attention to contracture of the pelvis as a factor in delayed or difficult labor, and suggested that molding of the fetal head could result in brain injury (Kriewall, 1960). In 1752, William Smellie (1697-1763) called attention to the dangers of trauma and excessive molding (Roberts et al., 2010, Smellie, 1752)

By the middle of the 19th century, the notion that the forces of labor and delivery can injure the brain received compelling support from William Little (1810-1894), a London orthopedist. Little described "abundant instances of deformities arising after birth from disorders of the nervous system: disorders of nutrition, affecting the muscular and osseous structures, disorders from malposition and violence" (Little, 1862). In those infants who survived, he implicated difficult labors and mechanical injuries to the head and neck in later disorders of posture (Little, 1862). Unlike the previously held belief that the infant either survived the rigors of birth intact or died, Little espoused a "third option" for reproductive casualty, in that "many cases of deformity, [both] mental and physical, [were] traceable to potentially dangerous forces of labor and delivery including an increased intrauterine pressure attendant to contractions" (Little, 1862). For many years thereafter, the affliction we call cerebral palsy was referred to as "Little's disease" (Schifrin and Longo, 2000).

Despite obvious advancements in medical science and in clinical practice since Little's time, even up to the present day, nothing has mitigated the notion that excessive uterine activity and compressive forces on the fetal skull have the potential to injure the fetal brain during labor and delivery. In 1925, M.H. Roberts found that more than 10% of infants suffer trauma in the perinatal period, and a small fraction of these show conspicuous neurologic deficits later (Roberts, 1925). In 1930 Irving estimated the incidence of trauma as the cause of perinatal death to be 2% (Irving, 1930). These results emphasizing the frequency of intracranial hemorrhage and cerebral damage in newborn infants "due to pressures on the fetal head." acknowledge that birth "is a very traumatic event" (Yates, 1959).

During the 1960s and 1970s the prevalence of perinatal death decreased precipitously, a gratifying trend, but one that might have conferred neurologic injury on more surviving children. D.G. Wilson Clyne in Scotland and Cyril B. Courville (1900-1968) and Nathan Malamud (1903-2000) in California published detailed studies on stillbirths, neonatal, and later deaths from their respective communities during that era (Clyne, 1964, Courville, 1963, Malamud, 1970). They confirmed that mechanical trauma as well as lack of oxygen to the fetal brain during labor and delivery carried serious consequences for survival and subsequent motor and developmental handicap (Clyne, 1964, Courville, 1963, Malamud, 1970). The postmortem data were weighted in the direction of severe grades of neurological injury and mental retardation (and death) and may not apply to the entire population of mental or physical subnormality related to birth. The role of birth trauma in lesser degrees of handicap was largely unknown at the time, although it was understood from the work of Little that neurological signs of birth injury occur across a broad spectrum of presentations (Penrose, 1963). Moreover, the valuable insights obtainable from magnetic resonance imaging (MRI), diagnostic ultrasound, computerized axial tomography, electronic fetal monitoring (EFM) and umbilical blood gas analysis were unavailable to these investigators. For progress to continue in this regard, it would be necessary to visualize the brain without the benefit of autopsy. In addition, improved understanding was needed of the dynamics of uterine contractions and cerebral blood flow, along with an understanding of the timing and mechanisms of mechanical brain injuries, in order to mount strategies for their prevention.

The theory of causation of perinatal brain injury that holds most sway today derives from the observations in experimental animals of William Windle (1898-1985), Ronald Myers and their colleagues in the 1950s-1970s (Ranck and Windle, 1959, 1961, Windle, 1940). They purported to show the role of oxygen deprivation in reproducing the neurological lesions of human CP (Myers, 1967, 1972, Selzer et al., 1972). In these models, progressive asphyxiation results in impaired cardiac output ultimately causing diminished cerebral blood flow (ischemia) (Perlman, 2004, Shalak and Perlman, 2004). The differing patterns of brain pathology were related to the severity and time course of the asphyxial insult (Myers, 1972, Selzer et al., 1972, Shalak and Perlman, 2004). From this point onward, the focus on perinatal asphyxia greatly overshadowed the importance of mechanical factors, which were not studied in these experiments; indeed, they could not be studied. Unlike the human, the majority of experimental animals have smaller brains and skulls and less prominent faces and do not ordinarily undergo the mechanical rigors of human birth (including iatrogenic induction of labor oxytocin) (Lieberman, 2011). Further distracting attention from mechanical factors, these research efforts were conducted during the time when midforceps deliveries, complex obstetric maneuvers, and neglected labors as causes of obvious trauma were diminishing in favor of the rising use of cesarean delivery. Nevertheless, literature continued to reinforce the empirical relationship between mechanical forces of labor and fetal injury (Kriewall, 1960). Data from the Collaborative Perinatal Project, for example, implicated trauma specifically along with dysfunctional labor and midforceps delivery as strongly associated with neurologic damage (Clifford and Drorbaugh, 1970, Friedman and Acker, 1987, Friedman et al., 1984). These observations notwithstanding, the emphasis on the role of hypoxia and acidemia in brain injury has veiled recognition of the fact that permanent fetal brain injury associated with oxygen deprivation occurs as a consequence of ischemia, and not hypoxia per se (Paneth, 1986a, 1986b, 1993, Perlman, 2004). Indeed, in term infants who appear healthy, metabolic acidosis at birth is not associated with long-term developmental abnormalities (Hafstrom et al., 2012). Ischemia may well be the final common pathway for both severe hypoxia and the direct mechanical effects of excessive brain compression from forceps and vacuum, dysfunctional labor, and uterine hypercontractility.

Pathophysiology of Intrapartum Cerebral Ischemia

There is a biologic basis to support the idea that cerebral ischemia during labor can occur without without being precipitated by severe, systemic fetal hypoxia and acidemia. To appreciate the role of mechanical factors it is necessary to understand the several effects of uterine contractions on uterine blood flow, fetal oxygenation, fetal cerebral blood flow and head molding. Uterine contractions can decrease oxygen availability to the placenta and fetus by reducing flow in the uterine artery branches that traverse the myometrium. The longer, stronger, and more frequent the contractions, the less oxygen is available to the fetus and the greater the risk of adverse outcome. The association of excessive uterine activity with neonatal depression and adverse neurological outcome is usually thought to be related to asphyxia from impaired blood flow (Bakker et al., 2007a, Hayes et al., 2013)

It is less well appreciated that the fetal intracranial pressure (ICP) may be higher than the intrauterine pressure (IUP) and that descent of the fetal head raises the ICP further within the pliable portion of the fetal skull. (Lindgren, 1960, 1977, Schwarcz et al., 1969). Even normal strength contractions can moderate cerebral blood flow (Ueno, 1992). Fetal exposure to these forces, when excessive, may result in cerebral ischemia and injury even in the absence of systemic hypoxia or acidosis (Kelly, 1963, Lindgren, 1960, 1977, Schwarcz et al., 1969, Sorbe and Dahlgren, 1983). To maintain brain blood flow under conditions of elevated ICP the fetus must raise its blood pressure above the ICP (the differential pressure between the fetal blood pressure and the intracranial pressure is called the cerebral perfusion pressure, CPP). Figure 1 depicts schematically the relationships among intrauterine pressure (IUP), fetal intracranial pressure (ICP), mean arterial blood pressure (MAP) and cerebral perfusion pressure (CPP).

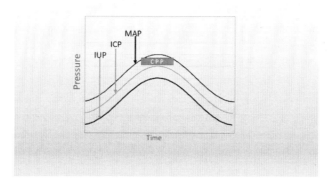

Figure 1. Schematic interrelationship of Intrauterine Pressure (IUP), Fetal Intracranial Pressure (ICP), and Mean Arterial Blood Pressure (MAP). The difference in pressure between the ICP and the MAP (MAP minus ICP) represents the cerebral perfusion pressure (CPP). In order to maintain CPP during a contraction, the fetal blood pressure must exceed the ICP.

When uterine contractions are of moderate intensity with an adequate time interval between them, the fetus compensates for the rise in ICP with a proportionate elevation of sympathetic tone, which raises arterial pressure so that CPP is maintained (the Cushing response) (Harris et al., 1989, 1992, 1998, Mann et al., 1972). As the amount of head compression is augmented from such factors as: increasing frequency and intensity of contractions, abnormal shape or resistance of the birth canal, cranial molding, maternal bearing-down efforts, rupture of the membranes, or dysfunctional labor, the fetus is required to mount more intense compensatory physiological responses (autoregulation and intracerebral shunting) in order to maintain cerebral perfusion (Harris et al., 1989, 1992, 1998).

At term, autoregulatory mechanisms can maintain a constant CBF over a broad range of perfusion pressures (Helou et al., 1994). Autoregulation, however, may be rendered inoperative by prolonged umbilical cord occlusion (Lotgering et al., 2003) impaired cerebral venous outflow, or extreme brain compression from excessive uterine forces, abetted by the effects of maternal bearing-down and molding (Volpe, 2008). Under these circumstances the ICP may become so high that it cannot be overcome by the limited capability of the fetus to elevate its blood pressure or of autoregulation to maintain flow, and normal brain perfusion would be curtailed, even in the face of pressures at which flow might otherwise be preserved (Fanaroff and Martin, 2002, Volpe, 2008). Also, compromised fetal autoregulation may lead to unchecked, pressure-passive blood flow and the potential for both hemorrhage and ischemic injury (Volpe, 2008). Ultimately, with sustained elevations of the ICP, even the most resilient fetus may be unable to maintain perfusion of the brain, resulting in critical reductions in CBF and the risk of ischemic injury (Volpe, 2001). Less severe restrictions of cerebral blood flow may result in redistribution to areas most vital to survival (basal ganglia and hippocampus at the expense of supratentorial white matter) (Volpe, 2008).

The fetus tolerates hypoxemia much more effectively than it does ischemia (Vannucci, 1993a, 1993b). In fact, it is very difficult to produce experimental fetal brain injury when perfusion is maintained, despite the presence of severe hypoxemia or acidemia (Volpe, 2008). With hypoxemia, brain blood flow and substrate availability are maintained [or even increased initially] despite low oxygen tensions (Bishai et al., 2003). However, with prolonged and severe oxygen deprivation, systemic acidosis develops along with reduced cardiac output and diminished brain perfusion, potentially resulting in ischemia. In contrast, ischemia from cord or head compression promptly prevents oxygenated blood from even reaching the fetal brain, depriving it of oxygen as well as energy-yielding substrates (Longo, 1987, Lotgering et al., 2003). For this reason, head (or cord) compression-related ischemia may promote more rapid injury than, for example, contraction-related hypoxia. Ultimately, whether the mechanism of fetal neurological injury derives from prolonged hypoxia and acidemia or from mechanical factors, the final common pathway is ischemia of the brain. In the former ischemia derives from depressed cardiac output and cerebral hypotension; (Perlman, 2004) in the latter, the effect on blood flow is direct (Ghosh et al., 2011, Recker et al., 2009). Irrespective of the initiating mechanism, increased intracranial pressure from any cause can only aggravate the ischemia and increase the risk of injury (Perlman and Risser, 1993, Stewart et al., 2012, Volpe, 2012).

Quantifying Intracranial Pressure

Theoretical Considerations

To explain the manner in which forces exerted on the fetal head could generate increased intracranial pressure that, if sufficiently high, could cause constriction or collapse of cerebral arteries and diminish CPP, we take a reductionist approach, in which the fetal skull is modeled as a closed sphere. The cranial vault constitutes the pliable portion of the fetal skull and is represented by a hemisphere, the wall of which is movable. The other hemisphere, representing the skull base, is rigid. External forces generated by the uterus, cervix or pelvic bones applied to the pliable part of the skull will increase the intracranial pressure only if they possess components normal to the movable parietal plates. Tangential components of the forces will not contribute significantly to a rise in pressure. To isolate the normal components, the hemispheric model of the skull can, therefore, be further reduced to that of a simple mechanical system composed of a piston within a rigid cylinder closed on one end. The space delimited by the piston and the cylinder is filled with an incompressible fluid, like water. The rigid cylinder mimics the skull base and the movement of the piston the pliable cranial vault. The intracranial pressure (P_{ICP}) will therefore arise from mechanical forces that are applied perpendicular to the piston surface as the piston is forced into the cylinder.

Imagine the piston/cylinder model of the fetal skull placed into the uterine cavity. The intrauterine pressure, (P_{IUP}), applies forces that are normal to the piston. Mechanical equilibrium therefore requires that the intracranial pressure equals the IUP, that is $P_{ICP}=P_{IUP}$. When the cranial vault contacts the cervix, additional labor forces may develop on the skull. We denote by f_C the surface density of the normal component of the force applied by the cervix, i.e., the head-to-cervix pressure (P_{HC}). Mechanical equilibrium of the uterus/skull/cervix system imposes the condition: $P_{ICP}=P_{IUP}+f_C=P_{IUP}+P_{HC}$. In this, we have assumed that the cervical force density is uniform. Of course the cervical force may not be uniform and may be applied only onto the region of the skull in contact with the cervix. In that case, one would need to address the mechanical equilibrium condition in the form of a surface integral equation. For the sake of simplicity we have not addressed this issue here, and consider only a uniform cervical force density.

Pu et al. investigated the effect of labor forces on the molding of the fetal skull and reported the application of P_{HC} four to five times that of P_{IUP} (Pu et al., 2011, 2013). With an average P_{IUP} of approximately 50 mmHg during the peak of a contraction, therefore, the head-to-cervix pressure would exceed 200 mmHg. The question that now arises is the extent to which an intracranial pressure of, say, 250 mmHg could cause collapse of cerebral arteries and subsequent reduction in perfusion of brain tissue. A sketch of an answer to this question can be drawn by considering the resistance to collapse of a tube under external pressure. The tube represents a cerebral artery within the skull (i.e. inside the chamber of our model cylinder/piston system).

An expression for the collapse strength of a tube under external pressure has been reported (Clinedinst, 1939, Holmquist and Nadai, 1939). There are two modes of collapse, namely elastic and plastic collapse. We limit our discussion here to elastic collapse, under normal conditions, as the walls of fetal arteries can be presumed to exhibit essentially elastic responses. Clinedist derived an expression for the elastic collapse pressure, P_{EC}, of a long tube with perfect roundness and no variation in its wall thickness:

$$P_{EC} = 2\frac{E}{1-v^2}\frac{1}{\frac{D}{t}\left(\frac{D}{t}-1\right)^2} \tag{1}$$

The factors that affect the collapse strength of tubes are the ratio of the outside diameter to the wall thickness (D/t), Young's modulus (E) and Poisson's ratio (v)[1] (Young's modulus is a measure of the stiffness of a material in tension. For a material subjected to tension in some direction, Poisson's ratio reflects the relative contraction of the material perpendicular to the applied tension). Under an external pressure that exceeds P_{EC}, the tube collapses and its cross section becomes oval and flattens thus inhibiting blood flow. In what follows we estimate P_{EC} for a newborn carotid artery, a vessel for which nearly consistent sets of morphometric and elastic data are available. Less is known about the cerebral vessels, but the diameter of the middle cerebral artery (the vessel often used as a marker for brain blood flow in Doppler ultrasound studies) is about 75-80% that of the internal carotid (Gielecki et al., 2009). It can be reasonably assumed that our calculations for the internal carotid would apply as well to one of its primary branches, the middle cerebral artery.

The diameter of the newborn internal carotid artery ranges from approximately 1.2 to 1.9 mm (Sehirli et al., 2005). We therefore used a value of D=1.5 mm for our estimate. Ultrasound measurements of the wall thickness of the common carotid artery in normal term newborns give of an average value for t of 0.37 mm (Hondappanavar et al., 2013). These measurements give an approximate value of D/t of 4.

We have not been able to find data for Poisson's ratio of newborn arteries, but ultrasonic non-invasive methods have been used to measure *in vivo* Poisson's ratio of the human carotid artery in a normal young subject; (Hasegawa et al., 1997) based on those data, a value of v=0.46 will be used here. It is also important to note that the sensitivity of P_{EC} on v is limited and uncertainties on that elastic property will not impact significantly the estimated value of P_{EC}.

The collapse strength is finally given by:

$$P_{EC}=5.28 \times 10^{-4}E \text{ (mmHg)} \tag{2}$$

where E is expressed in units of Pa. Reasonable values for Young's modulus in the carotid artery range from E=100 kPa to 900 kPa (13-117 mmHg) (Khamdaeng et al., 2012). This range was measured in individuals aged 28±3.6 years. We may estimate the Young's modulus for newborn cranial arteries by downscaling the values. We therefore used a range of values between 100 and 400 kPa (13-52 mmHg) for our estimation of the collapse pressure. Within this assumption for the range of values of the elastic modulus, the collapse strength takes on values ranging from P_{EC} ~50 mmHg to 200 mmHg. Resisting collapse would be the blood pressure within the artery. The condition for collapse of the artery is therefore attained when the difference between the intracranial pressure minus the systolic pressure (P_{Sys}) of the artery exceeds the collapse strength, that is, when $P_{ICP}-P_{Sys} > P_{EC}$. A systolic pressure of about 50 mmHg would exist in a normal term fetus. Values for $P_{ICP}-P_{Sys}$ in excess of 200 mmHg may be sufficient to lead to artery collapse. It is only for values of Young's modulus exceeding 400 kPa that artery collapse may not occur for intracranial pressures of less than 200 mmHg. These conditions are illustrated in figure 2. In that figure, the solid line represents the elastic collapse pressure given by equation (2) as a function of Young's modulus of the artery wall. The pressure difference that may drive collapse, $P_{ICP}-P_{Sys}=250-50 = 200$ mmHg, is represented as the dashed horizontal line. The condition for collapse of the arterial wall is marked by the brace in figure 2.

These estimates indicate that forces exerted on the fetal head (such as IUP combined with head-to-cervix pressure) could generate increased intracranial pressures that in turn could cause elastic collapse of cerebral arteries, diminishing perfusion of brain tissue. Moreover, if the blood pressure within brain vessels were to be diminished, such as by severe hypoxia, sepsis, or certain drugs, the vessels would be even more susceptible to collapse.

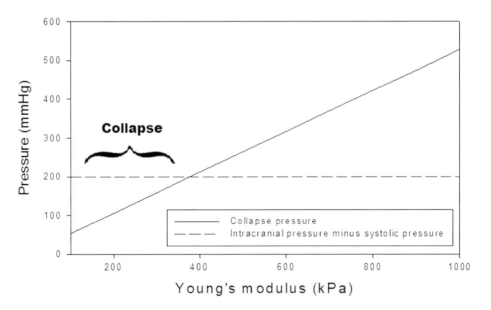

Figure 2. Graphical representation of the elastic collapse pressure, P_{EC}, (solid line) and of the intracranial pressure minus the systolic pressure, $P_{IC}-P_{Sys}$, (dashed line) as functions of Young's modulus of the cerebral arteries. Artery collapse will occur when $P_{ICP}-P_{Sys} > P_{EC.}$

Experimental Observations

Considerable clinical and laboratory evidence supports the theoretical model described above. Beginning in the 1960s several research groups studied the physical effects of contractions on the fetal head (Buhimschi et al., 2002a, 2002b, 2004, Lindgren, 1960, 1966, 1977). Using pressure sensors introduced between the uterine wall and the fetal head, Schwarcz et al. showed that during a contraction pressures exerted on the biparietal diameter level of the fetal head were up to 2.5 times higher than the intra-amniotic pressure (Schwarcz et al., 1969) (Figure 3). The difference between intrauterine pressure (IUP) and pressures on the skull are due to the resistance offered by the cervix as well as by muscular and bony pelvic structures. Of importance, this gradient increased further with rupture of the membranes, maternal bearing-down efforts, progress in descent and head molding. (Buhimschi et al., 2002b, 2004, Furuya et al., 1981). Other experiments using intrauterine transducers are consistent with these observations (Amiel-Tison et al., 1988, Lindgren, 1960, 1966, 1972, 1977, Rempen, 1993b, Rempen and Kraus, 1991). Some have shown that the cervix-to-head pressure could be at least 3 to 4 times the IUP, depending on the state of the membranes. Pressures on the skull also may not be uniform, may be influenced by fetal position and station and may be multiplied during instrumental delivery (Rempen, 1993a). These experiments echoed the findings in those isolated cases in which simultaneous intrauterine and intracranial catheters were inserted into anomalous or dead fetuses (Mocsary et al., 1970, Schwarcz et al., 1969) (Figures 3 and 4). In each case, the pressures within the skull were always greater than the intrauterine pressure, even between contractions. Two-dimensional color Doppler flow technology in normal term human fetuses has demonstrated that the resistance index of the middle cerebral artery correlated positively with the intrauterine pressure, and was highest with descent of the fetal head (Ueno, 1992).

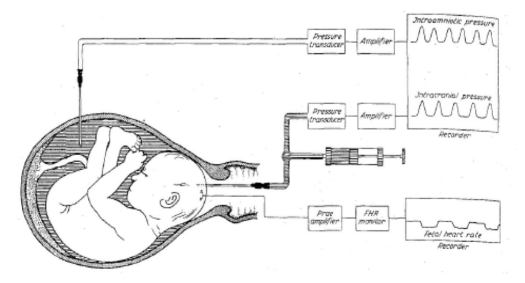

Figure 3. Illustration from Mocsary et al., revealing experimental set up in human (hydrocephalic) fetus. Measurements include intraamniotic pressure, fetal intracranial pressure and fetal heart rate pattern (Mocsary et al., 1970).

Experimental animal studies confirm that increased intracranial pressure can lead to brain ischemia and injury. In fetal lambs increased extracranial pressure caused vascular collapse and dramatically decreased blood flow to the brain (Mann et al., 1972, O'Brien et al., 1984). In one study increasing cerebral vascular resistance caused a 95% reduction in flow to the cerebral cortex, with less impairment to the brainstem and cerebellum (Mann et al., 1972, O'Brien et al., 1984). These studies make it clear that fetal head compression can cause substantial reduction in intracranial blood flow despite the absence of significant changes in systemic PO_2 and pH or in cardiac performance (O'Brien et al., 1984). When these laboratory studies are considered in conjunction with the theoretical model we have presented and the available human data, the evidence for the potential of forces of labor to produce brain ischemia is compelling.

The Neuroradiological Topography of Injury

In the more than half century since the first experimental production of brain injury by perinatal asphyxia, different patterns of injury have been attributed to the severity and duration of the hypoxic–ischemic insult (Barkovich, 2006, de Vries and Groenendaal, 2010, Myers, 1967) (Table 1). Although most neuroradiological lesions represent infarction in the distribution of the arterial circulation, some cases of perinatal injury seem to occur from in utero sinus or periventricular venous infarction (Berfelo et al., 2010, Takanashi et al., 2003).

While the injuries associated with acute catastrophic events and obvious neonatal compromise tend to be basal ganglia and hippocampal lesions, the majority of neuroradiological patterns are associated with white matter injury and often a less dramatic neonatal course (Miller et al., 2005). Clinically, neonatal seizures in association with fetal compromise and birth asphyxia are associated with worse neurodevelopmental outcome, independent of the severity of hypoxic-ischemic brain injury (Glass et al., 2009). Of importance, a significant number of infants with obvious encephalopathy have no lesions discernible on neuroimaging (Miller et al., 2005, Okereafor et al., 2008).

Neuroradiological imaging has proved useful in delimiting the timing of an injury to the perinatal period and not to some earlier time in gestation. Cowan et al. found that more than 90% of newborns with encephalopathy had evidence of perinatally acquired ischemic lesions on an MRI performed within the first 2 weeks after birth, with a very low rate of established antenatal brain injury (Cowan et al., 2003, Martinez-Biarge et al., 2012, 2013). Their results strongly point to the immediate perinatal period as a common factor in the development of ischemic encephalopathy. Accordingly, the absence of severe umbilical acidosis at birth in association with a recent ischemic injury is not consistent with the notion that the injury developed prenatally. While neuroimaging techniques are helpful in the timing of an injury, they can only approximate a window in time rather than determine the moment when injury occurred. (Table 2).

Table 1. Neuroradiological Findings in Perinatal Brain Injury

	Anatomic Features	Clinical Circumstances	Mechanism of injury	Neonatal Appearance	Follow-up Findings
Selective Neuronal Necrosis **Other Names:** Near-total acute asphyxia (TAA) Acute profound asphyxia (APA) Basal ganglia thalamic injury (BGT)	Involves central grey nuclei (ventrolateral thalami and posterior putamina) and perirolandic cortex bilaterally. Relative sparing of the cerebral hemispheres (though white matter may be involved). Involvement of the hippocampus and cerebellar nuclei not uncommon.	Short duration (minutes) event responsible. Considered "imaging signature" of acute, severe hypoxia-ischemia (often a sentinel event -such as placental abruption or cord prolapse.) Fetal bradycardia commonplace, often leading to death or delivery. Ischemic episode often brief, or else fetal demise/ stillbirth may occur.	Typically, an abrupt impairment of perfusion (ischemia) to entire brain; central grey matter, perirolandic cortex, cerebellar and brainstem nuclei preferentially damaged due to higher baseline metabolic rate and high density of NMDA receptors. Cerebral cortex may be spared from injury. Brain edema may be trivial or absent.	Infant tends to be profoundly depressed at delivery and often meets criteria for "intrapartum asphyxia." Variable tone is common, neonatal seizures are frequently not seen. Organ involvement may be absent.	Infant usually severely disabled due to dyskinetic/extrapyramidal cerebral palsy (CP). Fluctuating tone as infant then involuntary movements are seen. Cognition may be relatively spared due to less cortical damage.
White Matter/Cortical Injury **Other Names:** Prolonged, partial asphyxia (PPA) Watershed pattern. Most common pattern seen.	Supratentorial, predominantly white matter, though some grey matter injury generally to the vascular watershed zones (anterior –middle and posterior– middle cerebral arteries) of the cerebral hemispheres. Deep cortical infarcts (ulegyria) may be seen when severe. The injury may be unilateral or bilateral, posterior and/or	Subacute event (many minutes to hours) is responsible. More prolonged fetal distress is evident. Hypoxia to fetus is the mechanism with greater preservation of perfusion; may be seen in setting of uterine hyperstimulation - mechanical forces of labor, uteroplacental insufficiency.	Prolonged, sublethal hypoxia, less ischemia - often > 1 hour. Due to duration of hypoxic event, greater acidosis often seen. Cerebral cortex and WM involved, brain edema common. Neonatal seizures often occur, may be severe.	Neonatal encephalopathy, often severe. Neurologic manifestations often meet criteria for "intrapartum asphyxia" and for neuroprotection. Organ involvement is common. Extensive damage to the cerebral cortex and white matter may occur, ultimately resulting in cystic encephalomalacia.	Infant often has suboptimal head growth (microcephaly), cognitive impairment, spastic quadriplegic CP feeding problems and communication deficits.

Table 1. (Continued)

	Anatomic Features	Clinical Circumstances	Mechanism of injury	Neonatal Appearance	Follow-up Findings
Perinatal stroke **Other Names:** Perinatal arterial ischemic stroke (PAIS)	Typically, ischemic brain injury in the distribution of a single major vessel supplying the brain - the left middle cerebral artery (MCA) most common vessel involved. May have multiple, single vessels involved. anterior. Thalamus, basal ganglia and cerebellum / brainstem are typically spared.	More likely to occur around parturition than any other time in childhood. Associated with risk factors of late labor: trauma, perinatal asphyxia, prolonged rupture of membranes, FHR abnormalities, chorioamnionitis, dysfunctional labor, nulliparity, emergency cesarean section, higher birthweight.	Ischemic event - may have contribution from trauma, thrombophilic disorder, either genetic or acquired (inflammation), cardiac disease with embolus, congenital vascular anomaly, hyperviscosity.	May appear with little to no acute symptoms /signs ("normal newborn"). Severe neonatal depression is uncommon. May present with mild neonatal encephalopathy and/or seizures. Occasionally, neonatal hemiplegia may be evident.	Subsequent neurological deficits including cerebral palsy (often hemiplegic CP) and epilepsy occur in most survivors with varying effects on language, learning, vision (visual field cut), cognition and behavior that may continue to evolve over the several years of childhood.
Cerebral Sinovenous Thrombosis (CSVT) **Other Names:** Sinus Thrombosis	Critical to distinguish arterial from venous cerebral infarct. Parietal, thalamic occipital infarcts more common w CSVT. Superior sag sinus (55%), lateral sinus (51%), Straight sinus (24%) most common. Cortical Venous engorgement, may have hemorrhage.	Mean gestational age of 39 weeks (range, 30 to 42 weeks; preterm uncommon). "Assisted or complicated delivery" common. In the neonate, systemic illness/risk factors often present (infection, surgery, hypoxia, trauma, dehydration, thrombophilia)	Often precipitated by alteration in venous flow from reduced volume, inflammation, vessel / venous injury, hyperviscosity, abnl. clotting, with multiple risks often present. Parenchymal infarcts in approx 40%.	Seizures, partial or generalized, most common presenting symptom. 25-35% w encephalopathy, 30 % w focal signs. Symptoms developed at a median postnatal age of 15 days (range, 0 to 28 days). Head CT may miss diagnosis, MRV, Angiogram or power Doppler highest yield.	At follow-up (median age, 19 months; range, 3 to 72 months), moderate to severe neurological sequelae were present in 38%, mortality 8%. Approximately 50% w "normal" outcome, but limited follow-up into school age.

Table 2. Summary of Imaging Neuroradiological Findings in Relation to the Timing of Birth Injury*

Modality	Feature	Onset – From time of injury	Duration**
Proton MRI spectroscopy	Increased lactate.	First few hours	About 2 weeks
	Decreased N-acetyl aspartate	First few hours	Indefinitely
Diffusion Weighted MRI (DWI)	Reduced diffusion	12 hours (onset)	About 10 days duration
Tl-weighted MRI	Increased signal thalamus or basal ganglia	2-3 days	Months, becoming more localized and globular
	Loss of signal post limb of internal capsule	<24 hours	
T2-weighted MRI	Increased signal in cortex or deep nuclei	6-7 days	Months or indefinitely
	Decreased signal in deep grey nuclei	3-4 days	Several days
CT scan	Decreased density thalami or basal ganglia	18-24 hours	5-7 days – may be permanent
	May not be visible		
Ultrasonography	Increased echogenicity thalami or basal ganglia	Approximately 24 hours; may be earlier	Progresses over 2-3 days, persists 5-7 days
	Increased echogenicity in white matter		
	Loss of clarity (due to edema)		

Recent reports present a changing pattern of perinatal brain injury in term infants born in 2004-2009 with "perinatal depression" (Takenouchi et al., 2012). Injuries included hypoxic-ischemic encephalopathy (HIE), intracranial hemorrhage, and focal cerebral infarction. Of interest, 13 of 33 infants studied by Tekenouchi et al. were initially admitted to the well-baby nursery because they were asymptomatic in the delivery room. The authors averred that "... most cases attributable to perinatal brain injury [other than HIE] are not identified according to any perinatal characteristics until the onset of [neonatal] signs, limiting opportunities for prevention" (Takenouchi et al., 2012). They also opined that such injuries antedated the onset of labor. Unfortunately, they did not attempt to correlate the non-HIE injuries with a detailed analysis of either antepartum or intrapartum problems or the condition of the fetus at the outset of labor (Takenouchi et al., 2012).

The Nomenclature of Injury

The various terms that are applied to the appearance of the newborn and the lesions associated with neonatal encephalopathy and injury have not been consistent (Leviton, 2013, Volpe, 2012). HIE is widely used to refer to neonatal encephalopathy with evidence of hypoxia-ischemia during parturition. The term neonatal encephalopathy is commonly used to describe infants with an encephalopathy of any etiology, but often for those with the clinical and imaging characteristics of neonatal HIE (Volpe, 2012). Other terms, including acute near total asphyxia, partial prolonged asphyxia, birth trauma, birth injury, and perinatal asphyxia, have been used despite considerable variation in how they are defined (Table 1) (Gilbert et al., 2010, Shah and Perlman, 2009). Several years ago, the American College of Obstetricians and Gynecologists recommended that the term "perinatal asphyxia" be eliminated from the obstetrical lexicon (ACOG, 2004). Among the consequences of the confusing and sometimes contradictory descriptors of both the condition of the fetus at birth and the designation of perinatal brain injury is that it is difficult to be certain about both the prevalence and provenance of these illnesses. It stands to reason that we cannot fully understand or improve what we do not classify properly (Kodama et al., 2009). Changing the definition may cause dramatic changes in reporting statistics without changing the number of fetuses actually suffering from the problem (Dzakpasu et al., 2009, Kodama et al., 2009).

Volpe has pointed out that the terms perinatal trauma and birth injury have been given definitions so broad as to be confusing and nearly meaningless, and that the overlap between mechanical trauma and the occurrence of hypoxic-ischemic cerebral injury is important to recognize because perinatal mechanical insults may result in primarily hypoxic-ischemic cerebral injury" (Kodama et al., 2009, Volpe, 2001). Beyond the issues of nosology, there needs to be greater interdisciplinary cooperation in the study of the circumstances in which neonatal encephalopathies develop. Does the diagnosis of HIE, for example, require the presence of certain fetal heart rate patterns and/or a critical level of metabolic acidemia in the umbilical artery or severe signs and symptoms in the newborn? Do the neurological findings of HIE and near-normal umbilical blood gases exclude the events of labor as causative of injury? Does the presence of intracranial or extracranial hemorrhage and/or obvious skull trauma such as fracture, diffuse scalp swelling, marked molding and subgaleal hemorrhage mitigate the diagnosis of HIE irrespective of the umbilical artery pH? Does HIE with low Apgar scores and metabolic acidemia in the umbilical artery exclude mechanical factors? For the most part these and other issues remain unresolved with glaring differences in opinions among experts (ACOG, 2003a, Hayes et al., 2013, Shankaran et al., 2005).

Lee et al., have reminded us that "the clinical diagnosis of birth asphyxia is not specific for any single pathogenetic mechanism of brain injury" (Lee et al., 2005, Schifrin and Ater, 2006). To help clarify these manifold issues of nomenclature, we propose the concept of cranial compression ischemic encephalopathy (CCIE) and discuss below the various mechanical factors that may contribute to intrapartum fetal cerebral ischemia.

Head Molding

Head molding during labor and delivery refers to changes in the fetal cranial bone relationships that occur in response to the compressive forces of uterine contractions and the birth canal. Molding may contribute to progress in descent during labor and delivery by enabling the fetal head to accommodate to the geometry of the passage. The change in shape is possible because of the pliability of the bones and the loose connection they have with one another along the suture lines. This allows the cranial plates to override, thereby reducing the intracranial volume.

The response of normal fetal cranial bones to force is variable, and depends on a number of factors, including head position, labor character, gestational age, and pliability of the skull bones (Amiel-Tison et al., 1988). In general, the typical molded newborn head is elongated and cylindrical, reflecting misalignment among the bones of the cranial vault (parietal, frontal, and occipital bones) (Carlan et al., 1991, Sorbe and Dahlgren, 1983). Molding is a dynamic process that normally develops gradually during labor and begins to resolve after compressive forces are removed. The skull generally returns to a normal conformation within hours to days during the neonatal period. (Kriewall et al., 1977). It may not be recognized or described in the medical record and it is rarely quantitatively documented. While some molding is commonplace, "excessive molding" appears to be one of the mechanisms through which the forces of labor have the potential to impart traumatic physical damage to the fetal brain and surrounding tissues. Cranial compression of short duration, however, can produce substantially elevated intracranial pressure and cerebral ischemia without recognized head molding after birth.

Molding increases as labor progresses, especially when progress is slow and contractions are excessive. Overlap of the sagittal suture anticipates cephalopelvic disproportion (CPD) (Buchmann and Libhaber, 2008). The dislocation of the cranial bones can be large - up to 25 mm (Lindgren, 1977). In a study of 56 women with excessive uterine activity and slow progress, 16 (29%) of the infants died, all due to rupture of the tentorium cerebelli (Lindgren, 1977).

Using skull photographs obtained immediately after delivery and at three days of age of 319 vaginally delivered term babies, Sorbe and Dahlgren found that the mechanical forces of labor subjected the fetal head to considerable compression and molding and presumably, shearing forces. The region of the brain most affected and in greatest jeopardy of injury from these mechanical forces was not consistent, but depended upon the orientation of the head as it descended through the pelvis (Sorbe and Dahlgren, 1983). Not surprisingly, infants born after oxytocin stimulation of labor had significantly greater molding than those born after normal labor. Three days postpartum significant differences remained between the molding indices of the two groups. In comparing patients with prolonged labor in association with either "hypertonic" or "hypotonic" uterine contractions, they found that the amount of molding was related not to the duration of labor per se, but to the presence of frequent uterine contractions. Cerebral hemorrhage was 15 times more common as a cause of infant death in hypertonic inertia than in normal labor, and they concluded that intrapartum and neonatal death and injury can occur from mechanical trauma to the brain during birth (Sorbe and Dahlgren, 1983). Other investigations have also found an association between difficulty in labor and distortion of the fetal head (Aarnivala et al., 2014, Frymann, 1966)

Analysis of a non-linear model of the deformation of a complete fetal skull during the first stage of labor found that excessive molding could occur when labor is prolonged, when contractions are too forceful, when there is a malposition of the fetal head, or in association with "inept instrumental interference" (Lapeer and Prager, 2001). Excessive displacements of the skull bones may cause fractures, dural membrane injury, intracranial hypertension, congestion of the Galenic venous system and direct injury of major intracranial vessels (Lapeer and Prager, 2001). More advanced dilatations were associated with significantly higher head-to-cervix pressures and higher degrees of molding with an increased risk of injury (Govaert et al., 1992b, Lapeer and Prager, 2001, McPherson and Kriewall, 1980a, 1980b).

In a classic article, Roberto Caldeyro-Barcia (1921-1996) underscored the potentially adverse effects of early amniotomy and prolonged rupture of the membranes (Caldeyro-Barcia, 1974). Compared to membrane rupture late in labor, early amniotomy increased the amount of cranial molding which, if exaggerated, may produce cardiac decelerations, lesions in the fetal brain, and subdural hemorrhage, frequently located near the sutures (Caldeyro-Barcia, 1974).

These studies establish a link between excessive cranial molding and intracranial injury during labor. While the definition of "excessive" molding is elusive, it is clearly more likely to occur in the context of abnormal labor progress, high levels of uterine activity and ruptured membranes. Molding of the fetal head deserves more attention as a cause or as a marker for potential mechanical injury and abnormalities of neonatal adaptation (Frymann, 1976, Frymann, 1966).

Molding and Decreased Venous Return

Neuroradiological studies have shown that, in addition to the inverse relationship between cerebral arterial perfusion and intracranial pressure, there also is decreased venous return related specifically to both the resistance to flow and direct compression of the sagittal sinus (Barkovich, 2000a, Newton and Gooding, 1975, Towbin, 1998). While modest amounts of molding are considered commonplace and benign, such compression may increase cerebral venous pressure and precipitate intracerebral hemorrhage or cerebral venous thrombosis (Barkovich, 2000b, Berfelo et al., 2010, Newton and Gooding, 1975, Takanashi et al., 2003, Towbin, 1998). Hanigan and Tan and colleagues have called attention to the relationship of perinatal sinovenous thrombosis and sagittal sinus compression due to head molding during labor (Hanigan et al., 1985, 1990, Medlock and Hanigan, 1997, Tan et al., 2011).

Maternal Bearing-Down Efforts

The resilient fetus is usually able to tolerate considerable amounts of even excessive uterine activity in the first stage of labor (Stewart et al., 2012). The effects of contractions on fetal blood pressure, oxygen availability and head molding, are greatly exaggerated later in the first stage of labor and especially during the second stage when expulsive efforts may increase the IUP by an average of 62% and the risk of adverse outcome (Asicioglu et al., 2014, Buhimschi et al., 2002a, 2002b). With the combination of frequent and prolonged uterine contractions with maternal bearing-down efforts, or fundal pressure or vacuum application, intrauterine pressures above 250 mm Hg may be seen, along with a marked reduction in placental and fetal cerebral perfusion (Dupuis and Simon, 2008, Furuya et al., 1981). Undoubtedly, at this pressure, not only has uterine blood flow ceased but fetal cerebral blood flow has almost certainly ceased as well (Volpe, 2001). The maximum blood pressure response to head compression that the fetus can sustain has not been elucidated.

Considerable debate concerns the methodology, duration and impact of maternal pushing in the second stage of labor (Aldrich et al., 1995, Le Ray and Audibert, 2008, Petersen and Besuner, 1997, Schaal et al., 2008, Simpson, 2006). With coached Valsalva-based, maternal pushing, there may be several closely spaced, exaggerated peaks created by energetic pushing where the IUP may easily exceed, sometimes considerably, 100 mmHg. This dramatically increases the amplitude, duration and pattern of the IUP changes and potentially diminishes the relaxation time for recovery, thus imposing greater demands on the responsiveness of the fetal cardiovascular system (Lindgren, 1977). Alternatively, non-Valsalva pushing strategies with open glottis and slowly developing transient peak pressures not only appear to subject the fetus to less head compression, but also may improve Apgar scores and umbilical pH values at delivery (Yildirim and Beji, 2008).

Near infrared spectroscopy transducers in human subjects reveal a significant decrease in the calculated mean fetal cerebral oxygen saturation during pushing and a significant increase in the mean cerebral blood volume (Aldrich et al., 1995). While moderate pushing may not be detrimental if the fetus is healthy, the associated hemodynamic alterations may have important consequences if fetal oxygenation is already reduced prior to pushing, or if maternal effort is prolonged (Aldrich et al., 1995, Keeling, 1993, Svenningsen and Jensen, 1988).

Thus, during pushing, the pressures exerted on the fetal head are higher and more sustained than in the first stage of labor and the risks of significant ischemia and potential injury appear greatly increased, especially if decelerations are frequent and maternal pushing is relentless and unheeding of the responses of the fetus (Schifrin and Ater, 2006).

Occiput Posterior Position

The occiput posterior [OP] position is a malposition often associated with FHR decelerations, prolonged labor, especially in the second stage, marked cranial molding, an increased risk of failed instrumental vaginal delivery, cesarean delivery, and oxytocin administration (Porreco et al., 2004). OP is an independent risk factor for subsequent CP and low mental scores in the offspring (Badawi et al., 1998, Senecal et al., 2005) and accounts for a disproportionate share of such injuries. (Ater et al., 2008). To what extent these long-term disabilities are the consequence of excessive or asymmetric forces exerted on a fetal head positioned inappropriately is unknown. Uterine activity with the fetus in OP position, however, appears equivalent to that in OA position (Buhimschi et al., 2003). Manual rotation of the head in the fetus in the OP position to a more favorable position can, in some circumstances, reduce the duration of the second stage and the frequency of operative delivery (Le Ray et al., 2007, Shaffer et al., 2006). The impact of successful rotation on the risk of fetal injury is unknown (Govaert et al., 1992c, Gurbuz et al., 2006, O'Grady et al., 2000, Pollina et al., 2001, Towner et al., 1999)

Operative Vaginal Delivery

Operative vaginal delivery is a risk factor for mechanical, traumatic, and ischemic injury to the scalp and brain, including subgaleal hemorrhage (Govaert et al., 1992c, O'Grady et al., 2000). The risks increase if sequential instruments are used (Al-Kadri et al., 2003). While elective cesarean section appears to decrease the risk of neurological harm to the fetus, cesarean sections after the onset of labor, especially during the 2nd stage, appear to have higher risk of adverse outcome than does elective cesarean section (Asicioglu et al., 2014). Thus, a cesarean section performed too late in labor cannot be expected to prevent injury (Gurbuz et al., 2006, Towner et al., 1999). The ability to define the timing of injury and its antecedents are of crucial importance for determining both the timing of intervention and the institution of neuroprotective measures (Schifrin and Ater, 2006). More attention needs to be given to the circumstances of labor and the fetal condition prior to the application of vacuum or forceps.

Excessive Uterine Activity

Several quantitative formulations for representing normal and excessive uterine activity have been proposed (Henry et al., 1979). This broad range of options has led inescapably to marked variations in practice patterns and nomenclature. Moreover, irrespective of the definition used, excessive uterine activity is often simply unrecognized or ignored (Kunz et al., 2013, Murray and Huelsmann, 2008). This is not surprising, in that the assessment of contractility is not simple, and, importantly, the relationship between contractility and progress in labor is not well understood; it is certainly not linear, as is commonly thought.

Tachysystole defined as a frequency of greater than 5 contractions in 10 minutes, averaged over 30 minutes, has been introduced as a simplistic measure of "excessive uterine activity" despite the acknowledgement that other parameters such as duration, rest interval between contractions and uterine tone may be important (Macones et al., 2008). Because the adverse effects of increased uterine activity on uterine and cerebral blood flows are proportional to the frequency, amplitude and duration of contractions, contraction frequency by itself seems an insufficient measure of the fetal effects of contractions. With a contraction frequency of 5 per 10 minutes with an average contraction duration of 60 seconds, the cumulative rest time is 5 minutes or 50%. If the average duration is 90 or 120 seconds, then the cumulative percentage rest times are 25% and 0% respectively. The latter would be unsustainable for the fetus. In addition, it is clear that the effects on fetal oxygenation of an excessive frequency of contractions appear long before 30 minutes have elapsed, especially in the second stage, and that optimal "rest time", requires at least 2 minutes between contractions, at least when decelerations are present. (Peebles et al., 1994, Simpson and James, 2008, Westgate et al., 1999, 2007). An elevated baseline tone associated with placental abruption is also a risk factor for adverse fetal outcome (Odendaal and Burchell, 1985). External monitors, however, do not permit assessment of intrauterine pressures or baseline uterine tone.

Our understanding of the role of excessive uterine activity in intrapartum fetal brain injury is based on the flawed notion, detailed above, that the only potential adversity caused by contractions, excessive or not, is hypoxemia. In recent decades, only scant attention has been turned to the effects of the mechanical forces of labor and delivery on intracranial pressure, cerebral blood flow, fetal adaptive mechanisms, fetal head molding and descent. The prevailing monolithic view is that, as long as the FHR pattern does not show ominous, presumably hypoxemic, changes, contractile force cannot be "excessive" (ACOG, 2003b). Such an approach gives misguided acceptability to the notion that in an augmented labor it is permissible to increase oxytocin dose until the fetus manifests abnormal FHR patterns (Simpson and Knox, 2009, Tillett, 2011). During efforts to expedite delivery, this approach contributes to the dubious practice of encouraging aggressive maternal pushing to facilitate vaginal delivery in response to concerning FHR abnormalities in the second stage of labor. These attitudes account in part for the high prevalence of excessive uterine activity, the variability in response to its appearance depending on the presence or severity of associated FHR patterns, and in the widespread allegations of oxytocin abuse in medical and legal circles involving adverse neonatal outcomes (Berglund et al., 2008, Clark et al., 2009, Doyle et al., 2011, Simpson and James, 2008, Simpson and Knox, 2009).

In 1597 induced labors, Kunz et al. identified 661 instances of tachysystole (41%.). Fifty-four of 55 patients (98%) demonstrated one or more occurrences. More pertinently, we believe, they also found a diminished relaxation time (< 60 seconds rest between contractions) in 98% of women who received oxytocin for induction of labor (Kunz et al., 2013). Indeed, diminished relaxation time was nearly three times more sensitive for recognition of excessive uterine activity than was contraction frequency.

Inadequate relaxation time often accompanies tachysystole. It is strongly related to the adequacy of perfusion of the fetal brain between contractions. Bakker, et al. reported that reduced relaxation time between contractions was significantly correlated with fetal acidosis (umbilical artery pH <7.12), while contraction frequency greater than 5 per 10 minute period was not a sensitive measure for predicting acidosis (Bakker et al., 2007a). Uterine rest of more than 1 minute between moderate to strong contractions appears necessary to allow sufficient time for reperfusion and adequate oxygen delivery to the fetus (Bakker et al., 2007b, Johnson et al., 1994, McNamara and Johnson, 1995, Peebles et al., 1994, Simpson and James, 2008). These data affirm a positive relation between the patterns of uterine contractions and decreases in human fetal cerebral oxygen saturation, and suggest that contractions (of normal duration) should occur no more frequently than every 2 to 2.5 minutes. With shorter intervals, fetal cerebral oxygen saturation is likely to fall (Peebles et al., 1994).

Table 3 presents criteria for normal and excessive uterine activity using parameters readily discernable on the contraction monitor during labor. However defined, excessive uterine activity clearly is associated with diminished oxygenation of fetal blood and decreased umbilical artery pH at the time of delivery, abnormal FHR patterns, and even neonatal encephalopathy (Bakker and van Geijn, 2008, Bakker et al., 2007a, Graham, 2007, Hamilton et al., 2012, Hayes et al., 2013, Heuser et al., 2013, Simpson and James, 2008, Simpson and Knox, 2000, 2009). Of note, excessive uterine activity does not necessarily beget more rapid progress in the active phase of labor (Allman and Steer, 1993, Cohen et al., 1987, Ingemarsson et al., 1980, Steer, 1993). Indeed, there appears to be no relationship between the rate of progress after an arrest of labor and the frequency of oxytocin-induced contractions (Bidgood and Steer, 1987a, 1987b). Oppenheimer et al. have shown that optimal progress in labor is related to evenly spaced contractions of similar amplitude and duration rather than to their frequency (Oppenheimer et al., 2002).

Fetal Heart Rate Patterns

While there is agreement that FHR monitoring has revolutionized our understanding of fetal cardiovascular responses to hypoxia during labor and reliably anticipates fetal acidemia (Spong, 2008, Steer, 2008), it has also been deemed to be of little value over auscultation of the FHR and to neither predict fetal neurological injury nor to improve perinatal outcome (Alfirevic et al., 2006, Costantine and Saade, 2012, Graham et al., 2008, MacDonald et al., 1985, MacLennan et al., 2005, Spong, 2008). Realizing the benefits of EFM is highly dependent on accurate interpretation of these patterns. International guidelines for its use have not been consistent in their recommendations and interpretation has been shown to be of a low standard in both clinical practice and in allegations of malpractice (Berglund et al., 2008, Hill et al., 2012, Steer, 2008).

Numerous studies have explored the neuroradiological findings in infants with presumed HIE, but any study of their correlation with obstetrical events is severely limited. For example, we have no comprehensive understanding of the relations among FHR patterns, uterine activity patterns, the course of labor and delivery, neonatal clinical presentation, serial neuroradiological findings and long-term neurological outcome. Various studies relating FHR patterns to early outcome may involve only the last few minutes of labor, but irrespective of the duration of sampling they frequently fail to document the timing of injury (if any) and whether on admission to labor the fetus was normal (Cahill et al., 2012, Graham et al., 2006, Spencer et al., 1997).

Controlled studies of excessive uterine activity have shown an increased risk of abnormal FHR tracings, fetal acidosis and low Apgar score, but have no long-term follow-up (Bakker et al., 2007a, Jackson et al., 2011). Studies of neonatal encephalopathy identified a high incidence of abnormal FHR patterns, but generally have not commented on the presence of specific FHR patterns or of excessive uterine activity. In various studies, abnormal FHR patterns including fetal tachycardia were commonplace in babies with encephalopathy (Hayes et al., 2013, Kazandi et al., 2003, Kodama et al., 2009, Murray et al., 2009, Phelan and Ahn, 1998). The majority of infants in these studies had low, but not severely depressed Apgar scores and only a minority of patients had low umbilical cord blood pH values. Further, abnormal heart rate patterns persisted for over 1 hour in about half the patients with neonatal encephalopathy and over 2 hours in one third (Murray et al., 2009). A preliminary study of a group of neonates who suffered neurological injury during labor in association with prolonged excessive uterine activity [>2 hours] and other mechanical factors showed significant evidence of cranial trauma [marked molding, bruising, etc.] at birth (Ater et al., 2008), On neuroradiological examination they showed diverse, supratentorial white matter lesions [both focal and non-focal] compatible with ischemia. Basal ganglia and thalamic injury were uncommon. Forty-six percent had intracranial hemorrhage. The majority of the newborns displayed neither umbilical artery acidemia nor other systemic evidence of intrapartum asphyxia. Invariably, FHR patterns were abnormal, but other than the conversion pattern (see below) in about half of these infants, the abnormalities were diverse.

These data are all consistent with the hypothesis that intrapartum brain injury and consequent neonatal encephalopathy can develop in association with abnormal FHR patterns, but without severe asphyxia or fetal acidosis. The ischemic and hemorrhagic injuries appearing during labor in such cases are likely the consequence of brain ischemia produced by mechanical compression or deformation of the head, and not primarily by systemic fetal hypoxia or asphyxia (Ater et al., 2008). It becomes understandable that contemporary techniques of fetal surveillance including conventional electronic FHR monitoring, even abetted by detailed analysis of FECG complexes for asphyxia (STAN monitor), fetal pulse oximetry, and fetal blood gas analysis are unlikely to be helpful in this regard (Bloom et al., 2006, Dokus et al., 2013, Schifrin, 2003). Indeed, in one study, withdrawal of the STAN monitor was associated with an improvement in umbilical blood gases although the cesarean section rate increased (Dokus et al., 2013).

Table 3. Uterine Activity Parameters

Parameter	Normal Range	Excessive (a)
Contraction Frequency	2 – 4.5 / 10 min.	>5/10 min. (b)
Contraction Intensity [Amplitude]	25 – 75 mmHg	Not defined
Contraction Duration	60 – 90 sec.	>90 sec.
Resting Tone (IUPC)	15 – 20 mmHg	>25 mmHg
Interval [peak-peak]	>2 – 4 min.	>2min
Interval [end-beginning]	1 -2 min	< 1 min
Rest time (Duty cycle) (c)	<= 50 %	> 50%
Montevideo Units (Average amplitude above baseline x frequency / 10 minutes)	200-250 MVU	>300 MVU

(a) Must persist, alone or in combination, continuously for at least 20 minutes
(b) Called "tachysystole" (>5 contractions / 10 minutes - averaged over 30 minutes)
(c) The percentage of time that the uterus is at rest (not contracting).
IUPC = intrauterine pressure catheter

The contemporary classification of fetal heart rate identifies categories (I, II, III) of tracings according to their likelihood of associated fetal acidemia (Macones et al., 2008). Though the severity of acidemia increases with increasing severity of the patterns, they are in fact, poor predictors of either fetal acidemia or of subsequent cerebral palsy (Cahill et al., 2012, Dennis et al., 1989, Dijxhoorn et al., 1985, 1986, 1987, Ruth and Raivio, 1988, Schwarcz et al., 1969). Data from neonatal cooling studies strongly suggest that no single quantitative value of fetal arterial pH serves to define a point of hypoxia-induced damage applicable to all fetuses (Clark et al., 2013, Shankaran et al., 2005).

The current system of intrapartum fetal surveillance predicated on rapid intervention in the presence of acidemia or an acute clinical event is unlikely to diminish the risk of neurological injury. It has, however, reduced dramatically the risk of intrapartum fetal death attributable to intrapartum hypoxia at the same time increasing the cesarean section rate (Steer, 2009, Walsh et al., 2008). To obtain greater clinical benefit from EFM, it will be necessary to modify the precepts of EFM by using FHR and uterine contraction patterns not only for the detection of hypoxia (where it has high sensitivity, but low specificity) , but also to estimate directly whether or not the fetus is at risk of cranial compression ischemia or has already suffered neurological harm irrespective of its pH (Schifrin and Ater, 2006, Tranquilli et al., 2013).

Abundant data support the idea that, properly interpreted, FHR patterns are better predictors of neurological injury than is umbilical acidemia (Clapp et al., 1988, Dijxhoorn et al., 1985, 1986, 1987). Experimental evidence from Ikeda et al., bears directly on this issue (Ikeda et al., 1998a, 1998b). In a study of fetal lambs severely asphyxiated by prolonged cord compression, they found that the severity of subsequent neurological injury was not related to the duration of the bradycardia or the severity of the drop in pH or base excess, but rather to the duration of the hypotension (with its potential for ischemia) and to the abnormal fetal heart rate pattern after the recovery from the deceleration. The latter is analogous to a pattern observed in human fetuses, which we have called the "conversion pattern" (Schifrin and Ater, 2006). The term refers to a sudden evolution of the behaviorally normal fetus with absent hypoxia to one with a pattern of absent variability and tachycardia (Asakura et al., 1994, Bennet et al., 2005, Clark et al., 2013, Schifrin and Ater, 2006, Shields and Schifrin, 1988).

Finally, authors have found abnormal FHR patterns, but absent acidemia, associated with oxytocin use, fetuses laboring in the OP position, and with intrauterine bacterial infection and subsequent CP (Porreco et al., 2004). Miller and Hankins and their colleagues have proposed that elective cesarean section offers significant benefits for the reduction of CP – a benefit of avoiding the rigors of labor –especially the 2nd stage of labor (Asicioglu et al., 2014, Hankins et al., 2006, Ingemarsson et al., 1980, Miller and Ferriero, 2013).

It is tempting to believe that above a certain ICP or compromise of fetal CBF decelerations occur, but the available evidence for such a pathognomonic sequence is conflicting and the reliability of FHR monitoring for detecting pathologic impairment of CBF is uncertain as are the parallels to be drawn from animal experiments. In the experiments with intracranial pressure catheters inserted into hydrocephalic fetuses (Figure 4), Mocsary et al. found recurrent decelerations with significant elevations of ICP. In some of these, the recovery of the deceleration was delayed beyond the end of the contraction (late deceleration). When the ICP was elevated significantly the fetus exhibited a sustained bradycardia that recovered to baseline only after the pressure was relieved (Mocsary et al., 1970). Caldeyro-Barcia and colleagues called attention to the high prevalence of early decelerations in patients with early rupture of the membranes and exaggerated molding, and to the appearance of these decelerations with high uterine pressures or pressure on the fetal skull (Figure 5) (Amiel-Tison et al., 1988, Caldeyro-Barcia, 1974, Schwarcz et al., 1969). In the study of Ueno cited above a high resistance index of the middle cerebral artery was negatively correlated with FHR. (Ueno, 1992). Early decelerations appeared in 67% of the cases with absent end-diastolic flow velocity, and in 100% of cases with reversed diastolic flow even in fetuses with normal outcomes. Nor are such decelerations present at modest elevations of pressure despite activation of the Cushing response (Harris et al., 1989, 1992). In the experiments of Mann and colleagues, the heart rate decreased in eleven experiments increased in twelve and remained unchanged in seven (Mann et al., 1972). There is also compelling evidence that head (or ocular) compression may cause variable decelerations, especially in the second stage of labor (Sholapurkar, 2012). It seems necessary to revise the concept that early decelerations are invariably benign or that variable decelerations only indicate umbilical cord compression and may be tolerated indefinitely (Amiel-Tison et al., 1988, Sholapurkar, 2012). Ultimately, even late decelerations, thought to represent fetal hypoxia, may represent delayed recovery from elevated intracranial pressure (Mocsary et al., 1970).

The objective of surveillance, therefore, must go beyond the search for hypoxia and take advantage of both the FHR and uterine contraction patterns and the factors related to progress in labor to minimize the frequency and duration of those factors that reveal or suggest a potential adverse impact on the cerebral circulation – irrespective of their effect on fetal pH or fetal heart rate patterns. The absence of decelerations makes highly improbable the presence of significant hypoxia and acidemia, but does not eliminate the potential for excessive mechanical forces acting on the brain and diminishing cerebral blood flow.

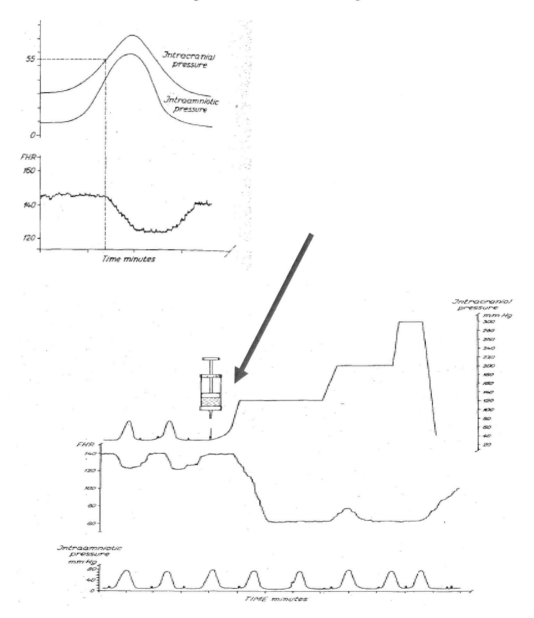

Figure 4. Relationship of fetal heart rate changes to spontaneous contractions and artificial increases in intracranial pressure (at arrow). Notice the appearance of fetal cardiac decelerations (beginning somewhat later in the contraction cycle - inset) and the appearance of prolonged decelerations when the intracranial pressure is artificially increased above 100 mmHg. Release of the pressure is accompanied by the return of the fetal heart rate (Mocsary et al., 1970).

FHR patterns do not represent the totality of intrapartum care, which must include a detailed evaluation of the course of labor and the position, molding and descent of the head, among other factors. Accordingly, efforts to reduce the risk of intrapartum injury to the fetus will require more appropriate recognition of the risks, proper classification of the role of mechanical factors [CCIE] and more suitable evaluation of the obstetrical antecedents of those identified as injured. Extensive evidence supports the concept that excessive fetal head compression during labor and delivery can result in reduced brain blood flow and consequent ischemic brain injury, even in the absence of superficial trauma, hemorrhage or acidemia (Clark et al., 2009, Geirsson, 1988, Govaert et al., 1992c, Keeling, 1981, Volpe, 2008, Welch and Strand, 1986). In the presence of hypoxia and hypotension from other causes excess head compression can further diminish cerebral perfusion and increase the risk of injury.

Toward Reducing the Risk of Mechanical Injury

Evidence for the potential of head compression to cause injury is both clinical and experimental. Its significance has been overlooked, however, due in largest part to the widespread assumption that neonatal ischemic injuries are asphyxial, not mechanical, in origin. By consequence, there has been a dearth of research in this area (ACOG, 2003a, Volpe, 2012).

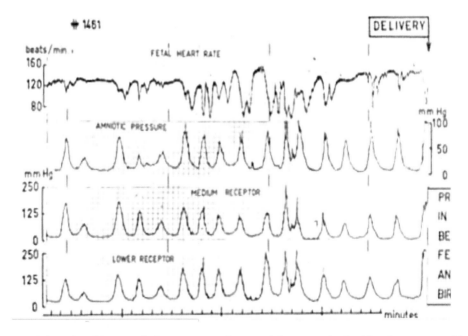

Figure 5. Relationship of intraamniotic pressure and external forces on the fetal head as measured by sensors between the fetal head and the birth canal and the response of the fetal heart rate. Notice that pressures exerted on the head during a contraction are consistently greater than the intrauterine pressure. Note also the association of decelerations with increasing pressures as the head approaches delivery (Schwarcz et al., 1969).

Many, probably most, newborns diagnosed with ischemic encephalopathy (absent an acute event) were not exposed to severe global asphyxia in utero. Their brain ischemia more likely represents a contribution of the effects of mechanical trauma in addition to the various pharmacological, infectious, hypoxemic factors during labor. Trauma could be caused by excessive uterine activity abetted by neglected dysfunctional labor in the presence of cephalopelvic disproportion, malposition, prolonged rupture of the membranes, molding of the fetal head, operative vaginal delivery or excessive maternal pushing in the second stage of labor. The overall contribution of these forces to ischemic brain injury during labor is difficult to establish, in no small measure because in modern obstetrics necessary details about these various factors are often unmeasured, unrecorded and not considered. To isolate the contribution of mechanical factors it will be necessary for epidemiologic studies to adjust for the role of potentially mitigating factors, including any prenatal, genetic, or hypoxemic contributors to injury. If inferences about the cause of the brain injury are to be accurate, studies of newborns with encephalopathy need to incorporate detailed obstetric data, including estimates of neurological integrity at the outset of labor and uterine activity measures. In so doing we will better understand the concept of CCIE and its contribution to neonatal morbidity. Injury related to CCIE may be far more common than generally appreciated.

With these historical perspectives and evolving pathophysiological concepts in mind we offer the following principles of fetal surveillance during labor. Assuming the well-being of the mother, the program is dependent upon a thoughtful analysis of the FHR pattern, the uterine activity pattern, and the course of labor.

Avoiding the need to rescue the fetus from serious adversity is a priority. Delivering a fetus under emergency circumstances, regardless of the outcome, is not a goal to which we should aspire. Emergency deliveries disrupt care of other patients and are more likely to beget complications in fetus and mother (Tolcher et al., 2014).

The avoidance of hypoxic, ischemic, and mechanical stresses is best realized by:

- The scrupulous avoidance of excessive uterine activity under any circumstances. (The definition of "excessive" must include the frequency duration and rest time between contractions or between expulsive efforts). A normal fetal heart rate tracing should never be considered reassuring if uterine activity is excessive - especially in late labor.
- With decelerations in the fetal heart rate, the fetus should be allowed to recover to its previously normal (and stable) baseline rate and variability if possible, before oxytocin or pushing is resumed. Failure to recover as defined requires the further application of conservative measures (cessation of pushing, lateral positioning, maternal oxygenation) and consideration of intervention as dictated by the expected course of labor (Clark et al., 2013).
- Close attention to the course of cervical dilatation and descent with prompt recognition and response to dysfunctional labor patterns. Decisions to use oxytocin should incorporate information about cephalopelvic relations (including pelvic architecture, station molding, position, attitude) as well as the FHR and contraction patterns.
- In the second stage of labor, maternal expulsive efforts are conducted only with, not between, contractions. If contractions are close together or decelerations are present,

encourage pushing only with every other or every third contraction, especially if epidural anesthesia is in place. Encourage pushing using the open glottis technique.

Conclusion– Perspective

Fetal neurological injury during labor may derive from pharmacological, infectious, and hypoxemic factors and from mechanical trauma. Elucidating their individual contributions is difficult because of limited intrapartum and follow up data and a current perspective of injury slanted almost exclusively to identifying severe fetal hypoxia.

Mechanical forces resulting in fetal craniocerebral vascular insufficiency during labor may result in ischemic cerebral injury in the absence of obvious superficial trauma, hemorrhage or acidemia (Clark et al., 2009, Geirsson, 1988, Govaert et al., 1992a, Keeling, 1981, Volpe, 2001, Welch and Strand, 1986). In the presence of pre-existing hypoxia and/or hypotension, contractions, especially with pushing, can further diminish cerebral perfusion. Mechanical forces in the form of cranio-cerebral compression are an overlooked mechanism of injury. To isolate the contribution of mechanical factors it will be necessary to eliminate or minimize the role of potentially mitigating factors, including any prenatal, genetic, or hypoxemic cause of injury and perhaps, with newfound understanding, identify it specifically. We propose the concept of cranial compression ischemic encephalopathy (CCIE). Injury related to CCIE, may indeed be the more important link to intrapartum ischemic injury and its prevention than is the detection of hypoxia. The objective of enlightened obstetrical care is to avoid these adverse consequences. We must learn more about the ability of the fetal skull to protect the fetal brain.

References

Aarnivala, H.E.I., Valkama, A.M. & Pirttiniemi, P.M. (2014). Cranial shape, size and cervical motion in normal newborns. Early Hum Devel, 90 425-430.

Al-Kadri, H., Sabr, Y., Al-Saif, S., Abulaimoun, B., Ba'Aqeel, H. & Saleh, A. (2003). Failed individual and sequential instrumental vaginal delivery: contributing risk factors and maternal-neonatal complications. *Acta Obstet Gynecol Scand, 82*, 642-8.

Aldrich, C. J., D'Antona, D., Spencer, J. A., Wyatt, J. S., Peebles, D. M., Delpy, D. T., et al. (1995). The effect of maternal pushing on fetal cerebral oxygenation and blood volume during the second stage of labour. *Br J Obstet Gynaecol, 102*, 448-53.

Alfirevic, Z., Devane, D. & Gyte, G. M. (2006). Continuous cardiotocography (CTG) as a form of electronic fetal monitoring (EFM) for fetal assessment during labour. *Cochrane Database Syst Rev, (3)*, CD006066.

Allman, A. C. & Steer, P. J. (1993). Monitoring uterine activity. *Br J Hosp Med*, 49, 649-53.

American College of Obstetricians and Gynecologists (ACOG). (2003a). *Neonatal encephalopathy and cerebral palsy: Defining the pathogenesis and pathophysiology.* Washington, D. C.: American College of Obstetricians and Gynecologists.

American College of Obstetricians and Gynecologists Committee on Practice Bulletins-Obstetrics (ACOG). (2003b). ACOG Practice Bulletin Number 49, December 2003: Dystocia and augmentation of labor. *Obstet Gynecol*, *102*, 1445-54.

American College of Obstetricians and Gynecologists Committee on Obstetric Practice (ACOG). (2004). ACOG Committee Opinion #303: Inappropriate use of the terms fetal distress and birth asphyxia. *Obstet Gynecol*, *104*, 903.

Amiel-Tison, C. (1988). Neurological morbidity of term infants as an indicator of safe obstetrical practice. In: *Perinatal events and brain damage in surviving children*. Kubli, F., Patel, N., Schmidt, W., Linderkamp, O. (Eds). Berlin: Springer-Verlag, 175-191.

Amiel-Tison, C., Sureau, C. & Shnider, S. M. (1988). Cerebral handicap in full-term neonates related to the mechanical forces of labour. *Baillieres Clin Obstet Gynaecol*, *2*, 145-65.

Asakura, H., Schifrin, B. S. & Myers, S. A. (1994). Intrapartum, atraumatic, non-asphyxial, intracranial hemorrhage in a full-term infant. *Obstet Gynecol*, *84*, 680-3.

Asicioglu, O., Gungorduk, K., Yildirim, G., Asicioglu, B.B., Gungorduk, O.C., Ark, C., et al. (2014). Second-stage vs first stage cesarean delivery: comparison of maternal and perinatal outcomes. J. Obstet Gynaecol, 1-7.

Ater, S., Schifrin, B., Glass, S. & Eden, R. (2008). Neonatal Presentation after Intrapartum Fetal Injury Associated with Uterine Hyperstimulation. *Ann Neurol*, *64*, Suppl S12, S133-4.

Badawi, N., Kurinczuk, J. J., Keogh, J. M., Alessandri, L. M., O'Sullivan, F., Burton, P. R., et al. (1998). Intrapartum risk factors for newborn encephalopathy: the Western Australian case-control study. *BMJ*, *317*, 1554-8.

Bakker, P. C., Kurver, P. H., Kuik, D. J. & Van Geijn, H. P. (2007a). Elevated uterine activity increases the risk of fetal acidosis at birth. *Am J Obstet Gynecol*, *196*, 313. e1-6.

Bakker, P. C. & van Geijn, H. P. (2008). Uterine activity: implications for the condition of the fetus. *J Perinat Med*, *36*, 30-7.

Bakker, P. C., Van Rijswijk, S. & van Geijn, H. P. (2007b). Uterine activity monitoring during labor. *J Perinat Med*, *35*, 468-77.

Barkovich, A. J. (2000a). Brain and spine injuries in infancy and childhood. In: *Pediatric Neuroimaging. 3rd* Edition, Chapter 4. Philadelphia: Lippincott Williams & Wilkins.

Barkovich, A. J. (2000b). *Pediatric Neuroimaging*. 3rd Edition. Philadelphia: Lippincott Williams & Wilkins.

Barkovich, A. J. (2006). MR imaging of the neonatal brain. *Neuroimaging Clin N Am*, *16*, 117-35, viii-ix.

Bennet, L., Westgate, J. A., Liu, Y. C., Wassink, G. & Gunn, A. J. (2005). Fetal acidosis and hypotension during repeated umbilical cord occlusions are associated with enhanced chemoreflex responses in near-term fetal sheep. *J Appl Physiol*, *99*, 1477-82.

Berfelo, F. J., Kersbergen, K. J., van Ommen, C. H., Govaert, P., van Straaten, H. L., Poll-The, B. T., et al. (2010). Neonatal cerebral sinovenous thrombosis from symptom to outcome. *Stroke*, *41*, 1382-8.

Berglund, S., Gruenwald, C., Pettersson, H. & Cnattingius, S. (2008). Severe asphyxia due to delivery-related malpractice in Sweden 1990-2005. *BJOG*, *115*, 316-23.

Bidgood, K. A. & Steer, P. J. (1987a). A randomized control study of oxytocin augmentation of labour. 1. Obstetric outcome. *Br J Obstet Gynaecol*, *94*, 512-7.

Bidgood, K. A. & Steer, P. J. (1987b). A randomized control study of oxytocin augmentation of labour. 2. Uterine activity. *Br J Obstet Gynaecol*, *94*, 518-22.

Bishai, J. M., Blood, A. B., Hunter, C. J., Longo, L. D. & Power, G. G. (2003). Fetal lamb cerebral blood flow (CBF) and oxygen tensions during hypoxia: a comparison of laser Doppler and microsphere measurements of CBF. *J Physiol, 546*, 869-78.

Blair, E. & Stanley, F. J. (1988). Intrapartum asphyxia: a rare cause of cerebral palsy. *J Pediatr, 112*, 515-9.

Bloom, S. L., Spong, C. Y., Thom, E., Varner, M. W., Rouse, D. J., Weininger, S., et al. (2006). Fetal pulse oximetry and cesarean delivery. *N Engl J Med, 355*, 2195-202.

Buchmann, E. J. & Libhaber, E. (2008). Sagittal suture overlap in cephalopelvic disproportion: blinded and non-participant assessment. *Acta Obstet Gynecol Scand, 87*, 731-7.

Buhimschi, C. S., Buhimschi, I. A., Malinow, A. M., Kopelman, J. N. & Weiner, C. P. (2002a). The effect of fundal pressure manoeuvre on intrauterine pressure in the second stage of labour. *BJOG, 109*, 520-6.

Buhimschi, C. S., Buhimschi, I. A., Malinow, A. M., Kopelman, J. N. & Weiner, C. P. (2002b). Pushing in labor: performance and not endurance. *Am J Obstet Gynecol, 186*, 1339-44.

Buhimschi, C. S., Buhimschi, I. A., Malinow, A. M. & Weiner, C. P. (2003). Uterine contractility in women whose fetus is delivered in the occipitoposterior position. *Am J Obstet Gynecol, 188,* 734-9.

Buhimschi, C. S., Buhimschi, I. A., Malinow, A. M. & Weiner, C. P. (2004). Intrauterine pressure during the second stage of labor in obese women. *Obstet Gynecol, 103*, 225-30.

Cahill, A. G., Roehl, K. A., Odibo, A. O. & Macones, G. A. (2012). Association and prediction of neonatal acidemia. *Am J Obstet Gynecol, 207*, 206. e1-8.

Caldeyro-Barcia, R. (1974). Adverse perinatal effects of early amniotomy during labor. In: *Modern perinatal medicine.* Gluck, L. (Ed). Chicago: Year Book Medical Publ.

Carlan, S. J., Wyble, L., Lense, J., Mastrogiannis, D. S. & Parsons, M. T. (1991). Fetal head molding. Diagnosis by ultrasound and a review of the literature. *J Perinatol, 11*, 105-11.

Clapp, J. F., Peress, N. S., Wesley, M. & Mann, L. I. (1988). Brain damage after intermittent partial cord occlusion in the chronically instrumented fetal lamb. *Am J Obstet Gynecol, 159*, 504-9.

Clark, S. L., Miller, D. D., Belfort, M. A., Dildy, G. A., Frye, D. K. & Meyers, J. A. (2009). Neonatal and maternal outcomes associated with elective term delivery. *Am J Obstet Gynecol, 200*, 156. e1-4.

Clark, S. L., Nageotte, M. P., Garite, T. J., Freeman, R. K., Miller, D. A., Simpson, K. R., et al. (2013). Intrapartum management of category II fetal heart rate tracings: towards standardization of care. *Am J Obstet Gynecol, 209*, 89-97.

Clinedinst, W. O. (1939). *A rational expression for the critical collapsing pressure of pipe under external pressure.* Drilling Production Practice, American Petroleum Institute (API), 383.

Clyne, D. G. (1964). Traumatic versus anoxic damage to the foetal brain. *Dev Med Child Neurol, 91*, 455-7.

Cohen, G. R., O'Brien, W. F., Lewis, L. & Knuppel, R. A. (1987). A prospective randomized study of the aggressive management of early labor. *Am J Obstet Gynecol, 157*, 1174-7.

Costantine, M. M. & Saade, G. R. (2012). The first cesarean: role of "fetal distress" diagnosis. *Semin Perinatol, 36*, 379-83.

Courville, C. B. (1963). Birth and brain damage. Traumatic versus anoxic damage to the fetal brain. *Bull Los Angel Neuro Soc, 28*, 209-16.

Cowan, F., Rutherford, M., Groenendaal, F., Eken, P., Mercuri, E., Bydder, G. M., et al. 2003. Origin and timing of brain lesions in term infants with neonatal encephalopathy. *Lancet, 361*, 736-42.

De Vries, L. S. & Groenendaal, F. (2010). Patterns of neonatal hypoxic-ischaemic brain injury. *Neuroradiology, 52*, 555-66.

Dennis, J., Johnson, A., Mutch, L., Yudkin, P. & Johnson, P. (1989). Acid-base status at birth and neurodevelopmental outcome at four and one-half years. *Am J Obstet Gynecol, 161*, 213-20.

Dijxhoorn, M. J., Visser, G. H., Fidler, V. J., Touwen, B. C. & Huisjes, H. J. (1986). Apgar score, meconium and acidaemia at birth in relation to neonatal neurological morbidity in term infants. *Br J Obstet Gynaecol, 93*, 217-22.

Dijxhoorn, M. J., Visser, G. H., Huisjes, H. J., Fidler, V. & Touwen, B. C. (1985). The relation between umbilical pH values and neonatal neurological morbidity in full term appropriate-for-dates infants. *Early Hum Dev, 11*, 33-42.

Dijxhoorn, M. J., Visser, G. H., Touwen, B. C. & Huisjes, H. J. (1987). Apgar score, meconium and acidaemia at birth in small-for-gestational age infants born at term, and their relation to neonatal neurological morbidity. *Br J Obstet Gynaecol, 94*, 873-9.

Dokus, K., Zubor, P., Matasova, K., Visnovsky, J. & Danko, J. (2013). Impact of fetal pulse oximetry and ST analysis surveillance withdrawal on rates of obstetric surgery and frequency of low birth umbilical artery pH: a cause of rising caesarean rates? *J Obstet Gynaecol, 33*, 685-8.

Doyle, J., Kenny, T. H., Burkett, A. M. & Von Gruenigen, V. E. (2011). A performance improvement process to tackle tachysystole. *J Obstet Gynecol Neonatal Nurs, 40*, 512-9.

Dupuis, O. & Simon, A. (2008). [Fetal monitoring during the active second stage of labor]. *J Gynecol Obstet Biol Reprod (Paris), 37*, Suppl 1, S93-100.

Dzakpasu, S., Joseph, K. S., Huang, L., Allen, A., Sauve, R. & Young, D. (2009). Decreasing diagnoses of birth asphyxia in Canada: fact or artifact. *Pediatrics, 123*, e668-72.

Fanaroff, A. A. & Martin, R. J. (2002). *Neonatal-perinatal medicine, diseases of the fetus and infant*. 7th Ed. St. Louis: Mosby.

Ferriero, D. M. (2004). Neonatal brain injury. *N Engl J Med, 351*, 1985-95.

Foley, M. E., Alarab, M., Daly, L., Keane, D., Macquillan, K. & O'Herlihy, C. (2005). Term neonatal asphyxial seizures and peripartum deaths: lack of correlation with a rising cesarean delivery rate. *Am J Obstet Gynecol, 192*, 102-8.

Frey, H. A., Tuuli, M. G., Roehl, K. A., Odibo, A. O., Macones, G. A. & Cahill, A. G. (2013). Can contraction patterns predict neonatal outcomes? *J Matern Fetal Neonatal Med.*

Friedman, E. A. & Acker, D. B. (1987). Use of midforceps and associated risk. *Am J Obstet Gynecol, 156*, 764-6.

Friedman, E. A., Sachtleben-Murray, M. R., Dahrouge, D. & Neff, R. K. (1984). Long-term effects of labor and delivery on offspring: a matched-pair analysis. *Am J Obstet Gynecol, 150*, 941-5.

Frymann, V. (1966). Relation of disturbances of craniosacral mechanism to symptomatology of the newborn: study of 1250 infants. *J Am Osteopath Assoc, 65*, 1059-75.

Frymann, V. M. (1976). The trauma of birth. *Osteopathic Annals, 5*, 197-205.

Furuya, H., Hashimoto, T., Kokuho, K., Kino, H. & Fukamauchi, K. (1981). [Pressures on the human fetus during labor - intrauterine and on the fetal head (author's transl)]. *Nippon Sanka Fujinka Gakkai Zasshi*, *33*, 2173-81.

Geirsson, R. T. (1988). Birth trauma and brain damage. *Baillieres Clin Obstet Gynaecol*, *2*, 195-212.

Ghosh, N., Recker, R., Shah, A., Bhanu, B., Ashwal, S. & Obenaus, A. (2011). Automated ischemic lesion detection in a neonatal model of hypoxic ischemic injury. *J Magn Reson Imaging*, *33*, 772-81.

Gielecki, J., Zurada, A., Kozlowska, H., Nowak, D. & Loukas, M. (2009). Morphometric and volumetric analysis of the middle cerebral artery in human fetuses. *Acta Neurobiol Exp (Wars)*, *69*, 129-37.

Gilbert, W. M., Jacoby, B. N., Xing, G., Danielsen, B. & Smith, L. H. (2010). Adverse obstetric events are associated with significant risk of cerebral palsy. *Am J Obstet Gynecol*, *203*, 328. e1-5.

Glass, H. C., Glidden, D., Jeremy, R. J., Barkovich, A. J., Ferriero, D. M. & Miller, S. P. (2009). Clinical Neonatal Seizures are Independently Associated with Outcome in Infants at Risk for Hypoxic-Ischemic Brain Injury. *J Pediatr*, *155*, 318-23.

Govaert, P., Achten, E., Vanhaesebrouck, P., De Praeter, C. & Van Damme, J. (1992a). Deep cerebral venous thrombosis in thalamo-ventricular hemorrhage of the term newborn. *Pediatr Radiol*, *22*, 123-7.

Govaert, P., Vanhaesebrouck, P. & De Praeter, C. (1992b). Traumatic neonatal intracranial bleeding and stroke. *Arch Dis Child*, *67*, 840-5.

Govaert, P., Vanhaesebrouck, P., De Praeter, C., Moens, K. & Leroy, J. (1992c). Vacuum extraction, bone injury and neonatal subgaleal bleeding. *Eur J Pediatr*, *151*, 532-5.

Graham, E. M. (2007). Elevated uterine activity increases the risk of fetal acidosis at birth. *Am J Obstet Gynecol*, *197*, 441, author reply 441-2.

Graham, E. M., Petersen, S. M., Christo, D. K. & Fox, H. E. (2006). Intrapartum electronic fetal heart rate monitoring and the prevention of perinatal brain injury. *Obstet Gynecol*, *108*, 656-66.

Graham, E. M., Ruis, K. A., Hartman, A. L., Northington, F. J. & Fox, H. E. (2008). A systematic review of the role of intrapartum hypoxia-ischemia in the causation of neonatal encephalopathy. *Am J Obstet Gynecol*, *199*, 587-95.

Gurbuz, A., Karateke, A., Yilmaz, U. & Kabaca, C. (2006). The role of perinatal and intrapartum risk factors in the etiology of cerebral palsy in term deliveries in a Turkish population. *J Matern Fetal Neonatal Med*, *19*, 147-55.

Hafstrom, M., Ehnberg, S., Blad, S., Noren, H., Renman, C., Rosen, K. G., et al. (2012). Developmental outcome at 6. 5 years after acidosis in term newborns: a population-based study. *Pediatrics*, *129*, e1501-7.

Hagberg, B., Hagberg, G., Beckung, E. & Uvebrant, P. (2001). Changing panorama of cerebral palsy in Sweden. VIII. Prevalence and origin in the birth year period 1991-94. *Acta Paediatr*, *90*, 271-7.

Hamilton, E., Warrick, P., Knox, E., O'Keeffe, D. & Garite, T. (2012). High uterine contraction rates in births with normal and abnormal umbilical artery gases. *J Matern Fetal Neonatal Med*, *25*, 2302-7.

Hanigan, W. C., Ali, M. B., Cusack, T. J., Miller, T. C. & Shah, J. J. (1985). Diagnosis of subdural hemorrhage in utero. Case report. *J Neurosurg*, *63*, 977-9.

Hanigan, W. C., Morgan, A. M., Stahlberg, L. K. & Hiller, J. L. (1990). Tentorial hemorrhage associated with vacuum extraction. *Pediatrics, 85,* 534-9.

Hankins, G. D., Clark, S. M. & Munn, M. B. (2006). Cesarean section on request at 39 weeks: impact on shoulder dystocia, fetal trauma, neonatal encephalopathy, and intrauterine fetal demise. *Semin Perinatol, 30,* 276-87.

Harris, A. P., Helou, S., Traystman, R. J., Jones, M. D., Jr. & Koehler, R. C. (1998). Efficacy of the cushing response in maintaining cerebral blood flow in premature and near-term fetal sheep. *Pediatr Res, 43,* 50-6.

Harris, A. P., Koehler, R. C., Gleason, C. A., Jones, M. D., Jr. & Traystman, R. J. (1989). Cerebral and peripheral circulatory responses to intracranial hypertension in fetal sheep. *Circ Res, 64,* 991-1000.

Harris, A. P., Koehler, R. C., Nishijima, M. K., Traystman, R. J. & Jones, M. D., Jr. (1992). Circulatory dynamics during periodic intracranial hypertension in fetal sheep. *Am J Physiol, 263,* R95-102.

Hasegawa, H., Kanai, H., Chubachi, N. & Koiwa, Y. (1997). Non-invasive evaluation of Poisson's ratio of arterial wall using ultrasound. *Electronics Lett, 33,* 340.

Hayes, B. C., McGarvey, C., Mulvany, S., Kennedy, J., Geary, M. P., Matthews, T. G., et al. (2013). A case-control study of hypoxic-ischemic encephalopathy in newborn infants at >36 weeks gestation. *Am J Obstet Gynecol, 209,* 29. e1-29. e19.

Helou, S., Koehler, R. C., Gleason, C. A., Jones, M. D., Jr. & Traystman, R. J. (1994). Cerebrovascular autoregulation during fetal development in sheep. *Am J Physiol, 266,* H1069-74.

Henry, M. J., McColl, D. D., Crawford, J. W. & Patel, N. (1979). Computing techniques for intrapartum physiological data reduction. I. Uterine activity. *J Perinat Med, 7,* 209-14.

Heuser, C. C., Knight, S., Esplin, M. S., Eller, A. G., Holmgren, C. M., Richards, D., et al. (2013). Tachysystole in term labor: incidence, risk factors, outcomes, and effect on fetal heart tracings. *Am J Obstet Gynecol, 209,* 32. e1-6.

Hill, J. B., Chauhan, S. P., Magann, E. F., Morrison, J. C. & Abuhamad, A. Z. (2012). Intrapartum fetal surveillance: review of three national guidelines. *Am J Perinatol, 29,* 539-50.

Himmelmann, K., Ahlin, K., Jacobsson, B., Cans, C. & Thorsen, P. (2011). Risk factors for cerebral palsy in children born at term. *Acta Obstet Gynecol Scand, 90,* 1070-81.

Holmquist, J. L. & Nadai, A. (1939). A theoretical approach to the problem of collapse of deep well casing. *Drilling Production Practice, API,* 392.

Hondappanavar, A., Sodhi, K. S., Dutta, S., Saxena, A. K. & Khandelwal, N. (2013). Quantitative ultrasound measurement of intima-media thickness of abdominal aorta and common carotid arteries in normal term newborns. *Pediatr Cardiol, 34,* 364-9.

Ikeda, T., Murata, Y., Quilligan, E. J., Choi, B. H., Parer, J. T., Doi, S., et al. (1998a). Physiologic and histologic changes in near-term fetal lambs exposed to asphyxia by partial umbilical cord occlusion. *Am J Obstet Gynecol, 178,* 24-32.

Ikeda, T., Murata, Y., Quilligan, E. J., Parer, J. T., Theunissen, I. M., Cifuentes, P., et al. (1998b). Fetal heart rate patterns in postasphyxiated fetal lambs with brain damage. *Am J Obstet Gynecol, 179,* 1329-37.

Ingemarsson, E., Ingemarsson, I., Solum, T. & Westgren, M. (1980). Influence of occiput posterior position on the fetal heart rate pattern. *Obstet Gynecol, 55,* 301-4.

Irving, F. C. (1930). Obstetrical aspects of intracranial hemorrhage. *JAMA, 203,* 499.

Jackson, M., Holmgren, C. M., Esplin, M. S., Henry, E. & Varner, M. W. (2011). Frequency of fetal heart rate categories and short-term neonatal outcome. *Obstet Gynecol*, *118*, 803-8.

Johnson, N., van Oudgaarden, E., Montague, I. & McNamara, H. (1994). The effect of oxytocin-induced hyperstimulation on fetal oxygen. *Br J Obstet Gynaecol*, *101*, 805-7.

Kazandi, M., Sendag, F., Akercan, F., Terek, M. C. & Gundem, G. (2003). Different types of variable decelerations and their effects to neonatal outcome. *Singapore Med J*, *44*, 243-7.

Keeling, J. (1993). *Fetal and neonatal pathology*. London: Springer Verlag.

Keeling, J. W. (1981). Iatrogenic disease in the newborn. *Virchows Arch A Pathol Anat Histol*, *394*, 1-29.

Kelly, J. V. (1963). Compression of the fetal brain. *Am J Obstet Gynecol*, *85*, 687-94.

Khamdaeng, T., Luo, J., Vappou, J., Terdtoon, P. & Konofagou, E. E. (2012). Arterial stiffness identification of the human carotid artery using the stress-strain relationship in vivo. *Ultrasonics*, *52*, 402-11.

Kodama, Y., Sameshima, H., Ikeda, T. & Ikenoue, T. (2009). Intrapartum fetal heart rate patterns in infants (> or =34 weeks) with poor neurological outcome. *Early Hum Dev*, *85*, 235-8.

Kriewall, T. J. (1960). Effects of uterine contractility on the fetal cranium. In: *A short history of obstetrics and gynecology*. Cianfrani, T. (Ed). Springfield: C. C. Thomas.

Kriewall, T.J., Stys, S.J., McPherson, G.K. 1977. Neonatal head shape after delivery: an index of molding. J Perinat Med, 5,260-7.

Kunz, M. K., Loftus, R. J. & Nichols, A. A. (2013). Incidence of uterine tachysystole in women induced with oxytocin. *J Obstet Gynecol Neonatal Nurs*, *42*, 12-8.

Lapeer, R. J. & Prager, R. W. (2001). Fetal head moulding: finite element analysis of a fetal skull subjected to uterine pressures during the first stage of labour. *J Biomech*, *34*, 1125-33.

Laugesaar, R., Kolk, A., Tomberg, T., Metsvaht, T., Lintrop, M., Varendi, H., et al. (2007). Acutely and retrospectively diagnosed perinatal stroke: a population-based study. *Stroke*, *38*, 2234-40.

Le Ray, C. & Audibert, F. (2008). [Duration of pushing in labor: literature review]. *J Gynecol Obstet Biol Reprod (Paris)*, *37*, 325-8.

Le Ray, C., Serres, P., Schmitz, T., Cabrol, D. & Goffinet, F. (2007). Manual rotation in occiput posterior or transverse positions: risk factors and consequences on the cesarean delivery rate. *Obstet Gynecol*, *110*, 873-9.

Lee, J., Croen, L. A., Lindan, C., Nash, K. B., Yoshida, C. K., Ferriero, D. M., et al. (2005). Predictors of outcome in perinatal arterial stroke: a population-based study. *Ann Neurol*, *58*, 303-8.

Leviton, A. (2013). Why the term neonatal encephalopathy should be preferred over neonatal hypoxic-ischemic encephalopathy. *Am J Obstet Gynecol*, *208*, 176-80.

Lieberman, D. E. (2011). *The evolution of the human head*. Cambridge, MA: Harvard University Press.

Lindgren, L. (1960). The causes of foetal head moulding in labour. *Acta Obstet Gynecol Scand*, *39*, 46-62.

Lindgren, L. (1966). Cervical dilatation with respect to the resistance of the lower parts of the uterus during labour. *Bibl Gynaecol*, *42*, 148-64.

Lindgren, L. (1972). The engagement of the foetal head in the uterus when the vertex presents. *Acta Obstet Gynecol Scand*, *51*, 37-45.

Lindgren, L. (1977). The influence of pressure upon the fetal head during labour. *Acta Obstet Gynecol Scand*, *56*, 303-9.

Little, W. J. (1862). On the influence of abnormal paturition, difficult labors, premature birth, and asphyxia neonatorum, on the mental and physical conditions of the child, especially in relation to deformities. *Trans Obstet Soc Lond*, *3*, 293-344. [Republished in *Clin Orthop Relat Res*, *46*, 7-22, 1966].

Longo, L. D. (1987). Physiologic assessment of fetal compromise: biomarkers of toxic exposure. *Environ Health Perspect*, *74*, 93-101.

Lotgering, F. K., Bishai, J. M., Struijk, P. C., Blood, A. B., Hunter, C. J., Power, G. G., et al. (2003). Ten-minute umbilical cord occlusion markedly reduces cerebral blood flow and heat production in fetal sheep. *Am J Obstet Gynecol*, *189*, 233-8.

MacDonald, D., Grant, A., Sheridan-Pereira, M., Boylan, P. & Chalmers, I. (1985). The Dublin randomized controlled trial of intrapartum fetal heart rate monitoring. *Am J Obstet Gynecol*, *152*, 524-39.

MacLennan, A., Nelson, K. B., Hankins, G. & Speer, M. (2005). Who will deliver our grandchildren? Implications of cerebral palsy litigation. *JAMA*, *294*, 1688-90.

Macones, G. A., Hankins, G. D., Spong, C. Y., Hauth, J. & Moore, T. (2008). The 2008 National Institute of Child Health and Human Development workshop report on electronic fetal monitoring: update on definitions, interpretation, and research guidelines. *J Obstet Gynecol Neonatal Nurs*, *37*, 510-5.

Malamud, N. (1970). Trauma and mental retardation. In: *Physical trauma as an etiological agent in mental retardation*. Washington, D. C.: US Department of Health, Education and Welfare.

Mann, L. I., Carmichael, A. & Duchin, S. (1972). The effect of head compression on FHR, brain metabolism and function. *Obstet Gynecol*, *39*, 721-6.

Martinez-Biarge, M., Diez-Sebastian, J., Wusthoff, C. J., Mercuri, E. & Cowan, F. M. (2013). Antepartum and intrapartum factors preceding neonatal hypoxic-ischemic encephalopathy. *Pediatrics*, *132*, e952-9.

Martinez-Biarge, M., Madero, R., Gonzalez, A., Quero, J. & Garcia-Alix, A. (2012). Perinatal morbidity and risk of hypoxic-ischemic encephalopathy associated with intrapartum sentinel events. *Am J Obstet Gynecol*, *206*, 148. e1-7.

McLean, C. & Ferriero, D. (2004). Mechanisms of hypoxic-ischemic injury in the term infant. *Semin Perinatol*, *28*, 425-32.

McNamara, H. & Johnson, N. (1995). The effect of uterine contractions on fetal oxygen saturation. *Br J Obstet Gynaecol*, *102*, 644-7.

McPherson, G. K. & Kriewall, T. J. (1980a). The elastic modulus of fetal cranial bone: a first step towards an understanding of the biomechanics of fetal head molding. *J Biomech*, *13*, 9-16.

McPherson, G. K. & Kriewall, T. J. (1980b). Fetal head molding: an investigation utilizing a finite element model of the fetal parietal bone. *J Biomech*, *13*, 17-26.

Medlock, M. D. & Hanigan, W. C. (1997). Neurologic birth trauma. Intracranial, spinal cord, and brachial plexus injury. *Clin Perinatol*, *24*, 845-57.

Miller, S. P. & Ferriero, D. M. (2013). Paediatric neurology: improved care of the developing brain. *Lancet Neurol*, *12*, 16-8.

Miller, S. P., Ramaswamy, V., Michelson, D., Barkovich, A. J., Holshouser, B., Wycliffe, N., et al. (2005). Patterns of brain injury in term neonatal encephalopathy. *J Pediatr*, *146*, 453-60.

Mocsary, P., Gaal, J., Komaromy, B., Mihaly, G., Pohanka, O. & Suranyi, S. (1970). Relationship between fetal intracranial pressure and fetal heart rate during labor. *Am J Obstet Gynecol*, *106*, 407-11.

Murray, D. M., O'Riordan, M. N., Horgan, R., Boylan, G., Higgins, J. R. & Ryan, C. A. (2009). Fetal heart rate patterns in neonatal hypoxic-ischemic encephalopathy: relationship with early cerebral activity and neurodevelopmental outcome. *Am J Perinatol*, *26*, 605-12.

Murray, M. & Huelsmann, G. (2008). Uterine Hyperstimulation: Physiologic and Pharacologic Causes with Results from a Survey of 1000 Nurses. Albuquerque.

Myers, R. E. (1967). Experimental brain damage in the newborn monkey. *J Neuropathol Exp Neurol*, *26*, 172.

Myers, R. E. (1972). Two patterns of perinatal brain damage and their conditions of occurrence. *Am J Obstet Gynecol*, *112*, 246-76.

Newton, T. H. & Gooding, C. A. (1975). Compression of superior sagittal sinus by neonatal calvarial molding. *Radiology*, *115*, 635-40.

O'Brien, W. F., Davis, S. E., Grissom, M. P., Eng, R. R. & Golden, S. M. (1984). Effect of cephalic pressure on fetal cerebral blood flow. *Am J Perinatol*, *1*, 223-6.

O'Grady, J. P., Pope, C. S. & Patel, S. S. (2000). Vacuum extraction in modern obstetric practice: a review and critique. *Curr Opin Obstet Gynecol*, *12*, 475-80.

Odendaal, H. J. & Burchell, H. (1985). Raised uterine resting tone in patients with abruptio placentae. *Int J Gynaecol Obstet*, *23*, 121-4.

Okereafor, A., Allsop, J., Counsell, S. J., Fitzpatrick, J., Azzopardi, D., Rutherford, M. A., et al. (2008). Patterns of brain injury in neonates exposed to perinatal sentinel events. *Pediatrics*, *121*, 906-14.

Oppenheimer, L. W., Bland, E. S., Dabrowski, A., Holmes, P., McDonald, O. & Wen, S. W. (2002). Uterine contraction pattern as a predictor of the mode of delivery. *J Perinatol*, *22*, 149-53.

Paneth, N. (1986a). Birth and the origins of cerebral palsy. *N Engl J Med*, *315*, 124-6.

Paneth, N. (1986b). Etiologic factors in cerebral palsy. *Pediatr Ann*, *15*, 191, 194-5, 197-201.

Paneth, N. (1993). The causes of cerebral palsy. Recent evidence. *Clin Invest Med*, *16*, 95-102.

Paneth, N. (2001). Cerebral palsy in term infants--birth or before birth? *J Pediatr*, *138*, 791-2.

Peebles, D. M., Spencer, J. A., Edwards, A. D., Wyatt, J. S., Reynolds, E. O., Cope, M., et al. (1994). Relation between frequency of uterine contractions and human fetal cerebral oxygen saturation studied during labour by near infrared spectroscopy. *Br J Obstet Gynaecol*, *101*, 44-8.

Penrose, L. S. (1963). *The biology of mental defect*. New York: Grune & Stratton.

Perlman, J. M. (2004). Brain injury in the term infant. *Semin Perinatol*, *28*, 415-24.

Perlman, J. M. (2006). Intrapartum asphyxia and cerebral palsy: is there a link? *Clin Perinatol*, *33*, 335-53.

Perlman, J. M. & Risser, R. (1993). Severe fetal acidemia: neonatal neurologic features and short-term outcome. *Pediatr Neurol*, *9*, 277-82.

Petersen, L. & Besuner, P. (1997). Pushing techniques during labor: issues and controversies. *J Obstet Gynecol Neonatal Nurs, 26,* 719-26.

Phelan, J. P. & Ahn, M. O. (1998). Fetal Heart Rate Observations in 300 Term Brain-damaged Infants. *J Matern Fetal Investig, 8,* 1-5.

Pollina, J., Dias, M. S., Li, V., Kachurek, D. & Arbesman, M. (2001). Cranial birth injuries in term newborn infants. *Pediatr Neurosurg, 35,* 113-9.

Porreco, R. P., Boehm, F. H., Dildy, G. A., Miller, H. S., Wickstrom, E. A., Garite, T. J., et al. (2004). Dystocia in nulliparous patients monitored with fetal pulse oximetry. *Am J Obstet Gynecol, 190,* 113-7.

Pu, F., Xu, L., Li, D., Li, S., Sun, L., Wang, L., et al. (2011). Effect of different labor forces on fetal skull molding. *Med Eng Phys, 33,* 620-5.

Pu, F., Xu, L., Li, D., Li, S., Sun, L., Wang, L., et al. (2013). Response of the authors on: comments on "Effect of different labor forces on fetal skull molding" by Pu et al., Med Eng Phys. 33 (2011) 620-625. *Med Eng Phys, 35,* 419.

Ranck, J. B., Jr. & Windle, W. F. (1959). Brain damage in the monkey, macaca mulatta, by asphyxia neonatorum. *Exp Neurol, 1,* 130-54.

Ranck, J. B., Jr. & Windle, W. F. (1961). Asphyxiation of adult rhesus monkeys. *Exp Neurol, 3,* 122-5.

Recker, R., Adami, A., Tone, B., Tian, H. R., Lalas, S., Hartman, R. E., et al. (2009). Rodent neonatal bilateral carotid artery occlusion with hypoxia mimics human hypoxic-ischemic injury. *J Cereb Blood Flow Metab, 29,* 1305-16.

Rempen, A. (1993a). [Pressure on the fetal head in vacuum extraction]. *Geburtshilfe Frauenheilkd, 53,* 337-41.

Rempen, A. (1993b). [Stress on the head of the fetus in spontaneous labor in relation to perinatal factors]. *Z Geburtshilfe Perinatol, 197,* 77-83.

Rempen, A. & Kraus, M. (1991). Pressures on the fetal head during normal labor. *J Perinat Med, 19,* 199-206.

Roberts, A. D., Baskett, T. F., Calder, A. A. & Arulkumaran, S. (2010). William Smellie and William Hunter: two great obstetricians and anatomists. *J R Soc Med, 103,* 205-6.

Roberts, M. H. (1925). The spinal fluid in the newborn with especial reference to intracranial hemorrhage. *AMA Am J Dis Child, 85,* 500.

Ruth, V. J. & Raivio, K. O. (1988). Perinatal brain damage: predictive value of metabolic acidosis and the Apgar score. *BMJ, 297,* 24-7.

Schaal, J. P., Dreyfus, M., Bretelle, F., Carbonne, B., Dupuis, O., Foulhy, C., et al. 2008. [Length of pushing efforts: pushing is not playing. Reply to the article of C. Le Ray and F. Audibert]. *J Gynecol Obstet Biol Reprod (Paris), 37,* 715-23.

Schifrin, B. S. (2003). Is fetal pulse oximetry ready for clinical practice?: Writing for the CON position. *MCN Am J Matern Child Nurs, 28,* 65.

Schifrin, B. S. & Ater, S. (2006). Fetal hypoxic and ischemic injuries. *Curr Opin Obstet Gynecol, 18,* 112-22.

Schifrin, B. S. & Longo, L. D. (2000). William John Little and cerebral palsy. A reappraisal. *Eur J Obstet Gynecol Reprod Biol, 90,* 139-44.

Schwarcz, R., Strada-Saenz, G. Althabe, O. Fernandez-Funes, J. & Caldeyro-Barcia, R. (1969). Pressure exerted by uterine contractions on the head of the human fetus during labor. In: *Perinatal factors affecting human development.* World Health Organization. Washington, D. C.: Pan American Health organization.

Sehirli, U. S., Yalin, A., Tulay, C. M., Cakmak, Y. O. & Gurdal, E. (2005). The diameters of common carotid artery and its branches in newborns. *Surg Radiol Anat*, *27*, 292-6.

Selzer, M. E., Myers, R. E. & Holstein, S. B. (1972). Prolonged partial asphyxia: effects on fetal brain water and electrolytes. *Neurology*, *22*, 732-7.

Senecal, J., Xiong, X. & Fraser, W. D. (2005). Effect of fetal position on second-stage duration and labor outcome. *Obstet Gynecol*, *105*, 763-72.

Shaffer, B. L., Cheng, Y. W., Vargas, J. E., Laros, R. K., Jr. & Caughey, A. B. (2006). Manual rotation of the fetal occiput: predictors of success and delivery. *Am J Obstet Gynecol*, *194*, e7-9.

Shah, P. S. & Perlman, M. (2009). Time courses of intrapartum asphyxia: neonatal characteristics and outcomes. *Am J Perinatol*, *26*, 39-44.

Shalak, L. & Perlman, J. M. (2004). Hypoxic-ischemic brain injury in the term infant-current concepts. *Early Hum Dev*, *80*, 125-41.

Shankaran, S., Laptook, A. R., Ehrenkranz, R. A., Tyson, J. E., McDonald, S. A., Donovan, E. F., et al. (2005). Whole-body hypothermia for neonates with hypoxic-ischemic encephalopathy. *N Engl J Med*, *353*, 1574-84.

Shields, J. R. & Schifrin, B. S. (1988). Perinatal antecedents of cerebral palsy. *Obstet Gynecol*, *71*, 899-905.

Sholapurkar, S. L. (2012). The conundrum of vanishing early decelerations in British obstetrics, a step backwards? Detailed appraisal of British and American classifications of fetal heart rate decelerations - fallacies of emphasis on waveform and putative aetiology. *J Obstet Gynaecol*, *32*, 505-11.

Simpson, K. R. (2006). When and how to push: providing the most current information about second-stage labor to women during childbirth education. *J Perinat Educ*, *15*, 6-9.

Simpson, K. R. & James, D. C. (2008). Effects of oxytocin-induced uterine hyperstimulation during labor on fetal oxygen status and fetal heart rate patterns. *Am J Obstet Gynecol*, *199*, 34. e1-5.

Simpson, K. R. & Knox, G. E. (2000). Risk management and electronic fetal monitoring: decreasing risk of adverse outcomes and liability exposure. *J Perinat Neonatal Nurs*, *14*, 40-52.

Simpson, K. R. & Knox, G. E. (2009). Oxytocin as a high-alert medication: implications for perinatal patient safety. *MCN Am J Matern Child Nurs*, *34*, 8-15; quiz 16-7.

Smellie, W. (1752). *A treatise on the theory and practice of midwifery*. London: D. Wilson.

Sorbe, B. & Dahlgren, S. (1983). Some important factors in the molding of the fetal head during vaginal delivery--a photographic study. *Int J Gynaecol Obstet*, *21*, 205-12.

Spencer, J. A., Badawi, N., Burton, P., Keogh, J., Pemberton, P. & Stanley, F. (1997). The intrapartum CTG prior to neonatal encephalopathy at term: a case-control study. *Br J Obstet Gynaecol*, *104*, 25-8.

Spong, C. Y. (2008). Electronic fetal heart rate monitoring: another look. *Obstet Gynecol*, *112*, 506-7.

Steer, P. J. (1993). Standards in fetal monitoring--practical requirements for uterine activity measurement and recording. *Br J Obstet Gynaecol*, *100*, Suppl 9, 32-6.

Steer, P. J. (2008). Has electronic fetal heart rate monitoring made a difference. *Semin Fetal Neonatal Med*, *13*, 2-7.

Steer, P. J. (2009). Surveillance during labour. *J Perinat Med*, *37*, 451-6.

Stewart, R. D., Bleich, A. T., Lo, J. Y., Alexander, J. M., McIntire, D. D. & Leveno, K. J. (2012). Defining uterine tachysystole: how much is too much? *Am J Obstet Gynecol*, *207*, 290. e1-6.

Svenningsen, L. & Jensen, O. (1988). A method for objective measurement of fetal head compression during the second stage of labor. *Gynecol Obstet Invest*, *26*, 219-24.

Takanashi, J., Barkovich, A. J., Ferriero, D. M., Suzuki, H. & Kohno, Y. (2003). Widening spectrum of congenital hemiplegia: Periventricular venous infarction in term neonates. *Neurology*, *61*, 531-3.

Takenouchi, T., Kasdorf, E., Engel, M., Grunebaum, A. & Perlman, J. M. (2012). Changing pattern of perinatal brain injury in term infants in recent years. *Pediatr Neurol*, *46*, 106-10.

Tan, M., Deveber, G., Shroff, M., Moharir, M., Pontigon, A. M., Widjaja, E., et al. (2011). Sagittal sinus compression is associated with neonatal cerebral sinovenous thrombosis. *Pediatrics*, *128*, e429-35.

Tillett, J. 2011. "Pit to distress": is this an evidence-based strategy? J. Perinat Neonatal Nurs, 25, 302-4.

Tolcher, M. C., Johnson, R. L., El-Nashar, S. A. & West, C. P. (2014). Decision-to-incision time and neonatal outcomes: a systematic review and meta-analysis. *Obstet Gynecol*, *123*, 536-48.

Towbin, A. (1998). *Brain damage in the newborn and its neurologic sequels: pathologic and clinical correlation*. Danvers, MA: PRM Publishing.

Towner, D., Castro, M. A., Eby-Wilkens, E. & Gilbert, W. M. (1999). Effect of mode of delivery in nulliparous women on neonatal intracranial injury. *N Engl J Med*, *341*, 1709-14.

Tranquilli, A. L., Biagini, A., Greco, P., Di Tommaso, M. & Giannubilo, S. R. (2013). The correlation between fetal bradycardia area in the second stage of labor and acidemia at birth. *J Matern Fetal Neonatal Med*, *26*, 1425-9.

Ueno, N. (1992). [Studies on fetal middle cerebral artery blood flow velocity waveforms in the intrapartum period]. *Nihon Sanka Fujinka Gakkai Zasshi*, *44*, 97-104.

Vannucci, R. C. (1993a). Experimental models of perinatal hypoxic-ischemic brain damage. *APMIS Suppl*, *40*, 89-95.

Vannucci, R. C. (1993b). Mechanisms of perinatal hypoxic-ischemic brain damage. *Semin Perinatol*, *17*, 330-7.

Volpe, J. J. (2001). *Neurology of the newborn*. 4th ed. Philadelphia: W. B. Saunders.

Volpe, J. J. (2008). *Neurology of the newborn*. 5th ed. Philadelphia: Saunders/Elsevier.

Volpe, J. J. (2012). Neonatal encephalopathy: an inadequate term for hypoxic-ischemic encephalopathy. *Ann Neurol*, *72*, 156-66.

Walsh, C. A., McMenamin, M. B., Foley, M. E., Daly, S. F., Robson, M. S. & Geary, M. P. (2008). Trends in intrapartum fetal death, 1979-2003. *Am J Obstet Gynecol*, *198*, 47. e1-7.

Welch, K. & Strand, R. (1986). Traumatic parturitional intracranial hemorrhage. *Dev Med Child Neurol*, *28*, 156-64.

Westgate, J. A., Bennet, L. & Gunn, A. J. (1999). Fetal heart rate variability changes during brief repeated umbilical cord occlusion in near term fetal sheep. *Br J Obstet Gynaecol*, *106*, 664-71.

Westgate, J. A., Wibbens, B., Bennet, L., Wassink, G., Parer, J. T. & Gunn, A. J. (2007). The intrapartum deceleration in center stage: a physiologic approach to the interpretation of fetal heart rate changes in labor. *Am J Obstet Gynecol, 197*, 236. e1-11.

Windle, W. F. (1940). *Physiology of the fetus; origin and extent of function and prenatal life.* Philadelphia: W. B. Saunders.

Yates, P. O. (1959). Birth trauma to the vertebral arteries. *Arch Dis Child, 34*, 436-41.

Yeh, P., Emary, K. & Impey, L. (2012). The relationship between umbilical cord arterial pH and serious adverse neonatal outcome: analysis of 51,519 consecutive validated samples. *BJOG, 119*, 824-31.

Yildirim, G. & Beji, N. K. (2008). Effects of pushing techniques in birth on mother and fetus: a randomized study. *Birth, 35*, 25-30.

Index

C

E

H

I

N

O

P

Q

R